PART ONE

CALCULUS

ONE AND SEVERAL VARIABLES

Sir Isaac Newton

S.L. SALAS   EINAR HILLE
JOHN T. ANDERSON

PART ONE

CALCULUS

FIFTH EDITION

ONE AND SEVERAL VARIABLES
WITH ANALYTIC GEOMETRY

John Wiley and Sons/New York/Chichester/Brisbane/Toronto/Singapore

IN FOND REMEMBRANCE OF
EINAR HILLE

Text design: Levavi/Levavi
Cover design: Karin Gerdes Kincheloe
Cover illustration: Steve Jenkins
Production: Philip McCaffrey
Editorial supervision: Deborah Herbert
Copyediting: Trumbull Rogers

Library of Congress Cataloging-in-Publication Data

Salas, Saturnino L.
  Calculus: one and several variables, with analytic
geometry.

  Includes indexes.
  1. Calculus. I. Hille, Einar, 1894–1979.
II. Anderson, John T. III. Title
QA303.S17 1986b   515   85-29518

Printed in Singapore
10 9 8 7 6 5 4 3 2 1

Preface

At the suggestion of several valued reviewers we have made some substantial changes in the organization of the text and in the treatment of certain topics: you will now find an early treatment of the calculus of the trigonometric functions, an increased use of the Riemann definition of the integral, the introduction of several numerical techniques, a relatively early chapter on mathematical modeling, expanded and balanced (odd/even) exercise sets. Other changes: additional detail, suggested procedures for problem solving, revised proofs, and additional examples. All is geared toward providing a complete mathematical treatment that is accessible to students. A detailed description of these and other changes is given on page vii.

As before, *Calculus: One and Several Variables* is available in a single complete volume and in two parts:

Part I—Functions of one variable, differential equations, analytic geometry, sequences and series (Chapters 1–13 of the complete volume);
Part II—Sequences and series, vector calculus, functions of several variables (Chapters 12–19 of the complete volume).

Many people have contributed to this revision. We are particularly indebted to the following mathematicians for their comments and suggestions:

W. W. Comfort, *Wesleyan University;* Hudson Kronk, *SUNY, Binghamton;* Giles Maloof, *Boise State University;* Gordon D. Prichett, *Babson College;* John Saber,

Babson College; Ted Scheick, *Ohio State University;* and Donald Sherbert, *University of Illinois, Urbana.*

Special thanks go to Elaine Rauschal and Philip McCaffrey, who supervised production and to Karin Kincheloe, who supervised the design. The commitment to excellence on the part of Wiley's mathematics editor Carolyn Moore is deeply appreciated. Finally, we are grateful to Charles G. Salas for keeping a careful eye on the development of this revision, from initial draft to finished product.

S. L. SALAS
Haddam, CT

JOHN T. ANDERSON
Clinton, NY

A Note From The Publisher. A *Student Solutions Manual* with complete solutions to all the odd-numbered exercises is available. Also available is a *Teacher's Manual,* which includes notes to the instructor, tests, all exercises together with selected solutions. A *Complex Variables/Differential Equations Supplement,* chapters 20 and 21 of the Fourth Edition, is free to those who wish to cover this material. Finally, there is a *Testing Disk,* for Apple and IBM, which includes a set of test questions for each chapter.

THE CHANGES

The major changes are highlighted below.

- Trigonometric functions are treated in such a way that the instructor can use them from the outset (Chapter 2 on limits) or postpone the work to as late as Chapter 7 on the natural logarithm without disrupting the flow of the course. Sections 2.5, 3.7, 5.12, and 7.6 are devoted to the trigonometric functions. Exercises and a few examples are given in most of the other intervening sections.
- Exercise sets have been expanded (approximately 1100 new exercises) and balanced (odd/even). The answer section at the back of the text and the *Student Solutions Manual* cover odd-numbered exercises only.
- Chapters 3 and 4 have been significantly rearranged with tangent-line problems and motion problems treated much sooner to provide greater motivation and to permit more variety in the exercise sets.
- Numerical techniques are given much fuller treatment: bisection method (Section 2.6), Newton-Raphson method (Section 3.12), Euler and Runge-Kutta methods (Section 8.9), numerical integration with error estimates (Section 9.9).
- Basic applications of the integral are treated sooner (Chapter 6) and are based on the Riemann definition of the integral. The notion of integral is still introduced with the Darboux definition.
- Chapter 8 is devoted to mathematical modeling and differential equations for the benefit of those instructors who are following the CUPM recommendations and experimenting with UMAP modules or comparable materials in the traditional second semester. The first five sections include topics (exponential growth and harmonic motion) typically covered in Chapter 7 on logarithms and may be treated earlier. Subsequent sections include topics (mechanical vibrations, a predator–prey model, numerical methods) whose coverage can be postponed.
- Additional work with u-substitutions has been provided.
- Integration by parts has been placed with other techniques of integration in Chapter 9.
- Graphing techniques in polar coordinates (Section 11.2) and parametric equations (Section 11.5) are presented at a slower pace in much more detail.
- Series solutions of differential equations are introduced in Section 13.11.
- More explanation and additional hints to some exercises have made it unnecessary to label any material as optional. (Of course, some material can still be omitted.)
- The preliminaries in Chapter 1 are treated at a more relaxed pace. Appendices on radian measure and complex numbers have been added.
- The treatment of max–min problems in several variables has been expanded to include boundary-value problems.
- Suggested procedures for solving certain kinds of problems, such as max–min problems, have been added.
- Chapter summaries with page references to key terms and results are provided.

For the benefit of those instructors familiar with the fourth edition of the text we provide a broad overview of the reorganization:

Chapters 3 and 4 are shuffled,
Chapter 6 is the old Chapter 10,
Chapter 7 combines portions of the old Chapters 6 and 7,

Chapter 8 combines some new material with portions of the old Chapters 6, 7, and 21,
Chapter 9 is the old Chapter 10,
Chapter 10 is the old Chapter 9.

Here is a list of *a few key sections* that contain new material or have been revised extensively:

1.9, 2.6, 3.12, 3.5, 3.6, 3.11, 4.7, 6.4, 8.1, 8.8, 8.9, 11.2, 11.5, 13.11, and 17.5.

Finally, Chapter 20 on complex functions and Chapter 21 on the theory and applications of differential equations from the fourth edition are not bound in the text, but are now available as a supplement.

The Greek Alphabet

A	α	alpha
B	β	beta
Γ	γ	gamma
Δ	δ	delta
E	ϵ	epsilon
Z	ζ	zeta
H	η	eta
Θ	θ	theta
I	ι	iota
K	κ	kappa
Λ	λ	lambda
M	μ	mu
N	ν	nu
Ξ	ξ	xi
O	o	omicron
Π	π	pi
P	ρ	rho
Σ	σ	sigma
T	τ	tau
Y	υ	upsilon
Φ	ϕ	phi
X	χ	chi
Ψ	ψ	psi
Ω	ω	omega

Contents

Chapter 10   THE CONIC SECTIONS   501

Chapter 11   POLAR COORDINATES; PARAMETRIC EQUATIONS   535

Chapter 12   SEQUENCES; INDETERMINATE FORMS; IMPROPER INTEGRALS   593

Gottfried Leibniz

PART ONE

CALCULUS

ONE AND SEVERAL VARIABLES

Introduction

1.1 ······WHAT IS CALCULUS?

To a Roman in the days of the empire a "calculus" was a pebble used in counting and in gambling. Centuries later "calculare" came to mean "to compute," "to reckon," "to figure out." To the mathematician, physical scientist, and social scientist of today calculus is elementary mathematics (algebra, geometry, trigonometry) enhanced by *the limit process.*

Calculus takes ideas from elementary mathematics and extends them to a more general situation. Here are some examples. On the left-hand side you will find an idea from elementary mathematics; on the right, this same idea as extended by calculus.

Elementary Mathematics	*Calculus*

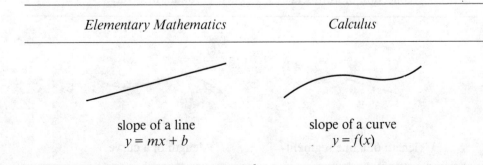

slope of a line	slope of a curve
$y = mx + b$	$y = f(x)$

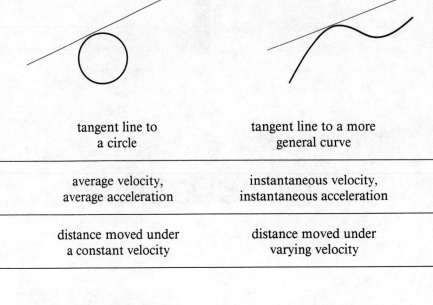

| tangent line to a circle | tangent line to a more general curve |

| average velocity, average acceleration | instantaneous velocity, instantaneous acceleration |

| distance moved under a constant velocity | distance moved under varying velocity |

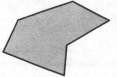

| area of a region bounded by line segments | area of a region bounded by curves |

| sum of a finite collection of numbers $a_1 + a_2 + \cdots + a_n$ | sum of an infinite series $a_1 + a_2 + \cdots + a_n + \cdots$ |

| average of a finite collection of numbers | average value of a function on an interval |

| length of a line segment | length of a curve |

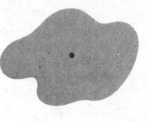

center of a circle   centroid of a region

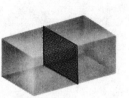

volume of
a rectangular solid

volume of a solid
with a curved boundary

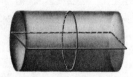

surface area of
a cylinder

surface area of
a more general solid

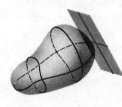

tangent plane to
a sphere

tangent plane to
a more general surface

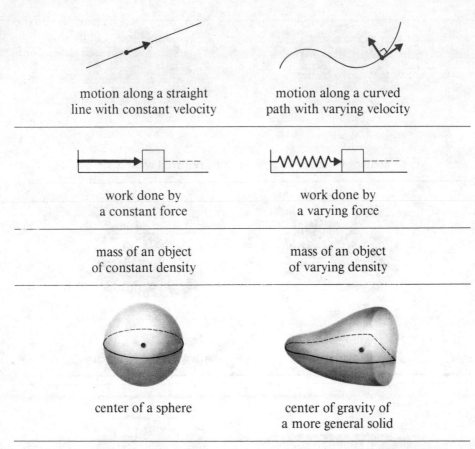

motion along a straight
line with constant velocity

motion along a curved
path with varying velocity

work done by
a constant force

work done by
a varying force

mass of an object
of constant density

mass of an object
of varying density

center of a sphere

center of gravity of
a more general solid

It is fitting to say something about the history of calculus. The origins can be traced back to ancient Greece. The ancient Greeks raised many questions (often paradoxical) about tangents, motion, area, the infinitely small, the infinitely large — questions that today are clarified and answered by calculus. Here and there the Greeks themselves provided answers (some very elegant), but mostly they provided only questions.

After the Greeks, progress was slow. Communication was limited, and each scholar was obliged to start almost from scratch. Over the centuries some ingenious solutions to calculus-type problems were devised, but no general techniques were put forth. Progress was impeded by the lack of a convenient notation. Algebra, founded in the ninth century by Arab scholars, was not fully systemized until the sixteenth century. Then, in the seventeenth century, Descartes established analytic geometry, and the stage was set.

The actual invention of calculus is credited to Sir Isaac Newton (1642–1727) and to Gottfried Wilhelm Leibniz (1646–1716), an Englishmen and a German. Newton's invention is one of the few good turns that the great plague did mankind. The plague forced the closing of Cambridge University in 1665 and young Isaac Newton of Trinity College returned to his home in Lincolnshire for eighteen months of meditation, out of which grew his *method of fluxions,* his *theory of gravitation,* and his *theory of light.* The method of fluxions is what concerns us here. A treatise with this title was written by Newton in 1672, but it remained unpublished until 1736, nine years after his death. The new method (calculus to us) was first announced in 1687, but in vague general terms without symbolism, formulas, or applications. Newton himself seemed reluctant to publish anything tangible about his new method, and it is not surprising that the development on the Continent, in spite of a late start, soon overtook Newton and went beyond him.

Leibniz started his work in 1673, eight years after Newton. In 1675 he initiated the basic modern notation: dx and $\int$. His first publications appeared in 1684 and 1686. These made little stir in Germany, but the two brothers Bernoulli of Basel (Switzerland) took up the ideas and added profusely to them. From 1690 onward calculus grew rapidly and reached roughly its present state in about a hundred years. Certain theoretical subtleties were not fully resolved until the twentieth century.

1.2 ······ NOTIONS AND FORMULAS FROM ELEMENTARY MATHEMATICS

The following outline is presented for review and easy reference.

I. SETS

the object x is in the set A (*x* is an element of *A*)	$x \in A$
the object x is not in the set A	$x \notin A$
subset, containment	$A \subseteq B$
union	$A \cup B$
intersection	$A \cap B$
Cartesian products	$A \times B,\ A \times B \times C$
empty set	$\varnothing$
the set of all x for which property P holds	$\{x : P\}$

(These are the only notions from set theory that you will need for this book. If you are not familiar with them, see Appendix A.1 at the back of the book.)

II. REAL NUMBERS

Classification

integers	$0, 1, -1, 2, -2, 3, -3$, etc.
rational numbers	p/q with p and q integers, $q \neq 0$; for example, $\frac{2}{5}, -\frac{9}{2}, \frac{4}{1} = 4$.
irrational numbers	real numbers that are not rational; for example, $\sqrt{2}, \pi$.

Order Properties

    (i) Either $a < b$, $b < a$, or $a = b$.   (trichotomy)
    (ii) If $a < b$ and $b < c$, then $a < c$.
    (iii) If $a < b$, then $a + c < b + c$ for all real numbers c.
    (iv) If $a < b$ and $c > 0$, then $ac < bc$.
        If $a < b$ and $c < 0$, then $ac > bc$.

(Techniques for solving inequalities are reviewed in Section 1.4.)

Density

Between any two real numbers there are infinitely many rational numbers and infinitely many irrational numbers. In particular, *there is no smallest positive real number.*

Absolute Value

$$\text{\textit{definition}} \qquad |a| = \begin{cases} a, & \text{if } a \geq 0 \\ -a, & \text{if } a \leq 0 \end{cases}.$$

other characterizations $|a| = \max\{a, -a\}$; $|a| = \sqrt{a^2}$.

geometric interpretation $|a|$ = distance between a and 0.
                           $|a - c|$ = distance between a and c.

properties   (i) $|a| = 0$ iff $a = 0$.†
             (ii) $|-a| = |a|$.
             (iii) $|ab| = |a||b|$.
             (iv) $|a + b| \leq |a| + |b|$.   (the triangle inequality)††
             (v) $\big||a| - |b|\big| \leq |a - b|$.   (a variant of the triangle inequality)

(The solution of inequalities involving absolute values is reviewed in Section 1.5.)

Intervals

Suppose that $a < b$. The *open interval* (a, b) is the set of all numbers between a and b:

$$(a, b) = \{x : a < x < b\}.$$

The *closed interval* $[a, b]$ is the open interval (a, b) together with the endpoints a and b:

$$[a, b] = \{x : a \leq x \leq b\}.$$

---

† By "iff" we mean "if and only if." This expression is used so often in mathematics that it's convenient to have an abbreviation for it.

†† The absolute value of the sum of two numbers cannot exceed the sum of their absolute values, just as in a triangle the length of a side cannot exceed the sum of the lengths of the other two sides.

There are seven other types of intervals:

$$(a, b] = \{x : a < x \leq b\}.$$
$$[a, b) = \{x : a \leq x < b\}.$$
$$(a, \infty) = \{x : a < x\}.$$
$$[a, \infty) = \{x : a \leq x\}.$$
$$(-\infty, b) = \{x : x < b\}.$$
$$(-\infty, b] = \{x : x \leq b\}.$$
$$(-\infty, \infty) = \text{set of real numbers}.$$

This interval notation is easy to remember: we use a bracket to include an endpoint; otherwise a parenthesis. The symbol ∞, read "infinity," has no meaning by itself. Just as in ordinary language we use syllables to construct words and need assign no meaning to the syllables themselves, so in mathematics we can use symbols to construct mathematical expressions, assigning no separate meaning to the individual symbols. While ∞ has no meaning, $(a, \infty), [a, \infty), (-\infty, b), (-\infty, b], (-\infty, \infty)$ do have meaning, and that meaning is given above.

Boundedness

A set S of real numbers is said to be

(i) *bounded above* iff there exists a real number M such that

$$x \leq M \qquad \text{for all } x \in S.$$

M is called an *upper bound* for S.

(ii) *bounded below* iff there exists a real number m such that

$$m \leq x \qquad \text{for all } x \in S.$$

m is called a *lower bound* for S.

(iii) *bounded* iff it is bounded above and below.

For example, the intervals $(-\infty, 2]$ and $(-\infty, 2)$ are bounded above but not below. The set of positive integers is bounded below but not above. The intervals $[0, 1]$, $(0, 1)$, and $(0, 1]$ are bounded (both above and below).

III. ALGEBRA AND GEOMETRY

General Quadratic Formula

The roots of a quadratic equation

$$ax^2 + bx + c = 0, \qquad a \neq 0$$

are given by

$$x = \frac{-b \pm \sqrt{b^2 - 4ac}}{2a}.$$

The expression under the radical, $b^2 - 4ac$, is called the *discriminant*.

Elementary Figures

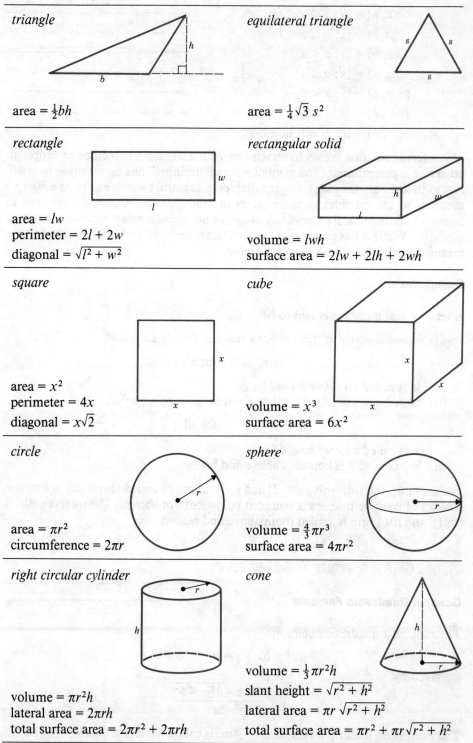

triangle

area = $\frac{1}{2}bh$

equilateral triangle

area = $\frac{1}{4}\sqrt{3}\,s^2$

rectangle

area = lw
perimeter = $2l + 2w$
diagonal = $\sqrt{l^2 + w^2}$

rectangular solid

volume = lwh
surface area = $2lw + 2lh + 2wh$

square

area = x^2
perimeter = $4x$
diagonal = $x\sqrt{2}$

cube

volume = x^3
surface area = $6x^2$

circle

area = πr^2
circumference = $2\pi r$

sphere

volume = $\frac{4}{3}\pi r^3$
surface area = $4\pi r^2$

right circular cylinder

volume = $\pi r^2 h$
lateral area = $2\pi rh$
total surface area = $2\pi r^2 + 2\pi rh$

cone

volume = $\frac{1}{3}\pi r^2 h$
slant height = $\sqrt{r^2 + h^2}$
lateral area = $\pi r\sqrt{r^2 + h^2}$
total surface area = $\pi r^2 + \pi r\sqrt{r^2 + h^2}$

Polynomials

A *polynomial* is a function of the form

$$P(x) = a_n x^n + a_{n-1} x^{n-1} + \cdots + a_1 x + a_0$$

where n is a positive integer. If $a_n \neq 0$, the polynomial is said to have *degree n*.

Recall the *factor theorem*: if P is a polynomial and c is a real number, then

$$x - c \text{ is a factor of } P(x) \quad \text{iff} \quad P(c) = 0.$$

Factorials

$$0! = 1$$
$$1! = 1$$
$$2! = 2 \cdot 1$$
$$3! = 3 \cdot 2 \cdot 1$$
$$\cdot$$
$$\cdot$$
$$\cdot$$
$$n! = n(n-1) \cdots (2)(1).$$

IV. ANALYTIC GEOMETRY

Rectangular Coordinates: The Distance and Midpoint Formulas

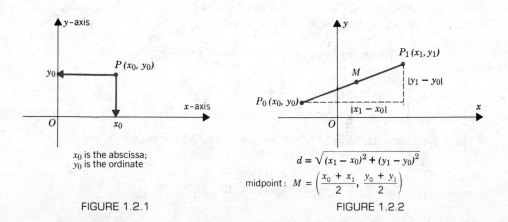

x_0 is the abscissa;
y_0 is the ordinate

FIGURE 1.2.1

$$d = \sqrt{(x_1 - x_0)^2 + (y_1 - y_0)^2}$$

midpoint: $M = \left(\dfrac{x_0 + x_1}{2}, \dfrac{y_0 + y_1}{2} \right)$

FIGURE 1.2.2

Lines

(i) Slope of a nonvertical line:

$$m = \frac{y_1 - y_0}{x_1 - x_0}$$

where $P_0(x_0, y_0)$ and $P_1(x_1, y_1)$ are any two points on the line;

$$m = \tan \theta$$

where θ, called the *inclination* of the line, is the angle between the line and the x-axis measured counterclockwise from the x-axis.

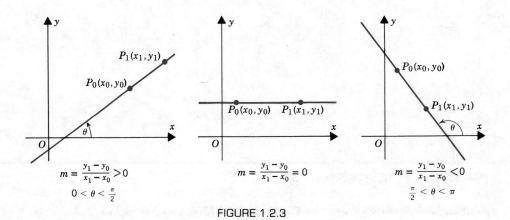

FIGURE 1.2.3

(ii) Equations for lines:

general form	$Ax + By + C = 0$, with A and B not both 0.
vertical line	$x = a$.
slope-intercept form	$y = mx + b$.
point-slope form	$y - y_0 = m(x - x_0)$.
two-point form	$y - y_0 = \dfrac{y_1 - y_0}{x_1 - x_0}(x - x_0)$.
two-intercept form	$\dfrac{x}{a} + \dfrac{y}{b} = 1$.

(iii) Two nonvertical lines $l_1: y = m_1 x + b_1$ and $l_2: y = m_2 x + b_2$ are

$$\text{\textit{parallel} \quad iff \quad } m_1 = m_2;$$
$$\text{\textit{perpendicular} \quad iff \quad } m_1 m_2 = -1.$$

The angle α (taken between $0°$ and $90°$) formed by two intersecting nonvertical lines can be obtained from the relation

$$\tan \alpha = \left| \frac{m_1 - m_2}{1 + m_1 m_2} \right|.$$

(Some review problems on lines are given in Section 1.3.)

Equations of Conic Sections

circle of radius r centered at the origin	$x^2 + y^2 = r^2.$
circle of radius r centered at $P(x_0, y_0)$	$(x - x_0)^2 + (y - y_0)^2 = r^2.$
parabolas	$x^2 = 4cy, \quad y^2 = 4cx.$
ellipse	$\dfrac{x^2}{a^2} + \dfrac{y^2}{b^2} = 1.$
hyperbolas	$\dfrac{x^2}{a^2} - \dfrac{y^2}{b^2} = 1, \quad xy = c.$

(The conic sections are discussed extensively in Chapter 10.)

V. TRIGONOMETRY

Angle Measurement

$$\pi \cong 3.14159.†$$

2π radians = 360 degrees = one complete revolution.

One radian $= \dfrac{180}{\pi}$ degrees $\cong 57.296$ degrees.

One degree $= \dfrac{\pi}{180}$ radians $\cong 0.0175$ radians.

(For a discussion of radian measure, see Appendix A.2.)

Sectors

Figure 1.2.4 displays a sector in a circle of radius r. If θ is the central angle measured in radians, then

---

† We use $\cong$ to indicate approximate equality.

the length of the subtended arc = $r\theta$,   the area of the sector = $\frac{1}{2}r^2\theta$.

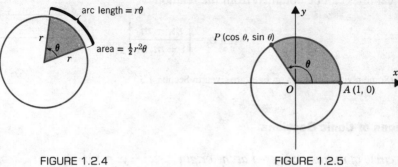

FIGURE 1.2.4   FIGURE 1.2.5

Sine and Cosine

Take θ in the interval $[0, 2\pi)$. In the unit circle (Figure 1.2.5) mark off the sector OAP with a central angle of θ radians:

$$\cos\theta = x\text{-coordinate of } P, \quad \sin\theta = y\text{-coordinate of } P.$$

These definitions are extended periodically:

$$\cos\theta = \cos(\theta + 2n\pi), \quad \sin\theta = \sin(\theta + 2n\pi).$$

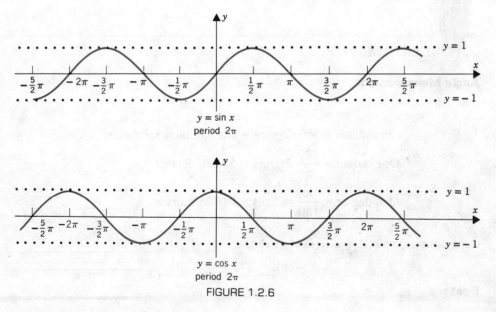

$y = \sin x$
period 2π

$y = \cos x$
period 2π

FIGURE 1.2.6

Other Trigonometric Functions

$$\tan\theta = \frac{\sin\theta}{\cos\theta}, \quad \cot\theta = \frac{\cos\theta}{\sin\theta},$$

$$\sec\theta = \frac{1}{\cos\theta}, \quad \csc\theta = \frac{1}{\sin\theta}.$$

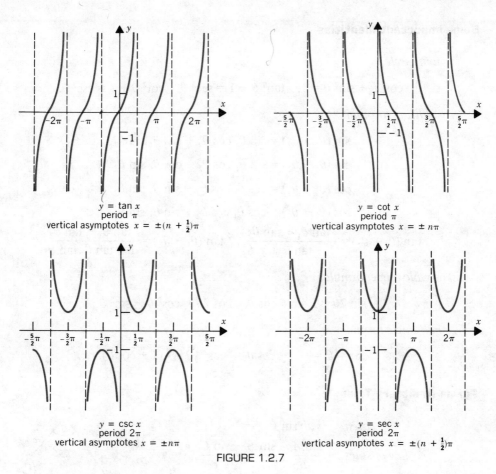

$y = \tan x$
period π
vertical asymptotes $x = \pm(n + \frac{1}{2})\pi$

$y = \cot x$
period π
vertical asymptotes $x = \pm n\pi$

$y = \csc x$
period 2π
vertical asymptotes $x = \pm n\pi$

$y = \sec x$
period 2π
vertical asymptotes $x = \pm(n + \frac{1}{2})\pi$

FIGURE 1.2.7

In Terms of a Right Triangle

For θ between 0 and $\frac{1}{2}\pi$,

$$\sin \theta = \frac{\text{opposite side}}{\text{hypotenuse}}, \qquad \cos \theta = \frac{\text{adjacent side}}{\text{hypotenuse}},$$

$$\tan \theta = \frac{\text{opposite side}}{\text{adjacent side}}, \qquad \cot \theta = \frac{\text{adjacent side}}{\text{opposite side}},$$

$$\sec \theta = \frac{\text{hypotenuse}}{\text{adjacent side}}, \qquad \csc \theta = \frac{\text{hypotenuse}}{\text{opposite side}}.$$

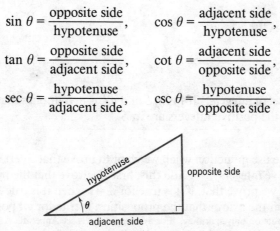

FIGURE 1.2.8

Some Important Identities

(i) *unit circle*

$$\cos^2\theta + \sin^2\theta = 1, \quad \tan^2\theta + 1 = \sec^2\theta, \quad \cot^2\theta + 1 = \csc^2\theta.$$

(ii) *addition formulas*

$$\sin(\theta_1 + \theta_2) = \sin\theta_1\cos\theta_2 + \cos\theta_1\sin\theta_2,$$
$$\sin(\theta_1 - \theta_2) = \sin\theta_1\cos\theta_2 - \cos\theta_1\sin\theta_2,$$
$$\cos(\theta_1 + \theta_2) = \cos\theta_1\cos\theta_2 - \sin\theta_1\sin\theta_2,$$
$$\cos(\theta_1 - \theta_2) = \cos\theta_1\cos\theta_2 + \sin\theta_1\sin\theta_2;$$
$$\tan(\theta_1 + \theta_2) = \frac{\tan\theta_1 + \tan\theta_2}{1 - \tan\theta_1\tan\theta_2}, \quad \tan(\theta_1 - \theta_2) = \frac{\tan\theta_1 - \tan\theta_2}{1 + \tan\theta_1\tan\theta_2}.$$

(iii) *double-angle formulas*

$$\sin 2\theta = 2\sin\theta\cos\theta, \quad \cos 2\theta = \cos^2\theta - \sin^2\theta.$$

(iv) *half-angle formulas*

$$\sin^2\tfrac{1}{2}\theta = \tfrac{1}{2}(1 - \cos\theta), \quad \cos^2\tfrac{1}{2}\theta = \tfrac{1}{2}(1 + \cos\theta).$$

For an Arbitrary Triangle

area $\tfrac{1}{2}ab\sin C.$

law of sines $\dfrac{\sin A}{a} = \dfrac{\sin B}{b} = \dfrac{\sin C}{c}.$

law of cosines $a^2 = b^2 + c^2 - 2bc\cos A.$

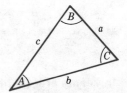

FIGURE 1.2.9

VI. INDUCTION

AXIOM

Let S be a set of integers. If 1 is in S and if k is in S implies that $k + 1$ is in S, then all the positive integers are in S.

In general, we use induction when we want to prove that a certain proposition is true for all positive integers n. To do this, first we prove that the proposition is true for $n = 1$. Next we prove that, if it is true for $n = k$, then it is true for $n = k + 1$. It follows then from the axiom that the proposition is true for all positive integers n.

(We will use induction only sparingly. For a discussion of it see Appendix A.3.)

1.3 ·····SOME PROBLEMS ON LINES

PROBLEM. Find the slope and *y*-intercept of each of the following lines:

$$l_1: 20x - 24y - 30 = 0, \qquad l_2: 2x - 3 = 0, \qquad l_3: 4y + 5 = 0.$$

Solution. The equation of l_1 can be written

$$y = \tfrac{5}{6}x - \tfrac{5}{4}.$$

This is in the form $y = mx + b$. The slope is $\tfrac{5}{6}$, and the *y*-intercept is $-\tfrac{5}{4}$.
    The equation of l_2 can be written

$$x = \tfrac{3}{2}.$$

The line is vertical and the slope is not defined. Since the line does not cross the *y*-axis, it has no *y*-intercept.
    The third equation can be written

$$y = -\tfrac{5}{4}.$$

The line is horizontal. Its slope is 0 and the *y*-intercept is $-\tfrac{5}{4}$. The three lines are drawn in Figure 1.3.1. □

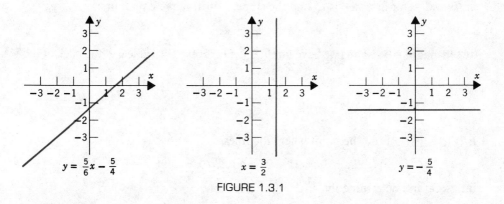

FIGURE 1.3.1

PROBLEM. Write an equation for the line l_2 that is parallel to

$$l_1: 3x - 5y + 8 = 0$$

and passes through the point $P(-3, 2)$.

Solution. We can rewrite the equation of l_1 as

$$y = \tfrac{3}{5}x + \tfrac{8}{5}.$$

The slope of l_1 is $\tfrac{3}{5}$. The slope of l_2 must also be $\tfrac{3}{5}$. (*Remember:* For nonvertical parallel lines $m_1 = m_2$.)
    Since l_2 passes through $(-3, 2)$ with slope $\tfrac{3}{5}$, we can use the point-slope formula and write the equation as

$$y - 2 = \tfrac{3}{5}(x + 3). \quad □$$

PROBLEM.   Write an equation for the line that is perpendicular to

$$l_1: x - 4y + 8 = 0$$

and passes through the point $P(2, -4)$.

Solution.   The equation for l_1 can be written

$$y = \tfrac{1}{4}x + 2.$$

The slope of l_1 is $\tfrac{1}{4}$.   The slope of l_2 is therefore -4.   (*Remember:* For nonvertical perpendicular lines $m_1 m_2 = -1$.)

Since l_2 passes through $(2, -4)$ with slope -4, we can use the point-slope formula and write the equation as

$$y + 4 = -4(x - 2). \quad \square$$

PROBLEM.   Find the inclination θ of the line

$$3x - 4y + 2 = 0.$$

Solution.   Our first step is to find the slope.   Writing the equation as

$$y = \tfrac{3}{4}x + \tfrac{1}{2},$$

we see that $m = \tfrac{3}{4}$.   Thus we have $\tan \theta = \tfrac{3}{4} = 0.7500$.   By Table 5 at the back of the book, $\theta \cong 37°$. $\square$

PROBLEM.   Find the point where the lines

$$l_1: 2x - 7y + 31 = 0 \quad \text{and} \quad l_2: x - 2y + 7 = 0$$

intersect, and determine the angle of intersection.

Solution.   To find the point of intersection we solve the two equations simultaneously.   As you can check, this gives $x = \tfrac{13}{3}$, $y = \tfrac{17}{3}$.   The point of intersection is $P(\tfrac{13}{3}, \tfrac{17}{3})$.

To find the angle of intersection we use the formula

$$\tan \alpha = \left| \frac{m_1 - m_2}{1 + m_1 m_2} \right|.$$

Here, as you can verify, $m_1 = \tfrac{2}{7}$ and $m_2 = \tfrac{1}{2}$, so that

$$\tan \alpha = \left| \frac{\tfrac{2}{7} - \tfrac{1}{2}}{1 + (\tfrac{2}{7})(\tfrac{1}{2})} \right| = \frac{3}{16} = 0.1875.$$

By Table 5 at the back of the book, $\alpha \cong 11°$. $\square$

EXERCISES

(The odd-numbered exercises have answers at the back of the book.)

Find the slope of the line through the given points.

1. $P_0(-2, 5)$, $P_1(4, 1)$.   **2.** $P_0(4, -3)$, $P_1(-2, -7)$.   **3.** $P_0(4, 2)$, $P_1(-3, 2)$.
4. $P_0(5, 0)$, $P_1(0, 5)$.   **5.** $P(a, b)$, $Q(b, a)$.   **6.** $P(4, -1)$, $Q(-3, -1)$.
7. $P(x_0, 0)$, $Q(0, y_0)$.   **8.** $O(0, 0)$, $P(x_0, y_0)$.

Find the slope and y-intercept.

9. $y = 2x - 4$.   **10.** $6 - 5x = 0$.   **11.** $3y = x + 6$.   **12.** $y = 4x - 2$.
13. $4x = 1$.   **14.** $6y - 3x + 8 = 0$.   **15.** $7x - 3y + 4 = 0$.   **16.** $4y = 3$.
17. $7y - 5 = 0$.   **18.** $4y = x - 5$.

Write an equation for the line with

19. slope 5 and y-intercept 2.   **20.** slope 5 and y-intercept -2.
21. slope -5 and y-intercept 2.   **22.** slope -5 and y-intercept -2.

Write an equation for the horizontal line 3 units

23. above the x-axis.   **24.** below the x-axis.

Write an equation for the vertical line 3 units

25. to the left of the y-axis.   **26.** to the right of the y-axis.

Find an equation for the line that passes through the point $P(2, 7)$ and is

27. parallel to the x-axis.
28. parallel to the y-axis.
29. parallel to the line $3y - 2x + 6 = 0$.
30. perpendicular to the line $y - 2x + 5 = 0$.
31. perpendicular to the line $3y - 2x + 6 = 0$.
32. parallel to the line $y - 2x + 5 = 0$.

Write the equation $3y + 6x - 12 = 0$

33. in slope-intercept form.   **34.** in two-intercept form.
35. in point-slope form using the point $P(1, 2)$.

Write the equation $4y - 2x + 12 = 0$

36. in slope-intercept form.   **37.** in two-intercept form.
38. in point-slope form using the point $P(-1, 4)$.

Find the inclination of the line.

39. $x - y + 2 = 0$.   **40.** $6y + 5 = 0$.   **41.** $2x - 3 = 0$.
42. $x + y - 3 = 0$.   **43.** $3x + 4y - 12 = 0$.   **44.** $2x - y + 4 = 0$.

Write an equation for the line with

45. inclination 30°, y-intercept 2.   **46.** inclination 60°, y-intercept 2.
47. inclination 120°, y-intercept 3.   **48.** inclination 135°, y-intercept 3.

Find the point where the lines intersect and determine the angle of intersection.

49. l_1: $2x - 3y - 3 = 0$, l_2: $3x - 2y - 3 = 0$.
50. l_1: $3x + 10y + 4 = 0$, l_2: $7x - 10y - 1 = 0$.
51. l_1: $4x - y + 2 = 0$, l_2: $19x + y = 0$.
52. l_1: $5x - 6y + 1 = 0$, l_2: $8x + 5y + 2 = 0$.

Find the angles of the triangle with the given vertices.

53. $(-2, 5)$, $(0, 0)$, $(5, -2)$.   **54.** $(1, -1)$, $(4, 0)$, $(3, 2)$.
55. $(-4, -2)$, $(0, -1)$, $(1, 1)$.   **56.** $(-4, 2)$, $(1, 0)$, $(1, 1)$.

57. (a) Find an equation for the line l' that is perpendicular to the line

$$l: Ax + By + C = 0$$

and passes through the origin.
(b) Find the point Q where l' and l intersect.
(c) What is the distance between l and the origin?

1.4 ······INEQUALITIES

In this section and the next, we work with the sort of inequalities that abound in calculus, inequalities that involve a variable.

To solve an equation in x is to find the set of numbers x for which the equation holds. To solve an inequality in x is to find the set of numbers x for which the inequality holds.

The way we solve an inequality is very similar to the way we solve an equation, but there is one important difference. We can maintain an inequality by adding the same number to both sides, or by subtracting the same number from both sides, or by multiplying both sides by the same *positive* number. But if we multiply by a *negative* number, then the inequality is *reversed*:

$$x - 2 < 5 \quad \text{gives} \quad x < 7,$$
$$x + 2 < 5 \quad \text{gives} \quad x < 3,$$
$$\tfrac{1}{2}x < 5 \quad \text{gives} \quad x < 10,$$

but

$$-\tfrac{1}{2}x < 5 \quad \text{gives} \quad x > -10.$$

(note ↓)

PROBLEM. Solve the inequality

$$\tfrac{1}{2}(1 + x) \leq 6.$$

Solution. The idea is to "unwrap" the x. We can eliminate the $\frac{1}{2}$ by multiplying through by 2. This gives

$$1 + x \leq 12.$$

Substracting 1 from both sides, we get

$$x \le 11.$$

The solution is thus the interval $(-\infty, 11]$.   ☐

PROBLEM.   Solve the inequality

$$-3(4 - x) < 12.$$

Solution.   Multiplying both sides of the inequality by $-\frac{1}{3}$, we have

$$4 - x > -4. \qquad \text{(the inequality has been reversed)}$$

Subtracting 4, we get

$$-x > -8.$$

To isolate x, we multiply by -1. This gives

$$x < 8. \qquad \text{(the inequality has been reversed again)}$$

The solution is the interval $(-\infty, 8)$.   ☐

    There are generally several ways to solve a given inequality. For example, the last inequality could have been solved this way:

$$-3(4 - x) < 12,$$
$$-12 + 3x < 12,$$
$$3x < 24, \qquad \text{(we added 12)}$$
$$x < 8. \qquad \text{(divided by 3)}$$

The solution, of course, is once again $(-\infty, 8)$.

    The usual way to solve a quadratic inequality is to factor the quadratic.

PROBLEM.   Solve the inequality

$$\tfrac{1}{5}(x^2 - 4x + 3) < 0.$$

Solution.   First we eliminate the outside factor $\frac{1}{5}$ by multiplying through by 5: this gives

$$x^2 - 4x + 3 < 0.$$

Factoring the quadratic, we have

$$(x - 1)(x - 3) < 0.$$

The product $(x - 1)(x - 3)$ is zero at 1 and 3. We mark these points on a number line (Figure 1.4.1). The points 1 and 3 separate three intervals:

$$(-\infty, 1), \qquad (1, 3), \qquad (3, \infty).$$

On each of these intervals the product $(x - 1)(x - 3)$ keeps a constant sign:

on $(-\infty, 1)$ [to the left of 1]

$$\text{sgn}\,[(x - 1)(x - 3)] = (-)(-) = +;$$

on $(1, 3)$ [between 1 and 3]

$$\text{sgn}\,[(x - 1)(x - 3)] = (+)(-) = -;$$

on $(3, \infty)$ [to the right of 3]

$$\text{sgn}\,[(x - 1)(x - 3)] = (+)(+) = +.$$

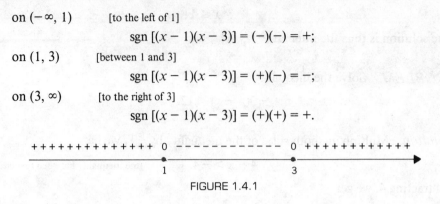

FIGURE 1.4.1

The product $(x - 1)(x - 3)$ is negative only on $(1, 3)$. The solution is the open interval $(1, 3)$. ☐

PROBLEM. Solve the inequality

$$2x^2 - 2x > 4.$$

Solution

$$2x^2 - 2x > 4,$$
$$2x^2 - 2x - 4 > 0, \qquad\qquad \text{(we subtracted 4)}$$
$$x^2 - x - 2 > 0, \qquad\qquad \text{(divided by 2)}$$
$$(x + 1)(x - 2) > 0. \qquad\qquad \text{(factored)}$$

On the number line we mark the points -1 and 2 where the product $(x + 1)(x - 2)$ is zero. See Figure 1.4.2. These points separate the intervals

$$(-\infty, -1), \qquad (-1, 2), \qquad (2, \infty).$$

On each of these intervals the product $(x + 1)(x - 2)$ keeps a constant sign:

on $(-\infty, -1)$ [to the left of -1]

$$\text{sgn}\,[(x + 1)(x - 2)] = (-)(-) = +;$$

on $(-1, 2)$ [between -1 and 2]

$$\text{sgn}\,[(x + 1)(x - 2)] = (+)(-) = -;$$

on $(2, \infty)$ [to the right of 2]

$$\text{sgn}\,[(x + 1)(x - 2)] = (+)(+) = +.$$

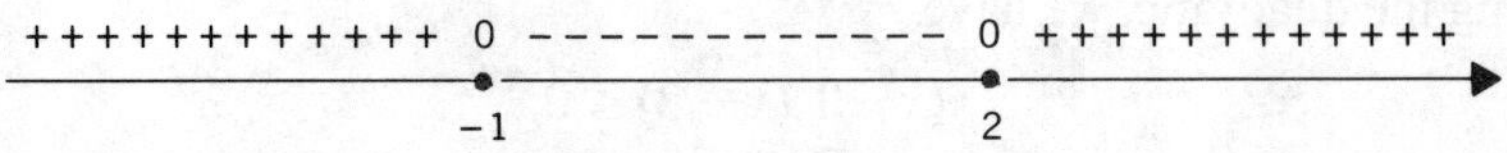

```
+ + + + + + + + + + + +  0  - - - - - - - - - - - -  0  + + + + + + + + + + + +
─────────────────────────●───────────────────────────●──────────────────────►
                        −1                            2
```

FIGURE 1.4.2

The product $(x + 1)(x - 2)$ is positive on $(-\infty, -1)$ and on $(2, \infty)$. The solution is the union of these two intervals $(-\infty, -1) \cup (2, \infty)$. ☐

More generally, consider an expression of the form

$$(x - a_1)(x - a_2) \cdots (x - a_n) \qquad \text{with } a_1 < a_2 < \cdots < a_n.$$

Such an expression is zero at $a_1, a_2, \ldots, a_n$. It is positive on those intervals where an even number of terms are negative, and it is negative on those intervals where an odd number of terms are negative.

As an example, take the expression

$$(x + 2)(x - 1)(x - 3).$$

This product is zero at $-2, 1, 3$. It is

$$
\begin{array}{ll}
\text{negative on } (-\infty, -2), & \text{(3 negative terms)} \\
\text{positive on } (-2, 1), & \text{(2 negative terms)} \\
\text{negative on } (1, 3), & \text{(1 negative term)} \\
\text{positive on } (3, \infty). & \text{(0 negative terms)}
\end{array}
$$

PROBLEM. Solve the inequality

$$(x + 3)^5(x - 1)(x - 4)^2 < 0.$$

Solution. We view $(x + 3)^5(x - 1)(x - 4)^2$ as the product of three factors: $(x + 3)^5$, $(x - 1)$, $(x - 4)^2$. The product is zero at $-3, 1,$ and 4. These points separate the intervals

$$(-\infty, -3), \qquad (-3, 1), \qquad (1, 4), \qquad (4, \infty).$$

On each of these intervals the product keeps a constant sign. It is

$$
\begin{array}{ll}
\text{positive on } (-\infty, -3), & \text{(2 negative factors)} \\
\text{negative on } (-3, 1), & \text{(1 negative factor)} \\
\text{positive on } (1, 4), & \text{(0 negative factors)} \\
\text{positive on } (4, \infty). & \text{(0 negative factors)}
\end{array}
$$

The solution is the open interval $(-3, 1)$. $\square$

PROBLEM. Solve the inequality

$$x^2 + 4x - 2 \le 0.$$

Solution. To factor the quadratic we first transpose the -2 and then complete the square on the left:

$$x^2 + 4x \le 2,$$
$$x^2 + 4x + 4 \le 2 + 4,$$
$$(x + 2)^2 \le 6.$$

Now we subtract 6 from both sides:

$$(x + 2)^2 - 6 \le 0$$

and factor the expression as the difference of two squares:

$$(x + 2 + \sqrt{6})(x + 2 - \sqrt{6}) \le 0.$$

The product is 0 at $-2 - \sqrt{6}$ and at $-2 + \sqrt{6}$. It is negative between these two numbers. The solution is the closed interval $[-2 - \sqrt{6}, -2 + \sqrt{6}]$. □

REMARK. The roots of the quadratic $x^2 + 4x - 2 = 0$ could have been obtained from the general quadratic formula. □

In solving inequalities that involve quotients we use the fact that

(1.4.1)
$$\frac{a}{b} > 0 \quad \text{iff} \quad ab > 0 \quad \text{and} \quad \frac{a}{b} < 0 \quad \text{iff} \quad ab < 0.$$

PROBLEM. Solve the inequality

$$\frac{x+2}{1-x} > 1.$$

Solution

$$\frac{x+2}{1-x} > 1,$$

$$\frac{x+2}{1-x} - 1 > 0,$$

$$\frac{x + 2 - (1 - x)}{1 - x} > 0,$$

$$\frac{2x+1}{1-x} > 0,$$

$$(2x+1)(1-x) > 0, \qquad\qquad\qquad \text{[by (1.4.1)]}$$

$$(2x+1)(x-1) < 0, \qquad\qquad \text{(we multiplied by } -1)$$

$$(x + \tfrac{1}{2})(x-1) < 0. \qquad\qquad \text{(divided by 2)}$$

The product $(x + \tfrac{1}{2})(x - 1)$ is zero at $-\tfrac{1}{2}$ and 1. As you can check, it is negative only on the open interval $(-\tfrac{1}{2}, 1)$. This open interval is the solution to our inequality. □

PROBLEM. Solve the inequality

$$\frac{(x+4)(x-5)^2}{x^3(x-2)} > 0.$$

Solution. By (1.4.1) this inequality has the same solution as the inequality

$$(x+4)(x-5)^2 x^3(x-2) > 0.$$

We will work with this second inequality. The product on the left is 0 at

$$-4, \quad 5, \quad 0, \quad 2.$$

We rewrite these numbers in their natural order:

$$-4, \quad 0, \quad 2, \quad 5$$

and rewrite the product accordingly:

$$(x + 4)x^3(x - 2)(x - 5)^2.$$

The points $-4, 0, 2, 5$ separate the intervals

$$(-\infty, -4), \quad (-4, 0), \quad (0, 2), \quad (2, 5), \quad (5, \infty).$$

On each of these intervals the product $(x + 4)x^3(x - 2)(x - 5)^2$ keeps a constant sign. It is

$$\begin{array}{ll}
\text{negative on } (-\infty, -4), & \text{(3 negative factors)} \\
\text{positive on } (-4, 0), & \text{(2 negative factors)} \\
\text{negative on } (0, 2), & \text{(1 negative factor)} \\
\text{positive on } (2, 5), & \text{(0 negative factors)} \\
\text{positive on } (5, \infty). & \text{(0 negative factors)}
\end{array}$$

The solution is the union $(-4, 0) \cup (2, 5) \cup (5, \infty)$. □

EXERCISES

Solve the following inequalities.

1. $2 + 3x < 5$.
2. $\frac{1}{2}(2x + 3) < 6$.
3. $16x + 64 \le 16$.
4. $3x + 5 > \frac{1}{4}(x - 2)$.
5. $\frac{1}{2}(1 + x) < \frac{1}{3}(1 - x)$.
6. $3x - 2 \le 1 + 6x$.
7. $x^2 - 1 < 0$.
8. $x^2 + x - 2 \le 0$.
9. $4(x^2 - 3x + 2) > 0$.
10. $x^2 + 9x + 20 < 0$.
11. $x(x - 1)(x - 2) > 0$.
12. $x(2x - 1)(3x - 5) \le 0$.
13. $x^3 - 2x^2 + x \ge 0$.
14. $x^2 - 4x + 4 \le 0$.
15. $x^2 + 1 > 4x$.
16. $2 - x^2 \ge -4x$.
17. $\frac{1}{2}(1 + x)^2 < \frac{1}{3}(1 - x)^2$.
18. $2x^2 + 9x + 6 \ge x + 2$.
19. $1 - 3x^2 < \frac{1}{2}(2 - x^2)$.
20. $6x^2 + 4x + 4 \le 4(x - 1)^2$.

21. $\dfrac{1}{x} < x$.
22. $x + \dfrac{1}{x} \ge 1$.

23. $\dfrac{x}{x - 5} \ge 0$.
24. $\dfrac{x}{x + 5} < 0$.

25. $\dfrac{x}{x - 5} > \dfrac{1}{4}$.
26. $\dfrac{1}{3x - 5} < 2$.

27. $\dfrac{x^2 - 9}{x + 1} > 0$.
28. $\dfrac{x^2}{x^2 - 4} < 0$.

29. $x^3(x - 2)(x + 3)^2 < 0$.
30. $x^2(x - 3)(x + 4)^2 > 0$.
31. $x^2(x - 2)(x + 6) > 0$.
32. $x^3(x + 3)(x - 5) > 0$.
33. $5x(x - 3)^2 < 0$.
34. $7x(x - 4)^2 < 0$.

35. $\dfrac{2x}{x^2 - 4} > 0.$

36. $\dfrac{x^2 - 9}{3x} > 0.$

37. $\dfrac{x - 1}{9 - x^2} < 0.$

38. $\dfrac{x^2 - 4}{(x + 4)^2} < 0.$

39. $\dfrac{1}{x - 1} + \dfrac{4}{x - 6} > 0.$

40. $\dfrac{3}{x - 2} - \dfrac{5}{x - 6} < 0.$

41. $\dfrac{2x - 6}{x^2 - 6x + 5} < 0.$

42. $\dfrac{2x + 8}{x^2 + 8x + 7} > 0.$

43. $\dfrac{x + 3}{x^2(x - 5)} < 0.$

44. $\dfrac{x^2 - 4x}{x + 2} > 0.$

45. $\dfrac{x^2 - 4x + 3}{x^2} > 0.$

46. $\dfrac{x^2 - 2x + 1}{x^2 + 2x - 3} < 0.$

47. Arrange the following in order:

$$1, \quad x, \quad \sqrt{x}, \quad \frac{1}{x}, \quad \frac{1}{\sqrt{x}}$$

given that (a) $1 < x$. (b) $0 < x < 1$.

48. Compare

$$\sqrt{\frac{x}{x + 1}} \quad \text{and} \quad \sqrt{\frac{x + 1}{x + 2}} \quad \text{given that } x > 0.$$

49. Verify (1.4.1).   HINT: $\dfrac{a}{b} = \dfrac{ab}{b^2}$ iff $b \neq 0$.

50. Let a and b be nonnegative numbers. Show that

$$\text{if} \quad a^2 \leq b^2 \quad \text{then} \quad a \leq b.$$

HINT: $b^2 - a^2 = (b + a)(b - a)$.

51. Show that

$$\text{if} \quad 0 \leq a \leq b \quad \text{then} \quad \frac{a}{1 + a} \leq \frac{b}{1 + b}.$$

52. Let a, b, c be nonnegative numbers. Show that

$$\text{if} \quad a \leq b + c \quad \text{then} \quad \frac{a}{1 + a} \leq \frac{b}{1 + b} + \frac{c}{1 + c}.$$

1.5 ······INEQUALITIES AND ABSOLUTE VALUE

Here we take up some inequalities that involve absolute values. With an eye toward Chapter 2 we introduce two Greek letters: δ (delta) and ϵ (epsilon). You can find the complete Greek alphabet in the front matter.

Recall that for each real number a

$$|a| = \begin{cases} a, & \text{if } a \geq 0 \\ -a, & \text{if } a \leq 0 \end{cases}, \qquad |a| = \max \{a, -a\}, \qquad |a| = \sqrt{a^2}.$$

We begin with the inequality

$$|x| < \delta$$

where δ is some positive number. To say that $|x| < \delta$ is to say that x lies within δ units of 0, or, equivalently, that x lies between $-\delta$ and δ. Thus

(1.5.1) $|x| < \delta$ iff $-\delta < x < \delta$.

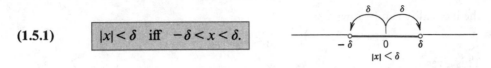

To say that $|x - c| < \delta$ is to say that x lies within δ units of c, or, equivalently, that x lies between $c - \delta$ and $c + \delta$. Thus

(1.5.2) $|x - c| < \delta$ iff $c - \delta < x < c + \delta$.

Somewhat more delicate is the inequality

$$0 < |x - c| < \delta.$$

Here we have $|x - c| < \delta$ with the additional requirement that x cannot be c. Consequently

(1.5.3) $0 < |x - c| < \delta$ iff $c - \delta < x < c$ or $c < x < c + \delta$.

EXAMPLES

1. $|x| < \frac{1}{2}$ iff $-\frac{1}{2} < x < \frac{1}{2}$.   *Solution.* $(-\frac{1}{2}, \frac{1}{2})$.

2. $|x - 5| < 1$ iff $4 < x < 6$.   *Solution.* $(4, 6)$.

3. $0 < |x - 5| < 1$ iff $4 < x < 5$ or $5 < x < 6$. *Solution.* $(4, 5) \cup (5, 6)$. □

PROBLEM. Solve the inequality

$$|x + 2| < 3.$$

Solution. We use (1.5.2) taking $c = -2$ and $\delta = 3$. Accordingly,

$$|x + 2| < 3 \quad \text{iff} \quad -2 - 3 < x < -2 + 3.$$

The solution is the open interval $(-5, 1)$. □

PROBLEM. Solve the inequality

$$|3x - 4| < 2.$$

Solution. Since

$$|3x - 4| = |3(x - \tfrac{4}{3})| = |3||x - \tfrac{4}{3}| = 3|x - \tfrac{4}{3}|,$$

the inequality can be rewritten

$$3|x - \tfrac{4}{3}| < 2.$$

This gives

$$|x - \tfrac{4}{3}| < \tfrac{2}{3},$$
$$\tfrac{4}{3} - \tfrac{2}{3} < x < \tfrac{4}{3} + \tfrac{2}{3},$$
$$\tfrac{2}{3} < x < 2.$$

The solution is the open interval $(\tfrac{2}{3}, 2)$. □

Let $\epsilon > 0$. If you think of $|a|$ as the distance between a and 0, then obviously

(1.5.4) $\boxed{|a| > \epsilon \ \text{ iff } \ a > \epsilon \ \text{ or } \ a < -\epsilon.}$

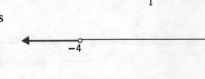

PROBLEM. Solve the inequality

$$|2x + 3| > 5.$$

Solution. As you saw, in general

$$|a| > \epsilon \qquad \text{iff} \qquad a > \epsilon \ \text{ or } \ a < -\epsilon.$$

So here

$$2x + 3 > 5 \quad \text{or} \quad 2x + 3 < -5.$$

The first possibility gives $2x > 2$ and thus

$$x > 1.$$

The second possibility gives $2x < -8$ and thus

$$x < -4.$$

The total solution is therefore the union

$$(-\infty, -4) \cup (1, \infty). \quad □$$

One of the fundamental inequalities of calculus is the *triangle inequality*: for all real numbers a and b,

(1.5.5) $\boxed{|a + b| \le |a| + |b|.}$

Proof. The proof is easy if you think of $|x|$ as $\sqrt{x^2}$. Note first that

$$(a + b)^2 = a^2 + 2ab + b^2 \le |a|^2 + 2|a||b| + |b|^2 = (|a| + |b|)^2.$$

Comparing the extremes of the inequality and taking square roots, we have

$$\sqrt{(a + b)^2} \le |a| + |b|. \qquad \text{(Exercise 50, Section 1.4)}$$

The result follows from observing that

$$\sqrt{(a + b)^2} = |a + b|. \quad \square$$

Here is a variant of the triangle inequality that also comes up in calculus: for all real numbers a and b,

(1.5.6)
$$\boxed{\big||a| - |b|\big| \le |a - b|.}$$

The proof is left to you in the exercises.

EXERCISES

Solve the following inequalities.

1. $|x| < 2$.
2. $|x| \ge 1$.
3. $|x| > 3$.
4. $|x - 1| < 1$.
5. $|x - 2| < \frac{1}{2}$.
6. $|x - \frac{1}{2}| < 2$.
7. $|x + 2| < \frac{1}{4}$.
8. $|x - 3| < \frac{1}{4}$.
9. $0 < |x| < 1$.
10. $0 < |x| < \frac{1}{2}$.
11. $0 < |x - 2| < \frac{1}{2}$.
12. $0 < |x - \frac{1}{2}| < 2$.
13. $0 < |x - 3| < 8$.
14. $0 < |x - 2| < 8$.
15. $|2x - 3| < 1$.
16. $|3x - 5| < 3$.
17. $|2x + 1| < \frac{1}{4}$.
18. $|5x - 3| < \frac{1}{2}$.
19. $|2x + 5| > 3$.
20. $|3x + 1| > 5$.
21. $|5x - 1| > 9$.

Find the inequality of the form $|x - c| < \delta$ the solution of which is the given open interval.

22. $(-2, 2)$.
23. $(-3, 3)$.
24. $(0, 4)$.
25. $(-3, 7)$.
26. $(-4, 0)$.
27. $(-7, 3)$.

Determine all values of $A > 0$ for which the statement is true.

28. If $|x - 2| < 1$, then $|2x - 4| < A$.
29. If $|x - 2| < A$, then $|2x - 4| < 3$.
30. If $|x + 1| < A$, then $|3x + 3| < 4$.
31. If $|x + 1| < 2$, then $|3x + 3| < A$.

32. Prove that for all real numbers a and b

$$|a - b| \le |a| + |b|.$$

33. Prove (1.5.6).   HINT: Calculate $\big||a| - |b|\big|^2$ and use the fact that $ab \le |a||b|$.

34. Show that equality holds in (1.5.5) iff $ab \ge 0$.

1.6 ······FUNCTIONS

The fundamental processes of calculus (called *differentiation* and *integration*) are processes applied to functions. To understand these processes and to be able to carry them out, you have to be thoroughly familiar with functions. Here we review some of the basic notions.

Domain, Range, Graph

First we need a working definition for the word *function*. Let D be a set of real numbers. By a *function* on D we mean a rule that assigns a unique number to each number in D. The set D is called the *domain* of the function. The set of assignments that the function makes (the set of values that the function takes on) is called the *range* of the function.

Here are some examples. We begin with the squaring function

$$f(x) = x^2, \qquad x \text{ real.}$$

The domain of f is explicitly given as the set of all real numbers. As x runs through all the real numbers, x^2 runs through all the nonnegative numbers. The range is therefore $[0, \infty)$. In abbreviated form we write

$$\text{dom } (f) = (-\infty, \infty) \quad \text{and} \quad \text{ran } (f) = [0, \infty)$$

and say that f *maps* $(-\infty, \infty)$ *onto* $[0, \infty)$.

Now take the function

$$g(x) = \sqrt{x + 4}, \qquad x \in [0, 5].$$

The domain of g is given as the closed interval $[0, 5]$. At 0, g takes on the value 2:

$$g(0) = \sqrt{0 + 4} = \sqrt{4} = 2.$$

At 5, g takes on the value 3:

$$g(5) = \sqrt{5 + 4} = \sqrt{9} = 3.$$

As x runs through all the numbers from 0 to 5, $g(x)$ runs through all the numbers from 2 to 3. The range of g is therefore the closed interval $[2, 3]$. In abbreviated form

$$\text{dom } (g) = [0, 5], \qquad \text{ran } (g) = [2, 3].$$

The function g maps $[0, 5]$ onto $[2, 3]$.

If f is a function with domain D, the *graph* of f is by definition the set of all points

$$P(x, f(x)) \qquad \text{with } x \in D.$$

The graph of the squaring function

$$f(x) = x^2, \qquad x \text{ real}$$

is the parabola shown in Figure 1.6.1. The graph of the function

$$g(x) = \sqrt{x + 4}, \qquad x \in [0, 5]$$

is the arc drawn in Figure 1.6.2.

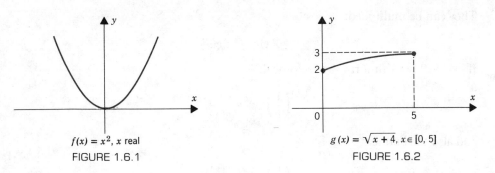

$f(x) = x^2$, x real
FIGURE 1.6.1

$g(x) = \sqrt{x + 4}$, $x \in [0, 5]$
FIGURE 1.6.2

Sometimes the domain of a function is not explicitly given. Thus, for example, we might write

$$f(x) = x^3 \quad \text{or} \quad f(x) = \sqrt{x} \qquad \text{(Figure 1.6.3)}$$

without further explanation. In such cases, take as the domain the maximal set of real numbers x for which $f(x)$ is itself a real number. For the cubing function, take dom $(f) = (-\infty, \infty)$, and for the square root function, take dom $(f) = [0, \infty)$.

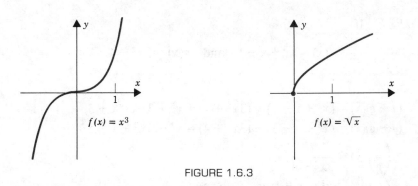

$f(x) = x^3$

$f(x) = \sqrt{x}$

FIGURE 1.6.3

PROBLEM. Find the domain and range of

$$f(x) = \frac{1}{\sqrt{2 - x}} + 5.$$

Solution. First we look for the domain. To be able to form $\sqrt{2 - x}$ we need $2 - x \geq 0$ and therefore $x \leq 2$. But at $x = 2$, $\sqrt{2 - x} = 0$ and its reciprocal is not defined. We must therefore restrict x to $x < 2$. The domain is $(-\infty, 2)$.

Now we look for the range. As x runs through $(-\infty, 2)$, $\sqrt{2 - x}$ takes on all positive values and so does its reciprocal. The range of f is therefore $(5, \infty)$. $\square$

Algebraic Combinations of Functions

Functions with a common domain can be added and subtracted:

$$(f + g)(x) = f(x) + g(x), \qquad (f - g)(x) = f(x) - g(x).$$

They can be multiplied:

$$(fg)(x) = f(x)g(x).$$

If $g(x) \neq 0$, we can form the reciprocal:

$$\left(\frac{1}{g}\right)(x) = \frac{1}{g(x)},$$

and also the quotient:

$$\left(\frac{f}{g}\right)(x) = \frac{f(x)}{g(x)}.$$

With α and β real, we can form *scalar multiples*:

$$(\alpha f)(x) = \alpha f(x)$$

and *linear combinations*:

$$(\alpha f + \beta g)(x) = \alpha f(x) + \beta g(x).$$

EXAMPLE. If

$$f(x) = x^3 + x - 1 \quad \text{and} \quad g(x) = 3x^2 + 4,$$

then

$$(f + g)(x) = (x^3 + x - 1) + (3x^2 + 4) = x^3 + 3x^2 + x + 3,$$
$$(f - g)(x) = (x^3 + x - 1) - (3x^2 + 4) = x^3 - 3x^2 + x - 5,$$
$$\left(\frac{1}{g}\right)(x) = \frac{1}{3x^2 + 4},$$
$$\left(\frac{f}{g}\right)(x) = \frac{x^3 + x - 1}{3x^2 + 4},$$
$$(6f)(x) = 6(x^3 + x - 1),$$
$$(6f - 5g)(x) = 6(x^3 + x - 1) - 5(3x^2 + 4) = 6x^3 - 15x^2 + 6x - 26. \quad \square$$

EXAMPLE. Now consider two functions defined piecewise:

$$f(x) = \begin{bmatrix} 1 - x^2, & x \leq 0 \\ x, & x > 0 \end{bmatrix}, \quad g(x) = \begin{bmatrix} -2x, & x < 1 \\ 1 - x, & x \geq 1 \end{bmatrix}.$$

To find $f + g, f - g, fg$, we must fit the pieces together; namely, we must break up the domain of both functions in the same manner:

$$f(x) = \begin{bmatrix} 1 - x^2, & x \leq 0 \\ x, & 0 < x < 1 \\ x, & 1 \leq x \end{bmatrix}, \quad g(x) = \begin{bmatrix} -2x, & x \leq 0 \\ -2x, & 0 < x < 1 \\ 1 - x, & 1 \leq x \end{bmatrix}.$$

The rest is straightforward:

$$(f + g)(x) = f(x) + g(x) = \begin{cases} 1 - 2x - x^2, & x \leq 0 \\ -x, & 0 < x < 1 \\ 1, & 1 \leq x \end{cases},$$

$$(f - g)(x) = f(x) - g(x) = \begin{cases} 1 + 2x - x^2, & x \leq 0 \\ 3x, & 0 < x < 1 \\ -1 + 2x, & 1 \leq x \end{cases},$$

$$(fg)(x) = f(x)g(x) = \begin{cases} -2x + 2x^3, & x \leq 0 \\ -2x^2, & 0 < x < 1 \\ x - x^2, & 1 \leq x \end{cases}. \quad \square$$

EXERCISES

Find the number(s), if any, where f takes on the value 1.

1. $f(x) = |2 - x|$.   **2.** $f(x) = \sqrt{1 + x}$.   **3.** $f(x) = x^2 + 4x + 5$.

4. $f(x) = 4 + 10x - x^2$.   **5.** $f(x) = 1 + \sin x$.   **6.** $f(x) = \tan x$.

7. $f(x) = \cos 2x$.   **8.** $f(x) = -1 + \cos x$.

Find the domain and the range.

9. $f(x) = |x|$.   **10.** $g(x) = x^2 - 1$.   **11.** $f(x) = 2x - 1$.

12. $g(x) = \sqrt{x} - 1$.   **13.** $f(x) = \dfrac{1}{x^2}$.   **14.** $g(x) = \dfrac{1}{x}$.

15. $f(x) = \sqrt{1 - x}$.   **16.** $g(x) = \sqrt{x - 1}$.   **17.** $f(x) = \sqrt{1 - x} - 1$.

18. $g(x) = \sqrt{x - 1} - 1$.   **19.** $f(x) = \dfrac{1}{\sqrt{1 - x}}$.   **20.** $g(x) = \dfrac{1}{\sqrt{4 - x^2}}$.

21. $f(x) = |\sin x|$.   **22.** $f(x) = \sin^2 x + \cos^2 x$.   **23.** $f(x) = 2 \cos 3x$.

24. $f(x) = \sqrt{\cos^2 x}$.   **25.** $f(x) = 1 + \tan^2 x$.   **26.** $f(x) = 1 + \sin x$.

Sketch the graph.

27. $f(x) = 1$.   **28.** $f(x) = -1$.   **29.** $f(x) = 2x$.

30. $f(x) = 2x + 1$.   **31.** $f(x) = \frac{1}{2}x$.   **32.** $f(x) = -\frac{1}{2}x$.

33. $f(x) = \frac{1}{2}x + 2$.   **34.** $f(x) = -\frac{1}{2}x - 3$.   **35.** $f(x) = \sqrt{4 - x^2}$.

36. $f(x) = \sqrt{9 - x^2}$.   **37.** $f(x) = 3 \sin 2x$.   **38.** $f(x) = 1 + \sin x$.

39. $f(x) = 1 - \cos x$.   **40.** $f(x) = \tan \frac{1}{2}x$.   **41.** $f(x) = \sqrt{\sin^2 x}$.

42. $f(x) = -2 \cos x$.

Sketch the graph and specify the domain and range.

43. $f(x) = \begin{cases} -1, & x < 0 \\ 1, & x > 0 \end{cases}$.   **44.** $f(x) = \begin{cases} x^2, & x \leq 0 \\ 1 - x, & x > 0 \end{cases}$.

45. $f(x) = \begin{cases} 1 + x, & 0 \leq x \leq 1 \\ x, & 1 < x < 2 \\ \frac{1}{2}x + 1, & 2 \leq x \end{cases}$.   **46.** $f(x) = \begin{cases} x^2, & x < 0 \\ -1, & 0 < x < 2 \\ x, & 2 < x \end{cases}$.

47. Given that

$$f(x) = \sqrt{x} + \frac{1}{\sqrt{x}} \quad \text{and} \quad g(x) = \sqrt{x} - \frac{2}{\sqrt{x}},$$

find   (a) $6f + 3g$,   (b) fg,   (c) f/g.

48. Given that

$$f(x) = \begin{cases} x, & x \le 0 \\ -1, & x > 0 \end{cases} \quad \text{and} \quad g(x) = \begin{cases} -x, & x < 1 \\ x^2, & x \ge 1 \end{cases},$$

find   (a) $f + g$,   (b) $f - g$,   (c) fg.

49. Given that

$$f(x) = \begin{cases} 1 - x, & x \le 1 \\ 2x - 1, & x > 1 \end{cases} \quad \text{and} \quad g(x) = \begin{cases} 0, & x < 2 \\ -1, & x \ge 2 \end{cases},$$

find   (a) $f + g$,   (b) $f - g$,   (c) fg.

Sketch the graphs of the following functions with f and g as in Figure 1.6.4.

50. $2f$.   **51.** $\frac{1}{2}f$.   **52.** $-f$.   **53.** $2g$.   **54.** $\frac{1}{2}g$.   **55.** $-2g$.

56. $f + g$.   **57.** $f - g$.   **58.** $f + 2g$.

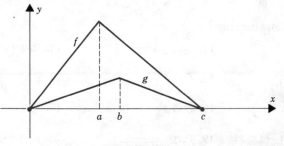

FIGURE 1.6.4

A function f is called *even* iff $f(-x) = f(x)$ for all $x \in \text{dom} (f)$.   It is called *odd* iff $f(-x) = -f(x)$ for all $x \in \text{dom} (f)$.

Test each of the functions below for evenness and oddness.

59. $f(x) = x^3$.   **60.** $f(x) = x^2$.   **61.** $g(x) = x(x - 1)$.

62. $g(x) = x(x^2 + 1)$.   **63.** $f(x) = \dfrac{x^2}{1 - |x|}$.   **64.** $f(x) = x + \dfrac{1}{x}$.

65. $f(x) = \sin x$.   **66.** $f(x) = \tan x$.   **67.** $f(x) = \cos x$.

68. What can you conclude about the product of two odd functions?

69. What can you conclude about the product of two even functions?

70. What can you conclude about the product of an odd function and an even function?

71. What is the characteristic feature of the graph of an even function?

72. What is the characteristic feature of the graph of an odd function?

73. Given that the function f is defined for all real numbers, show that the function $g(x) = f(x) + f(-x)$ is an even function.

74. Show that every function defined for all real numbers can be written as the sum of an even function and an odd function.   HINT: See Exercise 73.

1.7 ······ THE COMPOSITION OF FUNCTIONS

In the last section, you saw how to combine functions algebraically. There is another way to combine functions, called *composition*. To describe it, we begin with two functions f and g and a number x in the domain of g. By applying g to x, we get the number $g(x)$. If $g(x)$ is in the domain of f, then we can apply f to $g(x)$ and thereby obtain the number $f(g(x))$.

What is $f(g(x))$? It is the result of first applying g to x and then applying f to $g(x)$. The idea is illustrated in Figure 1.7.1.

If the range of g is completely contained in the domain of f (namely, if each value that g takes on is in the domain of f), then we can form $f(g(x))$ for *each x* in the domain of g and in this manner create a new function. This new function — it takes each x in the domain of g and assigns to it the value $f(g(x))$ — is called the *composition* of f and g and is denoted by the symbol $f \circ g$. What is this function $f \circ g$? It is the function that results from first applying g and then f. (Figure 1.7.2)

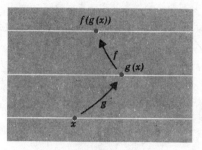

FIGURE 1.7.1

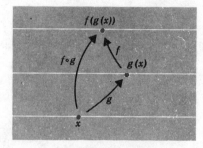

FIGURE 1.7.2

DEFINITION 1.7.1   COMPOSITION

If the range of the function g is contained in the domain of the function f, then the *composition* $f \circ g$ (read "f circle g") is the function defined on the domain of g by setting

$$(f \circ g)(x) = f(g(x)).$$

EXAMPLE. Suppose that

$$g(x) = x^2 \qquad \text{(the squaring function)}$$

and

$$f(x) = x + 1. \qquad \text{(the function that adds 1)}$$

Then

$$(f \circ g)(x) = f(g(x)) = g(x) + 1 = x^2 + 1.$$

In other words, $f \circ g$ is the function that *first* squares and *then* adds 1.

On the other hand,

$$(g \circ f)(x) = g(f(x)) = [f(x)]^2 = (x + 1)^2.$$

Thus $g \circ f$ is the function that *first* adds 1 and *then* squares. Notice that $g \circ f$ is *not* the same as $f \circ g$. □

EXAMPLE. If

$$g(x) = \frac{1}{x} + 1 \qquad\qquad (g \text{ adds 1 to the reciprocal})$$

and

$$f(x) = x^2 - 5, \qquad\qquad (f \text{ subtracts 5 from the square})$$

then

$$(f \circ g)(x) = f(g(x)) = [g(x)]^2 - 5 = \left(\frac{1}{x} + 1\right)^2 - 5.$$

Here $f \circ g$ *first* adds 1 to the reciprocal and *then* subtracts 5 from the square. □

EXAMPLE. If

$$f(x) = \frac{1}{x} + x^2 \quad \text{and} \quad g(x) = \frac{x^2 + 1}{x^4 + 1},$$

then

$$(f \circ g)(x) = f(g(x)) = \frac{1}{g(x)} + [g(x)]^2 = \frac{x^4 + 1}{x^2 + 1} + \left(\frac{x^2 + 1}{x^4 + 1}\right)^2. \quad □$$

It is possible to form the composition of more than two functions. For example, the triple composition $f \circ g \circ h$ consists of first h, then g, and then f:

$$(f \circ g \circ h)(x) = f(g(h(x))).$$

We can go on in this manner with as many functions as we like.

EXAMPLE. If

$$f(x) = \frac{1}{x}, \qquad g(x) = x + 2, \qquad h(x) = (x^2 + 1)^2,$$

then

$$(f \circ g \circ h)(x) = f(g(h(x))) = \frac{1}{g(h(x))} = \frac{1}{h(x) + 2} = \frac{1}{(x^2 + 1)^2 + 2}. \quad □$$

To apply some of the techniques of calculus you will need to be able to recognize composites. You will need to be able to start with a function, say $F(x) = (x + 1)^5$, and recognize how it is a composition.

PROBLEM. Find functions f and g such that $f \circ g = F$ if

$$F(x) = (x + 1)^5.$$

A Solution. The function consists of first adding 1 and then taking the fifth power. We can therefore set

$$g(x) = x + 1 \qquad \text{(adding 1)}$$

and

$$f(x) = x^5. \qquad \text{(taking the fifth power)}$$

As you can see,

$$(f \circ g)(x) = f(g(x)) = [g(x)]^5 = (x + 1)^5. \quad \square$$

PROBLEM. Find functions f and g such that $f \circ g = F$ if

$$F(x) = \frac{1}{x} - 6.$$

A Solution. F takes the reciprocal and then subtracts 6. We can therefore set

$$g(x) = \frac{1}{x} \qquad \text{(taking the reciprocal)}$$

and

$$f(x) = x - 6. \qquad \text{(subtracting 6)}$$

As you can check,

$$(f \circ g)(x) = f(g(x)) = g(x) - 6 = \frac{1}{x} - 6. \quad \square$$

PROBLEM. Find three functions f, g, h such that $f \circ g \circ h = F$ if

$$F(x) = \frac{1}{|x| + 3}.$$

A Solution. F takes the absolute value, adds 3, and then inverts. Let h take the absolute value:

$$\text{set} \quad h(x) = |x|.$$

Let g add 3:

$$\text{set} \quad g(x) = x + 3.$$

Let f do the inverting:

$$\text{set} \quad f(x) = \frac{1}{x}.$$

With this choice of f, g, h, we have

$$(f \circ g \circ h)(x) = f(g(h(x))) = \frac{1}{g(h(x))} = \frac{1}{h(x) + 3} = \frac{1}{|x| + 3}. \quad \square$$

In the next problem we start with the same function

$$F(x) = \frac{1}{|x| + 3},$$

but this time we are asked to break it up as the composition of only two functions.

PROBLEM. Find two functions f and g such that $f \circ g = F$ if

$$F(x) = \frac{1}{|x| + 3}.$$

Some Solutions. F takes the absolute value, adds 3, and then inverts. We can let g do the first two things by setting

$$g(x) = |x| + 3$$

and then let f do the inverting by setting

$$f(x) = \frac{1}{x}.$$

Or, we could let g just take the absolute value,

$$g(x) = |x|,$$

and then have f add 3 and invert:

$$f(x) = \frac{1}{x + 3}. \quad \Box$$

EXERCISES

Form the composition $f \circ g$.

1. $f(x) = 2x + 5, \quad g(x) = x^2.$ **2.** $f(x) = x^2, \quad g(x) = 2x + 5.$

3. $f(x) = \sqrt{x}, \quad g(x) = x^2 + 5.$ **4.** $f(x) = x^2 + x, \quad g(x) = \sqrt{x}.$

5. $f(x) = \frac{1}{x}, \quad g(x) = \frac{1}{x}.$ **6.** $f(x) = x^2, \quad g(x) = \frac{1}{x - 1}.$

7. $f(x) = x - 1, \quad g(x) = \frac{1}{x}.$ **8.** $f(x) = x^2 - 1, \quad g(x) = x(x - 1).$

9. $f(x) = \frac{1}{\sqrt{x} - 1}, \quad g(x) = (x^2 + 2)^2.$ **10.** $f(x) = \frac{1}{x} - \frac{1}{x + 1}, \quad g(x) = \frac{1}{x^2}.$

Form the composition $f \circ g \circ h$:

11. $f(x) = 4x, \quad g(x) = x - 1, \quad h(x) = x^2.$ **12.** $f(x) = x - 1, \quad g(x) = 4x, \quad h(x) = x^2.$

13. $f(x) = x^2, \quad g(x) = x - 1, \quad h(x) = x^4.$ **14.** $f(x) = x - 1, \quad g(x) = x^2, \quad h(x) = 4x.$

15. $f(x) = \frac{1}{x}, \quad g(x) = \frac{1}{2x + 1}, \quad h(x) = x^2.$

16. $f(x) = \frac{x + 1}{x}, \quad g(x) = \frac{1}{2x + 1}, \quad h(x) = x^2.$

Find f such that $f \circ g = F$ given that

17. $g(x) = \dfrac{1 + x^2}{1 + x^4}$ and $F(x) = \dfrac{1 + x^4}{1 + x^2}$.   **18.** $g(x) = x^2$ and $F(x) = ax^2 + b$.

19. $g(x) = 3x$ and $F(x) = 2 \sin 3x$.   **20.** $g(x) = -x^2$ and $F(x) = \sqrt{a^2 + x^2}$.

Find g such that $f \circ g = F$ given that

21. $f(x) = x^3$ and $F(x) = \left(1 - \dfrac{1}{x^4}\right)^2$.

22. $f(x) = x + \dfrac{1}{x}$ and $F(x) = a^2 x^2 + \dfrac{1}{a^2 x^2}$.

23. $f(x) = x^2 + 1$ and $F(x) = (2x^3 - 1)^2 + 1$.

24. $f(x) = \sin x$ and $F(x) = \sin \dfrac{1}{x}$.

Form $f \circ g$ and $g \circ f$.

25. $f(x) = \sqrt{x}$, $g(x) = x^2$.   **26.** $f(x) = 3x + 1$, $g(x) = x^2$.

27. $f(x) = 2x$, $g(x) = \sin x$.   **28.** $f(x) = 2x$, $g(x) = \frac{1}{2}$.

29. $f(x) = \begin{cases} 1 - x, & x \le 0 \\ x^2, & x > 0 \end{cases}$, $g(x) = \begin{cases} -x, & x < 1 \\ 1 + x, & x \ge 1 \end{cases}$.

30. $f(x) = \begin{cases} 1 - 2x, & x < 1 \\ 1 + x, & x \ge 1 \end{cases}$, $\cdot g(x) = \begin{cases} x^2, & x < 0 \\ 1 - x, & x \ge 0 \end{cases}$.

1.8 ······ONE-TO-ONE FUNCTIONS; INVERSES

One-to-One Functions

A function can take on the same value at different points of the domain. Constant functions, for example, take on the same value at all points of the domain. The squaring function takes on the same value at $-c$ as it does at c; so does the absolute-value function. The function

$$f(x) = 1 + (x - 3)(x - 5)$$

takes on the same value at $x = 5$ as it does at $x = 3$:

$$f(3) = 1, \qquad f(5) = 1.$$

Functions for which this kind of repetition does *not* occur are called *one-to-one*.

DEFINITION 1.8.1 ·

A function f is said to be *one-to-one* if and only if there are no two points at which it takes on the same value:

$$f(x_1) = f(x_2) \quad \text{implies} \quad x_1 = x_2.$$

As examples, take

$$f(x) = x^3 \quad \text{and} \quad g(x) = \sqrt{x}.$$

The cubing function is one-to-one because no two numbers have the same cube. The square-root function is one-to-one because no two numbers have the same square root.

There is a simple geometric test for one-to-oneness. Look at the graph of the function. If some horizontal line intersects the graph of the function more than once, then the function is not one-to-one (Figure 1.8.1). If, on the other hand, no horizontal line intersects the graph more than once, then the function is one-to-one (Figure 1.8.2).

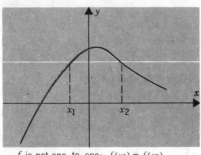

f is not one-to-one: $f(x_1) = f(x_2)$

FIGURE 1.8.1

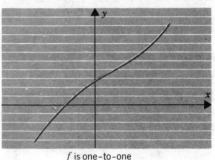

f is one-to-one

FIGURE 1.8.2

Inverses

I am thinking of a real number and its cube is 8. Can you figure out the number? Obviously, yes. It must be 2.

Now I am thinking of another number and its square is 9. Can you figure out the number? No, not unless you are clairvoyant. It could be 3, but it could also be -3.

The difference between the two situations can be phrased this way: In the first case we are dealing with a one-to-one function — no two numbers have the same cube. So, knowing the cube, we can work back to the original number. In the second case we are dealing with a function that is not one-to-one — different numbers can have the same square. Knowing the square, we still can't figure out what the original number was.

Throughout the rest of this section we will be looking at functional values and tracing them back to where they came from. So as to be able to trace these values back, we will restrict ourselves entirely to functions that are one-to-one.

We begin with a theorem about one-to-one functions.

THEOREM 1.8.2

If f is a one-to-one function, then there is one and only one function g that is defined on the range of f and satisfies the equation

$$f(g(x)) = x \qquad \text{for all } x \text{ in the range of } f.$$

Proof. The proof is easy. If x is in the range of f, then f must take on the value x at some number. Since f is one-to-one, there can be only one such number. We've called it $g(x)$. □

The function that we've named g in the theorem is called the *inverse* of f and is usually denoted by f^{-1}.

DEFINITION 1.8.3 INVERSE FUNCTION

Let f be a one-to-one function. The *inverse* of f, denoted by f^{-1}, is the unique function that is defined on the range of f and satisfies the equation

$$f(f^{-1}(x)) = x \qquad \text{for all } x \text{ in the range of } f.$$

PROBLEM. You have seen that the cubing function

$$f(x) = x^3$$

is one-to-one. Find the inverse.

Solution. We set $t = f^{-1}(x)$ and solve the equation $f(t) = x$ for t:

$$f(t) = x \qquad\qquad\qquad (1.8.3)$$
$$t^3 = x \qquad\qquad (f \text{ is the cubing function})$$
$$t = x^{1/3}.$$

Substituting $f^{-1}(x)$ back in for t, we have

$$f^{-1}(x) = x^{1/3}.$$

The inverse of the cubing function is the cube-root function. □

REMARK. We substitute t for $f^{-1}(x)$ merely to simplify the calculations. It's easier to work with t than with $f^{-1}(x)$. □

PROBLEM. Show that the linear function

$$f(x) = 3x - 5$$

is one-to-one. Then find the inverse.

Solution. To show that f is one-to-one, let's suppose that

$$f(x_1) = f(x_2).$$

Then

$$3x_1 - 5 = 3x_2 - 5$$

$$3x_1 = 3x_2$$
$$x_1 = x_2.$$

The function is one-to-one since

$$f(x_1) = f(x_2) \quad \text{implies} \quad x_1 = x_2.$$

(Another way to see that this function is one-to-one is to note that the graph is a line of slope 3 and as such cannot be intersected by a horizontal line more than once.)

Now let's find the inverse.   To do this, we set $t = f^{-1}(x)$ and solve the equation $f(t) = x$ for t:

$$f(t) = x$$
$$3t - 5 = x$$
$$3t = x + 5$$
$$t = \tfrac{1}{3}x + \tfrac{5}{3}.$$

Substituting $f^{-1}(x)$ back in for t, we have

$$f^{-1}(x) = \tfrac{1}{3}x + \tfrac{5}{3}. \quad \square$$

PROBLEM.   Show that the function

$$f(x) = (1 - x^3)^{1/5} + 2$$

is one-to-one.   What is the inverse?

Solution.   First we show that f is one-to-one.   Suppose that

$$f(x_1) = f(x_2).$$

Then

$$(1 - x_1^3)^{1/5} + 2 = (1 - x_2^3)^{1/5} + 2$$
$$(1 - x_1^3)^{1/5} = (1 - x_2^3)^{1/5}$$
$$1 - x_1^3 = 1 - x_2^3$$
$$x_1^3 = x_2^3$$
$$x_1 = x_2.$$

The function is one-to-one since

$$f(x_1) = f(x_2) \quad \text{implies} \quad x_1 = x_2.$$

To find the inverse we set $t = f^{-1}(x)$ and solve the equation $f(t) = x$ for t:

$$f(t) = x$$
$$(1 - t^3)^{1/5} + 2 = x$$
$$(1 - t^3)^{1/5} = x - 2$$
$$1 - t^3 = (x - 2)^5$$
$$t^3 = 1 - (x - 2)^5$$
$$t = [1 - (x - 2)^5]^{1/3}.$$

Substituting $f^{-1}(x)$ back in for t, we have

$$f^{-1}(x) = [1 - (x - 2)^5]^{1/3}. \quad \square$$

By definition f^{-1} satisfies the equation

(1.8.4) $f(f^{-1}(x)) = x$ for all x in the range of f.

It is also true that

(1.8.5) $f^{-1}(f(x)) = x$ for all x in the domain of f.

Proof.   Take x in the domain of f and set $y = f(x)$.   Since y is in the range of f,

$$f(f^{-1}(y)) = y. \tag{1.8.4}$$

This means that

$$f(f^{-1}(f(x))) = f(x)$$

and tells us that f takes on the same value at $f^{-1}(f(x))$ as it does at x.   With f one-to-one, this can only happen if

$$f^{-1}(f(x)) = x. \quad \square$$

Equation (1.8.5) tells us that f^{-1} "undoes" the work of f:

if f takes x to $f(x)$,   then f^{-1} takes $f(x)$ back to x.   (Figure 1.8.3)

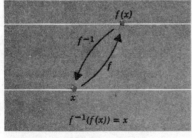

FIGURE 1.8.3

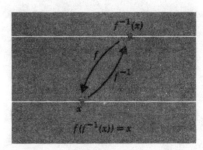

FIGURE 1.8.4

Equation (1.8.4) tells us that f "undoes" the work of f^{-1}:

if f^{-1} takes x to $f^{-1}(x)$,   then f takes $f^{-1}(x)$ back to x.   (Figure 1.8.4)

The Graphs of f and f^{-1}

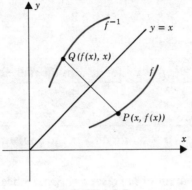

FIGURE 1.8.5

There is an important relation between the graph of a one-to-one function f and the graph of f^{-1}. (See Figure 1.8.5.) The graph of f consists of points of the form $P(x, f(x))$. Since f^{-1} takes on the value x at $f(x)$, the graph of f^{-1} consists of points of the form $Q(f(x), x)$. Since, for each x, P and Q are symmetric with respect to the line $y = x$, the graph of f^{-1} is the graph of f reflected in the line $y = x$.

PROBLEM. Given the graph of f in Figure 1.8.6, sketch the graph of f^{-1}.

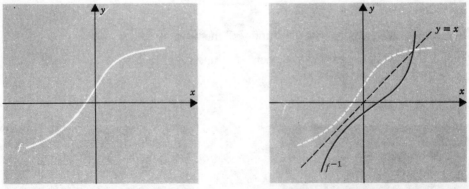

FIGURE 1.8.6   FIGURE 1.8.7

Solution. First draw in the line $y = x$. Then reflect the graph of f in that line. See Figure 1.8.7. ☐

EXERCISES

Determine whether or not the given function is one-to-one and, if so, find its inverse.

1. $f(x) = 5x + 3$.   **2.** $f(x) = 3x + 5$.   **3.** $f(x) = 4x - 7$.
4. $f(x) = 7x - 4$.   **5.** $f(x) = 1 - x^2$.   **6.** $f(x) = x^5$.
7. $f(x) = x^5 + 1$.   **8.** $f(x) = x^2 - 3x + 2$.   **9.** $f(x) = 1 + 3x^3$.

10. $f(x) = x^3 - 1$.

11. $f(x) = (1 - x)^3$.

12. $f(x) = (1 - x)^4$.

13. $f(x) = (x + 1)^3 + 2$.

14. $f(x) = (4x - 1)^3$.

15. $f(x) = x^{3/5}$.

16. $f(x) = 1 - (x - 2)^{1/3}$.

17. $f(x) = (2 - 3x)^3$.

18. $f(x) = (2 - 3x^2)^3$.

19. $f(x) = \dfrac{1}{x}$.

20. $f(x) = \dfrac{1}{1 - x}$.

21. $f(x) = x + \dfrac{1}{x}$.

22. $f(x) = \dfrac{x}{|x|}$.

23. $f(x) = \dfrac{1}{x^3 + 1}$.

24. $f(x) = \dfrac{1}{1 - x} - 1$

25. $f(x) = \dfrac{x + 2}{x + 1}$.

26. $f(x) = \dfrac{1}{(x + 1)^{2/3}}$.

27. What is the relation between f and $(f^{-1})^{-1}$?

Sketch the graph of f^{-1} given the graph of f.

28.

29.

30.

31.

32.

33.

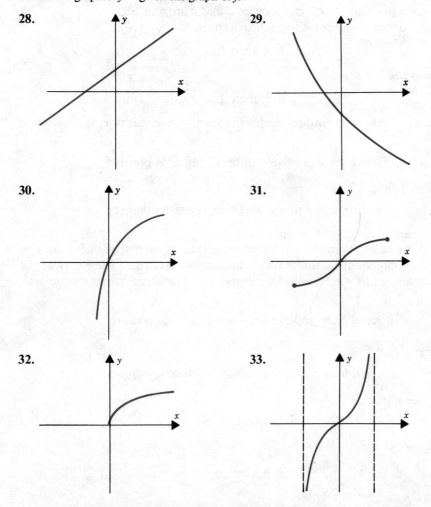

34. (a) Show that the composition of two one-to-one functions is one-to-one.
   (b) Express $(f \circ g)^{-1}$ in terms of f^{-1} and g^{-1}.

1.9 ·······A NOTE ON MATHEMATICAL PROOF

The notion of proof goes back to Euclid's *Elements*, and the rules of proof have changed little since they were formulated by Aristotle. We work in a deductive system where truth is argued on the basis of assumptions, definitions, and previously proved results. We cannot claim that such and such is true without clearly stating the basis on which we make that claim.

A theorem is an implication; it consists of a hypothesis and a conclusion:

if (hypothesis) . . . , then (conclusion) . . . .

Here is an example:

if a and b are positive numbers, then ab is positive.

A common mistake is to ignore the hypothesis and persist with the conclusion: to insist, for example, that $ab > 0$ just because a and b are numbers.

Another common mistake is to confuse a theorem

if A, then B

with its converse

if B, then A.

The fact that a theorem is true does not mean that its converse is true: While it's true that

if a and b are positive numbers, then ab is positive

it is *not* true that

if ab is positive, then a and b are positive numbers.

[$(-2)(-3)$ is positive, but -2 and -3 are not positive.]

A third, more subtle mistake is to presume that the hypothesis of a theorem represents the only condition under which the conclusion is true. There may well be other conditions under which the conclusion is true. Thus, for example, not only is it true that

if a and b are positive numbers, then ab is positive

but it is also true that

if a and b are negative numbers, then ab is positive.

In the event that a theorem

if A, then B

and its converse

if B, then A

are both true, then we can write

A if and only if B or more briefly A iff B.

We know, for example, that

$$\text{if} \quad x \geq 0, \qquad \text{then} \quad |x| = x;$$

we also know that

$$\text{if} \quad |x| = x, \qquad \text{then} \quad x \geq 0.$$

We can summarize by writing

$$x \geq 0 \qquad \text{iff} \qquad |x| = x.$$

A final point. One way of proving

$$\text{if } A, \text{ then } B$$

is to assume that

(1) A holds and B does not hold

and then arrive at a contradiction. The contradiction is taken to indicate that (1) is false and therefore

$$\text{if } A \text{ holds, then } B \text{ must hold.}$$

Some of the theorems of calculus are proved by this method.

Calculus provides procedures for solving a wide range of problems in the physical and social sciences. The fact that these procedures give us answers that seem to make sense is comforting, but it is only because we can prove our theorems that we can be confident in the results. Accordingly, your study of calculus should include the study of some proofs.

Limits and Continuity

2.1 ⋯⋯THE IDEA OF LIMIT

Introduction

We could begin by saying that limits are important in calculus, but that would be a pathetic understatement. *Without limits calculus simply does not exist. Every single notion of calculus is a limit in one sense or another.*

What is instantaneous velocity?   It is the limit of average velocities.

What is the slope of a curve?   It is the limit of slopes of secant lines.

What is the length of a curve?   It is the limit of the lengths of polygonal paths.

What is the sum of an infinite series?   It is the limit of its partial sums.

What is the area of a region bounded by curves?   It is the limit of areas of regions bounded by line segments.   See the next page.

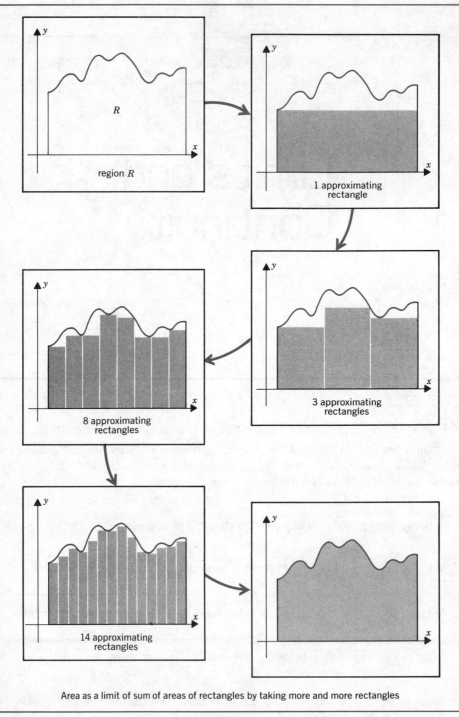

region R

1 approximating
rectangle

3 approximating
rectangles

8 approximating
rectangles

14 approximating
rectangles

Area as a limit of sum of areas of rectangles by taking more and more rectangles

FIGURE 2.1.1

The Idea of Limit

We begin with a number l and a function f defined *near the number c but not necessarily defined at c itself.* A rough translation of

$$\lim_{x \to c} f(x) = l$$

(the limit of f(x) as x tends to c is l)

might read

as x approaches c, f(x) approaches l

or, equivalently,

for *x close* to *c* but *different* from *c*, *f(x)* is *close* to *l*.

We illustrate the idea in Figure 2.1.2. The curve represents the graph of a function f. The number c appears on the x-axis, the limit l on the y-axis. As x approaches c along the x-axis, $f(x)$ approaches l along the y-axis.

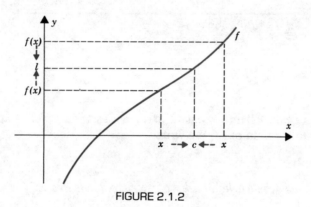

FIGURE 2.1.2

In taking the limit as x approaches c, it does not matter whether or not f is defined at c and, if so, how it is defined there. The only thing that matters is how f is defined *near c.* For example, in Figure 2.1.3 the graph of f is a broken curve defined peculiarly at c,

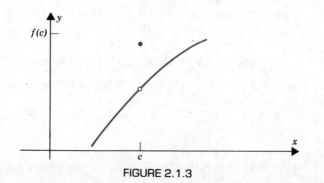

FIGURE 2.1.3

and yet

$$\lim_{x \to c} f(x) = l$$

because, as suggested in Figure 2.1.4,

as x approaches c, $f(x)$ approaches l.

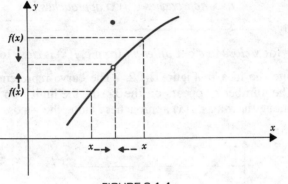

FIGURE 2.1.4

Numbers x near c fall into two natural categories: those that lie to the left of c and those that lie to the right of c. We write

$$\lim_{x \to c^-} f(x) = l$$

(*the left-hand limit of $f(x)$ as x tends to c is l*)

to indicate that

as x approaches c *from the left*, $f(x)$ approaches l.

Similarly,

$$\lim_{x \to c^+} f(x) = l$$

(*the right-hand limit of $f(x)$ as x tends to c is l*)

indicates that

as x approaches c *from the right*, $f(x)$ approaches l. †

For an example, see Figure 2.1.5. Note that in this case the left-hand limit and the right-hand limit are not the same.

---

† The left-hand limit is sometimes written $\lim_{x \uparrow c} f(x)$ and the right-hand limit, $\lim_{x \downarrow c} f(x)$.

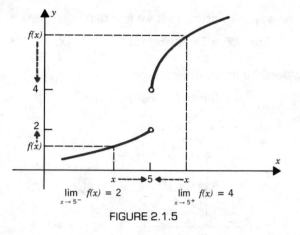

$$\lim_{x \to 5^-} f(x) = 2 \qquad\qquad \lim_{x \to 5^+} f(x) = 4$$

FIGURE 2.1.5

The left- and right-hand limits are called *one-sided limits*. As must be intuitively obvious (and everything we say in this section is only intuitive)

$$\lim_{x \to c} f(x) = l$$

if and only if both

$$\lim_{x \to c^-} f(x) = l \qquad and \qquad \lim_{x \to c^+} f(x) = l.$$

EXAMPLE. For the function f graphed in Figure 2.1.6

$$\lim_{x \to -2^-} f(x) = 5 \qquad and \qquad \lim_{x \to -2^+} f(x) = 5$$

and therefore

$$\lim_{x \to -2} f(x) = 5.$$

It does not matter that $f(-2) = 3$.

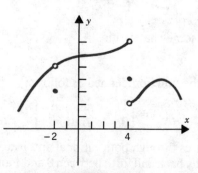

FIGURE 2.1.6

Examining the graph of f near $x = 4$, we find that

$$\lim_{x \to 4^-} f(x) = 7 \qquad \text{whereas} \qquad \lim_{x \to 4^+} f(x) = 2.$$

Since these one-sided limits are different,

$$\lim_{x \to 4} f(x) \quad \text{does not exist.} \quad \square$$

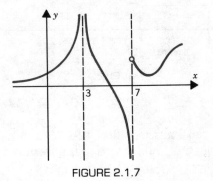

FIGURE 2.1.7

EXAMPLE. Consider the function f graphed in Figure 2.1.7. As x approaches 3 from either side, $f(x)$ becomes arbitrarily large. Becoming arbitrarily large, $f(x)$ cannot stay close to any fixed number l. Therefore

$$\lim_{x \to 3} f(x) \quad \text{does not exist.}$$

Now let's focus on what happens near 7. As x approaches 7 from the left, $f(x)$ becomes arbitrarily large negative (i.e., less than any preassigned number). Under these circumstances $f(x)$ can't possibly approach a fixed number. Thus

$$\lim_{x \to 7^-} f(x) \quad \text{does not exist.}$$

Since the left-hand limit at $x = 7$ does not exist,

$$\lim_{x \to 7} f(x) \quad \text{does not exist.} \quad \square$$

Our next example is somewhat exotic.

EXAMPLE. Let f be the function defined as follows:

$$f(x) = \begin{cases} 1, & x \text{ rational} \\ 0, & x \text{ irrational} \end{cases}. \qquad \text{(Figure 2.1.8)}$$

As x approaches c, x passes through both rational and irrational numbers. As this happens, $f(x)$ jumps wildly back and forth between 0 and 1 and thus cannot stay close to any fixed number l. Therefore $\lim_{x \to c} f(x)$ does not exist. $\square$

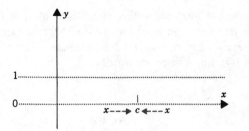

FIGURE 2.1.8

We go on with examples. Where a graph has not been provided, you may find it useful to sketch one.

EXAMPLE

$$\lim_{x \to 3} (2x + 5) = 11.$$

As x approaches 3, $2x$ approaches 6, and $2x + 5$ approaches 11. □

EXAMPLE

$$\lim_{x \to 2} (x^2 - 1) = 3.$$

As x approaches 2, x^2 approaches 4, and $x^2 - 1$ approaches 3. □

EXAMPLE

$$\lim_{x \to 3} \frac{1}{x - 1} = \frac{1}{2}.$$

As x approaches 3, $x - 1$ approaches 2, and $1/(x - 1)$ approaches $\frac{1}{2}$. □

EXAMPLE

$$\lim_{x \to 2} \frac{1}{x - 2} \quad \text{does not exist.} \quad \square \qquad \text{(Figure 2.1.9)}$$

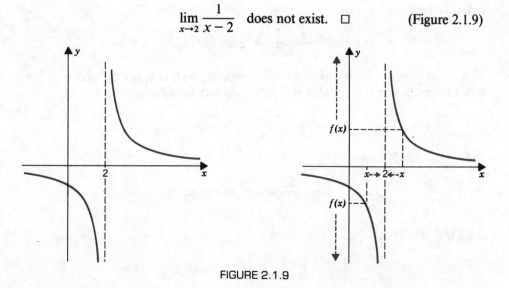

FIGURE 2.1.9

Before going on to the next examples, remember that, in taking the limit as x approaches a given number c, it does not matter whether or not the function is defined at the number c and, if so, how it is defined there. The only thing that matters is how the function is defined *near* the number c.

EXAMPLE

$$\lim_{x \to 2} \frac{x^2 - 4x + 4}{x - 2} = 0.$$

At $x = 2$, the function is undefined: both numerator and denominator are 0. But that doesn't matter. For all $x \neq 2$, and therefore *for all x near* 2,

$$\frac{x^2 - 4x + 4}{x - 2} = x - 2.$$

It follows that

$$\lim_{x \to 2} \frac{x^2 - 4x + 4}{x - 2} = \lim_{x \to 2} (x - 2) = 0. \quad \square$$

EXAMPLE

$$\lim_{x \to 2} \frac{x - 2}{x - 2} = 1.$$

At $x = 2$, the function is undefined: both numerator and denominator are 0. But, as we said before, that doesn't matter. For all $x \neq 2$, and therefore for all x near 2,

$$\frac{x - 2}{x - 2} = 1 \quad \text{so that} \quad \lim_{x \to 2} \frac{x - 2}{x - 2} = \lim_{x \to 2} 1 = 1. \quad \square$$

EXAMPLE

$$\lim_{x \to 2} \frac{x - 2}{x^2 - 4x + 4} \quad \text{does not exist.}$$

This result does not follow from the fact that the function is not defined at 2, but rather from the fact that for all $x \neq 2$, and therefore for all x near 2,

$$\frac{x - 2}{x^2 - 4x + 4} = \frac{1}{x - 2}$$

and, as you saw before,

$$\lim_{x \to 2} \frac{1}{x - 2} \quad \text{does not exist.} \quad \square$$

EXAMPLE

If $f(x) = \begin{cases} 3x - 1, & x \neq 2 \\ 45, & x = 2 \end{cases}$, then $\lim_{x \to 2} f(x) = 5.$

It doesn't matter to us that $f(2) = 45$. For $x \neq 2$, and thus for all x near 2,

$$f(x) = 3x - 1 \quad \text{so that} \quad \lim_{x \to 2} f(x) = \lim_{x \to 2} (3x - 1) = 5. \quad \square$$

EXAMPLE

If $f(x) = \begin{cases} -2x, & x < 1 \\ 2x, & x > 1 \end{cases}$, then $\lim_{x \to 1} f(x)$ does not exist.

The limit does not exist since the one-sided limits are different:

$$\lim_{x \to 1^-} f(x) = \lim_{x \to 1^-} (-2x) = -2, \qquad \lim_{x \to 1^+} f(x) = \lim_{x \to 1^+} 2x = 2. \quad \square$$

EXAMPLE

If $f(x) = \begin{cases} -2x, & x < 1 \\ 2x, & x > 1 \end{cases}$, then $\lim_{x \to 1.03} f(x) = 2.06$.

Notice that for values of x sufficiently near 1.03, the values of the function are computed using the rule $2x$ whether x is to the left or the right of 1.03. $\square$

If you've found all this very imprecise, you're absolutely right. It is imprecise, but it need not remain so. One of the great triumphs of calculus has been its capacity to formulate limit statements with precision, but for this precision you'll have to wait until Section 2.2.

EXERCISES

Use the graph of f to find

(a) $\lim_{x \to c^-} f(x)$ (b) $\lim_{x \to c^+} f(x)$ (c) $\lim_{x \to c} f(x)$ (d) $f(c)$

for the given value of c.

1. $c = 2$.

2. $c = 3$.

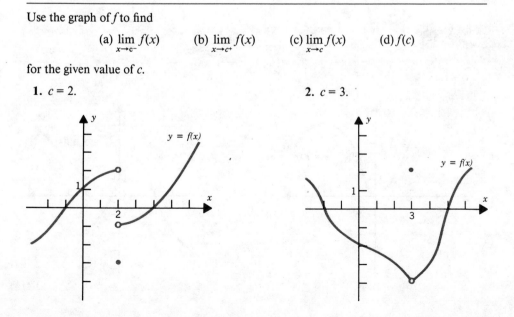

3. $c = 3$.

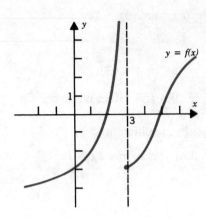

4. $c = 4$.

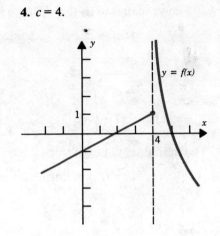

5. $c = -2$.

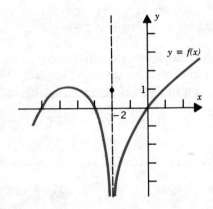

6. $c = 1$.

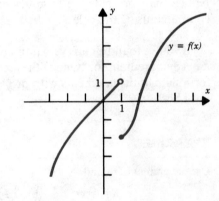

7. $c = 1$.

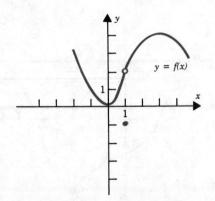

8. $c = -1$.

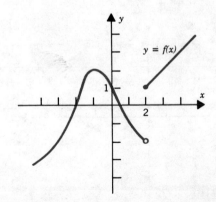

9. $c = 3$.

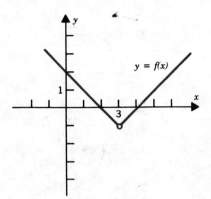

10. $c = 3$.

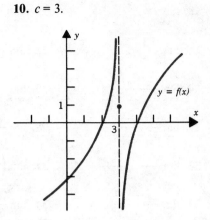

11. $c = 2$.

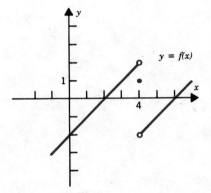

12. $c = -2$.

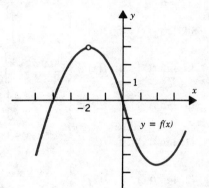

State the values of c for which $\lim\limits_{x \to c} f(x)$ does not exist.

13.   **14.**

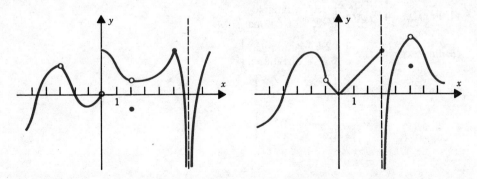

Decide on intuitive grounds whether or not the indicated limit exists. Evaluate the limits which do exist.

15. $\lim\limits_{x \to 0} (2x - 1)$.   **16.** $\lim\limits_{x \to 1} (2 - 5x)$.   **17.** $\lim\limits_{x \to -2} x^2$.

18. $\lim\limits_{x \to 4} \sqrt{x}$.

19. $\lim\limits_{x \to -3} (|x| - 2)$.

20. $\lim\limits_{x \to 0} \dfrac{1}{|x|}$.

21. $\lim\limits_{x \to 1} \dfrac{3}{x + 1}$.

22. $\lim\limits_{x \to 0} \dfrac{4}{x + 1}$.

23. $\lim\limits_{x \to -1} \dfrac{2}{x + 1}$.

24. $\lim\limits_{x \to 2} \dfrac{1}{3x - 6}$.

25. $\lim\limits_{x \to 3} \dfrac{2x - 6}{x - 3}$.

26. $\lim\limits_{x \to 3} \dfrac{x^2 - 6x + 9}{x - 3}$.

27. $\lim\limits_{x \to 3} \dfrac{x - 3}{x^2 - 6x + 9}$.

28. $\lim\limits_{x \to 2} \dfrac{x^2 - 3x + 2}{x - 2}$.

29. $\lim\limits_{x \to 2} \dfrac{x - 2}{x^2 - 3x + 2}$.

30. $\lim\limits_{x \to 1} \dfrac{x - 2}{x^2 - 3x + 2}$.

31. $\lim\limits_{x \to 0} \left(x + \dfrac{1}{x}\right)$.

32. $\lim\limits_{x \to 1} \left(x + \dfrac{1}{x}\right)$.

33. $\lim\limits_{x \to 0} \dfrac{2x - 5x^2}{x}$.

34. $\lim\limits_{x \to 3} \dfrac{x - 3}{6 - 2x}$.

35. $\lim\limits_{x \to 1} \dfrac{x^2 - 1}{x - 1}$.

36. $\lim\limits_{x \to 1} \dfrac{x^3 - 1}{x - 1}$.

37. $\lim\limits_{x \to 1} \dfrac{x^2 + 1}{x^2 - 1}$.

38. $\lim\limits_{x \to 0} f(x)$ if $f(x) = \begin{bmatrix} 1, & x \neq 0 \\ 3, & x = 0 \end{bmatrix}$.

39. $\lim\limits_{x \to 1} f(x)$ if $f(x) = \begin{bmatrix} 3x, & x < 1 \\ 3, & x > 1 \end{bmatrix}$.

40. $\lim\limits_{x \to 4} f(x)$ if $f(x) = \begin{bmatrix} x^2, & x \neq 4 \\ 0, & x = 4 \end{bmatrix}$.

41. $\lim\limits_{x \to 0} f(x)$ if $f(x) = \begin{bmatrix} -x^2, & x < 0 \\ x^2, & x > 0 \end{bmatrix}$.

42. $\lim\limits_{x \to 0} f(x)$ if $f(x) = \begin{cases} x^2, & x < 0 \\ 1 + x, & x > 0 \end{cases}$.

43. $\lim\limits_{x \to 1} f(x)$ if $f(x) = \begin{cases} 2x, & x < 1 \\ x^2 + 1, & x > 1 \end{cases}$.

44. $\lim\limits_{x \to 0} f(x)$ if $f(x) = \begin{cases} 2, & x \text{ rational} \\ -2, & x \text{ irrational} \end{cases}$.

45. $\lim\limits_{x \to 1} f(x)$ if $f(x) = \begin{cases} 2x, & x \text{ rational} \\ 2, & x \text{ irrational} \end{cases}$.

46. $\lim\limits_{x \to 2} f(x)$ if $f(x) = \begin{cases} 3x, & x < 1 \\ x + 2, & x \geq 1 \end{cases}$.

47. $\lim\limits_{x \to 0} f(x)$ if $f(x) = \begin{cases} 2x, & x \leq 1 \\ x + 1, & x > 1 \end{cases}$.

2.2 ⸻ DEFINITION OF LIMIT

As we indicated in Section 2.1,

$$\lim_{x \to c} f(x) = l$$

means, *roughly speaking,* that

for x close to c but different from c, $f(x)$ is close to l,

which is to say

if $|x - c|$ is small but different from zero, then $|f(x) - l|$ is small.

It is time to be more precise.

Let f be a function and let c be a real number. We do not require that f be defined at c, but, to avoid complications at this stage, we will assume that f is defined at least on a set of the form $(a, c) \cup (c, d)$. To say that

$$\lim_{x \to c} f(x) = l$$

is to say that

$\|f(x) - l\|$ can be made arbitrarily small	you pick $\epsilon > 0$; $\|f(x) - l\|$ can be made less than ϵ
simply by requiring that	simply by requiring that
$\|x - c\|$ be sufficiently small but different from zero.	$\|x - c\|$ satisfy an inequality of the form $0 < \|x - c\| < \delta$ for δ sufficiently small.

Putting the various pieces together in compact form we have the following *fundamental definition.*

DEFINITION 2.2.1   THE LIMIT OF A FUNCTION

$$\lim_{x \to c} f(x) = l \quad \text{iff} \quad \begin{cases} \text{for each } \epsilon > 0 \text{ there exists } \delta > 0 \text{ such that} \\ \text{if } \quad 0 < |x - c| < \delta, \quad \text{ then } \quad |f(x) - l| < \epsilon. \end{cases}$$

Figures 2.2.1 and 2.2.2 illustrate this definition.

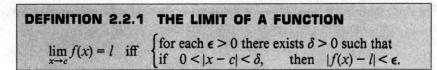

FIGURE 2.2.1

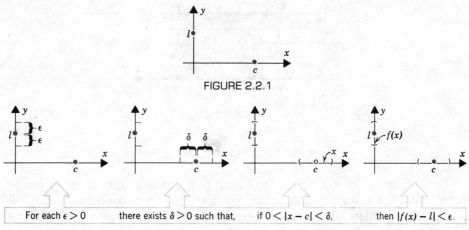

For each $\epsilon > 0$ there exists $\delta > 0$ such that,   if $0 < |x - c| < \delta$,   then $|f(x) - l| < \epsilon$.

FIGURE 2.2.2

In general, the choice of δ depends upon the previous choice of ϵ. We do not require that there exist a number δ which "works" for *all* ϵ but, rather, that for *each* ϵ there exist a δ which "works" for it.

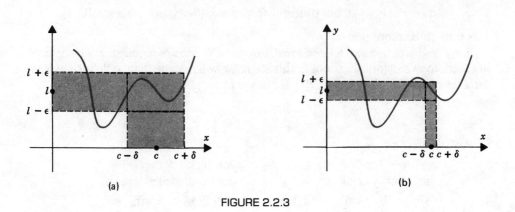

(a)   (b)

FIGURE 2.2.3

In Figure 2.2.3, we give two choices of ϵ and for each we display a suitable δ. For a δ to be suitable, all the points within δ of c (with the possible exception of c itself) must be taken by the function to within ϵ of l. In part (b) of the figure we began with a smaller ϵ and had to use a smaller δ.

The δ of Figure 2.2.4 is too large for the given ϵ. In particular the points marked x_1 and x_2 in the figure are not taken by the function to within ϵ of l.

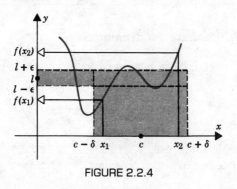

FIGURE 2.2.4

Next we apply the ϵ, δ definition of limit to a variety of functions. If you've never run across ϵ, δ arguments before, you may find them confusing at first. It usually takes a little while for the ϵ, δ idea to take hold.

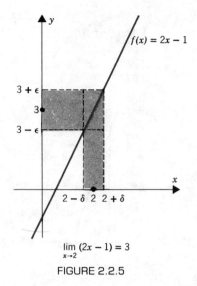

$$\lim_{x \to 2} (2x - 1) = 3$$

FIGURE 2.2.5

EXAMPLE. Show that

$$\lim_{x \to 2} (2x - 1) = 3. \qquad \text{(Figure 2.2.5)}$$

Finding a δ. Let $\epsilon > 0$. We seek a number $\delta > 0$ such that,

$$\text{if} \quad 0 < |x - 2| < \delta, \quad \text{then} \quad |(2x - 1) - 3| < \epsilon.$$

What we have to do first is establish a connection between

$$|(2x - 1) - 3| \quad \text{and} \quad |x - 2|.$$

The connection is simple:

$$|(2x - 1) - 3| = |2x - 4|$$

so that

(1) $$|(2x - 1) - 3| = 2|x - 2|.$$

To make $|(2x - 1) - 3|$ less than ϵ, we need only make $|x - 2|$ twice as small. This suggests that we choose $\delta = \frac{1}{2}\epsilon$.

Showing that the δ "works." If $0 < |x - 2| < \frac{1}{2}\epsilon$, then $2|x - 2| < \epsilon$ and, by (1), $|(2x - 1) - 3| < \epsilon$.† □

---

† Here we chose $\delta = \frac{1}{2}\epsilon$, but we could have chosen any positive $\delta \leq \frac{1}{2}\epsilon$. In general, if a certain δ "works," then any smaller $\delta > 0$ will also work.

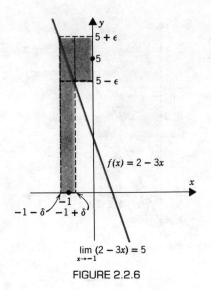

$$\lim_{x \to -1} (2 - 3x) = 5$$

FIGURE 2.2.6

EXAMPLE. Show that

$$\lim_{x \to -1} (2 - 3x) = 5. \qquad \text{(Figure 2.2.6)}$$

Finding a δ. Let $\epsilon > 0$. We seek a number $\delta > 0$ such that

$$\text{if } \quad 0 < |x - (-1)| < \delta, \quad \text{then } \quad |(2 - 3x) - 5| < \epsilon.$$

To find a connection between

$$|x - (-1)| \quad \text{and} \quad |(2 - 3x) - 5|,$$

we simplify both expressions:

$$|x - (-1)| = |x + 1|$$

and

$$|(2 - 3x) - 5| = |-3x - 3| = 3|-x - 1| = 3|x + 1|.$$

We can conclude that

(2) $$|(2 - 3x) - 5| = 3|x - (-1)|.$$

We can make the expression on the left less than ϵ by making $|x - (-1)|$ three times as small. This suggests that we set $\delta = \frac{1}{3}\epsilon$.

Showing that the δ "works." If $0 < |x - (-1)| < \frac{1}{3}\epsilon$, then $3|x - (-1)| < \epsilon$ and, by (2), $|(2 - 3x) - 5| < \epsilon$. $\square$

EXAMPLE

(2.2.2) $$\lim_{x \to c} |x| = |c|. \qquad \text{(Figure 2.2.7)}$$

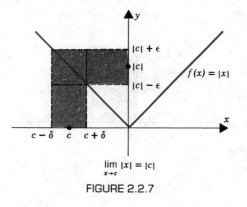

$$\lim_{x \to c} |x| = |c|$$

FIGURE 2.2.7

Proof. Let $\epsilon > 0$. We seek $\delta > 0$ such that

$$\text{if} \quad 0 < |x - c| < \delta, \quad \text{then} \quad \big||x| - |c|\big| < \epsilon.$$

Since

$$\big||x| - |c|\big| \le |x - c|, \tag{1.5.6}$$

we can choose $\delta = \epsilon$; for

$$\text{if} \quad 0 < |x - c| < \epsilon, \quad \text{then} \quad \big||x| - |c|\big| < \epsilon. \quad \square$$

EXAMPLE

(2.2.3) $$\lim_{x \to c} x = c.$$ (Figure 2.2.8)

Proof. Let $\epsilon > 0$. Here we must find $\delta > 0$ such that

$$\text{if} \quad 0 < |x - c| < \delta, \quad \text{then} \quad |x - c| < \epsilon.$$

Obviously we can choose $\delta = \epsilon$. $\quad \square$

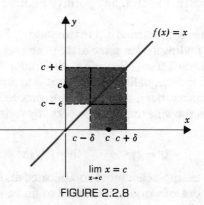

$$\lim_{x \to c} x = c$$

FIGURE 2.2.8

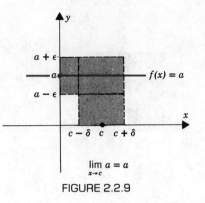

$$\lim_{x \to c} a = a$$

FIGURE 2.2.9

EXAMPLE

(2.2.4) $$\lim_{x \to c} a = a.$$ (Figure 2.2.9)

Proof. Here we are dealing with the constant function

$$f(x) = a.$$

Let $\epsilon > 0$. We must find $\delta > 0$ such that

$$\text{if} \quad 0 < |x - c| < \delta, \qquad \text{then} \quad |a - a| < \epsilon.$$

Since

$$|a - a| = 0,$$

we always have

$$|a - a| < \epsilon$$

no matter how δ is chosen; in short, any positive number will do for δ. □

Usually ϵ, δ arguments are carried out in two stages. First we do a little algebraic scratchwork, labeled "finding a δ" in some of the examples above. This scratchwork involves working backward from $|f(x) - l| < \epsilon$ to find a $\delta > 0$ sufficiently small so that we can begin with the inequality $0 < |x - c| < \delta$ to arrive at $|f(x) - l| < \epsilon$. This first stage is just preliminary, but it shows us how to proceed in the second stage. The second stage consists of showing that the δ "works" by verifying that for our choice of δ the implication

$$\text{if} \quad 0 < |x - c| < \delta, \qquad \text{then} \quad |f(x) - l| < \epsilon$$

is true. The next two examples are more complicated and therefore may give you a better feeling for this idea of working backward to find a δ.

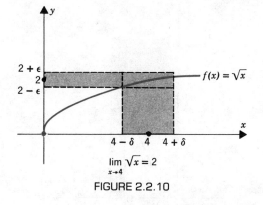

$$\lim_{x \to 4} \sqrt{x} = 2$$

FIGURE 2.2.10

EXAMPLE

$$\lim_{x \to 4} \sqrt{x} = 2. \qquad\qquad \text{(Figure 2.2.10)}$$

Finding a δ. Let $\epsilon > 0$. We seek $\delta > 0$ such that

$$\text{if} \quad 0 < |x - 4| < \delta, \quad \text{then} \quad |\sqrt{x} - 2| < \epsilon.$$

First we want a relation between $|x - 4|$ and $|\sqrt{x} - 2|$. To be able to form $\sqrt{x}$ at all we need $x \geq 0$. To ensure this we must have $\delta \leq 4$. (Why?)

Remembering that we must have $\delta \leq 4$, let's go on. If $x \geq 0$, then we can form $\sqrt{x}$ and write

$$x - 4 = (\sqrt{x})^2 - 2^2 = (\sqrt{x} + 2)(\sqrt{x} - 2).$$

Taking absolute values, we have

$$|x - 4| = |\sqrt{x} + 2||\sqrt{x} - 2|.$$

Since $|\sqrt{x} + 2| > 1$, we have

$$|\sqrt{x} - 2| < |x - 4|.$$

This last inequality suggests that we simply set $\delta = \epsilon$. But remember now the previous requirement $\delta \leq 4$. We can meet all requirements by setting $\delta =$ minimum of 4 and ϵ.

Showing that the δ "works." Let $\epsilon > 0$. Choose $\delta = \min\{4, \epsilon\}$ and assume that

$$0 < |x - 4| < \delta.$$

Since $\delta \leq 4$, we have $x \geq 0$ and can write

$$|x - 4| = |\sqrt{x} + 2||\sqrt{x} - 2|.$$

Since $|\sqrt{x} + 2| > 1$, we can conclude that

$$|\sqrt{x} - 2| < |x - 4|.$$

Since $|x - 4| < \delta$ and $\delta \leq \epsilon$, it does follow that

$$|\sqrt{x} - 2| < \epsilon. \quad \square$$

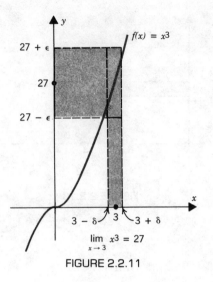

FIGURE 2.2.11

EXAMPLE

$$\lim_{x\to 3} x^3 = 27. \qquad\qquad \text{(Figure 2.2.11)}$$

Finding a δ. Let $\epsilon > 0$. We seek $\delta > 0$ such that

$$\text{if} \quad 0 < |x - 3| < \delta, \qquad \text{then} \quad |x^3 - 27| < \epsilon.$$

The needed connection between

$$|x - 3| \quad \text{and} \quad |x^3 - 27|$$

is found by factoring:

$$x^3 - 27 = (x - 3)(x^2 + 3x + 9)$$

and thus

(*) $$|x^3 - 27| = |x - 3||x^2 + 3x + 9|.$$

At this juncture we need to get a handle on the size of $|x^3 + 3x + 9|$ for x close to 3. For convenience let's take x within one unit of 3.

If $|x - 3| < 1$, then $2 < x < 4$ and

$$|x^2 + 3x + 9| \leq |x^2| + |3x| + |9|$$
$$= |x|^2 + 3|x| + 9$$
$$< 16 + 12 + 9 = 37.$$

It follows by (*) that

(**) $$\text{if} \quad |x - 3| < 1, \qquad \text{then} \quad |x^3 - 27| < 37|x - 3|.$$

If, in addition, $|x - 3| < \epsilon/37$, then it will follow that

$$|x^3 - 27| < 37(\epsilon/37) = \epsilon.$$

This means that we can take $\delta =$ minimum of 1 and $\epsilon/37$.

Showing that the δ "works." Let $\epsilon > 0$. Choose $\delta = \min\{1, \epsilon/37\}$ and assume that

$$0 < |x - 3| < \delta.$$

Then

$$|x - 3| < 1 \quad \text{and} \quad |x - 3| < \epsilon/37.$$

By (**)

$$|x^3 - 27| < 37|x - 3|,$$

which, since $|x - 3| < \epsilon/37$, gives

$$|x^3 - 27| < 37(\epsilon/37) = \epsilon. \quad \square$$

There are many different ways of formulating the same limit statement. Sometimes one formulation is more convenient, sometimes another. In any case, it is useful to recognize that the following are equivalent:

(2.2.5)

> (i) $\lim\limits_{x \to c} f(x) = l.$ (ii) $\lim\limits_{x \to c} (f(x) - l) = 0.$
>
> (iii) $\lim\limits_{x \to c} |f(x) - l| = 0.$ (iv) $\lim\limits_{h \to 0} f(c + h) = l.$

The equivalence of these four statements is obvious. It is, however, a good exercise in ϵ, δ technique to show that (i) is equivalent to (iv).

EXAMPLE. For $f(x) = x^3$, we have

$$\lim_{x \to 2} x^3 = 8, \qquad \lim_{x \to 2} (x^3 - 8) = 0,$$

$$\lim_{x \to 2} |x^3 - 8| = 0, \quad \lim_{h \to 0} (2 + h)^3 = 8. \quad \square$$

While we are on the subject of equivalent statements, note that

$$\lim_{x \to c} f(x) = l \quad \text{and} \quad \lim_{x \to c} |f(x)| = |l|$$

are *not* equivalent. While

$$\lim_{x \to c} f(x) = l \quad \text{implies} \quad \lim_{x \to c} |f(x)| = |l|, \qquad \text{(Exercise 33)}$$

the converse is false. There are instances in which

$$\lim_{x \to c} |f(x)| \text{ exists} \quad \text{but} \quad \lim_{x \to c} f(x) \text{ does not.} \qquad \text{(Exercise 34)}$$

We come now to the ϵ, δ definitions of one-sided limits.

DEFINITION 2.2.6 LEFT-HAND LIMIT

Let f be a function defined at least on an interval of the form (a, c).

$$\lim_{x \to c^-} f(x) = l \quad \text{iff} \quad \begin{cases} \text{for each } \epsilon > 0 \text{ there exists } \delta > 0 \text{ such that} \\ \text{if } \ c - \delta < x < c, \quad \text{then } \ |f(x) - l| < \epsilon. \end{cases}$$

DEFINITION 2.2.7 RIGHT-HAND LIMIT

Let f be a function defined at least on an interval of the form (c, d).

$$\lim_{x \to c^+} f(x) = l \quad \text{iff} \quad \begin{cases} \text{for each } \epsilon > 0 \text{ there exists } \delta > 0 \text{ such that} \\ \text{if } \ c < x < c + \delta, \quad \text{then } \ |f(x) - l| < \epsilon. \end{cases}$$

As indicated in Section 2.1, one-sided limits give us a simple way of determining whether or not a (two-sided) limit exists:

(2.2.8) $\quad \displaystyle\lim_{x \to c} f(x) = l \quad$ iff $\quad \displaystyle\lim_{x \to c^-} f(x) = l \quad$ and $\quad \displaystyle\lim_{x \to c^+} f(x) = l.$

The proof is left as an exercise. It is easy because any δ that "works" for the limit will work for both one-sided limits and any δ that "works" for both one-sided limits will work for the limit.

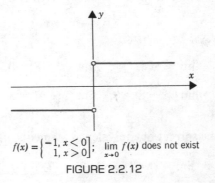

$f(x) = \begin{cases} -1, x < 0 \\ 1, x > 0 \end{cases}$; $\displaystyle\lim_{x \to 0} f(x)$ does not exist

FIGURE 2.2.12

EXAMPLE

If $f(x) = \begin{cases} -1, & x < 0 \\ 1, & x > 0 \end{cases}$,   then $\displaystyle\lim_{x \to 0} f(x)$ does not exist.   (Figure 2.2.12)

Proof. It is clear that

$$\lim_{x \to 0^-} f(x) = -1 \quad \text{and} \quad \lim_{x \to 0^+} f(x) = 1.$$

Since these one-sided limits are different,

$$\lim_{x \to 0} f(x) \text{ does not exist.} \quad \square$$

EXERCISES

Decide in the manner of Section 2.1 whether or not the indicated limit exists. Evaluate the limits which do exist.

1. $\lim_{x \to 1} \dfrac{x}{x+1}$.

2. $\lim_{x \to 0} \dfrac{x^2(1+x)}{2x}$.

3. $\lim_{x \to 0} \dfrac{x(1+x)}{2x^2}$.

4. $\lim_{x \to 4} \dfrac{x}{\sqrt{x+1}}$.

5. $\lim_{x \to 4} \dfrac{x}{\sqrt{x+1}}$.

6. $\lim_{x \to -1} \dfrac{1-x}{x+1}$.

7. $\lim_{x \to 1} \dfrac{x^4-1}{x-1}$.

8. $\lim_{x \to 2} \dfrac{x}{|x|}$.

9. $\lim_{x \to 0} \dfrac{x}{|x|}$.

10. $\lim_{x \to 1} \dfrac{x^2-1}{x^2-2x+1}$.

11. $\lim_{x \to -2} \dfrac{|x|}{x}$.

12. $\lim_{x \to 9} \dfrac{x-3}{\sqrt{x}-3}$.

13. $\lim_{x \to 2} f(x)$ if $f(x) = \begin{cases} 3, & \text{if } x \text{ is an integer} \\ 1, & \text{otherwise} \end{cases}$.

14. $\lim_{x \to 3} f(x)$ if $f(x) = \begin{cases} x^2 & x < 3 \\ 7, & x = 3 \\ 2x+3, & x > 3 \end{cases}$.

15. $\lim_{x \to \sqrt{2}} f(x)$ if $f(x) = \begin{cases} 3, & \text{if } x \text{ is an integer} \\ 1, & \text{otherwise} \end{cases}$.

16. $\lim_{x \to 2} f(x)$ if $f(x) = \begin{cases} x^2, & x \le 1 \\ 5x, & x > 1 \end{cases}$.

17. Which of the δ's displayed in Figure 2.2.13 "works" for the given ϵ?

18. For which of the ϵ's given in Figure 2.2.14 does the specified δ work?

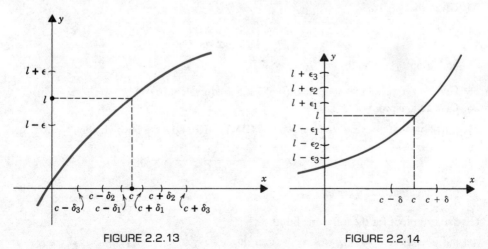

FIGURE 2.2.13   FIGURE 2.2.14

For the following limits, find the largest δ that "works" for a given arbitrary ϵ.

19. $\lim\limits_{x \to 1} 2x = 2.$ **20.** $\lim\limits_{x \to 4} 5x = 20.$ **21.** $\lim\limits_{x \to 2} \frac{1}{2}x = 1.$ **22.** $\lim\limits_{x \to 2} \frac{1}{5}x = \frac{2}{5}.$

Give an ϵ, δ proof for the following limits.

23. $\lim\limits_{x \to 4} (2x - 5) = 3.$ **24.** $\lim\limits_{x \to 2} (3x - 1) = 5.$ **25.** $\lim\limits_{x \to 3} (6x - 7) = 11.$

26. $\lim\limits_{x \to 0} (2 - 5x) = 2.$ **27.** $\lim\limits_{x \to 2} |1 - 3x| = 5.$ **28.** $\lim\limits_{x \to 2} |x - 2| = 0.$

29. Assume for some function f you know that

$$\text{if } \quad 0 < |x - 3| < 1, \quad \text{then} \quad |f(x) - 5| < 0.1.$$

Which of the following statements are necessarily true?
(a) If $|x - 3| < 1,$ then $|f(x) - 5| < 0.1.$
(b) If $|x - 2.5| < 0.3,$ then $|f(x) - 5| < 0.1.$
(c) $\lim\limits_{x \to 3} f(x) = 5.$

(d) If $0 < |x - 3| < 2,$ then $|f(x) - 5| < 0.1.$
(e) If $0 < |x - 3| < 0.5,$ then $|f(x) - 5| < 0.1.$
(f) If $0 < |x - 3| < \frac{1}{4},$ then $|f(x) - 5| < \frac{1}{4}(0.1).$
(g) If $0 < |x - 3| < 1,$ then $|f(x) - 5| < 0.2.$
(h) If $0 < |x - 3| < 1,$ then $|f(x) - 4.95| < 0.05.$
(i) If $\lim\limits_{x \to 3} f(x) = l,$ then $4.9 \le l \le 5.1.$

30. Suppose $|A - B| < \epsilon$ for each $\epsilon > 0$. Prove that $A = B$.
HINT: Consider what happens if $A \ne B$ and $\epsilon = \frac{1}{2}|A - B|$.

Give the four limit statements displayed in 2.2.5, taking

31. $f(x) = \dfrac{1}{x - 1}, \quad c = 3.$ **32.** $f(x) = \dfrac{x}{x^2 + 2}, \quad c = 1.$

33. Show that, if $\lim\limits_{x \to c} f(x) = l$, then $\lim\limits_{x \to c} |f(x)| = |l|$.

34. Given that

$$f(x) = \begin{cases} -1, & x < 0 \\ 1, & x > 0 \end{cases},$$

find (a) $\lim\limits_{x \to 0} f(x)$ and (b) $\lim\limits_{x \to 0} |f(x)|$.

35. Give an ϵ, δ proof that statement (i) of 2.2.5 is equivalent to (iv).
36. Give an ϵ, δ proof of (2.2.8).

37. (a) Show that $\lim\limits_{x \to c} \sqrt{x} = \sqrt{c}$ for $c > 0$.   HINT: If x and c are positive, then

$$0 \le |\sqrt{x} - \sqrt{c}| = \frac{|x - c|}{\sqrt{x} + \sqrt{c}} < \frac{1}{\sqrt{c}}|x - c|.$$

(b) Show that $\lim\limits_{x \to 0^+} \sqrt{x} = 0$.

Give an ϵ, δ proof for the following limits.

38. $\lim\limits_{x \to 2} x^2 = 4.$ **39.** $\lim\limits_{x \to 1} x^3 = 1.$ **40.** $\lim\limits_{x \to 3} \sqrt{x + 1} = 2.$ **41.** $\lim\limits_{x \to 3^-} \sqrt{3 - x} = 0.$

Prove the following statements.

42. If $g(x) = \begin{cases} x, & x \text{ rational} \\ 0, & x \text{ irrational} \end{cases}$, then $\lim_{x \to 0} g(x) = 0$.

43. If $f(x) = \begin{cases} 1, & x \text{ rational} \\ 0, & x \text{ irrational} \end{cases}$, then for no number c does $\lim_{x \to c} f(x)$ exist.

44. $\lim_{x \to c^-} f(x) = l$ iff $\lim_{h \to 0} f(c - |h|) = l$.

45. $\lim_{x \to c^+} f(x) = l$ iff $\lim_{h \to 0} f(c + |h|) = l$.

2.3 ······SOME LIMIT THEOREMS

As you saw in the last section, it can be rather tedious to apply the ϵ, δ limit test to individual functions. By proving some general theorems about limits we can avoid some of this repetitive work. The theorems themselves, of course (at least the first ones), will have to be proved by ϵ, δ methods.

We begin by showing that, if a limit exists, it is unique.

THEOREM 2.3.1　THE UNIQUENESS OF A LIMIT

If

$$\lim_{x \to c} f(x) = l \quad \text{and} \quad \lim_{x \to c} f(x) = m,$$

then

$$l = m.$$

Proof. We will show that $l = m$ by proving that the assumption that $l \neq m$ leads to the contradiction

$$|l - m| < |l - m|.$$

Let's assume that $l \neq m$. Then $|l - m|/2 > 0$. Since

$$\lim_{x \to c} f(x) = l,$$

we know that there exists $\delta_1 > 0$ such that

(1) $\qquad$ if $\ 0 < |x - c| < \delta_1,$ $\quad$ then $\quad |f(x) - l| < \dfrac{|l - m|}{2}.$ †

Since

$$\lim_{x \to c} f(x) = m,$$

---

† We are using $|l - m|/2$ as ϵ.

we know that there exists $\delta_2 > 0$ such that

(2)   if $\;0 < |x - c| < \delta_2,\quad$ then $\;|f(x) - m| < \dfrac{|l - m|}{2}.$

Now take x_1 as a number that satisfies the inequality

$$0 < |x_1 - c| < \text{minimum of } \delta_1 \text{ and } \delta_2.$$

Then by (1) and (2)

$$|f(x_1) - l| < \frac{|l - m|}{2} \quad \text{and} \quad |f(x) - m| < \frac{|l - m|}{2}.$$

It follows that

$$|l - m| = |[l - f(x_1)] + [f(x_1) - m]|$$

by the triangle $\quad\uparrow$
inequality
$$\le |l - f(x_1)| + |f(x_1) - m|$$

$|a| = |-a|$ $\quad\longrightarrow\quad = |f(x_1) - l| + |f(x_1) - m|$

$$< \frac{|l - m|}{2} + \frac{|l - m|}{2} = |l - m|. \quad \square$$

THEOREM 2.3.2

If

$$\lim_{x \to c} f(x) = l \quad \text{and} \quad \lim_{x \to c} g(x) = m,$$

then

(i) $\displaystyle \lim_{x \to c} [f(x) + g(x)] = l + m,$

(ii) $\displaystyle \lim_{x \to c} [\alpha f(x)] = \alpha l \quad$ for each real $\alpha,$

(iii) $\displaystyle \lim_{x \to c} [f(x)g(x)] = lm.$

Proof. Let $\epsilon > 0$. To prove (i) we must show that there exists $\delta > 0$ such that

$$\text{if } \; 0 < |x - c| < \delta, \quad \text{then} \quad |[f(x) + g(x)] - [l + m]| < \epsilon.$$

Note that

(*) $$|[f(x) + g(x)] - [l + m]| = |[f(x) - l] + [g(x) - m]|$$
$$\le |f(x) - l| + |g(x) - m|.$$

We will make

$$|[f(x) + g(x)] - [l + m]|$$

less than ϵ by making

$$|f(x) - l| \quad \text{and} \quad |g(x) - m|$$

each less than $\frac{1}{2}\epsilon$. Since $\epsilon > 0$, we know that $\frac{1}{2}\epsilon > 0$. Since

$$\lim_{x \to c} f(x) = l \quad \text{and} \quad \lim_{x \to c} g(x) = m,$$

we know that there exist positive numbers δ_1 and δ_2 such that

$$\text{if} \quad 0 < |x - c| < \delta_1, \quad \text{then} \quad |f(x) - l| < \tfrac{1}{2}\epsilon$$

and

$$\text{if} \quad 0 < |x - c| < \delta_2, \quad \text{then} \quad |g(x) - m| < \tfrac{1}{2}\epsilon.$$

Now we set $\delta = $ minimum of δ_1 and δ_2 and note that, if $0 < |x - c| < \delta$, then

$$|f(x) - l| < \tfrac{1}{2}\epsilon \quad \text{and} \quad |g(x) - m| < \tfrac{1}{2}\epsilon$$

and thus by (*)

$$|[f(x) + g(x)] - [l + m]| < \epsilon.$$

In summary, by setting $\delta = \min \{\delta_1, \delta_2\}$, we found that,

$$\text{if} \quad 0 < |x - c| < \delta, \quad \text{then} \quad |[f(x) + g(x)] - [l + m]| < \epsilon.$$

Thus (i) is proved. For proofs of (ii) and (iii), see the supplement at the end of this section. $\square$

The results of Theorem 2.3.2 are easily extended (by mathematical induction) to any finite collection of functions; namely, if

$$\lim_{x \to c} f_1(x) = l_1, \quad \lim_{x \to c} f_2(x) = l_2, \ldots, \quad \lim_{x \to c} f_n(x) = l_n$$

then

$$(2.3.3) \qquad \lim_{x \to c} [\alpha_1 f_1(x) + \alpha_2 f_2(x) + \cdots + \alpha_n f_n(x)] = \alpha_1 l_1 + \alpha_2 l_2 + \cdots + \alpha_n l_n$$

and

$$(2.3.4) \qquad \lim_{x \to c} [f_1(x) f_2(x) \cdots f_n(x)] = l_1 l_2 \cdots l_n.$$

It follows that for every polynomial $P(x) = a_n x^n + \cdots + a_1 x + a_0$

$$(2.3.5) \qquad \boxed{\lim_{x \to c} P(x) = P(c).}$$

Proof. We already know that

$$\lim_{x \to c} x = c.$$

Applying (2.3.4) to $f(x) = x$ multiplied k times by itself, we have

$$\lim_{x \to c} x^k = c^k \qquad \text{for each positive integer } k.$$

We also know that

$$\lim_{x \to c} a_0 = a_0.$$

If follows now from (2.3.3) that

$$\lim_{x \to c} (a_n x^n + \cdots + a_1 x + a_0) = a_n c^n + \cdots + a_1 c + a_0;$$

that is,

$$\lim_{x \to c} P(x) = P(c). \quad \square$$

EXAMPLES

$$\lim_{x \to 1} (5x^2 - 12x + 2) = 5(1)^2 - 12(1) + 2 = -5,$$

$$\lim_{x \to 0} (14x^5 - 7x^2 + 2x + 8) = 14(0)^5 - 7(0)^2 + 2(0) + 8 = 8,$$

$$\lim_{x \to -1} (2x^3 + x^2 - 2x - 3) = 2(-1)^3 + (-1)^2 - 2(-1) - 3 = -2. \quad \square$$

We come now to reciprocals and quotients.

THEOREM 2.3.6

If $\displaystyle \lim_{x \to c} g(x) = m$ and $m \neq 0$, then $\displaystyle \lim_{x \to c} \frac{1}{g(x)} = \frac{1}{m}$.

Proof. See the supplement at the end of this section. $\square$

EXAMPLES

$$\lim_{x \to 4} \frac{1}{x^2} = \frac{1}{16}, \qquad \lim_{x \to 2} \frac{1}{x^3 - 1} = \frac{1}{7}, \qquad \lim_{x \to -3} \frac{1}{|x|} = \frac{1}{|-3|} = \frac{1}{3}. \quad \square$$

Once you know that reciprocals present no trouble, quotients become easy to handle.

THEOREM 2.3.7

If

$$\lim_{x \to c} f(x) = l \quad \text{and} \quad \lim_{x \to c} g(x) = m \quad \text{with} \quad m \neq 0,$$

then

$$\lim_{x \to c} \frac{f(x)}{g(x)} = \frac{l}{m}.$$

Proof. The key here is to observe that the quotient can be written as a product:

$$\frac{f(x)}{g(x)} = f(x)\,\frac{1}{g(x)}.$$

With

$$\lim_{x \to c} f(x) = l \quad \text{and} \quad \lim_{x \to c} \frac{1}{g(x)} = \frac{1}{m},$$

the product rule [part (iii) of Theorem 2.3.2] gives

$$\lim_{x \to c} \frac{f(x)}{g(x)} = l\,\frac{1}{m} = \frac{l}{m}. \quad \square$$

As an immediate consequence of this theorem on quotients you can see that, if P and Q are polynomials and $Q(c) \neq 0$, then

(2.3.8)
$$\lim_{x \to c} \frac{P(x)}{Q(x)} = \frac{P(c)}{Q(c)}.$$

EXAMPLES

$$\lim_{x \to 2} \frac{3x - 5}{x^2 + 1} = \frac{6 - 5}{4 + 1} = \frac{1}{5}, \qquad \lim_{x \to 3} \frac{x^3 - 3x^2}{1 - x^2} = \frac{27 - 27}{1 - 9} = 0. \quad \square$$

There is no point looking for a limit that does not exist. The next theorem gives a condition under which a quotient does not have a limit.

THEOREM 2.3.9

If

$$\lim_{x \to c} f(x) = l \quad \text{with } l \neq 0 \qquad \text{and} \qquad \lim_{x \to c} g(x) = 0,$$

then

$$\lim_{x \to c} \frac{f(x)}{g(x)} \quad \text{does not exist.}$$

Proof. Suppose, on the contrary, that there exists a real number L such that

$$\lim_{x \to c} \frac{f(x)}{g(x)} = L.$$

Then

$$l = \lim_{x \to c} f(x) = \lim_{x \to c} \left[g(x) \cdot \frac{f(x)}{g(x)} \right] = \lim_{x \to c} g(x) \cdot \lim_{x \to c} \frac{f(x)}{g(x)} = 0 \cdot L = 0,$$

which contradicts our assumption that $l \neq 0$. $\quad \square$

EXAMPLES. From Theorem 2.3.9 you can see that

$$\lim_{x \to 1} \frac{x^2}{x - 1}, \qquad \lim_{x \to 2} \frac{3x - 7}{x^2 - 4}, \qquad \text{and} \qquad \lim_{x \to 0} \frac{5}{x}$$

all fail to exist. □

PROBLEM. Evaluate the limits that exist:

(a) $\displaystyle\lim_{x \to 3} \frac{x^2 - x - 6}{x - 3}$ (b) $\displaystyle\lim_{x \to 4} \frac{(x^2 - 3x - 4)^2}{x - 4}$ (c) $\displaystyle\lim_{x \to -1} \frac{x + 1}{(2x^2 + 7x + 5)^2}.$

Solution. In each case both numerator and denominator tend to zero, and so we have to be careful.

(a) First we factor the numerator:

$$\frac{x^2 - x - 6}{x - 3} = \frac{(x + 2)(x - 3)}{x - 3}.$$

For $x \neq 3$,

$$\frac{x^2 - x - 6}{x - 3} = x + 2.$$

Thus

$$\lim_{x \to 3} \frac{x^2 - x - 6}{x - 3} = \lim_{x \to 3} (x + 2) = 5.$$

(b) Note that

$$\frac{(x^2 - 3x - 4)^2}{x - 4} = \frac{[(x + 1)(x - 4)]^2}{x - 4} = \frac{(x + 1)^2(x - 4)^2}{x - 4}$$

so that, for $x \neq 4$,

$$\frac{(x^2 - 3x - 4)^2}{x - 4} = (x + 1)^2(x - 4).$$

It follows then that

$$\lim_{x \to 4} \frac{(x^2 - 3x - 4)^2}{x - 4} = \lim_{x \to 4} (x + 1)^2(x - 4) = 0.$$

(c) Since

$$\frac{x + 1}{(2x^2 + 7x + 5)^2} = \frac{x + 1}{[(2x + 5)(x + 1)]^2} = \frac{x + 1}{(2x + 5)^2(x + 1)^2},$$

you can see that, for $x \neq -1$,

$$\frac{x + 1}{(2x^2 + 7x + 5)^2} = \frac{1}{(2x + 5)^2(x + 1)}.$$

By Theorem 2.3.9,

$$\lim_{x \to -1} \frac{1}{(2x + 5)^2(x + 1)} \qquad \text{does not exist,}$$

and therefore

$$\lim_{x \to -1} \frac{x+1}{(2x^2 + 7x + 5)^2} \quad \text{does not exist either.} \quad \square$$

CAUTION. Even though the "arithmetic of limits" provided by the theorems above has not presented any surprises, you should be careful in paraphrasing the results. For example, it is *not* quite true that "the limit of a sum is the sum of the limits." This is but the conclusion of the theorem. We need to remember the hypothesis. A correct paraphrase might run

> "the limit of a sum is the sum of the limits
> *provided these latter limits exist*."   (Exercise 54)

A similar caution applies to the other results. $\square$

Suppose that, for x close to c but different from c, a function f is trapped between two functions h and g. If, as x tends to c, both $h(x)$ and $g(x)$ tend to the same limit l (see Figure 2.3.1), then $f(x)$ also tends to l. This is the substance of what we call the *pinching theorem*.

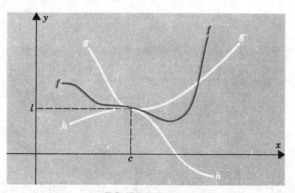

FIGURE 2.3.1

THEOREM 2.3.10   THE PINCHING THEOREM

Let $p > 0$. Suppose that, for all x such that $0 < |x - c| < p$,

$$h(x) \le f(x) \le g(x).$$

If

$$\lim_{x \to c} h(x) = l \quad \text{and} \quad \lim_{x \to c} g(x) = l,$$

then

$$\lim_{x \to c} f(x) = l.$$

Proof.   Let $\epsilon > 0$.   Let $p > 0$ be such that

$$\text{if}\quad 0 < |x - c| < p,\qquad \text{then}\quad h(x) \leq f(x) \leq g(x).$$

Choose $\delta_1 > 0$ such that

$$\text{if}\quad 0 < |x - c| < \delta_1,\qquad \text{then}\quad l - \epsilon < h(x) < l + \epsilon.$$

Choose $\delta_2 > 0$ such that

$$\text{if}\quad 0 < |x - c| < \delta_2,\qquad \text{then}\quad l - \epsilon < g(x) < l + \epsilon.$$

Let $\delta = \min\{p, \delta_1, \delta_2\}$.   For x satisfying $0 < |x - c| < \delta$, we have

$$l - \epsilon < h(x) \leq f(x) \leq g(x) < l + \epsilon$$

and thus

$$|f(x) - l| < \epsilon.\quad \square$$

EXAMPLE.   Suppose that

$$x^2 + 12x - 9 \leq f(x) \leq 5x^2 \qquad \text{for all}\ \ x \neq \tfrac{3}{2}.$$

As you can check,

$$\lim_{x \to 3/2} (x^2 + 12x - 9) = \tfrac{45}{4}\ \ \text{and}\ \ \lim_{x \to 3/2} 5x^2 = \tfrac{45}{4}.$$

It follows from the pinching theorem that

$$\lim_{x \to 3/2} f(x) = \tfrac{45}{4}.\quad \square$$

EXAMPLE

$$\text{If}\ \ f(x) = \begin{cases} x^2, & x\ \text{rational} \\ x^4, & x\ \text{irrational} \end{cases},\qquad \text{then}\quad \lim_{x \to 0} f(x) = 0.$$

To verify this, note that, for $|x| < 1$,

$$0 \leq f(x) \leq x^2. \qquad\qquad\qquad\qquad \text{(explain)}$$

Since

$$\lim_{x \to 0} x^2 = 0, \qquad\qquad (\text{and, of course, } \lim_{x \to 0} 0 = 0)$$

the pinching theorem guarantees that

$$\lim_{x \to 0} f(x) = 0.\quad \square$$

REMARK.   Results like those proved in this section for two-sided limits also hold for one-sided limits.   (Exercises 61 and 62.)

EXERCISES

1. Given that

$$\lim_{x \to c} f(x) = 2, \quad \lim_{x \to c} g(x) = -1, \quad \text{and} \quad \lim_{x \to c} h(x) = 0$$

evaluate the limits that exist.

(a) $\lim_{x \to c} [f(x) - g(x)]$.   (b) $\lim_{x \to c} [f(x)]^2$.   (c) $\lim_{x \to c} \dfrac{f(x)}{g(x)}$.

(d) $\lim_{x \to c} \dfrac{h(x)}{f(x)}$.   (e) $\lim_{x \to c} \dfrac{f(x)}{h(x)}$.   (f) $\lim_{x \to c} \dfrac{1}{f(x) - g(x)}$.

2. Given that

$$\lim_{x \to c} f(x) = 3, \quad \lim_{x \to c} g(x) = 0, \quad \text{and} \quad \lim_{x \to c} h(x) = -2$$

evaluate the limits that exist.

(a) $\lim_{x \to c} [3f(x) + 2h(x)]$.   (b) $\lim_{x \to c} [h(x)]^3$.   (c) $\lim_{x \to c} \dfrac{h(x)}{x - c}$.

(d) $\lim_{x \to c} \dfrac{g(x)}{h(x)}$.   (e) $\lim_{x \to c} \dfrac{4}{f(x) - h(x)}$.   (f) $\lim_{x \to c} [3 + g(x)]^2$.

3. When asked to evaluate

$$\lim_{x \to 4} \left(\frac{1}{x} - \frac{1}{4} \right)\left(\frac{1}{x - 4} \right),$$

a student responds that the limit is zero since $\lim_{x \to 4} [1/x - \frac{1}{4}] = 0$ and cites Theorem 2.3.2 (limit of a product) as justification.   Verify that the actual value of the limit is $-\frac{1}{16}$ and identify the student's error.

4. When asked to evaluate

$$\lim_{x \to 3} \frac{x^2 + x - 12}{x - 3},$$

a student responds that the limit does not exist since $\lim_{x \to 3} (x - 3) = 0$ and cites Theorem 2.3.9 (limit of a quotient) as justification.   Verify that the actual value of the limit is 7 and identify the student's error.

Evaluate the limits that exist.

5. $\lim_{x \to 2} 3$.

6. $\lim_{x \to 3} (5 - 4x)^2$.

7. $\lim_{x \to -4} (x^2 + 3x - 7)$.

8. $\lim_{x \to -2} 3|x - 1|$.

9. $\lim_{x \to \sqrt{3}} |x^2 - 8|$.

10. $\lim_{x \to 3} 2$.

11. $\lim_{x \to -1} \dfrac{x^2 + 1}{3x^5 + 4}$.

12. $\lim_{x \to 2} \dfrac{3x}{x + 4}$.

13. $\lim_{x \to 0} \left(x - \dfrac{4}{x} \right)$.

14. $\lim_{x \to 2} \dfrac{x^2 + x + 1}{x^2 + 2x}$.

15. $\lim_{x \to 5} \dfrac{2 - x^2}{4x}$.

16. $\lim_{x \to 0} \dfrac{x^2 + 1}{x}$.

17. $\lim_{x \to 0} \dfrac{x^2}{x^2 + 1}$.

18. $\lim_{x \to 2} \dfrac{x}{x^2 - 4}$.

19. $\lim_{h \to 0} h \left(1 - \dfrac{1}{h} \right)$.

20. $\lim\limits_{h\to 0} h\left(1+\dfrac{1}{h}\right).$

21. $\lim\limits_{x\to 2}\dfrac{x-2}{x^2-4}.$

22. $\lim\limits_{x\to 2}\dfrac{x^2-4}{x-2}.$

23. $\lim\limits_{x\to -2}\dfrac{(x^2-x-6)^2}{x+2}.$

24. $\lim\limits_{x\to 1}\dfrac{x-x^2}{1-x}.$

25. $\lim\limits_{x\to 1}\dfrac{x-x^2}{(3x-1)(x^4-2)}.$

26. $\lim\limits_{x\to 1}\dfrac{x^2-x-6}{(x+2)^2}.$

27. $\lim\limits_{x\to -2}\dfrac{x^2-x-6}{(x+2)^2}.$

28. $\lim\limits_{x\to 0}\dfrac{x^4}{3x^3+2x^2+x}.$

29. $\lim\limits_{h\to 0}\dfrac{1-1/h^2}{1-1/h}.$

30. $\lim\limits_{h\to 0}\dfrac{1-1/h^2}{1+1/h^2}.$

31. $\lim\limits_{h\to 0}\dfrac{1-1/h}{1+1/h}.$

32. $\lim\limits_{h\to 0}\dfrac{1+1/h}{1+1/h^2}.$

33. $\lim\limits_{t\to -1}\dfrac{t^2+6t+5}{t^2+3t+2}.$

34. $\lim\limits_{x\to -3}\dfrac{5x+15}{x^3+3x^2-x-3}.$

35. $\lim\limits_{t\to 0}\dfrac{t+a/t}{t+b/t}.$

36. $\lim\limits_{x\to 1}\dfrac{x^2-1}{x^3-1}.$

37. $\lim\limits_{x\to 1}\dfrac{x^5-1}{x^4-1}.$

38. $\lim\limits_{t\to 0}\dfrac{t+1/t}{t-1/t}.$

39. $\lim\limits_{h\to 0} h\left(1+\dfrac{1}{h^2}\right).$

40. $\lim\limits_{h\to 0} h^2\left(1+\dfrac{1}{h}\right).$

41. $\lim\limits_{x\to -4}\left(\dfrac{3x}{x+4}+\dfrac{8}{x+4}\right).$

42. $\lim\limits_{x\to -2}\dfrac{(x^2-x-6)^2}{(x+2)^2}.$

43. $\lim\limits_{t\to 1}\dfrac{t^2-2t+1}{t^3-3t^2+3t-1}.$

44. $\lim\limits_{x\to -4}\left(\dfrac{2x}{x+4}+\dfrac{8}{x+4}\right).$

45. Given that $f(x)=x^2-4x$, evaluate the limits that exist.

(a) $\lim\limits_{x\to 4}\dfrac{f(x)-f(4)}{x-4}.$

(b) $\lim\limits_{x\to 1}\dfrac{f(x)-f(1)}{x-1}.$

(c) $\lim\limits_{x\to 3}\dfrac{f(x)-f(1)}{x-3}.$

(d) $\lim\limits_{x\to 3}\dfrac{f(x)-f(2)}{x-3}.$

46. Given that $f(x)=x^3$, evaluate the limits that exist.

(a) $\lim\limits_{x\to 3}\dfrac{f(x)-f(3)}{x-3}.$

(b) $\lim\limits_{x\to 3}\dfrac{f(x)-f(2)}{x-3}.$

(c) $\lim\limits_{x\to 3}\dfrac{f(x)-f(3)}{x-2}.$

(d) $\lim\limits_{x\to 1}\dfrac{f(x)-f(1)}{x-1}.$

47. Find $\lim\limits_{x\to 0} f(x)$ given that $0\le f(x)\le |x|$ if $0<|x|<1$.

48. Find $\lim\limits_{x\to 0} f(x)$ given that $2-|x|\le f(x)\le 2+|x|$ for $x\ne 0$.

49. Find $\lim\limits_{x\to 3} f(x)$ given that $1\le f(x)\le (x-3)^2+1$ for $x\ne 3$.

50. Find $\lim\limits_{x\to 2} f(x)$ given that $-(x-2)^2\le f(x)\le 0$ if $0<|x-2|<1$.

51. Find $\lim\limits_{x\to 0} f(x)$ given that $\left|\dfrac{f(x)}{x}\right|\le M$ for $x\ne 0$.

52. Find $\lim\limits_{x \to c} f(x)$ given that $\left| \dfrac{f(x) - f(c)}{x - c} \right| \le M$ for $x \ne c$.

53. Given that

$$\lim_{x \to c} g(x) = 0 \quad \text{and} \quad f(x)g(x) = 1 \quad \text{for all real } x,$$

prove that $\lim\limits_{x \to c} f(x)$ does not exist.   HINT: Suppose that $\lim\limits_{x \to c} f(x)$ exists (say, it is equal to l) and deduce a contradiction.

54. Give an example to show that $\lim\limits_{x \to c} [f(x) + g(x)]$ may exist even if neither $\lim\limits_{x \to c} f(x)$ nor $\lim\limits_{x \to c} g(x)$ exists.

55. Give an example to show that $\lim\limits_{x \to c} [f(x)g(x)]$ may exist even if neither $\lim\limits_{x \to c} f(x)$ nor $\lim\limits_{x \to c} g(x)$ exists.

56. Give an example to show that $\lim\limits_{x \to c} \sqrt{f(x)}$ may not exist even if $\lim\limits_{x \to c} f(x)$ does exist.

57. (a) Verify that

$$\max \{f(x), g(x)\} = \tfrac{1}{2}\{[f(x) + g(x)] + |f(x) - g(x)|\}.$$

(b) Find a similar expression for $\min \{f(x), g(x)\}$.

58. Let

$$h(x) = \min \{f(x), g(x)\} \quad \text{and} \quad H(x) = \max \{f(x), g(x)\}.$$

Show that

if $\lim\limits_{x \to c} f(x) = l$ and $\lim\limits_{x \to c} g(x) = l,$ then $\lim\limits_{x \to c} h(x) = l$ and $\lim\limits_{x \to c} H(x) = l.$

HINT: Use Exercise 57.

59. Show that, if $\lim\limits_{x \to c} f(x) = l > 0$, then $f(x) > 0$ for all $x \ne c$ in an interval of the form $(c - \delta, c + \delta), \delta > 0.$ HINT: Use an ϵ, δ argument with $\epsilon = l$.

60. Show that, if $f(x) \le g(x)$ for all real x, then

$$\lim_{x \to c} f(x) \le \lim_{x \to c} g(x)$$

provided both limits exist.   HINT: Let $l = \lim\limits_{x \to c} f(x)$ and $m = \lim\limits_{x \to c} g(x)$; assume $l > m$ and derive a contradiction using $\epsilon = (l - m)/2.$

61. State and prove the pinching theorem (2.3.10) for right-hand limits.

62. State and prove statement (i) of (2.3.2) for left-hand limits.

Supplement to Section 2.3

Proof of Theorem 2.3.2 (ii). We consider two cases: $\alpha \ne 0$ and $\alpha = 0$. If $\alpha \ne 0$, then $\epsilon/|\alpha| > 0$ and, since

$$\lim_{x \to c} f(x) = l,$$

we know that there exists $\delta > 0$ such that,

$$\text{if} \quad 0 < |x - c| < \delta, \quad \text{then} \quad |f(x) - l| < \frac{\epsilon}{|\alpha|}.$$

From the last inequality we obtain

$$|\alpha||f(x) - l| < \epsilon \quad \text{and thus} \quad |\alpha f(x) - \alpha l| < \epsilon.$$

The case $\alpha = 0$ was treated before in (2.2.4). $\quad\square$

Proof of Theorem 2.3.2 (iii).   We begin with a little algebra:

$$\begin{aligned}
|f(x)g(x) - lm| &= |[f(x)g(x) - f(x)m] + [f(x)m - lm]| \\
&\leq |f(x)g(x) - f(x)m| + |f(x)m - lm| \\
&= |f(x)||g(x) - m| + |m||f(x) - l| \\
&\leq |f(x)||g(x) - m| + (1 + |m|)|f(x) - l|.
\end{aligned}$$

Now let $\epsilon > 0$.   Since

$$\lim_{x \to c} f(x) = l \quad \text{and} \quad \lim_{x \to c} g(x) = m,$$

we know

(1) that there exists $\delta_1 > 0$ such that, if $0 < |x - c| < \delta_1$, then

$$|f(x) - l| < 1 \quad \text{and thus} \quad |f(x)| < 1 + |l|;$$

(2) that there exists $\delta_2 > 0$ such that

$$\text{if} \quad 0 < |x - c| < \delta_2, \quad \text{then} \quad |g(x) - m| < \left(\frac{\frac{1}{2}\epsilon}{1 + |l|} \right);$$

(3) that there exists $\delta_3 > 0$ such that

$$\text{if} \quad 0 < |x - c| < \delta_3, \quad \text{then} \quad |f(x) - l| < \left(\frac{\frac{1}{2}\epsilon}{1 + |m|} \right).$$

We now set $\delta = \min \{\delta_1, \delta_2, \delta_3\}$ and observe that, if

$$0 < |x - c| < \delta,$$

then

$$|f(x)g(x) - lm| < |f(x)||g(x) - m| + (1 + |m|)|f(x) - l|$$

$$< \underset{\text{by (1)}}{\underbrace{(1 + |l|)}} \underset{\text{by (2)}}{\underbrace{\left(\frac{\frac{1}{2}\epsilon}{1 + |l|} \right)}} + (1 + |m|) \underset{\text{by (3)}}{\underbrace{\left(\frac{\frac{1}{2}\epsilon}{1 + |m|} \right)}} = \epsilon. \quad\square$$

Proof of Theorem 2.3.6.   For $g(x) \neq 0$,

$$\left| \frac{1}{g(x)} - \frac{1}{m} \right| = \frac{|g(x) - m|}{|m||g(x)|}.$$

Choose $\delta_1 > 0$ such that

$$\text{if} \quad 0 < |x - c| < \delta_1, \quad \text{then} \quad |g(x) - m| < \frac{|m|}{2}.$$

For such x,

$$|g(x)| > \frac{|m|}{2}, \qquad \frac{1}{|g(x)|} < \frac{2}{|m|}$$

and thus

$$\left| \frac{1}{g(x)} - \frac{1}{m} \right| \leq \frac{2}{|m|^2} |g(x) - m|.$$

Now let $\epsilon > 0$ and choose $\delta_2 > 0$ such that

$$\text{if} \quad 0 < |x - c| < \delta_2, \quad \text{then} \quad |g(x) - m| < \frac{|m|^2}{2} \epsilon.$$

Setting $\delta = \min \{\delta_1, \delta_2\}$, we find that

$$\text{if} \quad 0 < |x - c| < \delta, \quad \text{then} \quad \left| \frac{1}{g(x)} - \frac{1}{m} \right| < \epsilon. \quad \square$$

2.4 ······CONTINUITY

In ordinary language, to say that a certain process is "continuous" is to say that it goes on without interruption and without abrupt changes. In mathematics the word "continuous" has much the same meaning.

    The idea of continuity is so important to calculus that we will discuss it with some care. First we introduce the idea of continuity at a point (or number) c, and then we talk about continuity on an interval.

Continuity at a Point

Let f be a function defined at least on an open interval $(c - \delta, c + \delta)$.

DEFINITION 2.4.1

The function f is said to be *continuous at c* iff $\lim_{x \to c} f(x) = f(c)$.

    If the domain of f contains an interval $(c - \delta, c + \delta)$, then f can fail to be continuous at c only for one of two reasons: either $f(x)$ does not have a limit as x tends to c (in which case c is called an *essential discontinuity*), or it does have a limit, but the limit is not $f(c)$. In this case c is called a *removable discontinuity*; the discontinuity can be removed by redefining f at c. If the limit is l, define f at c to be l.

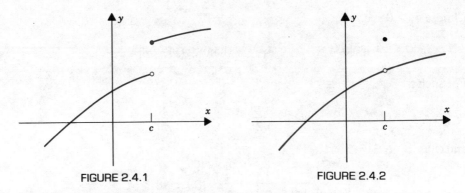

FIGURE 2.4.1   FIGURE 2.4.2

The function depicted in Figure 2.4.1 is discontinuous at c because it does not have a limit at c. The discontinuity is essential. .

The function depicted in Figure 2.4.2 does have a limit at c. It is discontinuous at c only because its limit at c is not its value at c. The discontinuity is removable; it can be removed by lowering the dot into place (by redefining f at c).

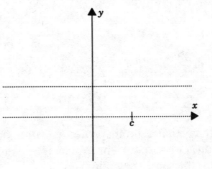

FIGURE 2.4.3

In Figure 2.4.3, we have tried to suggest the Dirichlet function

$$f(x) = \begin{cases} 1, & x \text{ rational} \\ 0, & x \text{ irrational} \end{cases}.$$

At no point c does f have a limit. It is therefore everywhere discontinuous and every point is an essential discontinuity.

Most of the functions that you have encountered so far are continuous at each point of their domains. In particular, this is true for polynomials,

$$\lim_{x \to c} P(x) = P(c), \tag{2.3.5}$$

for rational functions (quotients of polynomials),

$$\lim_{x \to c} \frac{P(x)}{Q(x)} = \frac{P(c)}{Q(c)} \quad \text{if} \quad Q(c) \neq 0, \tag{2.3.8}$$

and for the absolute-value function,

$$\lim_{x \to c} |x| = |c|. \tag{2.2.2}$$

In one of the exercises you showed (or at least were asked to show) that

$$\lim_{x \to c} \sqrt{x} = \sqrt{c} \qquad \text{for each } c > 0.$$

This makes the square-root function continuous at each positive number. What happens at 0, we discuss later.

With f and g continuous at c, we have

$$\lim_{x \to c} f(x) = f(c), \quad \lim_{x \to c} g(x) = g(c)$$

and thus, by the limit theorems,

$$\lim_{x \to c} [f(x) + g(x)] = f(c) + g(c)$$

$$\lim_{x \to c} [\alpha f(x)] = \alpha f(c) \qquad \text{for each real } \alpha$$

$$\lim_{x \to c} [f(x)g(x)] = f(c)g(c)$$

and, if $g(c) \neq 0$,

$$\lim_{x \to c} \frac{f(x)}{g(x)} = \frac{f(c)}{g(c)}.$$

In summary, we have the following theorem:

THEOREM 2.4.2

If f and g are continuous at c, then

  (i) $f + g$ is continuous at c,

  (ii) αf is continuous at c for each real α,

  (iii) fg is continuous at c,

  (iv) f/g is continuous at c provided $g(c) \neq 0$.

Parts (i) and (iii) can be extended to any finite number of functions.

EXAMPLE. The function

$$F(x) = 3|x| + \frac{x^3 - x}{x^2 - 5x + 6} + 4$$

is continuous at all real numbers other than 2 and 3. You can see this by noting that $F = 3f + g/h + k$ where

$$f(x) = |x|, \quad g(x) = x^3 - x, \quad h(x) = x^2 - 5x + 6, \quad \text{and} \quad k(x) = 4.$$

Since f, g, h, and k are everywhere continuous, F is continuous except at 2 and 3, the numbers where h takes on the value 0. $\square$

Our next topic is the continuity of composite functions. Before getting into this, however, let's take a look at continuity in terms of ϵ, δ. A direct translation of

$$\lim_{x \to c} f(x) = f(c)$$

into ϵ, δ terms reads like this: for each $\epsilon > 0$ there exists $\delta > 0$ such that

$$\text{if} \quad 0 < |x - c| < \delta \qquad \text{then} \quad |f(x) - f(c)| < \epsilon.$$

Here the restriction $0 < |x - c|$ is unnecessary. We can allow $|x - c| = 0$ because then $x = c$, $f(x) = f(c)$, and thus $|f(x) - f(c)| = 0$. Being 0, $|f(x) - f(c)|$ is certainly less than ϵ.

In summary, an ϵ, δ characterization of continuity at c reads as follows:

(2.4.3) f is continuous at c iff $\begin{cases} \text{for each } \epsilon > 0 \text{ there exists } \delta > 0 \text{ such that} \\ \text{if } |x - c| < \delta \qquad \text{then} \quad |f(x) - f(c)| < \epsilon. \end{cases}$

In simple intuitive language

f is continuous at c iff   for x close to c, $f(x)$ is close to $f(c)$.

We are now ready to take up the continuity of composites. Remember the defining formula: $(f \circ g)(x) = f(g(x))$.

THEOREM 2.4.4

If g is continuous at c and f is continuous at $g(c)$, then the composition $f \circ g$ is continuous at c.

The idea here is simple: with g continuous at c, we know that

$$\text{for } x \text{ close to } c, \quad g(x) \text{ is close to } g(c);$$

from the continuity of f at $g(c)$, we know that

$$\text{with } g(x) \text{ close to } g(c), \quad f(g(x)) \text{ is close to } f(g(c)).$$

In summary,

$$\text{with } x \text{ close to } c, \quad f(g(x)) \text{ is close to } f(g(c)). \quad \square$$

The argument we just gave is too vague to be a proof. Here in contrast is a proof. We begin with $\epsilon > 0$. We must show that there exists some number $\delta > 0$ such that

$$\text{if} \quad |x - c| < \delta, \qquad \text{then} \quad |f(g(x)) - f(g(c))| < \epsilon.$$

In the first place, we observe that, since f is continuous at $g(c)$, there does exist a number $\delta_1 > 0$ such that

(1) $\text{if} \quad |t - g(c)| < \delta_1, \qquad \text{then} \quad |f(t) - f(g(c))| < \epsilon.$

With $\delta_1 > 0$, we know from the continuity of g at c that there exists a number $\delta > 0$ such that

(2)   if $|x - c| < \delta$,   then $|g(x) - g(c)| < \delta_1$.

Combining (2) and (1) we have what we want: by (2)

                              if $|x - c| < \delta$,   then $|g(x) - g(c)| < \delta_1$

so that by (1)

$$|f(g(x)) - f(g(c))| < \epsilon. \quad \square$$

This proof is illustrated in Figure 2.4.4. The numbers within δ of c are taken by g to within δ_1 of $g(c)$ and then by f to within ϵ of $f(g(c))$.

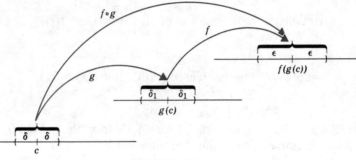

FIGURE 2.4.4

It's time to look at some examples.

EXAMPLE. The function

$$F(x) = \sqrt{\frac{x^2 + 1}{(x - 8)^3}}$$

is continuous at all numbers greater than 8. To see this, note that $F = f \circ g$, where

$$g(x) = \frac{x^2 + 1}{(x - 8)^3} \quad \text{and} \quad f(x) = \sqrt{x}.$$

Now take $c > 8$. The function g is continuous at c, and since $g(c)$ is positive, f is continuous at $g(c)$. By the theorem F is continuous at c. $\quad \square$

The continuity of composites holds for any finite number of functions. The only requirement is that each function be continuous *where it is applied.*

EXAMPLE. The function

$$F(x) = \frac{1}{5 - \sqrt{x^2 + 16}}$$

is continuous everywhere except at $x = \pm 3$, where it is not defined. To see this, note that $F = f \circ g \circ k \circ h$, where

$$f(x) = \frac{1}{x}, \quad g(x) = 5 - x, \quad k(x) = \sqrt{x}, \quad h(x) = x^2 + 16$$

and observe that each of these functions is being applied only where it is continuous. In particular, f is being applied only to nonzero numbers and k is being applied only to positive numbers.   □

Just as we considered one-sided limits, we can consider one-sided continuity.

DEFINITION 2.4.5   ONE-SIDED CONTINUITY

A function f is called

$$\textit{continuous from the left at } c \quad \text{iff} \quad \lim_{x \to c^-} f(x) = f(c).$$

It is called

$$\textit{continuous from the right at } c \quad \text{iff} \quad \lim_{x \to c^+} f(x) = f(c).$$

In Figure 2.4.5 we have an example of continuity from the right at 0; in Figure 2.4.6 we have an example of continuity from the left at 0.

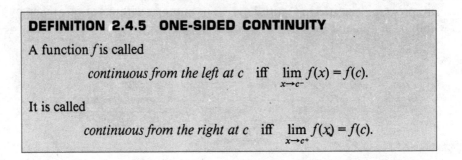

FIGURE 2.4.5   FIGURE 2.4.6

It's clear from (2.2.8) that a function f is continuous at c iff it is continuous there from both sides.   Thus

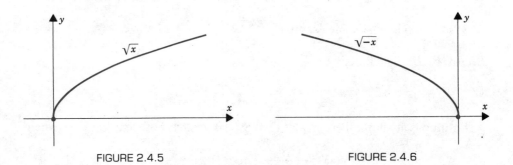

(2.4.6)

f is continuous at c iff the quantities

$$f(c), \quad \lim_{x \to c^-} f(x), \quad \lim_{x \to c^+} f(x)$$

all exist and are equal.

This is sometimes referred to as the *slot-machine test* for continuity.   We apply it below to a piecewise-defined function.

PROBLEM.   Determine the discontinuities of the following function:

$$f(x) = \begin{cases} x^3, & x \le -1 \\ x^2 - 2, & -1 < x < 0 \\ 3 - x, & 0 \le x < 2 \\ \dfrac{4x - 1}{x - 1}, & 2 \le x < 4 \\ \dfrac{15}{7 - x}, & 4 < x < 7 \\ 5x + 2, & 7 \le x \end{cases}$$

Solution.   It should be clear that f is continuous on the open intervals $(-\infty, -1)$, $(-1, 0)$, $(0, 2)$, $(2, 4)$, $(4, 7)$, and $(7, \infty)$.   All we have to check is the behavior of f at $x = -1, 0, 2, 4,$ and 7.   To do so, we apply (2.4.6).

At $x = -1$, f is continuous since $f(-1) = (-1)^3 = -1$,

$$\lim_{x \to -1^-} f(x) = \lim_{x \to -1^-} x^3 = -1, \quad \text{and} \quad \lim_{x \to -1^+} f(x) = \lim_{x \to -1^+} (x^2 - 2) = -1.$$

Our findings at the other four points are displayed in the chart below.   You should verify each entry.

c	$f(c)$	$\lim\limits_{x \to c^-} f(x)$	$\lim\limits_{x \to c^+} f(x)$	*conclusion*
0	3	-2	3	discontinuous
2	7	1	7	discontinuous
4	not defined	5	5	discontinuous
7	37	does not exist	37	discontinuous

Note that the discontinuity at $x = 4$ is removable; if we define $f(4) = 5$, f is now continuous at $x = 4$.   The discontinuities at $x = 0, 2,$ and 7 are essential (not removable) since the limit does not exist at these points.   □

Continuity on [a, b]

From a function defined on a closed interval $[a, b]$ the most continuity that we can possibly expect is

1. continuity at each point c of the open interval (a, b),
2. continuity from the right at a, and
3. continuity from the left at b.

Any function f that fulfills these requirements is called *continuous on* $[a, b]$.

As an example we take the function

$$f(x) = \sqrt{1 - x^2}.$$

Its graph is the semicircle displayed in Figure 2.4.7. The function is continuous on $[-1, 1]$ because it is continuous at each number c in $(-1, 1)$, continuous from the right at -1, and continuous from the left at 1.

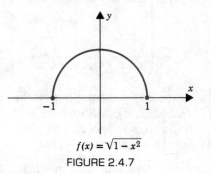

$$f(x) = \sqrt{1 - x^2}$$
FIGURE 2.4.7

Functions that are continuous on a closed interval $[a, b]$ have special properties that, in general, discontinuous functions do not have. We will focus on two of these properties and their applications in Section 2.6.

EXERCISES

Determine whether or not the function is continuous at the indicated point. If not, determine whether the discontinuity is essential or removable.

1. $f(x) = x^3 - 5x + 1$; $x = 2$.

2. $g(x) = \sqrt{(x - 1)^2 + 5}$; $x = 1$.

3. $f(x) = \sqrt{x^2 + 9}$; $x = 3$.

4. $f(x) = |4 - x^2|$; $x = 2$.

5. $f(x) = \begin{cases} x^2 + 4, & x < 2 \\ x^3, & x \geq 2 \end{cases}$; $x = 2$.

6. $h(x) = \begin{cases} x^2 + 5, & x < 2 \\ x^3, & x \geq 2 \end{cases}$; $x = 2$.

7. $g(x) = \begin{cases} x^2 + 4, & x < 2 \\ 5, & x = 2 \\ x^3, & x > 2 \end{cases}$; $x = 2$.

8. $g(x) = \begin{cases} x^2 + 5, & x < 2 \\ 10, & x = 2 \\ 1 + x^3, & x > 2 \end{cases}$; $x = 2$.

9. $f(x) = \begin{cases} -1, & x < 0 \\ 0, & x = 0 \\ 1, & x > 0 \end{cases}$; $x = 0$.

10. $f(x) = \begin{cases} 1 - x, & x < 1 \\ 1, & x = 1 \\ x^2 - 1, & x > 1 \end{cases}$; $x = 1$.

11. $h(x) = \begin{cases} \dfrac{x^2 - 1}{x + 1}, & x \neq -1 \\ -2, & x = -1 \end{cases}$; $x = -1$.

12. $g(x) = \begin{cases} \dfrac{1}{x + 1}, & x \neq -1 \\ 0, & x = -1 \end{cases}$; $x = -1$.

13. $f(x) = \begin{cases} -x^2, & x < 0 \\ 1 - \sqrt{x}, & x \geq 0 \end{cases}$; $x = 0$.

14. $g(x) = \dfrac{x(x + 1)(x + 2)}{\sqrt{(x - 1)(x - 2)}}$; $x = -2$.

Sketch the graph and classify the discontinuities (if any).

15. $f(x) = \dfrac{x^2 - 4}{x - 2}$.

16. $f(x) = \dfrac{x - 3}{x^2 - 9}$.

17. $f(x) = |x - 1|$.

18. $h(x) = |x^2 - 1|$.

19. $g(x) = \begin{cases} x - 1, & x < 1 \\ 0, & x = 1 \\ x^2, & x > 1 \end{cases}$.

20. $g(x) = \begin{cases} 2x - 1, & x < 1 \\ 0, & x = 1 \\ x^2, & x > 1 \end{cases}$.

21. $f(x) = \max \{x, x^2\}$.

22. $f(x) = \min \{x, x^2\}$.

23. $f(x) = \begin{cases} -1, & x < -1 \\ x^3, & -1 \le x \le 1 \\ 1, & 1 < x \end{cases}$.

24. $g(x) = \begin{cases} 1, & x \le -2 \\ \frac{1}{2}x, & -2 < x < 4 \\ \sqrt{x}, & 4 \le x \end{cases}$.

25. $h(x) = \begin{cases} 1, & x \le 0 \\ x^2, & 0 < x < 1 \\ 1, & 1 \le x < 2 \\ x, & 2 \le x \end{cases}$.

26. $g(x) = \begin{cases} -x^2, & x < -1 \\ 3, & x = -1 \\ 2 - x, & -1 < x \le 1 \\ x^2, & 1 < x \end{cases}$.

27. $f(x) = \begin{cases} 2x + 9, & x < -2 \\ x^2 + 1, & -2 < x \le 1 \\ 3x - 1, & 1 < x < 3 \\ x + 6, & 3 < x \end{cases}$.

28. $g(x) = \begin{cases} x + 7, & x < -3 \\ |x - 2|, & -3 < x < -1 \\ x^2 - 2x, & -1 < x < 3 \\ 2x - 3, & 3 \le x \end{cases}$.

Each of the functions f below is defined everywhere except at $x = 1$. Where possible, define $f(1)$ so that f becomes continuous at 1.

29. $f(x) = \dfrac{x^2 - 1}{x - 1}$.

30. $f(x) = \dfrac{1}{x - 1}$.

31. $f(x) = \dfrac{x - 1}{|x - 1|}$.

32. $f(x) = \dfrac{(x - 1)^2}{|x - 1|}$.

33. Let

$$f(x) = \begin{cases} x^2, & x < 1 \\ Ax - 3, & x \ge 1 \end{cases}.$$

Find A given that f is continuous at 1.

34. Let

$$f(x) = \begin{cases} A^2x^2, & x \le 2 \\ (1 - A)x, & x > 2 \end{cases}.$$

For what values of A is f continuous at 2?

35. Give necessary and sufficient conditions on A and B for the function

$$f(x) = \begin{cases} Ax - B, & x \le 1 \\ 3x, & 1 < x < 2 \\ Bx^2 - A, & 2 \le x \end{cases}$$

to be continuous at $x = 1$ but discontinuous at $x = 2$.

36. Give necessary and sufficient conditions on A and B for the function in Exercise 35 to be continuous at $x = 2$ but discontinuous at $x = 1$.

Define a function that is everywhere continuous from

37. the left but discontinuous from the right at $x = \frac{1}{2}$.

38. the right but discontinuous from the left at $x = \frac{1}{2}$.

At what points (if any) are the following functions continuous?

39. $f(x) = \begin{bmatrix} 1, & x\text{ rational} \\ 0, & x\text{ irrational} \end{bmatrix}$.

40. $g(x) = \begin{bmatrix} x, & x\text{ rational} \\ 0, & x\text{ irrational} \end{bmatrix}$.

41. $g(x) = \begin{bmatrix} 2x, & x\text{ is an integer} \\ x^2, & \text{otherwise} \end{bmatrix}$.

42. $f(x) = \begin{bmatrix} 4, & x\text{ is an integer} \\ x^2, & \text{otherwise} \end{bmatrix}$.

43. (*Important*) Prove that

$$f\text{ is continuous at } c \quad \text{iff} \quad \lim_{h \to 0} f(c + h) = f(c).$$

44. (*Important*) Let f and g be continuous at c. Prove that if
(a) $f(c) > 0$, then there exists $\delta > 0$ such that

$$f(x) > 0 \qquad \text{for all } x \in (c - \delta, c + \delta).$$

(b) $f(c) < 0$, then there exists $\delta > 0$ such that

$$f(x) < 0 \qquad \text{for all } x \in (c - \delta, c + \delta).$$

(c) $f(c) < g(c)$, then there exists $\delta > 0$ such that

$$f(x) < g(x) \qquad \text{for all } x \in (c - \delta, c + \delta).$$

2.5 ······TRIGONOMETRIC LIMITS

The basic result is this: *each trigonometric function is continuous on its entire domain.* That is, if f denotes any one of the six trigonometric functions and c is in the domain of f, then

$$\lim_{x \to c} f(x) = f(c).$$

We begin by showing that

(2.5.1)
$$\lim_{x \to 0} \sin x = 0 \quad \text{and} \quad \lim_{x \to 0} \cos x = 1.$$

Proof. First we prove that

$$\lim_{x \to 0} \sin x = 0.$$

To follow the argument see Figure 2.5.1.†

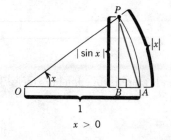
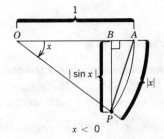

$x > 0$ $\qquad\qquad\qquad\qquad\qquad$ $x < 0$

FIGURE 2.5.1

---

† Recall that a central angle of θ radians in a circle of radius r subtends an arc of length $r\theta$. (See Figure 1.2.4.) In Figure 2.5.1 we have $r = 1$.

For small $x \neq 0$

$$|\sin x| = \text{length of } \overline{BP} < \text{length of } \overline{AP} < \text{length of } \widehat{AP} = |x|$$

so that

$$0 < |\sin x| < |x|.$$

Since

$$\lim_{x \to 0} 0 = 0 \quad \text{and} \quad \lim_{x \to 0} |x| = 0,$$

the pinching theorem (2.3.10) tells us that

$$\lim_{x \to 0} |\sin x| = 0 \quad \text{and thus} \quad \lim_{x \to 0} \sin x = 0.$$

The proof that $\lim_{x \to 0} \cos x = 1$ is left to you as an exercise. ☐

Next we can show that the sine and cosine are everywhere continuous: for all real numbers c

(2.5.2)
$$\lim_{x \to c} \sin x = \sin c \quad \text{and} \quad \lim_{x \to c} \cos x = \cos c.$$

Proof. By (2.2.5) we can write

$$\lim_{x \to c} \sin x \quad \text{as} \quad \lim_{x \to 0} \sin (c + x).$$

This form of the limit suggests we use the addition formula

$$\sin (c + x) = \sin c \cos x + \cos c \sin x.$$

Since $\sin c$ and $\cos c$ are constants, we may use (2.5.1) to conclude that

$$\lim_{x \to 0} \sin (c + x) = \sin c \lim_{x \to 0} \cos x + \cos c \lim_{x \to 0} \sin x$$

$$= (\sin c)(1) + (\cos c)(0)$$

$$= \sin c.$$

The proof that $\lim_{x \to c} \cos x = \cos c$ is left to you as an exercise. ☐

The other four trigonometric functions can be expressed in terms of sine and cosine:

$$\tan x = \frac{\sin x}{\cos x}, \quad \csc x = \frac{1}{\sin x}, \quad \sec x = \frac{1}{\cos x}, \quad \cot x = \frac{\cos x}{\sin x}.$$

We conclude from the limit theorem on quotients that, if f denotes any one of the six trigonometric functions and c is in the domain of f, then $\lim_{x \to c} f(x) = f(c)$.

We turn now to two limits, the importance of which will become clear in Chapter 3.

(2.5.3)
$$\lim_{x \to 0} \frac{\sin x}{x} = 1 \quad \text{and} \quad \lim_{x \to 0} \frac{1 - \cos x}{x} = 0.$$

Proof. First we prove that

$$\lim_{x \to 0} \frac{\sin x}{x} = 1.$$

To follow the argument see Figure 2.5.2.

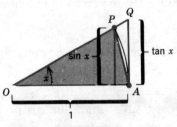

FIGURE 2.5.2

For small $x > 0$

$$\text{area of triangle } OAP = \frac{1}{2} \sin x,$$

$$\text{area of sector} = \frac{1}{2} x,$$

$$\text{area of triangle } OAQ = \frac{1}{2} \tan x = \frac{1}{2} \frac{\sin x}{\cos x}.$$

Since

$$\text{triangle } OAP \subseteq \text{sector} \subseteq \text{triangle } OAQ$$

(and these are all proper containments), we have

$$\frac{1}{2} \sin x < \frac{1}{2} x < \frac{1}{2} \frac{\sin x}{\cos x},$$

$$\sin x < x < \frac{\sin x}{\cos x},$$

$$\frac{\cos x}{\sin x} < \frac{1}{x} < \frac{1}{\sin x},$$

$$\cos x < \frac{\sin x}{x} < 1.$$

This last inequality was derived for small $x > 0$, but, since

$$\cos(-x) = \cos x \quad \text{and} \quad \frac{\sin(-x)}{-x} = \frac{-\sin x}{-x} = \frac{\sin x}{x},$$

the inequality also holds for small $x < 0$.

Since

$$\cos x < \frac{\sin x}{x} < 1 \quad \text{and} \quad \lim_{x \to 0} \cos x = 1,$$

we conclude from the pinching theorem that

$$\lim_{x \to 0} \frac{\sin x}{x} = 1.$$

We now show that

$$\lim_{x \to 0} \frac{1 - \cos x}{x} = 0.$$

For small $x \neq 0$,

$$\frac{1 - \cos x}{x} = \left(\frac{1 - \cos x}{x}\right)\left(\frac{1 + \cos x}{1 + \cos x}\right)^\dagger$$

$$= \frac{1 - \cos^2 x}{x(1 + \cos x)}$$

$$= \frac{\sin^2 x}{x(1 + \cos x)}$$

$$= \left(\frac{\sin x}{x}\right)\left(\frac{\sin x}{1 + \cos x}\right).$$

That

$$\lim_{x \to 0} \frac{1 - \cos x}{x} = 0$$

follows from noting that

$$\lim_{x \to 0} \frac{\sin x}{x} = 1 \quad \text{and} \quad \lim_{x \to 0} \frac{\sin x}{1 + \cos x} = 0. \quad \square$$

---

† This "trick" is a fairly common procedure with trigonometric expressions. It's much like using "conjugates" to revise algebraic expressions:

$$\frac{3}{4 + \sqrt{2}} = \frac{3}{4 + \sqrt{2}} \cdot \frac{4 - \sqrt{2}}{4 - \sqrt{2}} = \frac{3(4 - \sqrt{2})}{14}.$$

It is time for some sample problems.

PROBLEM. Find

$$\lim_{x \to 0} \frac{\sin 4x}{x}.$$

Solution. Earlier you saw that

$$\lim_{x \to 0} \frac{\sin x}{x} = 1.$$

From this it follows that

$$\lim_{x \to 0} \frac{\sin 4x}{4x} = 1 \qquad\qquad \text{(see Exercise 33)}$$

and therefore

$$\lim_{x \to 0} \frac{\sin 4x}{x} = \lim_{x \to 0} 4 \left(\frac{\sin 4x}{4x} \right) = 4. \quad \square$$

PROBLEM. Find

$$\lim_{x \to 0} x \cot 3x$$

Solution. We begin by writing

$$x \cot 3x = x \frac{\cos 3x}{\sin 3x}.$$

Since

$$\lim_{x \to 0} \frac{\sin x}{x} = 1 \quad \text{and equivalently} \quad \lim_{x \to 0} \frac{x}{\sin x} = 1,$$

we would like to "pair off" sin 3x with 3x. Thus, we write

$$x \frac{\cos 3x}{\sin 3x} = \frac{1}{3} \left(\frac{3x}{\sin 3x} \right) (\cos 3x).$$

Now we take the limit:

$$\lim_{x \to 0} x \cot 3x = \frac{1}{3} \left(\lim_{x \to 0} \frac{3x}{\sin 3x} \right) \left(\lim_{x \to 0} \cos 3x \right) = \frac{1}{3} (1)(1) = \frac{1}{3}. \quad \square$$

PROBLEM. Find

$$\lim_{x \to \frac{1}{4}\pi} \frac{\sin (x - \frac{1}{4}\pi)}{(x - \frac{1}{4}\pi)^2}.$$

Solution

$$\frac{\sin (x - \frac{1}{4}\pi)}{(x - \frac{1}{4}\pi)^2} = \left[\frac{\sin (x - \frac{1}{4}\pi)}{(x - \frac{1}{4}\pi)} \right] \cdot \frac{1}{x - \frac{1}{4}\pi}.$$

We know that

$$\lim_{x \to \frac{1}{4}\pi} \frac{\sin (x - \frac{1}{4}\pi)}{x - \frac{1}{4}\pi} = 1. \qquad (2.2.5)$$

Since $\lim_{x \to \frac{1}{4}\pi} (x - \frac{1}{4}\pi) = 0$, you can see by Theorem 2.3.9 that

$$\lim_{x \to \frac{1}{4}\pi} \frac{\sin (x - \frac{1}{4}\pi)}{(x - \frac{1}{4}\pi)^2} \quad \text{does not exist} \quad \square$$

PROBLEM. Find

$$\lim_{x \to 0} \frac{x^2}{\sec x - 1}.$$

Solution. The evaluation of this limit requires a little imagination. We cannot deal with the fraction as it stands because both numerator and denominator tend to zero with x and it isn't clear what happens to the fraction as x tends to 0. We can, however, rewrite the fraction in more amenable form:

$$\frac{x^2}{\sec x - 1} = \frac{x^2}{\sec x - 1} \cdot \frac{\sec x + 1}{\sec x + 1}$$

$$= \frac{x^2(\sec x + 1)}{\sec^2 x - 1}$$

$$= \frac{x^2(\sec x + 1)}{\tan^2 x}$$

$$= \frac{x^2 \cos^2 x (\sec x + 1)}{\sin^2 x}$$

$$= \left(\frac{x}{\sin x} \right)^2 (\cos^2 x)(\sec x + 1).$$

Since each of these expressions has a limit as x tends to 0, the fraction we began with has a limit:

$$\lim_{x \to 0} \frac{x^2}{\sec x - 1} = \lim_{x \to 0} \left(\frac{x}{\sin x} \right)^2 \cdot \lim_{x \to 0} \cos^2 x \cdot \lim_{x \to 0} (\sec x + 1)$$

$$= (1)(1)(2) = 2. \quad \square$$

EXERCISES

Evaluate the limits that exist.

1. $\lim_{x \to 0} \dfrac{\sin 3x}{x}.$ 2. $\lim_{x \to 0} \dfrac{2x}{\sin x}.$ 3. $\lim_{x \to 0} \dfrac{3x}{\sin 5x}.$

4. $\lim_{x \to 0} \dfrac{\sin 3x}{2x}.$ 5. $\lim_{x \to 0} \dfrac{\sin x^2}{x}.$ 6. $\lim_{x \to 0} \dfrac{\sin x^2}{x^2}.$

7. $\lim\limits_{x\to 0} \dfrac{\sin x}{x^2}$.

8. $\lim\limits_{x\to 0} \dfrac{\sin^2 x^2}{x^2}$.

9. $\lim\limits_{x\to 0} \dfrac{\sin^2 3x}{5x^2}$.

10. $\lim\limits_{x\to 0} \dfrac{\tan^2 3x}{4x^2}$.

11. $\lim\limits_{x\to 0} \dfrac{2x}{\tan 3x}$.

12. $\lim\limits_{x\to 0} \dfrac{4x}{\cot 3x}$.

13. $\lim\limits_{x\to 0} x \csc x$.

14. $\lim\limits_{x\to 0} \dfrac{\cos x - 1}{2x}$.

15. $\lim\limits_{x\to 0} \dfrac{x^2}{1 - \cos 2x}$.

16. $\lim\limits_{x\to 0} \dfrac{x^2 - 2x}{\sin 3x}$.

17. $\lim\limits_{x\to 0} \dfrac{1 - \sec^2 2x}{x^2}$.

18. $\lim\limits_{x\to 0} \dfrac{1}{2x \csc x}$.

19. $\lim\limits_{x\to 0} \dfrac{2x^2 + x}{\sin x}$.

20. $\lim\limits_{x\to 0} \dfrac{1 - \cos 4x}{9x^2}$.

21. $\lim\limits_{x\to 0} \dfrac{\tan 3x}{2x^2 + 5x}$.

22. $\lim\limits_{x\to 0} x^2(1 + \cot^2 3x)$.

23. $\lim\limits_{x\to 0} \dfrac{\sec x - 1}{x \sec x}$.

24. $\lim\limits_{x\to \pi/4} \dfrac{1 - \cos x}{x}$.

25. $\lim\limits_{x\to \pi/4} \dfrac{\sin x}{x}$.

26. $\lim\limits_{x\to 0} \dfrac{\sin^2 x}{x(1 - \cos x)}$.

27. $\lim\limits_{x\to \pi/4} \dfrac{\cos x}{x - \dfrac{\pi}{2}}$.

28. $\lim\limits_{x\to \pi} \dfrac{\sin x}{x - \pi}$.

29. $\lim\limits_{x\to \pi/4} \dfrac{\sin\left(x + \dfrac{\pi}{4}\right) - 1}{x - \dfrac{\pi}{4}}$.

30. $\lim\limits_{x\to \pi/6} \dfrac{\sin\left(x + \dfrac{\pi}{3}\right) - 1}{x - \dfrac{\pi}{6}}$.

31. Prove that $\lim\limits_{x\to 0} \cos x = 1$.   HINT: $\sin^2 x = \dfrac{1 - \cos 2x}{2}$

32. Prove that $\lim\limits_{x\to c} \cos x = \cos c$ for all real numbers c.

33. Show that

$$\text{if } \lim_{x\to 0} f(x) = l, \quad \text{then } \lim_{x\to 0} f(ax) = l \quad \text{for all } a \neq 0.$$

HINT: Let $\epsilon > 0$. If $\delta_1 > 0$ "works" for the first limit, then $\delta = \delta_1/|a|$ "works" for the second limit.

2.6 ······TWO BASIC THEOREMS

A function that is continuous on an interval does not "skip" any values, and thus its graph is an "unbroken curve." There are no "holes" in it and no "gaps." This is the idea behind the *intermediate-value theorem*.

THEOREM 2.6.1 THE INTERMEDIATE-VALUE THEOREM

If f is continuous on $[a, b]$ and C is a number between $f(a)$ and $f(b)$, then there is at least one number c between a and b for which $f(c) = C$.

We illustrate the theorem in Figure 2.6.1. What can happen in the discontinuous case is illustrated in Figure 2.6.2. There the number c has been "skipped." You can find a proof of the intermediate-value theorem in Appendix B. We'll assume the result and use it.

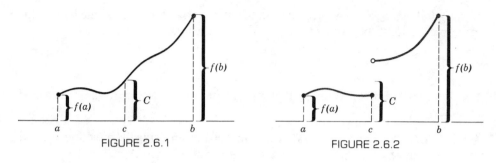

FIGURE 2.6.1   FIGURE 2.6.2

Suppose that f is continuous on $[a, b]$ and

$$f(a) < 0 < f(b) \quad \text{or} \quad f(b) < 0 < f(a).$$

Then, by the intermediate-value theorem, we know that the equation $f(x) = 0$ has at least one root in $[a, b]$. For simplicity let's assume that there is only one such root and call it c. How can we estimate the location of c? The intermediate-value theorem itself gives us no clue. The simplest method of finding the approximate location of c is called the *bisection method*.

The Bisection Method

The method is an iterative process. A basic step is repeated (iterated) over and over until the goal is reached, in this case an approximation for c that is as accurate as we wish.

It is standard practice to label the elements of successive iterations by using as subscripts $n = 1, 2, 3$, etc. We begin by setting $x_1 = a$ and $y_1 = b$. If c is not the midpoint of $[x_1, y_1]$ (that is, if $f([x_1 + y_1]/2) \neq 0$), then c must lie in either the left or the right half of $[x_1, y_1]$. Call the half interval in which c lies $[x_2, y_2]$. If c is not the midpoint of $[x_2, y_2]$, then c must lie in the left or the right half of $[x_2, y_2]$. Call this half $[x_3, y_3]$, and so on. The first three iterations for a particular function are depicted in Figure 2.6.3.

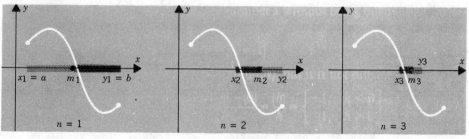

FIGURE 2.6.3

After n iterations we are examining the midpoint m_n of the interval $[x_n, y_n]$. We can thus be certain that

$$|c - m_n| \leq \frac{1}{2}(y_n - x_n) = \frac{1}{2}\left(\frac{y_{n-1} - x_{n-1}}{2}\right) = \cdots = \frac{b - a}{2^n}.$$

The quantity $(b - a)/2^n$ represents an upper bound estimate on the error we would make by taking m_n as an approximation for c. Clearly, if we specify the size of this error in advance to be ϵ or less, we can use the relation

$$\frac{b-a}{2^n} < \epsilon$$

to calculate the number of times n that we must iterate the process to gain the desired accuracy.

EXAMPLE. We approximate $\sqrt{2}$ to within 0.001 by applying the bisection method to the function $f(x) = x^2 - 2$, taking $a = x_1 = 1$ and $b = y_1 = 2$.

We begin by computing the number of times n we need to iterate the process. Here the relation

$$\frac{b-a}{2^n} < \epsilon$$

gives

$$\frac{2-1}{2^n} < 0.001 \quad \text{and thus} \quad 1000 < 2^n.$$

As you can check, the inequality is satisfied by taking $n \geq 10$. It will suffice to iterate the process 10 times.

$$x_1 = 1, \qquad y_1 = 2, \qquad m_1 = 1.5$$
$$f(x_1) = 1^2 - 2 < 0, \quad f(y_1) = 2^2 - 2 > 0, \quad f(m_1) = (1.5)^2 - 2 = 0.25 > 0$$

$$x_2 = x_1 = 1, \qquad y_2 = m_1 = 1.5, \qquad m_2 = 1.25$$
$$f(x_2) < 0, \quad f(y_2) > 0, \quad f(m_2) = (1.25)^2 - 2 = -0.4375 < 0$$

$$x_3 = m_2 = 1.25, \qquad y_3 = y_2 = 1.5, \qquad m_3 = 1.375$$
$$f(x_3) < 0, \quad f(y_3) > 0, \quad f(m_3) = (1.375)^2 - 2 = -0.109375 < 0$$

$$x_4 = m_3 = 1.375, \qquad y_4 = y_3 = 1.5, \qquad m_4 = 1.4375$$

etc.

The complete computations are summarized in Table 2.6.1. To increase readability, all the entries in the table have been rounded off to 5 decimal places.

TABLE 2.6.1

n	x_n	y_n	m_n	$f(m_n)$
1	1.00000	2.00000	1.50000	0.25000
2	1.00000	1.50000	1.25000	-0.43750
3	1.25000	1.50000	1.37500	-0.10938
4	1.37500	1.50000	1.43750	0.06641
5	1.37500	1.43750	1.40625	-0.02246
6	1.40625	1.43750	1.42187	0.02171
7	1.40625	1.42187	1.41406	-0.00043
8	1.41406	1.42187	1.41797	0.01064
9	1.41406	1.41797	1.41601	0.00508
10	1.41406	1.41601	1.41503	0.00231

We take $m_{10} = 1.41503$ as our approximation of $\sqrt{2}$. Note (from a table or your calculator) that $\sqrt{2} \cong 1.41421$ and $|m_{10} - 1.41421| = 0.00082 < 0.001$ as desired. □

We come now to the maximum-minimum property of continuous functions.

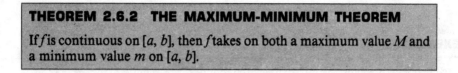

THEOREM 2.6.2   THE MAXIMUM-MINIMUM THEOREM

If f is continuous on $[a, b]$, then f takes on both a maximum value M and a minimum value m on $[a, b]$.

The situation is illustrated in Figure 2.6.4. The maximum value M is taken on at the point marked x_2, and the minimum value m is taken on at the point marked x_1.

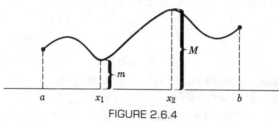

FIGURE 2.6.4

It is interesting to note that in the maximum-minimum theorem the full hypothesis is needed. If we drop the continuity requirement, the conclusion does not follow. As an example, we can take the function

$$f(x) = \begin{cases} 3, & x = 1 \\ x, & 1 < x < 5 \\ 3, & x = 5 \end{cases}.$$

The graph of this function is pictured in Figure 2.6.5. The function is defined on $[1, 5]$, but it takes on neither a maximum nor a minimum value. If, instead of dropping the continuity requirement, we drop the requirement that the interval be of the form $[a, b]$, then again the result fails. For example, in the case of

$$g(x) = x \qquad \text{for } x \in (1, 5),$$

g is continuous at each point of $(1, 5)$ but again there is no maximum value and no minimum value. See Figure 2.6.6.

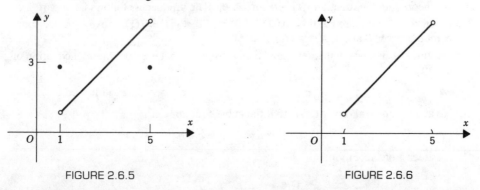

FIGURE 2.6.5   FIGURE 2.6.6

A proof of the maximum-minimum theorem appears in Appendix B. Techniques for determining the maximum and minimum values of functions are described in Chapter 4. These techniques require an understanding of "differentiation," the subject to which we devote Chapter 3.

EXERCISES

Use the bisection method to approximate the root of $f(x) = 0$ in $[a, b]$ to within 0.1.

1. $f(x) = 3x - 5$; $[1, 2]$.
2. $f(x) = 7x - 6$; $[0, 1]$.
3. $f(x) = 3 - 2x$; $[-1, 2]$.
4. $f(x) = 4 - 5x$; $[-2, 1]$.
5. $f(x) = x^2 - 3$; $[1, 2]$.
6. $f(x) = x^2 - 5$; $[2, 3]$.
7. $f(x) = 9 - x^2$; $[-5, -2]$.
8. $f(x) = 4 - x^2$; $[-3, 0]$.
9. $f(x) = 2x^2 + x - 1$; $[0, 2]$.
10. $f(x) = 2x^2 + x - 3$; $[-2, 0]$.

Sketch the graph of a continuous function on $[0, 6]$ that has

11. its maximum value at 1 and 3 and its minimum value at 4.
12. its maximum value at 2 and its minimum value at 3 and 5.
13. its maximum and minimum values at 2.
14. no maximum value.
15. no minimum value.
16. the same value for its maximum and minimum.

Define a function that is continuous on $(0, 1)$ and has

17. no maximum value there.
18. no minimum value there.
19. its minimum value at $\frac{1}{2}$ and has no maximum value.
20. its maximum value at $\frac{1}{2}$ and has no minimum value.

21. (*Fixed-point property*) Show that, if f is continuous and $0 \leq f(x) \leq 1$ for all $x \in [0, 1]$, then there exists at least one point c in $[0, 1]$ for which $f(c) = c$.   HINT: Apply the intermediate-value theorem to the function $g(x) = x - f(x)$.

22. Let n be a positive integer.
    (a) Prove that, if $0 \leq a < b$, then $a^n < b^n$.
    (b) Prove that every nonnegative real number x has a unique nonnegative nth root $x^{1/n}$.   HINT: The existence of $x^{1/n}$ can be seen by applying the intermediate-value theorem to the function $f(t) = t^n$ for $t \geq 0$.   The uniqueness follows from part (a).

23. Given that f and g are continuous and $f(0) < g(0) < g(1) < f(1)$, prove that, for some point c between 0 and 1, $f(c) = g(c)$.

24. The intermediate-value theorem can be used to prove that each polynomial equation of odd degree

$$x^n + a_{n-1}x^{n-1} + \cdots + a_1 x + a_0 = 0 \qquad \text{with } n \text{ odd}$$

has at least one real root. Prove that the cubic equation

$$x^3 + ax^2 + bx + c = 0$$

has at least one real root.

Calculator exercises.

Use the bisection method to approximate the root of $f(x) = 0$ in $[a, b]$ to within 0.001.

25. $f(x) = x^2 - 3$; $[1, 2]$.   **26.** $f(x) = 5 - x^2$; $[-3, -2]$.
27. $f(x) = x^2 + x - 1$; $[0, 1]$.   **28.** $f(x) = x^2 - x - 1$; $[1, 2]$.
29. $f(x) = x^3 + x - 10$; $[1, 4]$.   **30.** $f(x) = 2x^3 + 5x - 7$; $[-1, 2]$.
31. $f(x) = \cos x - x$; $[0, 1]$.   **32.** $f(x) = \cos x - 2x$; $[0, 1]$.

2.7 ······ADDITIONAL EXERCISES

Evaluate the limits that exist.

1. $\lim\limits_{x \to 3} \dfrac{x^2 - 3}{x - 3}$.

2. $\lim\limits_{x \to 2} \dfrac{x^2 + 4}{x^2 + 2x + 1}$.

3. $\lim\limits_{x \to 3} \dfrac{(x - 3)^2}{x + 3}$.

4. $\lim\limits_{x \to 0} \left(\dfrac{1}{x} - \dfrac{x}{1 - x} \right)$.

5. $\lim\limits_{x \to 3} \dfrac{x^2 - 9}{x^2 - 5x + 6}$.

6. $\lim\limits_{x \to 2+} \dfrac{x - 2}{|x - 2|}$.

7. $\lim\limits_{x \to 3-} \dfrac{x - 3}{|x - 3|}$.

8. $\lim\limits_{x \to -2} \dfrac{|x|}{x - 2}$.

9. $\lim\limits_{x \to 0} \left(\dfrac{1}{x} - \dfrac{1 - x}{x} \right)$.

10. $\lim\limits_{x \to -1} \dfrac{x^2 - x - 2}{x + 1}$.

11. $\lim\limits_{x \to 1-} \sqrt{|x| - x}$.

12. $\lim\limits_{x \to 3+} \dfrac{\sqrt{x - 3}}{|x - 3|}$.

13. $\lim\limits_{x \to 2+} \dfrac{x^2}{x + 2}$.

14. $\lim\limits_{x \to 1} \dfrac{|x - 1|}{x}$.

15. $\lim\limits_{x \to 1} \dfrac{x^3 - 1}{|x^3 - 1|}$.

16. $\lim\limits_{x \to 1+} \sqrt{|x| - x}$.

17. $\lim\limits_{x \to -1} \dfrac{1 + |x|}{1 - |x|}$.

18. $\lim\limits_{x \to 1} \dfrac{1 - 1/x}{1 - 1/x^2}$.

19. $\lim\limits_{x \to -1} \dfrac{1 + 1/x}{1 + 1/x^2}$.

20. $\lim\limits_{x \to 1} \dfrac{1 + 1/x}{1 - x^2}$.

21. $\lim\limits_{x \to 1} \dfrac{1 - 1/x}{1 - x^2}$.

22. $\lim\limits_{x \to 1} \dfrac{1 - 1/x^2}{1 - x}$.

23. $\lim\limits_{x \to 0+} \dfrac{1 + \sqrt{x}}{1 - \sqrt{x}}$.

24. $\lim\limits_{x \to -1} \dfrac{1 + 1/x^2}{1 - x}$.

25. $\lim\limits_{x \to 4} \left[\left(\dfrac{1}{x} - \dfrac{1}{4} \right) \left(\dfrac{1}{x - 4} \right) \right]$.

26. $\lim\limits_{x \to 1-} \dfrac{\sqrt{x} - 1}{x - 1}$.

27. $\lim\limits_{x \to 0-} \dfrac{\sqrt{x} - 1}{x - 1}$.

28. $\lim\limits_{x \to 0+} \dfrac{\sqrt{x} - 1}{x - 1}$.

29. $\lim\limits_{x \to 3+} \dfrac{x^2 - 2x - 3}{\sqrt{x - 3}}$.

30. $\lim\limits_{x \to 3+} \dfrac{\sqrt{x^2 - 2x - 3}}{x - 3}$.

31. $\lim\limits_{x \to 2+} \left(\dfrac{1}{x - 2} - \dfrac{1}{|x - 2|} \right)$.

32. $\lim\limits_{x \to 2-} \left(\dfrac{1}{x - 2} - \dfrac{1}{|x - 2|} \right)$.

33. $\lim\limits_{x \to 4} \dfrac{\sqrt{x + 5} - 3}{x - 4}$.

34. $\lim\limits_{x \to 2} \dfrac{x^3 - 8}{x^4 - 3x^2 - 4}$.

35. $\lim\limits_{x \to 0} \dfrac{5x}{\sin 2x}$.

36. $\lim\limits_{x \to 0} \dfrac{\tan^2 2x}{3x^2}$.

37. $\lim\limits_{x \to 0} 4x^2 \cot^2 3x$.

38. $\lim\limits_{x \to 0} x \csc 4x$.

39. $\lim\limits_{x \to 0} \dfrac{x^2 - 3x}{\tan x}$.

40. $\lim\limits_{x \to 0} \dfrac{x}{1 - \cos x}$.

41. $\lim\limits_{x \to \pi/2} \dfrac{\cos x}{2x - \pi}$.

42. $\lim\limits_{x \to 0} \dfrac{\sin 3x}{5x^2 - 4x}$.

43. $\lim\limits_{x \to 0} \dfrac{5x^2}{1 - \cos 2x}$.

44. $\lim\limits_{x \to -\pi} \dfrac{x + \pi}{\sin x}$.

45. $\lim\limits_{x \to 2} \dfrac{x^2 - 4}{x^3 - 8}$.

46. $\lim\limits_{x\to3}\left(3-\dfrac{1}{x}\right)\left(\dfrac{2x}{1-9x^2}\right).$

47. $\lim\limits_{x\to2^+}\dfrac{\sqrt{x-2}}{|x-2|}.$

48. $\lim\limits_{x\to2^-}\dfrac{x-2}{|x^2-4|}.$

49. $\lim\limits_{x\to2}\left(\dfrac{6}{x-2}-\dfrac{3x}{x-2}\right).$

50. $\lim\limits_{x\to2}\left(\dfrac{2x}{x^2-4}-\dfrac{x^2}{x^2-4}\right).$

51. $\lim\limits_{x\to-1^+}\dfrac{|x^2-1|}{x+1}.$

52. $\lim\limits_{x\to3}\dfrac{\sqrt{x+1}-2}{x-3}.$

53. $\lim\limits_{x\to2}\dfrac{1-2/x}{1-4/x^2}.$

54. $\lim\limits_{x\to-4^+}\dfrac{|x+4|}{\sqrt{x+4}}.$

55. $\lim\limits_{x\to2^+}\dfrac{\sqrt{x^2-3x+2}}{x-2}.$

56. $\lim\limits_{x\to1}\dfrac{x^2-1}{x^5-1}.$

57. $\lim\limits_{x\to2}\left(1-\dfrac{2}{x}\right)\left(\dfrac{3}{4-x^2}\right).$

58. $\lim\limits_{x\to1^+}\dfrac{x^2-3x+2}{\sqrt{x-1}}.$

59. $\lim\limits_{x\to7}\dfrac{x-7}{\sqrt{x+2}-3}.$

60. $\lim\limits_{x\to3}\dfrac{1-9/x^2}{1+3/x}.$

61. $\lim\limits_{x\to2} f(x)$ if $f(x)=\begin{cases} x^2, & \text{if } x \text{ is an integer} \\ 3x, & \text{otherwise} \end{cases}.$

62. $\lim\limits_{x\to3} f(x)$ if $f(x)=\begin{cases} x^2, & x \text{ rational} \\ 3x, & x \text{ irrational} \end{cases}.$

63. $\lim\limits_{x\to-2} f(x)$ if $f(x)=\begin{cases} 3+x, & x<-2 \\ 5, & x=-2 \\ x^2-3, & x>-2 \end{cases}.$

64. $\lim\limits_{x\to2} f(x)$ if $f(x)=\begin{cases} x+1, & x<1 \\ 3x-x^2, & x>1 \end{cases}.$

65. (a) Sketch the graph of

$$f(x)=\begin{cases} 3x+4, & x<-1 \\ 2x+3, & -1<x<1 \\ 4x+1, & 1<x<2 \\ 3x-2, & 2<x \\ x^2, & x=-1, 1, 2 \end{cases}.$$

(b) Evaluate the limits that exist.

    (i) $\lim\limits_{x\to-1^-} f(x).$ (ii) $\lim\limits_{x\to-1^+} f(x).$ (iii) $\lim\limits_{x\to-1} f(x).$

    (iv) $\lim\limits_{x\to1^-} f(x).$ (v) $\lim\limits_{x\to1^+} f(x).$ (vi) $\lim\limits_{x\to1} f(x).$

    (vii) $\lim\limits_{x\to2^-} f(x).$ (viii) $\lim\limits_{x\to2^+} f(x).$ (ix) $\lim\limits_{x\to2} f(x).$

(c) (i) At what points is f discontinuous from the left?
    (ii) At what points is f discontinuous from the right?
    (iii) Where are the removable discontinuities of f?
    (iv) Where are the essential discontinuities of f?

66. Exercise 65 with

$$f(x)=\begin{cases} -2x, & x<-1 \\ x^2+1, & -1<x<1 \\ \sqrt{2x}, & 1<x<2 \\ x, & 2<x \\ |x^2-3|, & x=-1, 1, 2 \end{cases}.$$

67. Find $\lim_{x \to c} f(x)$ given that $|f(x)| \le M|x - c|$ for all $x \ne c$.

68. Given that $\lim_{x \to 0} (f(x)/x)$ exists, prove that $\lim_{x \to 0} f(x) = 0$.

Give an, ϵ, δ proof for the following limits.

69. $\lim_{x \to 2} (5x - 4) = 6$.   **70.** $\lim_{x \to 3} (1 - 2x) = -5$.   **71.** $\lim_{x \to -4} |2x + 5| = 3$.

72. $\lim_{x \to 3} |1 - 2x| = 5$.   **73.** $\lim_{x \to 9} \sqrt{x - 5} = 2$.   **74.** $\lim_{x \to 2^+} \sqrt{x^2 - 4} = 0$.

75. Prove that there exists a real number x_0 such that

$$x_0^5 - 4x_0 + 1 = 7.21.$$

76. Let f be a continuous function and n a positive integer. Show that, if $0 \le f(x) \le 1$ for all $x \in [0, 1]$, then there exists at least one point c in $[0, 1]$ for which $f(c) = c^n$.

Use the bisection method to approximate the root of $f(x) = 0$ in $[a, b]$ to within 0.1.

77. $f(x) = x^2 + x - 6$; $[1, 4]$.   **78.** $f(x) = x^2 - 2$; $[-2, -1]$.

79. $f(x) = x^2 - 6$; $[2, 3]$.   **80.** $f(x) = x^2 + 3x - 4$; $[-1, 2]$.

2.8 CHAPTER SUMMARY

2.1 The Idea of Limit

Intuitively speaking, $\lim_{x \to c} f(x) = l$ can be taken to mean that

as x approaches c, $f(x)$ approaches l

or, equivalently,

for x close to c, $f(x)$ is close to l.

Restricting our attention to values of x to the left or to the right of c, we have *one-sided limits*: $\lim_{x \to c^-} f(x)$ and $\lim_{x \to c^+} f(x)$.

2.2 Definition of Limit

limit of a function (p. 59)
left-hand limit (p. 68)   right-hand limit (p. 68)

Equivalent formulations of the limit statement are given in (2.2.5) on p. 67.

2.3 Some Limit Theorems

uniqueness of limit (p. 71)   pinching theorem (p. 77)

The "arithmetic of limits" is based on the following results. Similar results hold for one-sided limits.   Suppose that $\lim_{x \to c} f(x) = l$ and $\lim_{x \to c} g(x) = m$; then

$$\lim_{x \to c} [f(x) + g(x)] = l + m, \qquad \lim_{x \to c} [\alpha f(x)] = \alpha l \quad \text{for each real } \alpha,$$

$$\lim_{x \to c} [f(x)g(x)] = m, \qquad \lim_{x \to c} \frac{f(x)}{g(x)} = \frac{l}{m} \quad \text{provided } m \neq 0.$$

If $m = 0$ and $l \neq 0$, then $\lim_{x \to c} \dfrac{f(x)}{g(x)}$ does not exist.

2.4 Continuity

continuity at c (p. 83)   one-sided continuity (p. 88)
slot-machine test (p. 88)   continuity on $[a, b]$ (p. 89)

The sum, difference, product, quotient, and composition of continuous functions are continuous where defined.   Polynomials and the absolute-value function are everywhere continuous.   Rational functions are continuous on their domains.   The square-root function is continuous at all positive numbers and continuous from the right at 0.

2.5 Trigonometric Limits

$$\lim_{x \to 0} \frac{\sin x}{x} = 1 \qquad \lim_{x \to 0} \frac{1 - \cos x}{x} = 0$$

Each trigonometric function is continuous on its domain.

2.6 Two Basic Theorems

intermediate-value theorem (p. 98)
bisection method (p. 99)
maximum-minimum theorem (p. 101)

2.7 Additional Exercises

3

Differentiation

3.1 ······THE DERIVATIVE

Introduction: The Tangent to a Curve

We begin with a function f, and on the graph we choose a point $(x, f(x))$. See Figure 3.1.1. What line, if any, should be called tangent to the graph at that point?

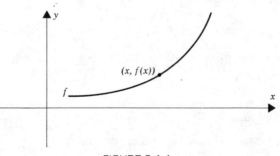

FIGURE 3.1.1

To answer this question, we choose a small number $h \neq 0$ and on the graph mark the point $(x + h, f(x + h))$. Now we draw the secant line that passes through these two points. The situation is pictured in Figure 3.1.2, first with $h > 0$ and then with $h < 0$.

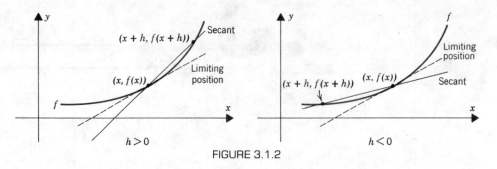

FIGURE 3.1.2

As h tends to zero from the right (see the figure), the secant line tends to a limiting position, and it tends to the same limiting position as h tends to zero from the left. The line at this limiting position is what we call "the tangent to the graph at the point $(x, f(x))$."

Since the approximating secants have slope of the form

(∗) $$\frac{f(x + h) - f(x)}{h},$$ (check this out)

you can expect the tangent, the limiting position of these secants, to have slope

(∗∗) $$\lim_{h \to 0} \frac{f(x + h) - f(x)}{h}.$$

While (∗) measures the steepness of the line that passes through $(x, f(x))$ and $(x + h, f(x + h))$, (∗∗) measures the steepness of the graph at $(x, f(x))$ and is called the "slope of the graph" at that point.

Derivatives and Differentiation

In the introduction we spoke informally about tangent lines and gave a geometric interpretation to limits of the form

$$\lim_{h \to 0} \frac{f(x + h) - f(x)}{h}.$$

Here we begin the systematic study of such limits, what mathematicians call the theory of *differentiation*.

DEFINITION 3.1.1

A function f is said to be *differentiable at x* iff

$$\lim_{h \to 0} \frac{f(x + h) - f(x)}{h} \quad \text{exists.}$$

If this limit exists, it is called the *derivative of f at x* and is denoted by $f'(x)$.†

---

† This prime notation goes back to the French mathematician Joseph Louis Lagrange (1736–1813). Another notation will be introduced later.

We interpret

$$f'(x) = \lim_{h \to 0} \frac{f(x + h) - f(x)}{h}$$

as the *slope of the graph at the point* $(x, f(x))$. The line that passes through the point $(x, f(x))$ with slope $f'(x)$ is called the *tangent line at* $(x, f(x))$. This is the line that best approximates the graph of f near the point $(x, f(x))$.

It is time we looked at some examples.

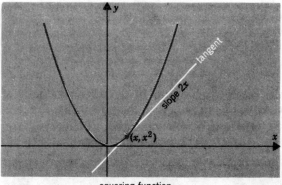

squaring function
FIGURE 3.1.3

EXAMPLE. We begin with the squaring function

$$f(x) = x^2. \qquad \text{(Figure 3.1.3)}$$

To find $f'(x)$ we form the *difference quotient*

$$\frac{f(x + h) - f(x)}{h} = \frac{(x + h)^2 - x^2}{h}.$$

Since

$$\frac{(x + h)^2 - x^2}{h} = \frac{x^2 + 2xh + h^2 - x^2}{h} = \frac{2xh + h^2}{h} = 2x + h,$$

we have

$$\frac{f(x + h) - f(x)}{h} = 2x + h,$$

and therefore

$$f'(x) = \lim_{h \to 0} \frac{f(x + h) - f(x)}{h} = \lim_{h \to 0} (2x + h) = 2x. \quad \square$$

EXAMPLE. In the case of a linear function

$$f(x) = mx + b$$

we have

$$f'(x) = m.$$

In other words, the slope is constantly m.   To verify this, note that

$$\frac{f(x+h) - f(x)}{h} = \frac{[m(x+h) + b] - [mx+b]}{h} = \frac{mh}{h} = m.$$

It follows that

$$f'(x) = \lim_{h \to 0} \frac{f(x+h) - f(x)}{h} = m. \quad \square$$

The derivative

$$f'(x) = \lim_{h \to 0} \frac{f(x+h) - f(x)}{h}$$

is a two-sided limit.   Therefore it cannot be taken at an endpoint of the domain.   In our next example we will be dealing with the square-root function.   Although this function is defined for all $x \geq 0$, you can expect a derivative only for $x > 0$.

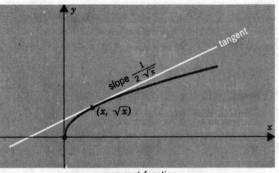

square root function
FIGURE 3.1.4

EXAMPLE.   The square-root function

$$f(x) = \sqrt{x}, \qquad x \geq 0 \qquad\qquad \text{(Figure 3.1.4)}$$

has derivative

$$f'(x) = \frac{1}{2\sqrt{x}}, \quad \text{for } x > 0.$$

To verify this, we begin with $x > 0$ and form the difference quotient

$$\frac{f(x+h) - f(x)}{h} = \frac{\sqrt{x+h} - \sqrt{x}}{h}.$$

To remove the radicals from the numerator we multiply both the numerator and the denominator by $\sqrt{x+h} + \sqrt{x}$. This gives

$$\frac{f(x+h)-f(x)}{h} = \left(\frac{\sqrt{x+h}-\sqrt{x}}{h}\right)\left(\frac{\sqrt{x+h}+\sqrt{x}}{\sqrt{x+h}+\sqrt{x}}\right)$$

$$= \frac{(x+h)-x}{h(\sqrt{x+h}+\sqrt{x})} = \frac{1}{\sqrt{x+h}+\sqrt{x}}$$

and thus

$$f'(x) = \lim_{h\to 0}\frac{f(x+h)-f(x)}{h} = \frac{1}{2\sqrt{x}}. \quad \square$$

To *differentiate* a function is to find its derivative.

EXAMPLE.   Here we differentiate the function

$$f(x) = \frac{1}{x}, \qquad x \neq 0. \qquad\qquad \text{(Figure 3.1.5)}$$

We form the difference quotient

$$\frac{f(x+h)-f(x)}{h} = \frac{\dfrac{1}{x+h}-\dfrac{1}{x}}{h}.$$

and simplify:

$$\frac{\dfrac{1}{x+h}-\dfrac{1}{x}}{h} = \frac{\dfrac{x}{x(x+h)}-\dfrac{x+h}{x(x+h)}}{h} = \frac{\dfrac{-h}{x(x+h)}}{h} = \frac{-1}{x(x+h)}.$$

Thus

$$f'(x) = \lim_{h\to 0}\frac{f(x+h)-f(x)}{h} = \lim_{h\to 0}\frac{-1}{x(x+h)} = -\frac{1}{x^2}. \quad \square$$

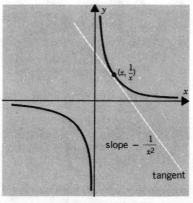

FIGURE 3.1.5

Evaluating Derivatives

PROBLEM. Find $f'(-2)$ given that

$$f(x) = 1 - x^2.$$

Solution. We can first find $f'(x)$:

$$f'(x) = \lim_{h \to 0} \frac{f(x + h) - f(x)}{h}$$

$$= \lim_{h \to 0} \frac{[1 - (x + h)^2] - [1 - x^2]}{h} = \lim_{h \to 0} \frac{-2xh - h^2}{h} = \lim_{h \to 0} (-2x - h) = -2x$$

and then substitute -2 for x:

$$f'(-2) = -2(-2) = 4.$$

We can also evaluate $f'(-2)$ directly:

$$f'(-2) = \lim_{h \to 0} \frac{f(-2 + h) - f(-2)}{h}$$

$$= \lim_{h \to 0} \frac{[1 - (-2 + h)^2] - [1 - (-2)^2]}{h} = \lim_{h \to 0} \frac{4h - h^2}{h} = \lim_{h \to 0} (4 - h) = 4. \quad \square$$

PROBLEM. Find $f'(-3)$ and $f'(1)$ given that

$$f(x) = \begin{cases} x^2, & x \le 1 \\ 2x - 1, & x > 1 \end{cases}.$$ (Figure 3.1.6)

Solution. By definition

$$f'(-3) = \lim_{h \to 0} \frac{f(-3 + h) - f(-3)}{h}.$$

For all x sufficiently close to -3, $f(x) = x^2$. Thus

$$f'(-3) = \lim_{h \to 0} \frac{f(-3 + h) - f(-3)}{h}$$

$$= \lim_{h \to 0} \frac{(-3 + h)^2 - (-3)^2}{h}$$

$$= \lim_{h \to 0} \frac{(9 - 6h + h^2) - 9}{h}$$

$$= \lim_{h \to 0} (-6 + h) = -6.$$

Now let's find

$$f'(1) = \lim_{h \to 0} \frac{f(1 + h) - f(1)}{h}.$$

Since f is not defined by the same formula on both sides of 1, we'll evaluate this limit by taking one-sided limits. Note that $f(1) = 1^2 = 1$.

To the left of 1, $f(x) = x^2$. Thus

$$\lim_{h \to 0^-} \frac{f(1 + h) - f(1)}{h} = \lim_{h \to 0^-} \frac{(1 + h)^2 - 1}{h}$$

$$= \lim_{h \to 0^-} \frac{(1 + 2h + h^2) - 1}{h} = \lim_{h \to 0^-} (2 + h) = 2.$$

To the right of 1, $f(x) = 2x - 1$. Thus

$$\lim_{h \to 0^+} \frac{f(1 + h) - f(1)}{h} = \lim_{h \to 0^+} \frac{[2(1 + h) - 1] - 1}{h} = \lim_{h \to 0^+} 2 = 2.$$

The limit of the difference quotient exists and is 2:

$$f'(1) = \lim_{h \to 0} \frac{f(1 + h) - f(1)}{h} = 2. \quad \square$$

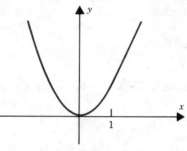

FIGURE 3.1.6

Tangent Lines and Normal Lines

We begin with a differentiable function f and choose a point (x_0, y_0) on the graph. As you know, the tangent line through this point has slope $f'(x_0)$. To get an equation for this tangent line, we use the point-slope formula

$$y - y_0 = m(x - x_0).$$

In this case $m = f'(x_0)$ and the equation becomes

(3.1.2) $$\boxed{y - y_0 = f'(x_0)(x - x_0).}$$

The line through (x_0, y_0) that is perpendicular to the tangent is called the *normal line*. Since the slope of the tangent is $f'(x_0)$, the slope of the normal is $-1/f'(x_0)$, provided of course that $f'(x_0) \neq 0$. (*Remember:* for nonvertical perpendicular lines, $m_1 m_2 = -1$.) As an equation for this normal line we have

(3.1.3) $$\boxed{y - y_0 = -\frac{1}{f'(x_0)}(x - x_0).}$$

Some tangents and normals are pictured in Figure 3.1.7.

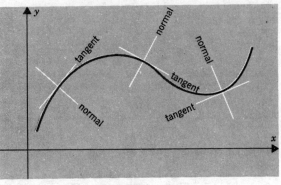

FIGURE 3.1.7

PROBLEM. Find equations for the tangent and normal to the graph of $f(x) = x^2$ at the point $(-3, f(-3)) = (-3, 9)$.

Solution. Earlier we saw that

$$f'(x) = 2x.$$

At the point $(-3, 9)$ the slope is $f'(-3) = -6$. As an equation for the tangent we have

$$y - 9 = -6(x - (-3)),$$

which simplifies to

$$y - 9 = -6(x + 3).$$

The equation for the normal can be written

$$y - 9 = \tfrac{1}{6}(x + 3). \quad \square$$

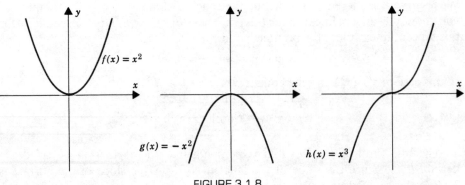

FIGURE 3.1.8

If $f'(x_0) = 0$, Equation (3.1.3) does not apply. If $f'(x_0) = 0$, the tangent line at (x_0, y_0) is horizontal (equation $y = y_0$) and the normal line is vertical (equation $x = x_0$). In Figure 3.1.8 you can see several instances of a horizontal tangent. In each case, the point of tangency is the origin, the tangent line is the x-axis ($y = 0$), and the normal line is the y-axis ($x = 0$).

A Note on Vertical Tangents

It is also possible for the graph of a function to have a vertical tangent. This cannot occur at a point of differentiability, but only at a point where the derivative becomes infinite. Take, for example, the cube-root function $f(x) = x^{1/3}$. The derivative becomes infinite at 0:

$$\lim_{h \to 0} \frac{f(0 + h) - f(0)}{h} = \lim_{h \to 0} \frac{h^{1/3} - 0}{h} = \lim_{h \to 0} \frac{1}{h^{2/3}} \quad \text{is infinite.}$$

At the origin the function has a vertical tangent ($x = 0$) and a horizontal normal ($y = 0$). See Figure 3.1.9.

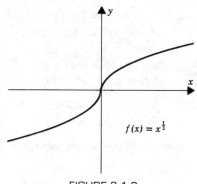

$$f(x) = x^{\frac{1}{3}}$$

FIGURE 3.1.9

Vertical tangents are mentioned here only in passing. They are discussed in detail in Section 4.8.

Differentiability and Continuity

A function can be continuous at some number x without being differentiable there. For example, the absolute-value function

$$f(x) = |x|$$

is continuous at 0 (it is everywhere continuous), but it is not differentiable at 0:

$$\frac{f(0 + h) - f(0)}{h} = \frac{|0 + h| - |0|}{h} = \frac{|h|}{h} = \begin{cases} -1, & h < 0 \\ 1, & h > 0 \end{cases},$$

so that

$$\lim_{h \to 0^-} \frac{f(0 + h) - f(0)}{h} = -1, \qquad \lim_{h \to 0^+} \frac{f(0 + h) - f(0)}{h} = 1$$

and thus

$$\lim_{h \to 0} \frac{f(0 + h) - f(0)}{h} \quad \text{does not exist.} \quad \square$$

In Figure 3.1.10 we have drawn the graph of the absolute-value function. The lack of differentiability at 0 is evident geometrically. At the point $(0, 0) = (0, f(0))$ the graph changes direction abruptly and there is no tangent line.

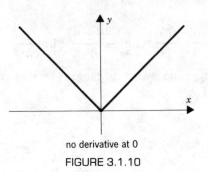

no derivative at 0

FIGURE 3.1.10

You can see a similar abrupt change of direction in the graph of

$$f(x) = \begin{cases} x^2, & x \le 1 \\ x, & x > 1 \end{cases} \qquad \text{(Figure 3.1.11)}$$

at the point $(1, 1)$. Once again f is everywhere continuous (you can verify that), but it is not differentiable at 1:

$$\lim_{h \to 0^-} \frac{f(1 + h) - f(1)}{h} = \lim_{h \to 0^-} \frac{(1 + h)^2 - 1}{h} = \lim_{h \to 0^-} \frac{h^2 + 2h}{h} = \lim_{h \to 0^-} (h + 2) = 2$$

and

$$\lim_{h \to 0^+} \frac{f(1 + h) - f(1)}{h} = \lim_{h \to 0^+} \frac{(1 + h) - 1}{h} = \lim_{h \to 0^+} 1 = 1.$$

Since these one-sided limits are different, the two-sided limit

$$f'(1) = \lim_{h \to 0} \frac{f(1 + h) - f(1)}{h} \quad \text{does not exist.} \quad \square$$

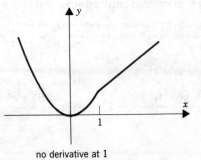

no derivative at 1

FIGURE 3.1.11

Although not every continuous function is differentiable, every differentiable function is continuous.

THEOREM 3.1.4

If f is differentiable at x, then f is continuous at x.

Proof. For $h \neq 0$ and $x + h$ in the domain of f,

$$f(x + h) - f(x) = \frac{f(x + h) - f(x)}{h} \cdot h.$$

With f differentiable at x,

$$\lim_{h \to 0} \frac{f(x + h) - f(x)}{h} = f'(x).$$

Since $\lim_{h \to 0} h = 0$, we have

$$\lim_{h \to 0} [f(x + h) - f(x)] = \left[\lim_{h \to 0} \frac{f(x + h) - f(x)}{h} \right] \cdot \left[\lim_{h \to 0} h \right] = f'(x) \cdot 0 = 0.$$

It follows that

$$\lim_{h \to 0} f(x + h) = f(x) \qquad \qquad \text{(explain)}$$

and thus (by Exercise 43, Section 2.4) that f is continuous at x. $\square$

EXERCISES

Differentiate each of the following functions by forming a suitable difference quotient and taking the limit as h tends to 0.

1. $f(x) = 4$.
2. $f(x) = c$.
3. $f(x) = 2 - 3x$.
4. $f(x) = 4x + 1$.
5. $f(x) = 5x - x^2$.
6. $f(x) = 2x^3 + 1$.
7. $f(x) = x^4$.
8. $f(x) = 1/(x + 3)$.
9. $f(x) = \sqrt{x - 1}$.
10. $f(x) = x^3 - 4x$.
11. $f(x) = 1/x^2$.
12. $f(x) = 1/\sqrt{x}$.

For each of the functions below, find $f'(2)$ by forming the difference quotient

$$\frac{f(2 + h) - f(2)}{h}$$

and taking the limit as $h \to 0$.

13. $f(x) = (3x - 7)^2$.
14. $f(x) = 7x - x^2$.
15. $f(x) = 9/(x + 4)$.
16. $f(x) = 5 - x^4$.
17. $f(x) = x + \sqrt{2x}$.
18. $f(x) = \sqrt{6 - x}$.

Find equations for the tangent and normal to the graph of f at the point $(a, f(a))$.

19. $f(x) = x^2$; $a = 2$.
20. $f(x) = \sqrt{x}$; $a = 4$.
21. $f(x) = 5x - x^2$; $a = 4$.
22. $f(x) = 5 - x^3$; $a = 2$.

23. $f(x) = |x|;$ $a = -4.$
25. $f(x) = 1/(x + 2);$ $a = -3.$
24. $f(x) = 7x + x^2;$ $a = -1.$
26. $f(x) = 1/x^2;$ $a = -2.$

Draw the graph of each of the following functions and indicate where it is not differentiable.

27. $f(x) = |x + 1|.$
29. $f(x) = \sqrt{|x|}.$
28. $f(x) = |2x - 5|.$
30. $f(x) = |x^2 - 4|.$

31. $f(x) = \begin{cases} x^2, & x \le 1 \\ 2 - x, & x > 1 \end{cases}.$

32. $f(x) = \begin{cases} x^2 - 1, & x \le 2 \\ 3, & x > 2 \end{cases}.$

Find $f'(c)$ if it exists.

33. $f(x) = \begin{cases} 4x, & x < 1 \\ 2x^2 + 2, & x \ge 1 \end{cases};$ $c = 1.$

34. $f(x) = \begin{cases} 3x^2, & x \le 1 \\ 2x^3 + 1, & x > 1 \end{cases};$ $c = 1.$

35. $f(x) = \begin{cases} x + 1, & x \le -1 \\ (x + 1)^2, & x > -1 \end{cases};$ $c = -1.$

36. $f(x) = \begin{cases} -\frac{1}{2}x^2, & x < 3 \\ -3x, & x \ge 3 \end{cases};$ $c = 3.$

Sketch the graph of the derivative of the function with the given graph.

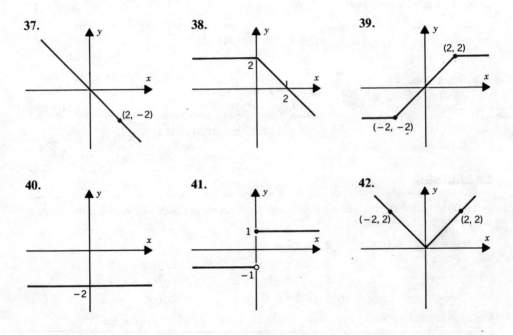

37.   (2, −2)

38.   2 ⋮ 2

39.   (2, 2)   (−2, −2)

40.   −2

41.   1   −1

42.   (−2, 2)   (2, 2)

43. Show that

$$f(x) = \begin{cases} x^2, & x \le 1 \\ 2x, & x > 1 \end{cases}$$

is not differentiable at $x = 1$.   HINT: Consider Theorem 3.1.4.

44. Find A and B given that the function

$$f(x) = \begin{cases} x^3, & x \le 1 \\ Ax + B, & x > 1 \end{cases}$$

is differentiable at $x = 1$.

45. Let

$$f(x) = \begin{cases} (x+1)^2, & x \le 0 \\ (x-1)^2, & x > 0 \end{cases}.$$

(a) Compute $f'(x)$ for $x \ne 0$.

(b) Show that f is not differentiable at $x = 0$.

46. Given that f is differentiable at x_0, show that the function

$$g(x) = \begin{cases} f(x), & x \le x_0 \\ f'(x_0)(x - x_0) + f(x_0), & x > x_0 \end{cases}$$

is differentiable at x_0. What is $g'(x_0)$?

Give an example of a function f that is defined for all real numbers and satisfies the given conditions.

47. $f'(x) = 0$ for all real x.

48. $f'(x) = 0$ for all $x \ne 0$; $f'(0)$ does not exist.

49. $f'(x)$ exists for all $x \ne -1$; $f'(-1)$ does not exist.

50. $f'(x)$ exists for all $x \ne \pm 1$;   neither $f'(1)$ nor $f'(-1)$ exists.

51. $f'(1) = 2$ and $f(1) = 7$.

52. $f'(2) = 5$ and $f(2) = 1$.

53. f is nowhere differentiable.

54. $f'(x) = 1$ for $x < 0$ and $f'(x) = -1$ for $x > 0$.

3.2 ·····SOME DIFFERENTIATION FORMULAS

Calculating the derivative of

$$f(x) = (x^3 - 2)(4x + 1) \quad \text{or} \quad f(x) = \frac{6x^2 - 1}{x^4 + 5x + 1}$$

by forming the proper difference quotient

$$\frac{f(x+h) - f(x)}{h}$$

and then taking the limit as h tends to 0 is somewhat laborious. Here we derive some general formulas that will enable us to calculate such derivatives quite quickly and easily.

We begin by pointing out that all constant functions have derivative 0:

(3.2.1) $\text{if } f(x) = \alpha, \quad \text{then } f'(x) = 0$

and the identity function has derivative 1:

(3.2.2) $\text{if } f(x) = x, \quad \text{then } f'(x) = 1.$

Proof.   For $f(x) = \alpha$,

$$f'(x) = \lim_{h \to 0} \frac{f(x + h) - f(x)}{h} = \lim_{h \to 0} \frac{\alpha - \alpha}{h} = \lim_{h \to 0} 0 = 0.$$

For $f(x) = x$,

$$f'(x) = \lim_{h \to 0} \frac{f(x + h) - f(x)}{h} = \lim_{h \to 0} \frac{(x + h) - x}{h}$$

$$= \lim_{h \to 0} \frac{h}{h} = \lim_{h \to 0} 1 = 1. \quad \square$$

DEFINITION 3.2.3   DERIVATIVES OF SUMS AND SCALAR MULTIPLES

Let α be a real number.   If f and g are differentiable at x, then $f + g$ and αf are differentiable at x.   Moreover,

$$(f + g)'(x) = f'(x) + g'(x) \quad \text{and} \quad (\alpha f)'(x) = \alpha f'(x).$$

Proof.   To verify the first formula note that

$$\frac{(f + g)(x + h) - (f + g)(x)}{h} = \frac{[f(x + h) + g(x + h)] - [f(x) + g(x)]}{h}$$

$$= \frac{f(x + h) - f(x)}{h} + \frac{g(x + h) - g(x)}{h}.$$

By definition

$$\lim_{h \to 0} \frac{f(x + h) - f(x)}{h} = f'(x), \qquad \lim_{h \to 0} \frac{g(x + h) - g(x)}{h} = g'(x).$$

Thus

$$\lim_{h \to 0} \frac{(f + g)(x + h) - (f + g)(x)}{h} = f'(x) + g'(x),$$

which means that

$$(f + g)'(x) = f'(x) + g'(x).$$

To verify the second formula we must show that

$$\lim_{h \to 0} \frac{(\alpha f)(x + h) - (\alpha f)(x)}{h} = \alpha f'(x).$$

This follows directly from the fact that

$$\frac{(\alpha f)(x + h) - (\alpha f)(x)}{h} = \alpha \left[\frac{f(x + h) - f(x)}{h} \right]. \quad \square$$

THEOREM 3.2.4 THE PRODUCT RULE

If f and g are differentiable at x, then so is their product, and

$$(fg)'(x) = f(x)g'(x) + g(x)f'(x).$$

Proof. We form the difference quotient

$$\frac{(fg)(x+h) - (fg)(x)}{h} = \frac{f(x+h)\,g(x+h) - f(x)g(x)}{h}$$

and rewrite it as

$$f(x+h)\left[\frac{g(x+h) - g(x)}{h}\right] + g(x)\left[\frac{f(x+h) - f(x)}{h}\right].$$

(Here we've added and subtracted $f(x+h)g(x)$ in the numerator and then regrouped the terms so as to display difference quotients for f and g.) Since f is differentiable at x, we know that f is continuous at x (Theorem 3.1.4) and thus

$$\lim_{h\to 0} f(x+h) = f(x).$$

Since

$$\lim_{h\to 0}\frac{g(x+h) - g(x)}{h} = g'(x) \quad\text{and}\quad \lim_{h\to 0}\frac{f(x+h) - f(x)}{h} = f'(x),$$

we obtain

$$\lim_{h\to 0}\frac{(fg)(x+h) - (fg)(x)}{h} = f(x)g'(x) + g(x)f'(x). \quad \square$$

Using the product rule, it's not hard to prove that

(3.2.5)

for each positive integer n

$p(x) = x^n$ has derivative $p'(x) = nx^{n-1}$.

In particular

$$p(x) = x \quad\quad \text{has derivative} \quad p'(x) = 1 \cdot x^0 = 1,$$
$$p(x) = x^2 \quad \text{has derivative} \quad p'(x) = 2x,$$
$$p(x) = x^3 \quad \text{has derivative} \quad p'(x) = 3x^2,$$
$$p(x) = x^4 \quad \text{has derivative} \quad p'(x) = 4x^3,$$

and so on.

Proof of (3.2.5). We proceed by induction on n. If $n = 1$, then we have the identity function

$$p(x) = x,$$

which we know satisfies

$$p'(x) = 1 = 1 \cdot x^0.$$

This means that the formula holds for $n = 1$.

We suppose now that the result holds for $n = k$ and go on to show that it holds for $n = k + 1$. We let

$$p(x) = x^{k+1}$$

and note that

$$p(x) = x \cdot x^k.$$

Applying the product rule (3.2.4) and our inductive hypothesis, we obtain

$$p'(x) = x \cdot kx^{k-1} + 1 \cdot x^k = (k + 1)x^k.$$

This shows that the formula holds for $n = k + 1$.

By the axiom of induction the formula holds for all positive integers n. □

The formula for differentiating polynomials follows from (3.2.3) and (3.2.5):

(3.2.6)

$$\boxed{\begin{array}{l} \text{if} \quad\quad P(x) = a_n x^n + \cdots + a_2 x^2 + a_1 x + a_0, \\ \text{then} \quad P'(x) = na_n x^{n-1} + \cdots + 2a_2 x + a_1. \end{array}}$$

For example,

$$P(x) = 12x^3 - 6x - 2 \quad \text{has derivative} \quad P'(x) = 36x^2 - 6$$

and

$$P(x) = \tfrac{1}{4}x^4 - 2x^2 + x + 5 \quad \text{has derivative} \quad P'(x) = x^3 - 4x + 1.$$

PROBLEM. Differentiate

$$F(x) = (x^3 - 2)(4x + 1)$$

and find $F'(-1)$.

Solution. We have a product $F(x) = f(x)g(x)$ with

$$f(x) = x^3 - 2 \quad \text{and} \quad g(x) = 4x + 1.$$

The product rule gives

$$\begin{aligned} F'(x) &= f(x)g'(x) + g(x)f'(x) \\ &= (x^3 - 2) \cdot 4 + (4x + 1)(3x^2) \\ &= 4x^3 - 8 + 12x^3 + 3x^2 \\ &= 16x^3 + 3x^2 - 8. \end{aligned}$$

Setting $x = -1$, we have

$$F'(-1) = 16(-1)^3 + 3(-1)^2 - 8 = -16 + 3 - 8 = -21. \quad \square$$

PROBLEM. Differentiate

$$F(x) = (ax + b)(cx + d).$$

Solution. We have a product $F(x) = f(x)g(x)$ with

$$f(x) = ax + b \quad \text{and} \quad g(x) = cx + d.$$

Again we use the product rule

$$F'(x) = f(x)g'(x) + g(x)f'(x).$$

In this case

$$F'(x) = (ax + b)c + (cx + d)a = 2acx + bc + ad.$$

We can also do the problem without using the product rule by first carrying out the multiplication:

$$F(x) = acx^2 + bcx + adx + bd$$

and then differentiating:

$$F'(x) = 2acx + bc + ad.$$

The result is the same.   □

We come now to reciprocals.

THEOREM 3.2.7 THE RECIPROCAL RULE

If g is differentiable at x and $g(x) \neq 0$, then $1/g$ is differentiable at x and

$$\left(\frac{1}{g}\right)'(x) = -\frac{g'(x)}{[g(x)]^2}.$$

Proof. Since g is differentiable at x, g is continuous at x (Theorem 3.1.4). Since $g(x) \neq 0$, we know that $1/g$ is continuous at x, and thus that

$$\lim_{h \to 0} \frac{1}{g(x + h)} = \frac{1}{g(x)}.$$

For h different from zero and sufficiently small, $g(x + h) \neq 0$ and

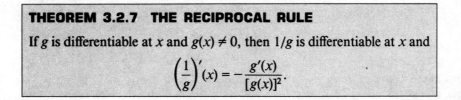

$$\frac{1}{h}\left[\frac{1}{g(x + h)} - \frac{1}{g(x)}\right] = -\left[\frac{g(x + h) - g(x)}{h}\right]\frac{1}{g(x + h)}\frac{1}{g(x)}.$$

Taking the limit as h tends to zero, we see that the right-hand side (and thus the left) tends to

$$-\frac{g'(x)}{[g(x)]^2}. \quad □$$

From this last result it is easy to see that the formula for the derivative of a power, x^n, also applies to negative powers; namely,

(3.2.8)

> for each negative integer n
>
> $$p(x) = x^n \quad \text{has derivative} \quad p'(x) = nx^{n-1}.$$

This formula holds except, of course, at $x = 0$ where no negative power is even defined. In particular

$$p(x) = x^{-1} \quad \text{has derivative} \quad p'(x) = (-1)x^{-2} = -x^{-2},$$
$$p(x) = x^{-2} \quad \text{has derivative} \quad p'(x) = -2x^{-3},$$
$$p(x) = x^{-3} \quad \text{has derivative} \quad p'(x) = -3x^{-4},$$

and so on.

Proof of (3.2.8).   Note that

$$p(x) = \frac{1}{g(x)} \quad \text{where} \quad g(x) = x^{-n} \text{ and } -n \text{ is a positive integer.}$$

The rule for reciprocals gives

$$p'(x) = -\frac{g'(x)}{[g(x)]^2} = -\frac{(-nx^{-n-1})}{x^{-2n}} = (nx^{-n-1})x^{2n} = nx^{n-1}. \quad \square$$

PROBLEM.   Differentiate

$$f(x) = \frac{5}{x^2} - \frac{6}{x}$$

and find $f'(\frac{1}{2})$.

Solution.   To apply (3.2.8) we write

$$f(x) = 5x^{-2} - 6x^{-1}.$$

Differentiation gives

$$f'(x) = -10x^{-3} + 6x^{-2}.$$

Back in fractional notation

$$f'(x) = -\frac{10}{x^3} + \frac{6}{x^2}.$$

Setting $x = \frac{1}{2}$, we have

$$f'(\tfrac{1}{2}) = -\frac{10}{(\frac{1}{2})^3} + \frac{6}{(\frac{1}{2})^2} = -80 + 24 = -56. \quad \square$$

PROBLEM. Differentiate

$$f(x) = \frac{1}{ax^2 + bx + c}.$$

Solution. Here we have a reciprocal $f(x) = 1/g(x)$ with

$$g(x) = ax^2 + bx + c.$$

The reciprocal rule (3.2.7) gives

$$f'(x) = -\frac{g'(x)}{[g(x)]^2} = -\frac{2ax + b}{[ax^2 + bx + c]^2}. \quad \square$$

Finally we come to quotients in general.

THEOREM 3.2.9 THE QUOTIENT RULE

If f and g are differentiable at x and $g(x) \neq 0$, then the quotient f/g is differentiable at x and

$$\left(\frac{f}{g}\right)'(x) = \frac{g(x)f'(x) - f(x)g'(x)}{[g(x)]^2}.$$

The proof is left to you.   HINT: $f/g = f \cdot 1/g$.
    From the quotient rule you can see that all rational functions (quotients of polynomials) are differentiable wherever they are defined.

PROBLEM. Differentiate

$$F(x) = \frac{ax + b}{cx + d}.$$

Solution. We are dealing with a quotient $F(x) = f(x)/g(x)$. The quotient rule,

$$F'(x) = \frac{g(x)f'(x) - f(x)g'(x)}{[g(x)]^2},$$

gives

$$F'(x) = \frac{(cx + d) \cdot a - (ax + b) \cdot c}{(cx + d)^2} = \frac{ad - bc}{(cx + d)^2}. \quad \square$$

PROBLEM. Differentiate

$$F(x) = \frac{6x^2 - 1}{x^4 + 5x + 1}.$$

Solution. Again we are dealing with a quotient $F(x) = f(x)/g(x)$. The quotient rule gives

$$F'(x) = \frac{(x^4 + 5x + 1)(12x) - (6x^2 - 1)(4x^3 + 5)}{(x^4 + 5x + 1)^2}. \quad \square$$

PROBLEM. Find $f'(0), f'(1)$, and $f'(2)$ for the function

$$f(x) = \frac{5x}{1 + x}.$$

Solution. First we find a general expression for $f'(x)$, and then we evaluate it at 0, 1, and 2. Using the quotient rule, we get

$$f'(x) = \frac{(1 + x)5 - 5x(1)}{(1 + x)^2} = \frac{5}{(1 + x)^2}.$$

This gives

$$f'(0) = \frac{5}{(1 + 0)^2} = 5, \quad f'(1) = \frac{5}{(1 + 1)^2} = \frac{5}{4}, \quad f'(2) = \frac{5}{(1 + 2)^2} = \frac{5}{9}. \quad \square$$

PROBLEM. Find $f'(-1)$ for

$$f(x) = \frac{x^2}{ax^2 + b}.$$

Solution. We first find $f'(x)$ in general by the quotient rule:

$$f'(x) = \frac{(ax^2 + b)2x - x^2(2ax)}{(ax^2 + b)^2} = \frac{2bx}{(ax^2 + b)^2}.$$

Now we evaluate f' at -1:

$$f'(-1) = -\frac{2b}{(a + b)^2}. \quad \square$$

REMARK. Some expressions are easier to differentiate if we rewrite them in more convenient form. For example, we can differentiate

$$f(x) = \frac{x^5 - 2x}{x^2}$$

by the quotient rule, or we can write

$$f(x) = (x^5 - 2x)x^{-2}$$

and use the product rule; even better, we can notice that

$$f(x) = x^3 - 2x^{-1}$$

and proceed from there:

$$f'(x) = 3x^2 + 2x^{-2}. \quad \square$$

EXERCISES

Differentiate the following functions.

1. $F(x) = 1 - x$.

2. $F(x) = 2(1 + x)$.

3. $F(x) = 11x^5 - 6x^3 + 8$.

4. $F(x) = \dfrac{x^4}{4} - \dfrac{x^3}{3} + \dfrac{x^2}{2} - \dfrac{x}{1}$.

5. $F(x) = ax^2 + bx + c$.

6. $F(x) = \dfrac{3}{x^2}$.

7. $F(x) = -\dfrac{1}{x^2}$.

8. $F(x) = \dfrac{(x^2 + 2)}{x^3}$.

9. $G(x) = (x^2 - 1)(x - 3)$.

10. $F(x) = x - \dfrac{1}{x}$.

11. $G(x) = \dfrac{x^3}{1 - x}$.

12. $F(x) = \dfrac{ax - b}{cx - d}$.

13. $G(x) = (x - 1)(x - 2)$.

14. $G(x) = \dfrac{7x^4 + 11}{x + 1}$.

15. $G(x) = \dfrac{x^2 - 1}{2x + 3}$.

16. $G(x) = \dfrac{2x^2 + 1}{x + 2}$.

17. $G(x) = \dfrac{6 - 1/x}{x - 2}$.

18. $G(x) = \dfrac{1 + x^4}{x^2}$.

19. $G(x) = (9x^8 - 8x^9)\left(x + \dfrac{1}{x}\right)$.

20. $G(x) = \left(1 + \dfrac{1}{x}\right)\left(1 + \dfrac{1}{x^2}\right)$.

Find $f'(0)$ and $f'(1)$.

21. $f(x) = \dfrac{1}{x - 2}$.

22. $f(x) = x^2(x + 1)$.

23. $f(x) = \dfrac{1 - x^2}{1 + x^2}$.

24. $f(x) = \dfrac{2x^2 + x + 1}{x^2 + 2x + 1}$.

25. $f(x) = \dfrac{ax + b}{cx + d}$.

26. $f(x) = \dfrac{ax^2 + bx + c}{cx^2 + bx + a}$.

Given that $h(0) = 3$ and $h'(0) = 2$, find $f'(0)$.

27. $f(x) = xh(x)$.

28. $f(x) = 3x^2h(x) - 5x$.

29. $f(x) = h(x) - \dfrac{1}{h(x)}$.

30. $f(x) = h(x) + \dfrac{x}{h(x)}$.

Find an equation for the tangent to the graph of f at the point $(a, f(a))$.

31. $f(x) = \dfrac{x}{x + 2}$; $a = -4$.

32. $f(x) = (x^3 - 2x + 1)(4x - 5)$; $a = 2$.

33. $f(x) = (x^2 - 3)(5x - x^3)$; $a = 1$.

34. $f(x) = x^2 - \dfrac{10}{x}$; $a = -2$.

35. $f(x) = 6/x^2$; $a = 3$.

36. $f(x) = \dfrac{3x + 5}{7x - 3}$; $a = 1$.

Find the points where the tangent to the curve is horizontal.

37. $f(x) = (x - 2)(x^2 - x - 11)$.   **38.** $f(x) = x^2 - \dfrac{16}{x}$.   **39.** $f(x) = \dfrac{5x}{x^2 + 1}$.

40. $f(x) = (x + 2)(x^2 - 2x - 8)$.   **41.** $f(x) = x + \dfrac{4}{x^2}$.   **42.** $f(x) = \dfrac{x^2 - 2x + 4}{x^2 + 4}$.

Find the points where the tangent to the curve

43. $f(x) = -x^2 - 6$ is parallel to the line $y = 4x - 1$.

44. $f(x) = x^3 - 3x$ is perpendicular to the line $5y - 3x - 8 = 0$.

45. $f(x) = x^3 - x^2$ is perpendicular to the line $5y + x + 2 = 0$.

46. $f(x) = 4x - x^2$ is parallel to the line $2y = 3x - 5$.

47. Find the area of the triangle formed by the x-axis and the lines tangent and normal to the curve $f(x) = 6x - x^2$ at the point $(5, 5)$.

48. Find the area of the triangle formed by the x-axis and the lines tangent and normal to the curve $f(x) = 9 - x^2$ at the point $(2, 5)$.

49. Determine the coefficients A, B, C so that the curve $f(x) = Ax^2 + Bx + C$ will pass through the point $(1, 3)$ and be tangent to the line $4x + y = 8$ at the point $(2, 0)$.

50. Determine A, B, C, D so that the curve $f(x) = Ax^3 + Bx^2 + Cx + D$ will be tangent to the line $y = 3x - 3$ at the point $(1, 0)$ and tangent to the line $y = 18x - 27$ at the point $(2, 9)$.

51. Prove the validity of the quotient rule.

52. Verify that, if f, g, h are differentiable, then

$$(fgh)'(x) = f'(x)g(x)h(x) + f(x)g'(x)h(x) + f(x)g(x)h'(x).$$

HINT: Apply the product rule to $[f(x)g(x)]h(x)$.

53. Use the product rule (3.2.4) to show that, if f is differentiable, then

$$g(x) = [f(x)]^2 \quad \text{has derivative} \quad g'(x) = 2f(x)f'(x).$$

54. Show that, if f is differentiable, then

$$g(x) = [f(x)]^n \quad \text{has derivative} \quad g'(x) = n[f(x)]^{n-1}f'(x)$$

for each nonzero integer n.   HINT: Mimic the inductive proof of (3.2.5).

55. Find A and B given that the derivative of

$$f(x) = \begin{cases} Ax^3 + Bx + 2, & x \le 2 \\ Bx^2 - A, & x > 2 \end{cases}$$

is continuous for all real x.   HINT: f itself must be continuous.

56. Find A and B given that the derivative of

$$f(x) = \begin{cases} Ax^2 + B, & x < -1 \\ Bx^5 + Ax + 4, & x \ge -1 \end{cases}$$

is continuous for all real x.

3.3 ······THE d/dx NOTATION; DERIVATIVES OF HIGHER ORDER

The d/dx Notation

So far we have indicated the derivative by a prime, but there are other notations that are widely used, particularly in science and engineering. The most popular of these is the double-d notation of Leibniz. In the Leibniz notation the derivative of a function y is indicated by writing

$$\frac{dy}{dx}, \quad \frac{dy}{dt}, \quad \text{or} \quad \frac{dy}{dz}, \quad \text{etc.,}$$

depending upon whether the letter x, t, or z, etc., is being used for the elements of the domain of y. For instance, if y is initially defined by

$$y(x) = x^3,$$

then the Leibniz notation gives

$$\frac{dy(x)}{dx} = 3x^2.$$

Usually writers drop the (x) and simply write

$$y = x^3 \quad \text{and} \quad \frac{dy}{dx} = 3x^2.$$

The symbols

$$\frac{d}{dx}, \quad \frac{d}{dt}, \quad \frac{d}{dz}, \quad \text{etc.,}$$

are also used as prefixes before expressions to be differentiated. For example,

$$\frac{d}{dx}(x^3 - 4x) = 3x^2 - 4, \quad \frac{d}{dt}(t^2 + 3t + 1) = 2t + 3, \quad \frac{d}{dz}(z^5 - 1) = 5z^4.$$

In the Leibniz notation the differentiation formulas look like this:

I. $$\frac{d}{dx}[f(x) + g(x)] = \frac{d}{dx}[f(x)] + \frac{d}{dx}[g(x)].$$

II. $$\frac{d}{dx}[\alpha f(x)] = \alpha \frac{d}{dx}[f(x)].$$

III. $$\frac{d}{dx}[f(x)g(x)] = f(x)\frac{d}{dx}[g(x)] + g(x)\frac{d}{dx}[f(x)].$$

IV. $$\frac{d}{dx}\left[\frac{1}{g(x)}\right] = -\frac{1}{[g(x)]^2}\frac{d}{dx}[g(x)].$$

V. $$\frac{d}{dx}\left[\frac{f(x)}{g(x)}\right] = \frac{g(x)\frac{d}{dx}[f(x)] - f(x)\frac{d}{dx}[g(x)]}{[g(x)]^2}.$$

Often functions f and g are replaced by u and v and the x is left out altogether. Then the formulas look like this:

I. $$\frac{d}{dx}(u + v) = \frac{du}{dx} + \frac{dv}{dx}.$$

II. $$\frac{d}{dx}(\alpha u) = \alpha \frac{du}{dx}.$$

III.
$$\frac{d}{dx}(uv) = u\frac{dv}{dx} + v\frac{du}{dx}.$$

IV.
$$\frac{d}{dx}\left(\frac{1}{v}\right) = -\frac{1}{v^2}\frac{dv}{dx}.$$

V.
$$\frac{d}{dx}\left(\frac{u}{v}\right) = \frac{v\dfrac{du}{dx} - u\dfrac{dv}{dx}}{v^2}.$$

The only way to develop a feeling for this notation is to use it. Below we work out some practice problems.

PROBLEM. Find

$$\frac{dy}{dx} \quad \text{for} \quad y = \frac{3x-1}{5x+2}.$$

Solution. Here we can use the quotient rule (V):

$$\frac{dy}{dx} = \frac{(5x+2)\dfrac{d}{dx}(3x-1) - (3x-1)\dfrac{d}{dx}(5x+2)}{(5x+2)^2}$$

$$= \frac{(5x+2)(3) - (3x-1)(5)}{(5x+2)^2} = \frac{11}{(5x+2)^2}. \quad \square$$

PROBLEM. Find

$$\frac{dy}{dx} \quad \text{for} \quad y = (x^3+1)(3x^5+2x-1).$$

Solution. Here we can use the product rule (III):

$$\frac{dy}{dx} = (x^3+1)\frac{d}{dx}(3x^5+2x-1) + (3x^5+2x-1)\frac{d}{dx}(x^3+1)$$
$$= (x^3+1)(15x^4+2) + (3x^5+2x-1)(3x^2)$$
$$= (15x^7 + 15x^4 + 2x^3 + 2) + (9x^7 + 6x^3 - 3x^2)$$
$$= 24x^7 + 15x^4 + 8x^3 - 3x^2 + 2. \quad \square$$

PROBLEM. Find

$$\frac{d}{dt}\left(t^3 - \frac{t}{t^2-1}\right).$$

Solution

$$\frac{d}{dt}\left(t^3 - \frac{t}{t^2-1}\right) = \frac{d}{dt}(t^3) - \frac{d}{dt}\left(\frac{t}{t^2-1}\right)$$

$$= 3t^2 - \left[\frac{(t^2-1)(1) - t(2t)}{(t^2-1)^2}\right] = 3t^2 + \frac{t^2+1}{(t^2-1)^2}. \quad \square$$

PROBLEM. Find

$$\frac{du}{dx} \quad \text{for} \quad u = x(x+1)(x+2).$$

Solution. You can think of u as

$$[x(x+1)](x+2) \quad \text{or as} \quad x[(x+1)(x+2)].$$

From the first point of view,

$$\frac{du}{dx} = [x(x+1)](1) + (x+2)\frac{d}{dx}[x(x+1)]$$

$$= x(x+1) + (x+2)[x(1) + (x+1)(1)]$$

(∗) $$= x(x+1) + (x+2)(2x+1).$$

From the second point of view,

$$\frac{du}{dx} = x\frac{d}{dx}[(x+1)(x+2)] + (x+1)(x+2)(1)$$

$$= x[(x+1)(1) + (x+2)(1)] + (x+1)(x+2)$$

(∗∗) $$= x(2x+3) + (x+1)(x+2).$$

Both (∗) and (∗∗) can be multiplied out to give

$$\frac{du}{dx} = 3x^2 + 6x + 2.$$

This same result can be obtained by first carrying out the entire multiplication and then differentiating:

$$u = x(x+1)(x+2) = x(x^2 + 3x + 2) = x^3 + 3x^2 + 2x$$

so that

$$\frac{du}{dx} = 3x^2 + 6x + 2. \quad \square$$

PROBLEM. Evaluate dy/dx at $x = 0$ and $x = 1$ given that

$$y = \frac{x^2}{x^2 - 4}.$$

Solution

$$\frac{dy}{dx} = \frac{(x^2 - 4)2x - x^2(2x)}{(x^2 - 4)^2} = -\frac{8x}{(x^2 - 4)^2}.$$

At $x = 0$, $dy/dx = 0$; at $x = 1$, $dy/dx = -\frac{8}{9}$. $\quad \square$

Derivatives of Higher Order

If a function f is differentiable, then we can form a new function f'. If f' is itself differentiable, then we can form its derivative, called the *second derivative of f*, and denoted by f''. So long as we have differentiability, we can continue in this manner, forming f''', etc. The prime notation is not used beyond the third order. For the fourth derivative we write $f^{(4)}$ and more generally, for the nth derivative, $f^{(n)}$.

If $f(x) = x^5$, then

$$f'(x) = 5x^4, \quad f''(x) = 20x^3, \quad f'''(x) = 60x^2, \quad f^{(4)}(x) = 120x, \quad f^{(5)}(x) = 120.$$

All higher derivatives are identically zero. As a variant of this notation you can write $y = x^5$ and then

$$y' = 5x^4, \quad y'' = 20x^3, \quad y''' = 60x^2, \quad \text{etc.}$$

Since each polynomial P has a derivative P' that is in turn a polynomial, and each rational function Q has derivative Q' that is in turn a rational function, polynomials and rational functions have derivatives of all orders. In the case of a polynomial of degree n, derivatives of order greater than n are all identically zero. (Explain.)

In the Leibniz notation the derivatives of higher order are written

$$\frac{d^2y}{dx^2} = \frac{d}{dx}\left(\frac{dy}{dx}\right), \quad \frac{d^3y}{dx^3} = \frac{d}{dx}\left(\frac{d^2y}{dx^2}\right), \quad \ldots, \quad \frac{d^ny}{dx^n} = \frac{d}{dx}\left(\frac{d^{n-1}y}{dx^{n-1}}\right), \quad \ldots$$

or

$$\frac{d^2}{dx^2}[f(x)] = \frac{d}{dx}\left[\frac{d}{dx}[f(x)]\right], \quad \frac{d^3}{dx^3}[f(x)] = \frac{d}{dx}\left[\frac{d^2}{dx^2}[f(x)]\right], \quad \ldots,$$

$$\frac{d^n}{dx^n}[f(x)] = \frac{d}{dx}\left[\frac{d^{n-1}}{dx^{n-1}}[f(x)]\right], \quad \ldots$$

Below we work out some examples.

EXAMPLE. If

$$f(x) = x^4 - 3x^{-1} + 5,$$

then

$$f'(x) = 4x^3 + 3x^{-2}$$

and

$$f''(x) = 12x^2 - 6x^{-3}. \quad \square$$

EXAMPLE

$$\frac{d}{dx}[x^5 - 4x^3 + 7x] = 5x^4 - 12x^2 + 7$$

so that

$$\frac{d^2}{dx^2}[x^5 - 4x^3 + 7x] = \frac{d}{dx}[5x^4 - 12x^2 + 7] = 20x^3 - 24x$$

and

$$\frac{d^3}{dx^3}[x^5 - 4x^3 + 7x] = \frac{d}{dx}[20x^3 - 24x] = 60x^2 - 24. \quad \square$$

EXAMPLE. Finally we consider

$$y = x^{-1}.$$

In the Leibniz notation

$$\frac{dy}{dx} = -x^{-2}, \quad \frac{d^2y}{dx^2} = 2x^{-3}, \quad \frac{d^3y}{dx^3} = -6x^{-4}, \quad \frac{d^4y}{dx^4} = 24x^{-5}$$

and, more generally,

$$\frac{d^ny}{dx^n} = (-1)^n n! \, x^{-n-1}.$$

In the prime notation

$$y' = -x^{-2}, \quad y'' = 2x^{-3}, \quad y''' = -6x^{-4}, \quad y^{(4)} = 24x^{-5}$$

and

$$y^{(n)} = (-1)^n n! \, x^{-n-1}. \quad \square$$

EXERCISES

Find dy/dx.

1. $y = 3x^4 - x^2 + 1$. **2.** $y = x^2 + 2x^{-4}$. **3.** $y = x - \dfrac{1}{x}$.

4. $y = \dfrac{2x}{1-x}$. **5.** $y = \dfrac{x}{1+x^2}$. **6.** $y = x(x-2)(x+1)$.

7. $y = \dfrac{x^2}{1-x}$. **8.** $y = \left(\dfrac{x}{1+x}\right)\left(\dfrac{2-x}{3}\right)$. **9.** $y = \dfrac{x^3+1}{x^3-1}$.

10. $y = \dfrac{x^2}{(1+x)}$.

Find the indicated derivative.

11. $\dfrac{d}{dx}(2x-5)$. **12.** $\dfrac{d}{dx}(5x+2)$.

13. $\dfrac{d}{dx}[(3x^2 - x^{-1})(2x+5)]$. **14.** $\dfrac{d}{dx}[(2x^2 + 3x^{-1})(2x - 3x^{-2})]$.

15. $\dfrac{d}{dt}\left(\dfrac{t^2+1}{t^2-1}\right)$. **16.** $\dfrac{d}{dt}\left(\dfrac{2t^3+1}{t^4}\right)$.

17. $\dfrac{d}{dt}\left(\dfrac{t^4}{2t^3-1}\right)$. **18.** $\dfrac{d}{dt}\left[\dfrac{t}{(1+t)^2}\right]$.

19. $\dfrac{d}{du}\left(\dfrac{2u}{1-2u}\right)$. **20.** $\dfrac{d}{du}\left(\dfrac{u^2}{u^3+1}\right)$.

21. $\dfrac{d}{du}\left(\dfrac{u}{u-1} - \dfrac{u}{u+1}\right)$. **22.** $\dfrac{d}{du}[u^2(1-u^2)(1-u^3)]$.

23. $\dfrac{d}{dx}\left(\dfrac{x^2}{1-x^2}-\dfrac{1-x^2}{x^2}\right).$

24. $\dfrac{d}{dx}\left(\dfrac{3x^4+2x+1}{x^4+x-1}\right).$

25. $\dfrac{d}{dx}\left(\dfrac{x^3+x^2+x+1}{x^3-x^2+x-1}\right).$

26. $\dfrac{d}{dx}\left(\dfrac{x^3+x^2+x-1}{x^3-x^2+x+1}\right).$

Evaluate dy/dx at $x=2$.

27. $y=(x+1)(x+2)(x+3).$

28. $y=(x+1)(x^2+2)(x^3+3).$

29. $y=\dfrac{(x-1)(x-2)}{(x+2)}.$

30. $y=\dfrac{(x^2+1)(x^2-2)}{x^2+2}.$

Find the second derivative.

31. $f(x)=7x^3-6x^5.$

32. $f(x)=2x^5-6x^4+2x-1.$

33. $f(x)=\dfrac{x^2-3}{x}.$

34. $f(x)=x^2-\dfrac{1}{x^2}.$

35. $f(x)=(x^2-2)(x^{-2}+2).$

36. $f(x)=(2x-3)\left(\dfrac{2x+3}{x}\right).$

Find d^3y/dx^3.

37. $y=\tfrac{1}{3}x^3+\tfrac{1}{2}x^2+x+1.$

38. $y=(1+5x)^2.$

39. $y=(2x-5)^2.$

40. $y=\tfrac{1}{6}x^3-\tfrac{1}{4}x^2+x-3.$

41. $y=x^3-\dfrac{1}{x^3}.$

42. $y=\dfrac{x^4+2}{x}.$

Find the indicated derivatives.

43. $\dfrac{d}{dx}\left[x\dfrac{d}{dx}(x-x^2)\right].$

44. $\dfrac{d^2}{dx^2}\left[(x^2-3x)\dfrac{d}{dx}(x+x^{-1})\right].$

45. $\dfrac{d^4}{dx^4}[3x-x^4].$

46. $\dfrac{d^5}{dx^5}[ax^4+bx^3+cx^2+dx+e].$

47. $\dfrac{d^2}{dx^2}\left[(1+2x)\dfrac{d^2}{dx^2}(5-x^3)\right].$

48. $\dfrac{d^3}{dx^3}\left[\dfrac{1}{x}\dfrac{d^2}{dx^2}(x^4-5x^2)\right].$

49. Show that in general

$$(fg)''(x)\neq f(x)g''(x)+f''(x)g(x).$$

50. Verify the identity

$$f(x)g''(x)-f''(x)g(x)=\dfrac{d}{dx}[f(x)g'(x)-f'(x)g(x)].$$

Determine the values of x for which

  (a) $f''(x)=0.$ (b) $f''(x)>0.$ (c) $f''(x)<0.$

51. $f(x)=x^3.$

52. $f(x)=x^4.$

53. $f(x)=x^4+2x^3-12x^2+1.$

54. $f(x)=x^4+3x^3-6x^2-x.$

55. Prove by induction that

$$\text{if}\quad y=x^{-1},\qquad\text{then}\quad\dfrac{d^ny}{dx^n}=(-1)^n n!\,x^{-n-1}.$$

3.4 ······THE DERIVATIVE AS A RATE OF CHANGE

In the case of a linear function

$$y = mx + b$$

the graph is a straight line and the slope m measures the steepness of the line by giving the rate of climb of the line, *the rate of change of y with respect to x.*

As x changes from x_0 to x_1, y changes m times as much:

$$y_1 - y_0 = m(x_1 - x_0). \qquad \text{(Figure 3.4.1)}$$

Thus the slope m gives the change in y per unit change in x.

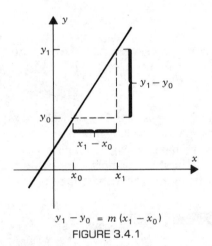

$$y_1 - y_0 = m (x_1 - x_0)$$

FIGURE 3.4.1

In the more general case of a differentiable function

$$y = f(x)$$

the graph is a curve. The slope

$$\frac{dy}{dx} = f'(x)$$

still gives *the rate of change of y with respect to x,* but this rate can vary from point to point. At $x = x_1$ (see Figure 3.4.2) the rate of change of y with respect to x is $f'(x_1)$;

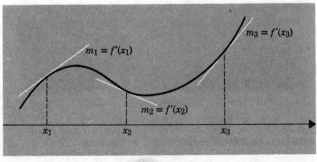

FIGURE 3.4.2

the steepness of the graph is that of a line of slope $f'(x_1)$. At $x = x_2$ the rate of change of y with respect to x is $f'(x_2)$; the steepness of the graph is that of a line of slope $f'(x_2)$. At $x = x_3$ the rate of change of y with respect to x is $f'(x_3)$; the steepness of the graph is that of a line of slope $f'(x_3)$.

From your understanding of slope it should be apparent to you when examining Figure 3.4.2 that $f'(x_1) > 0$, $f'(x_2) < 0$, and $f'(x_3) > 0$, and that, in general, a function increases on any interval where its derivative remains positive and decreases on any interval where its derivative remains negative. We'll take up this matter carefully in Chapter 4. Right now let's look at rates of change in the context of some simple geometric figures.

EXAMPLE. The area of a square is given by the formula $A = s^2$ where s is the length of a side. If s increases or decreases, A increases or decreases. The rate of change of A with respect to s is then given by the derivative

$$\frac{dA}{ds} = \frac{d}{ds}(s^2) = 2s.$$

When $s = \frac{1}{4}$, $dA/ds = \frac{1}{2}$: the area is changing only half as rapidly as s. When $s = \frac{1}{2}$, $dA/ds = 1$: at this point the area is changing at the same rate as s. When $s = 1$, $dA/ds = 2$: now the area is changing twice as rapidly as s.

In Figure 3.4.3 we have plotted A against s. The rate of change of A with respect to s at each of the indicated points appears as the slope of the tangent line. □

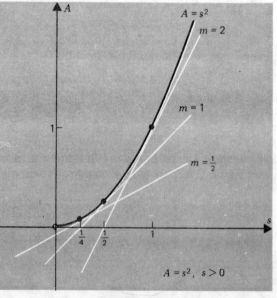

FIGURE 3.4.3

EXAMPLE. An equilateral triangle of side s has area

$$A = \tfrac{1}{4}\sqrt{3}\, s^2.$$ (check this out)

As s changes, the rate of change of A with respect to s is given by the derivative

$$\frac{dA}{ds} = \tfrac{1}{2}\sqrt{3}\ s.$$

When $s = 2\sqrt{3}$, the rate of change of A with respect to s is 3. In other words, when the side has length $2\sqrt{3}$, the area is changing three times as fast as the length of the side. ☐

EXAMPLE. The volume V of a circular cylinder of base radius r and height h is given by the formula

$$V = \pi r^2 h.$$

Let's suppose that r is increasing and let's try to find out how h must change with respect to r so as to keep V constant.

Differentiating $V = \pi r^2 h$ by the product rule, we find that

$$\frac{dV}{dr} = \pi r^2 \frac{dh}{dr} + h\frac{d}{dr}(\pi r^2) = \pi r^2 \frac{dh}{dr} + 2\pi rh.$$

If V is to remain constant, we must have $dV/dr = 0$ This gives

$$\pi r^2 \frac{dh}{dr} + 2\pi rh = 0.$$

Dividing through by πr, we have

$$r\frac{dh}{dr} + 2h = 0 \quad \text{and thus} \quad \frac{dh}{dr} = -\frac{2h}{r}.$$

For V to remain constant, h must *decrease* $2h/r$ times as quickly as r increases. ☐

The derivative as a rate of change is one of the fundamental ideas of calculus. We'll come back to it again and again. This brief section is only introductory.

EXERCISES

1. Find the rate of change of the area of a circle with respect to the radius r. What is the rate when $r = 2$?

2. Find the rate of change of the volume of a cube with respect to the length s of a side. What is the rate when $s = 4$?

3. Find the rate of change of the area of a square with respect to the length z of a diagonal. What is the rate when $z = 4$?

4. Find the rate of change of $y = 1/x$ with respect to x at $x = -1$.

5. Find the rate of change of $y = [x(x + 1)]^{-1}$ with respect to x at $x = 2$.

6. Find the values of x for which the rate of change of $y = x^3 - 12x^2 + 45x - 1$ with respect to x is zero.

7. Find the rate of change of the volume of a ball with respect to the radius.†

———

† Formulas for area, volume, etc. of the elementary geometric figures are listed in Section 1.2.

8. Find the rate of change of the surface area of a ball with respect to the radius given that $A = 4\pi r^2$. What is this rate of change when $r = r_0$? How must r_0 be chosen so that the rate of change is 1?

9. Find x_0 given that the rate of change of $y = 2x^2 + x - 1$ with respect to x is 4 at $x = x_0$.

10. Find the rate of change of the area A of a circle with respect to
   (a) the diameter d.   (b) the circumference C.

11. The volume of a cube is given by $V = s^3$ where s is the length of an edge. Find the rate of change of V with respect to
   (a) the length w of a diagonal on one of the faces.
   (b) the length z of one of the diagonals of the cube.

12. The dimensions of a rectangle are changing in such a way that the area of the rectangle remains constant. Find the rate of change of the height h with respect to the base b.

13. The area of a sector in a circle is given by the formula $A = \frac{1}{2}r^2\theta$ where r is the radius and θ is the central angle measured in radians.
   (a) Find the rate of change of A with respect to θ if r remains constant.
   (b) Find the rate of change of A with respect to r if θ remains constant.
   (c) Find the rate of change of θ with respect to r if A remains constant.

14. The total surface area of a right circular cylinder is given by the formula $A = 2\pi r(r + h)$ where r is the radius and h is the height.
   (a) Find the rate of change of A with respect to h if r remains constant.
   (b) Find the rate of change of A with respect to r if h remains constant.
   (c) Find the rate of change of h with respect to r if A remains constant.

15. For what value of x is the rate of change of

$$y = ax^2 + bx + c \quad \text{with respect to } x$$

the same as the rate of change of

$$z = bx^2 + ax + c \quad \text{with respect to } x?$$

Assume $a \neq b$.

16. Find the rate of change of the product $f(x)g(x)h(x)$ with respect to x at $x = 1$ given that

$$f(1) = 0, \quad g(1) = 2, \quad h(1) = -2,$$
$$f'(1) = 1, \quad g'(1) = -1, \quad h'(1) = 0.$$

3.5 ⋯⋯VELOCITY AND ACCELERATION

Suppose that an object is moving along a straight line and that, for each time t during a certain time interval, the object has position (coordinate) $x(t)$. If $x'(t)$ exists, then $x'(t)$ gives the *rate of change of position with respect to time* at time t. This rate of change of position is called the *velocity* of the object at time t; in symbols,

(3.5.1) $v(t) = x'(t).$

If the velocity function is itself differentiable, then its rate of change with respect to time at time t is called the *acceleration* at time t; in symbols,

(3.5.2) $$a(t) = v'(t) = x''(t).$$

In the Leibniz notation,

(3.5.3) $$v = \frac{dx}{dt} \quad \text{and} \quad a = \frac{dv}{dt} = \frac{d^2x}{dt^2}.$$

The absolute value of velocity is called *speed*:

(3.5.4) $$\text{speed at time } t = |v(t)|.$$

1. Positive velocity indicates motion in the positive direction (x is increasing). Negative velocity indicates motion in the negative direction (x is decreasing).

2. Positive acceleration indicates increasing velocity (increasing speed in the positive direction or decreasing speed in the negative direction). Negative acceleration indicates decreasing velocity (decreasing speed in the positive direction or increasing speed in the negative direction).

3. It follows from (2) that, if the velocity and acceleration have the same sign, the object is speeding up, but if the velocity and acceleration have opposite signs, the object is slowing down.

EXAMPLE. An object moves along the x-axis, its position at each time t given by the function

$$x(t) = t^3 - 12t^2 + 36t - 27.$$

Let's study the motion from time $t = 1$ to $t = 9$.

At time $t = 1$, the object is 2 units to the left of the origin:

$$x(1) = 1^3 - 12(1)^2 + 36(1) - 27 = -2.$$

At time $t = 9$, the object is 54 units to the right of the origin:

$$x(9) = 9^3 - 12(9)^2 + 36(9) - 27 = 54.$$

We obtain the velocity by differentiating the position function:

$$v(t) = x'(t) = 3t^2 - 24t + 36 = 3(t - 2)(t - 6).$$

We obtain the acceleration by differentiating the velocity function:

$$a(t) = v'(t) = 6t - 24 = 6(t - 4).$$

We record the sign of the velocity in a diagram and note that the object changes direction at times $t = 2$ and $t = 6$.†

---

† An object changes direction when the sign of $v(t)$ changes. However, $v(t)$ does *not* have to change sign when it becomes zero. For example, for the position function $x(t) = (t - 1)^3$, $v(t) = 3(t - 1)^2$. Note that $v(1) = 0$, but $v(t)$ is positive for all $t \neq 1$.

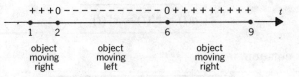

We then record the sign of the acceleration function:

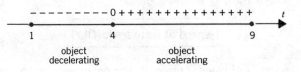

Combining the two diagrams, we have a brief description of the motion in a convenient form:

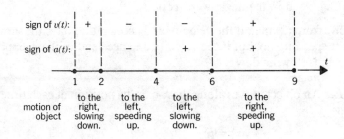

The direction of the motion at each time $t \in [1, 9]$ is represented schematically in Figure 3.5.1. Such figures are easy to draw but are of limited use.

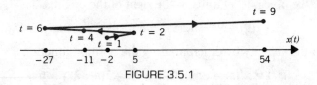

FIGURE 3.5.1

A better way to represent the motion is to graph x as a function of t, as we did in Figure 3.5.2. The velocity $v(t) = x'(t)$ then appears as the slope of the tangent to the curve. Note, for example, that at $t = 2$ and $t = 6$, the tangent is horizontal and the slope is 0. This reflects the fact that $v(2) = 0$ and $v(6) = 0$. ☐

Before going on, a word about units. If distance is measured in feet and time is measured in seconds, then velocity and speed are given in feet per second and acceleration is given in feet per second per second.

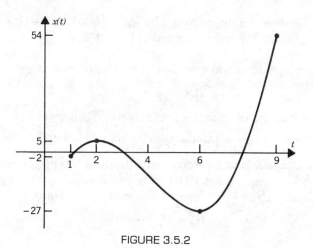

FIGURE 3.5.2

Now let's discuss the motion of a falling object. Let's assume that the object falls freely under the influence of gravity near the surface of the earth, and let's suppose that the air resistance is negligible. The height of the object at time t is then given by Galileo's formula

(3.5.5)
$$x(t) = -\tfrac{1}{2}gt^2 + v_0 t + x_0.\dagger$$

Since $x(0) = x_0$, the constant x_0 represents the height of the object at time $t = 0$. This is called *the initial position*. Differentiation gives

$$x'(t) = -gt + v_0.$$

Since $x'(0) = v_0$, the constant v_0 gives the velocity of the object at time $t = 0$. This is called *the initial velocity*. A second differentiation gives

$$x''(t) = -g.$$

The object falls with constant negative acceleration $-g$. (Why negative?) The constant g is a *gravitational constant*. If time is measured in seconds and distance is feet, then g is approximately 32 feet per second per second.†† In making numerical calculations we will take g as 32 feet per second per second. Equation 3.5.5 then reads

$$x(t) = -16t^2 + v_0 t + x_0.$$

---

† Galileo Galilei (1564–1642), a great Italian astronomer and mathematician, popularly known today for his early experiments with falling objects. His astronomical observations led him to support the Copernican view of the solar system. For this he was brought before the Inquisition.

†† The value of this constant varies with latitude and elevation. It is approximately 32 feet per second per second at the equator at elevation zero. In Greenland it's about 32.23.

PROBLEM. A stone is dropped from a height of 1600 feet. In how many seconds does it hit the ground? What is the speed at impact?

Solution. Here $x_0 = 1600$ and $v_0 = 0$. Consequently, by (3.5.5),

$$x(t) = -16t^2 + 1600.$$

To find t at the moment of impact we set $x(t) = 0$. This gives

$$-16t^2 + 1600 = 0, \quad t^2 = 100, \quad t = \pm 10.$$

We can disregard the negative answer because the stone was not dropped before time $t = 0$. We conclude that it takes 10 seconds for the stone to hit the ground.

The velocity at impact is the velocity at time $t = 10$. Since

$$v(t) = x'(t) = -32t,$$

we have

$$v(10) = -320.$$

The speed at impact is 320 feet per second. □

PROBLEM. An explosion causes debris to rise vertically with an initial velocity of 72 feet per second.

(a) In how many seconds does it attain maximum height?
(b) What is this maximum height?
(c) What is the speed of the debris as it reaches a height of 32 feet? (i) going up? (ii) coming back down?

Solution. The basic equation is again

$$x(t) = -16t^2 + v_0 t + x_0.$$

Here $x_0 = 0$ (it starts at ground level) and $v_0 = 72$ (the initial velocity is 72 feet per second). The equation of motion is therefore

$$x(t) = -16t^2 + 72t.$$

Differentiation gives

$$v(t) = x'(t) = -32t + 72.$$

The maximum height is attained when the velocity is 0. This occurs at time $t = \frac{72}{32} = \frac{9}{4}$. Since $x(\frac{9}{4}) = 81$, the maximum height attained is 81 feet.

To answer part (c) we must first find those times t for which $x(t) = 32$. Since

$$x(t) = -16t^2 + 72t,$$

the condition $x(t) = 32$ gives

$$16t^2 - 72t + 32 = 0.$$

This quadratic has two solutions, $t = \frac{1}{2}$ and $t = 4$. Since $v(\frac{1}{2}) = 56$ and $v(4) = -56$, the velocity going up is 56 feet per second and the velocity coming down is -56 feet per second. In each case the speed is 56 feet per second. □

EXERCISES

An object moves along a coordinate line, its position at each time $t \geq 0$ given by $x(t)$. Find the position, velocity, acceleration, and speed at time t_0.

1. $x(t) = 4 + 3t - t^2$; $t_0 = 5$.

2. $x(t) = 5t - t^3$; $t_0 = 3$.

3. $x(t) = t^3 - 6t$; $t_0 = 2$.

4. $x(t) = 4t^2 - 3t + 6$; $t_0 = 1$.

5. $x(t) = \dfrac{18}{t+2}$; $t_0 = 1$.

6. $x(t) = \dfrac{2t}{t+3}$; $t_0 = 3$.

7. $x(t) = (t^2 + 5t)(t^2 + t - 2)$; $t_0 = 1$.

8. $x(t) = (t^2 - 3t)(t^2 + 3t)$; $t_0 = 2$.

An object moves along a coordinate line, its position at each time $t \geq 0$ given by $x(t)$. Determine when, if ever, the object changes direction.

9. $x(t) = t^3 - 3t^2 + 3t$.

10. $x(t) = t + \dfrac{3}{t+1}$.

11. $x(t) = t + \dfrac{5}{t+2}$.

12. $x(t) = t^4 - 4t^3 + 6t^2 - 6t$.

13. $x(t) = \dfrac{t}{t^2 + 8}$.

14. $x(t) = 3t^5 + 10t^3 + 15t$.

Objects A, B, C move along the x-axis. Their positions from time $t = 0$ to time $t = t_3$ have been graphed in Figure 3.5.3.

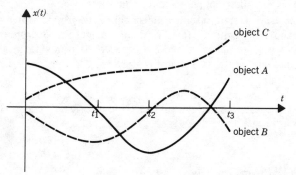

FIGURE 3.5.3

15. Which object begins furthest to the right?

16. Which object finishes furthest to the right?

17. Which object has the greatest speed at time t_1?

18. Which object maintains the same direction during the time interval $[t_1, t_3]$?

19. Which object begins by moving left?

20. Which object finishes moving left?

21. Which object changes direction at time t_2?

22. Which object speeds up during the time interval $[0, t_1]$?

23. Which object slows down during the time interval $[t_1, t_2]$?

24. Which objects changes direction during the time interval $[t_2, t_3]$?

An object moves along a coordinate line, its position at each time $t \geq 0$ given by $x(t)$. Determine the time interval(s), if any, during which the object satisfies the given condition.

25. $x(t) = t^4 - 12t^3 + 28t^2$; moving right.   26. $x(t) = t^3 - 12t^2 + 21t$; moving left.

27. $x(t) = 5t^4 - t^5$; speeding up.   28. $x(t) = 6t^2 - t^4$; slowing down.

29. $x(t) = t^3 - 6t^2 - 15t$; moving left and slowing down.

30. $x(t) = t^3 - 6t^2 - 15t$; moving right and slowing down.

31. $x(t) = t^4 - 8t^3 + 16t^2$; moving right and speeding up.

32. $x(t) = t^4 - 8t^3 + 16t^2$; moving left and speeding up.

33. An object is dropped and hits the ground 6 seconds later. From what height was it dropped?

34. Supplies are dropped from a helicopter and seconds later hit the ground at 384 feet per second. How high was the helicopter?

35. A rubber ball is thrown straight down from a height of 224 feet at a speed of 80 feet per second. If the ball always rebounds with one-fourth of its impact speed, what will be the speed of the ball the third time it hits the ground?

36. A ball is thrown straight up from ground level. How high will the ball go if it reaches a height of 64 feet in 2 seconds?

37. A stone is thrown upward from ground level. The initial speed is 32 feet per second. (a) In how many seconds will the stone hit the ground? (b) How high will it go? (c) With what minimum speed should the stone be thrown so as to reach a height of 36 feet?

38. To estimate the height of a bridge a man drops a stone into the water below. How high is the bridge (a) if the stone hits the water 3 seconds later? (b) if the man hears the splash 3 seconds later? (Use 1080 feet per second as the speed of sound.)

39. A falling stone is at a certain instant 100 feet above the ground. Two seconds later it is only 16 feet above the ground. (a) From what height was it dropped? (b) If it was thrown down with an initial speed of 5 feet per second, from what height was it thrown? (c) If it was thrown upward with an initial speed of 10 feet per second, from what height was it thrown?

40. A rubber ball is thrown straight down from a height of 4 feet. If the ball rebounds with one-half of its impact speed and returns exactly to its original height before falling again, how fast was it thrown originally?

3.6 ······THE CHAIN RULE

Here we take up the differentiation of composite functions. Until we get to Theorem 3.6.7, our approach is completely intuitive—no real definitions, no proofs, just informal discussion. Our purpose is to give you some experience with the standard computational procedures and some insight into why these procedures work. Theorem 3.6.7 puts it all on a sound footing.

Suppose that y is a differentiable function of u:

$$y = f(u)$$

and u in turn is a differentiable function of x:

$$u = g(x).$$

Then y is a composite function of x:

$$y = f(u) = f(g(x)).$$

Does y have a derivative with respect to x? Yes it does, and it's given by a formula that's easy to remember:

(3.6.1)
$$\frac{dy}{dx} = \frac{dy}{du}\frac{du}{dx}.$$

This formula, known as the *chain rule*, says that "the rate of change of y with respect to x is the rate of change of y with respect to u times the rate of change of u with respect to x." (Plausible as all this sounds, remember that we have proved nothing. All we've done is asserted that the composition of differentiable functions is differentiable and given you a formula, a formula that needs justification and is justified at the end of this section.)

Before using the chain rule in elaborate computations, let's confirm its validity in some simple instances.

If
$$y = 2u \quad \text{and} \quad u = 3x,$$

then
$$y = 6x.$$

Clearly
$$\frac{dy}{dx} = 6, \qquad \frac{dy}{du} = 2, \qquad \frac{du}{dx} = 3$$

and so, in this case certainly, the chain rule is confirmed:
$$\frac{dy}{dx} = \frac{dy}{du}\frac{du}{dx}.$$

If
$$y = u^3 \quad \text{and} \quad u = x^2,$$

then
$$y = (x^2)^3 = x^6.$$

This time
$$\frac{dy}{dx} = 6x^5, \qquad \frac{dy}{du} = 3u^2 = 3x^4, \qquad \frac{du}{dx} = 2x$$

and once again
$$\frac{dy}{dx} = \frac{dy}{du}\frac{du}{dx}.$$

PROBLEM. Find dy/dx by the chain rule given that
$$y = \frac{u-1}{u+1} \quad \text{and} \quad u = x^2.$$

Solution

$$\frac{dy}{dx} = \frac{(u+1)1 - (u-1)1}{(u+1)^2} = \frac{2}{(u+1)^2} \quad \text{and} \quad \frac{du}{dx} = 2x$$

so that

$$\frac{dy}{dx} = \frac{dy}{du}\frac{du}{dx} = \left[\frac{2}{(u+1)^2}\right]2x = \frac{4x}{(x^2+1)^2}. \quad \Box$$

REMARK. We could have obtained the same result without the chain rule by first writing y as a function of x and then differentiating: with

$$y = \frac{u-1}{u+1} \quad \text{and} \quad u = x^2$$

we have

$$y = \frac{x^2 - 1}{x^2 + 1}$$

and therefore

$$\frac{dy}{dx} = \frac{(x^2+1)2x - (x^2-1)2x}{(x^2+1)^2} = \frac{4x}{(x^2+1)^2}. \quad \Box$$

If f is a differentiable function of u and u is a differentiable function of x, then, according to (3.6.1),

(3.6.2)
$$\frac{d}{dx}[f(u)] = \frac{d}{du}[f(u)]\frac{du}{dx}.$$

[All we've done here is written y as $f(u)$.] This is the formulation of the chain rule that we will use most frequently in later work.

Suppose now that we were asked to calculate

$$\frac{d}{dx}(x^2 - 1)^{100}.$$

We could expand $(x^2 - 1)^{100}$ into polynomial form by using the binomial theorem or, if we were masochistic, by repeated multiplication, but we would have a terrible mess on our hands and we'd probably get a wrong answer. With (3.6.2) we can derive a formula that will render such calculations almost trivial.

Assuming (3.6.2), we can prove that, if u is a differentiable function of x and n is an integer, then

(3.6.3)
$$\frac{d}{dx}[u^n] = nu^{n-1}\frac{du}{dx}.$$

Proof. Set $f(u) = u^n$. Then according to (3.6.2),

$$\frac{d}{dx}[u^n] = \frac{d}{du}[u^n]\frac{du}{dx}.$$

Since

$$\frac{d}{du}[u^n] = nu^{n-1},$$

we have

$$\frac{d}{dx}[u^n] = nu^{n-1}\frac{du}{dx}$$

as asserted.   □

   To calculate

$$\frac{d}{dx}(x^2 - 1)^{100}$$

we set $u = x^2 - 1$.   Then by our formula

$$\frac{d}{dx}(x^2 - 1)^{100} = 100(x^2 - 1)^{99}\frac{d}{dx}(x^2 - 1)$$

$$= 100(x^2 - 1)^{99}2x = 200x(x^2 - 1)^{99}.$$

Here are more examples of a similar sort.

EXAMPLE

$$\frac{d}{dx}\left(x + \frac{1}{x}\right)^{-3} = -3\left(x + \frac{1}{x}\right)^{-4}\frac{d}{dx}\left(x + \frac{1}{x}\right) = -3\left(x + \frac{1}{x}\right)^{-4}\left(1 - \frac{1}{x^2}\right). \quad □$$

EXAMPLE

$$\frac{d}{dx}[1 - (2 + 3x)^2]^3 = 3[1 - (2 + 3x)^2]^2\frac{d}{dx}[1 - (2 + 3x)^2].$$

Since

$$\frac{d}{dx}[1 - (2 + 3x)^2] = -2(2 + 3x)\frac{d}{dx}(3x) = -6(2 + 3x),$$

we have

$$\frac{d}{dx}[1 - (2 + 3x)^2]^3 = -18(2 + 3x)[1 - (2 + 3x)^2]^2. \quad □$$

EXAMPLE

$$\frac{d}{dx}[4x(x^2 + 3)^2] = 4x\frac{d}{dx}(x^2 + 3)^2 + (x^2 + 3)^2\frac{d}{dx}(4x)$$

$$= 4x[2(x^2 + 3)2x] + 4(x^2 + 3)^2$$

$$= 16x^2(x^2 + 3) + 4(x^2 + 3)^2 = 4(x^2 + 3)(5x^2 + 3). \quad □$$

The formula

$$\frac{dy}{dx} = \frac{dy}{du}\frac{du}{dx}$$

can easily be extended to more variables. For example, if x itself depends on s, then we have

(3.6.4)
$$\frac{dy}{ds} = \frac{dy}{du}\frac{du}{dx}\frac{dx}{ds}.$$

If, in addition, s depends on t, then

(3.6.5)
$$\frac{dy}{dt} = \frac{dy}{du}\frac{du}{dx}\frac{dx}{ds}\frac{ds}{dt}$$

and so on. Each new dependence adds a new link to the chain.

PROBLEM. Find dy/ds given that

$$y = 3u + 1, \qquad u = x^{-2}, \qquad x = 1 - s.$$

Solution

$$\frac{dy}{du} = 3, \qquad \frac{du}{dx} = -2x^{-3}, \qquad \frac{dx}{ds} = -1.$$

Therefore

$$\frac{dy}{ds} = \frac{dy}{du}\frac{du}{dx}\frac{dx}{ds} = (3)(-2x^{-3})(-1) = 6x^{-3}. \quad \square$$

PROBLEM. Find dy/dt at $t = 9$ given that

$$y = \frac{u + 2}{u - 1}, \qquad u = (3s - 7)^2, \qquad s = \sqrt{t}.$$

Solution. As you can check,

$$\frac{dy}{du} = -\frac{3}{(u-1)^2}, \qquad \frac{du}{ds} = 6(3s - 7), \qquad \frac{ds}{dt} = \frac{1}{2\sqrt{t}}.\dagger$$

At $t = 9$, we have $s = 3$ and $u = 4$ so that

$$\frac{dy}{du} = -\frac{3}{(4-1)^2} = -\frac{1}{3}, \qquad \frac{du}{ds} = 6(9 - 7) = 12, \qquad \frac{ds}{dt} = \frac{1}{2\sqrt{9}} = \frac{1}{6}.$$

$\dagger$ It was shown in Section 3.1 that

$$\frac{d}{dx}(\sqrt{x}) = \frac{1}{2\sqrt{x}}.$$

Thus, at $t = 9$,

$$\frac{dy}{dt} = \frac{dy}{du}\frac{du}{ds}\frac{ds}{dt} = \left(-\frac{1}{3}\right)(12)\left(\frac{1}{6}\right) = -\frac{2}{3}. \quad \square$$

So far we've worked entirely in Leibniz's notation. What does the chain rule look like in prime notation?

Let's go back to the beginning. Once again let y be a differentiable function of u:

$$y = f(u),$$

and let u be a differentiable function of x:

$$u = g(x).$$

Then

$$y = f(u) = f(g(x)) = (f \circ g)(x)$$

and, according to the chain rule (as yet unproved),

$$\frac{dy}{dx} = \frac{dy}{du}\frac{du}{dx}.$$

Since

$$\frac{dy}{dx} = \frac{d}{dx}[(f \circ g)(x)] = (f \circ g)'(x), \qquad \frac{dy}{du} = f'(u) = f'(g(x)), \qquad \frac{du}{dx} = g'(x),$$

the chain rule can be written

(3.6.6) $$\boxed{(f \circ g)'(x) = f'(g(x))\, g'(x).}$$

The chain rule in prime notation says that "the derivative of a composition $f \circ g$ at x is the derivative of f at $g(x)$ times the derivative of g at x."

In Leibniz's notation the chain rule *appears* seductively simple, to some even obvious. "After all, to prove it, all you have to do is cancel the du's":

$$\frac{dy}{dx} = \frac{dy}{d\!\!\!/u}\frac{d\!\!\!/u}{dx}.$$

Of course, this is just nonsense. What would one cancel from

$$(f \circ g)'(x) = f'(g(x))\, g'(x)?$$

Although Leibniz's notation is useful for routine calculations, mathematicians generally turn to the prime notation when precision is required.

It is time for us to be precise. How do we know that the composition of differentiable functions is differentiable? What assumptions do we need? Precisely under what circumstances is it true that

$$(f \circ g)'(x) = f'(g(x))\, g'(x).$$

The following theorem provides the definitive answer.

THEOREM 3.6.7   THE CHAIN RULE THEOREM

If g is differentiable at x and f is differentiable at $g(x)$, then the composition $f \circ g$ is differentiable at x and

$$(f \circ g)'(x) = f'(g(x))\, g'(x).$$

A proof of this theorem appears in the supplement to this section. The argument is not as easy as "canceling" the du's.

EXERCISES

Differentiate.

1. $f(x) = (1 - 2x)^{-1}$.

2. $f(x) = (1 + 2x)^5$.

3. $f(x) = (x^5 - x^{10})^{20}$.

4. $f(x) = \left(x^2 + \dfrac{1}{x^2}\right)^3$.

5. $f(x) = \left(x - \dfrac{1}{x}\right)^4$.

6. $f(x) = \left(x + \dfrac{1}{x}\right)^3$.

7. $f(x) = (x - x^3 - x^5)^4$.

8. $f(t) = \left(\dfrac{1}{1 + t}\right)^4$.

9. $f(t) = (t^2 - 1)^{100}$.

10. $f(t) = (t - t^2)^3$.

11. $f(t) = (t^{-1} + t^{-2})^4$.

12. $f(x) = \left(\dfrac{4x + 3}{5x - 2}\right)^3$.

13. $f(x) = \left(\dfrac{3x}{x^2 + 1}\right)^4$.

14. $f(x) = [(2x + 1)^2 + (x + 1)^2]^3$.

15. $f(x) = (x^4 + x^2 + x)^2$.

16. $f(x) = (x^2 + 2x + 1)^3$.

17. $f(x) = \left(\dfrac{x^3}{3} + \dfrac{x^2}{2} + \dfrac{x}{1}\right)^{-1}$.

18. $f(x) = \left(\dfrac{x^2 + 2}{x^2 + 1}\right)^5$.

19. $f(x) = \left(\dfrac{1}{x + 2} - \dfrac{1}{x - 2}\right)^3$.

20. $f(x) = [(6x + x^5)^{-1} + x]^2$.

Find dy/dx at $x = 0$.

21. $y = \dfrac{1}{1 + u^2}$, $\quad u = 2x + 1$.

22. $y = u + \dfrac{1}{u}$, $\quad u = (3x + 1)^4$.

23. $y = \dfrac{2u}{1 - 4u}$, $\quad u = (5x^2 + 1)^4$.

24. $y = u^3 - u + 1$, $\quad u = \dfrac{1 - x}{1 + x}$.

Find dy/dt.

25. $y = \dfrac{1 - 7u}{1 + u^2}$, $\quad u = 1 + x^2$, $\quad x = 2t - 5$.

26. $y = 1 + u^2$, $\quad u = \dfrac{1 - 7x}{1 + x^2}$, $\quad x = 5t + 2$.

Find dy/dx at $x = 2$.

27. $y = (s + 3)^2$, $\quad s = \sqrt{t - 3}$, $\quad t = x^2$.

28. $y = \dfrac{1 + s}{1 - s}$, $\quad s = t - \dfrac{1}{t}$, $\quad t = \sqrt{x}$.

Given that

$$f(0) = 1, \quad f'(0) = 2, \quad f(1) = 0, \quad f'(1) = 1, \quad f(2) = 1, \quad f'(2) = 1,$$
$$g(0) = 2, \quad g'(0) = 1, \quad g(1) = 1, \quad g'(1) = 0, \quad g(2) = 2, \quad g'(2) = 1,$$
$$h(0) = 1, \quad h'(0) = 2, \quad h(1) = 2, \quad h'(1) = 1, \quad h(2) = 0, \quad h'(2) = 2,$$

evaluate the following.

29. $(f \circ g)'(0)$.   **30.** $(f \circ g)'(1)$.   **31.** $(f \circ g)'(2)$.   **32.** $(g \circ f)'(0)$.

33. $(g \circ f)'(1)$.   **34.** $(g \circ f)'(2)$.   **35.** $(f \circ h)'(0)$.   **36.** $(h \circ f)'(1)$.

37. $(h \circ f)'(0)$.   **38.** $(f \circ h \circ g)'(1)$.   **39.** $(g \circ f \circ h)'(2)$.   **40.** $(g \circ h \circ f)'(0)$.

Find the following derivatives.

41. $\dfrac{d}{dx}[f(x^2 + 1)]$.

42. $\dfrac{d}{dx}\left[f\left(\dfrac{x-1}{x+1}\right) \right]$.

43. $\dfrac{d}{dx}[[f(x)]^2 + 1]$.

44. $\dfrac{d}{dx}\left[\dfrac{f(x) - 1}{f(x) + 1} \right]$.

Determine the values of x for which

(a) $f'(x) = 0$.   (b) $f'(x) > 0$.   (c) $f'(x) < 0$.

45. $f(x) = (1 + x^2)^{-2}$.

46. $f(x) = (1 - x^2)^2$.

47. $f(x) = x(1 + x^2)^{-1}$.

48. $f(x) = x(1 - x^2)^3$.

An object moves along a coordinate line, its position at each time $t \geq 0$ given by $x(t)$. Determine when the object changes direction.

49. $x(t) = (t + 1)^2(t - 9)^3$.

50. $x(t) = t(t - 8)^3$.

51. $x(t) = (t^3 - 12t)^4$.

52. $x(t) = (t^2 - 8t + 15)^3$.

53. Show that if $(x - a)^2$ is a factor of the polynomial $p(x)$, then $x - a$ is a factor of $p'(x)$.

54. Let f be a differentiable function. Show that
(a) if f is even, then f' is odd.   (b) if f is odd, then f' is even.

Differentiate.

55. $f(x) = [(7x - x^{-1})^{-2} + 3x^2]^{-1}$.

56. $f(x) = [(x^2 - x^{-2})^3 - x]^5$.

57. $f(x) = [(x + x^{-1})^2 - (x^2 + x^{-2})^{-1}]^3$.

58. $f(x) = [(x^{-1} + 2x^{-2})^3 + 3x^{-3}]^4$.

Supplement to Section 3.6

To prove Theorem 3.6.7 it is convenient to use a slightly different formulation of derivative.

THEOREM 3.6.8

The function f is differentiable at x iff

$$\lim_{t \to x} \frac{f(t) - f(x)}{t - x} \quad \text{exists.}$$

If this limit exists, it is $f'(x)$.

Proof. For each t in the domain of f, $t \ne x$, define

$$G(t) = \frac{f(t) - f(x)}{t - x}.$$

The theorem follows from observing that f is differentiable at x iff

$$\lim_{h \to 0} G(x + h) \quad \text{exists,}$$

and noting that

$$\lim_{h \to 0} G(x + h) = l \quad \text{iff} \quad \lim_{t \to x} G(t) = l.† \quad \square$$

Proof of Theorem 3.6.7. By Theorem 3.6.8 it is enough to show that

$$\lim_{t \to x} \frac{f(g(t)) - f(g(x))}{t - x} = f'(g(x))\, g'(x).$$

We begin by defining an auxiliary function F on the domain of f by setting

$$F(y) = \begin{cases} \dfrac{f(y) - f(g(x))}{y - g(x)}, & y \ne g(x) \\[2mm] f'(g(x)), & y = g(x) \end{cases}.$$

F is continuous at $g(x)$ since

$$\lim_{y \to g(x)} F(y) = \lim_{y \to g(x)} \frac{f(y) - f(g(x))}{y - g(x)},$$

and the right-hand side is, by Theorem 3.6.8, $f'(g(x))$, which is the value of F at $g(x)$. For $t \ne x$,

(1) $$\frac{f(g(t)) - f(g(x))}{t - x} = F(g(t)) \left[\frac{g(t) - g(x)}{t - x} \right].$$

To see this we note that, if $g(t) = g(x)$, then both sides are 0. If $g(t) \ne g(x)$, then

$$F(g(t)) = \frac{f(g(t)) - f(g(x))}{g(t) - g(x)},$$

so that again we have equality.

Since g, being differentiable at x, is continuous at x and since F is continuous at $g(x)$, we know that the composition $F \circ g$ is continuous at x. Thus

$$\lim_{t \to x} F(g(t)) = F(g(x)) = f'(g(x)).$$

↑—— by our definition of F

This, together with Equation (1), gives

$$\lim_{t \to x} \frac{f(g(t)) - f(g(x))}{t - x} = f'(g(x))\, g'(x). \quad \square$$

_____

† (2.2.5).

3.7 ······DIFFERENTIATING THE TRIGONOMETRIC FUNCTIONS

The calculus of the trigonometric functions is simplified by the use of radian measure. Throughout our work we will use radian measure and refer to degrees only in passing. An outline review of trigonometry—identities and graphs—appears in Section 1.2.

The derivative of the sine function is the cosine function:

(3.7.1)
$$\frac{d}{dx}(\sin x) = \cos x.$$

Proof. For $h \neq 0$,

$$\frac{\sin (x + h) - \sin x}{h} = \frac{[\sin x \cos h + \cos x \sin h] - [\sin x]}{h}$$

$$= \sin x \frac{\cos h - 1}{h} + \cos x \frac{\sin h}{h}.$$

As shown earlier

$$\lim_{h \to 0} \frac{\cos h - 1}{h} = 0 \quad \text{and} \quad \lim_{h \to 0} \frac{\sin h}{h} = 1. \qquad (2.5.3)$$

Since $\sin x$ and $\cos x$ remain constant as h approaches zero,

$$\lim_{h \to 0} \frac{\sin (x + h) - \sin x}{h} = \sin x \left(\lim_{h \to 0} \frac{\cos h - 1}{h} \right) + \cos x \left(\lim_{h \to 0} \frac{\sin h}{h} \right)$$

$$= (\sin x)(0) + (\cos x)(1) = \cos x. \quad \square$$

The derivative of the cosine function is the negative of the sine function:

(3.7.2)
$$\frac{d}{dx}(\cos x) = -\sin x.$$

Proof

$$\cos (x + h) = \cos x \cos h - \sin x \sin h.$$

Therefore

$$\lim_{h \to 0} \frac{\cos (x + h) - \cos x}{h} = \lim_{h \to 0} \frac{[\cos x \cos h - \sin x \sin h] - [\cos x]}{h}$$

$$= \cos x \left(\lim_{h \to 0} \frac{\cos h - 1}{h} \right) - \sin x \left(\lim_{h \to 0} \frac{\sin h}{h} \right)$$

$$= -\sin x. \quad \square$$

EXAMPLE. To differentiate

$$f(x) = \cos x \sin x$$

we use the product rule:

$$f'(x) = \cos x \frac{d}{dx}(\sin x) + \sin x \frac{d}{dx}(\cos x)$$

$$= \cos x (\cos x) + \sin x (-\sin x)$$

$$= \cos^2 x - \sin^2 x. \quad \square$$

We come now to the tangent function. Since

$$\tan x = \frac{\sin x}{\cos x},$$

we have

$$\frac{d}{dx}(\tan x) = \frac{\cos x \dfrac{d}{dx}(\sin x) - \sin x \dfrac{d}{dx}(\cos x)}{\cos^2 x}$$

$$= \frac{\cos^2 x + \sin^2 x}{\cos^2 x} = \frac{1}{\cos^2 x} = \sec^2 x.$$

The derivative of the tangent function is the secant squared:

(3.7.3)
$$\frac{d}{dx}(\tan x) = \sec^2 x.$$

The derivatives of the other trigonometric functions are as follows:

(3.7.4)
$$\frac{d}{dx}(\cot x) = -\csc^2 x,$$

$$\frac{d}{dx}(\sec x) = \sec x \tan x,$$

$$\frac{d}{dx}(\csc x) = -\csc x \cot x.$$

The verification of these formulas is left as an exercise.
It is time for some sample problems.

PROBLEM. Find $f'(\pi/4)$ for

$$f(x) = x \cot x.$$

Solution. We first find $f'(x)$ by the product rule:

$$f'(x) = x \frac{d}{dx}(\cot x) + \cot x \frac{d}{dx}(x)$$

$$= -x \csc^2 x + \cot x.$$

Now we evaluate f' at $\pi/4$:

$$f'(\pi/4) = -\frac{\pi}{4} (\sqrt{2})^2 + 1 = 1 - \frac{\pi}{2}. \quad \square$$

PROBLEM. Find

$$\frac{d}{dx} \left[\frac{\sec x}{\tan x} \right].$$

Solution. We can differentiate directly by the quotient rule:

$$\frac{d}{dx} \left[\frac{\sec x}{\tan x} \right] = \frac{\tan x \dfrac{d}{dx} (\sec x) - \sec x \dfrac{\cdot d}{dx} (\tan x)}{\tan^2 x}$$

$$= \frac{\tan x (\sec x \tan x) - \sec x (\sec^2 x)}{\tan^2 x}$$

$$= \frac{\sec x [\tan^2 x - \sec^2 x]}{\tan^2 x}$$

$$= -\frac{\sec x}{\tan^2 x}$$

or, we can note that

$$\frac{\sec x}{\tan x} = \frac{\dfrac{1}{\cos x}}{\dfrac{\sin x}{\cos x}} = \frac{1}{\sin x} = \csc x$$

and then differentiate:

$$\frac{d}{dx} \left[\frac{\sec x}{\tan x} \right] = \frac{d}{dx} (\csc x) = -\csc x \cot x.$$

The answers appear different, but, as you can check, they are equal. $\quad \square$

PROBLEM. Find an equation for the tangent to the curve $y = \cos x$ at the point where $x = \pi/3$.

Solution. Since $\cos \pi/3 = \frac{1}{2}$, the point of tangency is $(\pi/3, \frac{1}{2})$. To find the slope of the tangent, we evaluate the derivative

$$\frac{dy}{dx} = -\sin x$$

at $x = \pi/3$. This gives $m = -\sqrt{3}/2$. The equation for the tangent can be written

$$y - \frac{1}{2} = -\frac{\sqrt{3}}{2} \left(x - \frac{\pi}{3} \right). \quad \square$$

PROBLEM. An object moves along the *x*-axis, its position at each time *t* given by the function

$$x(t) = t + 2 \sin t.$$

Determine those times *t* from 0 to 2π when the object is moving to the left.

Solution. The object is moving to the left only when $v(t) < 0$. Since

$$v(t) = x'(t) = 1 + 2 \cos t,$$

the object is moving to the left only when $\cos t < -\frac{1}{2}$. As you can check, the only *t* in $[0, 2\pi]$ for which $\cos t < -\frac{1}{2}$ are those *t* that lie between $2\pi/3$ and $4\pi/3$. Thus from time $t = 0$ to $t = 2\pi$, the object is moving left only during the time interval $(2\pi/3, 4\pi/3)$. □

The Chain Rule and the Trigonometric Functions

If *f* is a differentiable function of *u* and *u* is a differentiable function of *x*, then, as you saw in Section 3.6,

$$\frac{d}{dx}[f(u)] = \frac{d}{du}[f(u)]\frac{du}{dx}.$$

Written in this form, the derivatives of the six trigonometric functions appear as follows:

(3.7.5)

$$\frac{d}{dx}(\sin u) = \cos u \frac{du}{dx}. \qquad \frac{d}{dx}(\cos u) = -\sin u \frac{du}{dx}.$$

$$\frac{d}{dx}(\tan u) = \sec^2 u \frac{du}{dx}. \qquad \frac{d}{dx}(\cot u) = -\csc^2 u \frac{du}{dx}.$$

$$\frac{d}{dx}(\sec u) = \sec u \tan u \frac{du}{dx}. \qquad \frac{d}{dx}(\csc u) = -\csc u \cot u \frac{du}{dx}.$$

EXAMPLE

$$\frac{d}{dx}(\cos 2x) = -\sin 2x \frac{d}{dx}(2x) = -2 \sin 2x. \quad \square$$

EXAMPLE

$$\frac{d}{dx}[\sec (x^2 + 1)] = \sec (x^2 + 1) \tan (x^2 + 1) \frac{d}{dx}(x^2 + 1)$$

$$= 2x \sec (x^2 + 1) \tan (x^2 + 1). \quad \square$$

EXAMPLE

$$\frac{d}{dx}(\sin^3 \pi x) = 3 \sin^2 \pi x \frac{d}{dx}(\sin \pi x)$$

$$= 3 \sin^2 \pi x \cos \pi x \frac{d}{dx}(\pi x)$$

$$= 3\pi \sin^2 \pi x \cos \pi x. \quad \Box$$

Our treatment of the trigonometric functions has been based entirely on radian measure. When degrees are used, the derivatives of the trigonometric functions contain the extra factor $\frac{1}{180}\pi \approx 0.0175$.

PROBLEM. Find

$$\frac{d}{dx}(\sin x°).$$

Solution. Since $x° = \frac{1}{180}\pi x$ radians,

$$\frac{d}{dx}(\sin x°) = \frac{d}{dx}(\sin \tfrac{1}{180}\pi x) = \tfrac{1}{180}\pi \cos \tfrac{1}{180}\pi x = \tfrac{1}{180}\pi \cos x°. \quad \Box$$

The extra factor $\frac{1}{180}\pi$ is a disadvantage, particularly in problems where it occurs repeatedly. This tends to discourage the use of degree measure in theoretical work.

EXERCISES

Differentiate.

1. $y = 3 \cos x - 4 \sec x$.
2. $y = x^2 \sec x$.
3. $y = x^3 \csc x$.
4. $y = \sin^2 x$.
5. $y = \cos^2 t$.
6. $y = 3t^2 \tan t$.
7. $y = \sin^4 \sqrt{u}$.
8. $y = u \csc u^2$.
9. $y = \tan x^2$.
10. $y = \cos \sqrt{x}$.
11. $y = [x + \cot \pi x]^4$.
12. $y = [x^2 - \sec 2x]^3$.

Find the second derivative.

13. $y = \sin x$.
14. $y = \cos x$.
15. $y = \dfrac{\cos x}{1 + \sin x}$.
16. $y = \tan^3 2\pi x$.
17. $y = \cos^3 2u$.
18. $y = \sin^5 3t$.
19. $y = \tan 2t$.
20. $y = \cot 4u$.
21. $y = x^2 \sin 3x$.
22. $y = \dfrac{\sin x}{1 - \cos x}$.
23. $y = \sin^2 x + \cos^2 x$.
24. $y = \sec^2 x - \tan^2 x$.

Find the indicated derivative.

25. $\dfrac{d^4}{dx^4}(\sin x)$.
26. $\dfrac{d^4}{dx^4}(\cos x)$.
27. $\dfrac{d}{dt}\left[t^2 \dfrac{d^2}{dt^2}(t \cos 3t)\right]$.
28. $\dfrac{d}{dt}\left[t \dfrac{d}{dt}(\cos t^2)\right]$.
29. $\dfrac{d}{dx}[f(\sin 3x)]$.
30. $\dfrac{d}{dx}[\sin(f(3x))]$.

Find an equation for the tangent to the curve at $x = a$.

31. $y = \sin x$; $a = 0$.
32. $y = \tan x$; $a = \pi/6$.
33. $y = \cot x$; $a = \pi/6$.
34. $y = \cos x$; $a = 0$.
35. $y = \sec x$; $a = \pi/4$.
36. $y = \csc x$; $a = \pi/3$.

Determine the numbers x between 0 and 2π where the tangent to the curve is horizontal.

37. $y = \cos x$.
38. $y = \sin x$.
39. $y = \sin x + \sqrt{3} \cos x$.
40. $y = \cos x - \sqrt{3} \sin x$.
41. $y = \sin^2 x$.
42. $y = \cos^2 x$.
43. $y = \tan x - 2x$.
44. $y = 3 \cot x + 4x$.
45. $y = 2 \sec x + \tan x$.
46. $y = \cot x - 2 \csc x$.
47. $y = \dfrac{\csc x}{1 + \cot x}$.
48. $y = \dfrac{\sec x}{\tan x - 1}$.

An object moves along the x-axis, its position at each time t given by $x(t)$. Determine those times from $t = 0$ to $t = 2\pi$ when the object is moving to the right with increasing speed.

49. $x(t) = \sin 3t$.
50. $x(t) = \cos 2t$.
51. $x(t) = \sin t - \cos t$.
52. $x(t) = \sin t + \cos t$.
53. $x(t) = t + 2 \cos t$.
54. $x(t) = t - \sqrt{2} \sin t$.

Find dy/dt (a) by using (3.6.4) and (b) by writing y as a function of t and then differentiating.

55. $y = u^2 - 1$, $u = \sec x$, $x = \pi t$.
56. $y = \left(\dfrac{1 + u}{2}\right)^3$, $u = \cos x$, $x = 2t$.

57. $y = \left(\dfrac{1 - u}{2}\right)^4$, $u = \cos x$, $x = 2t$.
58. $y = 1 - u^2$, $u = \csc x$, $x = 3t$.

59. It can be shown by induction that the nth derivative of the sine function is given by the formula

$$\frac{d^n}{dx^n} (\sin x) = \left\{ \begin{matrix} (-1)^{(n-1)/2} \cos x, & n \text{ odd} \\ (-1)^{n/2} \sin x, & n \text{ even} \end{matrix} \right].$$

Persuade yourself that this formula is correct and obtain a similar formula for the nth derivative of the cosine function.

60. Show that $\dfrac{d}{dx} (\cot x) = -\csc^2 x$.
61. Show that $\dfrac{d}{dx} (\sec x) = \sec x \tan x$.

62. Show that $\dfrac{d}{dx} (\csc x) = -\csc x \cot x$.

3.8 ····· DIFFERENTIATING INVERSES; FRACTIONAL EXPONENTS
Differentiating Inverses

If f is a one-to-one function, then f has an inverse f^{-1}. This you already know. Suppose now that f is differentiable. Is f^{-1} necessarily differentiable? Yes, if f' does not take on the value 0. You'll find a proof of this in Appendix B.3. Right now we assume this result and go on to describe how to calculate the derivative of f^{-1}.

To simplify notation we set $f^{-1} = g$. Then

$$f(g(x)) = x \quad \text{for all } x \text{ in the range of } f.$$

Differentiation gives

$$\frac{d}{dx}[f(g(x))] = 1,$$

$$f'(g(x))\,g'(x) = 1, \qquad \text{(we are assuming that } f \text{ and } g \text{ are differentiable)}$$

$$g'(x) = \frac{1}{f'(g(x))}. \qquad \text{(we are assuming that } f' \text{ is never 0)}$$

Substituting f^{-1} back in for g, we have

(3.8.1)
$$(f^{-1})'(x) = \frac{1}{f'(f^{-1}(x))}.$$

This is the standard formula for the derivative of an inverse.

   In Leibniz's notation formula (3.8.1) reads simply

(3.8.2)
$$\frac{dx}{dy} = \frac{1}{dy/dx}.$$

The rate of change of x with respect to y is the reciprocal of the rate of change of y with respect to x.

   For some geometric reassurance of the validity of Formula 3.8.1 we refer you to Figure 3.8.1. The graphs of f and f^{-1} are reflections of one another in the line $y = x$. The tangent lines l_1 and l_2 are also reflections of one another. From the figure

$$(f^{-1})'(x) = \text{slope of } l_1 = \frac{f^{-1}(x) - b}{x - b}, \qquad f'(f^{-1}(x)) = \text{slope of } l_2 = \frac{x - b}{f^{-1}(x) - b};$$

namely, $(f^{-1})'(x)$ and $f'(f^{-1}(x))$ are indeed reciprocals.

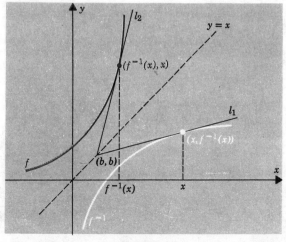

FIGURE 3.8.1

nth Roots

For $x > 0$, x^n is one-to-one and its derivative, nx^{n-1}, does not take on the value 0. The inverse $x^{1/n}$ is therefore differentiable and we can use the method just described to find its derivative.

$$(x^{1/n})^n = x,$$

$$\frac{d}{dx}[(x^{1/n})]^n = 1,$$

$$n(x^{1/n})^{n-1}\frac{d}{dx}[x^{1/n}] = 1,$$

$$\frac{d}{dx}[x^{1/n}] = \frac{1}{n}(x^{1/n})^{1-n}.$$

Since $(x^{1/n})^{1-n} = x^{(1/n)-1}$, we have the differentiation formula

(3.8.3)
$$\boxed{\frac{d}{dx}[x^{1/n}] = \frac{1}{n}x^{(1/n)-1}.}$$

We derived this formula for $x > 0$. If n is odd, then x^n is one-to-one everywhere and the formula also holds for $x < 0$. Same argument.

For suitable values of x,

$$\frac{d}{dx}(x^{1/2}) = \frac{1}{2}x^{-1/2}, \qquad \frac{d}{dx}(x^{1/3}) = \frac{1}{3}x^{-2/3}, \qquad \frac{d}{dx}(x^{1/4}) = \frac{1}{4}x^{-3/4}, \qquad \text{etc.}$$

Rational Powers

We come now to rational exponents p/q. We take q as positive and absorb the sign in p. You can see then that

$$\frac{d}{dx}[x^{p/q}] = \frac{d}{dx}[(x^{1/q})^p] = p(x^{1/q})^{p-1}\frac{d}{dx}[x^{1/q}] = p(x^{1/q})^{p-1}\frac{1}{q}x^{(1/q)-1} = \frac{p}{q}x^{(p/q)-1}.$$

power formula (3.6.2) ———   ———— root formula (3.8.3)

In short

(3.8.4)
$$\boxed{\frac{d}{dx}[x^{p/q}] = \frac{p}{q}x^{(p/q)-1}.}$$

Here are some simple examples:

$$\frac{d}{dx}(x^{2/3}) = \frac{2}{3}x^{-1/3}, \qquad \frac{d}{dx}(x^{5/2}) = \frac{5}{2}x^{3/2}, \qquad \frac{d}{dx}(x^{-7/9}) = -\frac{7}{9}x^{-16/9}. \quad \square$$

If u is a differentiable function of x, then, by the chain rule,

(3.8.5)
$$\frac{d}{dx} u^{p/q} = \frac{p}{q} u^{(p/q)-1} \frac{du}{dx}.$$

The verification of this is left to you.

The question of the applicability of (3.8.5) remains. If q is odd, then (3.8.5) is valid for all $u \neq 0$. If q is even, then (3.8.5) holds only for $u > 0$.

It's time for some examples.

EXAMPLE

$$\frac{d}{dx}[(x^2 + 1)^{1/5}] = \frac{1}{5}(x^2 + 1)^{-4/5} \cdot 2x = \frac{2}{5}x(x^2 + 1)^{-4/5}. \quad \square$$

EXAMPLE

$$\frac{d}{dx}[\sqrt[3]{3x^2 + 7}] = \frac{d}{dx}[(3x^2 + 7)^{1/3}] = \frac{1}{3}(3x^2 + 7)^{-2/3} \cdot 6x = \frac{2x}{(\sqrt[3]{3x^2 + 7})^2}. \quad \square$$

EXAMPLE

$$\frac{d}{dx}\left[\sqrt{\frac{x^2}{1 + x^2}}\right] = \frac{d}{dx}\left[\left(\frac{x^2}{1 + x^2}\right)^{1/2}\right]$$

$$= \frac{1}{2}\left(\frac{x^2}{1 + x^2}\right)^{-1/2} \frac{d}{dx}\left(\frac{x^2}{1 + x^2}\right)$$

$$= \frac{1}{2}\left(\frac{x^2}{1 + x^2}\right)^{-1/2} \frac{(1 + x^2)2x - x^2(2x)}{(1 + x^2)^2}$$

$$= \frac{1}{2}\left(\frac{1 + x^2}{x^2}\right)^{1/2} \frac{2x}{(1 + x^2)^2} = \frac{x}{(1 + x^2)^2}\sqrt{\frac{1 + x^2}{x^2}}. \quad \square$$

EXERCISES

Find dy/dx.

1. $y = (x^3 + 1)^{1/2}$.

2. $y = (x + 1)^{1/3}$.

3. $y = x\sqrt{x^2 + 1}$.

4. $y = x^2\sqrt{x^2 + 1}$.

5. $y = \sqrt[4]{2x^2 + 1}$.

6. $y = (x + 1)^{1/3}(x + 2)^{2/3}$.

7. $y = \sqrt{2 - x^2}\sqrt{3 - x^2}$.

8. $y = \sqrt{(x^4 - x + 1)^3}$.

Compute.

9. $\dfrac{d}{dx}\left(\sqrt{x} + \dfrac{1}{\sqrt{x}}\right).$

10. $\dfrac{d}{dx}\left(\sqrt{\dfrac{3x+1}{2x+5}}\right).$

11. $\dfrac{d}{dx}\left(\dfrac{x}{\sqrt{x^2+1}}\right).$

12. $\dfrac{d}{dx}\left(\dfrac{\sqrt{x^2+1}}{x}\right).$

13. $\dfrac{d}{dx}\left(\sqrt[3]{x} + \dfrac{1}{\sqrt[3]{x}}\right).$

14. $\dfrac{d}{dx}\left(\sqrt{\dfrac{ax+b}{cx+d}}\right).$

15. (*Important*) Show the general form of the graph.
   (a) $f(x) = x^{1/n}$, n a positive even integer.
   (b) $f(x) = x^{1/n}$, n a positive odd integer.
   (c) $f(x) = x^{2/n}$, n an odd integer greater than 1.

Find the second derivative.

16. $y = \sqrt{a^2 + x^2}.$

17. $y = \sqrt[3]{a + bx}.$

18. $y = x\sqrt{a^2 - x^2}.$

19. $y = \sqrt{a^2 - x^2}.$

20. $y = \sqrt{x}\tan\sqrt{x}.$

21. $y = \sqrt{x}\sin\sqrt{x}.$

22. Our geometric argument for the validity of Formula (3.8.1) collapses if the tangent marked l_1 in Figure 3.8.1 does not intersect the line $y = x$. Fill in this loophole.

Compute.

23. $\dfrac{d}{dx}[f(\sqrt{x} + 1)].$

24. $\dfrac{d}{dx}[\sqrt{[f(x)]^2 + 1}].$

25. $\dfrac{d}{dx}[\sqrt{f(x^2 + 1)}].$

26. $\dfrac{d}{dx}[f(\sqrt{x^2 + 1})].$

Find a formula for $(f^{-1})'(x)$ given that f is one-to-one and its derivative satisfies the indicated equation.

27. $f'(x) = f(x).$

28. $f'(x) = 1 + [f(x)]^2.$

29. $f'(x) = \sqrt{1 - [f(x)]^2}.$

In economics the *elasticity* of demand is given by the formula

$$\epsilon = \frac{P}{Q}\left|\frac{dQ}{dP}\right|$$

where P is price and Q quantity. The demand is said to be

$$\begin{cases} \text{inelastic} & \text{where } \epsilon < 1 \\ \text{unitary} & \text{where } \epsilon = 1 \\ \text{elastic} & \text{where } \epsilon > 1 \end{cases}.$$

Describe the elasticity of each of the following demand curves. Keep in mind that Q and P must remain positive.

30. $Q = \dfrac{1}{P^2}.$

31. $Q = \dfrac{1}{P}.$

32. $Q = \dfrac{1}{\sqrt{P}}.$

33. $Q = 200 - \frac{1}{5}P.$

34. $Q = 200 - 5P.$

35. $Q = \sqrt{300 - P}.$

3.9 ······ADDITIONAL PRACTICE IN DIFFERENTIATION

Differentiate.

1. $y = x^{2/3} - a^{2/3}.$

2. $y = 2x^{3/4} + 4x^{-1/4}.$

3. $y = \dfrac{a + bx + cx^2}{x}.$

4. $y = \dfrac{\sqrt{x}}{2} - \dfrac{2}{\sqrt{x}}.$

5. $y = \sqrt{ax} + \dfrac{a}{\sqrt{ax}}.$

6. $s = \dfrac{a + bt + ct^2}{\sqrt{t}}.$

7. $r = \sqrt{1 - 2\theta}.$

8. $f(t) = (2 - 3t^2)^3.$

9. $f(x) = \dfrac{1}{\sqrt{a^2 - x^2}}.$

10. $y = \left(a - \dfrac{b}{x}\right)^2.$

11. $y = \left(a + \dfrac{b}{x^2}\right)^3.$

12. $y = x\sqrt{a + bx}.$

13. $s = t\sqrt{a^2 + t^2}.$

14. $y = \dfrac{a - x}{a + x}.$

15. $y = \dfrac{a^2 + x^2}{a^2 - x^2}.$

16. $y = \dfrac{\sqrt{a^2 + x^2}}{x}.$

17. $y = \dfrac{2 - x}{1 + 2x^2}.$

18. $y = \dfrac{x}{\sqrt{a^2 - x^2}}.$

19. $y = \dfrac{x}{\sqrt{a - bx}}.$

20. $r = \theta^2\sqrt{3 - 4\theta}.$

21. $y = \sqrt{\dfrac{1 - cx}{1 + cx}}.$

22. $f(x) = x\sqrt[3]{2 + 3x}.$

23. $y = \sqrt{\dfrac{a^2 + x^2}{a^2 - x^2}}.$

24. $s = \sqrt[3]{\dfrac{2 + 3t}{2 - 3t}}.$

25. $r = \dfrac{\sqrt[3]{a + b\theta}}{\theta}.$

26. $s = \sqrt{2t - \dfrac{1}{t^2}}.$

27. $y = \dfrac{b}{a}\sqrt{a^2 - x^2}.$

28. $y = (a^{3/5} - x^{3/5})^{5/3}.$

29. $y = (a^{2/3} - x^{2/3})^{3/2}.$

30. $y = (x + 2)^2\sqrt{x^2 + 2}.$

31. $y = \sec x^2.$

32. $y = \tan \sqrt{x}.$

33. $y = \cot^3 2x.$

34. $y = \csc^4 (3 - 2x).$

35. $y = \sin (\cos x).$

36. $y = \cos (\sin x).$

Evaluate dy/dx at the given value of x.

37. $y = (x^2 - x)^3, \quad x = 3.$

38. $y = (4 - x^2)^3, \quad x = 3.$

39. $y = \sqrt[3]{x} + \sqrt{x}, \quad x = 64.$

40. $y = x\sqrt{3 + 2x}, \quad x = 3.$

41. $y = (2x)^{1/3} + (2x)^{2/3}, \quad x = 4.$

42. $y = \sqrt{9 + 4x^2}, \quad x = 2.$

43. $y = \dfrac{1}{\sqrt{25 - x^2}}, \quad x = 3.$

44. $y = \dfrac{x^2 + 2}{2 - x}, \quad x = 2.$

45. $y = \dfrac{\sqrt{16 + 3x}}{x}, \quad x = 3.$

46. $y = \dfrac{\sqrt{5 - 2x}}{2x + 1}, \quad x = \frac{1}{2}.$

47. $y = x\sqrt{8 - x^2}, \quad x = 2.$

48. $y = \sqrt{\dfrac{4x + 1}{5x - 1}}, \quad x = 2.$

49. $y = x^2\sqrt{1 + x^3}, \quad x = 2.$

50. $y = \sqrt{\dfrac{x^2 - 5}{10 - x^2}}, \quad x = 3.$

51. $y = \tan 2x; \quad x = \pi/6.$

52. $y = x^2 \sin^3 \pi x; \quad x = \frac{1}{6}.$

53. $y = \cos^3 4x; \quad x = \pi/12.$

54. $y = \cot 3x; \quad x = \pi/9.$

55. $y = x \csc \pi x; \quad x = \frac{1}{4}.$

56. $y = \sec^4 (x/4); \quad x = \pi.$

3.10····IMPLICIT DIFFERENTIATION

Suppose you know that y is a function of x that satisfies the equation

$$3x^3y - 4y - 2x + 1 = 0.$$

One way to find dy/dx is to solve first for y:

$$(3x^3y - 4)y - 2x + 1 = 0,$$
$$(3x^3 - 4)y = 2x - 1,$$
$$y = \frac{2x - 1}{3x^3 - 4},$$

and then differentiate:

$$\frac{dy}{dx} = \frac{(3x^3 - 4)2 - (2x - 1)(9x^2)}{(3x^3 - 4)^2}$$

$$= \frac{6x^3 - 8 - 18x^3 + 9x^2}{(3x^3 - 4)^2}$$

$$(1) \qquad\qquad = -\frac{12x^3 - 9x^2 + 8}{(3x^3 - 4)^2}.$$

It is also possible to find dy/dx without first solving the equation for y. The technique is called *implicit differentiation*.

Let's return to the equation

$$3x^3y - 4y - 2x + 1 = 0.$$

Differentiating both sides of this equation (remembering that y is a function of x), we have

$$\left(3x^3 \frac{dy}{dx} + 9x^2y \right) - 4\frac{dy}{dx} - 2 = 0,$$

by the product rule ——————

$$(3x^3 - 4)\frac{dy}{dx} = 2 - 9x^2y,$$

$$(2) \qquad\qquad \frac{dy}{dx} = \frac{2 - 9x^2y}{3x^3 - 4}.$$

The answer looks different from what we obtained before because this time y appears on the right-hand side. This is generally no disadvantage. To satisfy yourself that the two answers are really the same all you have to do is substitute

$$y = \frac{2x - 1}{3x^3 - 4}$$

in (2). This gives

$$\frac{dy}{dx} = \frac{2 - 9x^2\left(\dfrac{2x - 1}{3x^3 - 4} \right)}{3x^3 - 4} = \frac{6x^3 - 8 - 18x^3 + 9x^2}{(3x^3 - 4)^2} = -\frac{12x^3 - 9x^2 + 8}{(3x^3 - 4)^2}$$

which is the answer (1) we obtained before.

Implicit differentiation is particularly useful where it is inconvenient (or impossible) to first solve the given equation for y.

PROBLEM.   Find the slope of the curve

$$x^3 - 3xy^2 + y^3 = 1 \qquad \text{at } (2, -1).$$

Solution.   Differentiation gives

$$3x^2 - 3\left[x\left(2y \frac{dy}{dx}\right) + y^2 \right] + 3y^2 \frac{dy}{dx} = 0$$

(by the chain rule)

$$3x^2 - 6xy \frac{dy}{dx} - 3y^2 + 3y^2 \frac{dy}{dx} = 0.$$

At $x = 2$ and $y = -1$, the equation becomes

$$12 + 12 \frac{dy}{dx} - 3 + 3 \frac{dy}{dx} = 0$$

$$15 \frac{dy}{dx} = -9$$

$$\frac{dy}{dx} = -\frac{3}{5}.$$

The slope is $-\frac{3}{5}$.   □

We can also find higher derivatives by implicit differentiation.

PROBLEM.   Find d^2y/dx^2 given that

$$y^3 - x^2 = 4.$$

Solution.   Differentiation with respect to x gives

(1) $$3y^2 \frac{dy}{dx} - 2x = 0.$$

Differentiating again we have

(2) $$3y^2 \left(\frac{d^2y}{dx^2}\right) + 6y \left(\frac{dy}{dx}\right)^2 - 2 = 0.$$

From (1) we know that

$$\frac{dy}{dx} = \frac{2x}{3y^2}.$$

Substituting this in (2) we have

$$3y^2 \left(\frac{d^2y}{dx^2}\right) + 6y \left(\frac{2x}{3y^2}\right)^2 - 2 = 0$$

which, as you can check, gives

$$\frac{d^2y}{dx^2} = \frac{6y^3 - 8x^2}{9y^5}. \quad □$$

A Theoretical Aside.   If we differentiate

(1) $x^2 + y^2 = -1$

implicitly, we find that

$$2x + 2y \frac{dy}{dx} = 0$$

and therefore

$$\frac{dy}{dx} = -\frac{x}{y}.$$

However, the result is meaningless.   It is meaningless because there is no real-valued function y of x that satisfies Equation (1).   Implicit differentiation can be applied meaningfully to an equation in x and y only if there is a function y of x that satisfies the equation.   You can assume that such is the case for all the equations that appear in the exercises.

EXERCISES

Use implicit differentiation to obtain dy/dx in terms of x and y.

1. $x^2 + y^2 = 4$.   2. $x^3 + y^3 - 3xy = 0$.   3. $4x^2 + 9y^2 = 36$.
4. $\sqrt{x} + \sqrt{y} = 4$.   5. $x^4 + 4x^3y + y^4 = 1$.   6. $x^2 - x^2y + xy^2 + y^2 = 1$.
7. $(x - y)^2 - y = 0$.   8. $(y + 3x)^2 - 4x = 0$.   9. $\sin(x + y) = xy$.
10. $\tan xy = xy$.

Express d^2y/dx^2 in terms of x and y.

11. $y^2 + 2xy = 16$.   12. $x^2 - 2xy + 4y^2 = 3$.
13. $y^2 + xy - x^2 = 9$.   14. $x^2 - 3xy = 18$.

Find dy/dx and d^2y/dx^2 at the given point.

15. $x^2 - 4y^2 = 9$;   (5, 2).   16. $x^2 + 4xy + y^3 + 5 = 0$;   (2, -1).
17. $\cos(x + 2y) = 0$; $(\pi/6, \pi/6)$.   18. $x = \sin^2 y$; $(\frac{1}{2}, \pi/4)$.

Find equations for the tangent and normal at the indicated point.

19. $2x + 3y = 5$;   (-2, 3).   20. $9x^2 + 4y^2 = 72$;   (2, 3).
21. $x^2 + xy + 2y^2 = 28$;   (-2, -3).   22. $x^3 - axy + 3ay^2 = 3a^3$;   (a, a).

23. Show that all normals to the circle $x^2 + y^2 = r^2$ pass through the center of the circle.
24. Determine the x-intercept of the tangent to the parabola $y^2 = x$ at the point where $x = a$.

The angle between two curves is the angle between their tangents at the point of intersection. If the slopes are m_1 and m_2, then the angle of intersection α can be obtained from the formula

$$\tan \alpha = \left| \frac{m_1 - m_2}{1 + m_1 m_2} \right|.$$

25. At what angles do the parabolas $y^2 = 2px + p^2$ and $y^2 = p^2 - 2px$ intersect?
26. At what angle does the line $y = 2x$ intersect the curve $x^2 - xy + 2y^2 = 28$?

27. Show that the hyperbola $x^2 - y^2 = 5$ and the ellipse $4x^2 + 9y^2 = 72$ intersect at right angles.

28. Find the angles at which the circles $(x - 1)^2 + y^2 = 10$ and $x^2 + (y - 2)^2 = 5$ intersect.

29. Find equations for the tangents to the ellipse $4x^2 + y^2 = 72$ that are perpendicular to the line $2y + x + 3 = 0$.

30. Find equations for the normals to the hyperbola $4x^2 - y^2 = 36$ that are parallel to the line $2x + 5y - 4 = 0$.

3.11····RATES OF CHANGE PER UNIT TIME

Earlier you saw that velocity is the rate of change of position with respect to time t, and acceleration the rate of change of velocity. In this section we work with other quantities that vary with time. The fundamental point is this: *If Q is a quantity that varies with time, then the derivative dQ/dt gives the rate of change of that quantity per unit time.*

PROBLEM.   A spherical balloon is expanding. If the radius is increasing at the rate of 2 inches per minute, at what rate is the volume increasing when the radius is 5 inches?

Solution

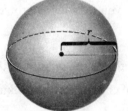

Find $\dfrac{dV}{dt}$ when $r = 5$ inches

given that $\dfrac{dr}{dt} = 2$ in./min.

$V = \frac{4}{3}\pi r^3$ (volume of a sphere of radius r)

Differentiating $V = \frac{4}{3}\pi r^3$ with respect to t, we have

$$\frac{dV}{dt} = 4\pi r^2 \frac{dr}{dt}.$$

Substituting $r = 5$ and $dr/dt = 2$, we find that

$$\frac{dV}{dt} = 4\pi(5)^2(2) = 200\pi.$$

When the radius is 5 inches, the volume is increasing at the rate of 200π cubic inches per minute. □

PROBLEM. A particle moves in circular orbit $x^2 + y^2 = 1$. As it passes through the point $(\frac{1}{2}, \frac{1}{2}\sqrt{3})$, its y-coordinate decreases at the rate of 3 units per second. At what rate is the x-coordinate changing?

Solution

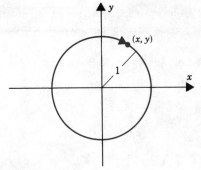

Find $\dfrac{dx}{dt}$ when $x = \tfrac{1}{2}$ and $y = \tfrac{1}{2}\sqrt{3}$

given that $\dfrac{dy}{dt} = -3$ units/sec.

$x^2 + y^2 = 1$

Differentiating $x^2 + y^2 = 1$ with respect to t, we have

$$2x \frac{dx}{dt} + 2y \frac{dy}{dt} = 0 \quad \text{and thus} \quad x \frac{dx}{dt} + y \frac{dy}{dt} = 0.$$

Substitution of $x = \tfrac{1}{2}$, $y = \tfrac{1}{2}\sqrt{3}$, and $dy/dt = -3$ gives

$$\frac{1}{2} \frac{dx}{dt} + \frac{1}{2}\sqrt{3}(-3) = 0 \quad \text{so that} \quad \frac{dx}{dt} = 3\sqrt{3}.$$

As the particle passes through the point $(\tfrac{1}{2}, \tfrac{1}{2}\sqrt{3})$, the x-coordinate is increasing at the rate of $3\sqrt{3}$ units per second. □

As you must have noticed, the first two sample problems were solved by the same general method, a method that we recommend to you for solving problems of this type:

Step 1. Draw a diagram, where relevant, and indicate the quantities that vary.

Step 2. Specify in mathematical form the rate of change you are looking for, and record all given information.

Step 3. Find an equation involving the variable whose rate of change is to be found.

Step 4. Differentiate with respect to time t the equation found in step 3.

Step 5. State the final answer in coherent form, specifying the units that you are using.

PROBLEM. A water trough with vertical cross section in the shape of an equilateral triangle is being filled at a rate of 4 cubic feet per minute. Given that the trough is 12 feet long, how fast is the level of the water rising at the instant that the water reaches a depth of $1\tfrac{1}{2}$ feet?

Solution. Let x be the depth of the water in feet and V the volume of water in cubic feet.

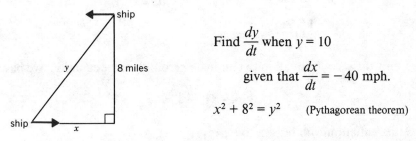

cross section of trough

Find $\dfrac{dx}{dt}$ when $x = \dfrac{3}{2}$

given that $\dfrac{dV}{dt} = 4$ cu. ft/min.

area of cross section $= \dfrac{\sqrt{3}}{3} x^2$

volume of water $= 12 \left(\dfrac{\sqrt{3}}{3} x^2 \right) = 4\sqrt{3} x^2$

Differentiation of $V = 4\sqrt{3} x^2$ with respect to t gives

$$\frac{dV}{dt} = 8\sqrt{3} x \frac{dx}{dt}.$$

Substituting $x = \frac{3}{2}$ and $dV/dt = 4$, we have

$$4 = 8\sqrt{3} \left(\frac{3}{2} \right) \frac{dx}{dt} \quad \text{and thus} \quad \frac{dx}{dt} = \frac{1}{9}\sqrt{3}.$$

At the instant that the water reaches a depth of $1\frac{1}{2}$ feet, the water level is rising at the rate of $\frac{1}{9}\sqrt{3}$ feet per second. $\square$

PROBLEM. Two ships, one heading west and the other east, approach each other on parallel courses 8 miles apart. Given that each ship is cruising at 20 miles per hour, at what rate is the distance between the ships diminishing when they are 10 miles apart?

Solution. Let y be the distance between the ships measured in miles.

Find $\dfrac{dy}{dt}$ when $y = 10$

given that $\dfrac{dx}{dt} = -40$ mph.

$x^2 + 8^2 = y^2$ (Pythagorean theorem)

(Note that dx/dt is taken as negative since x gets smaller.) Differentiating $x^2 + 8^2 = y^2$ with respect to t, we find that

$$2x \frac{dx}{dt} + 0 = 2y \frac{dy}{dt} \quad \text{and consequently} \quad x \frac{dx}{dt} = y \frac{dy}{dt}.$$

When $y = 10, x = 6$. (Why?) Substituting $x = 6, y = 10$, and $dx/dt = -40$, we have

$$6(-40) = 10 \frac{dy}{dt} \quad \text{so that} \quad \frac{dy}{dt} = -24.$$

(Note that dy/dt is negative since y is decreasing.)   When the two ships are 10 miles apart, the distance between them is diminishing at the rate of 24 miles per hour.   □

PROBLEM.   A conical paper cup 8 inches across the top and 6 inches deep is full of water.   The cup springs a leak at the bottom and loses water at the rate of 2 cubic inches per minute.   How fast is the water level dropping at the instant when the water is exactly 3 inches deep?

Solution.   We begin with a diagram that represents the situation after the cup has been leaking for a while (Figure 3.11.1).   We label the radius and height of the remaining "cone of water" r and h.   We can relate r and h by similar triangles (Figure 3.11.2).

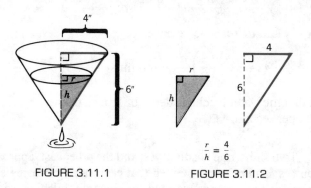

FIGURE 3.11.1   FIGURE 3.11.2

Let h be the depth of the water measured in inches.

Find $\dfrac{dh}{dt}$ when $h = 3$ given that $\dfrac{dV}{dt} = -2$ cu. in./min.

$$V = \frac{1}{3}\pi r^2 h \quad \text{(volume of a cone)} \qquad \text{and} \qquad \frac{r}{h} = \frac{4}{6} \quad \text{(similar triangles)}$$

Using the second equation to eliminate r from the first equation, we have

$$V = \frac{1}{3}\pi \left(\frac{2h}{3}\right)^2 h = \frac{4}{27}\pi h^3.$$

Differentiation with respect to t gives

$$\frac{dV}{dt} = \frac{4}{9}\pi h^2 \frac{dh}{dt}.$$

Substituting $h = 3$ and $dV/dt = -2$, we have

$$-2 = \frac{4}{9}\pi(3)^2 \frac{dh}{dt} \quad \text{and thus} \quad \frac{dh}{dt} = -\frac{1}{2\pi}.$$

At the instant when the water is exactly 3 inches deep, the water level is dropping at the rate of $1/2\pi$ inches per minute.   □

PROBLEM. A balloon leaves the ground 500 feet away from an observer and rises vertically at the rate of 140 feet per minute. At what rate is the angle of inclination of the observer's line of sight increasing at the instant when the balloon is exactly 500 feet above the ground?

Solution. Let x be the altitude of the balloon and θ the angle of inclination of the observer's line of sight.

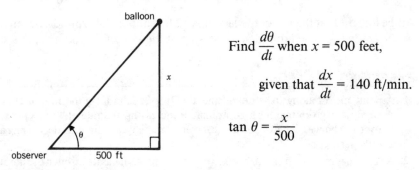

Find $\dfrac{d\theta}{dt}$ when $x = 500$ feet,

given that $\dfrac{dx}{dt} = 140$ ft/min.

$$\tan\theta = \frac{x}{500}$$

Differentiation with respect to t gives

$$\sec^2\theta\,\frac{d\theta}{dt} = \frac{1}{500}\frac{dx}{dt}.$$

When $x = 500$, the triangle is isosceles, and therefore $\sec\theta = \sqrt{2}$. Substituting $\sec\theta = \sqrt{2}$ and $dx/dt = 140$, we have

$$(\sqrt{2})^2\,\frac{d\theta}{dt} = \frac{1}{500}(140) \quad \text{and therefore} \quad \frac{d\theta}{dt} = 0.14.$$

At the instant when the balloon is exactly 500 feet above the ground, the inclination of the observer's line of sight is increasing at the rate of 0.14 radians per minute. □

PROBLEM. A ladder 13 feet long is leaning against the side of a building. If the foot of the ladder is pulled away from the building at the rate of 0.1 feet per second, how fast is the angle formed by the ladder and the ground changing at the instant when the top of the ladder is 12 feet above the ground?

Solution

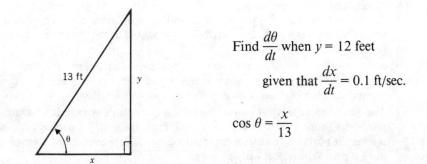

Find $\dfrac{d\theta}{dt}$ when $y = 12$ feet

given that $\dfrac{dx}{dt} = 0.1$ ft/sec.

$$\cos\theta = \frac{x}{13}$$

Differentiation with respect to t gives

$$-\sin\theta\,\frac{d\theta}{dt} = \frac{1}{13}\frac{dx}{dt}.$$

When $y = 12$, $\sin\theta = \frac{12}{13}$. Substituting $\sin\theta = \frac{12}{13}$ and $dx/dt = 0.1$, we have

$$-\left(\frac{12}{13}\right)\frac{d\theta}{dt} = \frac{1}{13}(0.1) \quad\text{and thus}\quad \frac{d\theta}{dt} = -\frac{1}{120}.$$

At the instant that the top of the ladder is 12 feet above the ground, the angle formed by the ladder and the ground is decreasing at the rate of $\frac{1}{120}$ radians per second.   □

EXERCISES

1. A point moves along the straight line $x + 2y = 2$. Find: (a) the rate of change of the y-coordinate, given that the x-coordinate is increasing at a rate of 4 units per second; (b) the rate of change of the x-coordinate, given that the y-coordinate is decreasing at a rate of 2 units per second.

2. A particle is moving in circular orbit $x^2 + y^2 = 25$. As it passes through the point $(3, 4)$, its y-coordinate is decreasing at the rate of 2 units per second. How is the x-coordinate changing?

3. A heap of rubbish in the shape of a cube is being compacted. Given that the volume decreases at a rate of 2 cubic meters per minute, find the rate of change of an edge of the cube when the volume is exactly 27 cubic meters. What is the rate of change at that instant of the surface area of the cube?

4. At a certain instant the dimensions of a rectangle are a and b. These dimensions are changing at the rates m, n, respectively. Find the rate at which the area is changing.

5. The volume of a spherical balloon is increasing at a constant rate of 8 cubic feet per minute. How fast is the radius increasing when the radius is exactly 10 feet? How fast is the surface area increasing at that instant?

6. At a certain instant the side of an equilateral triangle is α centimeters long and increasing at the rate of k centimeters per minute. How fast is the area increasing?

7. The perimeter of a rectangle is fixed at 24 centimeters. If the length l of the rectangle is increasing at the rate of 1 centimeter per second, for what value of l does the area of the rectangle start to decrease?

8. The dimensions of a rectangle are changing in such a way that the perimeter is always 24 inches. Show that, at the instant when the area is 32 square inches, the area is either increasing or decreasing 4 times as fast as the length is increasing.

9. A rectangle is inscribed in a circle of radius 5 inches. If the length of the rectangle is decreasing at the rate of 2 inches per second, how fast is the area changing at the instant when the length is 6 inches?   (HINT: A diagonal of the rectangle is a diameter of the circle.)

10. A boat is held by a bow line that is wound about a windlass 6 feet higher than the bow of the boat. If the boat is drifting away at the rate of 8 feet per minute, how fast is the line unwinding when the bow is exactly 30 feet from the windlass?

11. Two boats are racing with constant speed toward a finish marker, boat A sailing from the south at 13 mph and boat B approaching from the east. When equidistant from the marker the boats are 16 miles apart and the distance between them is decreasing at the rate of 17 mph. Which boat will win the race?

12. A ladder 13 feet long is leaning against a wall. If the foot of the ladder is pulled away from the wall at the rate of 0.5 feet per second, how fast will the top of the ladder be dropping at the instant when the base is 5 feet from the wall?

13. A tank contains 1000 cubic feet of natural gas at a pressure of 5 pounds per square inch. Find the rate of change of the volume if the pressure decreases at a rate of 0.05 pounds per square inch per hour. (Assume Boyle's law: *pressure × volume = constant*.)

14. The adiabatic law for the expansion of air is $PV^{1.4} = C$. At a given instant the volume is 10 cubic feet and the pressure 50 pounds per square inch. At what rate is the pressure changing if the volume is decreasing at a rate of 1 cubic foot per second?

15. A man standing 3 feet from the base of a lamp post casts a shadow 4 feet long. If the man is 6 feet tall and walks away from the lamp post at a speed of 400 feet per minute, at what rate will his shadow lengthen?

16. In the special theory of relativity the mass of a particle moving at velocity v is

$$m \left(1 - \frac{v^2}{c^2} \right)^{-1/2}$$

where m is the mass at rest and c is the speed of light. At what rate is the mass changing when the particle's velocity is $\frac{1}{2}c$ and the rate of change of the velocity is $0.01c$ per second?

17. The water level in a leaking paper cup 4 inches across the top and 6 inches deep is dropping at the rate of 0.3 inches per minute. How fast is the volume of water changing at the instant when the water is 5 inches deep?

18. Water flows from a faucet into a hemispherical basin 14 inches in diameter at a rate of 2 cubic inches per second. (Figure 3.11.3) How fast does the water rise (a) when the water is exactly halfway to the top? (b) just as it runs over? (The volume of a spherical segment is given by $\pi rh^2 - \frac{1}{3}\pi h^3$ where r is the radius of the sphere and h is the depth of the segment.)

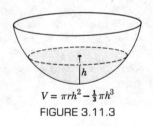

$$V = \pi rh^2 - \tfrac{1}{3}\pi h^3$$

FIGURE 3.11.3

19. The base of an isosceles triangle is 6 feet. If the altitude is 4 feet and increasing at the rate of 2 inches per minute, at what rate is the vertex angle changing?

20. As a boy winds up the cord, his kite is moving horizontally at a height of 60 feet with a speed of 10 feet per minute. How fast is the inclination of the cord changing when its length is 100 feet?

21. A revolving searchlight $\frac{1}{2}$ mile from shore makes 1 revolution per minute. How fast is the light traveling along the straight beach at the instant it passes over a shorepoint 1 mile away from the shorepoint nearest to the searchlight.

22. Two cars, car A traveling east at 30 mph and car B traveling north at 22.5 mph, are heading toward an intersection I. At what rate is angle IAB changing at the instant when cars A and B are 300 feet and 400 feet, respectively, from the intersection?

23. A rope 32 feet long is attached to a weight and passed over a pulley 16 feet above the

ground. The other end of the rope is pulled away along the ground at the rate of 3 feet per second. At what rate is the angle between the rope and the ground changing at the instant when the weight is exactly 4 feet off the ground?

24. A slingshot is made by fastening the two ends of a 10-inch rubber strip 6 inches apart. If the midpoint of the strip is drawn back at the rate of 1 inch per second, at what rate is the angle between the segments of the strip changing 8 seconds later?

25. A balloon is released 500 feet away from an observer. If the balloon rises vertically at the rate of 100 feet per minute and at the same time the wind is carrying it horizontally away from the observer at the rate of 75 feet per minute, at what rate is the angle of inclination of the observer's line of sight changing 6 minutes after the balloon has been released?

26. A searchlight is trained on a plane that flies directly above the light at an altitude of 2 miles at a speed of 400 miles per hour. How fast must the light be turning 2 seconds after the plane passes directly overhead?

3.12 ···· DIFFERENTIALS; NEWTON-RAPHSON APPROXIMATIONS

Differentials

In Figure 3.12.1 you can see the graph of a function f and below it the graph of the tangent line at the point $(x, f(x))$. As the figure suggests, for small h, $f(x + h) - f(x)$,

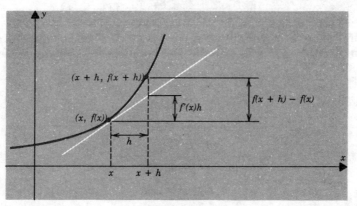

FIGURE 3.12.1

the change in f from x to $x + h$, can be approximated by the product $f'(x)h$:

(3.12.1)
$$f(x + h) - f(x) \cong f'(x)h.$$

How good is this approximation? It is good in the sense that, for small h, the difference between the two quantities,

$$[f(x + h) - f(x)] - f'(x)h,$$

is small compared to h. How small? Small enough that the ratio

$$\frac{[f(x + h) - f(x] - f'(x)h}{h}$$

tends to 0 as h tends to 0:

$$\lim_{h \to 0} \frac{f(x+h) - f(x) - f'(x)h}{h} = \lim_{h \to 0} \frac{f(x+h) - f(x)}{h} - \lim_{h \to 0} \frac{f'(x)h}{h}$$

$$= f'(x) - f'(x) = 0.$$

The quantities $f(x + h) - f(x)$ and $f'(x)h$ have names:

DEFINITION 3.12.2

The difference $f(x + h) - f(x)$ is called the *increment* (of f from x to $x + h$) and is denoted by Δf:

$$\Delta f = f(x+h) - f(x).\dagger$$

The product $f'(x)h$ is called the *differential* (at x with increment h) and is denoted by df:

$$df = f'(x)h.$$

Display (3.12.1) says that, for small h, Δf and df are approximately equal:

$$\Delta f \cong df.$$

How approximately equal are they? Enough so that the ratio

$$\frac{\Delta f - df}{h}$$

tends to 0 as h tends to 0.

Let's see what all this amounts to in a very simple case. The area of a square of side x is given by the function

$$f(x) = x^2, \qquad x > 0.$$

If the length of each side is increased from x to $x + h$, the area increases from $f(x)$ to $f(x + h)$. The change in area is the increment Δf:

$$\Delta f = f(x+h) - f(x) = (x+h)^2 - x^2 = (x^2 + 2xh + h^2) - x^2 = 2xh + h^2.$$

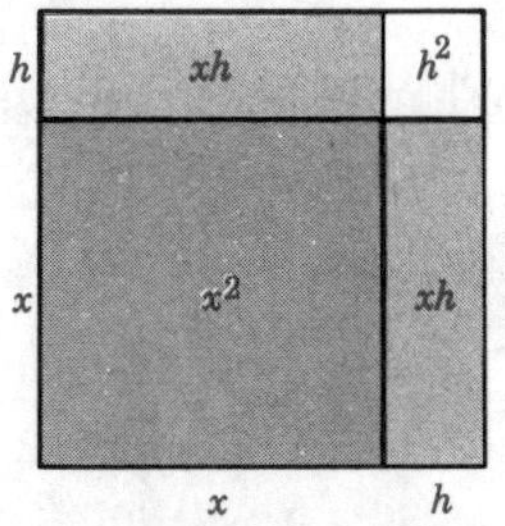

FIGURE 3.12.2

---

† The symbol Δ is a capital δ; Δf is read "delta f."

As an estimate for this change we can use the differential

$$df = f'(x)h = 2xh. \qquad \text{(Figure 3.12.2)}$$

The error of this estimate, the difference between the actual change Δf and the estimated change df, is the difference

$$\Delta f - df = h^2.$$

As promised, the error is small compared to h in the sense that

$$\frac{\Delta f - df}{h} = \frac{h^2}{h} = h$$

tends to 0 as h tends to 0.

PROBLEM.   Given that

$$f(x) = x^{2/5},$$

use a differential to estimate the change in f

(a) if x is increased from 32 to 34.   (b) if x is decreased from 1 to $\frac{9}{10}$.

Solution.   Since

$$f'(x) = \tfrac{2}{5}(1/x)^{3/5},$$

we have

$$df = f'(x)h = \tfrac{2}{5}(1/x)^{3/5}h.$$

For part (a) we set $x = 32$ and $h = 2$.   The differential then becomes

$$\tfrac{2}{5}(\tfrac{1}{32})^{3/5}(2) = \tfrac{1}{10} = 0.10.$$

A change in x from 32 to 34 increases the value of f by approximately 0.10.
    For part (b) we set $x = 1$ and $h = -\frac{1}{10}$.   The differential then becomes

$$\tfrac{2}{5}(\tfrac{1}{1})^{3/5}(-\tfrac{1}{10}) = -\tfrac{2}{50} = -\tfrac{1}{25} = -0.04.$$

A change in x from 1 to $\frac{9}{10}$ decreases the value of f by approximately 0.04.   □

PROBLEM.   Use a differential to estimate $\sqrt{104}$.

Solution.   We know $\sqrt{100}$.   What we need is an estimate for the increase of

$$f(x) = \sqrt{x}$$

from 100 to 104.   Differentiation gives

$$f'(x) = \frac{1}{2\sqrt{x}}$$

so that in general

$$df = f'(x)h = \frac{h}{2\sqrt{x}}.$$

With $x = 100$ and $h = 4$, df becomes

$$\frac{4}{2\sqrt{100}} = \frac{1}{5} = 0.2.$$

A change in x from 100 to 104 increases the value of the square root by approximately 0.2. It follows that

$$\sqrt{104} \cong \sqrt{100} + 0.2 = 10 + 0.2 = 10.2.$$

As you can check, $(10.2)^2 = 104.04$, so that we are not far off. $\square$

Newton-Raphson Method

Let f be a differentiable function. Since the tangent to the graph of f at $(x_1, f(x_1))$ is the best linear approximation of f near $(x_1, f(x_1))$, it seems reasonable to hope that, if x_1 is close to a root c of the equation $f(x) = 0$, then the point x_2 where the tangent at x_1 intersects the x-axis is also close to the root c, if not closer (see Figure 3.12.3). The tangent at x_2 in turn produces the value x_3, which may be even closer to the root c (see Figure 3.12.4). Iteration of this procedure is known as the *Newton-Raphson method* for approximating solutions of the equation $f(x) = 0$. There are instances in which the method does not work. We'll take note of those later. At this point let's look into the method a little further.

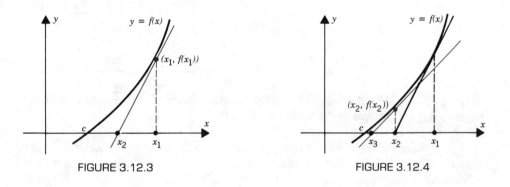

FIGURE 3.12.3   FIGURE 3.12.4

To identify the connection between successive approximations x_n and x_{n+1}, we examine the general case (see Figure 3.12.5). We begin by writing the equation for the tangent at $(x_n, f(x_n))$:

$$y - f(x_n) = f'(x_n)(x - x_n).$$

The x-intercept x_{n+1} of this line can be found by setting $y = 0$:

$$0 - f(x_n) = f'(x_n)(x_{n+1} - x_n).$$

Solving this equation for x_{n+i}, we have

(3.12.3) $$x_{n+1} = x_n - \frac{f(x_n)}{f'(x_n)}.$$

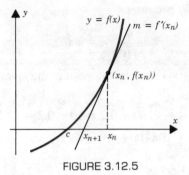

FIGURE 3.12.5

EXAMPLE. We approximate $\sqrt{3}$ by applying the Newton-Raphson method to the function $f(x) = x^2 - 3$, choosing $x_1 = 2$ as our first approximation. Since $f'(x) = 2x$, we have by Equation (3.12.3)

$$(1) \qquad x_{n+1} = x_n - \frac{x_n^2 - 3}{2x_n} = \frac{x_n^2 + 3}{2x_n} = \frac{1}{2}\left(x_n + \frac{3}{x_n}\right).$$

Here are the computations based on (1).

n	x_n	$\dfrac{3}{x_n}$	$x_{n+1} = \dfrac{1}{2}\left(x_n + \dfrac{3}{x_n}\right)$
1	2.0000000	1.5000000	1.7500000
2	1.7500000	1.7142857	1.7321428
3	1.7321428	1.7319588	1:7320508

Since $(1.7320508)^2 = 2.9999999$ (on the calculator used for these computations), the method has generated a fairly accurate estimate for $\sqrt{3}$ in only three steps. □

Clearly, the method fails if it ever happens that $f'(x_n) = 0$ (and $f(x_n) \neq 0$). (See Figure 3.12.6.) It is also possible that the values of x_n may oscillate between several values rather than approaching some limiting value. (See Figure 3.12.7.) Also, the

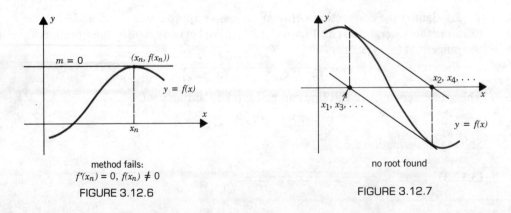

method fails:
$f'(x_n) = 0, f(x_n) \neq 0$

FIGURE 3.12.6

no root found

FIGURE 3.12.7

method may identify a root other than the one desired. (See Figure 3.12.8.) Finally, it is shown in more advanced mathematics that, if on the interval between the root c and the first estimate x_1 the curve is "flexed" toward the x-axis (see Figure 3.12.9), then the method will identify the root c.

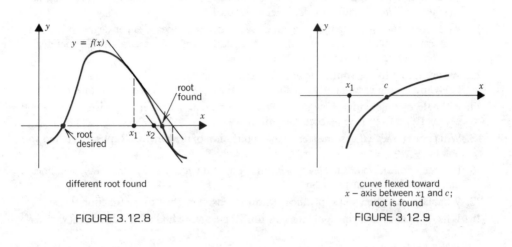

FIGURE 3.12.8

different root found

FIGURE 3.12.9

curve flexed toward
x – axis between x_1 and c;
root is found

EXERCISES

1. Use a differential to estimate the change in the volume of a cube caused by an increase h in the length of each side. Interpret geometrically the error of your estimate $\Delta V - dV$.

2. Use a differential to estimate the area of a ring of inner radius r and width h. What is the exact area?

Estimate the following by differentials.

3. $\sqrt[3]{1010}$.   4. $\sqrt{125}$.   5. $\sqrt[4]{15}$.   6. $\dfrac{1}{\sqrt{24}}$.

7. $\sqrt[5]{30}$.   8. $(26)^{2/3}$.   9. $(33)^{3/5}$.   10. $(33)^{-1/5}$.

Remembering that the domain of a trigonometric function is measured in radians rather than degrees, use differentials to estimate the following.

11. $\sin 46°$.   12. $\cos 62°$.   13. $\tan 28°$.   14. $\sin 43°$.

15. Estimate $f(2.8)$ given that $f(3) = 2$ and $f'(x) = (x^3 + 5)^{1/5}$.

16. Estimate $f(5.4)$ given that $f(5) = 1$ and $f'(x) = \sqrt[3]{x^2 + 2}$.

17. Find the approximate volume of a thin cylindrical sheet with open ends given that the inner radius is r, the height is h, and the thickness is t.

18. The diameter of a steel ball is measured to be 16 centimeters, with a maximum error of 0.3 centimeters. Estimate by differentials the maximum error in (a) the surface area when calculated by the formula $S = 4\pi r^2$; (b) the volume when calculated by the formula $V = \frac{4}{3}\pi r^3$.

19. A box is to be constructed in the form of a cube to hold 1000 cubic feet. Use a differential to estimate how accurately the inner edge must be made so that the volume will be correct to within 3 cubic feet.

20. Use differentials to estimate the values of x for which

   (a) $\sqrt{x+1} - \sqrt{x} < 0.01$.   (b) $\sqrt[4]{x+1} - \sqrt[4]{x} < 0.002$.

21. The duration of one vibration of a pendulum of length l is given by the formula $t = \pi\sqrt{l/g}$. Here t is measured in seconds, and l is measured in feet. Take $\pi \cong 3.14$ and $g \cong 32$. Given that a pendulum of length 3.26 feet vibrates once a second, find the approximate change in t if the pendulum is lengthened by 0.01 feet.

22. As a metal cube is heated, the length of each edge increases $\frac{1}{10}\%$ per degree increase in temperature. Show by differentials that the surface area increases about $\frac{2}{10}\%$ per degree and the volume increases about $\frac{3}{10}\%$ per degree.

23. We are trying to determine the area of a circle by measuring the diameter. How accurately must we measure the diameter if our estimate is to be correct within 1%?

24. Estimate by differentials how precisely x must be determined if (a) x^n is to be accurate within 1%; (b) $x^{1/n}$ is to be accurate within 1%.

25. What does it mean if at some step in the application of the Newton-Raphson method you obtain $x_{n+1} = x_n$?

26. If in the application of the Newton-Raphson method you discover that $f(x_2) = 0$, does it mean that f is a linear function?

27. What happens when you apply the Newton-Raphson method to the function $f(x) = x^{1/3}$?

28. What happens when you apply the Newton-Raphson method to the function $f(x) = \sqrt{|x|}$?

Calculator exercises.

Use the Newton-Raphson method to approximate to the nearest hundredth a root of the equation $f(x) = 0$ by taking x_1 as the first estimate.

29. $f(x) = x^2 - 22;\quad x_1 = 5$.   30. $f(x) = x^3 - 8;\quad x_1 = 3$.

31. $f(x) = x^3 + 27;\quad x_1 = -2$.   32. $f(x) = x^2 - 2;\quad x_1 = 1$.

33. $f(x) = 4x^2 - 16x + 15;\quad x_1 = 3$.   34. $f(x) = 6x^2 - x - 1;\quad x_1 = -1$.

35. $f(x) = 4x^2 - 16x + 15;\quad x_1 = 1$.   36. $f(x) = 6x^2 - x - 1;\quad x_1 = 1$.

37. $f(x) = \tan x;\quad x_1 = 3$.   38. $f(x) = \cos x - x;\quad x_1 = 1$.

(*Important*) Little-$o(h)$; The Tangent Line as Best Approximation

Let g be a function defined at least on an open interval containing the number 0. We say that $g(h)$ is *little-o(h)* and write $g(h) = o(h)$ iff, for small h, $g(h)$ is small enough compared to h that

$$\lim_{h \to 0} \frac{g(h)}{h} = 0, \quad \text{or equivalently,} \quad \lim_{h \to 0} \frac{g(h)}{|h|} = 0.$$

39. Which of the following statements is true?

   (a) $h^3 = o(h)$.   (b) $\dfrac{h^2}{h-1} = o(h)$.   (c) $h^{1/3} = o(h)$.

40. Show that, if $g(h) = o(h)$, then $\lim_{h \to 0} g(h) = 0$.

41. Show that, if $g_1(h) = o(h)$ and $g_2(h) = o(h)$, then

$$g_1(h) + g_2(h) = o(h) \quad \text{and} \quad g_1(h)g_2(h) = o(h).$$

42. Figure 3.12.10 shows the graph of a differentiable function f and a line with slope m that passes through the point $(x, f(x))$. The vertical separation at $x + h$ between the line with slope m and the graph of f has been labeled $g(h)$.

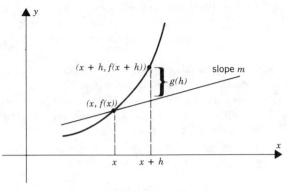

FIGURE 3.12.10

(a) Calculate $g(h)$.
(b) Show that, of all lines that pass through $(x, f(x))$, the tangent line is the line that best approximates the graph of f near the point $(x, f(x))$ by showing that

$$g(h) = o(h) \quad \text{iff} \quad m = f'(x).$$

3.13····ADDITIONAL EXERCISES

1. The rate of change of f at $x = x_0$ is twice as great as it is at $x = 1$. Find x_0 if
   (a) $f(x) = x^2$.   (b) $f(x) = 2x^3$.   (c) $f(x) = \sqrt{x}$.

2. For what value of x is the rate of change of

   $$y = ax^2 + bx + c \quad \text{with respect to } x$$

   the same as the rate of change of

   $$z = bx^2 + ax + c \quad \text{with respect to } x?$$

   Assume $a \neq b$.

3. Find the points on the curve $y = \frac{2}{3}x^{3/2}$ where the inclination of the tangent line is
   (a) $45°$. (b) $60°$. (c) $30°$.

4. Find an equation for the tangent to the curve $y = x^3$ that passes through the point $(0, 2)$.

5. Find an equation for the line tangent to the graph of f^{-1} at the point (b, a) given that the slope of the graph of f at (a, b) is m.

6. Find an equation for the normal to the parabola $y = 5x + x^2$ that makes an angle of $45°$ with the x-axis.

Find a formula for the nth derivative.   ·

7. $y = (a + bx)^n$.

8. $y = \dfrac{a}{bx + c}$.

9. If $y = 4x - x^3$ and x is increasing steadily at the rate of $\frac{1}{3}$ unit per second, how fast is the slope of the graph changing at the instant when $x = 2$?

10. A ball thrown straight up from the ground reaches a height of 24 feet in 1 second. How high will the ball go?

11. Find equations for all the tangents to the curve $y = x^3 - x$ that pass through the point $(-2, 2)$.   HINT: $(-2, 2)$ is not on the curve, so let (a, b) be the point of tangency. Calculate the slope of the tangent in two ways and then use the fact that (a, b) is on the curve.

12. A particle moves along the parabola $y^2 = 12x$. At what point of the parabola do the x- and y-coordinates of the particle increase at the same rate?

13. The radius of a cone is increasing at the rate of 0.3 inches per minute but the volume remains constant. At what rate is the height of the cone changing at the instant when the radius is 4 inches and the height is 15 inches?

14. The area of a square is increasing at the rate of 6 square inches per minute when the side of the square measures 14 inches. How fast is the perimeter of the square changing at that instant?

15. The dimensions of a rectangle are changing in such a way that the perimeter remains 20 centimeters. How fast is the area of the rectangle changing at the instant when one side is 7 centimeters long and is decreasing at the rate of 0.4 centimeters per minute?

16. The dimensions of a rectangle are changing in such a way that the area remains 24 square inches. At what rate is the perimeter changing at the instant when one side is 6 inches long and is increasing at the rate of 0.3 inches per minute?

17. At what rate is the volume of a sphere changing at the instant when the surface area is increasing at the rate of 4 square inches per minute and the radius is increasing at the rate of 0.1 inches per minute?

18. At what rate is the surface area of a cube changing at the instant when the volume is decreasing at the rate of 9 cubic centimeters per minute and the length of a side is decreasing at the rate of 4 centimeters per minute?

19. An object moves along a coordinate line, its position at time t given by the function $x(t) = t + 2 \cos t$. Find those times t from 0 to 2π when the object is slowing down.

20. An object moves along a coordinate line, its position at time t given by the function $x(t) = \sqrt{t + 1}$. (a) Show that the acceleration is negative and proportional to the cube of the velocity. (b) Use differentials to find numerical estimates for the position, velocity, and acceleration of the object at time $t = 17$. Base your estimate on $t = 15$.

21. As a metal sphere is heated, the length of the radius increases $\frac{1}{10}$% per degree increase in temperature. Show by differentials that the surface area increases about $\frac{2}{10}$% per degree and the volume increases about $\frac{3}{10}$% per degree.

22. An object moves along a coordinate line, its position at time t given by the function $x(t) = -t\sqrt{t + 1}$, $t \geq 0$. Find
   (a) the velocity at time $t = 1$.
   (b) the acceleration at time $t = 1$.
   (c) the speed at time $t = 1$.
   (d) the rate of change of the speed at time $t = 1$.

23. A horizontal trough 12 feet long has a vertical cross section in the shape of a trapezoid. The bottom is 3 feet wide, and the sides are inclined to the vertical at an angle whose sine is $\frac{4}{5}$. Given that water is poured into the trough at the rate of 10 cubic feet per minute, how fast is the water level rising when the water is exactly 2 feet deep?

24. In Exercise 23, at what rate is the water being drawn from the trough if the level is falling 0.1 feet per minute when the water is 3 feet deep?

25. A point P moves along the parabola $y = x^2$ so that its x-coordinate increases at the constant rate of k units per second. The projection of P on the x-axis is M. At what rate is the area of triangle OMP changing when P is at the point where $x = a$?

26. The diameter and height of a right circular cylinder are found at a certain instant to be 10

and 20 inches, respectively. If the diameter is increasing at the rate of 1 inch per minute, what change in the height will keep the volume constant?

27. Ballast dropped from a balloon that was rising at the rate of 5 feet per second reached the ground in 8 seconds. How high was the balloon when the ballast was dropped?

28. Had the balloon of Exercise 27 been falling at the rate of 5 feet per second, how long would it have taken for the ballast to reach the ground?

29. Isocost lines and indifference curves are studied in economics. For what value of C is the isocost line

$$Ax + By = 1 \qquad (A > 0, B > 0)$$

tangent to the difference curve

$$y = \frac{1}{x} + C, \qquad x > 0?$$

Find the point of tangency (called the *equilibrium point*).

30. Let

$$P = f(Q) \qquad\qquad (P = \text{price}, Q = \text{output})$$

be the supply function of Figure 3.13.1. Compare angles θ and ϕ at points where the elasticity

$$\epsilon = \frac{f(Q)}{Q|f'(Q)|}$$

(a) is 1.   (b) is less than 1.   (c) is greater than 1.

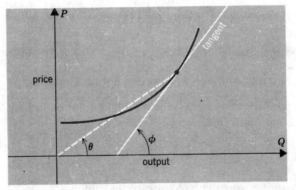

FIGURE 3.13.1

31. Determine the coefficients A, B, C so that the curve $y = Ax^2 + Bx + C$ will pass through the point $(1, 3)$ and be tangent to the line $x - y + 1 = 0$ at the point $(2, 3)$.

32. Find A, B, C, D given that the curve $y = Ax^3 + Bx^2 + Cx + D$ is tangent to the line $y = 5x - 4$ at the point $(1, 1)$ and tangent to the line $y = 9x$ at the point $(-1, -9)$.

33. An object moves along a coordinate line, its position at time t given by the function $x(t) = \cos 2t - 2 \cos t$. At what times t from 0 to 2π does the object change direction?

34. A boy walks on a straight horizontal path away from a light that hangs 12 feet above the path. How fast does his shadow lengthen if he is 5 feet tall and walks at a rate of 168 feet per minute?

35. A railroad track crosses a highway at an angle of 60°. A locomotive is 500 feet from the intersection and moving away from it at the rate of 60 miles per hour. An automobile is

500 feet from the intersection and moving toward it at the rate of 30 miles per hour. What is the rate of change of the distance between them?   HINT: Use the law of cosines.

36. One ship was sailing south at 6 miles per hour; another east at 8 miles per hour. At 4 P.M. the second crossed the track of the first, where the first had been 2 hours before. (a) How was the distance between the ships changing at 3 P.M.? (b) at 5 P.M.?

37. The period (P seconds) of a complete oscillation of a pendulum of length l inches is given by the formula $P = 0.32 \sqrt{l}$. (a) Find the rate of change of the period with respect to the length when $l = 9$ inches. (b) Use a differential to estimate the change in P caused by an increase in l from 9 to 9.2 inches.

3.14 CHAPTER SUMMARY

3.1 The Derivative

derivative of f (p. 108)   tangent line (p. 109)
normal line (p. 113)   vertical tangent (p. 115)

If f is differentiable at x, then f is continuous at x. (p. 115)   The converse is false.

3.2 Some Differentiation Formulas

$$(f + g)'(x) = f'(x) + g'(x) \qquad\qquad (\alpha f)'(x) = \alpha f'(x) \quad \text{for each real } \alpha$$

$$(fg)'(x) = f(x)g'(x) + g(x)f'(x) \qquad \left(\frac{f}{g}\right)'(x) = \frac{g(x)f'(x) - f(x)g'(x)}{[g(x)]^2} \quad (g(x) \neq 0)$$

For both positive and negative integers n, $p(x) = x^n$ has derivative $p'(x) = nx^{n-1}$.

3.3 The d/dx Notation; Derivatives of Higher Order

Another notation for the derivative is the double-d notation of Leibniz. For example, we can write the "sum rule"

$$(f + g)'(x) = f'(x) + g'(x) \qquad \text{as} \qquad \frac{d}{dx}[f(x) + g(x)] = \frac{d}{dx}[f(x)] + \frac{d}{dx}[g(x)].$$

Higher order derivatives are calculated by repeated differentiation. For example, the second derivative of $y = f(x)$ is the derivative of the derivative:

$$f''(x) = \frac{d^2y}{dx^2} = \frac{d}{dx}\left[\frac{dy}{dx}\right].$$

3.4 The Derivative as a Rate of Change

$\dfrac{dy}{dx}$ gives the rate of change of y with respect to x.

3.5 Velocity and Acceleration

velocity, acceleration and speed (p. 138–139)
motion of a falling object (p. 141)

If the velocity and acceleration have the same sign, the object is *speeding up*. If the velocity and acceleration have opposite signs, the object is *slowing down*.

3.6 The Chain Rule

$$\frac{dy}{dx} = \frac{dy}{du}\frac{du}{dx} \qquad\qquad \frac{dy}{ds} = \frac{dy}{du}\frac{du}{dx}\frac{dx}{ds}$$

$$\frac{d}{dx}[u^n] = nu^{n-1}\frac{du}{dx}$$

3.7 Differentiating the Trigonometric Functions

$$\frac{d}{dx}(\sin u) = \cos u\,\frac{du}{dx}, \qquad\qquad \frac{d}{dx}(\cos u) = -\sin u\,\frac{du}{dx},$$

$$\frac{d}{dx}(\tan u) = \sec^2 u\,\frac{du}{dx}, \qquad\qquad \frac{d}{dx}(\cot u) = -\csc^2 u\,\frac{du}{dx},$$

$$\frac{d}{dx}(\sec u) = \sec u \tan u\,\frac{du}{dx} \qquad \frac{d}{dx}(\csc u) = -\csc u \cot u\,\frac{du}{dx}$$

3.8 Differentiating Inverses: Fractional Exponents

$$(f^{-1})'(x) = \frac{1}{f'(f^{-1}(x))} \qquad \text{or} \qquad \frac{dx}{dy} = \frac{1}{dy/dx}$$

$$\frac{d}{dx}u^{p/q} = \frac{p}{q}u^{(p/q)-1}\frac{du}{dx}$$

3.9 Additional Practice in Differentiation

3.10 Implicit Differentiation

We can find dy/dx from an equation in x and y without first solving the equation for y.

3.11 Rates of Change per Unit Time

If Q is a quantity that varies with time, then the derivative dQ/dt gives the rate of change of that quantity per unit time.

A 5-step procedure for solving *related rates problems* is outlined on p. 168.

3.12 Differentials; Newton-Raphson Approximations

increment (Δf) and differential (df) (p. 175)
Newton-Raphson method (p. 177)

3.13 Additional Exercises

The Mean-Value Theorem and Applications

4.1 ······THE MEAN-VALUE THEOREM

In this section we prove a result known as *the mean-value theorem*. First stated by the French mathematician Joseph Louis Lagrange† (1736–1813), this theorem has come to permeate the theoretical structure of all calculus.

> **THEOREM 4.1.1 THE MEAN-VALUE THEOREM**
>
> If f is differentiable on (a, b) and continuous on $[a, b]$, then there is at least one number c in (a, b) for which
>
> $$f'(c) = \frac{f(b) - f(a)}{b - a}.$$

The number

$$\frac{f(b) - f(a)}{b - a}$$

---

† Lagrange, whom you encountered earlier in connection with the prime notation for differentiation, was born in Turin, Italy. He spent twenty years as mathematician in residence at the court of Frederick the Great. Later he taught at the renowned École Polytechnique.

is the slope of the line l that passes through the points $(a, f(a))$ and $(b, f(b))$. To say that there is at least one number c for which

$$f'(c) = \frac{f(b) - f(a)}{b - a}$$

is to say that the graph of f has at least one point $(c, f(c))$ at which the tangent is parallel to l. See Figure 4.1.1.

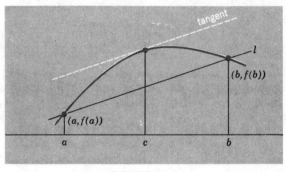

FIGURE 4.1.1

We will prove the mean-value theorem in steps. First we will show that, if a function f has a nonzero derivative at some point x_0, then, close to x_0, $f(x)$ is greater than $f(x_0)$ on one side of x_0 and less than $f(x_0)$ on the other side of x_0.

THEOREM 4.1.2

Let f be differentiable at x_0. If $f'(x_0) > 0$, then

$$f(x_0 - h) < f(x_0) < f(x_0 + h)$$

for all positive h sufficiently small. If $f'(x_0) < 0$, then

$$f(x_0 + h) < f(x_0) < f(x_0 - h)$$

for all positive h sufficiently small.

Proof. We take the case $f'(x_0) > 0$ and leave the other case to you. By the definition of derivative,

$$\lim_{k \to 0} \frac{f(x_0 + k) - f(x_0)}{k} = f'(x_0).$$

With $f'(x_0) > 0$ we can use $f'(x_0)$ itself as ϵ and conclude that there exists $\delta > 0$ such that

$$\text{if} \quad 0 < |k| < \delta, \quad \text{then} \quad \left| \frac{f(x_0 + k) - f(x_0)}{k} - f'(x_0) \right| < f'(x_0).$$

For such k we have

$$\frac{f(x_0 + k) - f(x_0)}{k} > 0. \qquad\qquad \text{(why?)}$$

If now $0 < h < \delta$, then

$$\frac{f(x_0 + h) - f(x_0)}{h} > 0 \quad \text{and} \quad \frac{f(x_0 - h) - f(x_0)}{-h} > 0,$$

and consequently

$$f(x_0) < f(x_0 + h) \quad \text{and} \quad f(x_0 - h) < f(x_0). \quad \square$$

Next we prove a special case of the mean-value theorem, known as Rolle's theorem (after the French mathematician Michel Rolle who first announced the result in 1691). In Rolle's theorem we make the additional assumption that $f(a)$ and $f(b)$ are both 0. (See Figure 4.1.2.) In this case the line joining $(a, f(a))$ to $(b, f(b))$ is horizontal. (It is the x-axis.) The conclusion is that there is a point $(c, f(c))$ at which the tangent is horizontal.

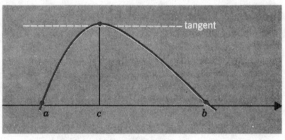

FIGURE 4.1.2

THEOREM 4.1.3   ROLLE'S THEOREM

Let f be differentiable on (a, b) and continuous on $[a, b]$. If $f(a)$ and $f(b)$ are both 0, then there is at least one number c in (a, b) for which

$$f'(c) = 0.$$

Proof. If f is constantly 0 on $[a, b]$, the result is obvious. If f is not constantly 0 on $[a, b]$, then either f takes on some positive values or some negative values. We assume the former and leave the other case to you.

Since f is continuous on $[a, b]$, at some point c of $[a, b]$, f must take on a maximum value. (Theorem 2.6.2.) This maximum value, $f(c)$, must be positive. Since $f(a)$ and $f(b)$ are both 0, c cannot be a and it cannot be b. This means that c must lie in the open interval (a, b) and therefore $f'(c)$ exists. Now $f'(c)$ cannot be greater than 0 and it cannot be less than 0 because each of these conditions would imply that f takes on values greater than $f(c)$. (This follows from Theorem 4.1.2.) We conclude therefore that $f'(c) = 0$. □

We are now ready to give a proof of the mean-value theorem.

Proof of the Mean-Value Theorem. We will create a function g that satisfies the conditions of Rolle's theorem and is so related to f that the conclusion $g'(c) = 0$ leads to the conclusion

$$f'(c) = \frac{f(b) - f(a)}{b - a}.$$

It is not hard to see that

$$g(x) = f(x) - \left[\frac{f(b) - f(a)}{b - a} (x - a) + f(a) \right]$$

is exactly such a function. Geometrically $g(x)$ is represented in Figure 4.1.3. The line that passes through $(a, f(a))$ and $(b, f(b))$ has the equation

$$y = \frac{f(b) - f(a)}{b - a} (x - a) + f(a).$$

[This is not hard to verify. The slope is right, and, when $x = a$, $y = f(a)$.] The difference

$$g(x) = f(x) - \left[\frac{f(b) - f(a)}{b - a} (x - a) + f(a) \right]$$

is simply the vertical separation between the graph of f and the line in question.

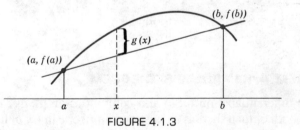

FIGURE 4.1.3

If f is differentiable on (a, b) and continuous on $[a, b]$, then so is g. As you can check, $g(a)$ and $g(b)$ are both 0. Therefore by Rolle's theorem there is at least one point c in (a, b) for which $g'(c) = 0$. Since in general

$$g'(x) = f'(x) - \frac{f(b) - f(a)}{b - a},$$

in particular

$$g'(c) = f'(c) - \frac{f(b) - f(a)}{b - a}.$$

With $g'(c) = 0$, we have

$$f'(c) = \frac{f(b) - f(a)}{b - a}. \quad \square$$

Note: The conclusion

$$f'(c) = \frac{f(b) - f(a)}{b - a}$$

is often written

$$f(b) - f(a) = f'(c)(b - a). \quad \square$$

EXERCISES

After verifying that the function satisfies the conditions of the mean-value theorem on the indicated interval, find the admissible values of c.

1. $f(x) = x^2$; [1, 2]. **2.** $f(x) = 3\sqrt{x} - 4x$; [1, 4]. **3.** $f(x) = x^3$; [1, 3].

4. $f(x) = x^{2/3}$; [1, 8]. **5.** $f(x) = \sqrt{1 - x^2}$; [0, 1]. **6.** $f(x) = x^3 - 3x$; [-1, 1].

7. Determine whether the function

$$f(x) = \frac{(1 - x^2)^{1/2}}{3 + x^2}$$

satisfies the conditions of Rolle's theorem on the interval $[-1, 1]$. If so, find the admissible values of c.

8. Sketch the graph of

$$f(x) = \begin{cases} 2 + x^3, & x \le 1 \\ 3x, & x > 1 \end{cases}$$

and compute the derivative. Determine whether f satisfies the conditions of the mean-value theorem on the interval $[-1, 2]$ and, if so, find the admissible values of c.

9. Sketch the graph of

$$f(x) = \begin{cases} 2x + 2, & x \le -1 \\ x^3 - x, & x > -1 \end{cases}$$

and compute the derivative. Determine whether f satisfies the conditions of the mean-value theorem on the interval $[-3, 2]$ and, if so, find the admissible values of c.

10. Set $f(x) = x^{-1}$, $a = -1$, $b = 1$. Verify that there is no number c for which

$$f'(c) = \frac{f(b) - f(a)}{b - a}.$$

Explain how this does not violate the mean-value theorem.

11. Exercise 10 with $f(x) = |x|$.

12. Graph the function $f(x) = |2x - 1| - 3$ and compute the derivative. Verify that $f(-1) = 0 = f(2)$ and yet $f'(x)$ is never 0. Explain how this does not violate Rolle's theorem.

13. Show that the equation $6x^4 - 7x + 1 = 0$ does not have more than two distinct real roots. (Use Rolle's theorem.)

14. Show that the equation $6x^5 + 13x + 1 = 0$ has exactly one real root. (Use Rolle's theorem and the intermediate-value theorem.)

15. Show that the equation $x^3 + 9x^2 + 33x - 8 = 0$ has exactly one real root.

16. Let f be twice differentiable. Show that, if the equation $f(x) = 0$ has n distinct real roots, then the equation $f'(x) = 0$ has at least $n - 1$ distinct real roots and the equation $f''(x) = 0$ has at least $n - 2$ distinct real roots.

17. Let P be a nonconstant polynomial

$$P(x) = a_n x^n + \cdots + a_1 x + a_0.$$

Show that between any two consecutive roots of the equation $P'(x) = 0$ there is at most one root of the equation $P(x) = 0$.

18. Show that the equation $x^3 + ax + b = 0$ has exactly one real root if $a \geq 0$ and at most one real root between $-\frac{1}{3}\sqrt{3}|a|$ and $\frac{1}{3}\sqrt{3}|a|$ if $a < 0$.

19. Given that $|f'(x)| \leq 1$ for all real numbers x, show that

$$|f(x_1) - f(x_2)| \leq |x_1 - x_2| \qquad \text{for all real numbers } x_1 \text{ and } x_2.$$

20. Let f be differentiable on an open interval I. Prove that, if $f'(x) = 0$ for all x in I, then f is constant on I.

21. Let f be differentiable on (a, b) with $f(a) = f(b) = 0$ and $f'(c) = 0$ for some c in (a, b). Show by example that f need not be continuous on $[a, b]$.

22. Prove that for all real x and y
(a) $|\cos x - \cos y| \leq |x - y|$.   (b) $|\sin x - \sin y| \leq |x - y|$.

23. An object moves along a coordinate line, its position at time t given by $f(t)$ where f is a differentiable function. (a) What does Rolle's theorem say about the motion? (b) What does the mean-value theorem say about the motion?

24. *(Important)* Use the mean-value theorem to show that, if f is continuous at x and $x + h$ and differentiable in between, then

$$f(x + h) - f(x) = f'(x + \theta h)h$$

for some number θ between 0 and 1. (In some texts this is how the mean-value theorem is stated.)

25. Let $h > 0$. Suppose that f is continuous on $[x_0 - h, x_0 + h]$ and differentiable on $(x_0 - h, x_0) \cup (x_0, x_0 + h)$. Show that if $\lim\limits_{x \to x_0^-} f'(x) = \lim\limits_{x \to x_0^+} f'(x) = L$, then f is differentiable at x_0 and $f'(x_0) = L$.   HINT: Use Exercise 24.

4.2 ·····INCREASING AND DECREASING FUNCTIONS

If f is a differentiable function, we can determine the intervals on which f "increases" and the intervals on which f "decreases" by examining the sign of the first derivative. As we shall show (and as you could well expect from recalling that the derivative is the slope of the graph),

(a) f "increases" on any interval on which the derivative is positive,

(b) f "decreases" on any interval on which the derivative is negative, and

(c) f is constant on any interval on which the derivative is identically 0.

To place our discussion on a solid footing we must define our terms.

> **DEFINITION 4.2.1**
>
> A function f is said to
>
>   (i) *increase* on the interval I iff for every two numbers x_1, x_2 in I
> $$x_1 < x_2 \quad \text{implies} \quad f(x_1) < f(x_2).$$
> (ii) *decrease* on the interval I iff for every two numbers x_1, x_2 in I
> $$x_1 < x_2 \quad \text{implies} \quad f(x_1) > f(x_2).$$

PRELIMINARY EXAMPLES

1. The squaring function
$$f(x) = x^2 \qquad \text{(Figure 4.2.1)}$$
decreases on $(-\infty, 0]$ and increases on $[0, \infty)$.

2. The function
$$f(x) = \begin{cases} 1, & x < 0 \\ x, & x \geq 0 \end{cases} \qquad \text{(Figure 4.2.2)}$$
is constant on $(-\infty, 0)$ and increases on $[0, \infty)$.

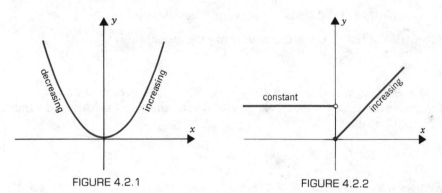

FIGURE 4.2.1   FIGURE 4.2.2

3. The cubing function
$$f(x) = x^3 \qquad \text{(Figure 4.2.3)}$$
is everywhere increasing.

4. In the case of the Dirichlet function
$$g(x) = \begin{cases} 1, & x \text{ rational} \\ 0, & x \text{ irrational} \end{cases}, \qquad \text{(Figure 4.2.4)}$$
there is no interval on which the function increases and no interval on which the function decreases. On every interval the function jumps back and forth between 0 and 1 an infinite number of times. □

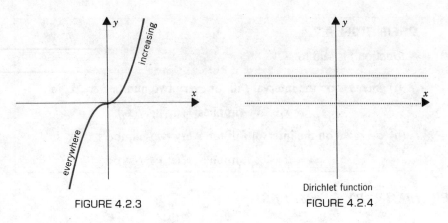

FIGURE 4.2.3   FIGURE 4.2.4

Now we start proving some theorems. As you will see, all of them are consequences of the mean-value theorem.

> ### THEOREM 4.2.2
>
> Let f be differentiable on an open interval I.
>
> (i) If $f'(x) > 0$ for all x in I, then f increases on I.
>
> (ii) If $f'(x) < 0$ for all x in I, then f decreases on I.
>
> (iii) If $f'(x) = 0$ for all x in I, then f is constant on I.

Proof. We take x_1 and x_2 in I with $x_1 < x_2$. Since f is differentiable on (x_1, x_2) and continuous on $[x_1, x_2]$, we see from the mean-value theorem that there is a number c in (x_1, x_2) for which

$$f'(c) = \frac{f(x_2) - f(x_1)}{x_2 - x_1}.$$

In (i), we have

$$\frac{f(x_2) - f(x_1)}{x_2 - x_1} > 0 \quad \text{and thus} \quad f(x_1) < f(x_2).$$

In (ii), we have

$$\frac{f(x_2) - f(x_1)}{x_2 - x_1} < 0 \quad \text{and thus} \quad f(x_1) > f(x_2).$$

In (iii), we have

$$\frac{f(x_2) - f(x_1)}{x_2 - x_1} = 0 \quad \text{and thus} \quad f(x_1) = f(x_2). \quad \square$$

CAUTION. The converse of Theorem 4.2.2 is not true. For example, we *cannot* conclude that, if f increases on I, then $f'(x) > 0$ for all x in I. Consider the cubing function $f(x) = x^3$. It is everywhere increasing even though $f'(0) = 0$. (Figure 4.2.3.) □

The theorem we just proved is useful, but it doesn't tell the complete story. Look, for example, at the squaring function $f(x) = x^2$. The derivative $f'(x) = 2x$ is negative for x in $(-\infty, 0)$, zero at $x = 0$, and positive for x in $(0, \infty)$. Theorem 4.2.2 assures us that

$$f \text{ decreases on } (-\infty, 0) \text{ and increases on } (0, \infty),$$

but actually

$$f \text{ decreases on } (-\infty, 0] \text{ and increases on } [0, \infty).$$

To get these stronger results we need a theorem that works for closed intervals.

To extend Theorem 4.2.2 so that it works for a closed interval I, the only additional condition we need is continuity at the endpoint(s).

THEOREM 4.2.3

Let f be continuous on a closed interval I and differentiable on the interior of I.

(i) If $f'(x) > 0$ for all x in the interior of I, then f increases on all of I.

(ii) If $f'(x) < 0$ for all x in the interior of I, then f decreases on all of I.

(iii) If $f'(x) = 0$ for all x in the interior of I, then f is constant on all of I.

A proof of this result is not hard to construct. As you can verify, a word-for-word repetition of our proof of Theorem 4.2.2 also works here.

It's time for examples.

EXAMPLE. The function

$$f(x) = \sqrt{1 - x^2}$$

has as its graph the upper semicircle of Figure 4.2.5. It is therefore obvious that f increases on $[-1, 0]$ and decreases on $[0, 1]$. With Theorem 4.2.3 we can get this information without reference to the figure.

That f increases on $[-1, 0]$ can be seen from the fact that the derivative

$$f'(x) = -\frac{x}{\sqrt{1 - x^2}}$$

is positive for x in $(-1, 0)$ and f itself is continuous on $[-1, 0]$. That f decreases on $[0, 1]$ can be seen from the fact that $f'(x)$ is negative for x in $(0, 1)$ and f is continuous on $[0, 1]$. □

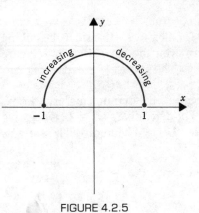

FIGURE 4.2.5

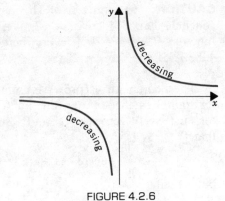

FIGURE 4.2.6

EXAMPLE. The function

$$f(x) = \frac{1}{x}$$

is defined for all $x \neq 0$. The derivative

$$f'(x) = -\frac{1}{x^2}$$

is negative for all $x \neq 0$. Thus the function f decreases both on $(-\infty, 0)$ and on $(0, \infty)$. (Figure 4.2.6.) □

EXAMPLE. The function

$$g(x) = 4x^5 - 15x^4 - 20x^3 + 110x^2 - 120x + 40$$

is a polynomial. It is therefore everywhere continuous and everywhere differentiable. Differentiation gives

$$\begin{aligned}
g'(x) &= 20x^4 - 60x^3 - 60x^2 + 220x - 120 \\
&= 20(x^4 - 3x^3 - 3x^2 + 11x - 6) \\
&= 20(x + 2)(x - 1)^2(x - 3).
\end{aligned}$$

The derivative g' takes on the value 0 at -2, at 1 and at 3. These numbers determine four intervals on which g' keeps a constant sign:

$$(-\infty, -2), \qquad (-2, 1), \qquad (1, 3), \qquad (3, \infty).$$

The sign of g' on these intervals and the consequences for g are as follows:

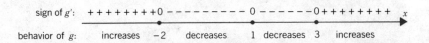

Since g is everywhere continuous, g increases on $(-\infty, -2]$, decreases on $[-2, 3]$ and increases on $[3, \infty)$. See Figure 4.2.7. □

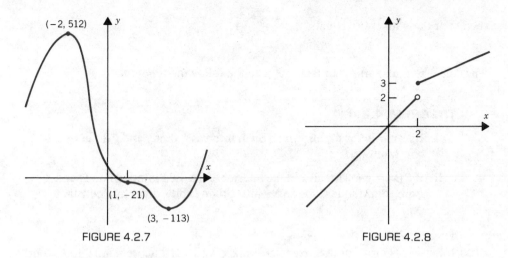

FIGURE 4.2.7   FIGURE 4.2.8

Theorems 4.2.2 and 4.2.3 have wide but limited applicability. If, for example, f is discontinuous at some point of its domain, then Theorems 4.2.2 and 4.2.3 do not tell the whole story.

EXAMPLE. The function

$$f(x) = \begin{cases} x, & x < 2 \\ \frac{1}{2}x + 2, & x \geq 2 \end{cases}$$

is graphed in Figure 4.2.8. Obviously there is a discontinuity at $x = 2$. Differentiation gives

$$f'(x) = \begin{cases} 1, & x < 2 \\ \text{does not exist,} & x = 2 \\ \frac{1}{2}, & x > 2 \end{cases}.$$

Since $f'(x) > 0$ on $(-\infty, 2)$, we know from Theorem 4.2.2 that f increases on $(-\infty, 2)$. Since $f'(x) > 0$ on $(2, \infty)$ and f is continuous on $[2, \infty)$, we know from Theorem 4.2.3 that f increases on $[2, \infty)$. The obvious fact that f increases on all of $(-\infty, \infty)$ is not derivable from the theorems.† □

Equality of Derivatives

If two differentiable functions differ by a constant,

$$f(x) = g(x) + C,$$

---

† The function

$$f(x) = \begin{cases} \frac{1}{2}x + 2, & x < 2 \\ x, & x \geq 2 \end{cases}$$

increases on $(-\infty, 2)$ and on $[2, \infty)$, but it does not increase on $(-\infty, \infty)$. Draw the graph.

then their derivatives are equal:

$$f'(x) = g'(x).$$

The converse is also true. In fact, we have the following theorem.

THEOREM 4.2.4

   I. If $f'(x) = g'(x)$ for all x in an open interval I, then f and g differ by a constant on I.

   II. If $f'(x) = g'(x)$ for all x in the interior of a closed interval I and f and g are continuous at the endpoint(s), then f and g differ by a constant on I.

Proof. Set $h = f - g$. For the first assertion apply (iii) of Theorem 4.2.2 to h. For the second assertion apply (iii) of Theorem 4.2.3 to h. We leave the details as an exercise. ☐

We illustrate the theorem in Figure 4.2.9. At points with the same x-coordinate the slopes are equal, and thus the curves have the same steepness. The separation between the curves remains constant.

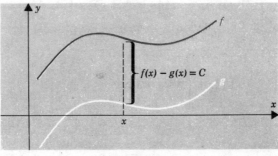

FIGURE 4.2.9

PROBLEM. Find f given that

$$f'(x) = 6x^2 - 7x - 5 \quad \text{for all real } x \quad \text{and} \quad f(2) = 1.$$

Solution. It's not hard to find a function with the right derivative:

$$\frac{d}{dx}[2x^3 - \tfrac{7}{2}x^2 - 5x] = 6x^2 - 7x - 5.$$

By Theorem 4.2.4 we know that $f(x)$ differs from $2x^3 - \tfrac{7}{2}x^2 - 5x$ only by some constant C. Thus we can write

$$f(x) = 2x^3 - \tfrac{7}{2}x^2 - 5x + C.$$

To evaluate C we use the fact that $f(2) = 1$. Since $f(2) = 1$ and also

$$f(2) = 2(2)^3 - \tfrac{7}{2}(2)^2 - 5(2) + C = 16 - 14 - 10 + C = -8 + C,$$

we have

$$-8 + C = 1 \quad \text{and} \quad C = 9.$$

Thus

$$f(x) = 2x^3 - \tfrac{7}{2}x^2 - 5x + 9. \quad \square$$

EXERCISES

Find the intervals on which f increases and the intervals on which f decreases.

1. $f(x) = x^3 - 3x + 2.$

2. $f(x) = x^3 - 3x^2 + 6.$

3. $f(x) = x + \dfrac{1}{x}.$

4. $f(x) = (x - 3)^3.$

5. $f(x) = x^3(1 + x).$

6. $f(x) = x(x + 1)(x + 2).$

7. $f(x) = (x + 1)^4.$

8. $f(x) = 2x - \dfrac{1}{x^2}.$

9. $f(x) = \dfrac{1}{|x - 2|}.$

10. $f(x) = \dfrac{x}{1 + x^2}.$

11. $f(x) = \dfrac{x^2 + 1}{x^2 - 1}.$

12. $f(x) = \dfrac{x^2}{x^2 + 1}.$

13. $f(x) = |x^2 - 5|.$

14. $f(x) = x^2(1 + x)^2.$

15. $f(x) = \dfrac{x - 1}{x + 1}.$

16. $f(x) = x^2 + \dfrac{16}{x^2}.$

17. $f(x) = \left(\dfrac{1 - \sqrt{x}}{1 + \sqrt{x}}\right)^7.$

18. $f(x) = \sqrt{\dfrac{2 + x}{1 + x}}.$

19. $f(x) = \sqrt{\dfrac{1 + x^2}{2 + x^2}}.$

20. $f(x) = |x + 1||x - 2|.$

21. $f(x) = \sqrt{\dfrac{3 - x}{x}}.$

22. $f(x) = x + \sin x, \quad 0 \le x \le 2\pi.$

23. $f(x) = x - \cos x, \quad 0 \le x \le 2\pi.$

24. $f(x) = \cos^2 x, \quad 0 \le x \le \pi.$

25. $f(x) = \cos 2x + 2 \cos x, \quad 0 \le x \le \pi.$

26. $f(x) = \sin^2 x - \sqrt{3} \sin x, \quad 0 \le x \le \pi.$

27. $f(x) = \sqrt{3}\, x - \cos 2x, \quad 0 \le x \le \pi.$

Find f given the following information.

28. $f'(x) = x^2 - 1$ for all real x and $f(0) = 1.$

29. $f'(x) = x^2 - 1$ for all real x and $f(1) = 2.$

30. $f'(x) = 2x - 5$ for all real x and $f(2) = 4.$

31. $f'(x) = 5x^4 + 4x^3 + 3x^2 + 2x + 1$ for all real x and $f(0) = 5.$

32. $f'(x) = 4x^{-3}$ for $x > 0$ and $f(1) = 0.$

33. $f'(x) = x^{1/3} - x^{1/2}$ for $x > 0$ and $f(0) = 1.$

34. $f'(x) = x^{-5} - 5x^{-1/5}$ for $x > 0$ and $f(1) = 0.$

35. $f'(x) = 2 + \sin x$ for all real x and $f(0) = 3.$

36. $f'(x) = 4x + \cos x$ for all real x and $f(0) = 1.$

Find f given the intervals on which f increases and the intervals on which f decreases.

37. $f(x) = \begin{cases} x + 7, & x < -3 \\ |x + 1|, & -3 \le x < 1 \\ 5 - 2x, & 1 \le x \end{cases}.$

38. $f(x) = \begin{cases} (x - 1)^2, & x < 1 \\ 5 - x, & 1 \le x < 3 \\ 7 - 2x, & 3 \le x \end{cases}.$

39. $f(x) = \begin{cases} 4 - x^2, & x < 1 \\ 7 - 2x, & 1 \le x < 3 \\ 3x - 10, & 3 \le x \end{cases}$.

40. $f(x) = \begin{cases} x + 2, & x < 0 \\ (x - 1)^2, & 0 < x < 3 \\ 8 - x, & 3 < x < 7 \\ 2x - 9, & 7 < x \\ 6, & x = 0, 3, 7 \end{cases}$.

41. Suppose that the function f increases on (a, b) and on (b, c). Suppose further that $\lim_{x \to b^-} f(x) = M$, $\lim_{x \to b^+} f(x) = N$ and $f(b) = L$. For which values of L, if any, can you conclude that f increases on (a, c) if (a) $M < N$? (b) $M > N$? (c) $M = N$?

42. Suppose that the function f increases on (a, b) and decreases on (b, c). Under what conditions can you conclude that f increases on $(a, b]$ and decreases on $[b, c)$?

43. Give an example of a function f that satisfies all of the following conditions: (i) f is defined for all real x, (ii) f' is positive wherever it exists, (iii) there is no interval on which f increases.

44. Prove Theorem 4.2.4.

45. Given that $f'(x) > g'(x)$ for all real x and $f(0) = g(0)$, compare $f(x)$ with $g(x)$ on $(-\infty, 0)$ and on $(0, \infty)$. Justify your answers.

46. Show, without making any assumptions of differentiability, that if f increases (decreases) on (a, b) and is continuous on $[a, b]$, then f increases (decreases) on $[a, b]$.

4.3 ⋯⋯MAXIMA AND MINIMA

In many problems of economics, engineering, and physics it is important to determine how large or how small a certain quantity can be. If the problem admits a mathematical formulation, it is often reducible to the problem of finding the maximum or minimum value of some function.

In this section we consider maximum and minimum values for functions defined on *an open interval* or on *the union of open intervals*. We begin with a definition.

DEFINITION 4.3.1   LOCAL EXTREMES

A function f is said to have a *local* (or *relative*) *maximum at c* iff

$$f(c) \ge f(x) \qquad \text{for all } x \text{ sufficiently close to } c.†$$

It is said to have a *local* (or *relative*) *minimum at c* iff

$$f(c) \le f(x) \qquad \text{for all } x \text{ sufficiently close to } c.$$

We illustrate these notions in Figure 4.3.1 and Figure 4.3.2. A careful look at the figures suggests that local maxima and minima occur only at points where the tangent is horizontal [$f'(c) = 0$] or where there is no tangent line [$f'(c)$ does not exist]. This is indeed the case.

---

† What do we mean by saying that "such and such is true *for all x sufficiently close to c?*" We mean that it's true for all x in some open interval $(c - \delta, c + \delta)$ centered at c.

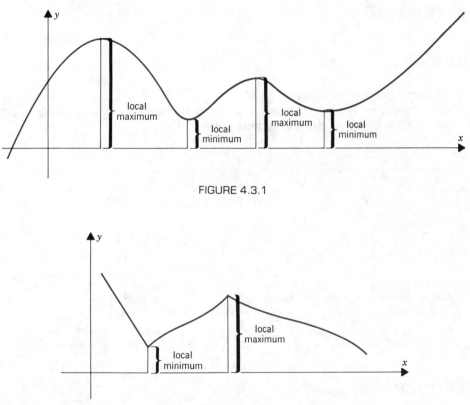

FIGURE 4.3.1

FIGURE 4.3.2

THEOREM 4.3.2

If f has a local maximum or minimum at c, then either

$$f'(c) = 0 \qquad \text{or} \qquad f'(c) \text{ does not exist.}$$

Proof. If $f'(c) > 0$ or $f'(c) < 0$, then, by Theorem 4.1.2, there must be numbers x_1 and x_2 that are arbitrarily close to c and yet satisfy

$$f(x_1) < f(c) < f(x_2).$$

This makes it impossible for a local maximum or minimum to occur at c. ☐

In view of this result, when searching for the local maxima and minima of a function f, the only points we need to test are *those points c in the domain of f for which $f'(c) = 0$ or $f'(c)$ does not exist.* Such points are called *critical points.*

We illustrate the technique for finding local maxima and minima by some examples. In each example the first step will be to find the critical points. We begin with very simple cases.

EXAMPLE. For

$$f(x) = 3 - x^2 \qquad \text{(Figure 4.3.3)}$$

the derivative

$$f'(x) = -2x$$

exists everywhere. Since $f'(x) = 0$ only at $x = 0$, 0 is the only critical point. The number $f(0) = 3$ is obviously a local maximum. ☐

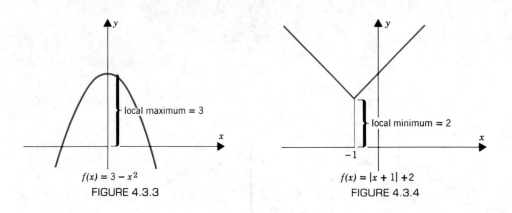

$f(x) = 3 - x^2$

FIGURE 4.3.3

$f(x) = |x + 1| + 2$

FIGURE 4.3.4

EXAMPLE. In the case of

$$f(x) = |x + 1| + 2 \qquad \text{(Figure 4.3.4)}$$

differentiation gives

$$f'(x) = \begin{cases} -1, & x < -1 \\ 1, & x > -1 \end{cases}.$$

This derivative is never 0. It fails to exist only at -1. The number -1 is the only critical point. The value $f(-1) = 2$ is a local minimum. ☐

EXAMPLE. In the case of

$$f(x) = \frac{1}{x - 1} \qquad \text{(Figure 4.3.5)}$$

the domain is $(-\infty, 1) \cup (1, \infty)$. The derivative

$$f'(x) = -\frac{1}{(x - 1)^2}$$

exists throughout the domain of f and is never 0. Thus there are no critical points and therefore no local extreme values. ☐

CAUTION. The fact that c is a critical point of f does not guarantee that $f(c)$ is a local extreme value. This is illustrated in the next two examples.

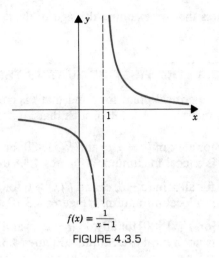

$$f(x) = \frac{1}{x-1}$$

FIGURE 4.3.5

EXAMPLE.　In the case of the cubing function

$$f(x) = x^3 \qquad\qquad \text{(Figure 4.3.6)}$$

the derivative $f'(x) = 3x^2$ is 0 at 0, but $f(0) = 0$ is not a local extreme value. The cubing function is everywhere increasing. □

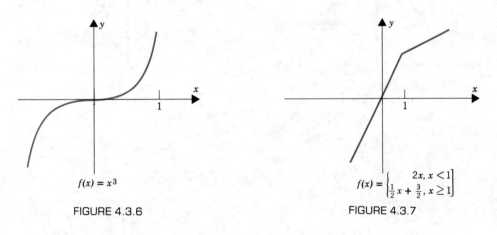

$f(x) = x^3$

FIGURE 4.3.6

$$f(x) = \begin{cases} 2x, & x < 1 \\ \frac{1}{2}x + \frac{3}{2}, & x \geq 1 \end{cases}$$

FIGURE 4.3.7

EXAMPLE.　The function

$$f(x) = \begin{cases} 2x, & x < 1 \\ \frac{1}{2}x + \frac{3}{2}, & x \geq 1 \end{cases}, \qquad\qquad \text{(Figure 4.3.7)}$$

is everywhere increasing. Although 1 is a critical point [$f'(1)$ does not exist], $f(1) = 2$ is not a local extreme value. □

There are two widely used tests for determining the behavior of a function at a critical point. The first test (given in Theorem 4.3.3) requires that we examine the sign of the first derivative on both sides of the critical point. The second test (given in

Theorem 4.3.4) requires that we examine the sign of the second derivative at the critical point itself.

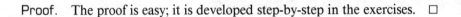

THEOREM 4.3.3　THE FIRST-DERIVATIVE TEST

Suppose that c is a critical point for f and that f is continuous at c. If there is an open interval $(c - \delta, c + \delta)$ such that

  (i) $f'(x) > 0$ for all x in $(c - \delta, c)$ and $f'(x) < 0$ for all x in $(c, c + \delta)$, then $f(c)$ is a local maximum. (Figures 4.3.8 and 4.3.9.)

  (ii) $f'(x) < 0$ for all x in $(c - \delta, c)$ and $f'(x) > 0$ for all x in $(c, c + \delta)$, then $f(c)$ is a local minimum. (Figures 4.3.10 and 4.3.11.)

  (iii) $f'(x) > 0$ [or, $f'(x) < 0$] for all x in $(c - \delta, c)$ and all x in $(c, c + \delta)$, then $f(c)$ is not a local extremum. (Figures 4.3.6 and 4.3.7.)

Proof. The proof is easy; it is developed step-by-step in the exercises. □

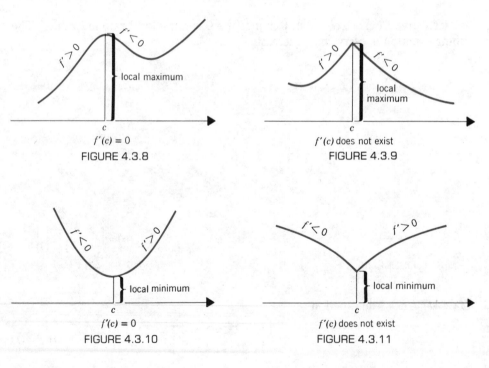

FIGURE 4.3.8

FIGURE 4.3.9

FIGURE 4.3.10

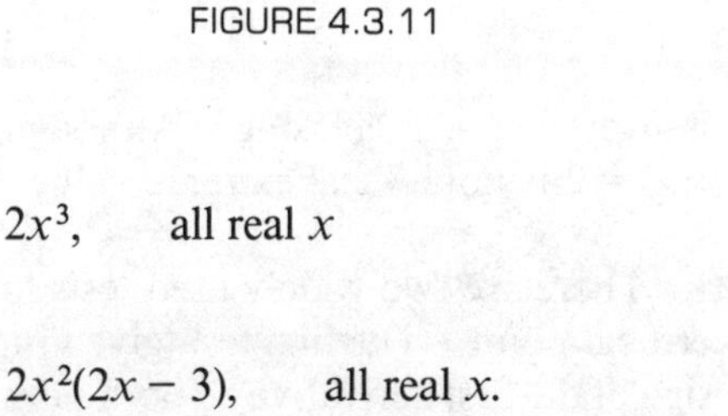

FIGURE 4.3.11

EXAMPLE. The function

$$f(x) = x^4 - 2x^3, \qquad \text{all real } x$$

has derivative

$$f'(x) = 4x^3 - 6x^2 = 2x^2(2x - 3), \qquad \text{all real } x.$$

The only critical points are 0 and $\frac{3}{2}$. The results of applying the first derivative test are shown in Figure 4.3.12. We find that there is no local extremum at $(0, 0)$, but there is a local minimum at $(\frac{3}{2}, -\frac{27}{16})$. The graph of f appears in Figure 4.3.13. $\square$

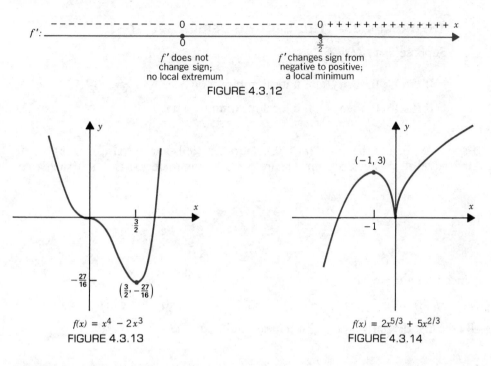

FIGURE 4.3.12

$f(x) = x^4 - 2x^3$
FIGURE 4.3.13

$f(x) = 2x^{5/3} + 5x^{2/3}$
FIGURE 4.3.14

REMARK. To save space on the number line we will write "dne" for "does not exist." $\square$

EXAMPLE. The function

$$f(x) = 2x^{5/3} + 5x^{2/3}, \qquad \text{all real } x$$

has derivative

$$f'(x) = \frac{10}{3}x^{2/3} + \frac{10}{3}x^{-1/3} = \frac{10}{3}x^{-1/3}(x + 1), \qquad x \neq 0.$$

Since $f'(-1) = 0$ and $f'(0)$ does not exist, the critical points are -1 and 0. The results of applying the first-derivative test are shown in Figure 4.3.15. We find a local maximum at $(-1, 3)$ and a local minimum at $(0, 0)$. The graph of f appears in Figure 4.3.14. $\square$

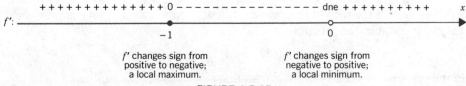

FIGURE 4.3.15

In certain cases it may be difficult to determine the sign of the first derivative both to the left of c and to the right of c. If f is twice differentiable at c, the following test may be easier to apply.

> ### THEOREM 4.3.4   THE SECOND-DERIVATIVE TEST
>
> Suppose that $f'(c) = 0$.
>
> If $f''(c) > 0$, then $f(c)$ is a local minimum value.
>
> If $f''(c) < 0$, then $f(c)$ is a local maximum value.

Proof. We handle the case $f''(c) > 0$. The other is left as an exercise. Since f'' is the derivative of f', we see from Theorem 4.1.2 that there exists $\delta > 0$ such that, if

$$c - \delta < x_1 < c < x_2 < c + \delta,$$

then

$$f'(x_1) < f'(c) < f'(x_2).$$

Since $f'(c) = 0$, we have

$$f'(x) < 0 \quad \text{for } x \text{ in } (c - \delta, c) \qquad \text{and} \qquad f'(x) > 0 \quad \text{for } x \text{ in } (c, c + \delta).$$

By the first-derivative test $f(c)$ is a local minimum.   □

EXAMPLE. For

$$f(x) = x^3 - x$$

we have

$$f'(x) = 3x^2 - 1 \quad \text{and} \quad f''(x) = 6x.$$

The critical points are $-\tfrac{1}{3}\sqrt{3}$ and $\tfrac{1}{3}\sqrt{3}$. At each of these points the derivative is 0. Since $f''(-\tfrac{1}{3}\sqrt{3}) < 0$ and $f''(\tfrac{1}{3}\sqrt{3}) > 0$, we can conclude from the second-derivative test that $f(-\tfrac{1}{3}\sqrt{3}) = \tfrac{2}{9}\sqrt{3}$ is a local maximum and $f(\tfrac{1}{3}\sqrt{3}) = -\tfrac{2}{9}\sqrt{3}$ is a local minimum.   □

We can apply the first-derivative test even at points where the function is not differentiable, provided that it is continuous there. On the other hand, the second-derivative test can only be applied at points where the function is twice differentiable and then only if the second derivative is different from zero. This is a drawback. Take, for example, the functions

$$f(x) = x^{4/3} \quad \text{and} \quad g(x) = x^4.$$

In the first case we have $f'(x) = \tfrac{4}{3}x^{1/3}$ so that

$$f'(0) = 0, \qquad f'(x) < 0 \quad \text{for } x < 0, \qquad f'(x) > 0 \quad \text{for } x > 0.$$

By the first-derivative test, $f(0) = 0$ is a local minimum. We cannot get this information from the second-derivative test because $f''(x) = \frac{4}{9}x^{-2/3}$ does not exist at $x = 0$. In the case of $g(x) = x^4$, we have $g'(x) = 4x^3$ so that

$$g'(0) = 0, \qquad g'(x) < 0 \quad \text{for } x < 0, \qquad g'(x) > 0 \quad \text{for } x > 0.$$

By the first-derivative test, $g(0) = 0$ is a local minimum. But here again the second-derivative test is of no avail: $g''(x) = 12x^2$ is 0 at $x = 0$.

EXERCISES

Find the critical points of f and the local extreme values.

1. $f(x) = x^3 + 3x - 2$.

2. $f(x) = 2x^4 - 4x^2 + 6$.

3. $f(x) = x + \dfrac{1}{x}$.

4. $f(x) = x^2 - \dfrac{3}{x^2}$.

5. $f(x) = x^2(1 - x)$.

6. $f(x) = (1 - x)^2(1 + x)$.

7. $f(x) = \dfrac{1 + x}{1 - x}$.

8. $f(x) = \dfrac{2 - 3x}{2 + x}$.

9. $f(x) = \dfrac{2}{x(x + 1)}$.

10. $f(x) = |x^2 - 16|$.

11. $f(x) = x^3(1 - x)^2$.

12. $f(x) = \left(\dfrac{x - 2}{x + 2}\right)^3$.

13. $f(x) = (1 - 2x)(x - 1)^3$.

14. $f(x) = (1 - x)(1 + x)^3$.

15. $f(x) = \dfrac{x^2}{1 + x}$.

16. $f(x) = \dfrac{|x|}{1 + |x|}$.

17. $f(x) = |x - 1||x + 2|$.

18. $f(x) = x \sqrt[3]{1 - x}$.

19. $f(x) = x^2 \sqrt[3]{2 + x}$.

20. $f(x) = \dfrac{1}{x + 1} - \dfrac{1}{x - 2}$.

21. $f(x) = |x - 3| + |2x + 1|$.

22. $f(x) = x^{7/3} - 7x^{1/3}$.

23. $f(x) = x^{2/3} + 2x^{-1/3}$.

24. $f(x) = \dfrac{x^3}{x + 1}$.

25. $f(x) = \sin x + \cos x, \quad 0 < x < 2\pi$.

26. $f(x) = x + \cos 2x, \quad 0 < x < \pi$.

27. $f(x) = \sin^2 x - \sqrt{3} \sin x, \quad 0 < x < \pi$.

28. $f(x) = \sin^2 x, \quad 0 < x < 2\pi$.

29. $f(x) = \sin x \cos x - 3 \sin x + 2x, \quad 0 < x < 2\pi$.

30. $f(x) = 2 \sin^3 x - 3 \sin x, \quad 0 < x < \pi$.

31. Justify each statement in the following proof of Theorem 4.3.3(i).
   (a) f increases on $(c - \delta, c)$ and f decreases on $(c, c + \delta)$.
   (b) f increases on $(c - \delta, c]$ and f decreases on $[c, c + \delta)$.
   (c) $f(x) \leq f(c)$ for all x in $(c - \delta, c + \delta)$.
   (d) $f(c)$ is a local maximum.

32. Prove Theorem 4.3.3(ii).

33. Prove Theorem 4.3.4(iii).

34. Prove the validity of the second-derivative test in the case that $f''(c) < 0$.

35. Find the critical points and the local extreme values of the polynomial

$$P(x) = x^4 - 8x^3 + 22x^2 - 24x + 4.$$

Then show that the equation $P(x) = 0$ has exactly two real roots, both positive.

4.4 ······MORE ON MAXIMA AND MINIMA

Endpoint Maxima and Minima

For functions defined on an open interval or on the union of open intervals the critical points are those where the derivative is 0 or the derivative does not exist. For functions defined on a closed or half-closed interval

$$[a, b], \quad [a, b), \quad (a, b], \quad [a, \infty), \quad \text{or} \quad (-\infty, b]$$

the *endpoints* of the domain (a and b in the case of $[a, b]$, a in the case of $[a, b)$ or $[a, \infty)$, and b in the case of $(a, b]$ or $(-\infty, b]$) are also called *critical points*.

Endpoints can give rise to what are called *endpoint maxima* and *endpoint minima*. See, for example, Figures 4.4.1, 4.4.2, 4.4.3, and 4.4.4.

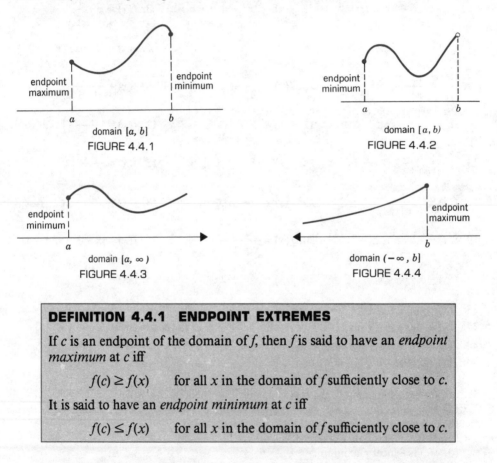

domain $[a, b]$
FIGURE 4.4.1

domain $[a, b)$
FIGURE 4.4.2

domain $[a, \infty)$
FIGURE 4.4.3

domain $(-\infty, b]$
FIGURE 4.4.4

> **DEFINITION 4.4.1   ENDPOINT EXTREMES**
>
> If c is an endpoint of the domain of f, then f is said to have an *endpoint maximum* at c iff
>
> $$f(c) \geq f(x) \qquad \text{for all } x \text{ in the domain of } f \text{ sufficiently close to } c.$$
>
> It is said to have an *endpoint minimum* at c iff
>
> $$f(c) \leq f(x) \qquad \text{for all } x \text{ in the domain of } f \text{ sufficiently close to } c.$$

Endpoints are usually tested by examining the sign of the derivative at nearby points. Suppose, for example, that a is the left endpoint and f is continuous from the right at a. If $f'(x) < 0$ for x close to a, then f decreases on an interval of the form $[a, a + \delta]$ and therefore $f(a)$ must be an endpoint maximum. (Figure 4.4.1.) On the other hand, if $f'(x) > 0$ for x close to a, then f increases on an interval of the form $[a, a + \delta]$ and therefore $f(a)$ must be an endpoint minimum. (Figure 4.4.2.) Similar reasoning can be applied to right endpoints.

Absolute Maxima and Minima

Whether or not a function f has a local or endpoint extreme at some point depends entirely on the behavior of f for x close to that point. Absolute extreme values, which we define below, depend on the behavior of the function on its entire domain.

We begin with a number d in the domain of f. Here d can be an interior point or an endpoint.

DEFINITION 4.4.2 ABSOLUTE EXTREMES

$f(d)$ is called *the absolute maximum (value)* of f iff

$$f(d) \geq f(x) \qquad \text{for all } x \text{ in the domain of } f;$$

$f(d)$ is called *the absolute minimum (value)* of f iff

$$f(d) \leq f(x) \qquad \text{for all } x \text{ in the domain of } f.$$

A function can be continuous on an interval (or even differentiable there) without taking on any absolute extreme values. All we can say in general is that, if f takes on an absolute extreme value, then it does so at a critical point. If, however, the domain is a bounded closed interval $[a, b]$, then the continuity of the function guarantees the existence of both an absolute maximum and an absolute minimum (Theorem 2.6.2). In this case the most practical way to determine the absolute extremes is to gather together the local extremes and the endpoint extremes. The largest of these numbers is obviously the absolute maximum, and the smallest is the absolute minimum.

If the domain is a half-closed interval or a bounded open interval,

$$(a, b], \quad [a, b), \quad \text{or} \quad (a, b),$$

the behavior of the function near a "missing endpoint" may preclude (rule out) the existence of an absolute extremum. As an example, consider the function graphed in Figure 4.4.2. In this case

$$\lim_{x \to b^-} f(x) > f(x) \qquad \text{for all } x \text{ in } [a, b).$$

This function approaches, but does not attain, an absolute maximum, and thus has no absolute maximum.

If the domain contains an unbounded interval

$$[a, \infty), \quad (a, \infty), \quad (-\infty, b], \quad (-\infty, b) \quad \text{or} \quad (-\infty, \infty),$$

we must examine what happens as x increases without bound (written $x \to \infty$) and/or what happens as x decreases without bound (written $x \to -\infty$). This too may preclude the existence of an absolute extremum. As an example, consider the function

$$f(x) = \frac{x^2}{x^2 + 1} = 1 - \frac{1}{x^2 + 1}, \qquad \text{all real } x.$$

This function has no absolute maximum since $f(x) \to 1$ as $x \to \infty$ (and as $x \to -\infty$), but, as you can readily see, $f(x) < 1$ for all real x.

We look into this notation more carefully in Section 4.8, where we discuss asymptotes. For the moment the following examples should suffice to establish the notation.

EXAMPLES

As $x \to \infty$, $x^3 \to \infty$.   As $x \to \infty$, $\sqrt{x} \to \infty$.   As $x \to \infty$, $\dfrac{1}{x} \to 0$.

As $x \to -\infty$, $\dfrac{1}{x} \to 0$.   As $x \to -\infty$, $x^2 \to \infty$.   As $x \to -\infty$, $x^{1/3} \to -\infty$. $\square$

Summary

We summarize here the central ideas of these last two sections by outlining a step-by-step procedure for finding all the extreme values (local, endpoint, and absolute) of a function f. We assume that f is continuous where defined.

1. Find the critical points. These are the interior points c at which $f'(c) = 0$ or $f'(c)$ does not exist, and the endpoints of the domain.

2. Test each interior critical point for local extremes:
   (a) by applying the first-derivative test,
   (b) or, if $f''(c)$ exists and is not 0, by applying the second-derivative test.

3. Test each endpoint for endpoint extremes. (If necessary, by checking the sign of f' at nearby points.)

4. Determine whether any of the local or endpoint extremes are absolute extremes.

PROBLEM. Find the critical points and classify the extreme values of

$$f(x) = x^2 - 2|x| + 2, \qquad x \in [-\tfrac{1}{2}, \tfrac{3}{2}].$$

Solution. First we check the interior points $x \in (-\tfrac{1}{2}, \tfrac{3}{2})$. On the open interval $(-\tfrac{1}{2}, \tfrac{3}{2})$ the function is differentiable except at 0:

$$f'(x) = \begin{cases} 2x + 2, & -\tfrac{1}{2} < x < 0 \\ 2x - 2, & 0 < x < \tfrac{3}{2} \end{cases}.$$ (check this out)

This makes 0 a critical point. Since $f'(x) = 0$ at $x = 1$, 1 is a critical point. The endpoints $-\tfrac{1}{2}$ and $\tfrac{3}{2}$ are also critical points.

An analysis of the sign of f' yields the information displayed in Figure 4.4.5.

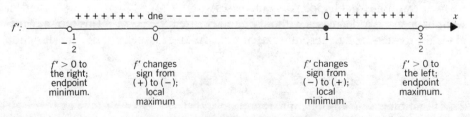

FIGURE 4.4.5

Using that information we can summarize as follows:

$f(-\frac{1}{2}) = 1\frac{1}{4}$ is an endpoint minimum.

$f(0) = 2$ is a local maximum; it is also the absolute maximum.

$f(1) = 1$ is a local minimum; it is also the absolute minimum.

$f(\frac{3}{2}) = 1\frac{1}{4}$ is an endpoint maximum.

The graph of f is shown in Figure 4.4.6.   □

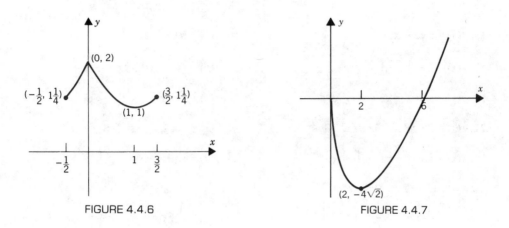

FIGURE 4.4.6   FIGURE 4.4.7

PROBLEM. Find the critical points and classify the extreme values of

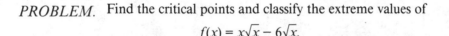

$$f(x) = x\sqrt{x} - 6\sqrt{x}.$$

Solution. The domain here is $[0, \infty)$. First we check the interior points $x \in (0, \infty)$. On $(0, \infty)$ the function f is differentiable and

$$f'(x) = \frac{3}{2}x^{1/2} - 3x^{-1/2} = \frac{3(x-2)}{2\sqrt{x}}. \qquad \text{(check this out)}$$

Since $f'(x) = 0$ at $x = 2$, we see that 2 is a critical point. The endpoint 0 is also a critical point.

A little to the right of $0, f' < 0$; it follows that $f(0) = 0$ is an endpoint maximum. Since f' changes sign from $(-)$ to $(+)$ at $x = 2$, we know that $f(2) = -4\sqrt{2}$ is a local minimum; it is also the absolute minimum. Finally, $f(x) = \sqrt{x}(x - 6) \to \infty$ as $x \to \infty$; therefore there is no absolute maximum. The graph of f is given in Figure 4.4.7.   □

EXERCISES

Find the critical points and classify the extreme values.

1. $f(x) = \sqrt{x + 2}$.   **2.** $f(x) = (x - 1)(x - 2)$.

3. $f(x) = x^2 - 4x + 1, \quad x \in [0, 3]$.   **4.** $f(x) = 2x^2 + 5x - 1, \quad x \in [-2, 0]$.

5. $f(x) = x^2 + \dfrac{1}{x}$.

6. $f(x) = x + \dfrac{1}{x^2}$.

7. $f(x) = x^2 + \dfrac{1}{x}, \quad x \in [\frac{1}{10}, 2]$.

8. $f(x) = x + \dfrac{1}{x^2}, \quad x \in [1, \sqrt{2}]$

9. $f(x) = (x - 1)(x - 2), \quad x \in [0, 2]$.

10. $f(x) = (x - 1)^2(x - 2)^2, \quad x \in [0, 4]$.

11. $f(x) = \dfrac{x}{4 + x^2}, \quad x \in [-3, 1]$.

12. $f(x) = \dfrac{x^2}{1 + x^2}, \quad x \in [-1, 2]$.

13. $f(x) = (x - \sqrt{x})^2$.

14. $f(x) = x\sqrt{4 - x^2}$.

15. $f(x) = x\sqrt{3 - x}$.

16. $f(x) = \sqrt{x} - \dfrac{1}{\sqrt{x}}$.

17. $f(x) = 1 - \sqrt[3]{x - 1}$.

18. $f(x) = (4x - 1)^{1/3}(2x - 1)^{2/3}$.

19. $f(x) = \sin^2 x - \sqrt{3}\cos x, \quad 0 \le x \le \pi$.

20. $f(x) = \cot x + x, \quad 0 < x \le \dfrac{2\pi}{3}$.

21. $f(x) = 2\cos^3 x + 3\cos x, \quad 0 \le x \le \pi$.

22. $f(x) = \sin 2x - x, \quad 0 \le x \le \pi$.

23. $f(x) = \tan x - x, \quad -\dfrac{\pi}{3} \le x < \dfrac{\pi}{2}$.

24. $f(x) = \sin^4 x - \sin^2 x, \quad 0 \le x \le \dfrac{2\pi}{3}$.

25. $f(x) = \begin{cases} -2x, & 0 \le x < 1 \\ x - 3, & 1 \le x \le 4 \\ 5 - x, & 4 < x \le 7 \end{cases}$.

26. $f(x) = \begin{cases} x + 9, & -8 \le x < -3 \\ x^2 + x, & -3 \le x \le 2 \\ 5x - 4, & 2 < x < 5 \end{cases}$.

27. $f(x) = \begin{cases} x^2 + 1, & -2 \le x < -1 \\ 5 + 2x - x^2, & -1 \le x \le 3 \\ x - 1, & 3 < x < 6 \end{cases}$.

28. $f(x) = \begin{cases} 2 - 2x - x^2, & -2 \le x \le 0 \\ |x - 2|, & 0 < x < 3 \\ \frac{1}{3}(x - 2)^3, & 3 \le x \le 4 \end{cases}$.

29. $f(x) = \begin{cases} |x + 1|, & -3 \le x < 0 \\ x^2 - 4x + 2, & 0 \le x < 3 \\ 2x - 7, & 3 \le x < 4 \end{cases}$.

30. $f(x) = \begin{cases} -x^2, & 0 \le x < 1 \\ -2x, & 1 < x < 2 \\ -\frac{1}{2}x^2, & 2 \le x \le 3 \end{cases}$.

31. Suppose that c is a critical point for f and $f'(x) > 0$ for $x \ne c$. Prove that, if $f(c)$ is a local maximum, then f is not continuous at c.

32. What can be said about the function f continuous on $[a, b]$, if for some c in (a, b), $f(c)$ is both a local maximum and a local minimum?

33. Suppose that f is continuous on its domain $[a, b]$ and $f(a) = f(b)$. Prove that f has at least one critical point in (a, b).

34. Suppose that $c_1 < c_2$ and that both $f(c_1)$ and $f(c_2)$ are local maximums. Prove that, if f is continuous on $[c_1, c_2]$, then, for some c in (c_1, c_2), $f(c)$ is a local minimum.

4.5 ······SOME MAX-MIN PROBLEMS

The techniques of the last two sections can be brought to bear on a wide variety of max-min problems. The *key step* in solving such problems is to express the quantity to be maximized or minimized as a function of one variable. If the function is differentiable, we can then differentiate and analyze the results.

PROBLEM. A mirror in the shape of a rectangle capped by a semicircle is to have perimeter p. Choose the radius of the semicircular part so that the mirror has maximum area.

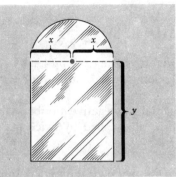

FIGURE 4.5.1

Solution. As in Figure 4.5.1 we let x be the radius of the semicircular part and y the height of the rectangular part. We want to express the area

$$A = \tfrac{1}{2}\pi x^2 + 2xy$$

as a function of x alone. To do this, we must express y in terms of x.

Since the perimeter is p, we have

$$p = 2x + 2y + \pi x$$

and thus

$$y = \tfrac{1}{2}[p - (2 + \pi)x].$$

Since y must be positive, x must remain between 0 and $p/(2 + \pi)$.

The area can now be expressed in terms of x alone:

$$
\begin{aligned}
A(x) &= \tfrac{1}{2}\pi x^2 + 2xy \\
&= \tfrac{1}{2}\pi x^2 + 2x\{\tfrac{1}{2}[p - (2 + \pi)x]\} \\
&= \tfrac{1}{2}\pi x^2 + px - (2 + \pi)x^2 = px - (2 + \tfrac{1}{2}\pi)x^2.
\end{aligned}
$$

We want to maximize the function

$$A(x) = px - (2 + \tfrac{1}{2}\pi)x^2, \qquad x \in \left(0, \frac{p}{2 + \pi}\right).$$

(Key step completed.)

The derivative

$$A'(x) = p - (4 + \pi)x$$

is 0 only at

$$x = \frac{p}{4 + \pi}.$$

Since

$$A'(x) > 0 \quad \text{for} \quad 0 < x < \frac{p}{4 + \pi}$$

and

$$A'(x) < 0 \quad \text{for} \quad \frac{p}{4 + \pi} < x < \frac{p}{2 + \pi},$$

the function A is maximized by setting $x = p/(4 + \pi)$. The mirror has maximum area when the radius of the semicircular part is $p/(4 + \pi)$. □

PROBLEM. The sum of two nonnegative numbers is 3. Find the two numbers if the square of twice the first, diminished by twice the square of the second, is a minimum.

Solution. Denote the first number by x; the second number becomes $3 - x$. Since both x and $3 - x$ are to be nonnegative, we must have $0 \le x \le 3$. We want the minimum value of

$$f(x) = (2x)^2 - 2(3 - x)^2, \qquad 0 \le x \le 3.$$

(Key step completed.)
    Since

$$f'(x) = 8x + 4(3 - x) = 4x + 12 = 4(x + 3),$$

we have $f'(x) > 0$ on $(0, 3)$. Since f is continuous on $[0, 3]$, f increases on $[0, 3]$. The minimum value of f occurs at $x = 0$. The first number must be 0 and the second 3. □

PROBLEM. Determine the dimensions of the rectangle of greatest area that can be inscribed in a 3-4-5 right triangle with one side of the rectangle resting on the hypotenuse of the triangle.

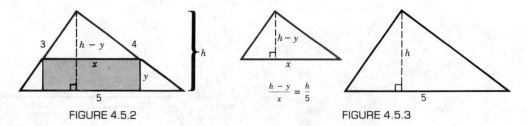

FIGURE 4.5.2   FIGURE 4.5.3

Solution. We label the dimensions as in Figure 4.5.2. To express the area $A = xy$ as a function of x alone, we need y in terms of x. We can get y in terms of x by similar triangles. The triangles of interest have been redrawn separately in Figure 4.5.3. From these triangles we see that

$$\frac{h - y}{x} = \frac{h}{5}$$

and therefore

(1) $y = h(1 - \frac{1}{5}x)$.

We can determine h by calculating the area of the 3-4-5 triangle in two different ways:

$$\tfrac{1}{2}(5)(h) = \tfrac{5}{2}h \quad \text{and} \quad \tfrac{1}{2}(3)(4) = 6.$$

Therefore $\frac{5}{2}h = 6$ and thus $h = \frac{12}{5}$.
    Substituting $h = \frac{12}{5}$ in equation (1) we have

(2) $y = \frac{12}{5}(1 - \frac{1}{5}x) = \frac{12}{25}(5 - x)$.

Since both x and y must be positive, x must remain between 0 and 5. Since the area of the rectangle is the product

$$xy = x\tfrac{12}{25}(5 - x) = \tfrac{12}{5}x - \tfrac{12}{25}x^2,$$

the function we want to maximize is the function

$$A(x) = \tfrac{12}{5}x - \tfrac{12}{25}x^2, \qquad 0 < x < 5.$$

(Key step completed.)
    As you can check by differentiation, this function takes on its absolute maximum value at $x = \frac{5}{2}$. Using (2) you can see that when $x = \frac{5}{2}$, $y = \frac{6}{5}$. The rectangle of greatest area that satisfies the conditions of this problem is a rectangle of length $\frac{5}{2}$ and width $\frac{6}{5}$. □

PROBLEM.   A lighthouse lies 3 miles offshore directly across from a point A of a straight coastline. Five miles down the coast from A there is a general store. The lighthouse keeper can row his boat at 4 miles per hour and he can walk at 6 miles per hour. To what point of the shore should he row so as to reach the store as quickly as possible?

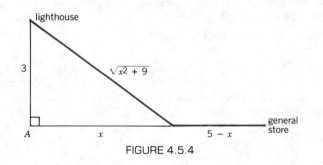

FIGURE 4.5.4

Solution.   Figure 4.5.4 shows the geometry of the problem. If the lighthouse keeper lands x miles from A, he must row for $\sqrt{x^2 + 9}$ miles and walk for $5 - x$ miles. The total time required on that route is

$$\frac{\text{distance rowed}}{\text{rowing rate}} + \frac{\text{distance walked}}{\text{walking rate}} = \frac{\sqrt{x^2 + 9}}{4} + \frac{5 - x}{6}.$$

We want to find the value of x that minimizes the function

$$T(x) = \frac{\sqrt{x^2 + 9}}{4} + \frac{5 - x}{6}, \qquad 0 \le x \le 5.$$

(Key step completed.)
Differentiation gives

$$T'(x) = \frac{x}{4\sqrt{x^2 + 9}} - \frac{1}{6}, \qquad 0 < x < 5.$$

Setting $T'(x) = 0$, we find that

$$6x = 4\sqrt{x^2 + 9}$$
$$36x^2 = 16(x^2 + 9)$$
$$20x^2 = 144$$
$$x = \pm\tfrac{6}{5}\sqrt{5}.$$

The solution $x = -\tfrac{6}{5}\sqrt{5}$ is an extraneous root we introduced when we did the squaring. The value we want is $x = \tfrac{6}{5}\sqrt{5}$. As you can check by examining the sign of the derivative, T decreases for $0 < x < \tfrac{6}{5}\sqrt{5}$ and increases for $\tfrac{6}{5}\sqrt{5} < x < 5$. It follows that $x = \tfrac{6}{5}\sqrt{5}$ gives the absolute minimum value for T.

The lighthouse keeper can reach the general store most quickly by rowing to the point that lies $\tfrac{6}{5}\sqrt{5}$ miles (about 2.683 miles) down shore from A. □

EXERCISES

1. Find the greatest possible value for xy given that x and y are both positive and $x + y = 40$.
2. Find the dimensions of the rectangle of perimeter 24 that has the largest area.
3. A rectangular garden 200 square feet in area is to be fenced off against rabbits. Find the dimensions that will require the least amount of fencing if one side of the garden is already protected by a barn.
4. Find the largest possible area for a rectangle with base on the x-axis and upper vertices on the curve $y = 4 - x^2$.
5. Find the largest possible area for a rectangle inscribed in a circle of radius 4.
6. The cross section of a beam is in the form of a rectangle of length l and width w. (Figure 4.5.5.) Assuming that the strength of the beam varies directly with w^2l, what are the dimensions of the strongest beam that can be sawed from a round log of diameter 3 feet?

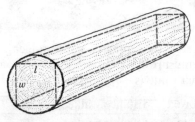

FIGURE 4.5.5

7. A rectangular playground is to be fenced off and divided in two by another fence parallel to one side of the playground. Six hundred feet of fencing is used. Find the dimensions of the playground that will enclose the greatest total area.

8. A Norman window is a window in the shape of a rectangle surmounted by a semicircle. Find the dimensions of the Norman window that admits the most light if the perimeter of the window is 30 feet.

9. Exercise 8, this time assuming that the semicircular portion of the window admits only one-third as much light per square foot as does the rectangular portion of the window.

10. One side of a rectangular field is bounded by a straight river. The other three sides are bounded by straight fences. The total length of the fence is 800 feet. Determine the dimensions of the field given that its area is a maximum.

11. Find the coordinates of P that maximize the area of the rectangle shown in Figure 4.5.6.

12. The base of a triangle is on the x-axis, one side lies along the line $y = 3x$, and the third side passes through the point $(1, 1)$. What is the slope of the third side if the area of the triangle is to be a minimum?

13. A triangle is formed by the coordinate axes and a line through the point $(2, 5)$ as in Figure 4.5.7. Determine the slope of this line if the area of the triangle is to be a minimum.

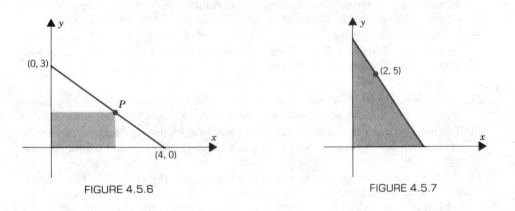

FIGURE 4.5.6   FIGURE 4.5.7

14. In the setting of Exercise 13 determine the slope of the line if the area is to be a maximum.

15. What are the dimensions of the base of the rectangular box of greatest volume that can be constructed from 100 square inches of cardboard if the base is to be twice as long as it is wide? Assume that the box has a top.

16. Exercise 15 under the assumption that the box has no top.

17. Find the dimensions of the isosceles triangle of largest area with perimeter 12.

18. Find the point(s) on the parabola $y = \frac{1}{8}x^2$ closest to the point $(0, 6)$.

19. Find the point(s) on the parabola $x = y^2$ closest to the point $(0, 3)$.

20. Find A and B given that the function $y = Ax^{-1/2} + Bx^{1/2}$ has a minimum value of 6 at $x = 9$.

21. A pentagon with a perimeter of 30 inches is to be constructed by adjoining an equilateral triangle to a rectangle. Find the dimensions of the rectangle and triangle that will maximize the area of the pentagon.

22. A 10-foot section of gutter is made from a 12-inch-wide strip of sheet metal by folding up 4-inch strips on each side so that they make the same angle with the bottom of the gutter.

Determine the depth of the gutter that has the greatest carrying capacity. *Caution:* there are two ways to sketch the trapezoidal cross section, as shown in Figure 4.5.8.

23. From a rectangular piece of cardboard of dimensions 8×15 four congruent squares are to be cut out, one at each corner. See Figure 4.5.9. The remaining crosslike piece is then to be folded into an open box. What size squares should be cut out if the volume of the resulting box is to be a maximum?

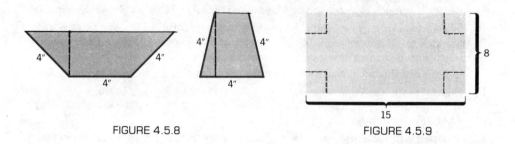

FIGURE 4.5.8   FIGURE 4.5.9

24. A page is to contain 81 square centimeters of print. The margins at the top and bottom are to be 3 centimeters each and, at the sides, 2 centimeters each. Find the most economical dimensions given that the cost of a page varies directly with the perimeter of the page.

25. Let ABC be a triangle with vertices $A = (-3, 0)$, $B = (0, 6)$, $C = (3, 0)$. Let P be a point on the line segment that joins B to the origin. Find the position of P that minimizes the sum of the distances between P and the vertices.

26. Solve Exercise 25 with $A = (-6, 0)$, $B = (0, 3)$, $C = (6, 0)$.

27. An 8-foot-high fence is located 1 foot from a building. Determine the length of the shortest ladder that can be leaned against the building and touch the top of the fence.

28. Two hallways, one 8 feet wide and the other 6 feet wide, meet at right angles. Determine the length of the longest ladder that can be carried horizontally from one hallway into the other.

29. A rectangular banner has a red border and a white center. The width of the border at top and bottom is 8 inches and along the sides it is 6 inches. The total area is 27 square feet. What should be the dimensions of the banner if the area of the white center is to be a maximum?

30. Find the absolute maximum value of $y = x(r^2 + x^2)^{-3/2}$.

31. A string 28 inches long is to be cut into two pieces, one piece to form a square and the other to form a circle. How should the string be cut so as to (a) maximize the sum of the two areas? (b) minimize the sum of the two areas?

32. What is the maximum volume for a rectangular box (square base, no top) made from 12 square feet of cardboard?

33. Figure 4.5.10 shows a cylinder inscribed in a right circular cone of height 8 and base radius 5. Find the dimensions of the cylinder if its volume is to be a maximum.

34. A variant of Exercise 33. This time find the dimensions of the cylinder if the area of its curved surface is to be a maximum.

35. A rectangular box with square base and top is to be made to contain 1250 cubic feet. The material for the base costs 35 cents per square foot, for the top 15 cents per square foot, and for the sides 20 cents per square foot. Find the dimensions that will maximize the cost of the box.

36. What is the largest possible area for a parallelogram inscribed in a triangle ABC in the manner of Figure 4.5.11?

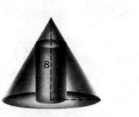

FIGURE 4.5.10

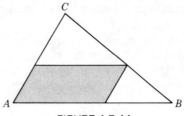

FIGURE 4.5.11

37. Find the dimensions of the isosceles triangle of least area that circumscribes a circle of radius r.

38. What is the maximal possible area for a triangle inscribed in a circle of radius r?

39. Figure 4.5.12 shows a cylinder inscribed in a sphere of radius R. Find the dimensions of the cylinder if its volume is to be a maximum.

40. A variant of Exercise 39. This time find the dimensions of the cylinder if the area of its curved surface is be a maximum.

41. A right circular cone is inscribed in a sphere of radius R as in Figure 4.5.13. Find the dimensions of the cone if its volume is to be a maximum.

FIGURE 4.5.12

FIGURE 4.5.13

42. What is the largest possible volume for a right circular cone of slant height a?

43. A power line is needed to connect a power station on the shore of a river to an island 4 kilometers downstream and 1 kilometer offshore. Find the minimum cost for such a line given that it costs $50,000 per kilometer to lay wire under water and $30,000 per kilometer to lay wire under ground.

44. A tapestry 7 feet high hangs on a wall. The lower edge is 9 feet above an observer's eye. How far from the wall should the observer stand to obtain the most favorable view? Namely, what distance from the wall maximizes the visual angle of the observer? HINT: Use the formula for $\tan (A - B)$.

45. A body of weight W is dragged along a horizontal plane by means of a force P whose line of action makes an angle θ with the plane. The magnitude of the force is given by the equation

$$P = \frac{mW}{m \sin \theta + \cos \theta}$$

where m denotes the coefficient of friction. For what value of θ is the pull a minimum?

46. If a projectile is fired from O so as to strike an inclined plane that makes a constant angle α with the horizontal, its range is given by the formula

$$R = \frac{2v^2 \cos \theta \sin (\theta - \alpha)}{g \cos^2 \alpha}$$

where v and g are constants and θ is the angle of elevation. Calculate θ for maximum range.

47. The lower edge of a movie theater screen 30 feet high is 6 feet above an observer's eye. How far from the screen should the observer sit to obtain the most favorable view? Namely, what distance from the screen maximizes the visual angle of the observer?

4.6 ⋯⋯CONCAVITY AND POINTS OF INFLECTION

We begin with a picture, Figure 4.6.1. To the left of c_1 and between c_2 and c_3, the graph "curves up" (we call it *concave up*); between c_1 and c_2 and to the right of c_3, the graph "curves down" (we call it *concave down*).

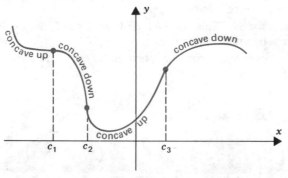

FIGURE 4.6.1

These terms deserve a precise definition.

DEFINITION 4.6.1   CONCAVITY

Let f be a function differentiable on an open interval I. The graph of f is said to be *concave up* on I iff f' increases on I; it is said to be *concave down* on I iff f' decreases on I.

In other words, the graph is concave up on an open interval where the slope increases and concave down on an open interval where the slope decreases.

Points that join arcs of opposite concavity are called *points of inflection*. The graph in Figure 4.6.1 has three of them: $(c_1, f(c_1))$, $(c_2, f(c_2))$, $(c_3, f(c_3))$.

Here is a formal definition.

DEFINITION 4.6.2   POINT OF INFLECTION

Let f be a function continuous at c. The point $(c, f(c))$ is called *a point of inflection* iff there exists $\delta > 0$ such that the graph of f is concave in one sense on $(c - \delta, c)$ and concave in the opposite sense on $(c, c + \delta)$.

EXAMPLES

1. The graph of the squaring function $f(x) = x^2$ is concave up everywhere since the derivative $f'(x) = 2x$ is everywhere increasing. (See Figure 4.6.2.) □

2. The graph of the cubing function $f(x) = x^3$ is concave down on $(-\infty, 0)$ and concave up on $(0, \infty)$:

   $$f'(x) = 3x^2 \quad \text{decreases on } (-\infty, 0) \text{ and increases on } (0, \infty).$$

   The origin is a point of inflection. (See Figure 4.6.3.) □

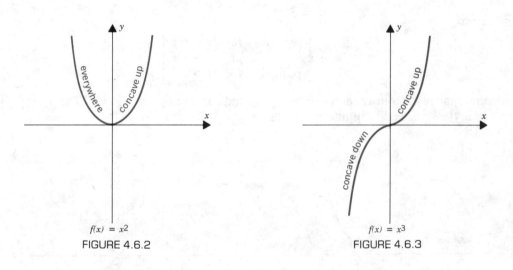

FIGURE 4.6.2   FIGURE 4.6.3

If f is twice differentiable, then, remembering that $f'' = (f')'$, we can determine the concavity of the graph by looking at the sign of the second derivative. If f'' is positive on I, then f' increases on I and the graph is concave up; if f'' is negative on I, then f' decreases on I and the graph is concave down.

The following result gives us a way of identifying possible points of inflection.

(4.6.3)   If $(c, f(c))$ is a point of inflection, then either
$$f''(c) = 0 \quad \text{or} \quad f''(c) \text{ does not exist.}$$

Proof.   Suppose that $(c, f(c))$ is a point of inflection. Let's assume that the graph is concave up to the left of c and concave down to the right of c. The other case can be handled in a similar manner.

In this situation f' increases on an interval $(c - \delta, c)$ and decreases on an interval $(c, c + \delta)$.

Suppose now that $f''(c)$ exists. Then f' is continuous at c. It follows that f' increases on the half-open interval $(c - \delta, c]$ and decreases on the half-open interval

$[c, c + \delta)$.† This says that f' has a local maximum at c. Since, by assumption, $f''(c)$ exists, $f''(c) = 0$. (Theorem 4.3.2 applied to f'.)

We have shown that, if $f''(c)$ exists, then $f''(c) = 0$. The other possibility, of course, is that $f''(c)$ does not exist. □

EXAMPLE. For the function

$$f(x) = x^3 + \tfrac{1}{2}x^2 - 2x + 1 \qquad\qquad \text{(Figure 4.6.4)}$$

we have

$$f'(x) = 3x^2 + x - 2 \quad \text{and} \quad f''(x) = 6x + 1.$$

Since

$$f''(x) \text{ is } \begin{cases} \text{negative,} & \text{for} \quad x < -\tfrac{1}{6} \\ 0, & \text{at} \quad x = -\tfrac{1}{6} \\ \text{positive,} & \text{for} \quad x > -\tfrac{1}{6} \end{cases},$$

the graph of f is concave down on $(-\infty, -\tfrac{1}{6})$ and concave up on $(-\tfrac{1}{6}, \infty)$. The point $(-\tfrac{1}{6}, f(-\tfrac{1}{6}))$ is a point of inflection. □

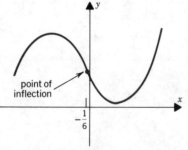

FIGURE 4.6.4

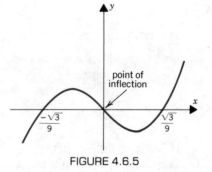

FIGURE 4.6.5

EXAMPLE. For

$$f(x) = 3x^{5/3} - x \qquad\qquad \text{(Figure 4.6.5)}$$

we have

$$f'(x) = 5x^{2/3} - 1 \quad \text{and} \quad f''(x) = \tfrac{10}{3}x^{-1/3}.$$

The second derivative does not exist at $x = 0$. Since

$$f''(x) \text{ is } \begin{cases} \text{negative,} & \text{for} \quad x < 0 \\ \text{positive,} & \text{for} \quad x > 0 \end{cases},$$

the graph is concave down on $(-\infty, 0)$ and concave up on $(0, \infty)$. Since f is continuous at 0, the point $(0, f(0)) = (0, 0)$ is a point of inflection. □

---

† See Exercise 46, Section 4.2.

CAUTION. The fact that

$$f''(c) = 0 \quad \text{or} \quad f''(c) \text{ does not exist}$$

does not guarantee that $(c, f(c))$ is a point of inflection. As you can verify, the function $f(x) = x^4$ satisfies $f''(0) = 0$, but the graph is always concave up and there are no points of inflection. If f is discontinuous at c, then $f''(c)$ does not exist but $(c, f(c))$ cannot be a point of inflection. A point of inflection occurs at c iff f is continuous at c and the point $(c, f(c))$ joins arcs of opposite concavity.

EXERCISES

Describe the concavity of the graph of f and find the points of inflection (if any).

1. $f(x) = \dfrac{1}{x}$.

2. $f(x) = x + \dfrac{1}{x}$.

3. $f(x) = x^3 - 3x + 2$.

4. $f(x) = 2x^2 - 5x + 2$.

5. $f(x) = \frac{1}{4}x^4 - \frac{1}{2}x^2$.

6. $f(x) = x^3(1 - x)$.

7. $f(x) = \dfrac{x}{x^2 - 1}$.

8. $f(x) = \dfrac{x + 2}{x - 2}$.

9. $f(x) = (1 - x)^2(1 + x)^2$.

10. $f(x) = \dfrac{6x}{x^2 + 1}$.

11. $f(x) = \dfrac{1 - \sqrt{x}}{1 + \sqrt{x}}$.

12. $f(x) = (x - 3)^{1/5}$.

13. $f(x) = (x + 2)^{5/3}$.

14. $f(x) = x\sqrt{4 - x^2}$.

15. $f(x) = \sin^2 x, \quad x \in [0, \pi]$.

16. $f(x) = 2\cos^2 x - x^2, \quad x \in [0, \pi]$.

17. $f(x) = x^2 + \sin 2x, \quad x \in [0, \pi]$.

18. $f(x) = \sin^4 x, \quad x \in [0, \pi]$.

19. Find d given that $(d, f(d))$ is a point of inflection of

$$f(x) = (x - a)(x - b)(x - c).$$

20. Find c given that the graph of $f(x) = cx^2 + x^{-2}$ has a point of inflection at $(1, f(1))$.

21. Find a and b given that the graph of $f(x) = ax^3 + bx^2$ passes through $(-1, 1)$ and has a point of inflection at $x = \frac{1}{3}$.

22. Determine A and B so that the curve $y = Ax^{1/2} + Bx^{-1/2}$ will have a point of inflection at $(1, 4)$.

23. Determine A and B so that the curve $y = A\cos 2x + B\sin 3x$ will have a point of inflection at $(\pi/6, 5)$.

24. Find necessary and sufficient conditions on A and B for

$$f(x) = Ax^2 + Bx + C$$

(a) to decrease between A and B with graph concave up.

(b) to increase between A and B with graph concave down.

4.7 ······SOME CURVE SKETCHING

During the course of the last few sections you have learned how to find the extreme values of a function, the intervals where it increases, the intervals where it decreases. You have also seen how to determine the concavity of the graph and how to find the points of inflection. This knowledge makes it possible to sketch the graph of a somewhat complicated function without having to plot point, after point, after point.

Before attempting to sketch the graph of a function f, we try to gather together the necessary information and record it in an organized form. Here is an outline of the procedure that we'll follow.

1. Preliminary general observations are made. (For example, we might note some obvious symmetry or what happens as $x \to \pm\infty$.)

2. The first and second derivatives are recorded, in factored form if possible.

3. *Possible* extrema are identified.

4. *Possible* points of inflection are identified.

5. The sign of f' is analyzed so as to determine actual extrema and intervals of increase or decrease.

6. The sign of f'' is analyzed so as to determine actual points of inflection and intervals of different concavity.

7. Points of interest from steps 5 and 6 are plotted in a preliminary sketch.

8. The final graph is sketched by "connecting the dots" from step 7. An eye is kept on the information obtained in steps 5 and 6 to ensure that the final sketch "rises," "falls," and "bends" in the proper way.

Some examples of the elements that constitute step 7 are given in Figure 4.7.1. Notice that information is sketched in an exaggerated fashion.

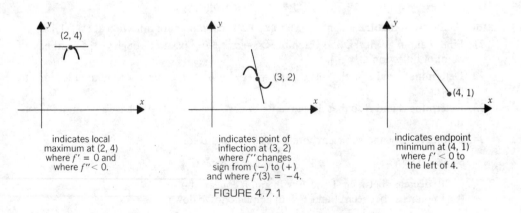

indicates local maximum at $(2, 4)$ where $f' = 0$ and where $f'' < 0$.

indicates point of inflection at $(3, 2)$ where f'' changes sign from $(-)$ to $(+)$ and where $f'(3) = -4$.

indicates endpoint minimum at $(4, 1)$ where $f' < 0$ to the left of 4.

FIGURE 4.7.1

It's time to apply what we've been talking about.

EXAMPLE. We begin with the function

$$f(x) = \tfrac{1}{3}x^3 + \tfrac{1}{2}x^2 - 2x - 1, \qquad \text{all real } x.$$

This is a polynomial of odd degree with a positive leading coefficient. Thus, we can expect that $f(x) \to -\infty$ as $x \to -\infty$ and $f(x) \to \infty$ as $x \to \infty$. Since $f(0) = -1$, the graph intersects the y-axis at the point $(0, -1)$.†

The next step is to work out $f'(x)$ and $f''(x)$. (So as not to clutter the page, we do this work on the side.) We record the results in factored form below $f(x)$:

$$f(x) = \tfrac{1}{3}x^3 + \tfrac{1}{2}x^2 - 2x - 1, \quad \text{all real } x.$$
$$f'(x) = (x + 2)(x - 1), \quad \text{all real } x.$$
$$f''(x) = 2(x + \tfrac{1}{2}), \quad \text{all real } x.$$

Possible extrema: $\begin{cases} f'(x) = 0: & x = -2, 1 \\ f' \text{ dne:} & \begin{bmatrix} \text{endpoints: none} \\ \text{other: none} \end{bmatrix} \end{cases}$.

Possible points of inflection: $\begin{bmatrix} f''(x) = 0: & x = -\tfrac{1}{2} \\ f'' \text{ dne:} & \text{none} \end{bmatrix}$.

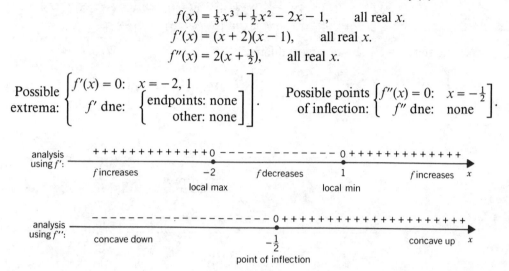

analysis using f':
$+ + + + + + + + + + + + 0 - - - - - - - - - - - - - - 0 + + + + + + + + + + + + + + \quad x$
f increases -2 f decreases 1 f increases
                     local max   local min

analysis using f'':
$- 0 + \quad x$
concave down $-\tfrac{1}{2}$ concave up
                          point of inflection

Summary of points of interest. (See Figure 4.7.2 for preliminary sketch.)

$(-2, 2\tfrac{1}{3})$: local maximum.
$(-\tfrac{1}{2}, \tfrac{1}{12})$: point of inflection; slope of $-\tfrac{9}{4}$.
$(0, -1)$: y-intercept.
$(1, -2\tfrac{1}{6})$: local minimum.

The final graph is given in Figure 4.7.3. □

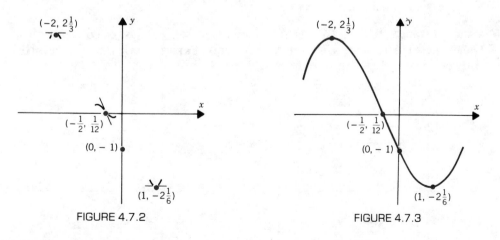

FIGURE 4.7.2   FIGURE 4.7.3

† It would be nice if we could also identify the point(s) where the graph intersects the x-axis, but this would require that we solve the cubic $\tfrac{1}{3}x^3 + \tfrac{1}{2}x^2 - 2x - 1 = 0$.

EXAMPLE. For the function

$$f(x) = x^4 - 4x^3 + 1, \qquad x \in [-1, 5)$$

we have

$$f'(x) = 4x^3 - 12x^2 = 4x^2(x - 3), \qquad x \in (-1, 5)$$
$$f''(x) = 12x^2 - 24x = 12x(x - 2), \qquad x \in (-1, 5).$$

We note that $x = 5$ is a "missing endpoint."

Possible extrema: $\left\{ \begin{array}{l} f'(x) = 0: \quad x = 0, 3 \\ f' \text{ dne:} \begin{cases} \text{endpoints: } x = -1 \\ \text{other: none} \end{cases} \end{array} \right]$.   Possible points of inflection: $\left\{ \begin{array}{l} f''(x) = 0: \quad x = 0, 2 \\ f'' \text{ dne: none} \end{array} \right]$.

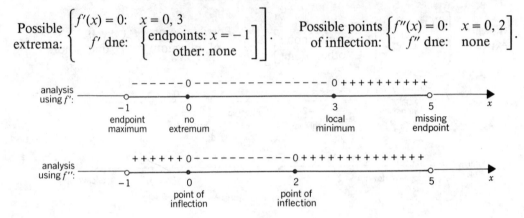

Summary of points of interest. (See Figure 4.7.4 for preliminary sketch.)

$(-1, 6)$:   endpoint maximum.

$(0, 1)$:   no extremum; point of inflection with horizontal tangent.

$(2, -15)$:   point of inflection; slope of -16.

$(3, -26)$:   local minimum.

As x approaches the missing endpoint 5 from the left, $f(x)$ increases toward a value of 126.

Since the range of f makes a scale drawing impractical, we must be content with a rough sketch as in Figure 4.7.5. In cases like this, it's particularly important to give the coordinates of the points of interest. □

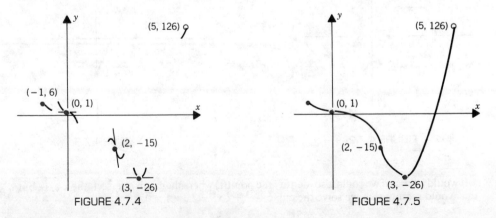

FIGURE 4.7.4   FIGURE 4.7.5

EXAMPLE. The function

$$f(x) = 5x - 3x^{5/3}, \qquad \text{all real } x$$

is an odd function: $f(-x) = -f(x)$. This means the graph of f is symmetric with respect to the origin.†

$$f'(x) = 5(1 + x^{1/3})(1 - x^{1/3}), \qquad \text{all real } x. \qquad \text{(verify this)}$$
$$f''(x) = -\tfrac{10}{3}x^{-1/3}, \qquad\qquad x \neq 0. \qquad \text{(verify this)}$$

Possible extrema: $\left\{ \begin{array}{l} f'(x) = 0: \quad x = -1,\, 1 \\ f' \text{ dne:} \quad \left[\begin{array}{l} \text{endpoints: none} \\ \text{other: none} \end{array}\right] \end{array} \right.$.   Possible points of inflection: $\left\{ \begin{array}{l} f''(x) = 0: \quad \text{none} \\ f'' \text{ dne:} \quad x = 0 \end{array} \right.$.

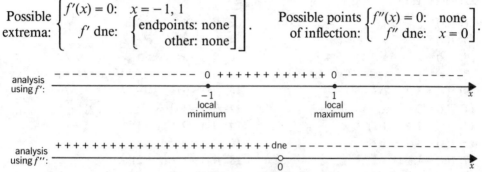

analysis using f':

analysis using f'':

Summary of points of interest. (See Figure 4.7.6 for preliminary sketch.)

$(-1, -2)$:   local minimum.

$(0, 0)$:   point of inflection; slope is 5.

$(1, 2)$:   local maximum.

The final graph appears in Figure 4.7.7.   □

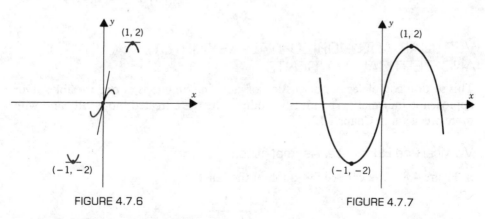

FIGURE 4.7.6   FIGURE 4.7.7

---

† For more information about odd functions (functions that satisfy $f(-x) = -f(x)$ for all x in their domains) and even functions (functions that satisfy $f(-x) = f(x)$ for all x in their domains), look again at Exercises 59–74 of Section 1.6. For graphing purposes it is enough to note that the graph of an odd function (such as $f(x) = x^3$ and $f(x) = \sin x$) is symmetric about the origin, while the graph of an even function (such as $f(x) = x^2$ and $f(x) = \cos x$) is symmetric about the y-axis.

REMARK. The most effective way to produce an accurate graph of a function is to take advantage of the graphic capabilities of some of today's computers.   By the method outlined in this chapter we can produce a rough sketch that gives the general shape of the graph and shows its salient features.   For most purposes this is sufficient. □

EXERCISES

Sketch the graph.

1. $f(x) = (x - 2)^2$.
2. $f(x) = 1 - (x - 2)^2$.
3. $f(x) = x^3 - 2x^2 + x + 1$.
4. $f(x) = x^3 - 9x^2 + 24x - 7$.
5. $f(x) = x^3 + 6x^2$, $x \in [-4, 4]$.
6. $f(x) = x^4 - 8x^2$, $x \in [0, \infty)$.
7. $f(x) = \frac{2}{3}x^3 - \frac{1}{2}x^2 - 10x - 1$.
8. $f(x) = 2 + (x - 4)^{1/3}$, $x \in [4, \infty)$.
9. $f(x) = 3x^4 - 4x^3 + 1$.
10. $f(x) = x(x^2 + 4)^2$.
11. $f(x) = 2\sqrt{x} - x$, $x \in [0, 4]$.
12. $f(x) = \frac{1}{4}x - \sqrt{x}$, $x \in [0, 9]$.
13. $f(x) = 2 + (x + 1)^{6/5}$.
14. $f(x) = 2 + (x + 1)^{7/5}$.
15. $f(x) = 3x^5 + 5x^3$.
16. $f(x) = 3x^4 + 4x^3$.
17. $f(x) = 1 + (x - 2)^{5/3}$.
18. $f(x) = 1 + (x - 2)^{4/3}$.
19. $f(x) = x^2(1 + x)^3$.
20. $f(x) = x^2(1 + x)^2$.
21. $f(x) = x\sqrt{1 - x}$.
22. $f(x) = \frac{1}{3}x^3 + x^2 - 8x + 4$.
23. $f(x) = x + \sin 2x$, $x \in [0, \pi]$.
24. $f(x) = \cos^3 x + 6 \cos x$, $x \in [0, \pi]$.
25. $f(x) = \cos^4 x$, $x \in [0, \pi]$.
26. $f(x) = \sqrt{3}\, x - \cos 2x$, $x \in [0, \pi]$.
27. $f(x) = 2 \sin^3 x + 3 \sin x$, $x \in [0, \pi]$.
28. $f(x) = \sin^4 x$, $x \in [0, \pi]$.

4.8 ······VERTICAL AND HORIZONTAL ASYMPTOTES; CUSPS AND VERTICAL TANGENTS

This section completes our discussion of graphing functions of one variable.   Our approach is informal.   The ideas introduced here are treated more fully and with more precision in Chapter 12.

Vertical and Horizontal Asymptotes

In Figure 4.8.1 you can see the graph of the function

$$f(x) = \frac{1}{|x - c|}$$

for values of x close to c. As x tends to c, $f(x)$ increases without bound. We write

$$\text{as } x \to c, \quad f(x) \to \infty.$$

We call the line $x = c$ a *vertical asymptote*.

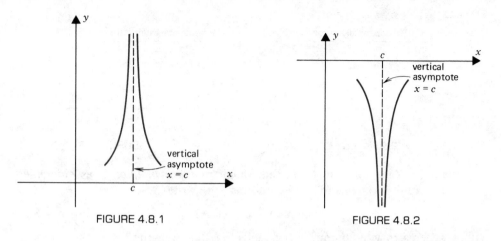

FIGURE 4.8.1   FIGURE 4.8.2

Figure 4.8.2 shows the graph of

$$g(x) = -\frac{1}{|x - c|}$$

for values of x close to c. In this case, as x tends to c, $f(x)$ decreases without bound. We write

$$\text{as } x \to c, \quad f(x) \to -\infty.$$

Again the line $x = c$ is a *vertical asymptote*.

   Vertical asymptotes can also arise from one-sided behavior. With f and g as in Figure 4.8.3, we write

$$\text{as } x \to c^-, \quad f(x) \to \infty \quad \text{and} \quad g(x) \to -\infty.$$

With f and g as in Figure 4.8.4, we write

$$\text{as } x \to c^+, \quad f(x) \to \infty \quad \text{and} \quad g(x) \to -\infty.$$

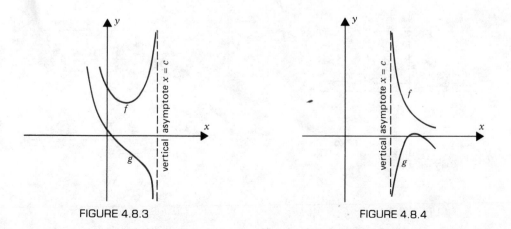

FIGURE 4.8.3   FIGURE 4.8.4

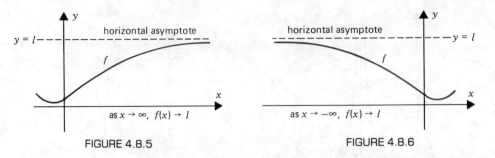

FIGURE 4.8.5   FIGURE 4.8.6

It's also possible for a function to have a *horizontal asymptote*. If, as x increases without bound, $f(x)$ tends to a finite number l, we write

$$\text{as } x \to \infty, \quad f(x) \to l. \qquad \text{(Figure 4.8.5)}$$

If, as x decreases without bound, $f(x)$ tends to l, then we write

$$\text{as } x \to -\infty, \quad f(x) \to l. \qquad \text{(Figure 4.8.6)}$$

In both cases the line $y = l$ is called a *horizontal asymptote*.

EXAMPLE. The function

$$f(x) = \frac{x}{x - 2}$$

is defined for all $x \neq 2$. As $x \to 2^+$, the denominator decreases toward 0 and $f(x) \to \infty$; as $x \to 2^-$, the denominator increases toward 0 and $f(x) \to -\infty$. The line $x = 2$ is a vertical asymptote.

As $x \to \pm\infty$ (that is, as $x \to \infty$ or $x \to -\infty$),

$$f(x) = \frac{x}{x - 2} = \frac{1}{1 - (2/x)} \to 1.$$

The line $y = 1$ is a horizontal asymptote. The graph is shown in Figure 4.8.7. □

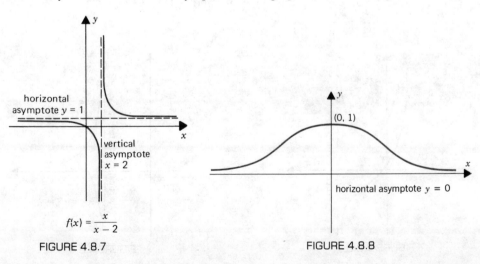

FIGURE 4.8.7   FIGURE 4.8.8

EXAMPLE. The function

$$g(x) = \frac{1}{1 + x^2}$$

is everywhere continuous, and thus there are no vertical asymptotes. As $x \to \pm\infty$, $g(x) \to 0$. The line $y = 0$ (the x-axis) is a horizontal asymptote. The graph of g is sketched in Figure 4.8.8. □

EXAMPLE. The function

$$f(x) = \frac{5 - 3x^2}{1 - x^2}$$

is continuous everywhere except at $x = \pm 1$. The asymptotic properties of f are made more apparent by writing

$$f(x) = \frac{3 - 3x^2 + 2}{1 - x^2} = 3 + \frac{2}{1 - x^2}.$$

In the first place,

as $x \to 1^-$, $1 - x^2$ decreases toward 0   and $f(x) \to \infty$

and

as $x \to 1^+$, $1 - x^2$ increases toward 0   and $f(x) \to -\infty$.

The line $x = 1$ is a vertical asymptote.

The line $x = -1$ is also a vertical asymptote:

as $x \to -1^-$, $1 - x^2$ increases toward 0   and $f(x) \to -\infty$

and

as $x \to -1^+$, $1 - x^2$ decreases toward 0   and $f(x) \to \infty$.

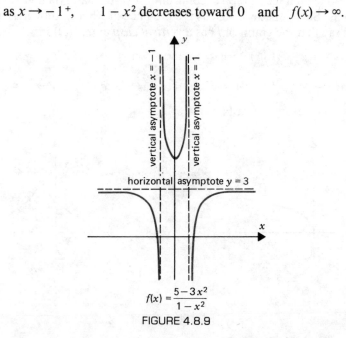

$$f(x) = \frac{5 - 3x^2}{1 - x^2}$$

FIGURE 4.8.9

The line $y = 3$ is a horizontal asymptote:

$$\text{as } x \rightarrow \pm\infty, \qquad \frac{2}{1 - x^2} \rightarrow 0 \quad \text{and} \quad f(x) \rightarrow 3.$$

The graph appears in Figure 4.8.9. □

Cusps and Vertical Tangents

For the remainder of this section take f as a function continuous at $x = c$ and differentiable for $x \neq c$.

We say that the graph of f has a *vertical tangent* at the point $(c, f(c))$ iff

$$\text{as } x \rightarrow c, \quad f'(x) \rightarrow \infty \text{ or } -\infty.$$

Figure 4.8.10 gives two examples.

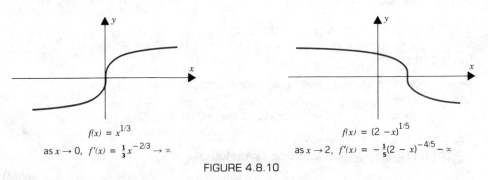

$f(x) = x^{1/3}$

as $x \rightarrow 0$, $f'(x) = \frac{1}{3}x^{-2/3} \rightarrow \infty$

$f(x) = (2 - x)^{1/5}$

as $x \rightarrow 2$, $f'(x) = -\frac{1}{5}(2 - x)^{-4/5} \rightarrow \infty$

FIGURE 4.8.10

On occasion you'll see a graph become almost vertical and then virtually double back on itself. Such a pattern signals the presence of what is known as a "vertical cusp." We say that the graph of f has a *vertical cusp* at $(c, f(c))$ iff

$$\text{as } x \rightarrow c^-, \quad f'(x) \rightarrow -\infty \quad \text{and} \quad \text{as } x \rightarrow c^+, \quad f'(x) \rightarrow \infty,$$

or

$$\text{as } x \rightarrow c^-, \quad f'(x) \rightarrow \infty \quad \text{and} \quad \text{as } x \rightarrow c^+, \quad f'(x) \rightarrow -\infty.$$

You can see some examples in Figure 4.8.11.

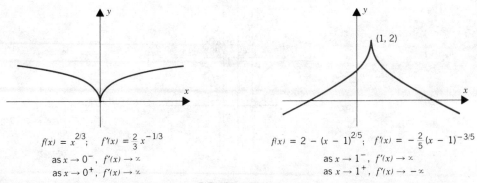

$f(x) = x^{2/3}$; $f'(x) = \frac{2}{3}x^{-1/3}$

as $x \rightarrow 0^-$, $f'(x) \rightarrow \infty$

as $x \rightarrow 0^+$, $f'(x) \rightarrow \infty$

$f(x) = 2 - (x - 1)^{2/5}$; $f'(x) = -\frac{2}{5}(x - 1)^{-3/5}$

as $x \rightarrow 1^-$, $f'(x) \rightarrow \infty$

as $x \rightarrow 1^+$, $f'(x) \rightarrow -\infty$

FIGURE 4.8.11

The fact that $f'(c)$ does not exist does *not* mean that the graph of f has either a vertical tangent or a vertical cusp at $(c, f(c))$. Unless the conditions spelled out above are met, the graph of f can simply be making a "corner" at $(c, f(c))$. For example, the function

$$f(x) = |x^3 - 1|$$

has derivative

$$f'(x) = \begin{cases} -3x^2, & x < 1 \\ \text{does not exist,} & x = 1 \\ 3x^2, & x > 1 \end{cases}.$$

As $x \rightarrow 1^-, f'(x) \rightarrow -3$, and as $x \rightarrow 1^+, f'(x) \rightarrow 3$. There is no vertical tangent here and no cusp. For the graph, see Figure 4.8.12.

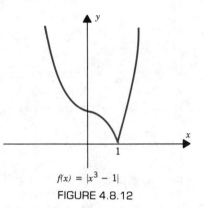

$f(x) = |x^3 - 1|$

FIGURE 4.8.12

EXERCISES

Find the vertical and horizontal asymptotes.

1. $f(x) = \dfrac{x}{3x - 1}$.

2. $f(x) = \dfrac{x^3}{x + 2}$.

3. $f(x) = \dfrac{x^2}{x - 2}$.

4. $f(x) = \dfrac{4x}{x^2 + 1}$.

5. $f(x) = \dfrac{2x}{x^2 - 9}$.

6. $f(x) = \dfrac{\sqrt{x}}{4\sqrt{x} - x}$.

7. $f(x) = \left(\dfrac{2x - 1}{4 + 3x}\right)^2$.

8. $f(x) = \dfrac{4x^2}{(3x - 1)^2}$.

9. $f(x) = \dfrac{3x}{(2x - 5)^2}$.

10. $f(x) = \left(\dfrac{x}{1 - 2x}\right)^3$.

11. $f(x) = \dfrac{3x}{\sqrt{4x^2 + 1}}$.

12. $f(x) = \dfrac{x^{1/3}}{x^{2/3} - 4}$.

13. $f(x) = \dfrac{\sqrt{x}}{2\sqrt{x} - x - 1}$.

14. $f(x) = \dfrac{2x}{\sqrt{x^2 - 1}}$.

15. $f(x) = \sqrt{x + 4} - \sqrt{x}$.

16. $f(x) = \sqrt{x} - \sqrt{x - 2}$.

17. $f(x) = \dfrac{\sin x}{\sin x - 1}$.

18. $f(x) = \dfrac{1}{\sec x - 1}$.

Determine whether or not the graph of f has a vertical tangent or a vertical cusp at c.

19. $f(x) = (x + 3)^{4/3}; \quad c = -3.$

20. $f(x) = 3 + x^{2/5}; \quad c = 0.$

21. $f(x) = (2 - x)^{4/5}; \quad c = 2.$

22. $f(x) = (x + 1)^{-1/3}; \quad c = -1.$

23. $f(x) = 2x^{3/5} - x^{6/5}; \quad c = 0.$

24. $f(x) = (x - 5)^{7/5}; \quad c = 5.$

25. $f(x) = (x + 2)^{-2/3}; \quad c = -2.$

26. $f(x) = 4 - (2 - x)^{3/7}; \quad c = 2.$

27. $f(x) = \sqrt{|x - 1|}; \quad c = 1.$

28. $f(x) = x(x - 1)^{1/3}; \quad c = 1.$

29. $f(x) = |(x + 8)^{1/3}|; \quad c = -8.$

30. $f(x) = \sqrt{4 - x^2}; \quad c = 2.$

31. $f(x) = \dfrac{x^{2/3} - 1}{|x^{1/3} - 1|}; \quad c = 0.$

32. $f(x) = |(4 + x)^{3/5}|; \quad c = -4.$

33. $f(x) = \begin{cases} x^{1/3} + 2, & x \le 0 \\ 1 - x^{1/5}, & x > 0 \end{cases}; \quad c = 0.$

34. $f(x) = \begin{cases} 1 + \sqrt{-x}, & x \le 0 \\ (4x - x^2)^{1/3}, & x > 0 \end{cases}; \quad c = 0.$

4.9 ······MORE GRAPHING PROBLEMS

Sketch the graph

1. $f(x) = (x + 1)^3 - 3(x + 1)^2 + 3(x + 1).$

2. $f(x) = (x - 1)^4 - 2(x - 1)^2.$

3. $f(x) = x^2(5 - x)^3.$

4. $f(x) = x^3(x + 5)^2.$

5. $f(x) = x^2 + \dfrac{2}{x}.$

6. $f(x) = x - \dfrac{1}{x}.$

7. $f(x) = \dfrac{x - 4}{x^2}.$

8. $f(x) = \dfrac{x + 2}{x^3}.$

9. $f(x) = 3 - |x^2 - 1|.$

10. $f(x) = 4 - |2x - x^2|.$

11. $f(x) = x^2 - 6x^{1/3}.$

12. $f(x) = x - x^{1/3}.$

13. $f(x) = x(x - 1)^{1/5}.$

14. $f(x) = x^2(x - 7)^{1/3}.$

15. $f(x) = \dfrac{2x}{4x - 3}.$

16. $f(x) = \dfrac{2x^2}{x + 1}.$

17. $f(x) = \dfrac{x}{(x + 3)^2}.$

18. $f(x) = \dfrac{x}{x^2 + 1}.$

19. $f(x) = \dfrac{x^2}{x^2 - 4}.$

20. $f(x) = \dfrac{2x}{x - 4}.$

21. $f(x) = \sqrt{\dfrac{x}{x - 2}}.$

22. $f(x) = \dfrac{2x}{\sqrt{x^2 + 1}}.$

23. $f(x) = \dfrac{x}{\sqrt{4x^2 + 1}}.$

24. $f(x) = \dfrac{x}{\sqrt{x^2 - 2}}.$

25. $f(x) = \dfrac{x^2}{\sqrt{x^2 - 2}}.$

26. $f(x) = \sqrt{\dfrac{x}{x + 4}}.$

27. $f(x) = 3 \sin 2x, \quad x \in [0, \pi].$

28. $f(x) = 4 \cos 3x, \quad x \in [0, \pi].$

29. $f(x) = 2 \sin 3x, \quad x \in [0, \pi].$

30. $f(x) = 3 \cos 4x, \quad x \in [0, \pi].$

31. $f(x) = (\sin x - \cos x)^2, \quad x \in [0, \pi].$ **32.** $f(x) = 3 + 2 \cot x + \csc^2 x, \quad x \in \left(0, \dfrac{\pi}{2}\right).$

33. $f(x) = 2 \tan x - \sec^2 x, \quad x \in \left(0, \dfrac{\pi}{2}\right).$ **34.** $f(x) = (\sin x + \cos x)^2, \quad x \in [0, \pi].$

4.10····MORE MAX-MIN PROBLEMS

This section is an exercise section. It's sole purpose is to give you more experience in working with max-min problems.

As prelude to the exercises, we'll work out a problem in which the function to be maximized is defined, not on an interval or union of intervals, but on a discrete set of points, in this case a finite collection of integers.

PROBLEM. A manufacturing plant has a capacity of 25 articles per week. Experience has shown that n articles per week can be sold at a price of p dollars each where $p = 110 - 2n$ and the cost of producing n articles is $600 + 10n + n^2$ dollars. How many articles should be made each week to give the largest profit?

Solution. The profit (P dollars) on the sale of n articles is

$$P = np - (600 + 10n + n^2).$$

With $p = 110 - 2n$, this simplifies to

$$P = 100n - 600 - 3n^2.$$

In this problem n must be an integer, and thus it makes no sense to differentiate P with respect to n. The formula shows that P is negative if n is less than 8 or greater than 25. By direct calculation we construct Table 4.10.1. The table shows that the largest profit comes from setting production at 17 articles per week.

TABLE 4.10.1

n	P	n	P	n	P
8	8	14	212	20	200
9	57	15	225	21	117
10	100	16	232	22	148
11	137	17	233	23	113
12	168	18	228	24	72
13	193	19	217	25	25

We can avoid such massive computation by considering the function

$$f(x) = 100x - 600 - 3x^2, \qquad 8 \le x \le 25. \qquad \text{(key step)}$$

This function is differentiable with respect to x, and for integral values of x it agrees with P. Differentiation of f gives

$$f'(x) = 100 - 6x.$$

Obviously, $f'(x) = 0$ at $x = \frac{100}{6} = 16\frac{2}{3}$. Since $f'(x) > 0$ on $(8, 16\frac{2}{3})$, f increases on $[8, 16\frac{2}{3}]$. Since $f'(x) < 0$ on $(16\frac{2}{3}, 25)$, f decreases on $[16\frac{2}{3}, 25]$. The largest value of f corresponding to an integral value of x will therefore occur at $x = 16$ or $x = 17$. Direct calculation of $f(16)$ and $f(17)$ shows that the choice of $x = 17$ is correct. □

EXERCISES

1. Davis Rent-A-TV derives an average net profit of $15 per customer if it services 1000 customers or less. If it services over 1000 customers, then the average profit decreases 1¢ for each customer above that number. How many customers give the maximum net profit?

2. A truck is to be driven 300 miles on a freeway at a constant speed of x miles per hour. Speed laws require that $35 \le x \le 55$. Assume that fuel costs $1.35 per gallon and is consumed at the rate of $2 + \frac{1}{600}x^2$ gallons per hour. Given that the driver's wages are $13 per hour, at what speed should the truck be driven to minimize the truck owner's expenses?

3. A triangle is formed by the coordinate axes and a line through the point (a, b) as in Figure 4.10.1. Determine the slope of this line if the area of the triangle is to be a minimum.

4. Find the coordinates of P that maximize the area of the rectangle shown in Figure 4.10.2.

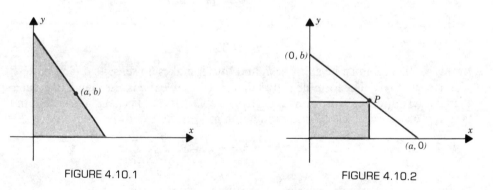

FIGURE 4.10.1   FIGURE 4.10.2

5. Let x and y be positive numbers such that $x + y = 100$; let n be a positive integer. Find the values of x and y that minimize $x^n + y^n$.

6. In Exercise 5 find the values of x and y that maximize $x^n y^n$.

7. Find the dimensions of the cylinder of greatest volume that can be inscribed in a right circular cone of height H and base radius R.

8. Let Q denote output, R revenue, C cost, and P profit. Given that $P = R - C$, what is the relation between marginal revenue dR/dQ and marginal cost dC/dQ when profit is at a maximum?

9. A manufacturer finds that the total cost of producing Q tons is $aQ^2 + bQ + c$ dollars and the price at which each ton can be sold is $\beta - \alpha Q$. Assuming that a, b, c, α, β are all positive, what is the output for maximum profit?

10. Let $P = f(Q)$ be a demand curve (P = price, Q = output). Show that at an output that maximizes total revenue (price × output) the elasticity

$$\epsilon = \frac{f(Q)}{Q|f'(Q)|}$$

is 1.

11. A manufacturer of customized lighting fixtures finds that it can sell x standing lamps per week at p dollars each where $5x = 375 - 3p$. The cost of production is $500 + 15x + \frac{1}{5}x^2$ dollars. Show that maximum profit is obtained by setting production at about 30 lamps per week.

12. Suppose that the relation between x and p in Exercise 11 is given by the equation $x = 100 - 4\sqrt{5p}$. Show that for maximum profit the manufacturer should produce only about 25 lamps per week.

13. Suppose that the relation between x and p in Exercise 11 is $x^2 = 2500 - 20p$. What production produces maximum profit in this instance?

14. The total cost of producing Q units per week is

$$C(Q) = \tfrac{1}{3}Q^3 - 20Q^2 + 600Q + 1000 \quad \text{dollars.}$$

Given that the total revenues are

$$R(Q) = 420Q - 2Q^2 \quad \text{dollars,}$$

find the output that maximizes profit.

15. A steel plant is capable of producing Q_1 tons per day of low-grade steel and Q_2 tons per day of high-grade steel, where

$$Q_2 = \frac{40 - 5Q_1}{10 - Q_1}.$$

If the market price of low-grade steel is half that of high-grade steel, show that about $5\frac{1}{2}$ tons of low-grade steel should be produced per day for maximum receipts.

16. The total cost of producing Q articles per week is $aQ^2 + bQ + c$ dollars, and the price at which each can be sold is $p = \beta - \alpha Q^2$. Show that the output for maximum profit is

$$Q = \frac{\sqrt{a^2 + 3\alpha(\beta - b)} - a}{3\alpha}. \qquad \text{(take } a, b, c, \alpha, \beta \text{ as positive)}$$

17. In a certain industry an output of Q units can be obtained at a total cost of

$$C(Q) = aQ^2 + bQ + c \quad \text{dollars,}$$

bringing in total revenues of

$$R(Q) = \beta Q - \alpha Q^2 \quad \text{dollars.}$$

The government decides to impose an excise tax on the product. What tax rate (dollars per unit) will maximize the government's revenues from this tax? (Take a, b, c, α, β as positive.)

18. Find the dimensions of the rectangle of perimeter p that has the largest area.

19. Find the largest possible area for a rectangle inscribed in a circle of radius r.

20. Find the dimensions of the isosceles triangle of largest area with perimeter p.

21. A local bus company offers charter trips to Blue Mountain Museum at a fare of $37 per person if 16 to 35 passengers sign up for the trip. The company does not charter trips for

fewer than 16 passengers. The bus has 48 seats. If more than 35 passengers sign up, then the fare for every passenger is reduced by 50 cents for each passenger in excess of 35 that signs up. Determine the number of passengers that generates the greatest revenue for the bus company.

22. The Hotwheels Rent-A-Car Co. derives an average net profit of $12 per customer if it services 50 customers or less. If it services over 50 customers, then the average net profit is decreased by 6 cents for each customer over 50. What number of customers produces the greatest total net profit for the company?

23. One side of a rectangular field is bounded by a straight river. The other three sides are bounded by straight fences. The total length of the fence is 800 feet. Each side of the field is at least 220 feet. Determine the dimensions of the field given that its area is a maximum.

24. An oil drum is to be made in the form of a right circular cylinder to contain 16π cubic feet. The upright drum is to be taller than it is wide but not more than 6 feet tall. Determine the dimensions of the drum with minimal surface area.

25. A closed rectangular box with a square base is to be built subject to the following specifications: the volume is to be 27 cubic feet, the area of the base may not exceed 18 square feet, the height of the box may not exceed 2 feet. Determine the dimensions for (a) minimal surface area; (b) maximal surface area.

26. Conical paper cups are usually made so that the depth is $\sqrt{2}$ times the radius of the rim. Show that this design requires the least amount of paper per unit volume.

27. An open box is made from a rectangular sheet of material measuring 8×15 inches by removing equal-sized squares from each corner of the sheet and folding up the sides. Each dimension of the resulting box is at least 2 inches. Determine the dimensions of the box of greatest volume.

28. A 28 inch piece of wire is to be cut into two pieces, one piece to form a circle and the other to form a square. Each piece is at least 9 inches long. How should the wire be cut so as to (a) maximize the sum of the two areas? (b) minimize the sum of the two areas?

29. Find the dimensions of the cylinder of maximum volume inscribable in a sphere of radius 6 inches. (Use the central angle θ subtended by the radius of the base.)

30. Solve Exercise 29 if the curved surface of the cylinder is to be a maximum.

31. The equation of the path of a ball is $y = mx - \frac{1}{800}(m^2 + 1)x^2$, where the origin is taken as the point from which the ball is thrown and m is the slope of the curve at the origin. For what value of m will the ball strike at the greatest distance along the same horizontal level?

32. In the setting of Exercise 31, for what value of m will the ball strike at the greatest height on a vertical wall 300 feet away?

33. The cost of erecting an office building is $1,000,000 for the first story, $1,100,000 for the second, $1,200,000 for the third, and so on. Other expenses (lot, basement, etc.) are $5,000,000. Assume that the net annual income is $200,000 per story. How many stories will provide the greatest rate of return on investment?

34. The sum of the surface areas of a sphere and a cube being given, show that the sum of the volumes will be least when the diameter of the sphere is equal to the edge of the cube. When will the sum of the volumes be greatest?

35. A miner wants to dig a tunnel from a point A in soft earth to a point B in bedrock 200 feet below and 600 feet to the east of A. The cost of tunneling through earth is $50 per linear foot and through rock $130. Find the minimum cost of a tunnel from A to B.

36. Given that $\overline{PQ}$ is the longest or shortest line segment that can be drawn from $P(a, b)$ to the differentiable curve $y = f(x)$, show that $\overline{PQ}$ is perpendicular to the curve at Q.

37. What point on the curve $y = x^{3/2}$ is closest to $P(\frac{1}{2}, 0)$?

38. Let $P(x_0, y_0)$ be a point in the first quadrant.   Draw a line through P that cuts the positive x-axis at $A(a, 0)$ and the positive y-axis at $B(0, b)$.   Choose a and b so that
    (a) the area of $\triangle OAB$ is a minimum.
    (b) the length of $\overline{AB}$ is a minimum.
    (c) $a + b$ is a minimum.
    (d) the perpendicular distance from O to $\overline{AB}$ is a maximum.

39. Two sources of heat are placed s meters apart: a source of intensity a at A and a source of intensity b at B.   The intensity of heat at a point P between A and B is then given by the formula

$$I = \frac{a}{x^2} + \frac{b}{(s - x)^2}$$

where x is the distance between P and A measured in meters.   At what point P between A and B will the temperature be lowest?

40. Draw the parabola $y = x^2$.   On the parabola mark a point $P \neq 0$.   Through P draw the normal line.   This normal line intersects the parabola at another point Q.   Show that the distance between P and Q is minimized by setting $P = (\pm\frac{1}{2}\sqrt{2}, \frac{1}{2})$.

41. *The problem of Viviani.*† Two parallel lines are cut by a given line AB.   See Figure 4.10.3.   From the point C we draw a line to the point marked Q.   How should Q be chosen so that the sum of the areas of the two triangles is a minimum?

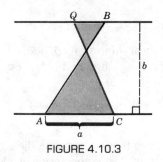

FIGURE 4.10.3

42. An isosceles trapezoid is inscribed in a circle of radius r.   (Figure 4.10.4)   Given that one base has length $2r$, find the length of the other base if the area is a maximum.

43. Find the dimensions of the rectangular solid of maximum volume that can be cut from a solid sphere of radius r.   (Figure 4.10.5)

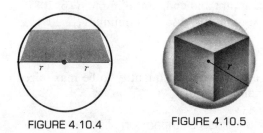

FIGURE 4.10.4   FIGURE 4.10.5

† Vicenzo Viviani (1622–1703), a pupil of Galileo.

44. Find the base and altitude of the isosceles triangle of minimum area that circumscribes the ellipse $b^2x^2 + a^2y^2 = a^2b^2$ if the base is parallel to the x-axis.

45. A triangle is formed in the first quadrant by the coordinate axes and a tangent to the ellipse $b^2x^2 + a^2y^2 = a^2b^2$. Find the point of tangency if the triangle is to have minimum area.

4.11 CHAPTER SUMMARY

4.1 The Mean-Value Theorem

mean-value theorem (p. 187)   Rolle's theorem (p. 189)

4.2 Increasing and Decreasing Functions

f increases (p. 193) f decreases (p. 193)

The derivative can be used to test for intervals of increase and decrease. For example, if $f'(x) > 0$ for all x in the interval I, then f increases on I, but not conversely. (p. 195)

If f and g have the same derivative on an interval, then f and g differ by a constant on that interval. (p. 198)

4.3 Maxima and Minima

local maximum and local minimum (p. 200)
critical point (p. 201)   first-derivative test (p. 204)
second-derivative test (p. 206)

If f has a local extremum at c, then either $f'(c) = 0$ or $f'(c)$ does not exist; the converse is false.

The first-derivative test requires that we examine the sign of the first-derivative on both sides of the critical point; the test is conclusive in all cases. The second-derivative test requires that we examine the sign of the second derivative at the critical point itself; the test is inconclusive if $f''(c) = 0$.

4.4 More on Maxima and Minima

endpoint maximum and endpoint minimum (p. 208)
absolute maximum and absolute minimum (p. 209)

4.5 Some Max-Min Problems

The *key step* here is to express the quantity to be maximized or minimized as a function of one variable.

4.6 Concavity and Points of Inflection

concave up and concave down (p. 220)
point of inflection (p. 220)

If $(c, f(c))$ is a point of inflection, then either $f''(c) = 0$ or $f''(c)$ does not exist; the converse is false.

4.7 Some Curve Sketching

An 8-step procedure for sketching the graph of a function is outlined on p. 224.

4.8 Vertical and Horizontal Asymptotes; Cusps and Vertical Tangents

vertical asymptote (p. 228)   horizontal asymptote (p. 230)
vertical tangent (p. 232)   vertical cusp (p. 232)

4.9 More Graphing Problems

4.10 More Max-Min Problems

5

Integration

5.1 ⋯⋯AN AREA PROBLEM; A SPEED AND DISTANCE PROBLEM

An Area Problem

In Figure 5.1.1 you can see a region Ω bounded above by the graph of a continuous nonnegative function f, bounded below by the x-axis, bounded to the left by $x = a$, and bounded to the right by $x = b$. The question before us is this: what number, if any, should be called the area of Ω?

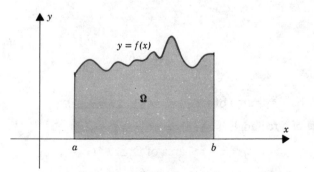

FIGURE 5.1.1

To begin to answer this question, we split up the interval $[a, b]$ into a finite number of nonoverlapping intervals

$$[x_0, x_1], [x_1, x_2], \ldots, [x_{n-1}, x_n] \quad \text{with} \quad a = x_0 < x_1 < \cdots < x_n = b.$$

This breaks up the region Ω into n subregions:

$$\Omega_1, \Omega_2, \ldots, \Omega_n. \qquad \text{(Figure 5.1.2)}$$

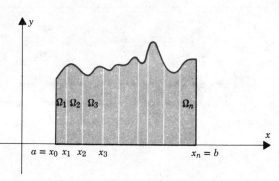

FIGURE 5.1.2

We can estimate the total area of Ω by estimating the area of each subregion Ω_j and adding up the results. Let's denote by M_j the maximum value of f on $[x_{j-1}, x_j]$ and by m_j the minimum value. Consider now the rectangles r_j and R_j of Figure 5.1.3.

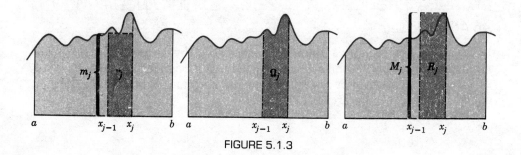

FIGURE 5.1.3

Since

$$r_j \subseteq \Omega_j \subseteq R_j,$$

we must have

$$\text{area of } r_j \leq \text{area of } \Omega_j \leq \text{area of } R_j.$$

Since the area of a rectangle is the length times the width,

$$m_j(x_j - x_{j-1}) \leq \text{area of } \Omega_j \leq M_j(x_j - x_{j-1}).$$

Setting $x_j - x_{j-1} = \Delta x_j$ we have

$$m_j \, \Delta x_j \leq \text{area of } \Omega_j \leq M_j \, \Delta x_j.$$

This inequality holds for $j = 1, j = 2, \ldots, j = n$. Adding up these inequalities we get on the one hand

(5.1.1) $m_1 \Delta x_1 + m_2 \Delta x_2 + \cdots + m_n \Delta x_n \leq$ area of Ω

and on the other hand

(5.1.2)   area of $\Omega \leq M_1 \Delta x_1 + M_2 \Delta x_2 + \cdots + M_n \Delta x_n$.

   A sum of the form

$$m_1 \Delta x_1 + m_2 \Delta x_2 + \cdots + m_n \Delta x_n \qquad \text{(Figure 5.1.4)}$$

is called a *lower sum for f.* A sum of the form

$$M_1 \Delta x_1 + M_2 \Delta x_2 + \cdots + M_n \Delta x_n \qquad \text{(Figure 5.1.5)}$$

is called an *upper sum for f.*

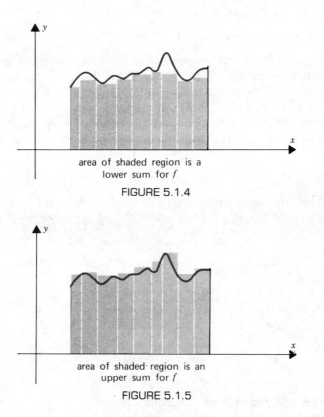

area of shaded region is a
lower sum for f

FIGURE 5.1.4

area of shaded region is an
upper sum for f

FIGURE 5.1.5

   Inequalities (5.1.1) and (5.1.2) together tell us that for a number to be a candidate for the title "area of Ω" it must be greater than or equal to every lower sum for f, and it must be less than or equal to every upper sum. By an argument that we omit here, it can be proved that with f continuous on $[a, b]$ there is one and only one such number. This number we call *the area of Ω.*

   Later we'll return to the subject of area. At this point we turn to a speed and distance problem. As you'll see, this new problem can be solved by the same technique that we just applied to the area problem.

A Speed and Distance Problem

If an object moves at a constant speed for a given period of time, then the total distance traveled is given by the familiar formula

$$\text{distance} = \text{speed} \times \text{time}.$$

Suppose now that during the course of the motion the speed does not remain constant but instead varies continuously. How can the total distance traveled be computed then?

   To answer this question, we suppose that the motion begins at time a, ends at time b, and that during the time interval $[a, b]$ the speed varies continuously.

   As in the case of the area problem we begin by breaking up the interval $[a, b]$ into a finite number of nonoverlapping intervals

$$[t_0, t_1], [t_1, t_2], \ldots, [t_{n-1}, t_n] \quad \text{with} \quad a = t_0 < t_1 < \cdots < t_n = b.$$

On each subinterval $[t_{j-1}, t_j]$ the object attains a certain maximum speed M_j and a certain minimum speed m_j. (How do we know this?) If throughout the time interval $[t_{j-1}, t_j]$ the object were to move constantly at its minimum speed, m_j, then it would cover a distance of $m_j \Delta t_j$ units. If instead it were to move constantly at its maximum speed, M_j, then it would cover a distance of $M_j \Delta t_j$ units. As it is, the actual distance traveled, call it s_j, must lie somewhere in between; namely, we must have

$$m_j \Delta t_j \leq s_j \leq M_j \Delta t_j.$$

The total distance traveled during the time interval $[a, b]$, call it s, must be the sum of the distances traveled during the subintervals $[t_{j-1}, t_j]$. In other words we must have

$$s = s_1 + s_2 + \cdots + s_n.$$

Since

$$m_1 \Delta t_1 \leq s_1 \leq M_1 \Delta t_1$$
$$m_2 \Delta t_2 \leq s_2 \leq M_2 \Delta t_2$$
$$\cdot$$
$$\cdot$$
$$\cdot$$
$$m_n \Delta t_n \leq s_n \leq M_n \Delta t_n,$$

it follows by the addition of these inequalities that

$$m_1 \Delta t_1 + m_2 \Delta t_2 + \cdots + m_n \Delta t_n \leq s \leq M_1 \Delta t_1 + M_2 \Delta t_2 + \cdots + M_n \Delta t_n.$$

A sum of the form

$$m \Delta t_1 + m_2 \Delta t_2 + \cdots + m_n \Delta t_n$$

is called a *lower sum* for the speed function. A sum of the form

$$M_1 \Delta t_1 + M_2 \Delta t_2 + \cdots + M_n \Delta t_n$$

is called an *upper sum* for the speed function. The inequality we just obtained for s tells us that s must be greater than or equal to every lower sum for the speed function, and it must be less than or equal to every upper sum. As in the case of the area problem, it turns out that there is one and only one such number, and this is the total distance traveled.

5.2 ......THE DEFINITE INTEGRAL OF A CONTINUOUS FUNCTION

The process we used to solve the two problems of Section 5.1 is called *integration,* and the end results of this process are called *definite integrals.* Our purpose here is to establish these notions more precisely.

(5.2.1)   By a *partition* of the closed interval $[a, b]$ we mean a finite subset of $[a, b]$ which contains the points a and b.

We index the elements of a partition according to their natural order. Thus, if we write

$$P = \{x_0, x_1, \ldots, x_n\} \text{ is a partition of } [a, b],$$

you can conclude that

$$a = x_0 < x_1 < \cdots < x_n = b.$$

EXAMPLE. The sets

$$\{0, 1\}, \quad \{0, \tfrac{1}{2}, 1\}, \quad \{0, \tfrac{1}{4}, \tfrac{1}{2}, 1\}, \quad \{0, \tfrac{1}{4}, \tfrac{1}{3}, \tfrac{1}{2}, \tfrac{5}{8}, 1\}$$

are all partitions of the interval $[0, 1]$. $\square$

If $P = \{x_0, x_1, \ldots, x_n\}$ is a partition of $[a, b]$, then P breaks up $[a, b]$ into a finite number of nonoverlapping intervals

$$[x_0, x_1], [x_1, x_2], \ldots, [x_{n-1}, x_n]$$

of lengths $\Delta x_1, \Delta x_2, \ldots, \Delta x_n$ respectively.

Suppose now that f is continuous on $[a, b]$. Then on each interval $[x_{j-1}, x_j]$ the function f takes on a maximum value, M_j, and a minimum value, m_j.

(5.2.2)   The number

$$U_f(P) = M_1 \Delta x_1 + M_2 \Delta x_2 + \cdots + M_n \Delta x_n$$

is called *the P upper sum for f,* and the number

$$L_f(P) = m_1 \Delta x_1 + m_2 \Delta x_2 + \cdots + m_n \Delta x_n$$

is called *the P lower sum for f.*

EXAMPLE. The squaring function

$$f(x) = x^2$$

is continuous on $[0, 1]$. The partition $P = \{0, \frac{1}{4}, \frac{1}{2}, 1\}$ breaks up $[0, 1]$ into three subintervals:

$$[x_0, x_1] = [0, \tfrac{1}{4}], \qquad [x_1, x_2] = [\tfrac{1}{4}, \tfrac{1}{2}], \qquad [x_2, x_3] = [\tfrac{1}{2}, 1]$$

of lengths

$$\Delta x_1 = \tfrac{1}{4} - 0 = \tfrac{1}{4}, \qquad \Delta x_2 = \tfrac{1}{2} - \tfrac{1}{4} = \tfrac{1}{4}, \qquad \Delta x_3 = 1 - \tfrac{1}{2} = \tfrac{1}{2}$$

respectively. The maximum values taken on by f on these intervals are

$$M_1 = f(\tfrac{1}{4}) = \tfrac{1}{16}, \qquad M_2 = f(\tfrac{1}{2}) = \tfrac{1}{4}, \qquad M_3 = f(1) = 1.$$

The minimum values are

$$m_1 = f(0) = 0, \qquad m_2 = f(\tfrac{1}{4}) = \tfrac{1}{16}, \qquad m_3 = f(\tfrac{1}{2}) = \tfrac{1}{4}.$$

Thus

$$U_f(P) = M_1 \Delta x_1 + M_2 \Delta x_2 + M_3 \Delta x_3 = \tfrac{1}{16}(\tfrac{1}{4}) + \tfrac{1}{4}(\tfrac{1}{4}) + 1(\tfrac{1}{2}) = \tfrac{37}{64}$$

and

$$L_f(P) = m_1 \Delta x_1 + m_2 \Delta x_2 + m_3 \Delta x_3 = 0(\tfrac{1}{4}) + \tfrac{1}{16}(\tfrac{1}{4}) + \tfrac{1}{4}(\tfrac{1}{2}) = \tfrac{9}{64}. \quad \square$$

EXAMPLE. This time we take the function

$$f(x) = -x - 1$$

on the closed interval $[-1, 0]$. The partition $P = \{-1, -\frac{1}{4}, 0\}$ breaks up $[-1, 0]$ into two intervals: $[-1, -\frac{1}{4}]$ and $[-\frac{1}{4}, 0]$. As you can check,

$$U_f(P) = (0)(\tfrac{3}{4}) + (-\tfrac{3}{4})(\tfrac{1}{4}) = -\tfrac{3}{16} \quad \text{and} \quad L_f(P) = (-\tfrac{3}{4})(\tfrac{3}{4}) + (-1)(\tfrac{1}{4}) = -\tfrac{13}{16}. \quad \square$$

By an argument that we omit here (it appears in Appendix B.4) it can be proved that, with f continuous on $[a, b]$, there is one and only one number I that satisfies the inequality

$$L_f(P) \le I \le U_f(P) \qquad \text{for } \textit{all} \text{ partitions } P \text{ of } [a, b].$$

This is the number we want.

DEFINITION 5.2.3   THE DEFINITE INTEGRAL

The unique number I that satisfies the inequality

$$L_f(P) \le I \le U_f(P) \qquad \text{for all partitions } P \text{ of } [a, b]$$

is called *the definite integral* (or more simply *the integral*) *of f from a to b* and is denoted by

$$\int_a^b f(x) \, dx.\dagger$$

$\dagger$ This is not the only notation. Some mathematicians omit the dx and write simply

$$\int_a^b f.$$

We will keep the dx. As we go on, you'll see that it does serve a useful purpose.

The symbol $\int$ dates back to Leibniz and is called an *integral sign*. It is really an elongated S—as in *Sum*. The numbers a and b are called *the limits of integration*, and we'll speak of *integrating* a function from a to b.† The function being integrated is called *the integrand*.

In the expression

$$\int_a^b f(x)\, dx$$

the letter x is a "dummy variable"; in other words, it may be replaced by any other letter not already engaged. Thus, for example, there is no difference between

$$\int_a^b f(x)\, dx, \qquad \int_a^b f(t)\, dt, \qquad \text{and} \qquad \int_a^b f(z)\, dz.$$

All of these denote the definite integral of f from a to b.

Section 5.1 gives two immediate applications of the definite integral:

I. If f is nonnegative on $[a, b]$, then

$$A = \int_a^b f(x)\, dx$$

gives the area below the graph of f. See Figure 5.1.1.

II. If $|v(t)|$ is the speed of an object at time t, then

$$s = \int_a^b |v(t)|\, dt$$

gives the distance traveled from time a to time b.

We'll come back to these ideas later. Right now, some simple computations.

EXAMPLE. If $f(x) = \alpha$ for all x in $[a, b]$, then

$$\int_a^b f(x)\, dx = \alpha(b - a).$$

To see this, take $P = \{x_0, x_1, \ldots, x_n\}$ as an arbitrary partition of $[a, b]$. Since f is constantly α on $[a, b]$, it is constantly α on each subinterval $[x_{j-1}, x_j]$. Thus, M_j and m_j are both α. It follows that

$$U_f(P) = \alpha\Delta x_1 + \alpha\Delta x_2 + \cdots + \alpha\Delta x_n$$
$$= \alpha(\Delta x_1 + \Delta x_2 + \cdots + \Delta x_n) = \alpha(b - a)$$

and

$$L_f(P) = \alpha\Delta x_1 + \alpha\Delta x_2 + \cdots + \alpha\Delta x_n$$
$$= \alpha(\Delta x_1 + \Delta x_2 + \cdots + \Delta x_n) = \alpha(b - a).$$

Obviously then

$$L_f(P) \le \alpha(b - a) \le U_f(P).$$

---

† The word "limit" here has no connection with the limits discussed in Chapter 2.

Since this inequality holds for all partitions P of $[a, b]$, we can conclude that

$$\int_a^b f(x)\, dx = \alpha(b - a). \quad \square$$

This last result can be written

(5.2.4)
$$\int_a^b \alpha\, dx = \alpha(b - a).$$

Thus for example

$$\int_{-1}^{1} 4\, dx = 4(2) = 8 \quad \text{and} \quad \int_{4}^{10} -2\, dx = -2(6) = -12.$$

If $\alpha > 0$, the region below the graph is a rectangle of height α erected on the interval $[a, b]$. (Figure 5.2.1) The integral gives the area of this rectangle.

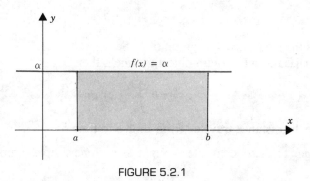

FIGURE 5.2.1

EXAMPLE

(5.2.5)
$$\int_a^b x\, dx = \tfrac{1}{2}(b^2 - a^2).$$

To see this, take $P = \{x_0, x_1, \ldots, x_n\}$ as an arbitrary partition of $[a, b]$. On each subinterval $[x_{j-1}, x_j]$ the function $f(x) = x$ has a maximum $M_j = x_j$ and a minimum $m_j = x_{j-1}$. It follows that

$$U_f(P) = x_1\Delta x_1 + x_2\Delta x_2 + \cdots + x_n\Delta x_n$$

and

$$L_f(P) = x_0\Delta x_1 + x_1\Delta x_2 + \cdots + x_{n-1}\Delta x_n.$$

For each index j

$$x_{j-1} \le \tfrac{1}{2}(x_j + x_{j-1}) \le x_j. \qquad \text{(explain)}$$

Multiplication by $\Delta x_j = x_j - x_{j-1}$ gives

$$x_{j-1}\Delta x_j \le \tfrac{1}{2}(x_j^2 - x_{j-1}^2) \le x_j\Delta x_j.$$

Summing from $j = 1$ to $j = n$, we find that

$$L_f(P) \le \tfrac{1}{2}(x_1^2 - x_0^2) + \tfrac{1}{2}(x_2^2 - x_1^2) + \cdots + \tfrac{1}{2}(x_n^2 - x_{n-1}^2) \le U_f(P).$$

The middle collapses to

$$\tfrac{1}{2}(x_n^2 - x_0^2) = \tfrac{1}{2}(b^2 - a^2).$$

Consequently we have

$$L_f(P) \le \tfrac{1}{2}(b^2 - a^2) \le U_f(P).$$

Since P was chosen arbitrarily, we can conclude that this inequality holds for all partitions P of $[a, b]$. It follows then that

$$\int_a^b x\,dx = \tfrac{1}{2}(b^2 - a^2). \quad \square$$

If the interval $[a, b]$ lies to the right of the origin, then the region below the graph of

$$f(x) = x, \qquad x \in [a, b]$$

is the trapezoid of Figure 5.2.2. The integral

$$\int_a^b x\,dx$$

gives the area of this trapezoid.

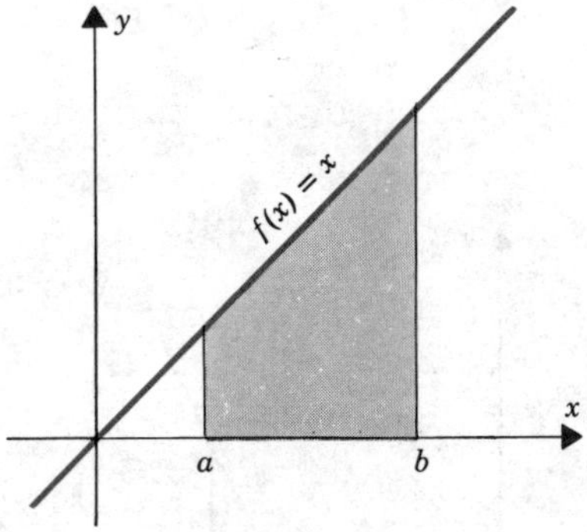

FIGURE 5.2.2

EXAMPLE

$$\int_0^1 x^2\,dx = \tfrac{1}{3}. \qquad\qquad \text{(Figure 5.2.3)}$$

This time take $P = \{x_0, x_1, \ldots, x_n\}$ as a partition of $[0, 1]$. On each subinterval $[x_{j-1}, x_j]$ the function $f(x) = x^2$ has a maximum $M_j = x_j^2$ and a minimum $m_j = x_{j-1}^2$.

It follows that

$$U_f(P) = x_1^2 \Delta x_1 + \cdots + x_n^2 \Delta x_n$$

and

$$L_f(P) = x_0^2 \Delta x_1 + \cdots + x_{n-1}^2 \Delta x_n.$$

For each index j,

$$x_{j-1}^2 \leq \tfrac{1}{3}(x_{j-1}^2 + x_{j-1}x_j + x_j^2) \leq x_j^2. \qquad \text{(check this out)}$$

We now multiply this inequality by $\Delta x_j = x_j - x_{j-1}$. The middle term reduces to

$$\tfrac{1}{3}(x_j^3 - x_{j-1}^3), \qquad \text{(check this out)}$$

showing us that

$$x_{j-1}^2 \Delta x_j \leq \tfrac{1}{3}(x_j^3 - x_{j-1}^3) \leq x_j^2 \Delta x_j.$$

The sum of the terms on the left is $L_f(P)$. The sum of all the middle terms collapses to $\tfrac{1}{3}$:

$$\tfrac{1}{3}(x_1^3 - x_0^3 + x_2^3 - x_1^3 + \cdots + x_n^3 - x_{n-1}^3) = \tfrac{1}{3}(x_n^3 - x_0^3) = \tfrac{1}{3}(1^3 - 0^3) = \tfrac{1}{3}.$$

The sum of the terms on the right is $U_f(P)$. Clearly then

$$L_f(P) \leq \tfrac{1}{3} \leq U_f(P).$$

Since P was chosen arbitrarily, we can conclude that this inequality holds for all partitions P of $[0, 1]$. It follows therefore that

$$\int_0^1 x^2 \, dx = \tfrac{1}{3}. \quad \square$$

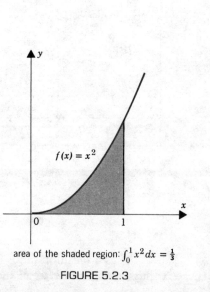

area of the shaded region: $\int_0^1 x^2 \, dx = \tfrac{1}{3}$

FIGURE 5.2.3

EXERCISES

Find $L_f(P)$ and $U_f(P)$.

1. $f(x) = 2x$, $x \in [0, 1]$; $P = \{0, \frac{1}{4}, \frac{1}{2}, 1\}$.

2. $f(x) = 1 - x$, $x \in [0, 2]$; $P = \{0, \frac{1}{3}, \frac{3}{4}, 1, 2\}$.

3. $f(x) = x^2$, $x \in [-1, 0]$; $P = \{-1, -\frac{1}{2}, -\frac{1}{4}, 0\}$.

4. $f(x) = 1 - x^2$, $x \in [0, 1]$; $P = \{0, \frac{1}{4}, \frac{1}{2}, 1\}$.

5. $f(x) = 1 + x^3$, $x \in [0, 1]$; $P = \{0, \frac{1}{2}, 1\}$.

6. $f(x) = \sqrt{x}$, $x \in [0, 1]$; $P = \{0, \frac{1}{25}, \frac{4}{25}, \frac{9}{25}, \frac{16}{25}, 1\}$.

7. $f(x) = |x|$, $x \in [-1, 1]$; $P = \{-1, -\frac{1}{2}, 0, \frac{1}{4}, 1\}$.

8. $f(x) = |x|$, $x \in [-1, 1]$; $P = \{-1, -\frac{1}{2}, -\frac{1}{4}, \frac{1}{2}, 1\}$.

9. $f(x) = x^2$, $x \in [-1, 1]$; $P = \{-1, -\frac{1}{4}, \frac{1}{4}, \frac{1}{2}, 1\}$.

10. $f(x) = x^2$, $x \in [-1, 1]$; $P = \{-1, -\frac{3}{4}, -\frac{1}{4}, \frac{1}{4}, \frac{1}{2}, 1\}$.

11. $f(x) = \sin x$, $x \in [0, \pi]$; $P = \left\{0, \dfrac{\pi}{6}, \dfrac{\pi}{2}, \pi\right\}$.

12. $f(x) = \cos x$, $x \in [0, \pi]$; $P = \left\{0, \dfrac{\pi}{3}, \dfrac{\pi}{2}, \pi\right\}$.

13. Explain why each of the following three statements is false. Take P as a partition of $[-1, 1]$.

   (a) $L_f(P) = 3$ and $U_f(P) = 2$.

   (b) $L_f(P) = 3$, $U_f(P) = 6$, and $\displaystyle\int_{-1}^{1} f(x)\, dx = 2.$

   (c) $L_f(P) = 3$, $U_f(P) = 6$, and $\displaystyle\int_{-1}^{1} f(x)\, dx = 10.$

14. (a) Given that $P = \{x_0, x_1, \ldots, x_n\}$ is an arbitrary partition of $[a, b]$, find $L_f(P)$ and $U_f(P)$ for $f(x) = x + 3$.

   (b) Use your answers to part (a) to evaluate

$$\int_a^b (x + 3)\, dx.$$

15. Exercise 14 with $f(x) = -3x$.

16. Exercise 14 with $f(x) = 1 + 2x$.

17. Evaluate

$$\int_0^1 x^3\, dx$$

by the methods of this section.   HINT: $b^4 - a^4 = (b^3 + b^2 a + ba^2 + a^3)(b - a)$.

18. Consider the Dirichlet function f on $[0, 1]$:

$$f(x) = \begin{bmatrix} 1, & x \text{ rational} \\ 0, & x \text{ irrational} \end{bmatrix}.$$

   (a) Show that $L_f(P) \leq \frac{1}{2} \leq U_f(P)$ for all partitions P of $[0, 1]$.

   (b) Explain why we can *not* conclude that

$$\int_0^1 f(x)\, dx = \frac{1}{2}.$$

19. We have assumed in (5.2.2) that f is continuous on $[a, b]$. However, $L_f(P)$ and $U_f(P)$ make sense for any function f as long as f has a maximum and a minimum on any closed subinterval of $[a, b]$. The function

$$f(x) = \begin{cases} 2, & x \in [0, 3) \cup (3, 4] \\ 7, & x = 3 \end{cases}$$

is just such a function. Use Definition 5.2.3 to show that

$$\int_0^4 f(x)\, dx = 8.$$

5.3 ⋯⋯ THE FUNCTION $F(x) = \displaystyle\int_a^x f(t)\, dt$

The evaluation of a definite integral

$$\int_a^b f(x)\, dx$$

directly from its definition as the unique number I satisfying the inequality

$$L_f(P) \le I \le U_f(P)$$

for all partitions P of $[a, b]$ is usually a laborious process. Try, for example, to evaluate

$$\int_2^5 \left(x^3 + x^{5/2} - \frac{2x}{1 - x^2} \right) dx \quad \text{or} \quad \int_{-1/2}^{1/4} \frac{x}{1 - x^2}\, dx$$

by this method. Theorem 5.4.2, called *the fundamental theorem of integral calculus,* gives us another way to evaluate such integrals. This other way depends on a connection between integration and differentiation described in Theorem 5.3.5. The main purpose of this section is to prove Theorem 5.3.5. Along the way we will pick up some information that is of interest in itself.

THEOREM 5.3.1

Let P and Q be partitions of the interval $[a, b]$. If $P \subseteq Q$, then

$$L_f(P) \le L_f(Q) \quad \text{and} \quad U_f(Q) \le U_f(P).$$

This result is easy to see. By adding points to a partition we tend to make the subintervals $[x_{j-1}, x_j]$ smaller. This tends to make the minima, m_j, larger and the maxima, M_j, smaller. Thus the lower sums are made bigger, and the upper sums are made smaller. The idea is illustrated (for a positive function) in Figures 5.3.1 and 5.3.2.

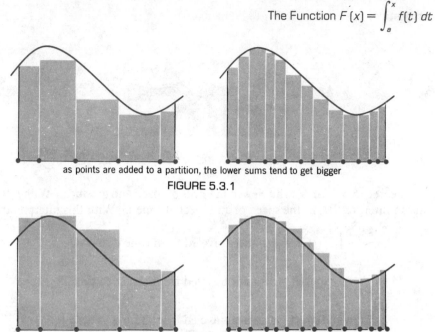

as points are added to a partition, the lower sums tend to get bigger

FIGURE 5.3.1

as points are added to a partition, the upper sums tend to get smaller

FIGURE 5.3.2

The next theorem says that the integral is *additive* on intervals.

THEOREM 5.3.2

If f is continuous on $[a, b]$ and $a < c < b$, then

$$\int_a^c f(t)\, dt + \int_c^b f(t)\, dt = \int_a^b f(t)\, dt.$$

For nonnegative functions f this theorem is easily understood in terms of area. The area of part I in Figure 5.3.3 is given by

$$\int_a^c f(t)\, dt;$$

the area of part II by

$$\int_c^b f(t)\, dt;$$

the area of the entire region by

$$\int_a^b f(t)\, dt.$$

The theorem says that

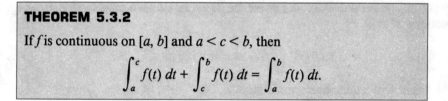

the area of part I + the area of part II = the area of the entire region.

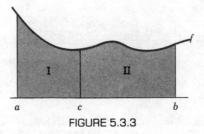

FIGURE 5.3.3

Theorem 5.3.2 can also be viewed in terms of speed and distance. With $f(t) \geq 0$, we can interpret $f(t)$ as the speed of an object at time t. With this interpretation,

$$\int_a^c f(t) \, dt = \text{distance traveled from time } a \text{ to time } c,$$

$$\int_c^b f(t) \, dt = \text{distance traveled from time } c \text{ to time } b,$$

$$\int_a^b f(t) \, dt = \text{distance traveled from time } a \text{ to time } b.$$

It is not surprising that the sum of the first two distances should equal the third.

The fact that the additivity theorem is so easy to understand does not relieve us of the necessity to prove it. Here is a proof.

Proof of Theorem 5.3.2. To prove the theorem we need only show that for each partition P of $[a, b]$

$$L_f(P) \leq \int_a^c f(t) \, dt + \int_c^b f(t) \, dt \leq U_f(P). \qquad \text{(why?)}$$

We begin with an arbitrary partition of $[a, b]$:

$$P = \{x_0, x_1, \ldots, x_n\}.$$

Since the partition $Q = P \cup \{c\}$ contains P, we know from Theorem 5.3.1 that

(1) $$L_f(P) \leq L_f(Q) \quad \text{and} \quad U_f(Q) \leq U_f(P).$$

The sets

$$Q_1 = Q \cap [a, c] \quad \text{and} \quad Q_2 = Q \cap [c, b]$$

are partitions of $[a, c]$ and $[c, b]$, respectively. Moreover

$$L_f(Q_1) + L_f(Q_2) = L_f(Q) \quad \text{and} \quad U_f(Q_1) + U_f(Q_2) = U_f(Q).$$

Since

$$L_f(Q_1) \leq \int_a^c f(t) \, dt \leq U_f(Q_1) \quad \text{and} \quad L_f(Q_2) \leq \int_c^b f(t) \, dt \leq U_f(Q_2),$$

we have

$$L_f(Q_1) + L_f(Q_2) \leq \int_a^c f(t) \, dt + \int_c^b f(t) \, dt \leq U_f(Q_1) + U_f(Q_2).$$

It follows that

$$L_f(Q) \leq \int_a^c f(t)\, dt + \int_c^b f(t)\, dt \leq U_f(Q)$$

and thus by (1) that

$$L_f(P) \leq \int_a^c f(t)\, dt + \int_c^b f(t)\, dt \leq U_f(P). \quad \square$$

Until now we have integrated only from left to right: from a number a to a number b greater than a. We integrate in the other direction by defining

(5.3.3)
$$\int_b^a f(t)\, dt = - \int_a^b f(t)\, dt.$$

The integral from any number to itself is defined to be zero:

(5.3.4)
$$\int_c^c f(t)\, dt = 0$$

for all real c. With these additional conventions, the additivity condition

$$\int_a^c f(t)\, dt + \int_c^b f(t)\, dt = \int_a^b f(t)\, dt$$

holds for all choices of a, b, c from an interval on which f is continuous, no matter what the order of a, b, c happens to be. We have left the proof of this to you as an exercise.

We are now ready to state the all-important connection that exists between integration and differentiation. Our first step is to point out that, if f is continuous on $[a, b]$, then for each x in $[a, b]$, the integral

$$\int_a^x f(t)\, dt$$

is a number, and consequently we can define a function F on $[a, b]$ by setting

$$F(x) = \int_a^x f(t)\, dt.$$

THEOREM 5.3.5

If f is continuous on $[a, b]$, the function F defined on $[a, b]$ by setting

$$F(x) = \int_a^x f(t)\, dt$$

is continuous on $[a, b]$, differentiable on (a, b), and has derivative

$$F'(x) = f(x) \qquad \text{for all } x \text{ in } (a, b).$$

Proof.   We begin with x in the half-open interval $[a, b)$ and show that

$$\lim_{h\to 0^+} \frac{F(x + h) - F(x)}{h} = f(x).$$

(For a pictorial outline of the proof for f nonnegative see Figure 5.3.4.)

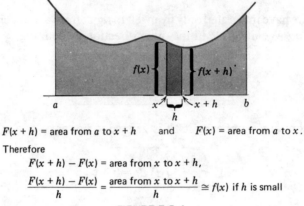

$F(x + h)$ = area from a to $x + h$ and $F(x)$ = area from a to x.

Therefore

$F(x + h) - F(x)$ = area from x to $x + h$,

$\dfrac{F(x + h) - F(x)}{h} = \dfrac{\text{area from } x \text{ to } x + h}{h} \cong f(x)$ if h is small

FIGURE 5.3.4

If $x < x + h \leq b$, then

$$F(x + h) - F(x) = \int_a^{x+h} f(t)\, dt - \int_a^x f(t)\, dt.$$

It follows that

$$F(x + h) - F(x) = \int_x^{x+h} f(t)\, dt.$$ (justify this step)

Now set

$$M_h = \text{maximum value of } f \text{ on } [x, x + h]$$

and

$$m_h = \text{minimum value of } f \text{ on } [x, x + h].$$

Since

$$M_h[(x + h) - x] = M_h \cdot h$$

is an upper sum for f on $[x, x + h]$ and

$$m_h[(x + h) - x] = m_h \cdot h$$

is a lower sum for f on $[x, x + h]$,

$$m_h \cdot h \leq \int_x^{x+h} f(t)\, dt \leq M_h \cdot h.$$

and, since $h > 0$,

$$m_h \le \frac{F(x+h) - F(x)}{h} \le M_h.$$

Since f is continuous on $[x, x+h]$,

(1) $$\lim_{h \to 0^+} m_h = f(x) = \lim_{h \to 0^+} M_h$$

and thus

(2) $$\lim_{h \to 0^+} \frac{F(x+h) - F(x)}{h} = f(x).$$

In a similar manner we can prove that, for x in the half-open interval $(a, b]$,

(3) $$\lim_{h \to 0^-} \frac{F(x+h) - F(x)}{h} = f(x).$$

For x in the open interval (a, b), both (2) and (3) hold, and we have

$$F'(x) = \lim_{h \to 0} \frac{F(x+h) - F(x)}{h} = f(x).$$

This proves that F is differentiable on (a, b) and has derivative $F'(x) = f(x)$.

All that's left to be shown is that F is continuous from the right at a and continuous from the left at b. Relation (2) at $x = a$ gives

$$\lim_{h \to 0^+} \frac{F(a+h) - F(a)}{h} = f(a).$$

It follows that

$$\lim_{h \to 0^+} [F(a+h) - F(a)] = 0 \qquad\qquad \text{(explain)}$$

and

$$\lim_{h \to 0^+} F(a+h) = F(a).$$

This shows that F is continuous from the right at a. That F is continuous from the left at b can be shown by applying relation (3) at $x = b$. $\square$

EXERCISES

1. Given that

$$\int_0^1 f(x)\, dx = 6, \qquad \int_0^2 f(x)\, dx = 4, \qquad \int_2^5 f(x)\, dx = 1,$$

find each of the following:

(a) $\displaystyle\int_0^5 f(x)\, dx.$ (b) $\displaystyle\int_1^2 f(x)\, dx.$ (c) $\displaystyle\int_1^5 f(x)\, dx.$

(d) $\displaystyle\int_0^0 f(x)\, dx.$ (e) $\displaystyle\int_2^0 f(x)\, dx.$ (f) $\displaystyle\int_5^1 f(x)\, dx.$

2. Given that

$$\int_1^4 f(x)\, dx = 5, \qquad \int_3^4 f(x)\, dx = 7, \qquad \int_1^8 f(x)\, dx = 11,$$

find each of the following:

(a) $\displaystyle\int_4^8 f(x)\, dx.$ (b) $\displaystyle\int_4^3 f(x)\, dx.$ (c) $\displaystyle\int_1^3 f(x)\, dx.$

(d) $\displaystyle\int_3^8 f(x)\, dx.$ (e) $\displaystyle\int_8^4 f(x)\, dx.$ (f) $\displaystyle\int_4^4 f(x)\, dx.$

3. Use upper and lower sums to show that

$$0.5 < \int_1^2 \frac{dx}{x} < 1.$$

4. Use upper and lower sums to show that

$$0.6 < \int_0^1 \frac{dx}{1 + x^2} < 1.$$

5. For $x > -1$ set $F(x) = \displaystyle\int_0^x t\sqrt{t + 1}\, dt.$

(a) Find $F(0)$.   (b) Find $F'(x)$.   (c) Find $F'(2)$.
(d) Express $F(2)$ as an integral of $t\sqrt{t + 1}$.
(e) Express $-F(x)$ as an integral of $t\sqrt{t + 1}$.

6. For $x > 0$ set $F(x) = \displaystyle\int_1^x \frac{dt}{t}.$

(a) Find $F(1)$.   (b) Find $F'(x)$.   (c) Find $F'(1)$.
(d) Express $F(2)$ as an integral of $1/t$.
(e) Express $-F(x)$ as an integral of $1/t$.

For the given function F compute the following:

(a) $F'(-1)$.   (b) $F'(0)$.   (c) $F'(\tfrac{1}{2})$.   (d) $F''(x)$.

7. $F(x) = \displaystyle\int_0^x \frac{dt}{t^2 + 9}.$ 8. $F(x) = \displaystyle\int_x^0 \sqrt{t^2 + 1}\, dt.$ 9. $F(x) = \displaystyle\int_x^1 t\sqrt{t^2 + 1}\, dt.$

10. $F(x) = \displaystyle\int_1^x \sin \pi t\, dt.$ 11. $F(x) = \displaystyle\int_1^x \cos \pi t\, dt.$ 12. $F(x) = \displaystyle\int_2^x (t + 1)^3\, dt.$

13. Explain why each of the following statements must be false.
(a) $U_f(P_1) = 4$ for the partition $P_1 = \{0, 1, \tfrac{3}{2}, 2\}$ and
    $U_f(P_2) = 5$ for the partition $P_2 = \{0, \tfrac{1}{4}, 1, \tfrac{3}{2}, 2\}$.
(b) $L_f(P_1) = 5$ for the partition $P_1 = \{0, 1, \tfrac{3}{2}, 2\}$ and
    $L_f(P_2) = 4$ for the partition $P_2 = \{0, \tfrac{1}{4}, 1, \tfrac{3}{2}, 2\}$.

14. Show that, if f is continuous on an interval I, then

$$\int_a^c f(t)\, dt + \int_c^b f(t)\, dt = \int_a^b f(t)\, dt$$

for *every* choice of a, b, c from I.   HINT: Assume $a < b$ and consider the four cases:
$c = a, c = b, c < a, b < c$.   Then consider what happens if $a > b$ or $a = b$.

15. (*The Mean-Value Theorem for Integrals.*) Show that, if f is continuous on $[a, b]$, then there is at least one number c in (a, b) for which

$$\int_a^b f(x)\, dx = f(c)(b - a).$$

HINT: Apply the mean-value theorem to the function

$$F(x) = \int_a^x f(t)\, dt \quad \text{on } [a, b].$$

16. Show the validity of equation (1) in the proof of Theorem 5.3.5.

17. Extend Theorem 5.3.5 by showing that, if f is continuous on $[a, b]$ and c is *any* number in $[a, b]$, then the function

$$F(x) = \int_c^x f(t)\, dt$$

is continuous on $[a, b]$, differentiable on (a, b), and satisfies

$$F'(x) = f(x) \qquad \text{for all } x \text{ in } (a, b).$$

HINT: $\displaystyle \int_c^x f(t)\, dt = \int_c^a f(t)\, dt + \int_a^x f(t)\, dt.$

18. Complete the proof of Theorem 5.3.5 by showing that

$$\lim_{h \to 0^-} \frac{F(x + h) - F(x)}{h} = f(x) \qquad \text{for all } x \text{ in } (a, b].$$

5.4 ······THE FUNDAMENTAL THEOREM OF INTEGRAL CALCULUS

DEFINITION 5.4.1   ANTIDERIVATIVE

A function G is called an *antiderivative* for f on $[a, b]$ iff

G is continuous on $[a, b]$ and $G'(x) = f(x)$ for all $x \in (a, b)$.

Theorem 5.3.5 says that, if f is continuous on $[a, b]$, then

$$F(x) = \int_a^x f(t)\, dt$$

is an antiderivative for f on $[a, b]$. This gives us a prescription for constructing antiderivatives. It tells us that we can construct an antiderivative for f by integrating f.

The so-called "fundamental theorem" goes the other way. It gives us a prescription, not for finding antiderivatives, but for evaluating integrals. It tells us that we can evaluate

$$\int_a^b f(t)\, dt$$

by finding an antiderivative for f.

THEOREM 5.4.2 THE FUNDAMENTAL THEOREM OF INTEGRAL CALCULUS

Let f be continuous on $[a, b]$. If G is an antiderivative for f on $[a, b]$, then

$$\int_a^b f(t)\, dt = G(b) - G(a).$$

Proof.   From Theorem 5.3.5 we know that the function

$$F(x) = \int_a^x f(t)\, dt$$

is an antiderivative for f on $[a, b]$. If G is also an antiderivative for f on $[a, b]$, then both F and G are continuous on $[a, b]$ and satisfy $F'(x) = G'(x)$ for all x in (a, b). From Theorem 4.2.4 we know that there exists a constant C such that

$$F(x) = G(x) + C \qquad \text{for all } x \text{ in } [a, b].$$

Since $F(a) = 0$,

$$G(a) + C = 0 \quad \text{and thus} \quad C = -G(a).$$

It follows that

$$F(x) = G(x) - G(a) \qquad \text{for all } x \text{ in } [a, b].$$

In particular,

$$F(b) = G(b) - G(a). \quad \square$$

We now evaluate some integrals by applying the fundamental theorem. In each case we use the simplest antiderivative we can think of.

PROBLEM. Evaluate

$$\int_1^4 x\, dx.$$

Solution. As an antiderivative for $f(x) = x$ we can use the function

$$G(x) = \tfrac{1}{2}x^2. \qquad\qquad \text{(check this out)}$$

By the fundamental theorem

$$\int_1^4 x\, dx = G(4) - G(1) = \tfrac{1}{2}(4)^2 - \tfrac{1}{2}(1)^2 = 7\tfrac{1}{2}. \quad \square$$

PROBLEM. Evaluate

$$\int_0^1 8x\, dx.$$

Solution. Here we can use the antiderivative $G(x) = 4x^2$:

$$\int_0^1 8x \, dx = G(1) - G(0) = 4(1)^2 - 4(0)^2 = 4. \quad \square$$

Expressions of the form $G(b) - G(a)$ are conveniently written

$$\left[G(x) \right]_a^b.$$

In this notation

$$\int_1^4 x \, dx = \left[\tfrac{1}{2}x^2 \right]_1^4 = \tfrac{1}{2}(4)^2 - \tfrac{1}{2}(1)^2 = 7\tfrac{1}{2},$$

and

$$\int_0^1 8x \, dx = \left[4x^2 \right]_0^1 = 4(1)^2 - 4(0)^2 = 4. \quad \square$$

From your study of differentiation you know that for all positive integers n

$$\frac{d}{dx}\left(\frac{1}{n+1} x^{n+1} \right) = x^n.$$

It follows that

(5.4.3)
$$\int_a^b x^n \, dx = \left[\frac{1}{n+1} x^{n+1} \right]_a^b = \frac{1}{n+1}(b^{n+1} - a^{n+1}).$$

Thus

$$\int_a^b x^2 \, dx = \left[\tfrac{1}{3}x^3 \right]_a^b = \tfrac{1}{3}(b^3 - a^3),$$

$$\int_a^b x^3 \, dx = \left[\tfrac{1}{4}x^4 \right]_a^b = \tfrac{1}{4}(b^4 - a^4),$$

$$\int_a^b x^4 \, dx = \left[\tfrac{1}{5}x^5 \right]_a^b = \tfrac{1}{5}(b^5 - a^5), \text{ etc. } \quad \square$$

PROBLEM. Evaluate

$$\int_0^1 (2x - 6x^4 + 5) \, dx.$$

Solution. As an antiderivative we use $G(x) = x^2 - \tfrac{6}{5}x^5 + 5x$:

$$\int_0^1 (2x - 6x^4 + 5) \, dx = \left[x^2 - \tfrac{6}{5}x^5 + 5x \right]_0^1 = 1 - \tfrac{6}{5} + 5 = 4\tfrac{4}{5}. \quad \square$$

PROBLEM. Evaluate

$$\int_{-1}^{1} (x - 1)(x + 2)\, dx.$$

Solution. First we carry out the indicated multiplication:

$$(x - 1)(x + 2) = x^2 + x - 2.$$

As an antiderivative we use $G(x) = \frac{1}{3}x^3 + \frac{1}{2}x^2 - 2x$:

$$\int_{-1}^{1} (x - 1)(x + 2)\, dx = \left[\frac{1}{3}x^3 + \frac{1}{2}x^2 - 2x \right]_{-1}^{1} = -\frac{10}{3}. \quad \square$$

Formula 5.4.3 holds not only for positive integer exponents but for all rational exponents other than -1 provided that the *integrand,* the function being integrated, is continuous over the interval of integration.   Thus

$$\int_{1}^{2} \frac{dx}{x^2} = \int_{1}^{2} x^{-2}\, dx = \left[-x^{-1} \right]_{1}^{2} = \left[-\frac{1}{x} \right]_{1}^{2} = (-\tfrac{1}{2}) - (-1) = \tfrac{1}{2},$$

$$\int_{4}^{9} \frac{dt}{\sqrt{t}} = \int_{4}^{9} t^{-1/2}\, dt = \left[2t^{1/2} \right]_{4}^{9} = 2(3) - 2(2) = 2,$$

$$\int_{0}^{1} t^{5/3}\, dt = \left[\tfrac{3}{8} t^{8/3} \right]_{0}^{1} = \tfrac{3}{8}(1)^{8/3} - \tfrac{3}{8}(0)^{8/3} = \tfrac{3}{8}. \quad \square$$

Finally, here are some slightly more complicated examples.   The essential step in each case is the determination of an antiderivative.   Check each computation in detail.

$$\int_{1}^{2} \frac{x^4 + 1}{x^2}\, dx = \int_{1}^{2} (x^2 + x^{-2})\, dx = \left[\tfrac{1}{3}x^3 - x^{-1} \right]_{1}^{2} = \tfrac{17}{6}.$$

$$\int_{1}^{5} \sqrt{x - 1}\, dx = \int_{1}^{5} (x - 1)^{1/2}\, dx = \left[\tfrac{2}{3}(x - 1)^{3/2} \right]_{1}^{5} = \tfrac{16}{3}.$$

$$\int_{0}^{1} (4 - \sqrt{x})^2\, dx = \int_{0}^{1} (16 - 8\sqrt{x} + x)\, dx = \left[16x - \tfrac{16}{3}x^{3/2} + \tfrac{1}{2}x^2 \right]_{0}^{1} = \tfrac{67}{6}.$$

$$\int_{1}^{2} -\frac{dt}{(t + 2)^2} = \int_{1}^{2} -(t + 2)^{-2}\, dt = \left[(t + 2)^{-1} \right]_{1}^{2} = -\tfrac{1}{12}. \quad \square$$

The Linearity of the Integral

Here are some simple properties of the integral that are often used in computation. Throughout take f and g as continuous functions.

I. Constants may be factored through the integral sign:

(5.4.4)
$$\int_{a}^{b} \alpha f(x)\, dx = \alpha \int_{a}^{b} f(x)\, dx.$$

EXAMPLES

$$\int_0^{10} \tfrac{3}{7}(x-5)\, dx = \tfrac{3}{7} \int_0^{10} (x-5)\, dx = \tfrac{3}{7} \left[\tfrac{1}{2}(x-5)^2 \right]_0^{10} = 0.$$

$$\int_0^1 \frac{8}{(x+1)^3}\, dx = 8 \int_0^1 \frac{dx}{(x+1)^3} = 8 \left[-\tfrac{1}{2}(x+1)^{-2} \right]_0^1 = 8(\tfrac{3}{8}) = 3. \quad \square$$

II. The integral of a sum is the sum of the integrals:

(5.4.5)
$$\int_a^b [f(x)+g(x)]\, dx = \int_a^b f(x)\, dx + \int_a^b g(x)\, dx.$$

EXAMPLE

$$\int_1^2 \left[(x-1)^2 + \frac{1}{(x+2)^2} \right] dx = \int_1^2 (x-1)^2\, dx + \int_1^2 \frac{dx}{(x+2)^2}$$

$$= \left[\tfrac{1}{3}(x-1)^3 \right]_1^2 + \left[-(x+2)^{-1} \right]_1^2$$

$$= \tfrac{1}{3} - \tfrac{1}{4} + \tfrac{1}{3} = \tfrac{5}{12}. \quad \square$$

III. The integral of a linear combination is the linear combination of the integrals:

(5.4.6)
$$\int_a^b [\alpha f(x) + \beta g(x)]\, dx = \alpha \int_a^b f(x)\, dx + \beta \int_a^b g(x)\, dx.$$

EXAMPLE

$$\int_2^{5/2} \left[\frac{3}{(x-1)^2} - 4x \right] dx = 3 \int_2^{5/2} \frac{dx}{(x-1)^2} - 2 \int_2^{5/2} 2x\, dx$$

$$= 3 \left[-(x-1)^{-1} \right]_2^{5/2} - 2 \left[x^2 \right]_2^{5/2}$$

$$= 3(-\tfrac{2}{3} + 1) - 2(\tfrac{25}{4} - 4) = -\tfrac{7}{2}. \quad \square$$

I and II are particular instances of III. To prove III, take F and G as antiderivatives for f and g, respectively, and observe that $\alpha F + \beta G$ is an antiderivative for $\alpha f + \beta g$. The details are left to you.

EXERCISES

Evaluate the following integrals.

1. $\displaystyle\int_0^1 (2x-3)\, dx.$ 2. $\displaystyle\int_0^1 (3x+2)\, dx.$ 3. $\displaystyle\int_{-1}^0 5x^4\, dx.$

4. $\displaystyle\int_1^2 (2x+x^2)\, dx.$ 5. $\displaystyle\int_1^4 \sqrt{x}\, dx.$ 6. $\displaystyle\int_0^4 \sqrt{x}\, dx.$

7. $\displaystyle\int_1^5 2\sqrt{x-1}\,dx.$

8. $\displaystyle\int_1^2 \left(\frac{3}{x^3}+5x\right)dx.$

9. $\displaystyle\int_{-2}^0 (x+1)(x-2)\,dx.$

10. $\displaystyle\int_2^0 \frac{dx}{(x+1)^2}.$

11. $\displaystyle\int_3^3 \sqrt{x}\,dx.$

12. $\displaystyle\int_{-1}^0 (t-2)(t+1)\,dt.$

13. $\displaystyle\int_0^1 \frac{dt}{(t+2)^3}.$

14. $\displaystyle\int_1^0 (t^3+t^2)\,dt.$

15. $\displaystyle\int_1^2 \left(3t+\frac{4}{t^2}\right)dt.$

16. $\displaystyle\int_{-1}^{-1} 7x^6\,dx.$

17. $\displaystyle\int_0^1 (x^{3/2}-x^{1/2})\,dx.$

18. $\displaystyle\int_0^1 (x^{3/4}-2x^{1/2})\,dx.$

19. $\displaystyle\int_0^1 (x+1)^{17}\,dx.$

20. $\displaystyle\int_0^a (a^2x-x^3)\,dx.$

21. $\displaystyle\int_0^a (\sqrt{a}-\sqrt{x})^2\,dx.$

22. $\displaystyle\int_{-1}^1 (x-2)^2\,dx.$

23. $\displaystyle\int_1^2 \frac{6-t}{t^3}\,dt.$

24. $\displaystyle\int_1^2 \frac{2-t}{t^3}\,dt.$

25. $\displaystyle\int_0^1 x^2(x-1)\,dx.$

26. $\displaystyle\int_1^3 \left(x^2-\frac{1}{x^2}\right)dx.$

27. $\displaystyle\int_1^2 2x(x^2+1)\,dx.$

28. $\displaystyle\int_0^1 3x^2(x^3+1)\,dx.$

29. $\displaystyle\int_0^{\pi/2} \cos x\,dx.$

30. $\displaystyle\int_0^\pi \sin x\,dx.$

31. $\displaystyle\int_0^{\pi/4} \sec^2 x\,dx.$

32. $\displaystyle\int_{\pi/6}^{\pi/3} \sec x \tan x\,dx.$

33. $\displaystyle\int_{\pi/6}^{\pi/4} \csc x \cot x\,dx.$

34. $\displaystyle\int_{\pi/4}^{\pi/3} \csc^2 x\,dx.$

35. $\displaystyle\int_0^{2\pi} \sin x\,dx.$

36. $\displaystyle\int_0^\pi \cos x\,dx.$

37. Define a function F on $[1, 8]$ such that $F'(x) = 1/x$ and (a) $F(2) = 0$; (b) $F(2) = -3$.

38. Define a function F on $[0, 4]$ such that $F'(x) = \sqrt{1 + x^2}$ and (a) $F(3) = 0$; (b) $F(3) = 1$.

39. Compare

$$\frac{d}{dx}\left[\int_a^x f(t)\,dt\right] \qquad \text{to} \qquad \int_a^x \frac{d}{dt}[f(t)]\,dt.$$

5.5 ······SOME AREA PROBLEMS

In Section 5.2 we noted that, if f is nonnegative and continuous on $[a, b]$, then the integral of f from a to b gives the area of the region below the graph of f. With Ω as in Figure 5.5.1

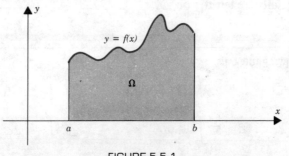

FIGURE 5.5.1

(5.5.1)
$$\text{area } (\Omega) = \int_a^b f(x)\, dx.$$

PROBLEM. Find the area below the graph of the square-root function from $x = 0$ to $x = 1$.

Solution. The graph is pictured in Figure 5.5.2. The area below the graph is $\tfrac{2}{3}$:

$$\int_0^1 \sqrt{x}\, dx = \int_0^1 x^{1/2}\, dx = \left[\tfrac{2}{3} x^{3/2} \right]_0^1 = \tfrac{2}{3}. \quad \square$$

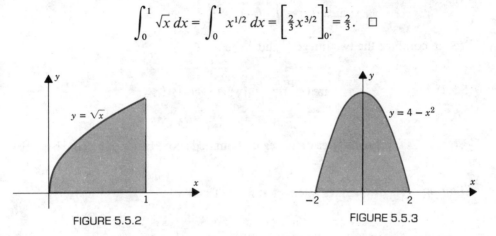

FIGURE 5.5.2   FIGURE 5.5.3

PROBLEM. Find the area of the region bounded above by the curve $y = 4 - x^2$ and below by the x-axis.

Solution. The curve intersects the x-axis at $x = -2$ and $x = 2$. See Figure 5.5.3. The area of the region is $\tfrac{32}{3}$:

$$\int_{-2}^2 (4 - x^2)\, dx = \left[4x - \tfrac{1}{3} x^3 \right]_{-2}^2 = \tfrac{32}{3}. \quad \square$$

Now we'll calculate the areas of somewhat more complicated regions such as region Ω shown in Figure 5.5.4. To avoid excessive repetition, let's agree at the outset that throughout this section the symbols f, g, h represent continuous functions.

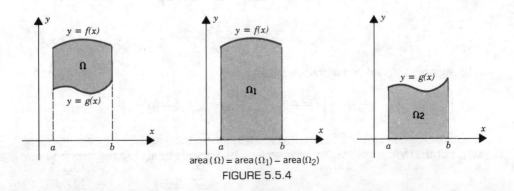

area $(\Omega) = $ area $(\Omega_1) - $ area (Ω_2)

FIGURE 5.5.4

Look at the region Ω shown in Figure 5.5.4. The upper boundary of Ω is the graph of a nonnegative function f and the lower boundary is the graph of a nonnegative function g. We can obtain the area of Ω by calculating the area of Ω_1 and subtracting off the area of Ω_2. Since

$$\text{area } (\Omega_1) = \int_a^b f(x)\, dx \qquad \text{and} \qquad \text{area } (\Omega_2) = \int_a^b g(x)\, dx,$$

we have

$$\text{area } (\Omega) = \int_a^b f(x)\, dx - \int_a^b g(x)\, dx.$$

We can combine the two integrals and write

(5.5.2)
$$\text{area } (\Omega) = \int_a^b [f(x) - g(x)]\, dx.$$

PROBLEM. Find the area of the region bounded above by $y = x + 2$ and below by $y = x^2$.

Solution. The two curves intersect at $x = -1$ and $x = 2$:

$$x + 2 = x^2 \qquad \text{iff} \qquad x^2 - x - 2 = 0 \qquad \text{iff} \qquad (x + 1)(x - 2) = 0.$$

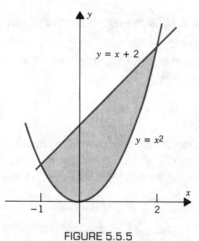

FIGURE 5.5.5

The region, sketched in Figure 5.5.5, has area $\tfrac{9}{2}$:

$$\int_{-1}^2 [(x + 2) - x^2]\, dx = \left[\frac{x^2}{2} + 2x - \frac{x^3}{3}\right]_{-1}^2 = (2 + 4 - \tfrac{8}{3}) - (\tfrac{1}{2} - 2 + \tfrac{1}{3}) = \tfrac{9}{2}. \quad \square$$

We derived Formula 5.5.2 under the assumption that f and g were both nonnegative, but that assumption is unnecessary. The formula holds for any region Ω that has an upper boundary of the form $y = f(x), \quad x \in [a, b]$

and

a lower boundary of the form $y = g(x), \quad x \in [a, b]$.

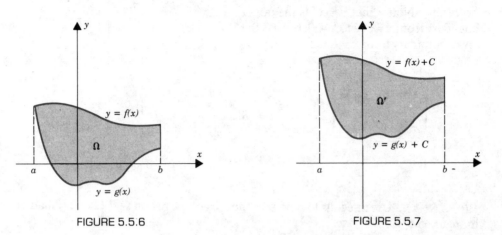

FIGURE 5.5.6   FIGURE 5.5.7

To see this, take Ω as in Figure 5.5.6. Obviously, Ω is congruent to the region marked Ω' in Figure 5.5.7. Ω' is Ω raised C units. Since Ω' lies entirely above the x-axis, the area of Ω' is given by the integral

$$\int_a^b \{[f(x) + C] - [g(x) + C]\}\, dx = \int_a^b [f(x) - g(x)]\, dx.$$

Since area (Ω) = area (Ω'),

$$\text{area } (\Omega) = \int_a^b [f(x) - g(x)]\, dx$$

as asserted.

PROBLEM. Find the area of the region shown in Figure 5.5.8.

Solution

$$\text{area } (\Omega) = \int_{\pi/4}^{5\pi/4} [\sin x - \cos x]\, dx$$

$$= \left[-\cos x - \sin x \right]_{\pi/4}^{5\pi/4}$$

$$= 2\sqrt{2}. \quad \square$$

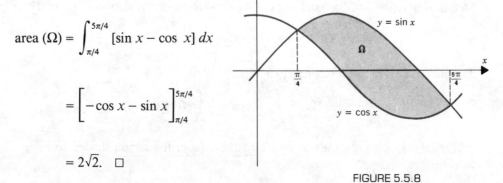

FIGURE 5.5.8

PROBLEM. Find the area between the curves $y = 4x$ and $y = x^3$ from $x = -2$ to $x = 2$. See Figure 5.5.9.

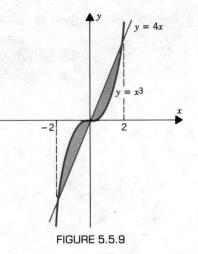

Solution. Notice that $y = x^3$ is the upper boundary from $x = -2$ to $x = 0$, but it is the lower boundary from $x = 0$ to $x = 2$. Thus

$$\text{area} = \int_{-2}^{0} [x^3 - 4x] \, dx + \int_{0}^{2} [4x - x^3] \, dx$$

$$= \left[\frac{x^4}{4} - 2x^2 \right]_{-2}^{0} + \left[2x^2 - \frac{x^4}{4} \right]_{0}^{2} = 8. \quad \square$$

FIGURE 5.5.9

PROBLEM. Use integrals to represent the area of the region $\Omega = \Omega_1 \cup \Omega_2$ shaded in Figure 5.5.10.

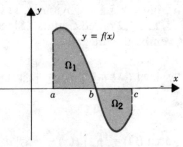

FIGURE 5.5.10

Solution. From $x = a$ to $x = b$, the curve $y = f(x)$ is above the x-axis. Therefore

$$\text{area} \, (\Omega_1) = \int_{a}^{b} f(x) \, dx.$$

From $x = b$ to $x = c$, the curve $y = f(x)$ is below the x-axis. The upper boundary for Ω_1 is the curve $y = 0$ (the x-axis) and the lower boundary is the curve $y = f(x)$. Thus

$$\text{area} \, (\Omega_2) = \int_{b}^{c} [0 - f(x)] \, dx = - \int_{b}^{c} f(x) \, dx.$$

The area of Ω is the sum of these two areas:

$$\text{area} \, (\Omega) = \int_{a}^{b} f(x) \, dx - \int_{b}^{c} f(x) \, dx. \quad \square$$

PROBLEM. Use integrals to represent the area of the region shaded in Figure 5.5.11.

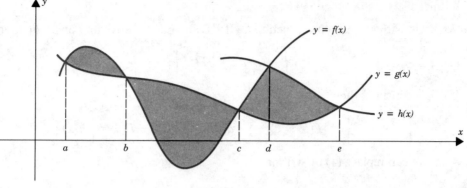

FIGURE 5.5.11

Solution

$$\text{Area} = \int_a^b [f(x) - g(x)]\, dx + \int_b^c [g(x) - f(x)]\, dx$$
$$+ \int_c^d [f(x) - g(x)]\, dx + \int_d^e [h(x) - g(x)]\, dx. \quad \square$$

EXERCISES

Find the area between the graph of f and the x-axis.

1. $f(x) = 2 + x^3, \quad x \in [0, 1].$

2. $f(x) = \dfrac{1}{(x + 1)^2}, \quad x \in [0, 2].$

3. $f(x) = \sqrt{x + 1}, \quad x \in [3, 8].$

4. $f(x) = x^2(3 + x), \quad x \in [0, 8].$

5. $f(x) = (2x^2 + 1)^2, \quad x \in [0, 1].$

6. $f(x) = \dfrac{1}{2\sqrt{x + 1}}, \quad x \in [0, 8].$

7. $f(x) = x^2 - 4, \quad x \in [1, 2].$

8. $f(x) = \cos x, \quad x \in \left[\dfrac{\pi}{6}, \dfrac{\pi}{3}\right].$

9. $f(x) = \sin x, \quad x \in \left[\dfrac{\pi}{3}, \dfrac{\pi}{2}\right].$

10. $f(x) = x^3 + 1, \quad x \in [-2, -1].$

Sketch the region bounded by the curves and find its area.

11. $y = \sqrt{x}, \quad y = x^2.$

12. $y = 6x - x^2, \quad y = 2x.$

13. $y = 5 - x^2, \quad y = 3 - x.$

14. $y = 8, \quad y = x^2 + 2x.$

15. $y = 8 - x^2, \quad y = x^2.$

16. $y = \sqrt{x}, \quad y = \tfrac{1}{4}x.$

17. $x^3 - 10y^2 = 0, \quad x - y = 0.$

18. $y^2 - 27x = 0, \quad x + y = 0.$

19. $x - y^2 + 3 = 0, \quad x - 2y = 0.$

20. $y^2 = 2x, \quad x - y = 4.$

21. $y = x, \quad y = 2x, \quad y = 4.$

22. $y = x^2, \quad y = -\sqrt{x}, \quad x = 4.$

23. $y = \cos x, \quad y = 4x^2 - \pi^2.$

24. $y = \sin x, \quad y = \pi x - x^2.$

25. $y = x, \quad y = \sin x, \quad x = \pi/2.$

26. $y = x + 1, \quad y = \cos x, \quad x = \pi.$

5.6 ······INDEFINITE INTEGRALS

We begin with a continuous function f. If F is an antiderivative for f on $[a, b]$, then

(1)
$$\int_a^b f(x)\, dx = \left[F(x) \right]_a^b.$$

If C is a constant, then

$$\left[F(x) + C \right]_a^b = [F(b) + C] - [F(a) + C] = F(b) - F(a) = \left[F(x) \right]_a^b.$$

Thus we can replace (1) by writing

$$\int_a^b f(x)\, dx = \left[F(x) + C \right]_a^b.$$

If we have no particular interest in the interval $[a, b]$ but wish instead to emphasize that F is an antiderivative for f on *some* interval, then we can omit the a and the b and simply write

$$\int f(x)\, dx = F(x) + C.$$

Antiderivatives expressed in this manner are called *indefinite integrals*. The constant C is called the *constant of integration*.

EXAMPLES

$$\int x^2\, dx = \tfrac{1}{3}x^3 + C, \qquad \int \sqrt{s}\, ds = \tfrac{2}{3}s^{3/2} + C,$$

$$\int \frac{4}{\sqrt{t+2}}\, dt = 8\sqrt{t+2} + C. \quad \square$$

The following problems will serve to illustrate the notation further.

PROBLEM. Find f given that $f'(x) = x^3 + 2$ and $f(0) = 1$.

Solution. Since f' is the derivative of f, f is an antiderivative for f'. Thus

$$f(x) = \int (x^3 + 2)\, dx = \tfrac{1}{4}x^4 + 2x + C.$$

To evaluate C we use the fact that $f(0) = 1$. Since

$$f(0) = 1 \qquad \text{and} \qquad f(0) = \tfrac{1}{4}(0)^4 + 2(0) + C = C,$$

we see that $C = 1$. Therefore

$$f(x) = \tfrac{1}{4}x^4 + 2x + 1. \quad \square$$

PROBLEM. Find f given that $f''(x) = 6x - 2$, $f'(1) = -5$, and $f(1) = 3$.

Solution. First we'll get f' by integrating f'':

$$f'(x) = \int (6x - 2)\, dx = 3x^2 - 2x + C.$$

Since

$$f'(1) = -5 \quad \text{and} \quad f'(1) = 3(1)^2 - 2(1) + C = 1 + C,$$

we have

$$-5 = 1 + C \quad \text{and thus} \quad C = -6.$$

Therefore

$$f'(x) = 3x^2 - 2x - 6.$$

Now we'll get to f by integrating f':

$$f(x) = \int (3x^2 - 2x - 6)\, dx = x^3 - x^2 - 6x + K.$$

(We're writing the constant of integration as K because we used C before and it would be confusing to have C with two different values in the same problem.) Since

$$f(1) = 3 \quad \text{and} \quad f(1) = (1)^3 - (1)^2 - 6(1) + C = -6 + C,$$

we have

$$3 = -6 + C \quad \text{and thus} \quad C = 9.$$

Therefore

$$f(x) = x^3 - x^2 - 6x + 9. \quad \square$$

EXERCISES

Calculate

1. $\int \dfrac{dx}{x^4}.$ **2.** $\int (x - 1)^2\, dx.$

3. $\int (ax + b)\, dx.$ **4.** $\int (ax^2 + b)\, dx.$

5. $\int \dfrac{dx}{\sqrt{1 + x}}.$ **6.** $\int \left(\dfrac{x^3 + 1}{x^5}\right) dx.$

7. $\int \left(\dfrac{x^3 - 1}{x^2}\right) dx.$ **8.** $\int \left(\sqrt{x} - \dfrac{1}{\sqrt{x}}\right) dx.$

9. $\int (t - a)(t - b)\, dt.$ **10.** $\int (t^2 - a)(t^2 - b)\, dt.$

11. $\int \dfrac{g'(x)}{[g(x)]^2}\, dx.$ **12.** $\int \dfrac{g(x)f'(x) - g'(x)f(x)}{[g(x)]^2}\, dx.$

13. $\int [f(x)\, g'(x) + f'(x)\, g(x)]\, dx.$ **14.** $\int 3\, g'(x)\, [g(x)]^2\, dx.$

15. $\displaystyle\int \cos t \, dt.$

16. $\displaystyle\int \csc t \cot t \, dt.$

17. $\displaystyle\int \sec^2 x \, dx.$

18. $\displaystyle\int \sin x \, dx.$

Find f from the information given.

19. $f'(x) = 2x - 1, \quad f(3) = 4.$

20. $f'(x) = 3 - 4x, \quad f(1) = 6.$

21. $f'(x) = ax + b, \quad f(2) = 0.$

22. $f'(x) = ax^2 + bx + c, \quad f(0) = 0.$

23. $f'(x) = \sin x, \quad f(0) = 2.$

24. $f'(x) = \cos x, \quad f(\pi) = 3.$

25. $f''(x) = 6x - 2, \quad f'(0) = 1, \quad f(0) = 2.$

26. $f''(x) = -12x^2, \quad f'(0) = 1, \quad f(0) = 2.$

27. $f''(x) = x^2 - x, \quad f'(1) = 0, \quad f(1) = 2.$

28. $f''(x) = 1 - x, \quad f'(2) = 1, \quad f(2) = 0.$

29. $f''(x) = \cos x, \quad f'(0) = 1, \quad f(0) = 2.$

30. $f''(x) = \sin x, \quad f'(0) = -2, \quad f(0) = 1.$

31. $f''(x) = 2x - 3, \quad f(2) = -1, \quad f(0) = 3.$

32. $f''(x) = 5 - 4x, \quad f(1) = 1, \quad f(0) = -2.$

33. Compare

$$\frac{d}{dx}\left[\int f(x) \, dx\right] \quad \text{to} \quad \int \frac{d}{dx}[f(x)] \, dx.$$

5.7 ······SOME MOTION PROBLEMS

PROBLEM. An object moves along a coordinate line with velocity

$$v(t) = 2 - 3t + t^2 \quad \text{units per second.}$$

Its initial position (position at time $t = 0$) is 2 units to the right of the origin. Find the position of the object 4 seconds later.

Solution. Let $x(t)$ be the position (coordinate) of the object at time t. We are given that $x(0) = 2$. Since $x'(t) = v(t)$,

$$x(t) = \int v(t) \, dt = \int (2 - 3t + t^2) \, dt = 2t - \tfrac{3}{2}t^2 + \tfrac{1}{3}t^3 + C.$$

Since

$$x(0) = 2 \quad \text{and} \quad x(0) = 2(0) - \tfrac{3}{2}(0)^2 + \tfrac{1}{3}(0)^3 + C = C,$$

we have $C = 2$ and

$$x(t) = 2t - \tfrac{3}{2}t^2 + \tfrac{1}{3}t^3 + 2.$$

The position of the object at time $t = 4$ is the value of this function at $t = 4$:

$$x(4) = 2(4) - \tfrac{3}{2}(4)^2 + \tfrac{1}{3}(4)^3 + 2 = 7\tfrac{1}{3}.$$

At the end of 4 seconds the object is $7\tfrac{1}{3}$ units to the right of the origin. □

Before getting to the next problem, recall that speed is the absolute value of velocity:

$$\text{speed at time } t = |v(t)|$$

and the integral of the speed function gives the distance traveled:

$$\int_a^b |v(t)|\, dt = \text{distance traveled from time } t = a \text{ to time } t = b.$$

PROBLEM.   An object moves along a coordinate line with acceleration $a(t) = 2t - 2$ units per second per second. Its initial position (position at time $t = 0$) is 5 units to the right of the origin. One second later the object is moving to the left at the rate of 4 units per second.

        (a) Find the position of the object when $t = 4$ seconds.

        (b) How far does the object travel during these 4 seconds?

Solution.   (a) Let $x(t)$ and $v(t)$ denote the position and velocity of the object at time t. We are given that $x(0) = 5$ and $v(1) = -4$. Since $v'(t) = a(t)$,

$$v(t) = \int a(t)\, dt = \int (2t - 2)\, dt = t^2 - 2t + C.$$

Since

$$v(1) = -4 \qquad \text{and} \qquad v(1) = (1)^2 - 2(1) + C = -1 + C,$$

we have $C = -3$ and

$$v(t) = t^2 - 2t - 3.$$

Since $x'(t) = v(t)$,

$$x(t) = \int v(t)\, dt = \int (t^2 - 2t - 3)\, dt = \tfrac{1}{3}t^3 - t^2 - 3t + K.$$

Since

$$x(0) = 5 \qquad \text{and} \qquad x(0) = \tfrac{1}{3}(0)^3 - (0)^2 - 3(0) + K = K,$$

we have $K = 5$. Therefore

$$x(t) = \tfrac{1}{3}t^3 - t^2 - 3t + 5.$$

As you can check, $x(4) = -\tfrac{5}{3}$. At time $t = 4$ the object is $\tfrac{5}{3}$ units to the left of the origin.

(b) The distance traveled from time $t = 0$ to $t = 4$ is given by the integral

$$s = \int_0^4 |v(t)|\, dt = \int_0^4 |t^2 - 2t - 3|\, dt.$$

To evaluate this integral we first remove the absolute-value sign. As you can verify,

$$|t^2 - 2t - 3| = \begin{cases} -(t^2 - 2t - 3), & 0 \le t \le 3 \\ t^2 - 2t - 3, & 3 \le t \le 4 \end{cases}.$$

Thus

$$s = \int_0^3 (3 + 2t - t^2)\, dt + \int_3^4 (t^2 - 2t - 3)\, dt$$

$$= \left[3t + t^2 - \tfrac{1}{3}t^3 \right]_0^3 + \left[\tfrac{1}{3}t^3 - t^2 - 3t \right]_3^4 = \tfrac{34}{3}.$$

During the 4 seconds the object travels a distance of $\tfrac{34}{3}$ units   □

PROBLEM. Find the general law of motion for an object that moves along a straight line with constant acceleration $-g$ from an initial position x_0 with initial velocity v_0.

Solution. Here $a(t) = -g$. Thus

$$v(t) = \int a(t)\, dt = \int -g\, dt = -gt + C.$$

The constant C is the initial velocity v_0:

$$v_0 = v(0) = (-g)(0) + C = C.$$

We replace C by v_0 and write

$$v(t) = -gt + v_0.$$

Now

$$x(t) = \int v(t)\, dt = \int (-gt + v_0)\, dt = -\tfrac{1}{2}gt^2 + v_0 t + K.$$

The constant K is the initial position x_0:

$$x_0 = x(0) = -\tfrac{1}{2}(g)(0)^2 + (v_0)(0) + K = K.$$

Replacing K by x_0, we have

$$x(t) = -\tfrac{1}{2}gt^2 + v_0 t + x_0.$$

You met this equation before in connection with free-falling bodies [Equation (3.5.5)].   □

EXERCISES

1. An object moves along a coordinate line with velocity $v(t) = 6t^2 - 6$ units per second. Its initial position (position at time $t = 0$) is 2 units to the left of the origin. (a) Find the position of the object 3 seconds later. (b) Find the total distance traveled by the object during those 3 seconds.

2. An object moves along a coordinate line with acceleration $a(t) = (t + 2)^3$ units per second per second. (a) Find the velocity function given that the initial velocity is 3 units per second. (b) Find the position function given that the initial velocity is 3 units per second and the initial position is the origin.

3. An object moves along a coordinate line with acceleration $a(t) = (t + 1)^{-1/2}$ units per

second per second. (a) Find the velocity function given that the initial velocity is 1 unit per second. (b) Find the position function given that the initial velocity is 1 unit per second and the initial position is the origin.

4. An object moves along a coordinate line with velocity $v(t) = t(1 - t)$ units per second. Its initial position is 2 units to the left of the origin. (a) Find the position of the object 10 seconds later. (b) Find the total distance traveled by the object during those 10 seconds.

Find the general law of motion of an object that moves in a straight line with acceleration $a(t)$. Write x_0 for initial position and v_0 for initial velocity.

5. $a(t) = 0$.   6. $a(t) = 45t^{1/2} + t^{-1/2}$.   7. $a(t) = 2A + 6Bt$.

8. $a(t) = -32$.   9. $a(t) = \sin t$.   10. $a(t) = \cos t$.

11. As a particle moves about the plane, its x-coordinate changes at the rate of $t^2 - 5$ units per second and its y-coordinate changes at the rate of $3t$ units per second. If the particle is at the point (4, 2) when $t = 2$ seconds, where is the particle 4 seconds later?

12. As a particle moves about the plane, its x-coordinate changes at the rate of $t - 2$ units per second and its y-coordinate changes at the rate of $\sqrt{t}$ units per second. If the particle is at the point (3, 1) when $t = 4$ seconds, where is the particle 5 seconds later?

13. A particle moves along the x-axis with velocity $v(t) = At + B$. Determine A and B given that the initial velocity of the particle is 2 units per second and the position of the particle after 2 seconds of motion is 1 unit to the left of the initial position.

14. A particle moves along the x-axis with velocity $v(t) = At^2 + 1$. Determine A given that $x(1) = x(0)$. Compute the total distance traveled by the particle during the first second.

15. An object moves along a coordinate line with velocity $v(t) = \sin t$ units per second. The object passes through the origin at time $t = \pi/6$ seconds. When is the next time that (a) the object passes through the origin? (b) the object passes through the origin moving from left to right?

16. Exercise 15 with $v(t) = \cos t$.

17. An automobile with varying velocity $v(t)$ moves in a fixed direction for 5 minutes and covers a distance of 4 miles. What theorem would you invoke to argue that for at least one instant the speedometer must have read 48 miles per hour?

18. Given that the acceleration of a particle is proportional to the square of the velocity,

$$a(t) = -k[v(t)]^2,$$

show that, if the initial velocity v_0 is different from zero, then

$$[v(t)]^{-1} = v_0^{-1} + kt.$$

5.8 ······THE *u*-SUBSTITUTION; CHANGE OF VARIABLES

When we differentiate a composite function, we do so by the chain rule. In trying to calculate an indefinite integral, we are often called upon to apply the chain rule in reverse. This process is usually facilitated by making what we call a "*u*-substitution." An integral of the form

$$\int f(g(x)) \, g'(x) \, dx$$

can be written

$$\int f(u)\, du$$

by setting

$$u = g(x), \qquad du = g'(x)\, dx.†$$

If F is an antiderivative for f, then

$$\int f(g(x))\, g'(x)\, dx = \int F'(g(x))\, g'(x)\, dx = F(g(x)) + C.$$

by the chain rule

We can obtain the same result by calculating

$$\int f(u)\, du$$

and then substituting $g(x)$ back in for u:

$$\int f(u)\, du = F(u) + C = F(g(x)) + C.$$

PROBLEM. Calculate

$$\int (x^2 - 1)^4\, 2x\, dx$$

and then check the result by differentiation.

Solution. Set

$$u = x^2 - 1 \qquad \text{so that} \qquad du = 2x\, dx.$$

Then

$$\int (x^2 - 1)^4\, 2x\, dx = \int u^4\, du = \tfrac{1}{5}u^5 + C = \tfrac{1}{5}(x^2 - 1)^5 + C.$$

Checking:

$$\frac{d}{dx}[\tfrac{1}{5}(x^2 - 1)^5 + C] = \tfrac{5}{5}(x^2 - 1)^4 \frac{d}{dx}(x^2 - 1) = (x^2 - 1)^4\, 2x. \quad \square$$

PROBLEM. Calculate

$$\int \frac{dx}{(3 + 5x)^2}$$

and then check the result by differentiation.

---

† Think of $du = g'(x)\, dx$ as a "formal differential," writing dx for h.

Solution. Set

$$u = 3 + 5x \qquad \text{so that} \qquad du = 5\ dx.$$

Then

$$\frac{dx}{(3 + 5x)^2} = \frac{\frac{1}{5}\,du}{u^2} = \frac{1}{5}\,\frac{du}{u^2}$$

and

$$\int \frac{dx}{(3 + 5x)^2} = \frac{1}{5} \int \frac{du}{u^2} = -\frac{1}{5u} + C\dagger = -\frac{1}{5(3 + 5x)} + C.$$

Checking:

$$\frac{d}{dx}\left(-\frac{1}{5(3 + 5x)} + C\right) = \frac{d}{dx}\left[-\tfrac{1}{5}(3 + 5x)^{-1}\right]$$

$$= (-\tfrac{1}{5})(-1)(3 + 5x)^{-2}(5) \overset{\checkmark}{=} \frac{1}{(3 + 5x)^2}. \quad \square$$

In the remaining problems we'll leave the checking to you.

PROBLEM. Calculate

$$\int x(2x^2 - 1)^3\ dx.$$

Solution. Set

$$u = 2x^2 - 1, \qquad du = 4x\ dx.$$

Then

$$x(2x^2 - 1)^3\ dx = \underbrace{(2x^2 - 1)^3}_{u^3}\,\underbrace{x\ dx}_{\frac{1}{4}\,du} = \tfrac{1}{4}u^3\ du$$

and

$$\int x(2x^2 - 1)^3\ dx = \tfrac{1}{4} \int u^3\ du = \tfrac{1}{16}\,u^4 + C = \tfrac{1}{16}(2x^2 - 1)^4 + C. \quad \square$$

The key step in making a *u*-substitution is to find a substitution $u = g(x)$ such that the expression $du = g'(x)\ dx$ appears in the original integral (at least up to a constant factor) and the new integral

$$\int f(u)\ du$$

is easier to calculate than the original integral. In most cases the form of the original integrand will suggest a good choice for *u*.

---

† One could write

$$\frac{1}{5} \int \frac{du}{u} = -\frac{1}{5}\left[\frac{1}{u} + C\right] = -\frac{1}{5u} + \frac{C}{5},$$

but, since *C* is arbitrary, *C*/5 is arbitrary, and we can therefore write *C* instead.

PROBLEM. Calculate

$$\int x^2 \sqrt{4 + x^3} \, dx.$$

Solution. Set

$$u = 4 + x^3, \qquad du = 3x^2 \, dx.$$

Then

$$x^2 \sqrt{4 + x^3} \, dx = \underbrace{\sqrt{4 + x^3}}_{\sqrt{u}} \underbrace{x^2 \, dx}_{\frac{1}{3} du} = \tfrac{1}{3}\sqrt{u} \, du$$

and

$$\int x^2 \sqrt{4 + x^3} \, dx = \tfrac{1}{3} \int \sqrt{u} \, du = \tfrac{2}{9} u^{3/2} + C = \tfrac{2}{9} (4 + x^3)^{3/2} + C. \quad \square$$

PROBLEM. Calculate

$$\int x(x - 3)^5 \, dx.$$

Solution. Set

$$u = x - 3, \qquad du = dx.$$

Then

$$x(x - 3)^5 \, dx = (u + 3)u^5 \, du = (u^6 + 3u^5) \, du$$

and

$$\int x(x - 3)^5 \, dx = \int (u^6 + 3u^5) \, du$$

$$= \tfrac{1}{7}u^7 + \tfrac{1}{2}u^6 + C = \tfrac{1}{7}(x - 3)^7 + \tfrac{1}{2}(x - 3)^6 + C. \quad \square$$

For definite integrals we have the following *change of variables formula:*

(5.8.1)
$$\int_a^b f(g(x)) \, g'(x) \, dx = \int_{g(a)}^{g(b)} f(u) \, du.$$

The formula holds provided that f and g' are both continuous. More precisely, g' must be continuous on an interval that joins a and b, and f must be continuous on the set of values taken on by g.

Proof. Let F be an antiderivative for f. Then $F' = f$ and

$$\int_a^b f(g(x)) \, g'(x) \, dx = \int_a^b F'(g(x)) \, g'(x) \, dx$$

$$= \left[F(g(x)) \right]_a^b = F(g(b)) - F(g(a)) = \int_{g(a)}^{g(b)} f(u) \, du. \quad \square$$

PROBLEM. Evaluate

$$\int_1^2 \frac{10x^2}{(x^3 + 1)^2} \, dx.$$

Solution. Set

$$u = x^3 + 1, \qquad du = 3x^2 \, dx.$$

Then

$$\frac{10x^2}{(x^3 + 1)^2} \, dx = 10 \frac{\overbrace{x^2 \, dx}^{\frac{1}{3} du}}{\underbrace{(x^3 + 1)^2}_{u^2}} = \frac{10}{3} \frac{du}{u^2}.$$

At $x = 1$, $u = 2$. At $x = 2$, $u = 9$. Therefore

$$\int_1^2 \frac{10x^2}{(x^3 + 1)^2} \, dx = \frac{10}{3} \int_2^9 \frac{du}{u^2} = \frac{10}{3} \left[-\frac{1}{u} \right]_2^9 = \frac{35}{27}. \quad \Box$$

PROBLEM. Evaluate

$$\int_0^2 x\sqrt{4x^2 + 9} \, dx.$$

Solution. Set

$$u = 4x^2 + 9, \qquad du = 8x \, dx.$$

Then

$$x\sqrt{4x^2 + 9} \, dx = \underbrace{\sqrt{4x^2 + 9}}_{\sqrt{u}} \underbrace{x \, dx}_{\frac{1}{8} du} = \frac{1}{8}\sqrt{u} \, du.$$

At $x = 0$, $u = 9$. At $x = 2$, $u = 25$. Thus

$$\int_0^2 x\sqrt{4x^2 + 9} \, dx = \frac{1}{8} \int_9^{25} \sqrt{u} \, du = \frac{1}{12} \left[u^{3/2} \right]_9^{25} = \frac{49}{6}. \quad \Box$$

PROBLEM. Evaluate

$$\int_0^{\sqrt{3}} x^5\sqrt{x^2 + 1} \, dx.$$

Solution. Set

$$u = x^2 + 1, \qquad du = 2x \, dx.$$

Then

$$x^5\sqrt{x^2 + 1} \, dx = \underbrace{x^4}_{(u-1)^2} \underbrace{\sqrt{x^2 + 1}}_{\sqrt{u}} \underbrace{x \, dx}_{\frac{1}{2} du} = \frac{1}{2}(u - 1)^2 \sqrt{u} \, du.$$

At $x = 0$, $u = 1$. At $x = \sqrt{3}$, $u = 4$. Thus

$$\int_0^{\sqrt{3}} x^5 \sqrt{x^2 + 1} \; dx = \tfrac{1}{2} \int_1^4 (u - 1)^2 \sqrt{u} \; du$$

$$= \tfrac{1}{2} \int_1^4 (u^{5/2} - 2u^{3/2} + u^{1/2}) \; du$$

$$= \tfrac{1}{2} \left[\tfrac{2}{7} u^{7/2} - \tfrac{4}{5} u^{5/2} + \tfrac{2}{3} u^{3/2} \right]_1^4$$

$$= \left[u^{3/2} (\tfrac{1}{7} u^2 - \tfrac{2}{5} u + \tfrac{1}{3}) \right]_1^4 = \tfrac{848}{105}. \quad \square$$

EXERCISES

Work out the following integrals by a u-substitution.

1. $\displaystyle\int \frac{dx}{(2 - 3x)^2}$.

2. $\displaystyle\int \frac{dx}{\sqrt{2x + 1}}$.

3. $\displaystyle\int \sqrt{2x + 1} \; dx$.

4. $\displaystyle\int \sqrt{ax + b} \; dx$.

5. $\displaystyle\int (ax + b)^{3/4} \; dx$.

6. $\displaystyle\int (2ax + b)(ax^2 + bx + c)^4 \; dx$.

7. $\displaystyle\int \frac{t}{(4t^2 + 9)^2} \; dt$.

8. $\displaystyle\int \frac{3t}{(t^2 + 1)^2} \; dt$.

9. $\displaystyle\int t^2 (5t^3 + 9)^4 \; dt$.

10. $\displaystyle\int t(1 + t^2)^3 \; dt$.

11. $\displaystyle\int x^2 (1 + x^3)^{1/4} \; dx$.

12. $\displaystyle\int x^{n-1} \sqrt{a + bx^n} \; dx$.

13. $\displaystyle\int \frac{s}{(1 + s^2)^3} \; ds$.

14. $\displaystyle\int \frac{2s}{\sqrt[3]{6 - 5s^2}} \; ds$.

15. $\displaystyle\int \frac{x}{\sqrt{x^2 + 1}} \; dx$.

16. $\displaystyle\int \frac{3ax^2 - 2bx}{\sqrt{ax^3 - bx^2}} \; dx$.

17. $\displaystyle\int \frac{b^3 x^3}{\sqrt{1 - a^4 x^4}} \; dx$.

18. $\displaystyle\int \frac{x^{n-1}}{\sqrt{a + bx^n}} \; dx$.

Evaluate the following integrals by a u-substitution.

19. $\displaystyle\int_0^1 x(x^2 + 1)^3 \; dx$.

20. $\displaystyle\int_{-1}^0 3x^2 (4 + 2x^3)^2 \; dx$.

21. $\displaystyle\int_0^1 5x(1 + x^2)^4 \; dx$.

22. $\displaystyle\int_1^2 (6 - x)^{-3} \; dx$.

23. $\displaystyle\int_{-1}^1 \frac{r}{(1 + r^2)^4} \; dr$.

24. $\displaystyle\int_0^3 \frac{r}{\sqrt{r^2 + 16}} \; dr$.

25. $\displaystyle\int_0^a y \sqrt{a^2 - y^2} \; dy$.

26. $\displaystyle\int_0^a y \sqrt{a^2 + y^2} \; dy$.

Work out the following integrals by a *u*-substitution.

27. $\displaystyle\int x\sqrt{x+1}\ dx.$ [set $u = x + 1$]   **28.** $\displaystyle\int 2x\sqrt{x-1}\ dx.$

29. $\displaystyle\int x\sqrt{2x-1}\ dx.$ **30.** $\displaystyle\int x^2\sqrt{x+1}\ dx.$

31. $\displaystyle\int y(y+1)^{12}\ dy.$ **32.** $\displaystyle\int y(y-1)^{-7}\ dy.$

33. $\displaystyle\int t^2(t-2)^5\ dt.$ **34.** $\displaystyle\int t(2t+3)^8\ dt.$

35. $\displaystyle\int_0^1 \frac{x+3}{\sqrt{x+1}}\ dx.$ **36.** $\displaystyle\int_0^1 \frac{x^2}{\sqrt{x+1}}\ dx.$

37. $\displaystyle\int_{-1}^0 x^3(x^2+1)^6\ dx.$ [set $u = x^2 + 1$]   **38.** $\displaystyle\int_1^{\sqrt{2}} x^3(x^2-1)^7\ dx.$

5.9 ······SOME FURTHER PROPERTIES OF THE DEFINITE INTEGRAL

In this section we feature some important general properties of the integral. The proofs are left mostly to you. You can assume throughout that the functions involved are continuous and that $a < b$.

   I. The integral of a nonnegative function is nonnegative:

(5.9.1)   if $f(x) \geq 0$ for all $x \in [a, b]$,   then $\displaystyle\int_a^b f(x)\ dx \geq 0.$

The integral of a positive function is positive:

(5.9.2)   if $f(x) > 0$ for all $x \in [a, b]$,   then $\displaystyle\int_a^b f(x)\ dx > 0.$

The next property is an immediate consequence of Property I and linearity (5.4.6).

   II. The integral is order-preserving:

(5.9.3)   if $f(x) \leq g(x)$ for all $x \in [a, b]$,   then $\displaystyle\int_a^b f(x)\ dx \leq \int_a^b g(x)\ dx$

and

(5.9.4)   if $f(x) < g(x)$ for all $x \in [a, b]$,   then $\displaystyle\int_a^b f(x)\ dx < \int_a^b g(x)\ dx.$

III. Just as the absolute value of a sum is less than or equal to the sum of the absolute values,

$$|x_1 + x_2 + \cdots + x_n| \leq |x_1| + |x_2| + \cdots + |x_n|,$$

the absolute value of an integral is less than or equal to the integral of the absolute value:

(5.9.5)
$$\left| \int_a^b f(x) \, dx \right| \leq \int_a^b |f(x)| \, dx.$$

Hint for Proof of (5.9.5). Show that

$$\int_a^b f(x) \, dx \qquad \text{and} \qquad - \int_a^b f(x) \, dx$$

are both less than or equal to

$$\int_a^b |f(x)| \, dx. \quad \square$$

The next property is one with which you are already familiar.

IV. If m is the minimum value of f on $[a, b]$ and M is the maximum value, then

(5.9.6)
$$m(b - a) \leq \int_a^b f(x) \, dx \leq M(b - a).$$

We come now to a generalization of Theorem 5.3.5. Its importance will become apparent in Chapter 7.

V. If u is a differentiable function of x and f is continuous, then

(5.9.7)
$$\frac{d}{dx} \left(\int_a^u f(t) \, dt \right) = f(u) \frac{du}{dx}.$$

Proof. The function

$$F(u) = \int_a^u f(t) \, dt$$

is differentiable with respect to u and

$$\frac{d}{du} [F(u)] = f(u). \qquad \text{(Theorem 5.3.5)}$$

Thus

$$\frac{d}{dx}\left(\int_a^u f(t)\, dt\right) = \frac{d}{dx}[F(u)] = \frac{d}{du}[F(u)]\frac{du}{dx} = f(u)\frac{du}{dx}. \quad \square$$

chain rule

PROBLEM. Find

$$\frac{d}{dx}\left(\int_0^{x^3} \frac{dt}{1+t}\right).$$

Solution. At this stage you'd probably be hard put to carry out the integration; it requires the logarithm function, not introduced in this text until Chapter 7. But, for our purposes, that doesn't matter. By (5.9.7) you know that

$$\frac{d}{dx}\left(\int_0^{x^3} \frac{dt}{1+t}\right) = \frac{1}{1+x^3}\, 3x^2 = \frac{3x^2}{1+x^3}$$

without carrying out the integration. $\square$

PROBLEM. Find

$$\frac{d}{dx}\left(\int_x^{2x} \frac{dt}{1+t^2}\right).$$

Solution. The idea is to express the integral in terms of integrals that have constant lower limits. Once we've done that, we can differentiate as before. By the additivity of the integral

$$\int_0^x \frac{dt}{1+t^2} + \int_x^{2x} \frac{dt}{1+t^2} = \int_0^{2x} \frac{dt}{1+t^2}.$$

Thus

$$\int_x^{2x} \frac{dt}{1+t^2} = \int_0^{2x} \frac{dt}{1+t^2} - \int_0^x \frac{dt}{1+t^2}.$$

Differentiation gives

$$\frac{d}{dx}\left(\int_x^{2x} \frac{dt}{1+t^2}\right) = \frac{d}{dx}\left(\int_0^{2x} \frac{dt}{1+t^2}\right) - \frac{d}{dx}\left(\int_0^x \frac{dt}{1+t^2}\right)$$

$$= \frac{1}{1+(2x)^2}\,(2) - \frac{1}{1+x^2}\,(1)$$

(5.9.7)

$$= \frac{2}{1+4x^2} - \frac{1}{1+x^2}. \quad \square$$

EXERCISES

Assume: f and g continuous, $a < b$, and

$$\int_a^b f(x)\, dx > \int_a^b g(x)\, dx.$$

Answer questions 1–6 giving supporting reasons.

1. Does it necessarily follow that $\int_a^b [f(x) - g(x)]\, dx > 0$?

2. Does it necessarily follow that $f(x) > g(x)$ for all $x \in [a, b]$?

3. Does it necessarily follow that $f(x) > g(x)$ for at least some $x \in [a, b]$?

4. Does it necessarily follow that $\left| \int_a^b f(x)\, dx \right| > \left| \int_a^b g(x)\, dx \right|$?

5. Does it necessarily follow that $\int_a^b |f(x)|\, dx > \int_a^b |g(x)|\, dx$?

6. Does it necessarily follow that $\int_a^b |f(x)|\, dx > \int_a^b g(x)\, dx$?

Assume: f continuous, $a < b$, and

$$\int_a^b f(x)\, dx = 0.$$

Answer questions 7–15 giving supporting reasons.

7. Does it necessarily follow that $f(x) = 0$ for all $x \in [a, b]$?

8. Does it necessarily follow that $f(x) = 0$ for at least some $x \in [a, b]$?

9. Does it necessarily follow that $\int_a^b |f(x)|\, dx = 0$?

10. Does it necessarily follow that $\left| \int_a^b f(x)\, dx \right| = 0$?

11. Must all upper sums $U_f(P)$ be nonnegative?

12. Must all upper sums $U_f(P)$ be positive?

13. Can a lower sum, $L_f(P)$, be positive?

14. Does it necessarily follow that $\int_a^b [f(x)]^2\, dx = 0$?

15. Does it necessarily follow that $\int_a^b [f(x) + 1]\, dx = b - a$?

Calculate the following derivatives.

16. $\dfrac{d}{dx}\left(\displaystyle\int_1^{x^2} \dfrac{dt}{t}\right).$

17. $\dfrac{d}{dx}\left(\displaystyle\int_0^{1+x^2} \dfrac{dt}{\sqrt{2t+5}}\right).$

18. $\dfrac{d}{dx}\left(\displaystyle\int_0^{x^3} \dfrac{dt}{\sqrt{1+t^2}}\right).$

19. $\dfrac{d}{dx}\left(\displaystyle\int_x^a f(t)\,dt\right).$

20. Show that, if u and v are differentiable functions of x and f is continuous, then

$$\frac{d}{dx}\left(\int_u^v f(t)\,dt\right) = f(v)\frac{dv}{dx} - f(u)\frac{du}{dx}.$$

HINT: Take a number a from the domain of f. Express the integral as the difference of two integrals, each with lower limit a.

Calculate the following derivatives using Exercise 20.

21. $\dfrac{d}{dx}\left(\displaystyle\int_x^{x^2} \dfrac{dt}{t}\right).$

22. $\dfrac{d}{dx}\left(\displaystyle\int_{1-x}^{1+x} \dfrac{t-1}{t}\,dt\right).$

23. $\dfrac{d}{dx}\left(\displaystyle\int_{x^{1/3}}^{2+3x} \dfrac{dt}{1+t^{3/2}}\right).$

24. $\dfrac{d}{dx}\left(\displaystyle\int_{\sqrt{x}}^{x^2+x} \dfrac{dt}{2+\sqrt{t}}\right).$

25. Verify Property I: (a) by considering lower sums $L_f(P)$; (b) by using an antiderivative.

26. Verify Property II.   **27.** Verify Property III.

28. Prove that, if f is continuous on $[a, b]$ and

$$\int_a^b |f(x)|\,dx = 0,$$

then $f(x) = 0$ for all x in $[a, b]$.   HINT: Exercise 44, Section 2.4.

29. Find $H'(2)$ given that

$$H(x) = \int_{2x}^{x^3-4} \frac{x}{1+\sqrt{t}}\,dt.$$

30. Find $H'(3)$ given that

$$H(x) = \frac{1}{x}\int_3^x [2t - 3H'(t)]\,dt.$$

5.10····AVERAGE VALUE; MEAN-VALUE THEOREM FOR INTEGRALS

You are familiar with averages in arithmetic. If $a_1, a_2, \ldots, a_n$ are numbers, then the average of these numbers is their sum divided by n:

$$\text{average} = (a_1 + a_2 + \cdots + a_n)/n.$$

Now suppose that f is a function continuous on some interval $[a, b]$. What number, if any, should we call the *average value* of f on $[a, b]$? Or, equivalently, the average value of f from $x = a$ to $x = b$?

We could define the average as $\frac{1}{2}[f(a) + f(b)]$, but that would take into consideration only what happens at the endpoints. We want a notion of average that takes into consideration what happens throughout the interval $[a, b]$.

To see how to proceed, let's look at averages in a more familiar setting. Think of a student taking tests. During the first marking period the student takes N_1 tests, during the next marking period N_2 tests, . . . , during the last marking period N_n tests. Now let N be the total number of tests taken by the student. Obviously

$$N = N_1 + \cdots + N_n.$$

If we give equal weight to each of the tests, then the student's average has the following two properties:

(i) lowest of the N grades $\leq$ average on the N tests $\leq$ highest of the N grades;

(ii) $\left(\begin{array}{c} \text{average on} \\ \text{the } N \text{ tests} \end{array} \right) \cdot N = \left(\begin{array}{c} \text{average on} \\ \text{first } N_1 \text{ tests} \end{array} \right) \cdot N_1 + \cdots + \left(\begin{array}{c} \text{average on} \\ \text{final } N_n \text{ tests} \end{array} \right) \cdot N_n.$

Property (i) is obvious. Property (ii) holds since each side of the equation represents the total number of points scored.

Now let's return to the function f. In view of (i) and (ii), we make two requirements of the number that we call the average of f:

Requirement 1. On each interval over which f is defined

$$\text{minimum value of } f \leq \text{average of } f \leq \text{maximum value of } f.$$

Requirement 2. If $P = \{x_0, x_1, \ldots, x_n\}$ is a partition of $[a, b]$, then

$$\left(\begin{array}{c} \text{average of } f \\ \text{on } [a, b] \end{array} \right)(b - a) = \left(\begin{array}{c} \text{average of } f \\ \text{on } [x_0, x_1] \end{array} \right) \Delta x_1 + \cdots + \left(\begin{array}{c} \text{average of } f \\ \text{on } [x_{n-1}, x_n] \end{array} \right) \Delta x_n.$$

To meet Requirements 1 and 2, there is only one way to define average, and that is to set

(5.10.1) $$\text{average of } f \text{ on } [a, b] = \frac{1}{b - a} \int_a^b f(x)\, dx.$$

Proof. Take an arbitrary partition $P = \{x_0, x_1, \ldots, x_n\}$ of $[a, b]$. For each subinterval $[x_{i-1}, x_i]$, Requirement 1 gives

$$m_i \leq \text{average of } f \text{ on } [x_{i-1}, x_i] \leq M_i,$$

where, as usual,

$$m_i = \text{minimum value of } f \text{ on } [x_{i-1}, x_i]$$

and

$$M_i = \text{maximum value of } f \text{ on } [x_{i-1}, x_i].$$

Multiplying by Δx_i, we have

$$m_i \Delta x_i \leq \left(\begin{array}{c} \text{average of } f \\ \text{on } [x_{i-1}, x_i] \end{array} \right) \Delta x_i \leq M_i \Delta x_i.$$

Summing from $i = 1$ to $i = n$, we get

$$L_f(P) \leq \left(\begin{array}{c} \text{average of } f \\ \text{on } [x_0, x_1] \end{array} \right) \Delta x_1 + \cdots + \left(\begin{array}{c} \text{average of } f \\ \text{on } [x_{n-1}, x_n] \end{array} \right) \Delta x_n \leq U_f(P).\dagger$$

Requirement 2 now gives

$$L_f(P) \leq \left(\begin{array}{c} \text{average of } f \\ \text{on } [a, b] \end{array} \right) (b - a) \leq U_f(P).$$

Since P was chosen arbitrarily, this inequality must hold for all partitions P. Since by assumption f is continuous, there is only one number with this property: the integral of f on $[a, b]$.$\dagger\dagger$ Thus we must have

$$\left(\begin{array}{c} \text{average of } f \\ \text{on } [a, b] \end{array} \right) (b - a) = \int_a^b f(x) \, dx$$

and

$$\text{average of } f \text{ on } [a, b] = \frac{1}{b - a} \int_a^b f(x) \, dx. \quad \square$$

This sense of average provides a powerful and intuitive way of viewing the definite integral. Think for a moment in terms of area. If f is constant and positive on $[a, b]$, then Ω, the region below the graph, is a rectangle. Its area is given by the formula

$$\text{area of } \Omega = (\text{constant value of } f \text{ on } [a, b]) \cdot (b - a). \quad \text{(Figure 5.10.1)}$$

If f is now allowed to vary continuously on $[a, b]$, then we have

$$\text{area of } \Omega = \int_a^b f(x) \, dx.$$

In terms of average values the formula reads

(5.10.2) | *area of Ω = (average value of f on $[a, b]$) $\cdot$ (b − a).* | (Figure 5.10.2)

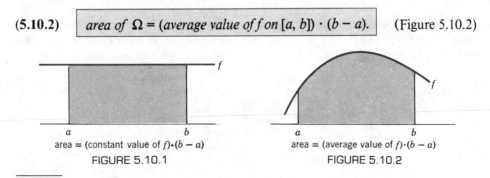

$\text{area} = (\text{constant value of } f) \cdot (b - a)$

FIGURE 5.10.1

$\text{area} = (\text{average value of } f) \cdot (b - a)$

FIGURE 5.10.2

$\dagger$ $L_f(P)$ and $U_f(P)$ are the lower and upper sums discussed in Section 5.2.

$\dagger\dagger$ See Section 5.2.

Think now in terms of motion. If an object moves along a line with constant speed $|v|$ during the time interval $[a, b]$, then

the distance traveled = (the constant value of $|v|$ on $[a, b]$) $\cdot$ $(b - a)$.

If the speed $|v|$ varies, then we have

$$\text{distance traveled} = \int_a^b |v(t)| \, dt$$

and the formula reads

(5.10.3) *distance traveled = (average value of $|v|$ on $[a, b]$) $\cdot$ $(b - a)$.*

In general, we have the identity

(5.10.4) $$\int_a^b f(x) \, dx = (\textit{average value of } f \textit{ on } [a, b]) \cdot (b - a).$$

THEOREM 5.10.5 THE MEAN-VALUE THEOREM FOR INTEGRALS

If f is continuous on $[a, b]$, then there is a number c in (a, b) such that

$$\int_a^b f(x) \, dx = f(c)(b - a).$$

In other words, there is a number c in (a, b) at which f takes on its average value.

Proof. Apply the mean-value theorem to the function

$$F(x) = \int_a^x f(t) \, dt \qquad \text{on } [a, b]. \quad \square$$

To see this theorem geometrically, look at Figure 5.10.3. Here we are assuming that f is positive. The theorem says that somewhere in (a, b) there exists a number c such that the rectangle displayed has the same area as the region under the curve.

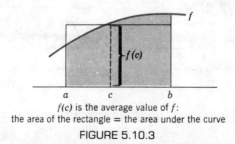

$f(c)$ is the average value of f:
the area of the rectangle = the area under the curve

FIGURE 5.10.3

EXERCISES

Determine the average value on the indicated interval and find a point in this interval at which the function takes on this average value.

1. $f(x) = mx + b$, $x \in [0, c]$.
2. $f(x) = x^2$, $x \in [-1, 1]$.
3. $f(x) = x^3$, $x \in [-1, 1]$.
4. $f(x) = x^{-2}$, $x \in [1, 4]$.
5. $f(x) = |x|$, $x \in [-2, 2]$.
6. $f(x) = x^{1/3}$, $x \in [-8, 8]$.
7. $f(x) = 2x - x^2$, $x \in [0, 2]$.
8. $f(x) = 3 - 2x$, $x \in [0, 3]$.
9. $f(x) = \sqrt{x}$, $x \in [0, 9]$.
10. $f(x) = 4 - x^2$, $x \in [-2, 2]$.
11. $f(x) = \sin x$, $x \in [0, 2\pi]$.
12. $f(x) = \cos x$, $x \in [0, \pi]$.

13. Solve the following equation for A:

$$\int_a^b [f(x) - A]\, dx = 0.$$

14. Given that f is continuous on $[a, b]$, compare

$$f(b)(b - a) \quad \text{and} \quad \int_a^b f(x)\, dx$$

if f is (a) constant on $[a, b]$; (b) increasing on $[a, b]$; (c) decreasing on $[a, b]$.

15. In Chapter 4, we viewed $[f(b) - f(a)]/(b - a)$ as the average rate of change of f on $[a, b]$ and $f'(t)$ as the instantaneous rate of change at time t. If our new sense of average is to be consistent with the old one, we must have

$$\frac{f(b) - f(a)}{b - a} = \text{average of } f' \text{ on } [a, b].$$

Prove that this is the case.

16. Determine whether the assertion is true or false.

(a) $\left(\begin{array}{c} \text{the average of } f + g \\ \text{on } [a, b] \end{array} \right) = \left(\begin{array}{c} \text{the average of } f \\ \text{on } [a, b] \end{array} \right) + \left(\begin{array}{c} \text{the average of } g \\ \text{on } [a, b] \end{array} \right).$

(b) $\left(\begin{array}{c} \text{the average of } \alpha f \\ \text{on } [a, b] \end{array} \right) = \alpha \left(\begin{array}{c} \text{the average of } f \\ \text{on } [a, b] \end{array} \right).$

(c) $\left(\begin{array}{c} \text{the average of } fg \\ \text{on } [a, b] \end{array} \right) = \left(\begin{array}{c} \text{the average of } f \\ \text{on } [a, b] \end{array} \right) \left(\begin{array}{c} \text{the average of } g \\ \text{on } [a, b] \end{array} \right).$

17. Find the average distance of the parabolic arc

$$y = x^2, \qquad x \in [0, \sqrt{3}]$$

from (a) the x-axis; (b) the y-axis; (c) the origin.

18. Find the average distance of the line segment

$$y = mx, \qquad x \in [0, 1]$$

from (a) the x-axis; (b) the y-axis; (c) the origin.

19. A stone falls from rest in a vacuum for x seconds. (a) Compare its terminal velocity to its average velocity; (b) compare its average velocity during the first $\frac{1}{2}x$ seconds to its average velocity during the next $\frac{1}{2}x$ seconds.

20. Let f be continuous. Show that, if f is an odd function, then its average value on every interval of the form $[-a, a]$ is zero.

21. Prove that two distinct continuous functions cannot have the same average on every interval.

22. Let f be continuous on $[a, b]$. Let $a < c < b$. Prove that

$$f(c) = \lim_{h \to 0^+} (\text{average value of } f \text{ on } [c - h, c + h]).$$

5.11 ····ADDITIONAL EXERCISES

Work out the following integrals.

1. $\displaystyle\int (\sqrt{x - a} - \sqrt{x - b})\, dx.$ 2. $\displaystyle\int ax\sqrt{1 + bx^2}\, dx.$ 3. $\displaystyle\int t^{-1/3}(t^{2/3} - 1)^2\, dt.$

4. $\displaystyle\int t^2(1 + t^3)^{10}\, dt.$ 5. $\displaystyle\int (1 + 2\sqrt{x})^2\, dx.$ 6. $\displaystyle\int \frac{1}{\sqrt{x}}(1 + 2\sqrt{x})^5\, dx.$

7. $\displaystyle\int \frac{(a + b\sqrt{y + 1})^2}{\sqrt{y + 1}}\, dy.$ 8. $\displaystyle\int y\sqrt{y}(1 + y^2\sqrt{y})^2\, dy.$ 9. $\displaystyle\int \frac{g'(x)}{[g(x)]^3}\, dx.$

10. $\displaystyle\int \frac{g(x)g'(x)}{\sqrt{1 + [g(x)]^2}}\, dx.$

Find the area below the graph.

11. $y = x\sqrt{2x^2 + 1},\quad x \in [0, 2].$ 12. $y = \dfrac{x}{(2x^2 + 1)^2},\quad x \in [0, 2].$

13. At every point of the curve the slope is given by the equation

$$\frac{dy}{dx} = x\sqrt{x^2 + 1}.$$

Find an equation for the curve given that it passes through the point $(0, 1)$.

14. Find the area of the portion of the first quadrant that is bounded

above by $y = 2x$ and   below by $y = x\sqrt{3x^2 + 1}.$

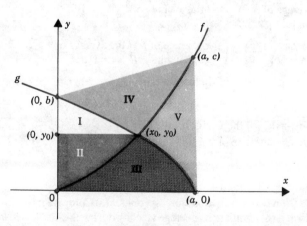

FIGURE 5.11.1

15. Find a formula for the area of each region drawn in Figure 5.11.1:

(a) I.   (b) II.   (c) III.   (d) IV.   (e) V.

Sketch the region bounded by the curves and find its area.

16. $y^2 = 2x$, $x^2 = 3y$.   **17.** $y^2 = 6x$, $x^2 + 4y = 0$.

18. $y = 4 - x^2$, $y = x + 2$.   **19.** $y = 4 - x^2$, $x + y + 2 = 0$.

20. $y = \sqrt{x}$, the x-axis, $y = 6 - x$.   **21.** $y = x^3$, the x-axis, $x + y = 2$.

22. $4y = x^2 - x^4$, $x + y + 1 = 0$.   **23.** $x^2 y = a^2$, the x-axis, $x = a$, $x = 2a$.

24. (*Important*) Let f be a continuous function. Show that

(5.11.1)

$$\text{(a) if } f \text{ is odd, then } \int_{-a}^{a} f(x)\, dx = 0;$$

$$\text{(b) if } f \text{ is even, then } \int_{-a}^{a} f(x)\, dx = 2 \int_{0}^{a} f(x)\, dx.$$

Assume that f and g are continuous, that $a < b$, and that

$$\int_{a}^{b} f(x)\, dx > \int_{a}^{b} g(x)\, dx.$$

Which of the following statements necessarily hold for all partitions P of $[a, b]$? Support your answers.

25. $L_g(P) < U_f(P)$.   **26.** $L_g(P) \leq L_f(P)$.   **27.** $L_g(P) < \int_{a}^{b} f(x)\, dx$.

28. $U_g(P) < U_f(P)$ **29.** $U_f(P) > \int_{a}^{b} g(x)\, dx$.   **30.** $U_g(P) < \int_{a}^{b} f(x)\, dx$.

A curve that passes through the point $(4, \frac{1}{3})$ has varying slope

$$\frac{dy}{dx} = -\frac{1}{2\sqrt{x}(1 + \sqrt{x})^2}.$$

31. Find an equation for the curve.

32. Sketch the curve.

33. Estimate the area under the curve between $x = 0$ and $x = 1$ by means of the partition $P = \{0, \frac{1}{25}, \frac{4}{25}, \frac{9}{25}, \frac{16}{25}, 1\}$.

Carry out the differentiation.

34. $\dfrac{d}{dx}\left(\displaystyle\int_{0}^{x} \dfrac{dt}{1 + t^2} \right).$ **35.** $\dfrac{d}{dx}\left(\displaystyle\int_{0}^{x^2} \dfrac{dt}{1 + t^2} \right).$ **36.** $\dfrac{d}{dx}\left(\displaystyle\int_{x}^{x^2} \dfrac{dt}{1 + t^2} \right).$

37. Where does the function

$$f(x) = \int_{0}^{x} \frac{t - 1}{1 + t^2}\, dt, \qquad x \in [0, 2]$$

take on its minimum value?

38. Show that

(a) $$\int_{a+c}^{b+c} f(x - c)\, dx = \int_{a}^{b} f(x)\, dx,$$

and, if $c \neq 0$,

(b)
$$\frac{1}{c} \int_{ac}^{bc} f\left(\frac{x}{c}\right) dx = \int_{a}^{b} f(x) \, dx.$$

Assume that f is everywhere continuous.

5.12····INTEGRATING THE TRIGONOMETRIC FUNCTIONS

In Section 3.7 you saw that each trigonometric function is differentiable on its domain and

(5.12.1)
$$\frac{d}{dx}(\sin x) = \cos x, \qquad \frac{d}{dx}(\cos x) = -\sin x,$$
$$\frac{d}{dx}(\tan x) = \sec^2 x, \qquad \frac{d}{dx}(\cot x) = -\csc^2 x,$$
$$\frac{d}{dx}(\sec x) = \sec x \tan x, \qquad \frac{d}{dx}(\csc x) = -\csc x \cot x.$$

Rewriting these formulas in integral form, we have

(5.12.2)
$$\int \cos x \, dx = \sin x + C, \qquad \int \sin x \, dx = -\cos x + C,$$
$$\int \sec^2 x \, dx = \tan x + C, \qquad \int \csc^2 x \, dx = -\cot x + C,$$
$$\int \sec x \tan x \, dx = \sec x + C, \qquad \int \csc x \cot x \, dx = -\csc x + C.$$

PROBLEM. Find
$$\int \sin x \cos x \, dx.$$

Solution. Set
$$u = \sin x, \qquad du = \cos x \, dx.$$

Then
$$\int \sin x \cos x \, dx = \int u \, du = \tfrac{1}{2}u^2 + C = \tfrac{1}{2}\sin^2 x + C. \quad \square$$

PROBLEM. Find
$$\int \sec^3 x \tan x \, dx.$$

Solution. Set

$$u = \sec x, \qquad du = \sec x \tan x \, dx.$$

Then

$$\sec^3 x \tan x \, dx = \underbrace{\sec^2 x}_{u^2} \underbrace{(\sec x \tan x) \, dx}_{du} = u^2 \, du$$

and

$$\int \sec^3 x \tan x \, dx = \int u^2 \, du = \tfrac{1}{3}u^3 + C = \tfrac{1}{3} \sec^3 x + C. \quad \square$$

Where an antiderivative is obvious, there is no need to make a substitution:

(1) $$\int \cos 3x \, dx = \tfrac{1}{3} \sin 3x + C$$

(2) $$\int \sec^2 \frac{\pi}{2} x \, dx = \frac{2}{\pi} \tan \frac{\pi}{2} x + C$$

(3) $$\int \sec (\pi - t) \tan (\pi - t) \, dt = - \sec (\pi - t) + C.$$

We can, of course, derive these results by substitution.
    For (1) set

$$u = 3x, \qquad du = 3 \, dx.$$

Then

$$\int \cos 3x \, dx = \tfrac{1}{3} \int \cos u \, du = \tfrac{1}{3} \sin u + C = \tfrac{1}{3} \sin 3x + C.$$

    For (2) set

$$u = \frac{\pi}{2} x, \qquad du = \frac{\pi}{2} \, dx.$$

Then

$$\int \sec^2 \frac{\pi}{2} x \, dx = \frac{2}{\pi} \int \sec^2 u \, du = \frac{2}{\pi} \tan u + C = \frac{2}{\pi} \tan \frac{\pi}{2} x + C.$$

    For (3) set

$$u = \pi - t, \qquad du = - dt.$$

Then

$$\int \sec (\pi - t) \tan (\pi - t) \, dt = - \int \sec u \tan u \, du$$

$$= - \sec u + C = - \sec (\pi - t) + C. \quad \square$$

PROBLEM. Find

$$\int x \cos \pi x^2 \, dx.$$

Solution. Set

$$u = \pi x^2, \qquad du = 2\pi x \, dx.$$

Then

$$x \cos \pi x^2 \, dx = \underbrace{\cos \pi x^2}_{\cos u} \underbrace{x \, dx}_{\frac{1}{2\pi} du} = \frac{1}{2\pi} \cos u \, du$$

and

$$\int x \cos \pi x^2 \, dx = \frac{1}{2\pi} \int \cos u \, du = \frac{1}{2\pi} \sin u + C = \frac{1}{2\pi} \sin \pi x^2 + C. \quad \square$$

PROBLEM. Find

$$\int x^2 \csc^2 x^3 \cot^4 x^3 \, dx.$$

Solution. We can effect some simplification by setting

$$u = x^3, \qquad du = 3x^2 \, dx.$$

Then

$$x^2 \csc^2 x^3 \cot^4 x^3 \, dx = \underbrace{\cot^4 x^3}_{\cot^4 u} \underbrace{\csc^2 x^3}_{\csc^2 u} \underbrace{x^2 \, dx}_{\frac{1}{3} du} = \tfrac{1}{3} \cot^4 u \csc^2 u \, du$$

and

$$\int x^2 \csc^2 x^3 \cot^4 x^3 \, dx = \tfrac{1}{3} \int \cot^4 u \csc^2 u \, du.$$

We can calculate the integral on the right by setting

$$t = \cot u, \qquad dt = - \csc^2 u \, du.$$

Then

$$\tfrac{1}{3} \int \cot^4 u \csc^2 u \, du = -\tfrac{1}{3} \int t^4 \, dt = -\tfrac{1}{15} t^5 + C = -\tfrac{1}{15} \cot^5 u + C,$$

and thus

$$\int x^2 \csc^2 x^3 \cot^4 x^3 \, dx = -\tfrac{1}{15} \cot^5 u + C = -\tfrac{1}{15} \cot^5 x^3 + C.$$

We arrived at this by making two consecutive substitutions. First we set $u = x^3$ and then we set $t = \cot u$. We could have saved ourselves some work by setting $u = \cot x^3$ at the very beginning. With

$$u = \cot x^3, \qquad du = - \csc^2 x^3 \cdot 3x^2 \, dx$$

we have

$$x^2 \csc^2 x^3 \cot^4 x^3 \, dx = \underbrace{\cot^4 x^3}_{u^4} \underbrace{\csc^2 x^3 \, x^2 \, dx}_{-\frac{1}{3} \, du} = -\tfrac{1}{3} u^4 \, du$$

and

$$\int x^2 \csc^2 x^3 \cot^4 x^3 \, dx = -\tfrac{1}{3} \int u^4 \, du = -\tfrac{1}{15} u^5 + C = -\tfrac{1}{15} \cot^5 x^3 + C. \quad \Box$$

REMARK. All the integrals that we have calculated in this section by substitution can be calculated without substitution. All that's required is a good sense of the chain rule.

1. $$\int \sin x \cos x \, dx$$

The cosine is the derivative of the sine. Thus

$$\int \sin x \cos x \, dx = \int \sin x \, \frac{d}{dx} (\sin x) \, dx = \tfrac{1}{2} \sin^2 x + C.$$

2. $$\int \sec^3 x \tan x \, dx$$

Write the integrand as

$$\sec^2 x \, (\sec x \tan x) = \sec^2 x \, \frac{d}{dx} (\sec x).$$

Then

$$\int \sec^3 x \tan x \, dx = \int \sec^2 x \, \frac{d}{dx} (\sec x) \, dx = \tfrac{1}{3} \sec^3 x + C.$$

3. $$\int x \cos \pi x^2 \, dx$$

The cosine is the derivative of the sine. Therefore

$$\frac{d}{dx} (\sin \pi x^2) = \cos \pi x^2 \cdot 2\pi x \qquad \text{and} \qquad x \cos \pi x^2 = \frac{1}{2\pi} \frac{d}{dx} (\sin \pi x^2).$$

Thus

$$\int x \cos \pi x^2 \, dx = \frac{1}{2\pi} \int \frac{d}{dx} (\sin \pi x^2) \, dx = \frac{1}{2\pi} \sin \pi x^2 + C.$$

4. $$\int x^2 \csc^2 x^3 \cot^4 x^3 \, dx.$$

This integral may look complicated, but looked at in the right way, it becomes very simple. You know that the derivative of the cotangent is the negative of the cosecant squared. Therefore, by the chain rule,

$$\frac{d}{dx}(\cot x^3) = -\csc^2 x^3 \cdot 3x^2$$

and

$$x^2 \csc^2 x^3 = -\frac{1}{3}\frac{d}{dx}(\cot x^3).$$

Thus

$$\int x^2 \csc^2 x^3 \cot^4 x^3 \, dx = -\frac{1}{3}\int \cot^4 x^3 \cdot \frac{d}{dx}(\cot x^3) \, dx$$
$$= -\tfrac{1}{15}\cot^5 x^3 + C.$$

There is nothing wrong with calculating integrals by substitution. All we're saying is that, with some experience, you'll be able to calculate many integrals without it. □

We'll return to the general subject of trigonometric integrals in later chapters (Chapters 7 and 9). But first, two formulas worth noting:

(5.12.3) $\quad \displaystyle\int \cos^2 x \, dx = \frac{x}{2} + \frac{\sin 2x}{4} + C \quad \text{and} \quad \int \sin^2 x \, dx = \frac{x}{2} - \frac{\sin 2x}{4} + C.$

You can derive these formulas by recalling that

$$\cos^2 x = \frac{1 + \cos 2x}{2} \quad \text{and} \quad \sin^2 x = \frac{1 - \cos 2x}{2}.$$

We leave the details to you.

EXERCISES

Calculate these indefinite integrals.

1. $\displaystyle\int \cos(3x - 1) \, dx.$

2. $\displaystyle\int \sin 2\pi x \, dx.$

3. $\displaystyle\int \csc^2 \pi x \, dx.$

4. $\displaystyle\int \sec 2x \tan 2x \, dx.$

5. $\displaystyle\int \sin(3 - 2x) \, dx.$

6. $\displaystyle\int \csc(1 - 2x) \cot(1 - 2x) \, dx.$

7. $\displaystyle\int \cos^4 x \sin x \, dx.$

8. $\displaystyle\int x \sec^2 x^2 \, dx.$

9. $\displaystyle\int \sqrt{1 + \sin x} \cos x \, dx.$

10. $\displaystyle\int \sin^2 x \cos x \, dx.$

11. $\displaystyle\int x^{-1/2} \sin x^{1/2} \, dx.$

12. $\displaystyle\int \frac{\sin x}{\sqrt{1 + \cos x}} \, dx.$

13. $\displaystyle\int \frac{1}{\cos^2 x}\,dx.$

14. $\displaystyle\int (1 + \tan^2 x)\sec^2 x\,dx.$

15. $\displaystyle\int x \sin^3 x^2 \cos x^2\,dx.$

16. $\displaystyle\int \sqrt{1 + \cot x}\,\csc^2 x\,dx.$

17. $\displaystyle\int (1 + \cot^2 x)\csc^2 x\,dx.$

18. $\displaystyle\int \cos^2 5x\,dx.$

19. $\displaystyle\int \sin^2 3x\,dx.$

20. $\displaystyle\int \frac{1}{\sin^2 x}\,dx.$

21. $\displaystyle\int \frac{\sec^2 x}{\sqrt{1 + \tan x}}\,dx.$

22. $\displaystyle\int x^2 \sin(4x^3 - 7)\,dx.$

Evaluate these integrals.

23. $\displaystyle\int_0^{2\pi} \sin x\,dx.$

24. $\displaystyle\int_{-\pi/3}^{\pi/3} \sec x \tan x\,dx.$

25. $\displaystyle\int_{1/4}^{1/3} \sec^2 \pi x\,dx.$

26. $\displaystyle\int_0^1 \cos^2 \frac{\pi}{2} x \sin \frac{\pi}{2} x\,dx.$

27. $\displaystyle\int_0^{\pi/2} \sin^3 x \cos x\,dx.$

28. $\displaystyle\int_0^{\pi} \cos x\,dx.$

29. $\displaystyle\int_{\pi/6}^{\pi/4} \csc x \cot x\,dx.$

30. $\displaystyle\int_0^{2\pi} \sin^2 x\,dx.$

31. $\displaystyle\int_0^{2\pi} \cos^2 x\,dx.$

32. $\displaystyle\int_{1/4}^{1/2} \csc^2 \pi x\,dx.$

33. Calculate

$$\int \sec^2 x \tan x\,dx$$

(a) by setting $u = \sec x$; (b) by setting $u = \tan x$. (c) Reconcile your answers to (a) and (b).

34. In the text we found that

$$\int \sin x \cos x\,dx = \tfrac{1}{2}\sin^2 x + C$$

by setting $u = \sin x$. Calculate the integral by setting $u = \cos x$ and show that your answer is the same.

5.13···· THE INTEGRAL AS THE LIMIT OF RIEMANN SUMS

Let f be some function continuous on a closed interval $[a, b]$. With our approach to integration (at this point we ask you to review Section 5.2) the definite integral

$$\int_a^b f(x)\,dx$$

is the unique number that satisfies the inequality

$$L_f(P) \le \int_a^b f(x)\,dx \le U_f(P)$$

for all partitions P of $[a, b]$. This method of obtaining the definite integral by *squeezing* toward it with upper and lower sums is called the *Darboux method*.†

There is another way to obtain the integral that is frequently used. Take a partition $P = \{x_0, x_1, \ldots, x_n\}$ of $[a, b]$. P breaks up $[a, b]$ into n subintervals

$$[x_0, x_1], [x_1, x_2], \ldots, [x_{n-1}, x_n]$$

of lengths

$$\Delta x_1, \Delta x_2, \ldots, \Delta x_n.$$

Now pick a point x_1^* from $[x_0, x_1]$ and form the product $f(x_1^*) \Delta x_1$; pick a point x_2^* from $[x_1, x_2]$ and form the product $f(x_2^*) \Delta x_2$; go on in this manner until you have formed the products

$$f(x_1^*) \Delta x_1, f(x_2^*) \Delta x_2, \ldots, f(x_n^*) \Delta x_n.$$

The sum of these products

$$S^*(P) = f(x_1^*) \Delta x_1 + f(x_2^*) \Delta x_2 + \cdots + f(x_n^*) \Delta x_n$$

is called a *Riemann sum*.††

The definite integral can be viewed as the *limit* of such Riemann sums in the following sense: define $\|P\|$, the *norm* of P, by setting

$$\|P\| = \max \Delta x_i \qquad i = 1, 2, \ldots, n;$$

given any $\epsilon > 0$, there exists a $\delta > 0$ such that

$$\text{if} \quad \|P\| < \delta \qquad \text{then} \quad \left| S^*(P) - \int_a^b f(x)\, dx \right| < \epsilon,$$

no matter how the x_i^* are chosen within $[x_{i-1}, x_i]$.

In symbols we write

$$(5.13.1) \qquad \int_a^b f(x)\, dx = \lim_{\|P\| \to 0} [f(x_1^*) \Delta x_1 + f(x_2^*) \Delta x_2 + \cdots + f(x_n^*) \Delta x_n].$$

A proof of this assertion appears in Appendix B.5. Figure 5.13.1 illustrates the idea. Here the base interval is broken up into 8 subintervals. The point x_1^* is chosen from $[x_0, x_1]$, x_2^* from $[x_1, x_2]$, and so on. While the integral represents the area under the curve, the Riemann sum represents the sum of the areas of the shaded rectangles. The difference between the two can be made as small as we wish (less than ϵ) simply by making the maximum length of the base subintervals sufficiently small—that is, by making $\|P\|$ sufficiently small.

---

† After the French mathematician J. G. Darboux (1842–1917).

†† After the German mathematician G. F. B. Riemann (1826–1866).

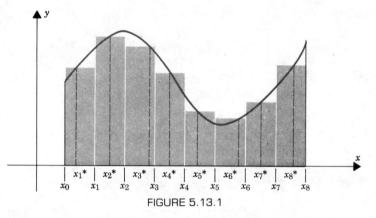

FIGURE 5.13.1

EXERCISES

1. Let Ω be the region below the graph of $f(x) = x^2$, $x \in [0,1]$. Draw a figure showing the Riemann sum $S^*(P)$ as an estimate for this area. Take

$$P = \{0, \tfrac{1}{4}, \tfrac{1}{2}, \tfrac{3}{4}, 1\} \quad \text{and} \quad x_1^* = \tfrac{1}{8}, \quad x_2^* = \tfrac{3}{8}, \quad x_3^* = \tfrac{5}{8}, \quad x_4^* = \tfrac{7}{8}.$$

2. Let Ω be the region below the graph of $f(x) = \tfrac{3}{2}x + 1$, $x \in [0, 2]$. Draw a figure showing the Riemann sum $S^*(P)$ as an estimate for this area. Take

$$P = \{0, \tfrac{1}{4}, \tfrac{3}{4}, 1, \tfrac{3}{2}, 2\} \quad \text{and let the } x_i \text{ be the midpoints of the subintervals.}$$

3. Set $f(x) = 2x$, $x \in [0, 1]$. Take $P = \{0, \tfrac{1}{8}, \tfrac{1}{4}, \tfrac{1}{2}, \tfrac{3}{4}, 1\}$ and set

$$x_1^* = \tfrac{1}{16}, \quad x_2^* = \tfrac{3}{16}, \quad x_3^* = \tfrac{3}{8}, \quad x_4^* = \tfrac{5}{8}, \quad x_5^* = \tfrac{3}{4}.$$

Calculate the following:

(a) $\Delta x_1, \Delta x_2, \Delta x_3, \Delta x_4, \Delta x_5$.   (b) $\|P\|$.   (c) m_1, m_2, m_3, m_4, m_5.

(d) $f(x_1^*), f(x_2^*), f(x_3^*), f(x_4^*), f(x_5^*)$.   (e) M_1, M_2, M_3, M_4, M_5.

(f) $L_f(P)$.   (g) $S^*(P)$.   (h) $U_f(P)$.   (i) $\displaystyle\int_a^b f(x)\, dx$.

4. Let f be continuous on $[a, b]$, let $P = \{x_0, x_1, \ldots, x_n\}$ be a partition of $[a, b]$, and let $S^*(P)$ be any Riemann sum generated by P. Show that

$$L_f(P) \leq S^*(P) \leq U_f(P).$$

In numerical computations the base interval $[a, b]$ is usually broken up into n subintervals each of length $(b - a)/n$. The Riemann sums then take the form

$$S_n^* = \frac{b - a}{n}[f(x_1^*) + f(x_2^*) + \cdots + f(x_n^*)].$$

Choose $\epsilon > 0$. Break up the interval $[0, 1]$ into n subintervals each of length $1/n$. Take $x_1^* = 1/n$, $x_2^* = 2/n$, $\ldots$, $x_n^* = n/n$.

5. (a) Determine the Riemann sum S_n^* for

$$\int_0^1 x\, dx.$$

(b) Show that

$$\left| S_n^* - \int_0^1 x \, dx \right| < \epsilon \qquad \text{if } n > 1/\epsilon.$$

HINT: $1 + 2 + \cdots + n = \frac{1}{2}n(n + 1)$.

6. (a) Determine the Riemann sum S_n^* for

$$\int_0^1 x^2 \, dx.$$

(b) Show that

$$\left| S_n^* - \int_0^1 x^2 \, dx \right| < \epsilon \qquad \text{if } n > 1/\epsilon.$$

HINT: $1^2 + 2^2 + \cdots + n^2 = \frac{1}{6}n(n + 1)(2n + 1)$.

7. (a) Determine the Riemann sum S_n^* for

$$\int_0^1 x^3 \, dx.$$

(b) Show that

$$\left| S_n^* - \int_0^1 x^3 \, dx \right| < \epsilon \qquad \text{if } n > 1/\epsilon.$$

HINT: $1^3 + 2^3 + \cdots + n^3 = (1 + 2 + \cdots + n)^2$.

5.14 CHAPTER SUMMARY

5.1 An Area Problem; A Speed and Distance Problem

5.2 The Definite Integral of a Continuous Function

partition (p. 247)   upper sum; lower sum (p. 247)
definite integral (p. 248)   limits of integration; integrand (p. 249)

5.3 The Function $F(x) = \int_a^x f(t) \, dt$

additive property of integrals (p. 255)

$$\frac{d}{dx}\left[\int_a^x f(t) \, dt \right] = f(x) \text{ (p. 257)}$$

5.4 The Fundamental Theorem of Integral Calculus

antiderivative (p. 261)   fundamental theorem (p. 262)

$$\int_a^b [\alpha f(x) + \beta g(x)] \, dx = \alpha \int_a^b f(x) \, dx + \beta \int_a^b g(x) \, dx$$

5.5 Some Area Problems

Suppose that f and g are continuous functions with $f(x) \geq g(x)$ for all x in some interval $[a, b]$. The area of the region between the graphs of f and g over $[a, b]$ is given by $\int_a^b [f(x) - g(x)] \, dx$.

5.6 Indefinite Integrals

indefinite integral; constant of integration (p. 272)

5.7 Some Motion Problems

For an object that moves along a coordinate line with velocity $v(t)$

$$\int_a^b |v(t)| \, dt = \text{distance traveled from time } t = a \text{ to time } t = b$$

whereas

$$\int_a^b v(t) \, dt = \text{net displacement from time } t = a \text{ to time } t = b.$$

5.8 The u-Substitution; Change of Variables

An integral of the form $\int f(g(x)) \, g'(x) \, dx$ can be written $\int f(u) \, du$ by setting

$$u = g(x), \qquad du = g'(x) \, dx.$$

For definite integrals

$$\int_a^b f(g(x)) \, g'(x) \, dx = \int_{g(a)}^{g(b)} f(u) \, du.$$

5.9 Some Further Properties of the Definite Integral

$$\left| \int_a^b f(x) \, dx \right| \leq \int_a^b |f(x)| \, dx, \qquad \frac{d}{dx}\left[\int_a^u f(t) \, dt \right] = f(u) \frac{du}{dx}$$

The integral of a nonnegative function is nonnegative; the integral of a positive function is positive; the integral is order-preserving. (p. 283)

5.10 Average Value; Mean-Value Theorem for Integrals

average of f (p. 288)   mean-value theorem for integrals (p. 290)

5.11 Additional Exercises

5.12 Integrating the Trigonometric Functions

$$\int \cos x \, dx = \sin x + C, \qquad \int \sin x \, dx = -\cos x + C,$$

$$\int \sec^2 x \, dx = \tan x + C, \qquad \int \csc^2 x \, dx = -\cot x + C,$$

$$\int \sec x \tan x \, dx = \sec x + C, \qquad \int \csc x \cot x \, dx = -\csc x + C,$$

$$\int \cos^2 x \, dx = \frac{x}{2} + \frac{\sin 2x}{4} + C, \qquad \int \sin^2 x \, dx = \frac{x}{2} - \frac{\sin 2x}{4} + C.$$

5.13 The Integral as the Limit of Riemann Sums

Darboux method (p. 300)   Riemann sum (p. 300)

Some Applications of the Integral

6.1 ·····MORE ON AREA

Representative Rectangles

You have seen that the definite integral can be viewed as the limit of Riemann sums:

$$(1) \qquad \int_a^b f(x)\, dx = \lim_{\|P\| \to 0} [f(x_1^*)\Delta x_1 + f(x_2^*)\Delta x_2 + \cdots + f(x_n^*)\Delta x_n].$$

With x_i^* chosen arbitrarily from $[x_{i-1}, x_i]$, you can think of $f(x_i^*)$ as a *representative* value of f for that interval. If f is positive, then the product

$$f(x_i^*)\Delta x_i$$

gives the area of the *representative rectangle* shown in Figure 6.1.1. Formula (1) tells us that we can approximate the area under the curve as closely as we wish by adding up the areas of representative rectangles. (Figure 6.1.2.)

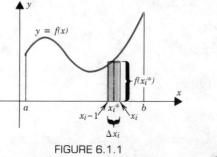

FIGURE 6.1.1

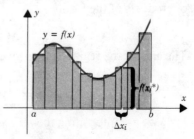

FIGURE 6.1.2

305

Figure 6.1.3 shows a region Ω bounded above by the graph of a function f and bounded below by the graph of a function g. As you've seen before, we can calculate the area of Ω by integrating with respect to x the *vertical separation*

$$f(x) - g(x)$$

from $x = a$ to $x = b$:

$$\text{area } (\Omega) = \int_a^b [f(x) - g(x)]\, dx.$$

In this case the approximating Riemann sums are of the form

$$[f(x_1^*) - g(x_1^*)]\, \Delta x_1 + [f(x_2^*) - g(x_2^*)]\, \Delta x_2 + \cdots + [f(x_n^*) - g(x_n^*)]\, \Delta x_n.$$

The dimensions of a representative rectangle are now

$$f(x_i^*) - g(x_i^*) \qquad \text{and} \qquad \Delta x_i.$$

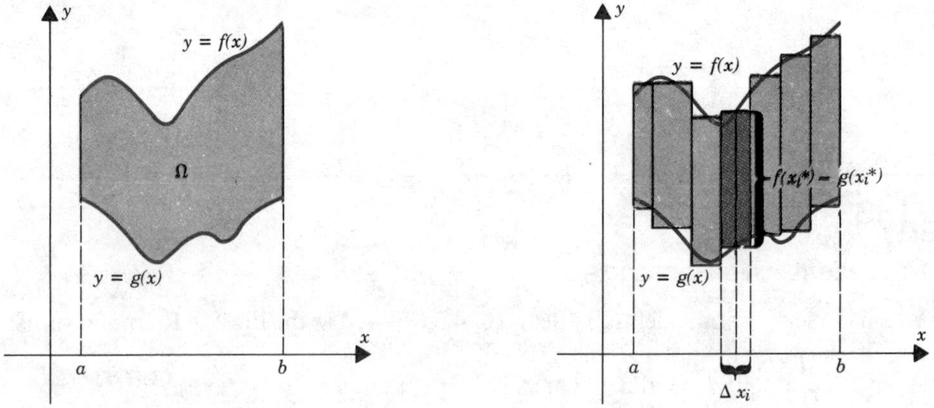

FIGURE 6.1.3

Areas by Integration with Respect to y

In Figure 6.1.4 you can see a region the boundaries of which are not functions of x but functions of y instead. In such a case we set the representative rectangles horizontally and we calculate the area of the region as the limit of Riemann sums composed of products of the form

$$[F(y_i^*) - G(y_i^*)]\, \Delta y_i.$$

The area of the region is thus given by the integral

$$\int_c^d [F(y) - G(y)]\, dy.$$

Here we are integrating the *horizontal separation*

$$F(y) - G(y)$$

with respect to y.

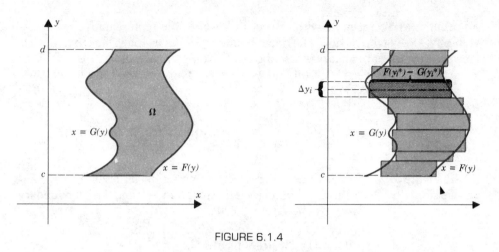

FIGURE 6.1.4

PROBLEM. Find the area of the region bounded on the left by $x = y^2$ and on the right by $x = 3 - 2y^2$.

Solution. The region is sketched in Figure 6.1.5. The easiest way to calculate the area is to set our representative rectangles horizontally and integrate with respect to y.

The two curves intersect at $y = -1$ and $y = 1$. We can find the area of the region by integrating the horizontal separation

$$(3 - 2y^2) - y^2 = 3 - 3y^2$$

from $y = -1$ to $y = 1$:

$$A = \int_{-1}^{1} (3 - 3y^2)\, dy = 4. \quad \square$$

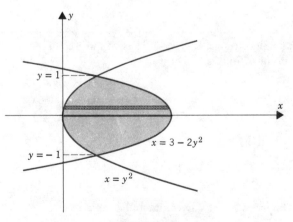

FIGURE 6.1.5

PROBLEM. Calculate the area of the region bounded by the curves $x = y^2$ and $x - y = 2$ by integrating (a) with respect to x, (b) with respect to y.

Solution. (a) To integrate with respect to x we set the representative rectangles vertically. See Figure 6.1.6. The upper boundary of the region is the curve $y = \sqrt{x}$. However, the lower boundary is described by two different equations: $y = -\sqrt{x}$ from $x = 0$ to $x = 1$ and $y = x - 2$ from $x = 1$ to $x = 4$. Thus, we need two integrals:

$$A = \int_0^1 [\sqrt{x} - (-\sqrt{x})]\, dx + \int_1^4 [\sqrt{x} - (x - 2)]\, dx$$

$$= 2\int_0^1 \sqrt{x}\, dx + \int_1^4 (\sqrt{x} - x + 2)\, dx = \left[\tfrac{4}{3}x^{3/2}\right]_0^1 + \left[\tfrac{2}{3}x^{3/2} - \tfrac{1}{2}x^2 + 2x\right]_1^4 = \tfrac{9}{2}.$$

(b) See Figure 6.1.7. To integrate with respect to y we set the representative rectangles horizontally. Now the right boundary is the line $x = y + 2$ and the left boundary is the curve $x = y^2$. Since y ranges from -1 to 2,

$$A = \int_{-1}^2 [(y + 2) - y^2]\, dy = \left[\tfrac{1}{2}y^2 + 2y - \tfrac{1}{3}y^3\right]_{-1}^2 = \tfrac{9}{2}. \quad \square$$

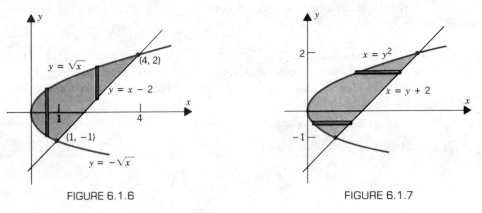

FIGURE 6.1.6   FIGURE 6.1.7

EXERCISES

Sketch the region bounded by the curves. Represent the area of the region as one or more integrals (a) in terms of x; (b) in terms of y.

1. $y = x^2$, $y = x + 2$.
2. $y = x^2$, $y = -4x$.
3. $y = x^3$, $y = 2x^2$.
4. $y = \sqrt{x}$, $y = x^3$.
5. $y = -\sqrt{x}$, $y = x - 6$, $y = 0$.
6. $x = y^3$, $x = 3y + 2$.
7. $y = |x|$, $3y - x = 8$.
8. $y = x$, $y = 2x$, $y = 3$.
9. $x + 4 = y^2$, $x = 5$.
10. $x = |y|$, $x = 2$.
11. $y = 2x$, $x + y = 9$, $y = x - 1$.
12. $y = x^3$, $y = x^2 + x - 1$.
13. $y = x^{1/3}$, $y = x^2 + x - 1$.
14. $y = x + 1$, $y + 3x = 13$, $3y + x + 1 = 0$.

Sketch the region bounded by the curves and find its area.

15. $4x = 4y - y^2$, $4x - y = 0$.
16. $x + y^2 - 4 = 0$, $x + y = 2$.
17. $x = y^2$, $x = 3 - 2y^2$.
18. $x + y = 2y^2$, $y = x^3$.
19. $x + y - y^3 = 0$, $x - y + y^2 = 0$.
20. $8x = y^3$, $8x = 2y^3 + y^2 - 2y$.

6.2 ······VOLUME BY PARALLEL CROSS SECTIONS; DISCS AND WASHERS

One way to calculate the volume of a solid is to introduce a coordinate axis and then examine the cross sections of the solid that are perpendicular to that axis. In Figure 6.2.1 we picture a solid and a coordinate axis that we label the x-axis. As in the figure, we suppose that the solid lies entirely between $x = a$ and $x = b$. The figure shows an arbitrary cross section perpendicular to the x-axis. By $A(x)$ we mean the area of the cross section that has coordinate x.

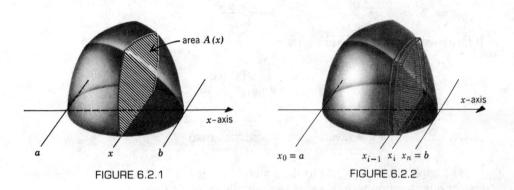

FIGURE 6.2.1   FIGURE 6.2.2

If the cross-sectional area, $A(x)$, varies continuously with x, then we can find the volume of the solid by integrating $A(x)$ from a to b:

(6.2.1)
$$V = \int_a^b A(x)\, dx.$$

To see this, let $P = \{x_0, x_1, \ldots, x_n\}$ be a partition of $[a, b]$. The volume of the solid from x_{i-1} to x_i can be approximated by a product of the form

$$A(x_i^*)\Delta x_i \qquad\qquad \text{(Figure 6.2.2)}$$

with x_i^* chosen arbitrarily from $[x_{i-1}, x_i]$. The volume of the entire solid can therefore be approximated by sums of the form

$$A(x_1^*)\Delta x_1 + A(x_2^*)\Delta x_2 + \cdots + A(x_n^*)\Delta x_n.$$

These are Riemann sums which, as $\|P\| \to 0$, converge to

$$\int_a^b A(x)\, dx.$$

For solids of constant cross-sectional area (such as those of Figure 6.2.3), the volume is simply the cross-sectional area times the thickness:

$$V = (\text{constant cross-sectional area}) \cdot (b - a).$$

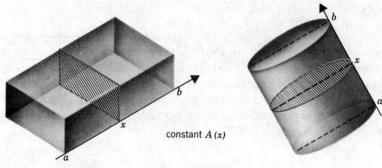

constant $A(x)$

FIGURE 6.2.3

If the cross-sectional area varies, then

$$V = \int_a^b A(x)\, dx,$$

and thus

(6.2.2) $\boxed{V = \text{(average cross-sectional area)} \cdot (b - a).}$ (5.10.1)

The application of (6.2.1) to the general case is left for Chapter 18. Here we restrict our attention to solids with very simple cross sections.

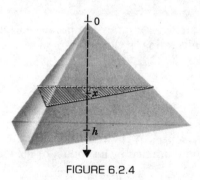

FIGURE 6.2.4

PROBLEM. Find the volume of a triangular pyramid with base area B and height h.

Solution. In Figure 6.2.4 you can see a coordinate line that passes through the apex and is perpendicular to the base. To the apex we assign coordinate 0, and to the base point coordinate h. The cross section at a distance of x units from the apex ($0 \le x \le h$) is a triangle similar to the base triangle. The corresponding sides of these triangles are proportional, the factor of proportionality being x/h. This means that the areas are also proportional, but now the factor of proportionality is $(x/h)^2$.†

———————

† If the base triangle has dimensions a, b, c, then its area is $ab \sin \theta$ where θ is the angle opposite the side of length c. For the x-level triangle the dimensions are $a(x/h)$, $b(x/h)$, $c(x/h)$, and the area is $a(x/h)b(x/h) \sin \theta = ab \sin \theta\, (x/h)^2$.

Thus we have

$$A(x) = B\,\frac{x^2}{h^2} \quad \text{and} \quad V = \int_0^h A(x)\,dx = \frac{B}{h^2}\int_0^h x^2\,dx = \tfrac{1}{3}Bh.$$

This formula was discovered in ancient times. It was known to Eudoxus of Cnidos (408?–355? B.C.). □

PROBLEM. The base of a solid is the region bounded by the ellipse

$$\frac{x^2}{a^2} + \frac{y^2}{b^2} = 1.$$

Find the volume of the solid given that the cross sections perpendicular to the x-axis are equilateral triangles.

FIGURE 6.2.5

Solution. Take x as in Figure 6.2.5. The cross section with coordinate x is an equilateral triangle with side $\overline{PQ}$. The equation of the ellipse can be written

$$y^2 = \frac{b^2}{a^2}(a^2 - x^2).$$

Since

$$\text{length of } \overline{PQ} = 2y = \frac{2b}{a}\sqrt{a^2 - x^2},$$

the equilateral triangle has area

$$A(x) = \frac{\sqrt{3}b^2}{a^2}(a^2 - x^2).\dagger$$

We find the volume of the solid by integrating $A(x)$ from $x = -a$ to $x = a$:

$$V = \int_{-a}^a A(x)\,dx = \frac{\sqrt{3}b^2}{a^2}\int_{-a}^a (a^2 - x^2)\,dx$$

$$= \frac{\sqrt{3}b^2}{a^2}\left[a^2 x - \frac{x^3}{3}\right]_{-a}^a = \frac{\sqrt{3}b^2}{a^2}\left(\frac{4}{3}a^3\right) = \frac{4}{3}\sqrt{3}\,ab^2. \quad \square$$

$\dagger$ In general, the area of an equilateral triangle is $\tfrac{1}{4}\sqrt{3}s^2$, where s is the length of a side.

PROBLEM.   The base of a solid is the region between the parabolas

$$x = y^2 \quad \text{and} \quad x = 3 - 2y^2.$$

Find the volume of the solid given that the cross sections perpendicular to the x-axis are squares.

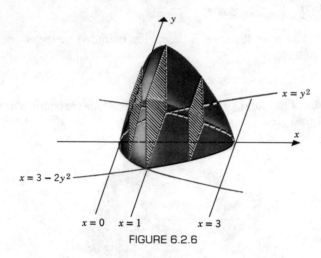

FIGURE 6.2.6

Solution.   The two parabolas intersect at $x = 1$.   (Figure 6.2.6.)   From $x = 0$ to $x = 1$, the cross section with coordinate x has area

$$A(x) = (2y)^2 = 4y^2 = 4x.$$

(Here we are measuring the span across the first parabola $x = y^2$.)   The volume of the solid from $x = 0$ to $x = 1$ is

$$V_1 = \int_0^1 4x \, dx = 4 \left[\tfrac{1}{2} x^2 \right]_0^1 = 2.$$

From $x = 1$ to $x = 3$, the cross section with coordinate x has area

$$A(x) = (2y)^2 = 4y^2 = 2(3 - x).$$

(Here we are measuring the span across the second parabola $x = 3 - 2y^2$.)   The volume of the solid from $x = 1$ to $x = 3$ is

$$V_2 = \int_1^3 2(3 - x) \, dx = 2 \left[-\tfrac{1}{2}(3 - x)^2 \right]_1^3 = 4.$$

The total volume is

$$V_1 + V_2 = 6. \quad \square$$

Solids of Revolution: Disc Method

Suppose that f is nonnegative and continuous on $[a, b]$.   (See Figure 6.2.7.)   If we revolve the region below the graph of f about the x-axis, we obtain a solid.   The

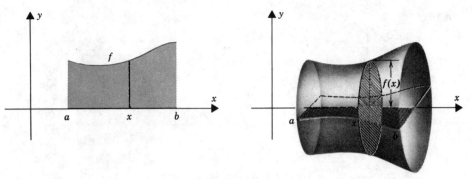

FIGURE 6.2.7

volume of this solid is given by the formula

(6.2.3)
$$V = \int_a^b \pi[f(x)]^2 \, dx.$$

Proof. The cross section with coordinate x is a circular *disc* of radius $f(x)$. The cross-sectional area is thus $\pi[f(x)]^2$. The result follows from Formula 6.2.1. □

As special instances of such solids of revolution we have the cone and the sphere.

EXAMPLE. To generate a cone of base radius r and height h, we can take

$$f(x) = \frac{r}{h} x, \qquad 0 \le x \le h$$

and revolve the region below the graph about the x-axis. Formula 6.2.3 then gives

$$V = \int_0^h \pi \frac{r^2}{h^2} x^2 \, dx = \tfrac{1}{3}\pi r^2 h. \quad □$$

EXAMPLE. A sphere of radius r can be obtained by revolving the region below the graph of

$$f(x) = \sqrt{r^2 - x^2}, \qquad -r \le x \le r$$

about the x-axis. Consequently, we have

$$\text{volume of sphere} = \int_{-r}^{r} \pi(r^2 - x^2) \, dx = \pi \left[r^2 x - \tfrac{1}{3}x^3 \right]_{-r}^{r} = \tfrac{4}{3}\pi r^3.$$

Incidentally, this result was obtained by Archimedes in the third century B.C. □

Solids of Revolution: Washer Method

The washer method is a slight generalization of the disc method. Suppose that f and g are nonnegative continuous functions with $g(x) \le f(x)$ for all x in $[a, b]$. (See Figure

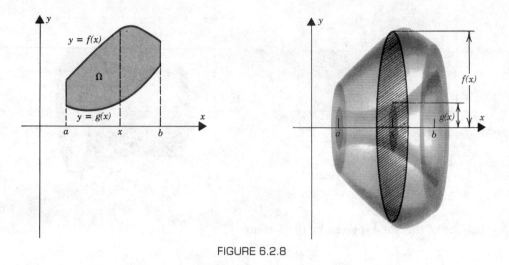

FIGURE 6.2.8

6.2.8.) If we revolve the region the region Ω about the x-axis, we obtain a solid. The volume of this solid is given by the formula

(6.2.4)
$$V = \int_a^b \pi([f(x)]^2 - [g(x)]^2)\, dx.$$
washer method
about x-axis

Proof. The cross section with coordinate x is a *washer* of outer radius $f(x)$, inner radius $g(x)$, and area

$$A(x) = \pi[f(x)]^2 - \pi[g(x)]^2 = \pi([f(x)]^2 - [g(x)]^2).$$

We can therefore get the volume of the solid by integrating this function from a to b. $\square$

Suppose now that the boundaries are functions of y rather than x. (See Figure 6.2.9.) By revolving Ω *about the y-axis,* we obtain a solid. It's clear from (6.2.4) that

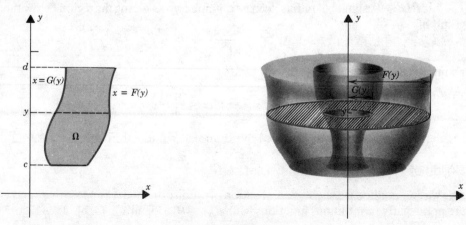

FIGURE 6.2.9

in this case

(6.2.5)

$$V = \int_c^d \pi([F(y)]^2 - [G(y)]^2)\, dy.$$

washer method
about y-axis

PROBLEM. Find the volume of the solid generated by revolving the region between

$$y = x^2 \qquad \text{and} \qquad y = 2x$$

about the x-axis.

Solution. We refer to Figure 6.2.10. For each x from 0 to 2, the x cross section is a washer of outer radius $2x$ and inner radius x^2. By (6.2.4)

$$V = \int_0^2 \pi[(2x)^2 - (x^2)^2]\, dx = \pi \int_0^2 (4x^2 - x^4)\, dx = \pi\left[\tfrac{4}{3}x^3 - \tfrac{1}{5}x^5\right]_0^2 = \frac{64\pi}{15}. \quad \square$$

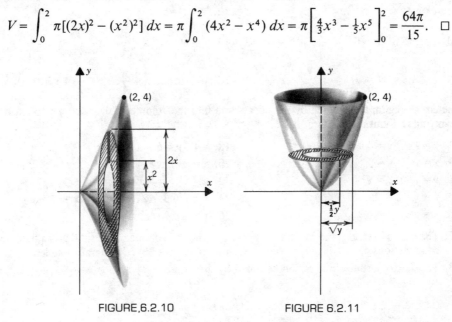

FIGURE 6.2.10   FIGURE 6.2.11

PROBLEM. Find the volume of the solid generated by revolving the region between

$$y = x^2 \qquad \text{and} \qquad y = 2x$$

about the y-axis.

Solution. The solid is depicted in Figure 6.2.11. For each y from 0 to 4, the y cross section is a washer of outer radius $\sqrt{y}$ and inner radius $\tfrac{1}{2}y$. By (6.2.5)

$$V = \int_0^4 \pi[(\sqrt{y})^2 - (\tfrac{1}{2}y)^2]\, dy = \pi \int_0^4 (y - \tfrac{1}{4}y^2)\, dy$$

$$= \pi\left[\tfrac{1}{2}y^2 - \tfrac{1}{12}y^3\right]_0^4 = \frac{8\pi}{3}. \quad \square$$

REMARK. These last two problems concerned solids generated by revolving the *same* region about *different* axes. Notice that the solids are different and have different volumes. This is generally the case. ☐

EXERCISES

Sketch the region Ω bounded by the curves and find the volume of the solid generated by revolving Ω about the x-axis.

1. $y = x$, $y = 0$, $x = 1$.

2. $x + y = 3$, $y = 0$, $x = 0$.

3. $y = x^2$, $y = 9$.

4. $y = x^3$, $y = 8$, $x = 0$.

5. $y = \sqrt{x}$, $y = x^3$.

6. $y = x^2$, $y = x^{1/3}$.

7. $y = x^3$, $x + y = 10$, $y = 1$.

8. $y = \sqrt{x}$, $x + y = 6$, $y = 1$.

9. $y = x^2$, $y = x + 2$.

10. $y = x^2$, $y = 2 - x$.

11. $y = \sqrt{4 - x^2}$, $y = 0$.

12. $y = 1 - |x|$, $y = 0$.

13. $y = \sec x$, $x = 0$, $x = \dfrac{\pi}{4}$, $y = 0$.

14. $y = \csc x$, $x = \dfrac{\pi}{4}$, $x = \dfrac{3\pi}{4}$, $y = 0$.

15. $y = \cos x$, $y = x + 1$, $x = \dfrac{\pi}{2}$.

16. $y = \sin x$, $x = \dfrac{\pi}{4}$, $x = \dfrac{\pi}{2}$, $y = 0$.

Sketch the region Ω bounded by the curves and find the volume of the solid generated by revolving Ω about the y-axis.

17. $y = 2x$, $y = 4$, $x = 0$.

18. $x + 3y = 6$, $x = 0$, $y = 0$.

19. $x = y^3$, $x = 8$, $y = 0$.

20. $x = y^2$, $x = 4$.

21. $y = \sqrt{x}$, $y = x^3$.

22. $y = x^2$, $y = x^{1/3}$.

23. $y = x$, $y = 2x$, $x = 4$.

24. $x + y = 3$, $2x + y = 6$, $x = 0$.

25. $x = y^2$, $x = 2 - y^2$.

26. $x = \sqrt{9 - y^2}$, $x = 0$.

27. The base of a solid is the circle $x^2 + y^2 = r^2$. Find the volume of the solid given that the cross sections perpendicular to the x-axis are (a) squares, (b) equilateral triangles.

28. The base of a solid is the region bounded by the ellipse

$$\frac{x^2}{a^2} + \frac{y^2}{b^2} = 1.$$

Find the volume of the solid given that the cross sections perpendicular to the x-axis are (a) isosceles right triangles each with hypotenuse on the xy-plane, (b) squares, (c) isosceles triangles of height 2.

29. The base of a solid is the region bounded by $y = x^2$ and $y = 4$. Find the volume given that the cross sections perpendicular to the x-axis are (a) squares, (b) semicircles, (c) equilateral triangles.

30. The base of a solid is the region between the parabolas

$$x = y^2 \quad \text{and} \quad x = 3 - 2y^2.$$

Find the volume given that the cross sections perpendicular to the x-axis are (a) rectangles of height h, (b) equilateral triangles, (c) isosceles right triangles each with hypotenuse on the xy-plane.

31. Exercise 29 with the cross sections perpendicular to the y-axis.

32. Exercise 30 with the cross sections perpendicular to the y-axis.

33. Find the volume enclosed by the surface generated by revolving the ellipse

$$\frac{x^2}{a^2} + \frac{y^2}{b^2} = 1$$

about the x-axis.

34. Exercise 33 with the ellipse revolved about the y-axis.

35. Derive a formula for the volume of the frustum of a cone in terms of its height h, the lower base radius R, and the upper base radius r.   (See Figure 6.2.12.)

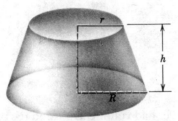

FIGURE 6.2.12

36. Find the volume enclosed by the surface that is generated by revolving the equilateral triangle with vertices $(0, 0)$, $(a, 0)$, $(\frac{1}{2}a, \frac{1}{2}\sqrt{3}a)$ about the x-axis.

37. A hemispheric basin of radius r feet is being used to store water. To what percent of capacity is it filled when the water is (a) $\frac{1}{2}r$ feet deep? (b) $\frac{1}{3}r$ feet deep?

38. A sphere of radius r is cut by two parallel planes: one, a units above the equator; the other, b units above the equator. Find the volume of the portion of the sphere that lies between the two planes. Assume that $a < b$.

39. Find the volume when the region OAB of Figure 6.2.13 is revolved about
    (a) the x-axis.   (b) AB.   (c) CA.   (d) the y-axis.

40. Find the volume when the region OAC of Figure 6.2.13 is revolved about
    (a) the y-axis.   (b) CA.   (c) AB.   (d) the x-axis.

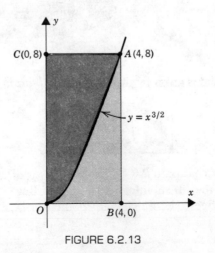

FIGURE 6.2.13

6.3 ······VOLUME BY THE SHELL METHOD

To describe the shell method of computing volumes, we begin with a solid cylinder of radius R and height h, and from it we cut out a cylindrical core of radius r. (Figure 6.3.1.)

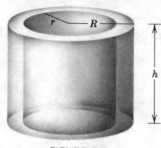

FIGURE 6.3.1

Since the original cylinder had volume $\pi R^2 h$ and the piece removed had volume $\pi r^2 h$, the solid cylindrical shell that remains has volume

(6.3.1) $$\pi R^2 h - \pi r^2 h = \pi h(R + r)(R - r).$$

We'll use this shortly.

Consider now a function f that is nonnegative and continuous on an interval $[a, b]$. For convenience assume that $a \geq 0$. If the region below the graph is revolved about the y-axis, then a solid T is generated. See Figure 6.3.2.

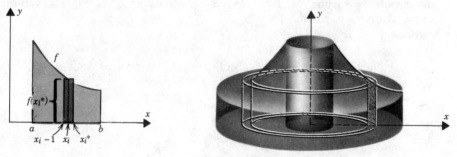

FIGURE 6.3.2

The volume of this solid is given by the *shell method formula*:

(6.3.2) $$V = \int_a^b 2\pi x\, f(x)\, dx.$$

To see this, we take a partition $P = \{x_0, x_1, \ldots, x_n\}$ of $[a, b]$ and concentrate on what's happening on the ith subinterval $[x_{i-1}, x_i]$. Recall that, when we form a Riemann sum, we are free to choose x_i^* as any point from $[x_{i-1}; x_i]$. For convenience we'll take x_i^* as the midpoint $\frac{1}{2}(x_{i-1} + x_i)$. The representative rectangle of height $f(x_i^*)$ and base Δx_i (see Figure 6.3.2) generates a cylindrical shell of height $h = f(x_i^*)$, inner radius $r = x_{i-1}$, and outer radius $R = x_i$. We can calculate the volume of this shell by (6.3.1). Since

$$h = f(x_i^*), \qquad R + r = x_i + x_{i-1} = 2x_i^*, \qquad \text{and} \qquad R - r = \Delta x_i,$$

the volume of this shell is

$$\pi h(R + r)(R - r) = 2\pi x_i^* f(x_i^*)\Delta x_i.$$

The volume of the entire solid can be approximated by adding up the volumes of such shells:

$$V \cong 2\pi x_1^* f(x_1^*)\Delta x_1 + 2\pi x_2^* f(x_2^*)\Delta x_2 + \cdots + 2\pi x_n^* f(x_n^*)\Delta x_n.$$

The sums on the right are Riemann sums which, as $\|P\| \to 0$, converge to

$$\int_a^b 2\pi x \, f(x) \, dx. \quad \square$$

For a geometric interpretation of Formula (6.3.2) we refer to Figure 6.3.3.

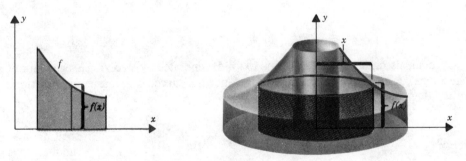

FIGURE 6.3.3

As the region below the graph of f is revolved about the y-axis, the line segment x units from the y-axis generates a cylinder of radius x, height $f(x)$, and lateral area $2\pi x \, f(x)$. The shell method formula

$$V = \int_a^b 2\pi x \, f(x) \, dx$$

expresses the volume of a solid of revolution as the average lateral area of these cylinders times the length of the base interval:

(6.3.3) $V = $ (average lateral area of the cylinders) $\cdot (b - a)$.

The shell method formula can be generalized. With Ω as in Figure 6.3.4, the volume generated by revolving Ω about the y-axis is given by the formula

(6.3.4)
$$V = \int_a^b 2\pi x[f(x) - g(x)]\, dx.$$

shell method
about y-axis

The integrand $2\pi x[f(x) - g(x)]$ is the lateral area of the cylinder shown in Figure 6.3.4.

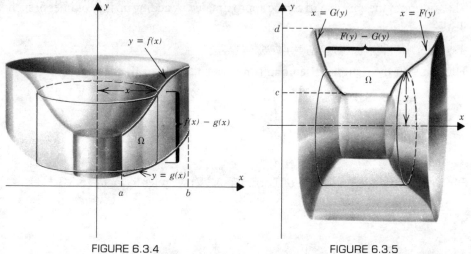

FIGURE 6.3.4   FIGURE 6.3.5

We can also apply the shell method to solids generated by revolving a region about the x-axis. (See Figure 6.3.5.) In this instance the curved boundaries are functions of y rather than x and we have

(6.3.5)
$$V = \int_c^d 2\pi y[F(y) - G(y)]\, dy.$$

shell method
about x-axis

The integrand $2\pi y[F(y) - G(y)]$ is the lateral area of the cylinder shown in Figure 6.3.5.

PROBLEM. Find the volume of the solid generated by revolving the region between

$$y = x^2 \quad \text{and} \quad y = 2x$$

about the y-axis.

Solution. We refer to Figure 6.3.6. For each x from 0 to 2 the line segment x units from the y-axis generates a cylinder of radius x, height $(2x - x^2)$, and lateral area $2\pi x(2x - x^2)$. By (6.3.4)

$$V = \int_0^2 2\pi x(2x - x^2)\, dx = 2\pi \int_0^2 (2x^2 - x^3)\, dx = 2\pi\left[\frac{2}{3}x^3 - \frac{1}{4}x^4\right]_0^2 = \frac{8\pi}{3}. \quad \square$$

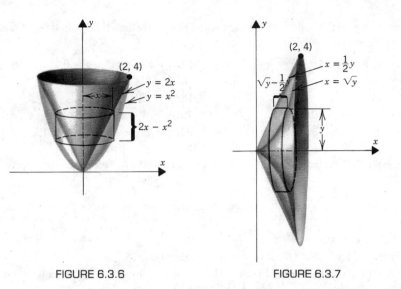

FIGURE 6.3.6   FIGURE 6.3.7

PROBLEM. Find the volume of the solid generated by revolving the region between

$$y = x^2 \quad \text{and} \quad y = 2x$$

about the x-axis.

Solution. We begin by expressing these boundaries as functions of y. We write $x = \sqrt{y}$ for the right boundary and $x = \frac{1}{2}y$ for the left boundary. (See Figure 6.3.7.) The shell of radius y has height $(\sqrt{y} - \frac{1}{2}y)$. Thus, by (6.3.5)

$$V = \int_0^4 2\pi y \left(\sqrt{y} - \frac{1}{2}y \right) dy = \pi \int_0^4 (2y^{3/2} - y^2)\, dy$$

$$= \pi \left[\frac{4}{5}y^{5/2} - \frac{1}{3}y^3 \right]_0^4 = \frac{64\pi}{15}. \quad \square$$

REMARK. In Section 6.2 we calculated the volumes of the same solids (and got the same answers) by the washer method. $\square$

EXERCISES

Sketch the region Ω bounded by the curves and use the shell method to find the volume of the solid generated by revolving Ω about the y-axis.

1. $y = x$, $y = 0$, $x = 1$.
2. $x + y = 3$, $y = 0$, $x = 0$.
3. $y = \sqrt{x}$, $x = 4$, $y = 0$.
4. $y = x^3$, $x = 2$, $y = 0$.
5. $y = \sqrt{x}$, $y = x^3$.
6. $y = x^2$, $y = x^{1/3}$.
7. $y = x$, $y = 2x$, $y = 4$.
8. $y = x$, $y = 1$, $x + y = 6$.
9. $x = y^2$, $x = y + 2$.
10. $x = y^2$, $x = 2 - y$.
11. $x = \sqrt{9 - y^2}$, $y = 0$.
12. $x = |y|$, $x = 2 - y^2$.

Sketch the region Ω bounded by the curves and use the shell method to find the volume of the solid generated by revolving Ω about the x-axis.

13. $x + 3y = 6$, $y = 0$, $x = 0$.   **14.** $y = x$, $y = 5$, $x = 0$.

15. $y = x^2$, $y = 9$.   **16.** $y = x^3$, $y = 8$, $x = 0$.

17. $y = \sqrt{x}$, $y = x^3$.   **18.** $y = x^2$, $y = x^{1/3}$.

19. $y = x^2$, $y = x + 2$.   **20.** $y = x^2$, $y = 2 - x$.

21. $y = x$, $y = 2x$, $x = 4$.   **22.** $y = x$, $x + y = 8$, $x = 1$.

23. $y = \sqrt{1 - x^2}$, $x + y = 1$.   **24.** $y = x^2$, $y = 2 - |x|$.

25. Use the shell method to find the volume enclosed by the surface generated by revolving the ellipse

$$\frac{x^2}{a^2} + \frac{y^2}{b^2} = 1$$

about the y-axis.

26. Exercise 25 with the ellipse revolved about the x-axis.

27. Find the volume enclosed by the surface generated by revolving the equilateral triangle with vertices $(0, 0)$, $(a, 0)$, $(\frac{1}{2}a, \frac{1}{2}\sqrt{3}a)$ about the y-axis.

28. A ball of radius r is cut into two pieces by a horizontal plane a units above the center of the ball. Determine the volume of the upper piece by using the shell method.

29. Carry out Exercise 39 of Section 6.2, this time using the shell method.

30. Carry out Exercise 40 of Section 6.2, this time using the shell method.

6.4 ······ A SUMMARY ON SOLIDS OF REVOLUTION

You may feel that you have been bombarded by a confusing array of formulas for calculating volumes of solids of revolution. Actually, we can boil it all down to two formulas:

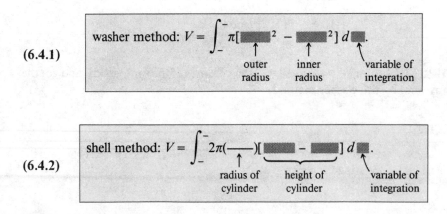

(6.4.1)
$$\text{washer method: } V = \int_{-}^{-} \pi[\quad^2 - \quad^2] \, d\,\blacksquare.$$
outer radius   inner radius   variable of integration

(6.4.2)
$$\text{shell method: } V = \int_{-}^{-} 2\pi(\underbrace{\quad})[\quad - \quad] \, d\,\blacksquare.$$
radius of cylinder   height of cylinder   variable of integration

These formulas can be used even if the axis of revolution is not one of the coordinate axes. For example, let's suppose that the region shown in Figure 6.4.1 is revolved about the line $y = 5$. We'll calculate the volume of the resulting solid of revolution first by the washer method and then by the shell method:

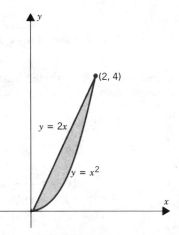

FIGURE 6.4.1

By The Washer Method   Referring to Figure 6.4.2 we see that the outer radius of the washer is $5 - x^2$ and the inner radius is $5 - 2x$. Since x ranges from 0 to 2,

$$V = \int_0^2 \pi[(5 - x^2)^2 - (5 - 2x)^2]\, dx = \frac{136\pi}{15}.$$

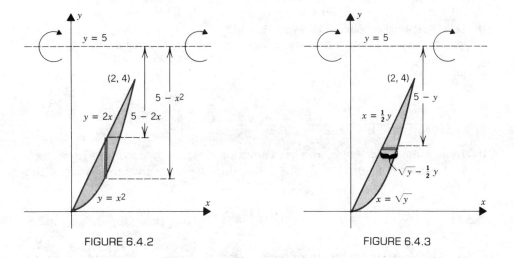

FIGURE 6.4.2   FIGURE 6.4.3

By The Shell Method   Referring to Figure 6.4.3 we see that the radius of the cylinder is $5 - y$ and the height of the shell is $\sqrt{y} - \frac{1}{2}y$. Since y ranges from 0 to 4,

$$V = \int_0^4 2\pi(5 - y)[\sqrt{y} - \tfrac{1}{2}y]\, dy = \frac{136\pi}{15}. \quad \square$$

EXERCISES

Sketch the region Ω bounded by the curves and find the volume of the solid generated by revolving Ω about.

      (a) the x-axis; use the washer method.   (b) the x-axis; use the shell method.
      (c) the y-axis; use the washer method.   (d) the y-axis; use the shell method.

1. $y = \sqrt{x}$, $y = 0$, $x = 4$.   ✓
2. $y = x^3$, $y = 0$, $x = 2$.
3. $y = x^2$, $y = x^{1/3}$.
4. $y = x^3$, $y = \sqrt{x}$.
5. $y = 2x$, $y = 2$, $x = 3$.
6. $y = 3x$, $y = 6$, $x = 1$.
7. $y = x^2 + 2$, $y = 6$, $x = 0$.
8. $y = x^2 + 1$, $y = 1$, $x = 3$.
9. $\sqrt{x} + \sqrt{y} = 1$, $x + y = 1$.
10. $y = \sqrt{1 - x^2}$, $x + y = 1$.
11. $y = x^2$, $x = 1$, $x = 2$.
12. $y = x^{1/3}$, $y = 1$, $x = 8$.
13. $y = x$, $x + y = 6$, $y = 1$.
14. $y = x$, $y = 2x$, $x = 3$.

15. Let Ω be the region bounded by the curves $y = x^3$, $y = 0$, and $x = 2$. Use an integral to represent the volume of the solid generated by revolving Ω about the
    (a) x-axis.   (b) line $x = 2$.   (c) line $x = -2$.
    (d) y-axis.   (e) line $y = 8$.   (f) line $y = -1$.

16. Let Ω be the region bounded by the curves $y = x^2$, $y = 0$, and $x = 2$. Use an integral to represent the volume of the solid generated by revolving Ω about the
    (a) x-axis.   (b) line $x = 2$.   (c) line $x = 4$.
    (d) y-axis.   (e) line $y = 4$.   (f) line $y = -3$.

17. Let Ω be the region bounded by the curves $y = x^2$, $y = 4$, and $x = 3$. Use an integral to represent the volume of the solid generated by revolving Ω about the
    (a) x-axis.   (b) line $x = -1$.   (c) line $x = 4$.
    (d) y-axis.   (e) line $y = 4$.   (f) line $y = 9$.

18. Let Ω be the region bounded by the curves $y = 2x - 3$, $y = 1$, and $x = 4$. Use an integral to represent the volume of the solid generated by revolving Ω about the
    (a) x-axis.   (b) line $x = 1$.   (c) line $x = 4$.
    (d) y-axis.   (e) line $y = -1$.   (f) line $y = 5$.

6.5 ······THE NOTION OF WORK

If an object moves a *distance s* in a fixed direction subject to a *constant force f* applied *in the direction of the motion,* then the *work* done by f is defined in physics by the equation

(6.5.1)

$$W = f \cdot s.$$
           (*work = force · distance*)

If force is measured in pounds and distance in feet, the units of work are foot-pounds: if a constant force of 500 pounds pushes a car for 60 feet, the work done is 30,000 foot-pounds.

    Now let's coordinatize the line of motion assigning coordinate a to the initial position, coordinate b ($b > a$) to the terminal position. The work done by a constant force f applied during the displacement is the product $f \cdot (b - a)$. If the force func-

FIGURE 6.5.1

tion f does not remain constant but instead varies continuously with position x, then the work done by f from $x = a$ to $x = b$ is by definition the *average value of the force function f times the displacement $b - a$*:

(6.5.2)
$$W = \int_a^b f(x)\, dx.$$
(Figure 6.5.1)

Hooke's Law

You can sense a variable force in the action of a steel spring. According to Hooke's law (Robert Hooke, 1635–1703), a spring stretched x units beyond its natural length exerts an elastic force that is proportional to the elongation x:

$$f(x) = kx.$$

The constant k depends on the spring and on the units used.

PROBLEM. A particular spring is found to exert a force of 10 pounds when stretched $\frac{1}{3}$ foot beyond its natural length. What is the work done in stretching the spring $\frac{1}{10}$ foot beyond its natural length? What is the work done in stretching it an additional $\frac{1}{10}$ foot?

Solution. We know that the force function is of the form

$$f(x) = kx.$$

Since $f(\frac{1}{3}) = 10$, we have

$$k \cdot \tfrac{1}{3} = 10,$$

so that $k = 30$. Thus, for this spring, the force function is

$$f(x) = 30x.$$

The work done in the initial stretching is

$$W_1 = \int_0^{1/10} 30x\, dx = 30 \left[\tfrac{1}{2}x^2 \right]_0^{1/10} = \tfrac{3}{20} \text{ foot-pounds.}$$

The work done in the next stretching is

$$W_2 = \int_{1/10}^{2/10} 30x\, dx = 30 \left[\tfrac{1}{2}x^2 \right]_{1/10}^{2/10} = \tfrac{9}{20} \text{ foot-pounds.} \quad \Box$$

Pumping Out a Tank

To lift an object we must counteract the force of gravity. Consequently, the work done in lifting an object is given by the formula

$$\text{work} = (\text{weight of the object}) \cdot (\text{distance lifted}).$$

If we lift a leaking sand bag or pump out a water tank from above, the calculation of work is more complicated. In the first instance the weight varies during the motion. (There's less sand in the bag as we keep lifting.) In the second instance the distance varies. (Water at the top of the tank doesn't have to be pumped as far as water at the bottom.) The sand bag problem is left to the exercises. Here we take up the second problem.

Figure 6.5.2 depicts a storage tank filled to within a feet of the top with some liquid, not necessarily water. Assume that the liquid is homogeneous and weighs σ pounds per cubic foot. Suppose now that this storage tank is pumped out from above until the level of the liquid drops to b feet below the top of the tank. How much work has been done?

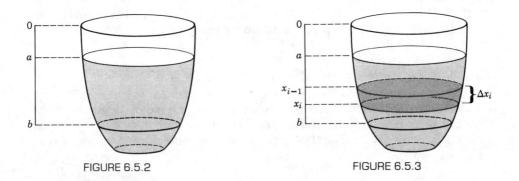

FIGURE 6.5.2   FIGURE 6.5.3

We can answer this question by the methods of integral calculus. For each $x \in [a, b]$, we let

$$A(x) = \text{cross-sectional area } x \text{ feet below the top of the tank,}$$

$$s(x) = \text{distance that the } x\text{-level must be lifted.}$$

We let $P = \{x_0, x_1, \ldots, x_n\}$ be an arbitrary partition of $[a, b]$ and focus our attention on the ith subinterval $[x_{i-1}, x_i]$. (Figure 6.5.3.) Taking x_i^* as an arbitrary point in the ith subinterval, we have

$$A(x_i^*)\Delta x_i = \text{approximate volume of the } i\text{th layer of liquid,}$$

$$\sigma A(x_i^*)\Delta x_i = \text{approximate weight of this volume,}$$

$$s(x_i^*) = \text{approximate distance this weight is to be moved,}$$

and therefore

$$\sigma s(x_i^*)A(x_i^*)\Delta x_i = \text{approximate work (weight} \times \text{distance) required to}$$
$$\text{pump this layer of liquid to the top of the tank.}$$

The work required to pump out all the liquid can be approximated by adding up all these last terms:

$$W \cong \sigma s(x_1^*)A(x_1^*)\Delta x_1 + \sigma s(x_2^*)A(x_2^*)\Delta x_2 + \cdots + \sigma s(x_n^*)A(x_n^*)\Delta x_n.$$

The sums on the right are Riemann sums which, as $\|P\| \to 0$, converge to give

(6.5.3)
$$W = \int_a^b \sigma s(x)A(x)\, dx. \qquad \square$$

We use this formula in the next problem.

PROBLEM. A hemispherical water tank of radius 10 feet is being pumped out. Find the work done in lowering the water level from 2 feet below the top of the tank to 4 feet below the top of the tank given that the pump is placed (a) at the top of the tank, (b) 3 feet above the top of the tank.

Solution. As the weight of water take 62.5 pounds per cubic foot. It's not hard to see that the cross section x feet from the top of the tank is a disc of radius $\sqrt{100 - x^2}$. Its area is therefore

$$A(x) = \pi(100 - x^2).$$

For part (a) we have $s(x) = x$, so that

$$W = \int_2^4 62.5\pi x(100 - x^2)\, dx = 33{,}750\pi \text{ foot-pounds.}$$

For part (b) we have $s(x) = x + 3$, so that

$$W = \int_2^4 62.5\pi(x + 3)(100 - x^2)\, dx = 67{,}750\pi \text{ foot-pounds.} \qquad \square$$

EXERCISES

1. A weight of 200 pounds stretches a certain spring 4 feet beyond its natural length. Find the work done in stretching the spring (a) 1 foot beyond its natural length, (b) $1\frac{1}{2}$ feet beyond its natural length.

2. A certain spring has natural length l. Given that W is the work done in stretching the spring from l feet to $l + a$ feet, find the work done in stretching the spring (a) from l feet to $l + 2a$ feet, (b) from l feet to $l + na$ feet, (c) from $l + a$ feet to $l + 2a$ feet, (d) from $l + a$ feet to $l + na$ feet.

3. Find the natural length of a heavy metal spring, given that the work done in stretching it from a length of 2 feet to a length of 3 feet is one-half the work done in stretching it from a length of 3 feet to a length of 4 feet.

4. A vertical cylindrical tank of radius 2 feet and height 6 feet is full of water. Find the work done in pumping out the water (a) to an outlet at the top of the tank, (b) to a level 5 feet above the top of the tank. (Assume that the water weighs 62.5 pounds per cubic foot.)

5. A horizontal cylindrical tank of radius 3 feet and length 8 feet is half full of oil weighing 60 pounds per cubic foot. What is the work done in pumping out the oil (a) to the top of the tank, (b) to a level 4 feet above the top of the tank?

6. What is the work done by gravity if the tank of Exercise 5 is completely drained through an opening at the bottom?

7. A conical container (vertex down) of radius r feet and height h feet is full of a liquid weighing σ pounds per cubic foot. Find the work done in pumping out the top $\frac{1}{2}h$ feet of liquid (a) to the top of the tank, (b) to a level k feet above the top of the tank.

8. What is the work done by gravity if the tank of Exercise 7 is completely drained through an opening at the bottom?

9. The force of gravity exerted by the earth on a mass m at a distance r from the center of the earth is given by Newton's formula

$$F = -G\frac{mM}{r^2}$$

where M is the mass of the earth and G is a gravitational constant. Find the work done by gravity in pulling a mass m from $r = r_1$ to $r = r_2$.

10. A box that weighs w pounds is dropped to the floor from a height of d feet. (a) What is the work done by gravity? (b) Show that the work is the same if the box slides to the floor along a smooth inclined plane.

11. A 100-pound bag of sand is lifted for 2 seconds at the rate of 4 feet per second. Find the work done in lifting the bag if the sand leaks out at the rate of $1\frac{1}{2}$ pounds per second.

12. A water container initially weighing w pounds is hoisted by a crane at the rate of n feet per second. What is the work done if the tank is raised m feet and the water leaks out constantly at the rate of p gallons per second? (Assume that the water weighs 8.3 pounds per gallon.)

13. A rope of length l feet that weighs σ pounds per foot is lying on the ground. What is the work done in lifting the rope so that it hangs from a beam (a) l feet high, (b) $2l$ feet high?

14. A load of weight w is lifted from the bottom of a shaft h feet deep. Find the work done given that the rope used to hoist the load weighs σ pounds per foot.

15. An 800-pound steel beam hangs from a 50-foot cable which weighs 6 pounds per foot. Find the work done in winding 20 feet of the cable about a steel drum.

6.6 ······FLUID PRESSURE

Here we take up the study of fluid pressure and discuss how to calculate the force exerted by a fluid on a vertical wall. By pressure we mean *force per unit area*.

When a horizontal surface is submerged in a liquid, the force against it is the total weight of the fluid *above it*. If the horizontal surface has area A, if the depth is h, and if the density of the fluid is σ, then the force is given by the formula

(6.6.1) $\boxed{f = \sigma h A.}$

In this discussion we'll measure area in square feet, depth in feet, and density in pounds per cubic foot. The force is then expressed in pounds.

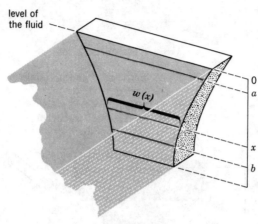

level of
the fluid

$w(x)$

0
a

x

b

FIGURE 6.6.1

In Figure 6.6.1 we have represented a vertical wall. By $w(x)$ we mean the width of the wall at depth x. To determine the force exerted on the wall by the fluid from depth a to depth b, we let $P = \{x_0, x_1, \ldots, x_n\}$ be a partition of $[a, b]$ and focus our attention on the portion of the wall that corresponds to the ith subinterval $[x_{i-1}, x_i]$. (See Figure 6.6.2.) With pressure the same in all directions (the physicists tell us that this is correct, and the skin diver confirms it), we can estimate the force against this ith strip. Taking x_i^* as an arbitrary point in the ith subinterval, we have

$$w(x_i^*) = \text{approximate width of the } i\text{th strip,}$$
$$w(x_i^*)\Delta x_i = \text{approximate area of this strip}$$

and by (6.6.1)

$$\sigma x_i^* w(x_i^*)\Delta x_i = \text{approximate force exerted by this strip.}$$

The force exerted by all the fluid can be approximated by adding up all these terms:

$$f \cong \sigma x_1^* w(x_1^*)\Delta x_1 + \sigma x_2^* w(x_2^*)\Delta x_2 + \cdots + \sigma x_n^* w(x_n^*)\Delta x_n.$$

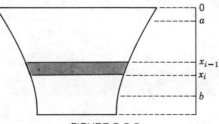

0
a

x_{i-1}
x_i

b

FIGURE 6.6.2

The sums on the right are Riemann sums which, as $\|P\| \to 0$, converge to give

(6.6.2)
$$f = \int_a^b \sigma x w(x)\, dx. \qquad \square$$

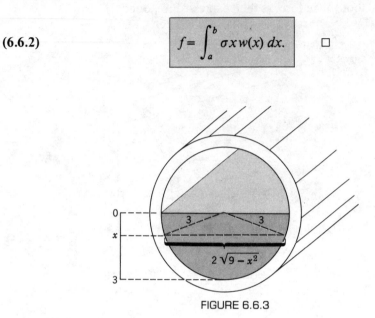

FIGURE 6.6.3

PROBLEM. A circular water main (Figure 6.6.3) 6 feet in diameter is capped when half full of water. What is the force of the water against the cap?

Solution. Here

$$w(x) = 2\sqrt{9 - x^2} \quad \text{and} \quad \sigma = 62.5 \text{ pounds per cubic foot.}$$

The force exerted against the cap is

$$f = \int_0^3 (62.5)x(2\sqrt{9 - x^2})\, dx = 62.5 \int_0^3 2x\sqrt{9 - x^2}\, dx = 1125 \text{ pounds.} \qquad \square$$

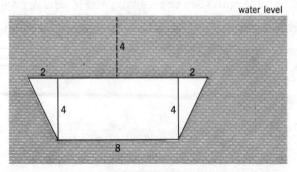

FIGURE 6.6.4

PROBLEM. The trapezoidal gate of a dam is shown in Figure 6.6.4. Find the force on the gate when the surface of the water is 4 feet above the top of the gate.

Solution. First we find the width of the gate x feet below the water level. By similar triangles (see Figure 6.6.5)

$$t = \tfrac{1}{2}(8 - x) \quad \text{so that} \quad w(x) = 8 + 2t = 16 - x.$$

The force against the gate is

$$f = \int_4^8 62.5x(16 - x)\, dx = 14{,}666\tfrac{2}{3} \text{ pounds.} \quad \square$$

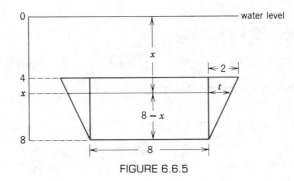

FIGURE 6.6.5

EXERCISES

1. Each end of a horizontal oil tank is an ellipse with horizontal axis 12 feet long and vertical axis 6 feet long. Calculate the force on one end when the tank is half full of oil weighing 60 pounds per cubic foot.

2. Each vertical end of a vat is a segment of a parabola (vertex down) 8 feet across the top and 16 feet deep. Calculate the force on an end when the vat is full of liquid weighing 70 pounds per cubic foot.

3. The vertical ends of a water trough are isosceles right triangles with the 90° angle at the bottom. Calculate the force on each triangle when the trough is full of water given that the legs of the triangle are 8 feet long.

4. The vertical ends of a water trough are isosceles triangles 5 feet across the top and 5 feet deep. Calculate the force on an end when the trough is full of water.

5. A horizontal cylindrical tank of diameter 8 feet is half full of oil weighing 60 pounds per cubic foot. Calculate the force on one end.

6. Calculate the force on one end if the tank of Exercise 5 is full.

7. A rectangular gate in a vertical dam is 10 feet wide and 6 feet high. (a) Find the force on the gate when the level of the water is 8 feet above the top of the gate. (b) How much higher must the water rise to double the force found in (a)?

8. A vertical cylindrical tank of diameter 30 feet and height 50 feet is full of oil weighing 60 pounds per cubic foot. Find the force on the curved surface.

6.7 CHAPTER SUMMARY

6.1 More on Area

representative rectangle (p. 305)
area by integration with respect to y (p. 306)

6.2 Volume by Parallel Cross Sections; Discs and Washers

volume by parallel cross sections (p. 309)
disc method (p. 313)
washer method (x-axis) (p. 314)
washer method (y-axis) (p. 315)

6.3 Volume by the Shell Method

shell method (y-axis) (p. 320)   shell method (x-axis) (p. 320)

6.4 A Summary on Solids of Revolution

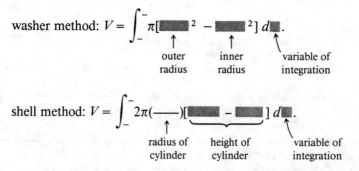

washer method: $V = \int_{-}^{-} \pi[\,\rule{1cm}{0.2cm}\,^2 - \,\rule{1cm}{0.2cm}\,^2]\, d\rule{0.3cm}{0.2cm}$.

outer radius   inner radius   variable of integration

shell method: $V = \int_{-}^{-} 2\pi(\,\rule{0.8cm}{0.02cm}\,)[\,\rule{1cm}{0.2cm}\, - \,\rule{0.8cm}{0.2cm}\,]\, d\rule{0.3cm}{0.2cm}$.

radius of cylinder   height of cylinder   variable of integration

6.5 The Notion of Work

Hooke's law (p. 325)   pumping out a tank (p. 327)

6.6 Fluid Pressure

force exerted by a fluid (p. 330)

The Transcendental Functions

If B is a positive number different from 1, the logarithm to the base B is defined in elementary mathematics by setting

$$C = \log_B A \quad \text{iff} \quad B^C = A.$$

Generally the base 10 is chosen and the defining relation becomes

$$C = \log_{10} A \quad \text{iff} \quad 10^C = A.$$

The basic properties of $\log_{10}$ can then be summarized as follows:

(a) $\log_{10}(XY) = \log_{10} X + \log_{10} Y.$ $(X > 0,\ Y > 0)$
(b) $\log_{10} 1 = 0.$
(c) $\log_{10}(1/Y) = -\log_{10} Y.$ $(Y > 0)$
(d) $\log_{10}(X/Y) = \log_{10} X - \log_{10} Y.$ $(X > 0,\ Y > 0)$
(e) $\log_{10} X^Y = Y \log_{10} X.$ $(X > 0)$
(f) $\log_{10} 10 = 1.$

This elementary notion of logarithm is inadequate for calculus. It is unclear: what is meant by 10^C if C is irrational? It does not lend itself well to the methods of calculus: how would you differentiate $Y = \log_{10} X$ knowing only that $10^Y = X$?

Here we take an entirely different approach to logarithms. Instead of trying to tamper with the elementary definition, we discard it altogether. From our point of view the fundamental property of logarithms is that they transform multiplication into addition:

$$\text{the log of a product} = \text{the sum of the logs.}$$

Taking this as the central idea we are led to a general notion of logarithm that encompasses the elementary notion, lends itself well to the methods of calculus, and leads us naturally to a choice of base that simplifies many calculations.

DEFINITION 7.1.1

A *logarithm* function is a nonconstant differentiable function f defined on the set of positive numbers such that for all $x > 0$ and $y > 0$

$$f(xy) = f(x) + f(y).$$

Let's assume for the time being that such logarithm functions exist, and let's see what we can find out about them. In the first place, if f is such a function, then

$$f(1) = f(1 \cdot 1) = f(1) + f(1) = 2f(1)$$

and so

$$f(1) = 0.$$

Taking $y > 0$, we have

$$0 = f(1) = f(y \cdot 1/y) = f(y) + f(1/y)$$

and therefore

$$f(1/y) = -f(y).$$

Taking $x > 0$ and $y > 0$, we have

$$f(x/y) = f(x \cdot 1/y) = f(x) + f(1/y),$$

which, in view of the previous result, means that

$$f(x/y) = f(x) - f(y).$$

We are now ready to look for the derivative. (Remember, we are *assuming* that f is differentiable.) We begin by forming the difference quotient

$$\frac{f(x + h) - f(x)}{h}.$$

From what we have discovered about f,

$$f(x + h) - f(x) = f\left(\frac{x + h}{x}\right) = f(1 + h/x),$$

and therefore

$$\frac{f(x + h) - f(x)}{h} = \frac{f(1 + h/x)}{h}.$$

Remembering that $f(1) = 0$ and multiplying the denominator by x/x, we have

$$\frac{f(x+h) - f(x)}{h} = \frac{1}{x}\left[\frac{f(1 + h/x) - f(1)}{h/x}\right].$$

As h tends to 0, the left side tends to $f'(x)$, and, while $1/x$ remains fixed, h/x tends to 0 and thus the bracketed expression tends to $f'(1)$. In short,

(7.1.2) $$\boxed{f'(x) = \frac{1}{x}f'(1).}$$

We have now established that, if f is a logarithm, then

$$f(1) = 0 \quad \text{and} \quad f'(x) = \frac{1}{x}f'(1).$$

We can't have $f'(1) = 0$ for that would make f constant. (Explain.) The most natural alternative is to set $f'(1) = 1$.† The derivative is then $1/x$.

This function, which takes on the value 0 at 1 and has derivative $1/x$ for $x > 0$, must, by the fundamental theorem of integral calculus, take the form

$$\int_1^x \frac{dt}{t}. \qquad \text{(check this out)}$$

7.2 ······THE LOGARITHM FUNCTION, PART I

> **DEFINITION 7.2.1**
>
> The function
>
> $$L(x) = \int_1^x \frac{dt}{t}, \qquad x > 0$$
>
> is called the (*natural*) *logarithm function.*

Here are some obvious properties of L:

(1) L is defined on $(0, \infty)$ with derivative

$$L'(x) = \frac{1}{x} \qquad \text{for all } x > 0.$$

L' is positive on $(0, \infty)$, and therefore L is an increasing function.

(2) L is continuous on $(0, \infty)$ since it is there differentiable.

(3) For $x > 1$, $L(x)$ gives the area of the region shaded in Figure 7.2.1.

(4) $L(x)$ is negative if $0 < x < 1$, zero at $x = 1$, positive if $x > 1$.

————

† This, as you'll see later, is tantamount to a choice of base.

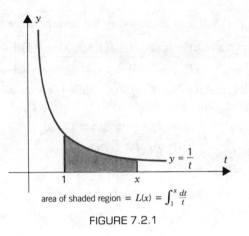

area of shaded region $= L(x) = \int_1^x \frac{dt}{t}$

FIGURE 7.2.1

The following result is fundamental.

THEOREM 7.2.2

If x and y are positive, then

$$L(xy) = L(x) + L(y).$$

Proof

$$L(xy) = \int_1^{xy} \frac{dt}{t} = \int_1^x \frac{dt}{t} + \int_x^{xy} \frac{dt}{t}.$$

Since

$$L(x) = \int_1^x \frac{dt}{t},$$

we need only show that

$$L(y) = \int_x^{xy} \frac{dt}{t}.$$

To do this, set

$$xu = t, \qquad x\,du = dt.$$

At $t = x$, $u = 1$ and at $t = xy$, $u = y$. Thus

$$\int_x^{xy} \frac{dt}{t} = \int_1^y \frac{x\,du}{xu} = \int_1^y \frac{du}{u} = L(y). \quad \square$$

We come now to another important result.

THEOREM 7.2.3

If x is positive and p/q is rational, then

$$L(x^{p/q}) = \frac{p}{q} L(x).$$

Proof. Since

$$\frac{d}{dx}(L(x^{p/q})) = \frac{d}{dx}\left(\int_1^{x^{p/q}} \frac{dt}{t}\right) = \left(\frac{1}{x^{p/q}}\right)\left(\frac{p}{q} x^{(p/q)-1}\right) = \frac{p}{qx}$$

by (5.9.7) ⟶

and

$$\frac{d}{dx}\left(\frac{p}{q} L(x)\right) = \frac{p}{q}\frac{d}{dx}(L(x)) = \left(\frac{p}{q}\right)\left(\frac{1}{x}\right) = \frac{p}{qx},$$

we know (from Theorem 4.2.4) that the two expressions differ by a constant:

$$L(x^{p/q}) = \frac{p}{q} L(x) + C.$$

The constant C is 0 since

$$L(1^{p/q}) = L(1) = 0 \quad \text{and} \quad \frac{p}{q} L(1) = 0. \quad \square$$

The domain of L is $(0, \infty)$. What is the range of L?

THEOREM 7.2.4

The range of L is $(-\infty, \infty)$.

Proof. Since L is continuous on $(0, \infty)$, we know from the intermediate-value theorem that it "skips" no values. Thus, its range is an interval. To show that the interval is $(-\infty, \infty)$, we need only show that it is unbounded above and unbounded below. We can do this by taking M as an arbitrary positive number and showing that L takes on values greater than M and values less than $-M$.

Since

$$L(2) = \int_1^2 \frac{dt}{t}$$

is positive (explain), we know that some positive multiple of $L(2)$ must be greater than M; namely, we know that there exists a positive integer n such that

$$nL(2) > M.$$

Multiplying this equation by -1 we have

$$-nL(2) < -M.$$

Since

$$nL(2) = L(2^n) \quad \text{and} \quad -nL(2) = L(2^{-n}),$$

we have

$$L(2^n) > M \quad \text{and} \quad L(2^{-n}) < -M.$$

This proves the unboundedness.   □

The Number e

Since the range of L is $(-\infty, \infty)$ and L is an increasing function, we know that L takes on every value and does so only once. In particular, there is one and only one number at which the function L takes on the value 1. *This unique number is denoted by the letter e.*†

Since

(7.2.5)
$$L(e) = \int_1^e \frac{dt}{t} = 1,$$

it follows from Theorem 7.2.3 that

(7.2.6)
$$L(e^{p/q}) = \frac{p}{q} \quad \text{for all rational numbers } \frac{p}{q}.$$

Because of this relation, we call L *the logarithm to the base e* and sometimes write

$$L(x) = \log_e x.$$

The number e arises naturally in many settings. Accordingly, we call $L(x)$ the natural logarithm and write

(7.2.7)
$$L(x) = \ln x. \quad ^{††}$$

----

† After the Swiss mathematician Leonhard Euler (1707–1783), considered by many the greatest mathematician of the eighteenth century.

†† Logarithms to bases other than e will be taken up later [they arise by other choices of $f'(1)$], but by far the most important logarithm in calculus is the logarithm to the base e. So much so, that when we speak of the logarithm of a number x and don't specify the base, you can be sure that we are talking about the *natural logarithm* $\ln x$.

Here are the basic properties we have established for ln x:

(7.2.8)

$$\ln 1 = 0, \qquad \ln e = 1.$$
$$\ln xy = \ln x + \ln y. \qquad\qquad (x > 0, y > 0)$$
$$\ln 1/x = -\ln x. \qquad\qquad\qquad (x > 0)$$
$$\ln x/y = \ln x - \ln y. \qquad\qquad (x > 0, y > 0)$$
$$\ln x^r = r \ln x. \qquad\qquad (x > 0, r \text{ rational})$$

Notice how closely these rules parallel the familiar rules for common logarithms (base 10). Later we'll show that the last of these rules also holds for irrational exponents.

The Graph of the Logarithm Function

You know that the logarithm function

$$\ln x = \int_1^x \frac{dt}{t}$$

has domain $(0, \infty)$, range $(-\infty, \infty)$, and derivative

$$\frac{d}{dx}(\ln x) = \frac{1}{x} > 0.$$

For small x the derivative is large (near 0 the curve is steep); for large x the derivative is small (far out the curve flattens out). At $x = 1$ the logarithm is 0 and its derivative $1/x$ is 1. (The graph crosses the x-axis at the point $(1, 0)$, and the tangent line at that point is parallel to the line $y = x$.) The second derivative

$$\frac{d^2}{dx^2}(\ln x) = -\frac{1}{x^2}$$

is negative on $(0, \infty)$. (The graph is concave down throughout.) We have sketched the graph in Figure 7.2.2. The y-axis is a vertical asymptote:

$$\text{as } x \to 0^+, \quad \ln x \to -\infty.$$

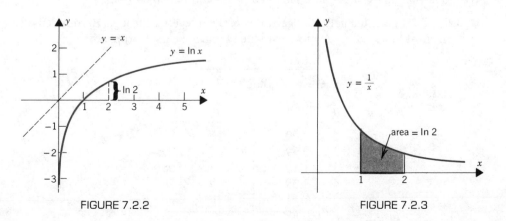

FIGURE 7.2.2   FIGURE 7.2.3

PROBLEM. Estimate ln 2.

Solution

$$\ln 2 = \int_1^2 \frac{dt}{t}. \qquad \text{(Figure 7.2.3)}$$

We can estimate the integral by upper and lower sums. Using the partition

$$P = \{1 = \tfrac{10}{10}, \tfrac{11}{10}, \tfrac{12}{10}, \tfrac{13}{10}, \tfrac{14}{10}, \tfrac{15}{10}, \tfrac{16}{10}, \tfrac{17}{10}, \tfrac{18}{10}, \tfrac{19}{10}, \tfrac{20}{10} = 2\},$$

we have

$$L_f(P) = \tfrac{1}{10}(\tfrac{10}{11} + \tfrac{10}{12} + \tfrac{10}{13} + \tfrac{10}{14} + \tfrac{10}{15} + \tfrac{10}{16} + \tfrac{10}{17} + \tfrac{10}{18} + \tfrac{10}{19} + \tfrac{10}{20})$$
$$= \tfrac{1}{11} + \tfrac{1}{12} + \tfrac{1}{13} + \tfrac{1}{14} + \tfrac{1}{15} + \tfrac{1}{16} + \tfrac{1}{17} + \tfrac{1}{18} + \tfrac{1}{19} + \tfrac{1}{20}$$

and

$$U_f(P) = \tfrac{1}{10}(\tfrac{10}{10} + \tfrac{10}{11} + \tfrac{10}{12} + \tfrac{10}{13} + \tfrac{10}{14} + \tfrac{10}{15} + \tfrac{10}{16} + \tfrac{10}{17} + \tfrac{10}{18} + \tfrac{10}{19})$$
$$= \tfrac{1}{10} + \tfrac{1}{11} + \tfrac{1}{12} + \tfrac{1}{13} + \tfrac{1}{14} + \tfrac{1}{15} + \tfrac{1}{16} + \tfrac{1}{17} + \tfrac{1}{18} + \tfrac{1}{19}.$$

Here a hand calculator can come in handy. After determining that

$$\tfrac{1}{10} = 0.100 \qquad 0.062 < \tfrac{1}{16} < 0.063$$
$$0.090 < \tfrac{1}{11} < 0.091 \qquad 0.058 < \tfrac{1}{17} < 0.059$$
$$0.083 < \tfrac{1}{12} < 0.084 \qquad 0.055 < \tfrac{1}{18} < 0.056$$
$$0.076 < \tfrac{1}{13} < 0.077 \qquad 0.052 < \tfrac{1}{19} < 0.053$$
$$0.071 < \tfrac{1}{14} < 0.072 \qquad 0.050 = \tfrac{1}{20}$$
$$0.066 < \tfrac{1}{15} < 0.067$$

you can see after a little addition that

$$0.663 < L_f(P) < \ln 2 < U_f(P) < 0.722.$$

The average of these two estimates is

$$\tfrac{1}{2}(0.663 + 0.722) = 0.6925.$$

We are not far off. Three-place tables carry the estimate 0.693. □

Table 7.2.1 gives the natural logarithms of the integers 2 through 10 rounded off to the nearest hundredth. A more extended table appears in Appendix C.

TABLE 7.2.1

n	$\ln n$	n	$\ln n$
1	0.00	6	1.79
2	0.69	7	1.95
3	1.10	8	2.08
4	1.39	9	2.20
5	1.61	10	2.30

PROBLEM. Use Table 7.2.1 to estimate the following logarithms:

(a) ln 0.2.   (b) ln 0.25.   (c) ln 2.4.   (d) ln 90.

Solution

(a) $\ln 0.2 = \ln \frac{1}{5} = -\ln 5 \cong -1.61$.

(b) $\ln 0.25 = \ln \frac{1}{4} = -\ln 4 \cong -1.39$.

(c) $\ln 2.4 = \ln \dfrac{12}{5} = \ln \dfrac{(3)(4)}{5} = \ln 3 + \ln 4 - \ln 5 \cong 0.88$.

(d) $\ln 90 = \ln [(9)(10)] = \ln 9 + \ln 10 \cong 4.50$. $\square$

PROBLEM. Use Table 7.2.1 to estimate e.

Solution. So far all we know is that $\ln e = 1$. From the table you can see that

$$3 \ln 3 - \ln 10 \cong 1.$$

The expression on the left can be written

$$\ln 3^3 - \ln 10 = \ln 27 - \ln 10 = \ln \tfrac{27}{10} = \ln 2.7.$$

With $\ln 2.7 \cong 1$ we have $e \cong 2.7$. (Eight-place tables give the estimate $e \cong 2.71828182$. For most purposes we take $e \cong 2.72$.) $\square$

EXERCISES

Use Table 7.2.1 to estimate the following natural logarithms.

1. ln 20.	**2.** ln 16.	**3.** ln 1.6.	**4.** ln 3^4.
5. ln 0.1.	**6.** ln 2.5.	**7.** ln 7.2.	**8.** ln $\sqrt{630}$.
9. ln $\sqrt{2}$.	**10.** ln 0.4.	**11.** ln 2^5.	**12.** ln 1.8.

13. Interpret the equation

$$\ln n = \ln mn - \ln m$$

in terms of area under the curve $y = 1/x$. Draw a figure.

14. Given that $0 < x < 1$, express as a logarithm the area under the curve $y = 1/t$ from $t = x$ to $t = 1$.

15. Estimate

$$\ln 1.5 = \int_1^{1.5} \frac{dt}{t}$$

using the approximation

$$\tfrac{1}{2}[L_f(P) + U_f(P)] \quad \text{with} \quad P = \{1 = \tfrac{8}{8}, \tfrac{9}{8}, \tfrac{10}{8}, \tfrac{11}{8}, \tfrac{12}{8} = 1.5\}.$$

16. Estimate

$$\ln 2.5 = \int_1^{2.5} \frac{dt}{t}$$

using the approximation

$$\tfrac{1}{2}[L_f(P) + U_f(P)] \quad \text{with} \quad P = \{1 = \tfrac{4}{4}, \tfrac{5}{4}, \tfrac{6}{4}, \tfrac{7}{4}, \tfrac{8}{4}, \tfrac{9}{4}, \tfrac{10}{4} = \tfrac{5}{2}\}.$$

17. Taking $\ln 5 \cong 1.61$, use differentials to estimate
  (a) $\ln 5.2$.   (b) $\ln 4.8$.   (c) $\ln 5.5$.
18. Taking $\ln 10 \cong 2.30$, use differentials to estimate
  (a) $\ln 10.3$.   (b) $\ln 9.6$.   (c) $\ln 11$.

Solve the following equations for x.

19. $\ln x = 2$.

20. $\ln x = -1$.

21. $(2 - \ln x) \ln x = 0$.

22. $\frac{1}{2} \ln x = \ln (2x - 1)$.

23. $\ln [(2x + 1)(x + 2)] = 2 \ln (x + 2)$.

24. $2 \ln (x + 2) - \frac{1}{2} \ln x^4 = 1$.

7.3 ·····THE LOGARITHM FUNCTION, PART II

Differentiation and Graphing

We know that for $x > 0$

$$\frac{d}{dx} [\ln x] = \frac{1}{x}.$$

If u is a positive differentiable function of x, then by the chain rule

$$\frac{d}{dx} [\ln u] = \frac{d}{du} [\ln u] \frac{du}{dx} = \frac{1}{u} \frac{du}{dx}.$$

Thus, for example,

$$\frac{d}{dx} [\ln (1 + x^2)] = \frac{1}{1 + x^2} \cdot 2x = \frac{2x}{1 + x^2} \qquad \text{for all real } x$$

and

$$\frac{d}{dx} [\ln (1 + 3x)] = \frac{1}{1 + 3x} \cdot 3 = \frac{3}{1 + 3x} \qquad \text{for all } x > -\frac{1}{3}.$$

PROBLEM. Find the domain of f and find $f'(x)$ if

$$f(x) = \ln (x\sqrt{1 + 3x}).$$

Solution. For x to be in the domain of f, we must have $x\sqrt{1 + 3x} > 0$, and conse-quently, $x > 0$. The domain is the set of positive numbers.

Before differentiating f, we make use of the special properties of the logarithm:

$$f(x) = \ln (x\sqrt{1 + 3x}) = \ln x + \ln [(1 + 3x)^{1/2}] = \ln x + \frac{1}{2} \ln (1 + 3x).$$

From this we have

$$f'(x) = \frac{1}{x} + \frac{1}{2} \left(\frac{3}{1 + 3x} \right). \quad \square$$

PROBLEM. Sketch the graph of

$$f(x) = \ln |x|.$$

Solution. This is an even function, $f(-x) = f(x)$, defined for all numbers $x \neq 0$. The graph has two branches:

$$y = \ln(-x), \quad x < 0 \qquad \text{and} \qquad y = \ln x, \quad x > 0.$$

Each branch is the mirror image of the other. (Figure 7.3.1) □

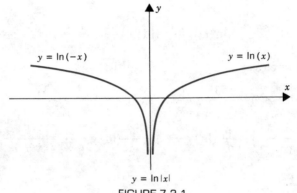

FIGURE 7.3.1

PROBLEM. Show that

(7.3.1) $$\frac{d}{dx}(\ln|x|) = \frac{1}{x} \qquad \text{for all } x \neq 0.$$

Solution. For $x > 0$,

$$\frac{d}{dx}(\ln|x|) = \frac{d}{dx}(\ln x) = \frac{1}{x}.$$

For $x < 0$, we have $|x| = -x > 0$, so that

$$\frac{d}{dx}(\ln|x|) = \frac{d}{dx}[\ln(-x)] = \frac{1}{-x}\frac{d}{dx}(-x) = \left(\frac{1}{-x}\right)(-1) = \frac{1}{x}. \quad □$$

PROBLEM. Find the domain of f and find $f'(x)$ given that

$$f(x) = (\ln x^2)^3.$$

Solution. Since the logarithm function is defined only for positive numbers, we must have $x^2 > 0$. The domain of f consists of all $x \neq 0$. Before differentiating note that

$$f(x) = (\ln x^2)^3 = (2 \ln|x|)^3 = 8(\ln|x|)^3.$$

It follows that

$$f'(x) = 24(\ln|x|)^2 \frac{d}{dx}(\ln|x|) = 24(\ln|x|)^2 \frac{1}{x} = \frac{24}{x}(\ln|x|)^2. \quad □$$

PROBLEM. Show that, if u is a differentiable function of x, then for $u \neq 0$

(7.3.2)
$$\frac{d}{dx}(\ln|u|) = \frac{1}{u}\frac{du}{dx}.$$

Solution

$$\frac{d}{dx}(\ln|u|) = \frac{d}{du}(\ln|u|)\frac{du}{dx} = \frac{1}{u}\frac{du}{dx}. \quad \square$$

Here are two examples:

$$\frac{d}{dx}(\ln|1-x^3|) = \frac{1}{1-x^3}\frac{d}{dx}(1-x^3) = \frac{-3x^2}{1-x^3} = \frac{3x^2}{x^3-1}.$$

$$\frac{d}{dx}\left(\ln\left|\frac{x-1}{x-2}\right|\right) = \frac{d}{dx}(\ln|x-1|) - \frac{d}{dx}(\ln|x-2|) = \frac{1}{x-1} - \frac{1}{x-2}.$$

PROBLEM. Let

$$f(x) = \ln\left(\frac{x^4}{x-1}\right).$$

(a) Specify the domain of f. (b) On what intervals does f increase? Decrease?
(c) Find the extreme values of f. (d) Determine the concavity of the graph and
find the points of inflection. (e) Sketch the graph specifying the asymptotes if any.

Solution. Since the logarithm function is defined only for positive numbers, the
domain of f is the open interval $(1, \infty)$.
    Making use of the special properties of the logarithm we write

$$f(x) = \ln x^4 - \ln(x-1) = 4\ln x - \ln(x-1).$$

Differentiation gives

$$f'(x) = \frac{4}{x} - \frac{1}{x-1} = \frac{3x-4}{x(x-1)}$$

and

$$f''(x) = -\frac{4}{x^2} + \frac{1}{(x-1)^2} = -\frac{(x-2)(3x-2)}{x^2(x-1)^2}.$$

Since the domain of f is $(1, \infty)$, we consider only the values of x greater than 1.
    It's not hard to see that

$$f'(x) \text{ is } \begin{cases} \text{negative,} & \text{for} \quad 1 < x < \frac{4}{3} \\ 0, & \text{at} \quad\quad x = \frac{4}{3} \\ \text{positive,} & \text{for} \quad\quad x > \frac{4}{3} \end{cases}.$$

This means that f decreases on $(1, \frac{4}{3}]$ and increases on $[\frac{4}{3}, \infty)$. By the first derivative
test

$$f(\tfrac{4}{3}) = 4 \ln 4 - 3 \ln 3 \cong 2.25 \qquad \text{(Table 1)†}$$

is a local and absolute minimum.   There are no other extreme values.
Since

$$f''(x) \text{ is } \begin{cases} \text{positive,} & \text{for} \quad 1 < x < 2 \\ \quad\quad 0, & \text{at} \quad\quad x = 2 \\ \text{negative,} & \text{for} \quad\quad x > 2 \end{cases},$$

the graph is concave up on $(1, 2)$ and concave down on $(2, \infty)$.   The point

$$(2, f(2)) = (2, 4 \ln 2) \cong (2, 2.77) \qquad \text{(Table 1)}$$

is the only point of inflection.
Before sketching the graph, note that the derivative

$$f'(x) = \frac{4}{x} - \frac{1}{x - 1}$$

is very large negative for x close to 1 and very close to 0 for x large.   This means that the graph is very steep for x close to 1 and very flat for x large.   See Figure 7.3.2.   The line $x = 1$ is a vertical asymptote: as $x \to 1^+$, $f(x) \to \infty$.   □

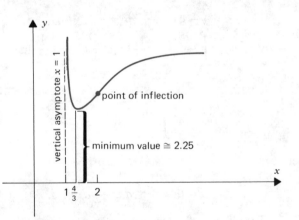

FIGURE 7.3.2

Integration

The integral counterpart of (7.3.1) takes the form

(7.3.3)
$$\int \frac{dx}{x} = \ln |x| + C.$$

In practice

$$\int \frac{g'(x)}{g(x)} \, dx \quad \text{is reduced to} \quad \int \frac{du}{u}$$

_____
† Appendix C.

by setting

$$u = g(x), \qquad du = g'(x)\, dx.$$

PROBLEM. Calculate

$$\int \frac{8x}{x^2 - 1}\, dx.$$

Solution. Set

$$u = x^2 - 1, \qquad du = 2x\, dx.$$

$$\int \frac{8x}{x^2 - 1}\, dx = 4 \int \frac{du}{u} = 4 \ln |u| + C = 4 \ln |x^2 - 1| + C. \quad \square$$

PROBLEM. Calculate

$$\int \frac{x^2}{1 - 4x^3}\, dx.$$

Solution. Set

$$u = 1 - 4x^3, \qquad du = -12x^2\, dx.$$

$$\int \frac{x^2}{1 - 4x^3}\, dx = -\frac{1}{12} \int \frac{du}{u} = -\frac{1}{12} \ln |u| + C = -\frac{1}{12} \ln |1 - 4x^3| + C. \quad \square$$

PROBLEM. Calculate

$$\int \frac{\ln x}{x}\, dx.$$

Solution. Set

$$u = \ln x, \qquad du = \frac{1}{x}\, dx.$$

$$\int \frac{\ln x}{x}\, dx = \int u\, du = \tfrac{1}{2}u^2 + C = \tfrac{1}{2}(\ln x)^2 + C. \quad \square$$

PROBLEM. Evaluate

$$\int_1^2 \frac{6x^2 - 2}{x^3 - x + 1}\, dx.$$

Solution. Set

$$u = x^3 - x + 1, \qquad du = (3x^2 - 1)\, dx.$$

At $x = 1$, $u = 1$; at $x = 2$, $u = 7$.

$$\int_1^2 \frac{6x^2 - 2}{x^3 - x + 1}\, dx = 2 \int_1^7 \frac{du}{u} = 2 \left[\ln |u| \right]_1^7 = 2(\ln 7 - \ln 1) = 2 \ln 7. \quad \square$$

Logarithmic Differentiation

We can differentiate a lengthy product

$$g(x) = g_1(x)g_2(x) \cdots g_n(x)$$

by first writing

$$\ln|g(x)| = \ln\left(|g_1(x)||g_2(x)| \cdots |g_n(x)|\right)$$
$$= \ln|g_1 x)| + \ln|g_2(x)| + \cdots + \ln|g_n(x)|$$

and then differentiating:

$$\frac{g'(x)}{g(x)} = \frac{g_1'(x)}{g_1(x)} + \frac{g_2'(x)}{g_2(x)} + \cdots + \frac{g_n'(x)}{g_n(x)}.$$

Multiplication by $g(x)$ gives

$$(7.3.4) \qquad \boxed{g'(x) = g(x)\left(\frac{g_1'(x)}{g_1(x)} + \frac{g_2'(x)}{g_2(x)} + \cdots + \frac{g_n'(x)}{g_n(x)}\right).}$$

The process by which $g'(x)$ was obtained is called *logarithmic differentiation*.
Logarithmic differentiation is valid at all points x where $g(x) \neq 0$. At points x where $g(x) = 0$, none of it makes sense.
A product of n factors

$$g(x) = g_1(x)g_2(x) \cdots g_n(x)$$

can, of course, also be differentiated by repeated applications of the product rule (3.2.4). The great advantage of logarithmic differentiation is that it gives us an explicit formula for the derivative, a formula that's easy to remember and easy to work with.

PROBLEM. Given that

$$g(x) = x(x - 1)(x - 2)(x - 3)$$

find $g'(x)$ for $x \neq 0, 1, 2, 3$.

Solution. We can write down $g'(x)$ directly from Formula 7.3.4.

$$g'(x) = x(x - 1)(x - 2)(x - 3)\left(\frac{1}{x} + \frac{1}{x - 1} + \frac{1}{x - 2} + \frac{1}{x - 3}\right).$$

Or, we can go through the process by which we derived Formula 7.3.4.

$$\ln|g(x)| = \ln|x| + \ln|x - 1| + \ln|x - 2| + \ln|x - 3|,$$
$$\frac{g'(x)}{g(x)} = \frac{1}{x} + \frac{1}{x - 1} + \frac{1}{x - 2} + \frac{1}{x - 3},$$
$$g'(x) = x(x - 1)(x - 2)(x - 3)\left(\frac{1}{x} + \frac{1}{x - 1} + \frac{1}{x - 2} + \frac{1}{x - 3}\right). \quad \square$$

Logarithmic differentiation can also be used with quotients.

PROBLEM. Given that

$$g(x) = \frac{(x^2 + 1)^3(2x - 5)^2}{(x^2 + 5)^2},$$

find $g'(x)$ for $x \neq \frac{5}{2}$.

Solution. Our first step is to write

$$g(x) = (x^2 + 1)^3(2x - 5)^2(x^2 + 5)^{-2}.$$

Then according to Formula 7.3.4

$$g'(x) = \frac{(x^2 + 1)^3(2x - 5)^2}{(x^2 + 5)^2}\left[\frac{3(x^2 + 1)^2(2x)}{(x^2 + 1)^3} + \frac{2(2x - 5)(2)}{(2x - 5)^2} + \frac{(-2)(x^2 + 5)^{-3}(2x)}{(x^2 + 5)^{-2}}\right]$$

$$= \frac{(x^2 + 1)^3(2x - 5)^2}{(x^2 + 5)^2}\left(\frac{6x}{x^2 + 1} + \frac{4}{2x - 5} - \frac{4x}{x^2 + 5}\right). \quad \square$$

EXERCISES

Determine the domain and find the derivative.

1. $f(x) = \ln 4x.$ **2.** $f(x) = \ln (2x + 1).$ **3.** $f(x) = \ln (x^3 + 1).$
4. $f(x) = \ln [(x + 1)^3].$ **5.** $f(x) = \ln \sqrt{1 + x^2}.$ **6.** $f(x) = (\ln x)^3.$

7. $f(x) = \ln |x^4 - 1|.$ **8.** $f(x) = \ln (\ln x).$ **9.** $f(x) = \dfrac{1}{\ln x}.$

10. $f(x) = \ln \left|\dfrac{x + 2}{x^3 - 1}\right|.$ **11.** $f(x) = x \ln x.$ **12.** $f(x) = \ln \sqrt[4]{x^2 + 1}.$

13. $f(x) = \dfrac{\ln (x + 1)}{x + 1}.$ **14.** $f(x) = \ln \sqrt{\dfrac{1 - x}{2 - x}}.$

Calculate the following integrals.

15. $\displaystyle\int \frac{dx}{x + 1}.$ **16.** $\displaystyle\int \frac{dx}{3 - x}.$ **17.** $\displaystyle\int \frac{x}{3 - x^2}\, dx.$

18. $\displaystyle\int \frac{x + 1}{x^2}\, dx.$ **19.** $\displaystyle\int \frac{x}{(3 - x^2)^2}\, dx.$ **20.** $\displaystyle\int \frac{\ln (x + a)}{x + a}\, dx.$

21. $\displaystyle\int \left(\frac{1}{x + 2} - \frac{1}{x - 2}\right) dx.$ **22.** $\displaystyle\int \frac{x^2}{2x^3 - 1}\, dx.$ **23.** $\displaystyle\int \frac{dx}{x(\ln x)^2}.$

24. $\displaystyle\int \left(\frac{1}{x - a} - \frac{1}{x - b}\right) dx.$ **25.** $\displaystyle\int \frac{\sqrt{x}}{1 + x\sqrt{x}}\, dx.$ **26.** $\displaystyle\int x\left(\frac{1}{x^2 - a^2} - \frac{1}{x^2 - b^2}\right) dx.$

Evaluate.

27. $\displaystyle\int_1^e \frac{dx}{x}.$ **28.** $\displaystyle\int_1^{e^2} \frac{dx}{x}.$ **29.** $\displaystyle\int_e^{e^2} \frac{dx}{x}.$ **30.** $\displaystyle\int_3^4 \frac{dx}{1 - x}.$

31. $\displaystyle\int_4^5 \frac{x}{x^2-1}\,dx.$

32. $\displaystyle\int_1^e \frac{\ln x}{x}\,dx.$

33. $\displaystyle\int_0^1 \frac{\ln(x+1)}{x+1}\,dx.$

34. $\displaystyle\int_0^1 \left(\frac{1}{x+1} - \frac{1}{x+2}\right)dx.$

Calculate the derivative by logarithmic differentiation.

35. $g(x) = (x^2+1)^2(x-1)^5 x^3.$

36. $g(x) = x(x+a)(x+b)(x+c).$

37. $g(x) = \dfrac{x^4(x-1)}{(x+2)(x^2+1)}.$

38. $g(x) = \dfrac{(1+x)(2+x)x}{(4+x)(2-x)}.$

39. $g(x) = \sqrt{\dfrac{(x-1)(x-2)}{(x-3)(x-4)}}.$

40. $g(x) = \dfrac{x^2(x^2+1)(x^2+2)}{(x^2-1)(x^2-5)}.$

Find the area of the part of the first quadrant that lies between

41. $x + 4y - 5 = 0$ and $xy = 1.$

42. $x + y - 3 = 0$ and $xy = 2.$

43. A particle moves along a line with acceleration $a(t) = -(t+1)^{-2}$ feet per second per second. Find the distance traveled by the particle during the time interval $[0, 4]$, given that the initial velocity $v(0)$ is 1 foot per second.

44. Exercise 43 with $v(0)$ as 2 feet per second.

Find a formula for the nth derivative.

45. $\dfrac{d^n}{dx^n}(\ln x).$

46. $\dfrac{d^n}{dx^n}[\ln(1-x)].$

47. $\dfrac{d^n}{dx^n}(\ln 2x).$

48. $\dfrac{d^n}{dx^n}\left(\ln\dfrac{1}{x}\right).$

49. (a) Verify that

$$\ln x = \int_1^x \frac{dt}{t} < \int_1^x \frac{dt}{\sqrt{t}} \qquad \text{for } x > 1.$$

(b) Use (a) to show that

$$0 < \ln x < 2(\sqrt{x} - 1) \qquad \text{for } x > 1.$$

(c) Use (b) to show that

$$2x\left(1 - \frac{1}{\sqrt{x}}\right) < x \ln x < 0 \qquad \text{for } 0 < x < 1.$$

(d) Use (c) to show that

$$\lim_{x \to 0^+} (x \ln x) = 0.$$

50. (a) Show that for $n = 2$ Formula 7.3.4 reduces to the product rule (3.2.4).
(b) Show that Formula 7.3.4 applied to

$$g(x) = \frac{g_1(x)}{g_2(x)}$$

reduces to the quotient rule (3.2.9).

For each of the functions below, (i) find the domain, (ii) find the intervals where the function increases and the intervals where it decreases, (iii) find the extreme values, (iv) determine the concavity of the graph and find the points of inflection, and finally, (v) sketch the graph, indicating asymptotes.

51. $f(x) = \ln 2x$.   **52.** $f(x) = x - \ln x$.   **53.** $f(x) = \ln (4 - x)$.

54. $f(x) = \ln (4 - x^2)$.   **55.** $f(x) = x \ln x$.   **56.** $f(x) = \ln (8x - x^2)$.

57. $f(x) = \ln \left(\dfrac{x}{1 + x^2} \right)$.   **58.** $f(x) = \ln \left(\dfrac{x^3}{x - 1} \right)$.

7.4 ······ THE EXPONENTIAL FUNCTION

Rational powers of e already have an established meaning: by $e^{p/q}$ we mean the qth root of e raised to the pth power. But what is meant by $e^{\sqrt{2}}$ or e^{π}?

Earlier we proved that each rational power $e^{p/q}$ had logarithm p/q:

(7.4.1)
$$\ln e^{p/q} = \frac{p}{q}.$$

The definition of e^z for z irrational is patterned after this relation.

DEFINITION 7.4.2

If z is irrational, then by e^z we mean the unique number which has logarithm z:

$$\ln e^z = z.$$

What is $e^{\sqrt{2}}$? It is the unique number that has logarithm $\sqrt{2}$. What is e^{π}? It is the unique number that has logarithm π. Note that e^x now has meaning for every real value of x: it is the unique number with logarithm x.

DEFINITION 7.4.3

The function

$$E(x) = e^x \qquad \text{for all real } x$$

is called the *exponential function.*

Some properties of the exponential function follow.

(1) In the first place

(7.4.4)
$$\ln e^x = x \qquad \text{for all real } x.$$

Writing $L(x) = \ln x$ and $E(x) = e^x$, we have

$$L(E(x)) = x \qquad \text{for all real } x.$$

This says that *the exponential function is the inverse of the logarithm function.*

(2) The graph of the exponential function appears in Figure 7.4.1. It can be obtained from the graph of the logarithm by reflection in the line $y = x$.

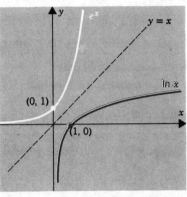

FIGURE 7.4.1

(3) Since the graph of the logarithm remains to the right of the y-axis, the graph of the exponential function remains above the x-axis:

(7.4.5) $$\boxed{e^x > 0 \qquad \text{for all real } x.}$$

(4) Since the graph of the logarithm crosses the x-axis at $(1, 0)$, the graph of the exponential function crosses the y-axis at $(0, 1)$:

$$\ln 1 = 0 \quad \text{gives} \quad e^0 = 1.$$

(5) Since the y-axis is a vertical asymptote for the graph of the logarithm function, the x-axis is a horizontal asymptote for the graph of the exponential function: as $x \to -\infty$, $e^x \to 0$.

(6) Since the exponential function is the inverse of the logarithm function, the logarithm function is the inverse of the exponential function; namely, we must have

(7.4.6) $$\boxed{e^{\ln x} = x \qquad \text{for all } x > 0.}$$

You can verify this equation directly by observing that both sides have the same logarithm:

$$\ln (e^{\ln x}) = \ln x,$$

since, for all real t, $\ln e^t = t$. $\square$

You know that for rational exponents

$$e^{(p/q + r/s)} = e^{p/q} \cdot e^{r/s}.$$

This property holds for all exponents, including irrational exponents.

THEOREM 7.4.7

$$e^{x+y} = e^x \cdot e^y \qquad \text{for all real } x \text{ and } y.$$

Proof

$$\ln (e^x \cdot e^y) = \ln e^x + \ln e^y = x + y = \ln e^{x+y}.$$

Since the logarithm is one-to-one, we must have

$$e^{x+y} = e^x \cdot e^y. \quad \square$$

We leave it to you to show that

(7.4.8)
$$e^{-y} = \frac{1}{e^y} \quad \text{and} \quad e^{x-y} = \frac{e^x}{e^y}.$$

Table 7.4.1 gives some values of the exponential function rounded off to the nearest hundredth.   More extended tables appear in Appendix C.

TABLE 7.4.1

x	e^x	x	e^x
0.1	1.11	1.1	3.00
0.2	1.22	1.2	3.32
0.3	1.35	1.3	3.67
0.4	1.49	1.4	4.06
0.5	1.65	1.5	4.48
0.6	1.82	1.6	4.95
0.7	2.01	1.7	5.47
0.8	2.23	1.8	6.05
0.9	2.46	1.9	6.68
1.0	2.72	2.0	7.39

PROBLEM.   Use Table 7.4.1 to estimate the following powers of e:

(a) $e^{-0.2}$.   (b) $e^{2.4}$.   (c) $e^{3.1}$.

Solution.   The idea, of course, is to use the laws of exponents.

(a) $e^{-0.2} = \dfrac{1}{e^{0.2}} \cong \dfrac{1}{1.22} \cong 0.82.$

(b) $e^{2.4} = e^{2+0.4} = (e^2)(e^{0.4}) \cong (7.39)(1.49) \cong 11.01.$

(c) $e^{3.1} = e^{1.7+1.4} = (e^{1.7})(e^{1.4}) \cong (5.47)(4.06) \cong 22.21.$ $\square$

We come now to one of the most important results in calculus. It is marvelously simple.

> **THEOREM 7.4.9**
>
> **The exponential function is its own derivative: for all real x**
>
> $$\frac{d}{dx}(e^x) = e^x.$$

Proof. The logarithm function is differentiable, and its derivative is never 0. It follows from our discussion in Section 3.8 that its inverse, the exponential function, is also differentiable. Knowing this, we can show that

$$\frac{d}{dx}(e^x) = e^x$$

by differentiating the identity

$$\ln e^x = x.$$

On the left-hand side, the chain rule gives

$$\frac{d}{dx}(\ln e^x) = \frac{1}{e^x}\frac{d}{dx}(e^x).$$

On the right-hand side, the derivative is 1:

$$\frac{d}{dx}(x) = 1.$$

Equating these derivatives, we have

$$\frac{1}{e^x}\frac{d}{dx}(e^x) = 1 \quad \text{and thus} \quad \frac{d}{dx}(e^x) = e^x. \quad \square$$

You will frequently run across expressions of the form e^u where u is a function of x. If u is differentiable, then the chain rule gives

(7.4.10)
$$\frac{d}{dx}[e^u] = e^u \frac{du}{dx}.$$

Proof

$$\frac{d}{dx}[e^u] = \frac{d}{du}[e^u]\frac{du}{dx} = e^u \frac{du}{dx}. \quad \square$$

EXAMPLES

$$\frac{d}{dx}(e^{kx}) = e^{kx} \cdot k = ke^{kx}.$$

$$\frac{d}{dx}(e^{\sqrt{x}}) = e^{\sqrt{x}}\frac{d}{dx}(\sqrt{x}) = e^{\sqrt{x}}\left(\frac{1}{2\sqrt{x}}\right) = \frac{1}{2\sqrt{x}}e^{\sqrt{x}}.$$

$$\frac{d}{dx}(e^{-x^2}) = e^{-x^2}\frac{d}{dx}(-x^2) = e^{-x^2}(-2x) = -2xe^{-x^2}. \quad \square$$

The relation

$$\frac{d}{dx}(e^x) = e^x \quad \text{and its corollary} \quad \frac{d}{dx}(e^{kx}) = ke^{kx}$$

have important applications to engineering, physics, chemistry, biology, and economics. We will discuss some of these applications in Section 8.3.

PROBLEM. Let

$$f(x) = xe^{-x} \qquad \text{for all real } x.$$

(a) On what intervals does *f* increase? Decrease? (b) Find the extreme values of *f*. (c) Determine the concavity of the graph and find the points of inflection. (d) Sketch the graph indicating the asymptotes if any.

Solution. We have

$$f(x) = xe^{-x},$$
$$f'(x) = xe^{-x}(-1) + e^{-x} = (1-x)e^{-x},$$
$$f''(x) = (1-x)e^{-x}(-1) - e^{-x} = (x-2)e^{-x}.$$

Since $e^x > 0$ for all real x,

$$f'(x) \text{ is } \begin{cases} \text{positive,} & \text{for} \quad x < 1 \\ 0; & \text{at} \quad x = 1 \\ \text{negative,} & \text{for} \quad x > 1 \end{cases}.$$

The function *f* increases on $(-\infty, 1]$ and decreases on $[1, \infty)$. The number

$$f(1) = \frac{1}{e} \cong \frac{1}{2.72} \cong 0.37$$

is a local and absolute maximum. There are no other extreme values. Since

$$f''(x) \text{ is } \begin{cases} \text{negative,} & \text{for} \quad x < 2 \\ 0, & \text{at} \quad x = 2 \\ \text{positive,} & \text{for} \quad x > 2 \end{cases},$$

the graph is concave down on $(-\infty, 2)$ and concave up on $(2, \infty)$. The point

$$(2, f(2)) = (2, 2e^{-2}) \cong \left(2, \frac{2}{(2.72)^2}\right) \cong (2, 0.27)$$

is the only point of inflection.   The graph is given in Figure 7.4.2.   The x-axis is a horizontal asymptote: as $x \to \infty$, $f(x) \to 0$.   □

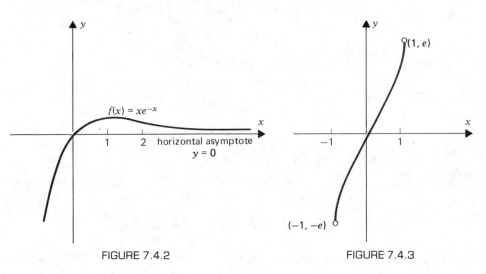

FIGURE 7.4.2   FIGURE 7.4.3

PROBLEM. Let

$$f(x) = xe^{x^2} \qquad \text{for all } x \in (-1, 1).$$

(a) On what intervals is f increasing? Decreasing? (b) Find the extreme values of f. (c) Determine the concavity of the graph and find the points of inflection. (d) Sketch the graph.

Solution. Here

$$f(x) = xe^{x^2},$$
$$f'(x) = xe^{x^2}(2x) + e^{x^2} = (1 + 2x^2)e^{x^2},$$
$$f''(x) = (1 + 2x^2)e^{x^2}(2x) + 4xe^{x^2} = 2x(2x^2 + 3)e^{x^2}.$$

Since $f'(x) > 0$ for all $x \in (-1, 1)$, f increases on $(-1, 1)$, and there are no extreme values.   Since

$$f''(x) \text{ is } \begin{cases} \text{negative,} & \text{for} \quad x \in (-1, 0) \\ 0, & \text{at} \quad x = 0 \\ \text{positive,} & \text{for} \quad x \in (0, 1) \end{cases},$$

the graph is concave down on $(-1, 0)$ and concave up on $(0, 1)$.   The point $(0, f(0)) = (0, 0)$ is the only point of inflection.   Since $f(-x) = -f(x)$, f is an odd function, and thus its graph (Figure 7.4.3) is symmetric with respect to the origin.   □

The integral counterpart of (7.4.9) takes the form

(7.4.11)

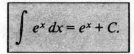

$$\int e^x \, dx = e^x + C.$$

In practice

$$\int e^{g(x)} g'(x) \, dx \quad \text{is reduced to} \quad \int e^u \, du$$

by setting

$$u = g(x), \quad du = g'(x) \, dx.$$

PROBLEM. Find

$$\int 9e^{3x} \, dx.$$

Solution. Set

$$u = 3x, \quad du = 3 \, dx.$$

$$\int 9e^{3x} \, dx = 3 \int e^u \, du = 3e^u + C = 3e^{3x} + C.$$

If you recognize at the very beginning that

$$3e^{3x} = \frac{d}{dx} (e^{3x}),$$

then you can dispense with the u-substitution and simply write

$$\int 9e^{3x} \, dx = 3 \int 3e^{3x} \, dx = 3e^{3x} + C. \quad \square$$

PROBLEM. Find

$$\int \frac{e^{\sqrt{x}}}{\sqrt{x}} \, dx.$$

Solution. Set

$$u = \sqrt{x}, \quad du = \frac{1}{2\sqrt{x}} \, dx.$$

$$\int \frac{e^{\sqrt{x}}}{\sqrt{x}} \, dx = 2 \int e^u \, du = 2e^u + C = 2e^{\sqrt{x}} + C.$$

If you recognize immediately that

$$\frac{1}{2} \left(\frac{e^{\sqrt{x}}}{\sqrt{x}} \right) = \frac{d}{dx} (e^{\sqrt{x}}),$$

then you can dispense with the u-substitution and integrate directly:

$$\int \frac{e^{\sqrt{x}}}{\sqrt{x}} \, dx = 2 \int \frac{1}{2} \left(\frac{e^{\sqrt{x}}}{\sqrt{x}} \right) dx = 2e^{\sqrt{x}} + C. \quad \square$$

PROBLEM.

$$\int \frac{e^{3x}}{e^{3x}+1}\, dx.$$

Solution. We can put this integral in the form

$$\int \frac{du}{u}$$

by setting

$$u = e^{3x}+1, \qquad du = 3e^{3x}\, dx.$$

Then

$$\int \frac{e^{3x}}{e^{3x}+1}\, dx = \frac{1}{3}\int \frac{du}{u} = \frac{1}{3}\ln|u| + C = \frac{1}{3}\ln(e^{3x}+1) + C. \quad \square$$

PROBLEM. Evaluate

$$\int_0^{\ln 2} e^x\, dx.$$

Solution

$$\int_0^{\ln 2} e^x\, dx = \left[e^x \right]_0^{\ln 2} = e^{\ln 2} - e^0 = 2 - 1 = 1. \quad \square$$

PROBLEM. Evaluate

$$\int_0^1 e^x(e^x+1)^{1/5}\, dx.$$

Solution. Set

$$u = e^x + 1, \qquad du = e^x\, dx.$$

At $x = 0$, $u = 2$; at $x = 1$, $u = e + 1$. Thus

$$\int_0^1 e^x(e^x+1)^{1/5}\, dx = \int_2^{e+1} u^{1/5}\, du = \left[\tfrac{5}{6} u^{6/5} \right]_2^{e+1} = \tfrac{5}{6}[(e+1)^{6/5} - 2^{6/5}]. \quad \square$$

REMARK. The u-substitution simplifies many calculations, but you'll find with experience that in many cases you can carry out the integration more quickly without it. $\square$

EXERCISES

Differentiate the following functions.

1. $y = e^{-2x}$.

2. $y = 3e^{2x+1}$.

3. $y = e^{x^2-1}$.

4. $y = 2e^{-4x}$.

5. $y = e^x \ln x$.

6. $y = x^2 e^x$.

7. $y = x^{-1}e^{-x}$.

8. $y = e^{\sqrt{x}+1}$.

9. $y = \frac{1}{2}(e^x + e^{-x})$.

10. $y = \frac{1}{2}(e^x - e^{-x})$.

11. $y = e^{\sqrt{x}} \ln \sqrt{x}$.

12. $y = (1 - e^{4x})^2$.

13. $y = (e^x + e^{-x})^2$.

14. $y = (3 - 2e^{-x})^3$.

15. $y = (e^{x^2} + 1)^2$.

16. $y = (e^{2x} - e^{-2x})^2$.

17. $y = (x^2 - 2x + 2)e^x$.

18. $y = x^2 e^x - x e^{x^2}$.

19. $y = \dfrac{e^x - 1}{e^x + 1}$.

20. $y = \dfrac{e^{2x} - 1}{e^{2x} + 1}$.

21. $y = \dfrac{e^{ax} - e^{bx}}{e^{ax} + e^{bx}}$.

22. $y = \ln e^{3x}$.

23. $y = e^{4\ln x}$.

24. $y = e^{\sqrt{1-x^2}}$.

Calculate the following indefinite integrals.

25. $\displaystyle\int e^{2x}\, dx$.

26. $\displaystyle\int e^{-2x}\, dx$.

27. $\displaystyle\int e^{kx}\, dx$.

28. $\displaystyle\int e^{ax+b}\, dx$.

29. $\displaystyle\int x e^{x^2}\, dx$.

30. $\displaystyle\int x e^{-x^2}\, dx$.

31. $\displaystyle\int \dfrac{e^{1/x}}{x^2}\, dx$.

32. $\displaystyle\int \dfrac{e^{2\sqrt{x}}}{\sqrt{x}}\, dx$.

33. $\displaystyle\int (e^x + e^{-x})^2\, dx$.

34. $\displaystyle\int e^{\ln x}\, dx$.

35. $\displaystyle\int \ln e^x\, dx$.

36. $\displaystyle\int (e^{-x} - 1)^2\, dx$.

37. $\displaystyle\int \dfrac{4}{\sqrt{e^x}}\, dx$.

38. $\displaystyle\int \dfrac{e^x}{e^x + 1}\, dx$.

39. $\displaystyle\int \dfrac{e^x}{\sqrt{e^x + 1}}\, dx$.

40. $\displaystyle\int \dfrac{2e^x}{\sqrt[3]{e^x + 1}}\, dx$.

41. $\displaystyle\int \dfrac{e^{2x}}{2e^{2x} + 3}\, dx$.

42. $\displaystyle\int \dfrac{x e^{ax^2}}{e^{ax^2} + 1}\, dx$.

Evaluate the following definite integrals.

43. $\displaystyle\int_0^1 e^x\, dx$.

44. $\displaystyle\int_0^1 e^{-kx}\, dx$.

45. $\displaystyle\int_0^{\ln \pi} e^{-6x}\, dx$.

46. $\displaystyle\int_0^1 x e^{-x^2}\, dx$.

47. $\displaystyle\int_0^1 \dfrac{e^x + 1}{e^x}\, dx$.

48. $\displaystyle\int_0^1 \dfrac{4 - e^x}{e^x}\, dx$.

49. $\displaystyle\int_0^{\ln 2} \dfrac{e^x}{e^x + 1}\, dx$.

50. $\displaystyle\int_0^1 \dfrac{e^x + e^{-x}}{2}\, dx$.

51. $\displaystyle\int_{\ln 2}^{\ln 3} (e^x - e^{-x})^2\, dx$.

52. $\displaystyle\int_0^1 \dfrac{e^x}{4 - e^x}\, dx$.

53. $\displaystyle\int_0^1 x(e^{x^2} + 2)\, dx$.

54. $\displaystyle\int_1^2 (2 - e^{-x})^2\, dx$.

Estimate using Table 7.4.1.

55. $e^{-0.4}$.

56. $e^{2.6}$.

57. $e^{2.8}$.

58. $e^{-2.1}$.

Estimate using differentials.

59. $e^{2.03}$. $(e^2 \cong 7.39)$

60. $e^{-0.15}$. $(e^0 = 1)$

61. $e^{2.85}$. $(e^3 \cong 20.09)$

62. e^{2a+h}. $(e^a = A)$

63. A particle moves on a coordinate line with its position at time t given by the function $x(t) = Ae^{ct} + Be^{-ct}$. Show that the acceleration of the particle is proportional to its position.

Sketch the region bounded by the curves and find its area.

64. $x = e^{2y}$, $x = e^{-y}$, $x = 4$.   **65.** $y = e^x$, $y = e^{2x}$, $y = e^4$.

66. $y = e^x$, $y = e$, $y = x$, $x = 0$.   **67.** $x = e^y$, $y = 1$, $y = 2$, $x = 2$.

68. Take $a > 0$ and refer to Figure 7.4.4. (a) Find the points of tangency, marked A and B. (b) Find the area of region I. (c) Find the area of region II.

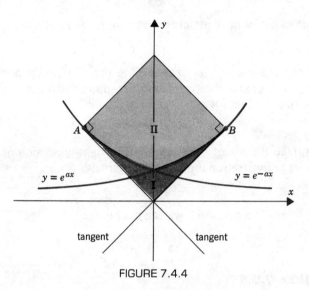

FIGURE 7.4.4

For each of the functions below, (i) find the domain, (ii) find the intervals where the function increases and the intervals where it decreases, (iii) find the extreme values, (iv) determine the concavity and find the points of inflection, and finally, (v) sketch the graph, indicating all asymptotes.

69. $f(x) = e^{x^2}$.   **70.** $f(x) = e^{-x^2}$.   **71.** $f(x) = \frac{1}{2}(e^x + e^{-x})$.

72. $f(x) = \frac{1}{2}(e^x - e^{-x})$.   **73.** $f(x) = xe^x$.   **74.** $f(x) = (1 - x)e^x$.

75. $f(x) = e^{(1/x)^2}$.   **76.** $f(x) = x^2 e^{-x}$

77. Prove that for all $x > 0$ and all positive integers n

$$e^x > 1 + x + \frac{x^2}{2!} + \frac{x^3}{3!} + \cdots + \frac{x^n}{n!},$$

where $n!$, read "n factorial," is shorthand for

$$n(n - 1)(n - 2) \cdots 2 \cdot 1.$$

HINT: $e^x = 1 + \int_0^x e^t \, dt > 1 + \int_0^x dt = 1 + x,$

$e^x = 1 + \int_0^x e^t \, dt > 1 + \int_0^x (1 + t) \, dt = 1 + x + \frac{x^2}{2},$ etc.

78. Prove that, if n is a positive integer, then

$$e^x > x^n \qquad \text{for all } x \text{ sufficiently large.}$$

HINT: Use Exercise 77.

7.5 ······ARBITRARY POWERS; OTHER BASES; ESTIMATING e

The Function x^r

The elementary notion of exponent applies only to rational numbers. Expressions such as

$$x^5, \quad x^{1/3}, \quad x^{-4/7}$$

make sense, but so far we have attached no meaning to expressions such as

$$x^{\sqrt{2}}, \quad x^\pi, \quad x^{-\sqrt{3}}.$$

The extension of our sense of exponent to allow for irrational exponents is conveniently done by making use of the logarithm and exponential functions. The heart of the matter is to observe that for $x > 0$ and p/q rational

$$x^{p/q} = e^{(p/q)\ln x}.$$

(To verify this, take the log of both sides.) The right-hand side of this equation already makes sense for irrational numbers z; namely,

$$e^{z\ln x}$$

already makes sense. To define x^z, we can simply set

$$x^z = e^{z\ln x}.$$

DEFINITION 7.5.1

If z is irrational and x is positive, we define the number x^z by setting

$$x^z = e^{z\ln x}.$$

Having made this definition, we now have

(7.5.2) $x^r = e^{r\ln x}$ for all real numbers r.

For example,

$$10^{\sqrt{2}} = e^{\sqrt{2}\ln 10}, \quad 2^\pi = e^{\pi\ln 2}, \quad 7^{-\sqrt{3}} = e^{-\sqrt{3}\ln 7}, \quad \pi^e = e^{e\ln\pi}. \quad \square$$

With this extended sense of exponent the usual laws of exponents

(7.5.3) $x^{r+s} = x^r x^s, \qquad x^{r-s} = \dfrac{x^r}{x^s}, \qquad (x^r)^s = x^{rs}$

still hold:

$$x^{r+s} = e^{(r+s)\ln x} = e^{r\ln x} \cdot e^{s\ln x} = x^r x^s,$$

$$x^{r-s} = e^{(r-s)\ln x} = e^{r\ln x} \cdot e^{-s\ln x} = \frac{e^{r\ln x}}{e^{s\ln x}} = \frac{x^r}{x^s},$$

$$(x^r)^s = e^{s\ln x^r} = e^{rs\ln x} = x^{rs}. \quad \square$$

The differentiation of arbitrary powers has a familiar look:

(7.5.4)
$$\frac{d}{dx}(x^r) = rx^{r-1} \qquad \text{for all } x > 0.$$

Proof

$$\frac{d}{dx}(x^r) = \frac{d}{dx}(e^{r\ln x}) = e^{r\ln x}\frac{d}{dx}(r\ln x) = x^r\frac{r}{x} = rx^{r-1}.$$

You can also set

$$f(x) = x^r$$

and use logarithmic differentiation:

$$\ln f(x) = r\ln x$$

$$\frac{f'(x)}{f(x)} = \frac{r}{x}$$

$$f'(x) = \frac{rf(x)}{x} = \frac{rx^r}{x} = rx^{r-1}. \quad \square$$

Thus

$$\frac{d}{dx}(x^{\sqrt{2}}) = \sqrt{2}\,x^{\sqrt{2}-1}, \qquad \frac{d}{dx}(x^\pi) = \pi x^{\pi-1}.$$

If *u* is a positive differentiable function of *x*, then, by the chain rule,

(7.5.5)
$$\frac{d}{dx}[u^r] = ru^{r-1}\frac{du}{dx}.$$

Proof

$$\frac{d}{dx}[u^r] = \frac{d}{du}[u^r]\frac{du}{dx} = ru^{r-1}\frac{du}{dx}. \quad \square$$

For example,

$$\frac{d}{dx}[(x^2+5)^{\sqrt{3}}] = \sqrt{3}(x^2+5)^{\sqrt{3}-1}(2x) = 2\sqrt{3}\,x(x^2+5)^{\sqrt{3}-1}.$$

PROBLEM. Find

$$\int \frac{x^3}{(2x^4+1)^\pi}\,dx.$$

Solution. Set

$$u = 2x^4 + 1, \qquad du = 8x^3\,dx.$$

$$\int \frac{x^3}{(2x^4+1)^\pi}\,dx = \frac{1}{8}\int \frac{du}{u^\pi} = \frac{1}{8}\left(\frac{u^{1-\pi}}{1-\pi}\right) + C = \frac{(2x^4+1)^{1-\pi}}{8(1-\pi)} + C. \quad \square$$

PROBLEM. Find

$$\frac{d}{dx}(x^x).$$

Solution. One way to find this derivative is to observe that

$$x^x = e^{x \ln x}$$

and then differentiate:

$$\frac{d}{dx}(x^x) = \frac{d}{dx}(e^{x \ln x}) = e^{x \ln x}\left(x \cdot \frac{1}{x} + \ln x\right) = x^x(1 + \ln x).$$

Another way to find the derivative of x^x is to set

$$f(x) = x^x$$

and use logarithmic differentiation:

$$\ln f(x) = x \ln x$$

$$\frac{f'(x)}{f(x)} = x \cdot \frac{1}{x} + \ln x = 1 + \ln x$$

$$f'(x) = f(x)(1 + \ln x) = x^x(1 + \ln x). \quad \square$$

The Function p^x

To form the function

$$f(x) = x^r$$

we take a positive variable x and raise it to a constant power r. To form the function

$$g(x) = p^x$$

we take a positive constant p and raise it to a variable power x.

The high status enjoyed by Euler's number e comes from the fact that

$$\frac{d}{dx}(e^x) = e^x.$$

For other bases the derivative is a little more complicated:

(7.5.6)

$$\frac{d}{dx}(p^x) = p^x \ln p.$$

Proof

$$\frac{d}{dx}(p^x) = \frac{d}{dx}[e^{x \ln p}] = e^{x \ln p} \ln p = p^x \ln p. \quad \square$$

If u is a differentiable function of x, then, by the chain rule,

(7.5.7)

$$\frac{d}{dx}[p^u] = p^u \ln p \frac{du}{dx}.$$

Proof

$$\frac{d}{dx}[p^u] = \frac{d}{du}[p^u]\frac{du}{dx} = p^u \ln p \frac{du}{dx}. \quad \Box$$

EXAMPLES

$$\frac{d}{dx}(e^x) = e^x \quad \text{but} \quad \frac{d}{dx}(2^x) = 2^x \ln 2.$$

$$\frac{d}{dx}(e^{3x^2}) = e^{3x^2}(6x) \quad \text{but} \quad \frac{d}{dx}(2^{3x^2}) = 2^{3x^2}(\ln 2)(6x) = 6x\, 2^{3x^2} \ln 2. \quad \Box$$

PROBLEM. Find

$$\int 2^x\, dx.$$

Solution. Set

$$u = 2^x, \quad du = 2^x \ln 2\, dx.$$

$$\int 2^x\, dx = \frac{1}{\ln 2}\int du = \frac{1}{\ln 2}u + C = \frac{1}{\ln 2}2^x + C. \quad \Box$$

PROBLEM. Evaluate

$$\int_1^2 3^{-x}\, dx.$$

Solution. Set

$$u = 3^{-x}, \quad du = -3^{-x}\ln 3\, dx.$$

At $x = 1$, $u = \frac{1}{3}$; at $x = 2$, $u = \frac{1}{9}$. Thus

$$\int_1^2 3^{-x}\, dx = -\frac{1}{\ln 3}\int_{1/3}^{1/9} du = -\frac{1}{\ln 3}\left(\frac{1}{9} - \frac{1}{3}\right) = \frac{2}{9\ln 3}. \quad \Box$$

The Function $log_p\, x$

If p is positive, then

$$\ln p^t = t \ln p.$$

If in addition p is different from 1, then $\ln p \neq 0$, and therefore

$$\frac{\ln p^t}{\ln p} = t.$$

This means that the function

$$f(x) = \frac{\ln x}{\ln p}$$

satisfies the relation

$$f(p^t) = t.$$

In view of this we call

$$\frac{\ln x}{\ln p}$$

the logarithm of x to the base p and write

(7.5.8)
$$\log_p x = \frac{\ln x}{\ln p}.$$

For example,

$$\log_2 32 = \frac{\ln 32}{\ln 2} = \frac{\ln 2^5}{\ln 2} = \frac{5 \ln 2}{\ln 2} = 5$$

and

$$\log_{100}\left(\tfrac{1}{10}\right) = \frac{\ln\left(\tfrac{1}{10}\right)}{\ln 100} = \frac{\ln 10^{-1}}{\ln 10^2} = \frac{-\ln 10}{2 \ln 10} = -\frac{1}{2}. \quad \square$$

We can obtain these same results more quickly by noting that

(7.5.9)
$$\log_p p^t = t.$$

Thus

$$\log_2 32 = \log_2 2^5 = 5 \quad \text{and} \quad \log_{100}\left(\tfrac{1}{10}\right) = \log_{100}(100^{-1/2}) = -\tfrac{1}{2}. \quad \square$$

By differentiating

$$\log_p x = \frac{\ln x}{\ln p}$$

we obtain the formula

(7.5.10)
$$\frac{d}{dx}(\log_p x) = \frac{1}{x \ln p}. \qquad †$$

---

† The function $f(x) = \log_p x$ satisfies

$$f'(x) = \frac{1}{x \ln p}, \qquad f'(1) = \frac{1}{\ln p}.$$

This means that in general

$$f'(x) = \frac{1}{x} f'(1).$$

We predicted this from general considerations in Section 7.1. (See Formula 7.1.2.)

When p is e, the factor $\ln p$ in the denominator becomes 1, and the formula is simply

$$\frac{d}{dx}(\log_e x) = \frac{1}{x}.$$

We view the logarithm to the base e, $\ln = \log_e$, as the "*natural logarithm*" because it is the logarithm with the simplest derivative.

For completeness note that, if u is a positive differentiable function of x, then, by the chain rule,

(7.5.11)

$$\frac{d}{dx}[\log_p u] = \frac{1}{u \ln p}\frac{du}{dx}.$$

This follows directly from (7.5.10) and the chain rule.

EXAMPLES

$$\frac{d}{dx}(\log_5 x) = \frac{1}{x \ln 5}, \qquad \frac{d}{dx}[\log_2 (3x^2 + 1)] = \frac{6x}{(3x^2 + 1)\ln 2}. \quad \square$$

Estimating the Number *e*

We defined the logarithm function by setting

$$\ln x = \int_1^x \frac{dt}{t}, \qquad x > 0.$$

We can derive a numerical estimate for e from this integral representation of the logarithm.

Since e is irrational (Exercise 36, Section 13.6), we cannot hope to express e as a terminating decimal. (Nor as a repeating decimal.) What we can do is describe a simple technique by which one can compute the value of e to any desired degree of accuracy.

THEOREM 7.5.12

For each positive integer n,

$$\left(1 + \frac{1}{n}\right)^n \le e \le \left(1 + \frac{1}{n}\right)^{n+1}.$$

Proof.   Refer throughout to Figure 7.5.1.

$$\ln\left(1 + \frac{1}{n}\right) = \int_1^{1+1/n} \frac{dt}{t} \le \int_1^{1+1/n} 1\, dt = \frac{1}{n}.$$

$\llcorner$ since $\dfrac{1}{t} \le 1$ throughout the interval of integration

$$\ln\left(1+\frac{1}{n}\right)=\int_{1}^{1+1/n}\frac{dt}{t}\geq\int_{1}^{1+1/n}\frac{dt}{1+1/n}=\frac{1}{1+1/n}\cdot\frac{1}{n}=\frac{1}{n+1}.$$

└ since $\dfrac{1}{t}\geq\dfrac{1}{1+1/n}$　throughout the interval of integration

We have now shown that

$$\frac{1}{n+1}\leq\ln\left(1+\frac{1}{n}\right)\leq\frac{1}{n}.$$

From the inequality on the right

$$1+\frac{1}{n}\leq e^{1/n}\qquad\text{and thus}\qquad\left(1+\frac{1}{n}\right)^{n}\leq e.$$

From the inequality on the left

$$e^{1/(n+1)}\leq 1+\frac{1}{n}\qquad\text{and thus}\qquad e\leq\left(1+\frac{1}{n}\right)^{n+1}.\quad\square$$

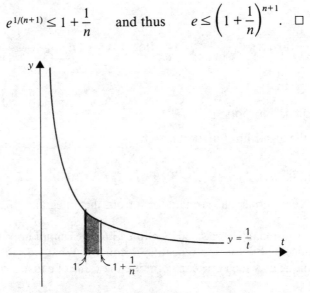

FIGURE 7.5.1

It's easy to see how to estimate e from this result.　Since

$$(1+\tfrac{1}{1})^{1}=2\qquad\text{and}\qquad(1+\tfrac{1}{1})^{2}=4,$$

we have

$$2\leq e\leq 4.$$

Since

$$(1+\tfrac{1}{2})^{2}=\tfrac{9}{4}=2.25\qquad\text{and}\qquad(1+\tfrac{1}{2})^{3}=\tfrac{27}{8}=3.375,$$

we have

$$2.25\leq e\leq 3.375.$$

With a little more patience you can verify that

$$2.59 \le (1 + \tfrac{1}{10})^{10} \quad \text{and} \quad (1 + \tfrac{1}{10})^{11} \le 2.86$$

and thus arrive at

$$2.59 \le e \le 2.86.$$

Lengthier calculations show that

$$2.70 \le (1 + \tfrac{1}{100})^{100} \quad \text{and} \quad (1 + \tfrac{1}{100})^{101} \le 2.74$$

and thus

$$2.70 \le e \le 2.74.$$

Still lengthier calculations show that

$$2.71 \le (1 + \tfrac{1}{200})^{200} \quad \text{and} \quad (1 + \tfrac{1}{200})^{201} \le 2.73.,$$

and thus

$$2.71 \le e \le 2.73.$$

A look at an eight-place table reveals the estimate

$$2.71828182.$$

For our purposes the estimate 2.72 is sufficient.

REMARK. The inequality

$$\left(1 + \frac{1}{n}\right)^n \le e \le \left(1 + \frac{1}{n}\right)^{n+1}$$

is rather elegant, but, as you saw, it does not provide a very efficient way of estimating *e*. (We have to go all the way to $n = 200$ to show that $2.71 \le e \le 2.73$.) We'll give a much more efficient way of estimating *e* in Chapter 13. □

EXERCISES

Find.

1. $\log_2 64$.   **2.** $\log_2 \tfrac{1}{64}$.   **3.** $\log_{64} \tfrac{1}{2}$.   **4.** $\log_{10} 0.01$.
5. $\log_5 1$.   **6.** $\log_5 0.2$.   **7.** $\log_5 125$.   **8.** $\log_2 4^3$.
9. $\log_{32} 8$.   **10.** $\log_{100} 10^{-4/5}$.   **11.** $\log_{10} 100^{-4/5}$.   **12.** $\log_9 \sqrt{3}$.

Show that

13. $\log_p xy = \log_p x + \log_p y$.   **14.** $\log_p \dfrac{1}{x} = -\log_p x$.

15. $\log_p x^y = y \log_p x$.   **16.** $\log_p \dfrac{x}{y} = \log_p x - \log_p y$.

Find those numbers *x*, if any, for which

17. $10^x = e^x$.   **18.** $\log_5 x = 0.04$.   **19.** $\log_x 10 = \log_4 100$.

20. $\log_x 2 = \log_3 x$.   **21.** $\log_2 x = \displaystyle\int_2^x \dfrac{dt}{t}$.   **22.** $\log_x 10 = \log_2 (\tfrac{1}{10})$.

23. Estimate $\ln a$ given that $e^{t_1} < a < e^{t_2}$.

24. Estimate e^b given that $\ln x_1 < b < \ln x_2$.

Calculate the following integrals.

25. $\displaystyle\int 3^x \, dx.$ **26.** $\displaystyle\int 2^{-x} \, dx.$ **27.** $\displaystyle\int (x^3 + 3^{-x}) \, dx.$

28. $\displaystyle\int x10^{-x^2} \, dx.$ **29.** $\displaystyle\int \frac{dx}{x \ln 5}.$ **30.** $\displaystyle\int \frac{\log_5 x}{x} \, dx.$

31. $\displaystyle\int \frac{\log_2 x^3}{x} \, dx.$ **32.** $\displaystyle\int \frac{\log_3 \sqrt{x} - 1}{x} \, dx.$ **33.** $\displaystyle\int x10^{x^2} \, dx.$

34. Show that, if a, b, c are positive, then

$$\log_a c = \log_a b \, \log_b c$$

provided that a and b are both different from 1.

Find $f'(e)$.

35. $f(x) = \log_3 x.$ **36.** $f(x) = x \log_3 x.$

37. $f(x) = \ln (\ln x).$ **38.** $f(x) = \log_3 (\log_2 x).$

Derive the formula for $f'(x)$ by logarithmic differentiation.

39. $f(x) = p^x.$ **40.** $f(x) = p^{g(x)}.$

Find by logarithmic differentiation.

41. $\displaystyle\frac{d}{dx} [(x + 1)^x].$ **42.** $\displaystyle\frac{d}{dx} [(\ln x)^x].$ **43.** $\displaystyle\frac{d}{dx} [(\ln x)^{\ln x}].$

44. $\displaystyle\frac{d}{dx} \left[\left(\frac{1}{x}\right)^x \right].$ **45.** $\displaystyle\frac{d}{dx} [(x^2 + 2)^{\ln x}].$ **46.** $\displaystyle\frac{d}{dx} [(\ln x)^{x^2+2}].$

Sketch figures in which you compare the following pairs of graphs.

47. $f(x) = e^x$ and $g(x) = 2^x.$ **48.** $f(x) = e^x$ and $g(x) = 3^x.$

49. $f(x) = e^x$ and $g(x) = e^{-x}.$ **50.** $f(x) = 2^x$ and $g(x) = 2^{-x}.$

51. $f(x) = \ln x$ and $g(x) = \log_3 x.$ **52.** $f(x) = \ln x$ and $g(x) = \log_2 x.$

53. $f(x) = 2^x$ and $g(x) = \log_2 x.$ **54.** $f(x) = 10^x$ and $g(x) = \log_{10} x.$

For each of the functions below (i) specify the domain, (ii) find the intervals where the function increases and those where it decreases, (iii) find the extreme values.

55. $f(x) = 10^{1-x^2}.$ **56.** $f(x) = 10^{1/(1-x^2)}.$

57. $f(x) = 10^{\sqrt{1-x^2}}.$ **58.** $f(x) = \log_{10} \sqrt{1 - x^2}.$

Evaluate.

59. $\displaystyle\int_1^2 2^{-x} \, dx.$ **60.** $\displaystyle\int_0^1 4^x \, dx.$ **61.** $\displaystyle\int_1^4 \frac{dx}{x \ln 2}.$

62. $\displaystyle\int_0^2 p^{x/2} \, dx.$ **63.** $\displaystyle\int_0^1 x10^{1+x^2} \, dx.$ **64.** $\displaystyle\int_1^3 \frac{\log_3 x}{x} \, dx.$

65. $\displaystyle\int_{10}^{100} \frac{dx}{x \log_{10} x}.$ **66.** $\displaystyle\int_0^1 \frac{5p^{\sqrt{x+1}}}{\sqrt{x+1}} \, dx.$ **67.** $\displaystyle\int_0^1 (2^x + x^2) \, dx.$

Use Table 7.2.1 to estimate the following logarithms.

68. $\log_{10} 4$.   **69.** $\log_{10} 7$.   **70.** $\log_{10} 12$.   **71.** $\log_{10} 45$.

72. Prove that

$$\lim_{h \to 0} (1 + h)^{1/h} = e.$$

HINT: At $x = 1$ the logarithm function has derivative 1:

$$\lim_{h \to 0} \frac{\ln (1 + h) - \ln 1}{h} = 1.$$

7.6 ⋯⋯MORE INTEGRATION OF TRIGONOMETRIC FUNCTIONS

In Section 5.12 you saw that

(7.6.1)

$$\int \cos x \, dx = \sin x + C, \qquad \int \sin x \, dx = -\cos x + C,$$

$$\int \sec^2 x \, dx = \tan x + C, \qquad \int \csc^2 x \, dx = -\cot x + C,$$

$$\int \sec x \tan x \, dx = \sec x + C, \qquad \int \csc x \cot x \, dx = -\csc x + C,$$

$$\int \cos^2 x \, dx = \frac{x}{2} + \frac{\sin 2x}{4} + C, \qquad \int \sin^2 x \, dx = \frac{x}{2} - \frac{\sin 2x}{4} + C.$$

Now that you are familiar with the logarithm function, we can add four more basic formulas to the list.

(7.6.2)

$$(i) \quad \int \tan x \, dx = \ln |\sec x| + C.$$

$$(ii) \quad \int \cot x \, dx = \ln |\sin x| + C.$$

$$(iii) \quad \int \sec x \, dx = \ln |\sec x + \tan x| + C.$$

$$(iv) \quad \int \csc x \, dx = \ln |\csc x - \cot x| + C.$$

Each of these formulas can be derived as follows:

$$\int \frac{g'(x)}{g(x)} \, dx = \int \frac{du}{u} = \ln |u| + C = \ln |g(x)| + C.$$

$$\underset{\text{set } u = g(x), \quad du = g'(x) \, dx}{\llcorner}$$

Derivation of Formulas (i)–(iii)

(i) $\displaystyle \int \tan x \, dx = \int \frac{\sin x}{\cos x} \, dx$ [set $u = \cos x, \quad du = -\sin x \, dx$]

$$= -\int \frac{du}{u} = -\ln |u| + C$$

$$= -\ln |\cos x| + C = \ln \left| \frac{1}{\cos x} \right| + C = \ln |\sec x| + C. \quad \square$$

(ii) $\displaystyle \int \cot x \, dx = \int \frac{\cos x}{\sin x} \, dx$ [set $u = \sin x, \quad du = \cos x \, dx$]

$$= \int \frac{du}{u} = \ln |u| + C = \ln |\sin x| + C. \quad \square$$

(iii) $\displaystyle \int \sec x \, dx \overset{\dagger}{=} \int \sec x \, \frac{\sec x + \tan x}{\sec x + \tan x} \, dx = \int \frac{\sec x \tan x + \sec^2 x}{\sec x + \tan x} \, dx$

[set $u = \sec x + \tan x, \quad du = (\sec x \tan x + \sec^2 x) \, dx$]

$$= \int \frac{du}{u} = \ln |u| + C = \ln |\sec x + \tan x| + C. \quad \square$$

The derivation of formula (iv) is left to you.

PROBLEM. Calculate

$$\int \cot \pi x \, dx.$$

Solution. Set

$$u = \pi x, \qquad du = \pi \, dx.$$

$$\int \cot \pi x \, dx = \frac{1}{\pi} \int \cot u \, du = \frac{1}{\pi} \ln |\sin u| + C = \frac{1}{\pi} \ln |\sin \pi x| + C. \quad \square$$

REMARK. The u-substitution simplifies many calculations, but you'll find with experience that you can carry out many integrations without it. $\square$

PROBLEM. Evaluate

$$\int_0^{\pi/8} \sec 2x \, dx.$$

Solution

$$\int_0^{\pi/8} \sec 2x \, dx = \frac{1}{2} \left[\ln |\sec 2x + \tan 2x| \right]_0^{\pi/8}$$

$$= \frac{1}{2} [\ln (\sqrt{2} + 1) - \ln 1] = \frac{1}{2} \ln (\sqrt{2} + 1). \quad \square$$

---

† Only experience prompts us to multiply numerator and denominator by $\sec x + \tan x$.

Whenever the integrand is a quotient, a useful tactic is to see if the integral can be written in the form $\int \dfrac{du}{u}$.

PROBLEM. Calculate

$$\int \frac{\cos 3x}{2 + \sin 3x}\, dx.$$

Solution. Set

$$u = 2 + \sin 3x, \qquad du = 3 \cos 3x\, dx.$$

$$\int \frac{\cos 3x}{2 + \sin 3x}\, dx = \frac{1}{3} \int \frac{du}{u} = \frac{1}{3} \ln |u| + C = \frac{1}{3} \ln |2 + \sin 3x| + C. \quad \square$$

PROBLEM. Evaluate

$$\int_{\pi/4}^{\pi/3} \frac{\sec^2 x}{1 + \tan x}\, dx.$$

Solution

$$\int_{\pi/4}^{\pi/3} \frac{\sec^2 x}{1 + \tan x}\, dx = \left[\ln (1 + \tan x) \right]_{\pi/4}^{\pi/3}$$

$$= \ln (1 + \sqrt{3}) - \ln (1 + 1) = \ln \left(\frac{1 + \sqrt{3}}{2} \right). \quad \square$$

EXERCISES

Calculate these indefinite integrals.

1. $\displaystyle\int \tan 3x\, dx.$

2. $\displaystyle\int \sec \frac{\pi}{2} x\, dx.$

3. $\displaystyle\int \csc \pi x\, dx.$

4. $\displaystyle\int \cot (\pi - x)\, dx.$

5. $\displaystyle\int e^x \cot e^x\, dx.$

6. $\displaystyle\int \frac{\csc^2 x}{2 + \cot x}\, dx.$

7. $\displaystyle\int \frac{\sin 2x}{3 - 2 \cos 2x}\, dx.$

8. $\displaystyle\int e^{\csc x} \csc x \cot x\, dx.$

9. $\displaystyle\int e^{\tan 3x} \sec^2 3x\, dx.$

10. $\displaystyle\int e^x \cos e^x\, dx.$

11. $\displaystyle\int x \sec x^2\, dx.$

12. $\displaystyle\int \frac{\sec e^{-2x}}{e^{2x}}\, dx.$

13. $\displaystyle\int \cot x \ln (\sin x)\, dx.$

14. $\displaystyle\int \frac{\tan (\ln x)}{x}\, dx.$

15. $\displaystyle\int (1 + \sec x)^2\, dx.$

16. $\displaystyle\int \tan x \ln (\sec x)\, dx.$

17. $\displaystyle\int \left(\frac{\csc x}{1 + \cot x} \right)^2 dx.$

18. $\displaystyle\int (3 - \csc x)^2\, dx.$

Evaluate these definite integrals.

19. $\displaystyle\int_{\pi/6}^{\pi/2} \frac{\cos x}{1 + \sin x}\, dx.$

20. $\displaystyle\int_{\pi/4}^{\pi/2} (1 + \csc x)^2\, dx.$

21. $\displaystyle\int_{\pi/4}^{\pi/2} \cot x\, dx.$

22. $\displaystyle\int_{1/4}^{1/3} \tan \pi x\, dx.$

23. $\displaystyle\int_{0}^{\ln \pi/4} e^x \sec e^x\, dx.$

24. $\displaystyle\int_{\pi/4}^{\pi/2} \frac{\csc^2 x}{3 + \cot x}\, dx.$

Sketch the region bounded by the curves and find its area.

25. $y = \sec x$, $y = 2$, $x = 0$, $x = \pi/6$.   **26.** $y = \csc \frac{1}{2}\pi x$, $y = x$, $x = \frac{1}{2}$.
27. $y = \tan x$, $y = 1$, $x = 0$.   **28.** $y = \sec x$, $y = \cos x$, $x = \pi/4$.

7.7 ······THE INVERSE TRIGONOMETRIC FUNCTIONS

Since none of the trigonometric functions are one-to-one, none of them have inverses. What then are the inverse trigonometric functions?

The Inverse Sine

The range of the sine function is the closed interval $[-1, 1]$. Although not one-to-one on its full domain, the sine function is one-to-one on the closed interval $[-\frac{1}{2}\pi, \frac{1}{2}\pi]$, and on that interval it takes on as a value every number in $[-1, 1]$. Thus, if $x \in [-1, 1]$, there is one and only one number in the interval $[-\frac{1}{2}\pi, \frac{1}{2}\pi]$ at which the sine function takes on the value x. This number is called the *inverse sine of x* and is written $\sin^{-1} x$.†

The *inverse sine function*

$$y = \sin^{-1} x, \qquad x \in [-1, 1]$$

is the inverse of the function

$$y = \sin x, \qquad x \in [-\tfrac{1}{2}\pi, \tfrac{1}{2}\pi].$$

The graphs of these functions are pictured in Figure 7.7.1. Each curve is the reflection of the other in the line $y = x$.

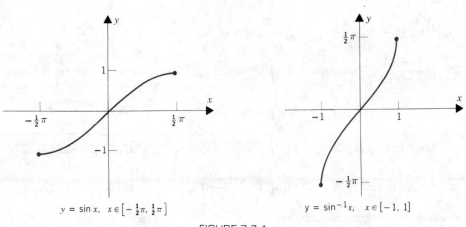

$$y = \sin x, \; x \in \left[-\tfrac{1}{2}\pi, \tfrac{1}{2}\pi\right] \qquad\qquad y = \sin^{-1}x, \; x \in [-1, 1]$$

FIGURE 7.7.1

---

† *Caution:* The -1 is not an exponent. Do not confuse $\sin^{-1} x$ with the reciprocal $1/(\sin x)$.

Because these functions are inverses,

(7.7.1) | for all $x \in [-1, 1]$ $\sin(\sin^{-1} x) = x$ |

and

(7.7.2) | for all $x \in [-\frac{1}{2}\pi, \frac{1}{2}\pi]$ $\sin^{-1}(\sin x) = x$. |

Table 7.7.1 gives some representative values of the sine function from $x = -\frac{1}{2}\pi$ to $x = \frac{1}{2}\pi$. Reversing the order of the columns we have a table for the inverse sine (Table 7.7.2).

TABLE 7.7.1			TABLE 7.7.2	
x	$\sin x$		x	$\sin^{-1} x$
$-\frac{1}{2}\pi$	-1		-1	$-\frac{1}{2}\pi$
$-\frac{1}{3}\pi$	$-\frac{1}{2}\sqrt{3}$		$-\frac{1}{2}\sqrt{3}$	$-\frac{1}{3}\pi$
$-\frac{1}{4}\pi$	$-\frac{1}{2}\sqrt{2}$		$-\frac{1}{2}\sqrt{2}$	$-\frac{1}{4}\pi$
$-\frac{1}{6}\pi$	$-\frac{1}{2}$		$-\frac{1}{2}$	$-\frac{1}{6}\pi$
0	0		0	0
$\frac{1}{6}\pi$	$\frac{1}{2}$		$\frac{1}{2}$	$\frac{1}{6}\pi$
$\frac{1}{4}\pi$	$\frac{1}{2}\sqrt{2}$		$\frac{1}{2}\sqrt{2}$	$\frac{1}{4}\pi$
$\frac{1}{3}\pi$	$\frac{1}{2}\sqrt{3}$		$\frac{1}{2}\sqrt{3}$	$\frac{1}{3}\pi$
$\frac{1}{2}\pi$	1		1	$\frac{1}{2}\pi$

On the basis of Table 7.7.2 one could guess that for all $x \in [-1, 1]$

$$\sin^{-1}(-x) = -\sin^{-1} x.$$

This is indeed the case. Being the inverse of an odd function ($\sin(-x) = -\sin x$ for all $x \in [-\frac{1}{2}\pi, \frac{1}{2}\pi]$), the inverse sine is itself an odd function. (Check that out.)

Table 4 at the back of the book gives the values of the principal trigonometric functions from 0 radians to 1.58 radians (approximately $\frac{1}{2}\pi$ radians). According to that table, for example,

$$\sin 0.32 \cong 0.315 \quad \text{and} \quad \sin 0.81 \cong 0.724.$$

Reading backward from that table and using the fact that the inverse sine is an odd function, we have

$$\sin^{-1} 0.315 \cong 0.32, \quad \sin^{-1}(-0.724) = -\sin^{-1} 0.724 \cong -0.81.$$

PROBLEM. Calculate if defined:

(a) $\sin^{-1}(\sin \frac{1}{16}\pi)$.   (b) $\sin^{-1}(\sin \frac{5}{2}\pi)$.   (c) $\sin(\sin^{-1} \frac{1}{3})$.

(d) $\sin^{-1}(\sin \frac{9}{5}\pi)$.   (e) $\sin(\sin^{-1} 2)$.

Solution

(a) Since $\frac{1}{16}\pi$ is within the interval $[-\frac{1}{2}\pi, \frac{1}{2}\pi]$, we know by (7.7.2) that

$$\sin^{-1}(\sin \tfrac{1}{16}\pi) = \tfrac{1}{16}\pi.$$

(b) Since $\frac{5}{2}\pi$ is not within the interval $[-\frac{1}{2}\pi, \frac{1}{2}\pi]$, we cannot apply (7.7.2) directly. However, $\frac{5}{2}\pi = \frac{1}{2}\pi + 2\pi$. Thus

$$\sin^{-1}(\sin \tfrac{5}{2}\pi) = \sin^{-1}(\sin(\tfrac{1}{2}\pi + 2\pi)) = \sin^{-1}(\sin \tfrac{1}{2}\pi) = \tfrac{1}{2}\pi.$$

by (7.7.2) ⌐

(c) By (7.7.1)

$$\sin(\sin^{-1}\tfrac{1}{3}) = \tfrac{1}{3}.$$

(d) Since $\frac{9}{5}\pi$ is not within the interval $[-\frac{1}{2}\pi, \frac{1}{2}\pi]$, we cannot apply (7.7.2) directly. However, $\frac{9}{5}\pi = 2\pi - \frac{1}{5}\pi$. Thus

$$\sin^{-1}(\sin \tfrac{9}{5}\pi) = \sin^{-1}(\sin(2\pi - \tfrac{1}{5}\pi)) = \sin^{-1}(\sin(-\tfrac{1}{5}\pi)) = -\tfrac{1}{5}\pi.$$

by (7.7.2) ⌐

(e) The expression $\sin(\sin^{-1} 2)$ makes no sense since 2 is not within the domain of the inverse sine. The inverse sine is defined only on $[-1, 1]$. □

If $0 < x < 1$, then $\sin^{-1} x$ is the radian measure of the acute angle that has sine x. We can construct an angle of radian measure $\sin^{-1} x$ by drawing a right triangle with a leg of length x and a hypotenuse of length 1. (Figure 7.7.2)

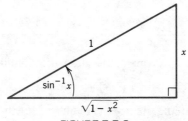

FIGURE 7.7.2

Reading from the figure we have

$$\sin(\sin^{-1} x) = x, \qquad\qquad \cos(\sin^{-1} x) = \sqrt{1 - x^2}$$

$$\tan(\sin^{-1} x) = \frac{x}{\sqrt{1 - x^2}}, \qquad \cot(\sin^{-1} x) = \frac{\sqrt{1 - x^2}}{x}$$

$$\sec(\sin^{-1} x) = \frac{1}{\sqrt{1 - x^2}}, \qquad \csc(\sin^{-1} x) = \frac{1}{x}.$$

Since the derivative of the sine function,

$$\frac{d}{dx}(\sin x) = \cos x,$$

does not take on the value 0 on the *open* interval $(-\frac{1}{2}\pi, \frac{1}{2}\pi)$, the inverse sine function is differentiable on the *open* interval $(-1, 1)$.† We can find the derivative as follows:

$$y = \sin^{-1} x,$$

$$\sin y = x,$$

$$\cos y \frac{dy}{dx} = 1,$$

$$\frac{dy}{dx} = \frac{1}{\cos y} = \frac{1}{\sqrt{1 - x^2}}. \quad \square$$

In short

(7.7.3)
$$\frac{d}{dx}(\sin^{-1} x) = \frac{1}{\sqrt{1 - x^2}}.$$

PROBLEM. Find

$$\frac{d}{dx}[\sin^{-1}(3x^2)].$$

Solution. In general, by the chain rule,

$$\frac{d}{dx}[\sin^{-1} u] = \frac{d}{du}[\sin^{-1} u]\frac{du}{dx} = \frac{1}{\sqrt{1 - u^2}}\frac{du}{dx}.$$

Thus

$$\frac{d}{dx}[\sin^{-1}(3x^2)] = \frac{1}{\sqrt{1 - (3x^2)^2}}\frac{d}{dx}(3x^2) = \frac{6x}{\sqrt{1 - 9x^4}}. \quad \square$$

PROBLEM. Show that for $a > 0$

(7.7.4)
$$\int \frac{dx}{\sqrt{a^2 - x^2}} = \sin^{-1}\left(\frac{x}{a}\right) + C.$$

Solution. We change variables so that the a^2 becomes 1 and we can use (7.7.3). We set

$$au = x, \qquad a\,du = dx.$$

Then

$$\int \frac{dx}{\sqrt{a^2 - x^2}} = \int \frac{a\,du}{\sqrt{a^2 - a^2 u^2}} = \int \frac{du}{\sqrt{1 - u^2}} = \sin^{-1} u + C = \sin^{-1}\left(\frac{x}{a}\right) + C. \quad \square$$

since $a > 0$ ⟶

---

† See the first paragraph of Section 3.8.

PROBLEM. Evaluate

$$\int_0^{\sqrt{3}} \frac{dx}{\sqrt{4-x^2}}.$$

Solution. By (7.7.4)

$$\int \frac{dx}{\sqrt{4-x^2}} = \sin^{-1}\left(\frac{x}{2}\right) + C.$$

It follows that

$$\int_0^{\sqrt{3}} \frac{dx}{\sqrt{4-x^2}} = \left[\sin^{-1}\left(\frac{x}{2}\right)\right]_0^{\sqrt{3}} = \sin^{-1}\frac{\sqrt{3}}{2} - \sin^{-1}0 = \frac{\pi}{3} - 0 = \frac{\pi}{3}. \quad \square$$

The Inverse Tangent

Although not one-to-one on its full domain, the tangent function is one-to-one on the open interval $(-\frac{1}{2}\pi, \frac{1}{2}\pi)$ and on that interval it takes on as a value every real number. Thus, if x is real, there is one and only one number in the open interval $(-\frac{1}{2}\pi, \frac{1}{2}\pi)$ at which the tangent function takes on the value x. This number is called the *inverse tangent of x* and is written $\tan^{-1} x$.

The *inverse tangent function*

$$y = \tan^{-1} x, \qquad x \text{ real}$$

is the inverse of the function

$$y = \tan x, \qquad x \in (-\tfrac{1}{2}\pi, \tfrac{1}{2}\pi).$$

The graphs of these two functions are given in Figure 7.7.3. Each curve is a reflection of the other in the line $y = x$. While the tangent has vertical asymptotes, the inverse tangent has horizontal asymptotes. Both functions are odd functions.

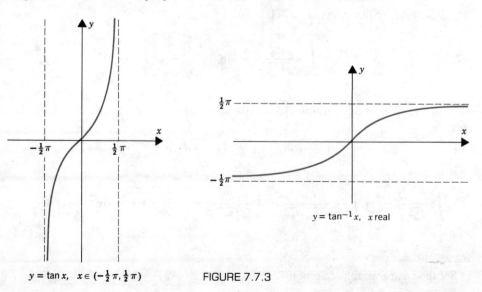

$y = \tan x, \quad x \in (-\tfrac{1}{2}\pi, \tfrac{1}{2}\pi)$ FIGURE 7.7.3

$y = \tan^{-1} x, \quad x \text{ real}$

Because these functions are inverses,

(7.7.5)   for all real numbers x $\tan (\tan^{-1} x) = x$

and

(7.7.6)   for all $x \in (-\tfrac{1}{2}\pi, \tfrac{1}{2}\pi)$ $\tan^{-1} (\tan x) = x.$

It's hard to make a mistake with the first relation since it applies for all real numbers. The second relation requires the usual care:

$$\tan^{-1} (\tan \tfrac{1}{4}\pi) = \tfrac{1}{4}\pi \quad \text{but} \quad \tan^{-1} (\tan \tfrac{7}{5}\pi) \neq \tfrac{7}{5}\pi.$$

We can calculate $\tan^{-1} (\tan \tfrac{7}{5}\pi)$ as follows:

$$\tan^{-1} (\tan \tfrac{7}{5}\pi) = \tan^{-1} (\tan (\tfrac{2}{5}\pi + \pi)) = \tan^{-1} (\tan \tfrac{2}{5}\pi) = \tfrac{2}{5}\pi.$$

The relation $\tan^{-1} (\tan \tfrac{2}{5}\pi) = \tfrac{2}{5}\pi$ is valid because $\tfrac{2}{5}\pi$ is within the interval $(-\tfrac{1}{2}\pi, \tfrac{1}{2}\pi)$.

If $x > 0$, then $\tan^{-1} x$ is the radian measure of the acute angle that has tangent x. We can construct an angle of radian measure $\tan^{-1} x$ by drawing a right triangle with legs of length x and 1 (Figure 7.7.4).

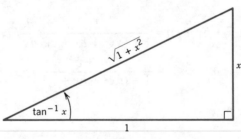

FIGURE 7.7.4

The values of

$$\tan (\tan^{-1} x), \quad \cot (\tan^{-1} x), \quad \sin (\tan^{-1} x),$$
$$\cos (\tan^{-1} x), \quad \sec (\tan^{-1} x), \quad \csc (\tan^{-1} x)$$

can all be read from this triangle.

Since the derivative of the tangent function

$$\frac{d}{dx} (\tan x) = \sec^2 x = \frac{1}{\cos^2 x},$$

is never 0, the inverse tangent function is everywhere differentiable (Section 3.8).

We can find the derivative as we did for the inverse sine:

$$y = \tan^{-1} x,$$
$$\tan y = x,$$
$$\sec^2 y \frac{dy}{dx} = 1,$$
$$\frac{dy}{dx} = \frac{1}{\sec^2 y} = \cos^2 y = \frac{1}{1 + x^2}. \quad \square$$

We have found that

(7.7.7)
$$\frac{d}{dx} (\tan^{-1} x) = \frac{1}{1 + x^2}.$$

PROBLEM. Calculate

$$\frac{d}{dx} [\tan^{-1} (ax^2 + bx + c)].$$

Solution. In general, by the chain rule,

$$\frac{d}{dx} [\tan^{-1} u] = \frac{d}{du} [\tan^{-1} u] \frac{du}{dx} = \frac{1}{1 + u^2} \frac{du}{dx}.$$

Thus

$$\frac{d}{dx} [\tan^{-1} (ax^2 + bx + c)] = \frac{1}{1 + (ax^2 + bx + c)^2} \frac{d}{dx} (ax^2 + bx + c)$$
$$= \frac{2ax + b}{1 + (ax^2 + bx + c)^2}. \quad \square$$

PROBLEM. Show that

(7.7.8)
$$\int \frac{dx}{a^2 + x^2} = \frac{1}{a} \tan^{-1} \left(\frac{x}{a} \right) + C.$$

Solution. We change variables so that the a^2 becomes 1 and we can use (7.7.7). We set

$$au = x, \qquad a \, du = dx.$$

Then

$$\int \frac{dx}{a^2 + x^2} = \int \frac{a \, du}{a^2 + a^2 u^2} = \frac{1}{a} \int \frac{du}{1 + u^2}$$
$$= \frac{1}{a} \tan^{-1} u + C = \frac{1}{a} \tan^{-1} \left(\frac{x}{a} \right) + C. \quad \square$$

PROBLEM. Evaluate

$$\int_0^2 \frac{dx}{4 + x^2}.$$

Solution. By (7.7.8)

$$\int \frac{dx}{4 + x^2} = \int \frac{dx}{2^2 + x^2} = \frac{1}{2} \tan^{-1}\left(\frac{x}{2}\right) + C$$

so that

$$\int_0^2 \frac{dx}{4 + x^2} = \left[\frac{1}{2} \tan^{-1}\left(\frac{x}{2}\right)\right]_0^2 = \frac{1}{2} \tan^{-1} 1 = \frac{\pi}{8}. \quad \square$$

The Other Trigonometric Inverses

There are four other trigonometric inverses:

the inverse cosine, $y = \cos^{-1} x$, is the inverse of

$$y = \cos x, \qquad x \in [0, \pi];$$

the inverse contangent, $y = \cot^{-1} x$, is the inverse of

$$y = \cot x, \qquad x \in (0, \pi);$$

the inverse secant, $y = \sec^{-1} x$, is the inverse of

$$y = \sec x, \qquad x \in [0, \tfrac{1}{2}\pi) \cup (\tfrac{1}{2}\pi, \pi];$$

the inverse cosecant, $y = \csc^{-1} x$, is the inverse of

$$y = \csc x, \qquad x \in [-\tfrac{1}{2}\pi, 0) \cup (0, \tfrac{1}{2}\pi].$$

Of these four functions only the first two are much used. Figure 7.7.5 shows them all between 0 and $\tfrac{1}{2}\pi$ in terms of right triangles.

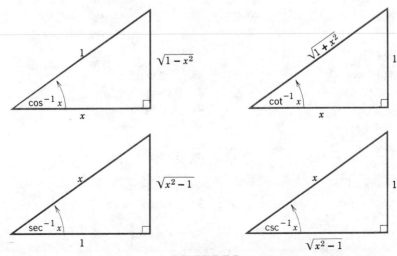

FIGURE 7.7.5

A Word on Notation

The ( )$^{-1}$ notation that we have been using for the trigonometric inverses is not the only notation in general use: the inverses

$$\sin^{-1} t, \quad \tan^{-1} t, \quad \cos^{-1} t, \quad \text{and so on}$$

are often written

$$\text{arc sin } t, \quad \text{arc tan } t, \quad \text{arc cos } t, \quad \text{etc.}$$

To familiarize you further with the notation, we use it in some of the exercises.

EXERCISES

Determine the exact value:

1. $\tan^{-1} 0$.
2. $\cos^{-1} 0$.
3. $\cos^{-1} \frac{1}{2}$.
4. $\tan^{-1} \sqrt{3}$.
5. $\tan^{-1} (-\sqrt{3})$.
6. $\cos^{-1} (-\frac{1}{2})$.
7. arc cos 1.
8. arc tan (-1).
9. arc sin $(-\frac{1}{2})$.
10. arc cos $(-\frac{1}{2}\sqrt{3})$.
11. $\cos (\cos^{-1} \frac{1}{2})$.
12. $\sin^{-1} (\sin \frac{7}{4}\pi)$.
13. $\tan^{-1} (\tan \frac{7}{4}\pi)$.
14. arc tan $(\tan \frac{5}{6}\pi)$.
15. $\cos (\text{arc sin } \frac{1}{2})$.
16. $\sin (\text{arc cos } \frac{1}{2})$.
17. $\tan^{-1} (\cos 0)$.
18. $\sin^{-1} (\sin (-\frac{7}{4}\pi))$.
19. $\sin (\cos^{-1} (-\frac{1}{2}))$.
20. arc tan $(\cos \frac{3}{2}\pi)$.

Find the approximate value by using Table 4 at the back of the book.

21. $\sin^{-1} 0.918$.
22. arc sin (-0.795).
23. $\tan^{-1} (-0.493)$.
24. arc tan 3.111.
25. arc cos (0.960).
26. $\cos^{-1} (-0.142)$.

Taking $x > 0$, calculate the following from Figure 7.7.4.

27. $\cos (\tan^{-1} x)$.
28. $\sin (\tan^{-1} x)$.
29. $\tan (\tan^{-1} x)$.
30. $\cot (\tan^{-1} x)$.
31. $\sec (\tan^{-1} x)$.
32. $\csc (\tan^{-1} x)$.

Taking $0 < x < 1$, calculate the following from an appropriate right triangle.

33. $\sin (\cos^{-1} x)$.
34. $\cos (\cot^{-1} x)$.
35. $\sec (\cot^{-1} x)$.
36. $\tan (\cos^{-1} x)$.
37. $\cot (\cos^{-1} x)$.
38. $\csc (\cot^{-1} x)$.

Differentiate.

39. $y = \tan^{-1} (x + 1)$.
40. $y = \tan^{-1} \sqrt{x}$.
41. $y = \sin^{-1} x^2$.
42. $f(x) = e^x \sin^{-1} x$.
43. $f(x) = x \sin^{-1} 2x$.
44. $f(x) = e^{\tan^{-1} x}$.
45. $u = (\sin^{-1} x)^2$.
46. $v = \tan^{-1} (e^x)$.

47. $y = \dfrac{\tan^{-1} x}{x}$.
48. $y = \tan^{-1} \left(\dfrac{2}{x}\right)$.

49. $f(x) = \sqrt{\tan^{-1} 2x}$.
50. $f(x) = \ln (\tan^{-1} x)$.
51. $y = \tan^{-1} (\ln x)$.
52. $y = \tan^{-1} (\sin x)$.

53. $\theta = \sin^{-1} (\sqrt{1 - r^2})$.
54. $\theta = \sin^{-1} \left(\dfrac{r}{r + 1}\right)$.

55. $\theta = \tan^{-1}\left(\dfrac{c+r}{1-cr}\right).$

56. $\theta = \tan^{-1}\left(\dfrac{1}{1+r^2}\right).$

57. $f(x) = \sqrt{c^2 - x^2} + c\,\sin^{-1}\left(\dfrac{x}{c}\right).$†

58. $f(x) = \tfrac{1}{3}\sin^{-1}(3x - 4x^2).$

59. $y = \dfrac{x}{\sqrt{c^2 - x^2}} - \sin^{-1}\left(\dfrac{x}{c}\right).$†

60. $y = x\sqrt{c^2 - x^2} + c^2\sin^{-1}\left(\dfrac{x}{c}\right).$†

61. Show that for $a > 0$

(7.7.9)
$$\int \frac{dx}{\sqrt{a^2 - (x+b)^2}} = \sin^{-1}\left(\frac{x+b}{a}\right) + C.$$

62. Show that for $a \neq 0$

(7.7.10)
$$\int \frac{dx}{a^2 + (x+b)^2} = \frac{1}{a}\tan^{-1}\left(\frac{x+b}{a}\right) + C.$$

Evaluate.

63. $\displaystyle\int_0^1 \frac{dx}{1 + x^2}.$

64. $\displaystyle\int_{-1}^1 \frac{dx}{1 + x^2}.$

65. $\displaystyle\int_0^{1/\sqrt{2}} \frac{dx}{\sqrt{1 - x^2}}.$

66. $\displaystyle\int_0^1 \frac{dx}{\sqrt{4 - x^2}}.$

67. $\displaystyle\int_0^5 \frac{dx}{25 + x^2}.$

68. $\displaystyle\int_{-4}^4 \frac{dx}{16 + x^2}.$

69. $\displaystyle\int_0^{3/2} \frac{dx}{9 + 4x^2}.$

70. $\displaystyle\int_2^5 \frac{dx}{9 + (x-2)^2}.$

71. $\displaystyle\int_{-3}^{-2} \frac{dx}{\sqrt{4 - (x+3)^2}}.$

72. $\displaystyle\int_{\ln 2}^{\ln 3} \frac{e^{-x}}{\sqrt{1 - e^{-2x}}}\,dx.$

73. $\displaystyle\int_0^{\ln 2} \frac{e^x}{1 + e^{2x}}\,dx.$

74. $\displaystyle\int_0^{1/2} \frac{1}{\sqrt{3 - 4x^2}}\,dx.$

75. Show that for $x < -1$ and $x > 1$

(7.7.11)
$$\frac{d}{dx}(\sec^{-1} x) = \frac{1}{|x|\sqrt{x^2 - 1}}.$$

Determine the following derivatives.

76. $\dfrac{d}{dx}(\cot^{-1} x)$ for all real x.

77. $\dfrac{d}{dx}(\cos^{-1} x)$ for $-1 < x < 1$.

78. $\dfrac{d}{dx}(\csc^{-1} x)$ for $x < -1$ and $x > 1$.

---

† Take $c > 0$

7.8 ······ADDITIONAL EXERCISES

1. Find the minimum value of $y = ae^{kx} + be^{-kx}$, $a > 0$, $b > 0$.
2. Show that, if $y = \frac{1}{2}a(e^{x/a} + e^{-x/a})$, then $y'' = y/a^2$.
3. Find the points of inflection of the graph of $y = e^{-x^2}$.
4. A rectangle has one side on the x-axis and the two upper vertices on the graph of $y = e^{-x^2}$. Where should the upper vertices be placed so as to maximize the area of the rectangle?
5. A telegraph cable consists of a core of copper wires with a covering made of nonconducting material. If x is the ratio of the radius of the core to the thickness of the covering, the speed of signaling is proportional to the product $x^2 \ln(1/x)$. For what value of x is the speed a maximum?
6. A rectangle has two sides along the coordinate axes and one vertex at a point P that moves along the curve $y = e^x$ in such a way that y increases at the rate of $\frac{1}{2}$ unit per minute. How fast is the area of the rectangle increasing when $y = 3$?
7. Find

$$\lim_{h \to 0} \frac{1}{h}(e^h - 1).$$

8. Find the extreme values and points of inflection of

$$y = \frac{x}{\ln x}.$$

Find the area below the graph.

9. $y = \dfrac{x}{x^2 + 1}$, $x \in [0, 1]$.

10. $y = \dfrac{1}{x^2 + 1}$, $x \in [0, 1]$.

11. $y = \dfrac{1}{\sqrt{1 - x^2}}$, $x \in [0, \frac{1}{2}]$.

12. $y = \dfrac{x}{\sqrt{1 - x^2}}$, $x \in [0, \frac{1}{2}]$.

A particle moves along a coordinate line so that at time t it has position $x(t)$, velocity $v(t)$, and acceleration $a(t)$. Find

13. $x(1)$ given that $x(0) = 0$ and $v(t) = 1/(t^2 + 1)$.
14. $a(1)$ given that $v(t) = 1/(t^2 + 1)$.
15. $a(0)$ given that $x(t) = \tan^{-1}(1 + t)$.
16. $v(0)$ given that $v(1) = 1$ and $a(t) = (\tan^{-1} t)/(t^2 + 1)$.

17. Show that the average slope of the logarithm curve from $x = a$ to $x = b$ is

$$\frac{1}{b - a} \ln \frac{b}{a}.$$

18. Find the average value of $\sin^2 x$ from $x = 0$ to $x = \pi$. (This average is used in the theory of alternating currents.)
19. Find the area of the region bounded by the curve $xy = a^2$, the x-axis, and the vertical lines $x = a$, $x = 2a$.
20. What are the averages of the sine and cosine on an interval of length 2π?
21. A ball is thrown from ground level. Take the origin as the point of release, take the x-axis as ground level, measure distances in feet, and take the path of the ball as given by the equation $y = x - \frac{1}{100}x^2$. (a) At what angle is the ball released? (b) At what angle will it strike a wall 75 feet away? (c) At what angle will it fall on a horizontal roof 16 feet high?

22. An object moves with acceleration $a(t) = g - kv(t)$, initial velocity $v = 0$, and initial position $x = 0$. Show that the following relations hold.

   (a) $v(t) = \dfrac{g}{k}(1 - e^{-kt})$.   (b) $x(t) = \dfrac{g}{k^2}(kt + e^{-kt} - 1)$.

   (c) $kx(t) + v(t) + \dfrac{g}{k}\ln\left(1 - \dfrac{kv(t)}{g}\right) = 0$.

Sketch the graph and find the volume generated by revolving the region below it about the x-axis.

23. $f(x) = \dfrac{1}{\sqrt{x}}, \quad x \in [1, 4]$.   **24.** $f(x) = \sin x, \quad x \in [0, \pi/4]$.

25. $f(x) = \dfrac{1}{\sqrt{1 + x^2}}, \quad x \in [0, 1]$.   **26.** $f(x) = e^x, \quad x \in [0, 1]$.

27. $f(x) = \cos\dfrac{\pi}{2}x, \quad x \in [0, 1]$.   **28.** $f(x) = \sqrt{\sec\dfrac{\pi}{2}x}, \quad x \in \left[-\dfrac{1}{2}, \dfrac{1}{2}\right]$.

29. Show that for all positive integers $m < n$

$$\ln\frac{n+1}{m} < \frac{1}{m} + \frac{1}{m+1} + \cdots + \frac{1}{n} < \ln\frac{n}{m-1}.$$

HINT:

$$\frac{1}{k+1} < \int_k^{k+1} \frac{dx}{x} < \frac{1}{k}.$$

30. Show that

$$\sin^{-1} x + \cos^{-1} x = \frac{\pi}{2} \qquad \text{for } x \in \left[0, \frac{\pi}{2}\right].$$

7.9 ······THE HYPERBOLIC SINE AND COSINE

The *hyperbolic sine* and *hyperbolic cosine* are the functions

(7.9.1) $\sinh x = \tfrac{1}{2}(e^x - e^{-x}), \qquad \cosh x = \tfrac{1}{2}(e^x + e^{-x})$.

The reasons for these names will become apparent as we go on.
   Since

$$\frac{d}{dx}(\sinh x) = \frac{d}{dx}[\tfrac{1}{2}(e^x - e^{-x})] = \tfrac{1}{2}(e^x + e^{-x})$$

and

$$\frac{d}{dx}(\cosh x) = \frac{d}{dx}[\tfrac{1}{2}(e^x + e^{-x})] = \tfrac{1}{2}(e^x - e^{-x}),$$

we have

(7.9.2)
$$\frac{d}{dx}(\sinh x) = \cosh x, \qquad \frac{d}{dx}(\cosh x) = \sinh x.$$

In short, each of these functions is the derivative of the other.

The Graphs

We begin with the hyperbolic sine. Since

$$\sinh(-x) = \tfrac{1}{2}(e^{-x} - e^{x}) = -\tfrac{1}{2}(e^{x} - e^{-x}) = -\sinh x,$$

the hyperbolic sine is an odd function. The graph is therefore symmetric about the origin. Since

$$\frac{d}{dx}(\sinh x) = \cosh x = \tfrac{1}{2}(e^{x} + e^{-x}) > 0 \qquad \text{for all real } x,$$

the hyperbolic sine increases everywhere. Since

$$\frac{d^{2}}{dx^{2}}(\sinh x) = \frac{d}{dx}(\cosh x) = \sinh x = \tfrac{1}{2}(e^{x} - e^{-x}),$$

you can see that

$$\frac{d^{2}}{dx^{2}}(\sinh x) \quad \text{is} \quad \begin{cases} \text{negative,} & \text{for} \quad x < 0 \\ 0, & \text{at} \quad x = 0 \\ \text{positive,} & \text{for} \quad x > 0 \end{cases}.$$

The graph is therefore concave down on $(-\infty, 0)$ and concave up on $(0, \infty)$. The point $(0, \sinh 0) = (0, 0)$ is the only point of inflection. The slope at the origin is $\cosh 0 = 1$. A sketch of the graph appears in Figure 7.9.1. $\square$

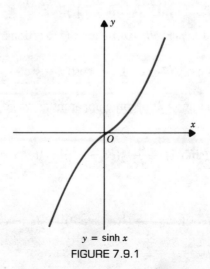

$y = \sinh x$

FIGURE 7.9.1

We turn now to the hyperbolic cosine. Since

$$\cosh(-x) = \tfrac{1}{2}(e^{-x} + e^x) = \tfrac{1}{2}(e^x + e^{-x}) = \cosh x,$$

the hyperbolic cosine is an even function. The graph is therefore symmetric about the y-axis. Since

$$\frac{d}{dx}(\cosh x) = \sinh x,$$

you can see that

$$\frac{d}{dx}(\cosh x) \quad \text{is} \quad \begin{cases} \text{negative,} & \text{for} \quad x < 0 \\ \quad\quad 0, & \text{at} \quad\;\; x = 0 \\ \text{positive,} & \text{for} \quad x > 0 \end{cases}.$$

The function therefore decreases on $(-\infty, 0]$ and increases on $[0, \infty)$. The number

$$\cosh 0 = \tfrac{1}{2}(e^0 + e^{-0}) = \tfrac{1}{2}(1 + 1) = 1$$

is a local and absolute minimum. There are no other extreme values. Since

$$\frac{d^2}{dx^2}(\cosh x) = \frac{d}{dx}(\sinh x) = \cosh x > 0 \qquad \text{for all real } x,$$

the graph is everywhere concave up. (Figure 7.9.2)   □

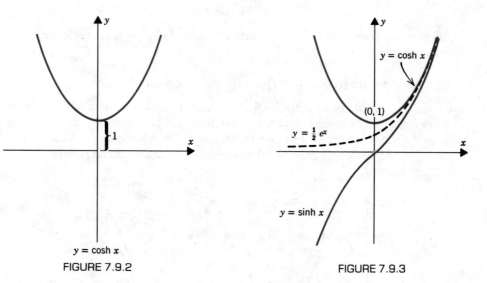

FIGURE 7.9.2   FIGURE 7.9.3

Figure 7.9.3 shows the graphs of three functions

$$y = \sinh x = \tfrac{1}{2}(e^x - e^{-x}), \qquad y = \tfrac{1}{2}e^x, \qquad y = \cosh x = \tfrac{1}{2}(e^x + e^{-x}).$$

For all real x

$$\sinh x < \tfrac{1}{2}e^x < \cosh x. \qquad\qquad (e^{-x} > 0)$$

Although markedly different for negative x, these functions are almost indistinguishable for large positive x. Reason: as $x \to \infty$, $e^{-x} \to 0$.

Identities

The hyperbolic sine and cosine satisfy identities similar to those satisfied by the "circular" sine and cosine.

(7.9.3)

$$\cosh^2 t - \sinh^2 t = 1,$$
$$\sinh (t + s) = \sinh t \cosh s + \cosh t \sinh s,$$
$$\cosh (t + s) = \cosh t \cosh s + \sinh t \sinh s,$$
$$\sinh 2t = 2 \sinh t \cosh t,$$
$$\cosh 2t = \cosh^2 t + \sinh^2 t.$$

The verification of these identities is left to you as an exercise.

Relation to the Hyperbola $x^2 - y^2 = 1$

The hyperbolic sine and cosine are related to the hyperbola $x^2 - y^2 = 1$ much as the "circular" sine and cosine are related to the circle $x^2 + y^2 = 1$:

1. For each real t

$$\cos^2 t + \sin^2 t = 1$$

and thus the point $(\cos t, \sin t)$ lies on the circle $x^2 + y^2 = 1$; for each real t

$$\cosh^2 t - \sinh^2 t = 1$$

and thus the point $(\cosh t, \sinh t)$ lies on the hyperbola $x^2 - y^2 = 1$.

2. For each t in $[0, 2\pi]$ (see Figure 7.9.4), the number $\frac{1}{2}t$ gives the area of the circular sector generated by the circular arc that begins at $(1, 0)$ and ends at $(\cos t, \sin t)$; as we prove below, for each $t > 0$ (see Figure 7.9.5), the number $\frac{1}{2}t$ gives the area of the hyperbolic sector generated by the hyperbolic arc that begins at $(1, 0)$ and ends at $(\cosh t, \sinh t)$.

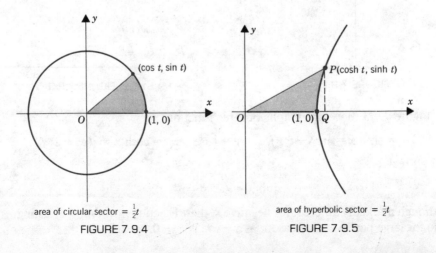

area of circular sector $= \frac{1}{2}t$

FIGURE 7.9.4

area of hyperbolic sector $= \frac{1}{2}t$

FIGURE 7.9.5

Proof.   Let's call the area of the hyperbolic sector $A(t)$.   It's not hard to see that

$$A(t) = \tfrac{1}{2} \cosh t \sinh t - \int_1^{\cosh t} \sqrt{x^2 - 1}\; dx.$$

The first term, $\tfrac{1}{2} \cosh t \sinh t$, gives the area of the triangle OPQ, and the integral

$$\int_1^{\cosh t} \sqrt{x^2 - 1}\; dx$$

gives the area of the unshaded portion of the triangle.   We wish to show that

$$A(t) = \tfrac{1}{2}t \qquad \text{for all } t \geq 0.$$

We will do so by showing that

$$A'(t) = \tfrac{1}{2} \quad \text{for all } t > 0 \qquad \text{and} \qquad A(0) = 0.$$

Differentiating $A(t)$, we have

$$A'(t) = \tfrac{1}{2}\left[\cosh t \,\frac{d}{dt}\,(\sinh t) + \sinh t \,\frac{d}{dt}\,(\cosh t)\right] - \frac{d}{dt}\!\left(\int_1^{\cosh t} \sqrt{x^2 - 1}\; dx\right)$$

and therefore

(1) $$A'(t) = \tfrac{1}{2}(\cosh^2 t + \sinh^2 t) - \frac{d}{dt}\!\left(\int_1^{\cosh t} \sqrt{x^2 - 1}\; dx\right).$$

Now we differentiate the integral:

$$\frac{d}{dt}\!\left(\int_1^{\cosh t} \sqrt{x^2 - 1}\; dx\right) = \underset{\underset{(5.9.7)}{\uparrow}}{\sqrt{\cosh^2 t - 1}}\; \frac{d}{dt}\,(\cosh t) = \sinh t \cdot \sinh t = \sinh^2 t.$$

Substituing this last expression into Equation (1), we have

$$A'(t) = \tfrac{1}{2}(\cosh^2 t + \sinh^2 t) - \sinh^2 t = \tfrac{1}{2}(\cosh^2 t - \sinh^2 t) = \tfrac{1}{2}.$$

It's not hard to see that $A(0) = 0$:

$$A(0) = \tfrac{1}{2} \cosh 0 \sinh 0 - \int_1^{\cosh 0} \sqrt{x^2 - 1}\; dx = 0. \quad \square$$

EXERCISES

Differentiate.

1. $y = \sinh x^2$.

2. $y = \cosh (x + a)$.

3. $y = \sqrt{\cosh ax}$.

4. $y = (\sinh ax)(\cosh ax)$.

5. $y = \dfrac{\sinh x}{\cosh x - 1}$.

6. $y = \dfrac{\sinh x}{x}$.

7. $y = a \sinh bx - b \cosh ax$.

8. $y = e^x (\cosh x + \sinh x)$.

9. $y = \ln |\sinh ax|$.

10. $y = \ln |1 - \cosh ax|$.

Verify the following identities.

11. $\cosh^2 t - \sinh^2 t = 1$.

12. $\sinh (t + s) = \sinh t \cosh s + \cosh t \sinh s$.

13. $\cosh(t + s) = \cosh t \cosh s + \sinh t \sinh s.$

14. $\sinh 2t = 2 \sinh t \cosh t.$

15. $\cosh 2t = \cosh^2 t + \sinh^2 t.$

Find the absolute extreme values.

16. $y = 5 \cosh x + 4 \sinh x.$ **17.** $y = -5 \cosh x + 4 \sinh x.$

18. $y = 4 \cosh x + 5 \sinh x.$

19. Show that for each positive integer n

$$(\cosh x + \sinh x)^n = \cosh nx + \sinh nx.$$

20. Verify that $y = A \cosh cx + B \sinh cx$ satisfies the equation $y'' - c^2 y = 0.$

21. Determine A, B, and c so that $y = A \cosh cx + B \sinh cx$ satisfies the conditions $y'' - 9y = 0$, $y(0) = 2$, and $y'(0) = 1$.   Take $c > 0$.

22. Determine A, B, and c so that $y = A \cosh cx + B \sinh cx$ satisfies the conditions $4y'' - y = 0$, $y(0) = 1$, and $y'(0) = 2$.   Take $c > 0$.

7.10····THE OTHER HYPERBOLIC FUNCTIONS

The hyperbolic tangent is defined by setting

$$\tanh x = \frac{\sinh x}{\cosh x} = \frac{e^x - e^{-x}}{e^x + e^{-x}}.$$

There is also a *hyperbolic cotangent*

$$\coth x = \frac{\cosh x}{\sinh x},$$

a *hyperbolic secant*

$$\operatorname{sech} x = \frac{1}{\cosh x},$$

and a *hyperbolic cosecant*

$$\operatorname{csch} x = \frac{1}{\sinh x}.$$

The derivatives are as follows:

(7.10.1)

$$\frac{d}{dx}(\tanh x) = \operatorname{sech}^2 x,$$

$$\frac{d}{dx}(\coth x) = -\operatorname{csch}^2 x,$$

$$\frac{d}{dx}(\operatorname{sech} x) = -\operatorname{sech} x \tanh x,$$

$$\frac{d}{dx}(\operatorname{csch} x) = -\operatorname{csch} x \coth x.$$

These formulas are easy to verify. For instance,

$$\frac{d}{dx}(\tanh x) = \frac{d}{dx}\left(\frac{\sinh x}{\cosh x}\right) = \frac{\cosh x \frac{d}{dx}(\sinh x) - \sinh x \frac{d}{dx}(\cosh x)}{\cosh^2 x}$$

$$= \frac{\cosh^2 x - \sinh^2 x}{\cosh^2 x} = \frac{1}{\cosh^2 x} = \operatorname{sech}^2 x.$$

We leave it to you to verify the other formulas. □

Let's examine the hyperbolic tangent a little further. Since

$$\tanh(-x) = \frac{\sinh(-x)}{\cosh(-x)} = \frac{-\sinh x}{\cosh x} = -\tanh x,$$

the hyperbolic tangent is an odd function and thus the graph is symmetric about the origin. Since

$$\frac{d}{dx}(\tanh x) = \operatorname{sech}^2 x > 0 \qquad \text{for all real } x,$$

the function is everywhere increasing. From the relation

$$\tanh x = \frac{e^x - e^{-x}}{e^x + e^{-x}} = 1 - \frac{2}{e^{2x} + 1}$$

you can see that $\tanh x$ always remains between -1 and 1. Moreover,

$$\text{as } x \to \infty, \quad \tanh x \to 1 \qquad \text{and} \qquad \text{as } x \to -\infty, \quad \tanh x \to -1.$$

The lines $y = 1$ and $y = -1$ are horizontal asymptotes. To check on the concavity of the graph, we take the second derivative:

$$\frac{d^2}{dx^2}(\tanh x) = \frac{d}{dx}(\operatorname{sech}^2 x) = 2\operatorname{sech} x \frac{d}{dx}(\operatorname{sech} x)$$

$$= 2\operatorname{sech} x (-\operatorname{sech} x \tanh x)$$

$$= -2\operatorname{sech}^2 x \tanh x.$$

Since

$$\tanh x = \frac{e^x - e^{-x}}{e^x + e^{-x}} \quad \text{is} \quad \left\{ \begin{array}{lll} \text{negative,} & \text{for} & x < 0 \\ 0, & \text{at} & x = 0 \\ \text{positive,} & \text{for} & x > 0 \end{array} \right\},$$

you can see that

$$\frac{d^2}{dx^2}(\tanh x) \quad \text{is} \quad \left\{ \begin{array}{lll} \text{positive,} & \text{for} & x < 0 \\ 0, & \text{at} & x = 0 \\ \text{negative,} & \text{for} & x > 0 \end{array} \right\}.$$

The graph is therefore concave up on $(-\infty, 0)$ and concave down on $(0, \infty)$. The point $(0, \tanh 0) = (0, 0)$ is a point of inflection. At the origin the slope is

$$\operatorname{sech}^2 0 = \frac{1}{\cosh^2 0} = 1.$$

For a picture of the graph see Figure 7.10.1.

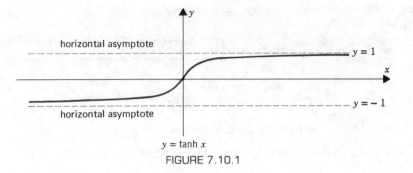

$y = \tanh x$

FIGURE 7.10.1

The Hyperbolic Inverses

The hyperbolic inverses that are important to us are the *inverse hyperbolic sine*, the *inverse hyperbolic cosine*, and the *inverse hyperbolic tangent*. These functions

$$y = \sinh^{-1} x, \qquad y = \cosh^{-1} x, \qquad y = \tanh^{-1} x$$

are the inverses of

$$y = \sinh x, \qquad y = \cosh x \quad (x \geq 0), \qquad y = \tanh x,$$

respectively.

THEOREM 7.10.2

   (i) $\sinh^{-1} x = \ln (x + \sqrt{x^2 + 1})$.   (*x* real)

   (ii) $\cosh^{-1} x = \ln (x + \sqrt{x^2 - 1})$.   ($x \geq 1$)

   (iii) $\tanh^{-1} x = \dfrac{1}{2} \ln \left(\dfrac{1 + x}{1 - x} \right)$.   ($-1 < x < 1$)

Proof.   To prove (i), we set

$$y = \sinh^{-1} x$$

and note that

$$\sinh y = x.$$

This gives in sequence

$$\tfrac{1}{2}(e^y - e^{-y}) = x, \qquad e^y - e^{-y} = 2x, \qquad e^{2y} - 2xe^y - 1 = 0.$$

This last equation is a quadratic equation in e^y. From the general quadratic formula we find that

$$e^y = \tfrac{1}{2}(2x \pm \sqrt{4x^2 + 4}) = x \pm \sqrt{x^2 + 1}.$$

Since $e^y > 0$, the minus sign on the right is impossible. Consequently, we have

$$e^y = x + \sqrt{x^2 + 1}$$

and, taking logs,

$$y = \ln (x + \sqrt{x^2 + 1}).$$

To prove (ii), we set

$$y = \cosh^{-1} x, \qquad x \geq 1$$

and note that

$$\cosh y = x \quad \text{and} \quad y \geq 0.$$

This gives in sequence

$$\tfrac{1}{2}(e^y + e^{-y}) = x, \qquad e^y + e^{-y} = 2x, \qquad e^{2y} - 2xe^y + 1 = 0.$$

Again we have a quadratic in e^y. Here the general quadratic formula gives

$$e^y = \tfrac{1}{2}(2x \pm \sqrt{4x^2 - 4}) = x \pm \sqrt{x^2 - 1}.$$

Since y is nonnegative,

$$e^y = x \pm \sqrt{x^2 - 1}$$

cannot be less than 1. This renders the negative sign impossible (check this out) and leaves

$$e^y = x + \sqrt{x^2 - 1}$$

as the only possibility. Taking logs, we get

$$y = \ln (x + \sqrt{x^2 - 1}).$$

The proof of (iii) is left as an exercise. $\square$

EXERCISES

Differentiate.

1. $y = \tanh^2 x.$ **2.** $y = \tanh^2 3x.$ **3.** $y = \ln (\tanh x).$

4. $y = \tanh (\ln x).$ **5.** $y = \sinh (\tan^{-1} e^{2x}).$ **6.** $y = \text{sech} (3x^2 + 1).$

7. $y = \coth (\sqrt{x^2 + 1}).$ **8.** $y = \ln (\text{sech} \, x).$

9. $y = \dfrac{\text{sech} \, x}{1 + \cosh x}.$ **10.** $y = \dfrac{\cosh x}{1 + \text{sech} \, x}.$

Verify the following differentiation formulas.

11. $\dfrac{d}{dx} (\coth x) = -\text{csch}^2 x.$ **12.** $\dfrac{d}{dx} (\text{sech} \, x) = -\text{sech} \, x \tanh x.$

13. $\dfrac{d}{dx} (\text{csch} \, x) = -\text{csch} \, x \coth x.$

14. Show that

$$\tanh (t + s) = \frac{\tanh t + \tanh s}{1 + \tanh t \tanh s}.$$

15. Given that $\tanh x_0 = \frac{4}{5}$, find

   (a) $\operatorname{sech} x_0$.   HINT: $1 - \tanh^2 x = \operatorname{sech}^2 x$.

   Then find

   (b) $\cosh x_0$.   (c) $\sinh x_0$.   (d) $\coth x_0$.   (e) $\operatorname{csch} x_0$.

16. Given that $\tanh t_0 = -\frac{5}{12}$, evaluate the remaining hyperbolic functions at t_0.

17. Show that

$$\text{if} \quad x^2 \geq 1 \quad \text{then} \quad x - \sqrt{x^2 - 1} \leq 1.$$

18. Show that

$$\tanh^{-1} x = \frac{1}{2} \ln\left(\frac{1 + x}{1 - x}\right), \qquad -1 < x < 1.$$

19. Show that

   (7.10.3)
$$\frac{d}{dx}(\sinh^{-1} x) = \frac{1}{\sqrt{x^2 + 1}}, \qquad x \text{ real.}$$

20. Show that

   (7.10.4)
$$\frac{d}{dx}(\cosh^{-1} x) = \frac{1}{\sqrt{x^2 - 1}}, \qquad x > 1.$$

21. Show that

   (7.10.5)
$$\frac{d}{dx}(\tanh^{-1} x) = \frac{1}{1 - x^2}, \qquad -1 < x < 1.$$

22. Sketch the graphs of

   (a) $y = \sinh^{-1} x$.   (b) $y = \cosh^{-1} x$.   (c) $y = \tanh^{-1} x$.

23. Given that

$$\tan \phi = \sinh x,$$

show that

   (a) $\dfrac{d\phi}{dx} = \operatorname{sech} x$.   (b) $x = \ln(\sec \phi + \tan \phi)$.   (c) $\dfrac{dx}{d\phi} = \sec \phi$.

7.11 CHAPTER SUMMARY

7.1 In Search of a Notion of Logarithm

definition of a logarithm function (p. 334)

7.2 The Logarithm Function, Part I

natural logarithm: $\ln x = \int_1^x \dfrac{dt}{t}$, $x > 0$;   range of $y = \ln x$ is $(-\infty, \infty)$

Suppose that x and y are positive and r is rational; then

$$\ln 1 = 0, \qquad \ln e = 1, \qquad \ln xy = \ln x + \ln y,$$

$$\ln \frac{1}{x} = -\ln x, \qquad \ln \frac{x}{y} = \ln x - \ln y, \qquad \ln x^r = r \ln x.$$

graph of $y = \ln x$ (p. 339)

7.3 The Logarithm Function, Part II

$$\frac{d}{dx}[\ln u] = \frac{1}{u}\frac{du}{dx} \qquad \int \frac{g'(x)}{g(x)}\,dx = \ln|g(x)| + C$$

logarithmic differentiation (p. 347)

7.4 The Exponential Function

The exponential function $y = e^x$ is the inverse of the logarithm function $y = \ln x$.

graph of $y = e^x$ (p. 351);   domain is $(-\infty, \infty)$, range is $(0, \infty)$

$$\ln(e^x) = x, \qquad e^{\ln x} = x, \qquad e^0 = 1, \qquad e^{-x} = \frac{1}{e^x}, \qquad e^{x+y} = e^x e^y, \qquad e^{x-y} = \frac{e^x}{e^y}$$

$$\frac{d}{dx}[e^u] = e^u \frac{du}{dx} \qquad \int e^{g(x)}g'(x)\,dx = e^{g(x)} + C$$

7.5 Arbitrary Powers; Other Bases; Estimating e

$$\frac{d}{dx}[p^u] = p^u \ln p \frac{du}{dx} \qquad (p \text{ a positive constant})$$

logarithm of x to the base p: $\log_p x = \dfrac{\ln x}{\ln p}$

$$\frac{d}{dx}[\log_p u] = \frac{1}{u \ln p}\frac{du}{dx}$$

$$\left(1 + \frac{1}{n}\right)^n \le e \le \left(1 + \frac{1}{n}\right)^{n+1} \qquad e \cong 2.71828182$$

7.6 More Integration of Trigonometric Functions

$$\int \tan x\,dx = \ln|\sec x| + C, \qquad \int \sec x\,dx = \ln|\sec x + \tan x| + C,$$

$$\int \cot x\,dx = \ln|\sin x| + C, \qquad \int \csc x\,dx = \ln|\csc x - \cot x| + C.$$

7.7 The Inverse Trigonometric Functions

inverse sine function: $y = \sin^{-1} x$; domain is $[-1, 1]$, range is $\left[-\dfrac{\pi}{2}, \dfrac{\pi}{2}\right]$.

$$\frac{d}{dx}[\sin^{-1} x] = \frac{1}{\sqrt{1 - x^2}} \qquad \int \frac{dx}{\sqrt{a^2 - x^2}} = \sin^{-1}\left(\frac{x}{a}\right) + C \quad (a > 0)$$

inverse tangent function: $y = \tan^{-1} x$; domain is $(-\infty, \infty)$, range is $(-1, 1)$.

$$\frac{d}{dx}[\tan^{-1} x] = \frac{1}{1 + x^2} \qquad \int \frac{dx}{a^2 + x^2} = \frac{1}{a}\tan^{-1}\left(\frac{x}{a}\right) + C \quad (a \neq 0)$$

graph of $y = \sin^{-1} x$ (p. 372)　　　　　　graph of $y = \tan^{-1} x$ (p. 376)

7.8 Additional Exercises

7.9 The Hyperbolic Sine and Cosine

$$\sinh x = \tfrac{1}{2}(e^x - e^{-x}) \qquad \cosh x = \tfrac{1}{2}(e^x + e^{-x})$$

$$\frac{d}{dx}[\sinh x] = \cosh x \qquad \frac{d}{dx}[\cosh x] = \sinh x$$

graphs (p. 385)　　　　　　　basic identities (p. 386)

7.10 The Other Hyperbolic Functions

$$\tanh x = \frac{\sinh x}{\cosh x}, \qquad \coth x = \frac{\cosh x}{\sinh x},$$

$$\text{sech } x = \frac{1}{\cosh x}, \qquad \text{csch } x = \frac{1}{\sinh x}$$

derivatives (p. 388)　　　　　hyperbolic inverses (p. 390)
derivatives of hyperbolic inverses (p. 392)

An Introduction to Differential Equations

Most real-world situations are dynamic: they change with time. If a variable quantity can be represented by a differentiable function y, then the description of how y changes is usually given by an equation that involves y and its derivatives. Such an equation is called a *differential equation*. Here are three examples:

$$y' = 2y, \qquad y'' + 9y = 0, \qquad y'' - 3y' + y = x.$$

Differential equations play an important role in mathematical modeling, the application of mathematical methods to the study of real-world situations. It would take volumes to describe in detail this growing field of study. We shall settle for a brief overview.

8.1 ······A NOTE ON MATHEMATICAL MODELING

More often than not the problems we might wish to study are too complex to allow easy analysis. For example, we might want to study the effects of a pollutant on the ecosystem or investigate the possible ramifications on the economy of a proposed change in the tax laws. Although it can be fairly easy to state a topic of interest, it's usually very difficult to arrive at significant conclusions. We are often confronted by hard-to-identify variables (such as the course of underground rivers) and by unanticipated variables (such as the incidence of major loan defaults). The interplay of the

395

seemingly significant elements of a problem may appear hopelessly complex. Moreover, the problem itself may change as the study is being carried out.

In order to get a handle on a problem it is usually necessary to begin with rather severe restrictive assumptions. For example, in working out some simple motion problems we assumed that the force of gravity was constant and that there was no air resistance.

The assumptions made must be stated clearly; otherwise the confusion is compounded. If the assumptions can be stated in mathematical terms, then mathematical tools can be brought to bear on the problem and we can use them to answer questions and make predictions. The whole process of translating, formulating, analyzing, and resolving a problem in a mathematical context is known as *mathematical modeling.*

The goal of mathematical modeling is to obtain a better understanding of a real-world situation. In some instances understanding is a goal unto itself. Most of the time, however, understanding is used to make predictions, which in turn provide an opportunity to change the course of events. For example, studies of a particular pollutant may lead to controls that can then be implemented to avoid serious contamination. An understanding of the implications of a proposed tax law before enactment may lead to a better law.

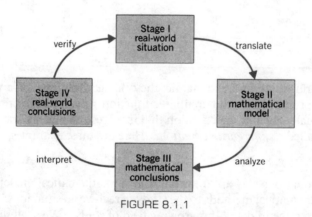

FIGURE 8.1.1

Mathematical modeling is generally thought of as an ongoing cycle with four stages. (See Figure 8.1.1.) We begin with a real-world question (Stage I). The transition to Stage II is based on some restrictive assumptions. Of the host of varying factors that may be interacting, we try to identify those that appear most influential. The forms of the mathematical representation (Stage II) are varied; we put off their description for the moment. Application of various mathematical techniques brings us to Stage III, where we formulate explanations and predictions about the mathematical version of the question. These predictions are then interpreted in the context of the real-world situation (Stage IV). At this point we can test the quality of our model. Sometimes our predictions can simply be compared to known results. Sometimes experiments have to be conducted to test the validity of our predictions. In any event we are in a position to reexamine the original assumptions that led to the mathematical model. Normally, modifications in the model are required. Perhaps

our model faithfully represents an overly idealized situation and now we can attempt
to alter the model to reflect reality more accurately.   Or, perhaps, our model has
approximated the real-world situation with some predictable, but unacceptable, level
of error.   In any event we recast the assumptions and basic descriptions in the model
and run this new variation through the cycle of design, analysis, interpretation, and
testing.   With each iteration of the cycle we hope to generate a model that offers a
better approximation of the real-world situation.

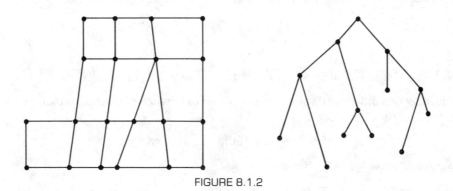

FIGURE 8.1.2

Some mathematical models are based on simple-looking diagrams consisting of
dots and line segments.   (See Figure 8.1.2.)   Such diagrams are called *graphs*.
Sometimes numbers are associated with the dots and line segments.   With numbers
representing traffic counts, for example, a metropolitan planning office can use a
graph that outlines the city streets to analyze the traffic flow.   With the numbers
representing the time needed to complete various tasks in a construction job, a
builder can use a graph to schedule various elements of a construction project.   In
general, graphs are used to display the interconnections of complicated systems, such
as pipeline networks, communications systems, transportation systems, etc.

Problems that involve time as a variable can be classified as *continuous* or *discrete*.   Continuous representations of time involve the passage of time in the manner
we ordinarily think of it.   For example, in our discussion of motion we used time as a
continuous variable.   Differential equations, our focus for the balance of this chapter, can be used to model continuous-time situations.   Discrete representations arise
when data are collected at regular intervals and a continuous representation is either
impossible or unnecessary.   For example, the concentration of some pollutant in a
lake may be under study on the basis of sample readings taken once a day or once a
week.   Such discrete-time situations are represented mathematically by what are
known as *difference equations,* very close in form to differential equations.

Models can be classified as either *deterministic* or *probabilistic*.   Deterministic
models lead to exact predictions, such as projecting the path of a comet approaching
our solar system.   Probabilistic models lead to predictions that state the likelihood of
certain outcomes.   These are the models used in small-particle physics.

The classification of mathematical modeling by type of mathematical tools used,
manner in which time is used as a variable, and style of predictions produced is a
rather technical matter.   What is not so technical but abundantly clear is that all these

variations have one essential feature in common. They are all based on deductive reasoning.

The role of intuition in these matters is somewhat delicate. Sometimes a model will lead to predictions that somehow seem "intuitively out of line," even if not exactly in direct conflict with recorded experience. If so, we try to reexamine the assumptions on which the model was based. On occasion we discover later that the model was correct after all and it was our intuition that had failed us. We simply had not understood the real-world situation as well as we thought we had.

8.2 ·····FIRST-ORDER LINEAR DIFFERENTIAL EQUATIONS

The *order* of a differential equation is the order of the highest derivative that appears in the equation. Thus

$$y' + 2y = x^3 \quad \text{and} \quad y' - xy = e^x$$

are equations of the first order;

$$y'' - 3y' + y = x \quad \text{and} \quad y'' + 4y = 0$$

are equations of the second order;

$$y''' - 3y'' + 3y' - y = x$$

is a differential equation of the third order. The differential equations that appear most frequently in applications are of order one or two.

A function y is called a *solution* of a differential equation iff it satisfies that differential equation. For example, the function

$$y = x + e^{-2x}$$

is a solution of the differential equation

$$y' + 2y = 2x + 1$$

since, for this choice of y,

$$y' + 2y = (1 - 2e^{-2x}) + 2(x + e^{-2x}) = 2x + 1.$$

In this section we'll be working with *linear differential equations of the first order:* equations of the form

$$y' + p(x)y = q(x).$$

Here p and q represent functions of x that are continuous where defined. In the simplest possible case, $p(x) = 0$ for all x, and the equation reduces to

$$(1) \qquad\qquad y' = q(x).$$

The solutions of this equation are the antiderivatives of q. If $y = Q(x)$ is a solution, then so is

$$(2) \qquad\qquad y = Q(x) + C$$

where C is an arbitrary constant. We call (2) the *general solution* and note that (by virtue of Theorem 4.2.4) every solution of (1) can be obtained from (2) by adjusting the constant C.

EXAMPLE. The function $y = x^2$ is a solution of the differential equation $y' = 2x$. The general solution is $y = x^2 + c$. $\square$

To solve an equation of the form

(8.2.1) $$\boxed{y' + p(x)y = q(x)}$$

we first calculate

$$P(x) = \int p(x)\, dx$$

(omitting the constant of integration) and form $e^{P(x)}$. We then multiply the differential equation by $e^{P(x)}$ obtaining

$$e^{P(x)}y' + e^{P(x)}p(x)y = e^{P(x)}q(x).$$

The rest is straightforward. The left side of the equation now has the form

$$\frac{d}{dx}[e^{P(x)}y] \qquad\qquad \text{(check this out)}$$

and the entire equation can thus be written

$$\frac{d}{dx}[e^{P(x)}y] = e^{P(x)}q(x).$$

Integration gives

$$e^{P(x)}y = \int e^{P(x)}q(x)\, dx + C$$

and thus

(8.2.2) $$\boxed{y = e^{-P(x)}\left\{\int e^{P(x)}q(x)\, dx + C\right\}.}$$

This is the *general solution* of Equation (8.2.1). Different choices of C give different *particular solutions*.

REMARK. The key step in solving a differential equation of the form

$$y' + p(x)y = q(x)$$

is multiplication by $e^{P(x)}$ where

$$P(x) = \int p(x)\, dx.$$

It is multiplication by $e^{P(x)}$ that enables us to write the left side of the equation in a form that we can integrate directly. We call $e^{P(x)}$ an *integrating factor*. □

EXAMPLE. We begin with a simple case:

$$y' + ay = b, \qquad a \neq 0.$$

Here $p(x) = a$ and so we use the integrating factor

$$e^{\int a\,dx} = e^{ax}.$$

Multiplication by e^{ax} gives

$$e^{ax}y' + e^{ax}ay = e^{ax}b$$

$$\frac{d}{dx}[e^{ax}y] = e^{ax}b$$

$$e^{ax}y = \frac{b}{a}e^{ax} + C$$

$$y = \frac{b}{a} + Ce^{-ax}. \quad \square$$

EXAMPLE. To solve the equation

$$y' + 2y = e^x$$

we use the integrating factor

$$e^{\int 2\,dx} = e^{2x}.$$

Multiplication by e^{2x} gives

$$e^{2x}y' + e^{2x}2y = e^{3x},$$

$$\frac{d}{dx}(e^{2x}y) = e^{3x},$$

$$e^{2x}y = \tfrac{1}{3}e^{3x} + C,$$

$$y = \tfrac{1}{3}e^x + Ce^{-2x}.$$

This is the general solution. Different choices of C give different particular solutions. Setting $C = 0$, we have

$$y = \tfrac{1}{3}e^x.$$

Setting $C = 1$, we have

$$y = \tfrac{1}{3}e^x + e^{-2x}.$$

If we want the solution that takes on the value 1 at 0, then we set

$$\tfrac{1}{3}e^0 + Ce^0 = 1.$$

This forces

$$\tfrac{1}{3} + C = 1, \qquad C = \tfrac{2}{3}$$

and gives

$$y = \tfrac{1}{3}e^x + \tfrac{2}{3}e^{-2x}. \quad \square$$

The general solution of a first-order differential equation contains one arbitrary constant. Differential equations of order two produce two arbitrary constants; and so on. When a differential equation is used in a mathematical model, there are usually initial conditions or side conditions that make it possible to evaluate whatever arbitrary constants appear. Finding the particular solution that satisfies certain given conditions is called solving an *initial-value problem*.

EXAMPLE. We will solve the initial-value problem

$$y' + 2xy = 0, \qquad y(0) = 4.$$

As an integrating factor we take

$$e^{\int 2x \, dx} = e^{x^2}.$$

Multiplying the equation by e^{x^2}, we have

$$e^{x^2}y' + e^{x^2}(2x)y = 0$$

$$\frac{d}{dx}[e^{x^2}y] = 0$$

$$e^{x^2}y = C$$

$$y = Ce^{-x^2}.$$

This is the general solution. We want the particular solution that satisfies $y(0) = 4$. Since

$$y(0) = Ce^0 = C,$$

we need only set $C = 4$. The solution to the initial-value problem is the function

$$y = 4e^{-x^2}. \quad \square$$

EXAMPLE. To solve the initial-value problem

$$xy' - 2y = 2x^4, \qquad y(-1) = 0$$

we first divide the equation by x so that the leading coefficient becomes 1:

$$y' - \frac{2}{x}y = 2x^3.$$

Now we form

$$\int -\frac{2}{x}\, dx = -2 \ln |x|.$$

As an integrating factor we can take

$$e^{-2\ln|x|} = e^{\ln|x|^{-2}} = e^{\ln x^{-2}} = x^{-2}.$$

Multiplication by x^{-2} gives

$$x^{-2}y' - 2x^{-3}y = 2x$$

$$\frac{d}{dx}(x^{-2}y) = 2x$$

$$x^{-2}y = x^2 + C$$

$$y = Cx^2 + x^4.$$

This is the general solution.   Now we must find the value of C for which $y(-1) = 0$. Since

$$y(-1) = C(-1)^2 + (-1)^4 = C + 1,$$

we must take $C = -1$.   The solution to the initial-value problem is the function

$$y = x^4 - x^2. \quad \square$$

EXERCISES

Find the general solution.

1. $y' - 2y = 1.$ 2. $xy' - 2y = -x.$ 3. $2y' + 5y = 2.$
4. $y' - y = -2e^{-x}.$ 5. $xy' - 4y = -2nx.$ 6. $xy' - 2y = -3x.$
7. $y' - e^x y = 0.$ 8. $y' - y = e^x.$ 9. $y' + 2xy = xe^{-x^2}.$

10. $xy' - y = 2x.$ 11. $y' + \dfrac{2}{x+1}\, y = 0.$ 12. $y' + \dfrac{2}{x+1}\, y = (x+1)^{5/2}.$

Solve the initial-value problem.

13. $y' + y = 1, \quad y(0) = 4.$ 14. $y' - y = e^x, \quad y(1) = 1.$

15. $y' + y = \dfrac{1}{1+e^x}, \quad y(0) = e.$ 16. $y' + y = \dfrac{1}{1+2e^x}, \quad y(0) = e.$

17. $xy' - 2y = x^3, \quad y(1) = 0.$ 18. $x^2 y' + 2xy = 1, \quad y(1) = 2.$
19. $y' + 2xy = 0, \quad y(2) = 1.$ 20. $xy' + 2y = 0, \quad y(1) = 3.$

21. Let f be a function continuous on $[0, \infty)$.   Find f given that $f(2) = 6$ and that the average value of f on every interval $[0, x]$ is one-half of the value of f at x.

22. Let x_0 be a positive number and let f be a function continuous on $[0, \infty)$, zero at $x = 0$, and positive for $x > 0$.   Find f given that the average value of f on every interval $[0, x]$ is one-third of the value of f at x and $f(x_0) = y_0$.

Let k be an integer different from 0 and 1.   By setting $v = y^{1-k}$, *Bernoulli's equation*

(8.2.3) $\boxed{y' + p(x)\, y = q(x)\, y^k}$

can be transformed into the linear equation

(8.2.4) $v' + (1 - k)p(x)\, v = (1 - k)q(x).$

Here p and q are continuous functions where defined.   Use this result to solve the following equations.

23. $y' + y = e^{3x}y^2.$ 24. $y' - y = e^{2x}y^2.$ 25. $y' + xy = xy^3.$
26. $y' - x^2 y = x^2 y^4.$ 27. $y' + (\tan x)y = (\cos^2 x)y^{-1}.$ 28. $y' + (\cot x)y = (\csc^3 x)y^{-1}.$
29. $xyy' - y^2 = x^4.$ 30. $xyy' + y^2 = x^2.$

31. Derive (8.2.4) from (8.2.3).

8.3 ······APPLICATIONS

In this section we consider several situations that can be modeled by a first-order linear differential equation.

Exponential Growth and Decline

Many quantities change with time at a rate proportional to the amount of the quantity present. The mathematical formulation of this phenomenon is the differential equation

(8.3.1)
$$y' = ky.$$

The number k is the constant of proportionality. Instances where Equation (8.3.1) has proved to be an effective model include population studies, radioactive decay, and some types of investment. Specific examples are worked out below.

To find the general solution of (8.3.1) we begin by rewriting it as a linear equation:

(1) $y' - ky = 0.$

Here we are viewing y as a function of time t. Multiplying (1) by the integrating factor

$$e^{\int -k\,dt} = e^{-kt}$$

we have

$$\frac{d}{dt}(ye^{-kt}) = 0$$

$$ye^{-kt} = C$$

$$y = Ce^{kt}.$$

The constant C is y_0, the value of y at time $t = 0$:

$$y_0 = y(0) = Ce^0 = C.$$

The general solution of (8.3.1) can therefore be written

(8.3.2)
$$y(t) = y_0 e^{kt}.$$

This is the basic law of exponential change (exponential growth if $k > 0$, exponential decline if $k < 0$).

Exponential Change Compared to Linear Change   Let y be a quantity that changes with time: $y = y(t)$.

If $y'(t)$ is constant, say

$$y'(t) = k \qquad \text{for all } t,$$

then y changes by the *same amount* during all periods of the same duration:

$$y'(t) = k \qquad \text{implies} \qquad y(t) = kt + y_0$$

and thus

$$y(t + \Delta t) = k(t + \Delta t) + y_0 = (kt + y_0) + k\Delta t = y(t) + k\Delta t.$$

During every period of duration Δt, y changes by the amount $k\Delta t$:

$$y(t + \Delta t) = y(t) + k\Delta t.$$

If $y'(t)/y(t)$ is constant, say

$$y'(t) = k\, y(t) \qquad \text{for all } t,$$

then y changes, not by the same amount, but by the *same factor* during all periods of the same duration:

$$y'(t) = k\, y(t) \qquad \text{implies} \qquad y(t) = y_0 e^{kt}$$

and thus

$$y(t + \Delta t) = y_0 e^{k(t+\Delta t)} = y_0 e^{kt} \cdot e^{k\Delta t} = e^{k\Delta t} y(t).$$

During every period of length Δt, $y = y_0 e^{kt}$ changes by a factor of $e^{k\Delta t}$.

REMARK. For the numerical calculations in the problems that follow, we refer to the tables in Appendix C. □

PROBLEM. Population tends to grow with time at a rate roughly proportional to the population present. According to the Bureau of the Census, the population of the United States in 1970 was approximately 203 million and in 1980, 227 million. Use this information to estimate in how many years the population of the United States will match the current (1985) world population of approximately 4.5 billion.

Solution. Let $P(t)$ be the population (in millions) of the United States t years after 1970. The basic equation is

$$P'(t) = kP(t)$$

so that

$$P(t) = Ce^{kt}.$$

Since $P(0) = 203$, we have

$$(1) \qquad\qquad P(t) = 203e^{kt}.$$

We can use the fact that $P(10) = 227$ to eliminate k from (1):

$$(*) \qquad 227 = 203e^{10k}, \qquad e^{10k} = \frac{227}{203}, \qquad e^k = \left(\frac{227}{203}\right)^{1/10},$$

and, thus, Equation (1) can be written

$$P(t) = 203\left(\frac{227}{203}\right)^{t/10}.$$

We want to find the value of t for which $P(t) = 4500$. Thus we set

$$203\left(\frac{227}{203}\right)^{t/10} = 4500$$

$$\ln 203 + \frac{t}{10}\ln\left(\frac{227}{203}\right) = \ln 4500$$

$$t = \frac{10\ln(4500/203)}{\ln(227/203)} \cong 10\left(\frac{3.10}{0.11}\right) \cong 282.$$

According to this growth model, the population of the United States will match the current world population sometime during the year $1970 + 282 = 2252$.   □

REMARK.   To solve this problem we did not need to find the value of k. Had we solved (∗) for k, we would have found that

$$k = \frac{1}{10} \ln \left(\frac{227}{203} \right) \cong 0.011.$$

As you'll see later from Formula (8.3.3), this means that the population of the United States is increasing at the rate of about 1.1% per year. By comparison the world population is currently increasing at the rate of about 2% per year.   □

PROBLEM.   The rate of decay of a radioactive substance is proportional to the amount of such substance present.
(a) Today we have A_0 grams of a radioactive substance. Given that one-third of the substance decays every 5 years, how much will be left t years from today?
(b) What is the *half-life* of the substance? (That is, how long does it take for half of the substance to decay?)

Solution.   (a) Let $A(t)$ be the amount of radioactive substance present t years from today. Since the rate of decay is proportional to the amount present, we know that

$$A'(t) = k A(t) \qquad \text{and thus} \qquad A(t) = C e^{kt}.$$

The constant C represents the amount at time $t = 0$. In this case $C = A_0$ and we have

(1) $$A(t) = A_0 e^{kt}.$$

At the end of 5 years, one-third of A_0 will have decayed and therefore two-thirds of A_0 will have remained:

$$A(5) = \tfrac{2}{3} A_0.$$

We can use this relation to eliminate k from (1):

$$A(5) = A_0 e^{5k} = \tfrac{2}{3} A_0, \qquad e^{5k} = \tfrac{2}{3}, \qquad e^k = (\tfrac{2}{3})^{1/5},$$

and consequently (1) can be written

$$A(t) = A_0 (\tfrac{2}{3})^{t/5}.$$

(b) To find the half-life of the substance we must find the value of t for which

$$A_0 (\tfrac{2}{3})^{t/5} = \tfrac{1}{2} A_0.$$

Dividing by A_0, we have

$$(\tfrac{2}{3})^{t/5} = \tfrac{1}{2}$$

so that

$$(\tfrac{2}{3})^t = (\tfrac{1}{2})^5, \qquad t \ln \tfrac{2}{3} = 5 \ln \tfrac{1}{2}, \qquad t(\ln 2 - \ln 3) = -5 \ln 2,$$

and

$$t = \frac{5 \ln 2}{\ln 3 - \ln 2} \text{ years.}$$

With $\ln 2 \cong 0.693$ and $\ln 3 \cong 1.099$, you'll find that $t \cong 8.53$ years.   The half-life of the substance is about $8\frac{1}{2}$ years.   □

Compound Interest

Consider money invested at interest rate r. If the accumulated interest is credited once a year, then the interest is said to be compounded annually; if twice a year, then semiannually; if four times a year, then quarterly. The idea can be pursued further. Interest can be credited every day, every hour, every second, every half-second, and so on. In the limiting case, interest is credited instantaneously. Economists call this *continuous compounding*.

The economists' formula for continuous compounding is a simple exponential:

(8.3.3)
$$A(t) = A_0 e^{rt}.$$

Here t is measured in years,

$$A(t) = \text{the principal in dollars at time } t,$$
$$A_0 = A(0) = \text{the initial investment},$$
$$r = \text{the annual interest rate}.$$

The rate r is called the *nominal* interest rate. Compounding makes the *effective* rate higher.

A Derivation of the Compound Interest Formula. We take h as a small time increment and observe that

$$A(t + h) - A(t) = \text{interest earned from time } t \text{ to time } t + h.$$

Had the principal remained $A(t)$ from time t to time $t + h$, the interest earned during this time period would have been

$$rh A(t).$$

Had the principal been $A(t + h)$ throughout the time interval, the interest earned would have been

$$rh A(t + h).$$

The actual interest earned must be somewhere in between:

$$rh A(t) \leq A(t + h) - A(t) \leq rh A(t + h).$$

Dividing by h, we get

$$rA(t) \leq \frac{A(t + h) - A(t)}{h} \leq rA(t + h).$$

If A varies continuously, then, as h tends to zero, $rA(t + h)$ tends to $rA(t)$ and (by the pinching theorem) the difference quotient in the middle must also tend to $rA(t)$:

$$\lim_{h \to 0} \frac{A(t + h) - A(t)}{h} = rA(t).$$

This says that

$$A'(t) = rA(t),$$

from which it follows that

$$A(t) = Ce^{rt}.$$

With A_0 as the initial investment, we have $C = A_0$ and

$$A(t) = A_0 e^{rt}. \quad \square$$

PROBLEM. Find the amount of interest earned by $100 compounded contin-
uously at 6% for 5 years.

Solution

$$A(5) = 100e^{(0.06)5} = 100e^{0.30} \cong 135.$$

The interest earned is approximately $35. $\square$

PROBLEM. A sum of money is earning interest at the rate of 10% compounded
continuously. What is the effective interest rate?

Solution. At the end of one year each dollar grows to

$$e^{0.10} \cong 1.105.$$

The interest earned is approximately $10\frac{1}{2}$ cents. The effective interest rate is about
$10\frac{1}{2}$%. $\square$

PROBLEM. How long does it take a sum of money to double at 5% compounded
continuously?

Solution. In general

$$A(t) = A_0 e^{0.05t}.$$

We set

$$2A_0 = A_0 e^{0.05t}$$

and solve for t:

$$2 = e^{0.05t}, \quad \ln 2 = 0.05t = \tfrac{1}{20}t, \quad t = 20 \ln 2 \cong 13.86.$$

It takes about 13 years, 10 months, and 14 days. $\square$

A dollar today is better than a dollar tomorrow because during that time we could
be earning interest.

PROBLEM. What is the present value of $1000 forty months from now? Assume
continuous compounding at 6%.

Solution.   We begin with

$$A(t) = A_0 e^{0.06t}$$

and solve for A_0:

$$A_0 = A(t)e^{-0.06t}.$$

Since forty months is $\frac{10}{3}$ years, $t = \frac{10}{3}$ and

$$A_0 = A(\tfrac{10}{3})e^{(-0.06)(10/3)} = 1000e^{-0.20} \cong 819.$$

The present value of $1000 forty months from now is about $819.   ⌐

PROBLEM.   Mr. A earns $15,000 a year.   How much will he have to be earning 10 years from today to retain his present purchasing power?   Assume a rate of inflation of 7%.

Solution.   The purchasing power of a dollar t years from now will have been eroded by a factor of $e^{-0.07t}$.   Earnings of S dollars a year 10 years from now will have the purchasing power of $Se^{-0.07(10)} = Se^{-0.7}$ dollars today.   Setting

$$15,000 = Se^{-0.7}$$

we have

$$S = (15,000)e^{0.7} \cong (15,000)(2.014) = 30,210.$$

Mr. A will have to be earning $30,210 a year to maintain his present purchasing power.   □

PROBLEM.   A producer of brandy finds that the value of his inventory (the price at which he can sell it) increases with time according to the formula

$$V(t) = V_0 e^{\sqrt{t}/2}. \qquad\qquad (t \text{ measured in years})$$

How long should he plan to keep the brandy in storage?   Neglect storage costs and assume an 8% annual rate of inflation.

Solution.   Future dollars should be discounted by a factor of $e^{-0.08t}$.   What we want to maximize is not $V(t)$ but the present value of the brandy

$$f(t) = V(t)e^{-0.08t} = V_0 e^{(\sqrt{t}/2)-0.08t}.$$

Differentiation gives

$$f'(t) = V_0 e^{(\sqrt{t}/2)-0.08t}\left(\frac{1}{4\sqrt{t}} - 0.08\right).$$

Setting $f'(t) = 0$, we find that

$$\frac{1}{4\sqrt{t}} = 0.08, \qquad \sqrt{t} = \frac{1}{0.32}, \qquad t = \left(\frac{1}{0.32}\right)^2 \cong 9.76.$$

He should plan to store it for about 9 years and 9 months.   □

A Mixing Problem

A fundamental assumption underlying the model for the following mixing problem is that a uniform concentration is maintained by some kind of "stirring."

PROBLEM. Water from a polluted reservoir (pollution level p_0 grams per liter) is being drawn off at the rate of n liters per hour and being replaced by less polluted water (pollution level p_1 grams per liter). Given that the reservoir contains M liters, how long will it take to reduce the pollution to p grams per liter?

Solution. Let $A(t)$ be the total number of grams of pollution in the reservoir at time t. We want to find the time t at which

$$\frac{A(t)}{M} = p.$$

At each time t, pollutants leave the reservoir at the rate of

$$n\frac{A(t)}{M} \quad \text{grams per hour}$$

and enter the reservoir at the rate of

$$np_1 \quad \text{grams per hour.}$$

It follows that

$$A'(t) = \text{rate in} - \text{rate out} = np_1 - n\frac{A(t)}{M}$$

and

$$A'(t) + \frac{n}{M}\,A(t) = np_1.$$

To solve the equation for $A(t)$ we multiply through by $e^{\int (n/M)\,dt} = e^{nt/M}$. This gives

$$e^{nt/M}A'(t) + e^{nt/M}\,\frac{n}{M}\,A(t) = np_1\,e^{nt/M},$$

$$\frac{d}{dt}\,[e^{nt/M}\,A(t)] = np_1\,e^{nt/M},$$

$$e^{nt/M}\,A(t) = Mp_1\,e^{nt/M} + C,$$

$$A(t) = Mp_1 + Ce^{-nt/M},$$

$$\frac{A(t)}{M} = p_1 + \frac{C}{M}\,e^{-nt/M}.$$

The constant C is determined by the initial pollution level p_0:

$$p_0 = \frac{A(0)}{M} = p_1 + \frac{C}{M} \qquad \text{so that} \qquad C = M(p_0 - p_1).$$

Using this value for C, we have

$$\frac{A(t)}{M} = p_1 + (p_0 - p_1)e^{-nt/M}.$$

This equation gives the pollution level at each time t. To find the time at which the pollution level has been reduced to p, we set

$$p_1 + (p_0 - p_1)e^{-nt/M} = p$$

and solve for t:

$$e^{-nt/M} = \frac{p - p_1}{p_0 - p_1}, \qquad -\frac{n}{M}t = \ln\frac{p - p_1}{p_0 - p_1}, \qquad t = \frac{M}{n}\ln\frac{p_0 - p_1}{p - p_1}. \quad \square$$

PROBLEM. In the problem just considered, how long would it take to reduce the pollution by 50% if the reservoir contained 50,000,000 liters, the water were replaced at the rate of 25,000 liters per hour, and the replacement water were completely pollution free?

Solution. In general

$$t = \frac{M}{n}\ln\frac{p_0 - p_1}{p - p_1}.$$

Here

$$M = 50{,}000{,}000, \quad n = 25{,}000, \quad p_1 = 0, \quad p = \tfrac{1}{2}p_0,$$

so that

$$t = 2000 \ln 2 \cong 2000(0.69) = 1380.$$

It would take about 1380 hours. $\square$

EXERCISES

A calculator or the tables in Appendix C may be needed to work many of the following exercises.

1. Find the amount of interest earned by $500 compounded continuously for 10 years (a) at 6%. (b) at 8%. (c) at 10%.
2. How long does it take for a sum of money to double when compounded continuously (a) at 6%. (b) at 8%. (c) at 10%?
3. What is the present value of a $1000 bond that matures in 5 years? Assume continuous compounding (a) at 6%. (b) at 8%. (c) at 10%.
4. At what rate r of continuous compounding does a sum of money increase by a factor of e (a) in one year? (b) in n years?
5. At what rate r of continuous compounding does a sum of money triple in 20 years?
6. At what rate r of continuous compounding does a sum of money double in 10 years?
7. At a certain moment a 100-gallon mixing tank is full of brine containing 0.25 pounds of salt per gallon. Find the amount of salt present t minutes later if the brine is being

continuously drawn off at the rate of 3 gallons per minute and replaced by brine containing 0.2 pounds of salt per gallon.

8. Water is pumped into a tank to dilute a saline solution. The volume of the solution, call it V, is kept constant by continuous outflow. The amount of salt in the tank, call it s, depends on the amount of water that has been pumped in, call this x. Given that

$$\frac{ds}{dx} = -\frac{s}{V},$$

find the amount of water that must be pumped into the tank to eliminate 50% of the salt. Take V as 10,000 gallons.

9. A 200-liter tank initially full of water develops a leak at the bottom. Given that 20% of the water leaks out in the first 5 minutes, find the amount of water left in the tank t minutes after the leak develops if the water drains off at a rate that is proportional to the product of the time elapsed and the amount of water present.

10. In Exercise 9 assume that the water drains off at a rate that is proportional to the amount of water present.

In Exercises 11–16 remember that the rate of decay of a radioactive substance is proportional to the amount of substance present.

11. What is the half-life of a radioactive substance if it takes 4 years for a quarter of the substance to decay?

12. A year ago there were 4 grams of a radioactive substance. Now there are 3 grams. How much was there 10 years ago?

13. Two years ago there were 5 grams of a radioactive substance. Now there are 4 grams. How much will remain 3 years from now?

14. What is the half-life of a radioactive substance if it takes 5 years for a third of the substance to decay?

15. Suppose the half-life of a radioactive substance is n years. What percentage of the substance present at the start of a year will decay during the ensuing year?

16. A radioactive substance weighed n grams at time $t = 0$. Today, 5 years later, the substance weighs m grams. How much will it weigh 5 years from now?

17. Atmospheric pressure p varies with altitude h according to the equation

$$\frac{dp}{dh} = kp, \qquad \text{where } k \text{ is a constant.}$$

Given that p is 15 pounds per square inch at sea level and 10 pounds per square inch at 10,000 feet, find p at (a) 5000 feet. (b) 15,000 feet.

18. Given that

$$f'(t) = k[2 - f(t)] \quad \text{and} \quad f(0) = 0,$$

show that the constant k satisfies the equation

$$k = \frac{1}{t} \ln \left[\frac{2}{2 - f(t)} \right].$$

19. During the process of inversion, the amount A of raw sugar present decreases at a rate proportional to A. During the first 10 hours, 1000 pounds of raw sugar have been reduced to 800 pounds. How many pounds will remain after 10 more hours of inversion?

20. Population tends to grow with time at a rate roughly proportional to the population present. According to the Bureau of the Census, the population of the United States in

1970 was approximately 203 million and in 1980, 227 million. Use this information to estimate the population of 1960. (The actual figure was about 179 million.)

21. (See Exercise 20) Predict the populations for 1990 and for the year 2000.

22. (See Exercise 20) Estimate how long it takes for the population to double.

23. A lumber company finds from experience that the value of its standing timber increases with time according to the formula

$$V(t) = V_0(\tfrac{3}{2})^{\sqrt{t}}.$$

Here t is measured in years and V_0 is the value at planting time. How long should the company wait before cutting the timber? Neglect costs and assume continuous compounding at 5%.

24. You are 45 years old and are looking toward an annual pension of $30,000 per year at age 65. What will be the present-day purchasing power of your pension if inflation over this period runs at (a) 6%? (b) 9%? (c) 10%?

25. Tuition at XYZ College is currently $3000. What would you expect to pay as tuition 3 years from now if inflation runs at (a) 5%? (b) 8%? (c) 12%?

26. The current i in an electric circuit varies with time t according to the formula

$$L\frac{di}{dt} + Ri = E$$

where E (the voltage), L (the inductance), and R (the resistance) are positive constants. Measure time in seconds, current in amperes, and suppose that the initial current is 0.
(a) Find a formula for the current at each subsequent time t.
(b) What upper limit does the current approach as t increases?
(c) In how many seconds will the current reach 90% of its upper limit?

27. An object falling in air is subject not only to gravitational force but also to air resistance. Find $v(t)$, the velocity of the object at time t, given that

$$v'(t) + Kv(t) = 32 \quad \text{and} \quad v(0) = 0. \qquad\qquad \text{(take } K > 0)$$

Show that $v(t)$ cannot exceed $32/K$. ($32/K$ is called the *terminal velocity*.)

28. *Newton's Law of Cooling* states that the rate of change of the temperature T of an object is proportional to the difference between T and the temperature τ of the surrounding medium:

$$\frac{dT}{dt} = -k(T - \tau)$$

where k is a positive constant.
(a) Solve this equation for T. (the general solution)
(b) Solve this equation for T given that $T(0) = T_0$.
(c) Take $T_0 > \tau$. What is the limiting temperature to which the object cools as t increases? What happens if $T_0 < \tau$?

29. A cup of coffee is served to you at 185° F in a room where the temperature is 65° F. Two minutes later the temperature of the coffee has dropped to 155° F. How many more minutes would you expect to wait for the coffee to cool to 105° F?   HINT: See Exercise 28.

30. A boat moving in still water is subject to a retardation proportional to its velocity. Show that the velocity t seconds after the power is shut off is given by the formula $v = ce^{-kt}$ where c is the velocity at the instant the power is shut off.

31. A boat is drifting in still water at 4 miles per hour; 1 minute later, at 2 miles per hour. How far has the boat drifted in that 1 minute? (See Exercise 30.)

32. The number of bacteria present in a given culture increases at a rate proportional to the number present. When first observed, the culture contained n_0 bacteria, an hour later, n_1.
    (a) Find the number present t hours after the observations began.
    (b) How long did it take for the number of bacteria to double?
33. Determine the time period during which $y = y_0 e^{kt}$ changes by a factor of q.

8.4 ······SEPARABLE EQUATIONS

An equation in x and y represents a curve in the xy-plane. An equation in x and y that contains an arbitrary constant represents a family of curves in the xy-plane.

Given a family of curves, say

$$x^2 - xy + y^2 = C,$$

we can find an equation for the slope y' by differentiating with respect to x:

$$2x - xy' - y + 2yy' = 0$$
$$2x - y + (2y - x)y' = 0.$$

Suppose now that we begin with an equation for y'. How can we recover the family of curves? In general, that's very difficult. It's easy, however, if y' satisfies an equation with *separated variables,* an equation of the form

(8.4.1)
$$p(x) + q(y)y' = 0.$$

Assuming that p and q are continuous, we can recover the family of curves (called the *integral curves*) by integrating separately with respect to x and with respect to y. To show this, we put the x's in the equation and write

$$p(x) + q(y(x)) y'(x) = 0.$$

Integrating with respect to x, we have

$$\int p(x) \, dx + \int q(y(x)) \, y'(x) \, dx = C.$$

We now write the second integral as an integral with respect to y. Setting

$$y = y(x) \quad \text{and} \quad dy = y'(x) \, dx,$$

we have

$$\int q(y(x)) \, y'(x) \, dx = \int q(y) \, dy$$

and therefore

(8.4.2)
$$\int p(x) \, dx + \int q(y) \, dy = C.$$

This equation, called the *general solution* of (8.4.1), gives all the integral curves of that differential equation.

EXAMPLE. The differential equation

$$x + yy' = 0$$

has the variables separated. We can solve the equation (that is, we can find the integral curves) by setting

$$\int x\,dx + \int y\,dy = C.$$

Carrying out the integrations, we have

$$\tfrac{1}{2}x^2 + \tfrac{1}{2}y^2 = C$$

and thus

$$x^2 + y^2 = 2C.$$

This is the general solution. The integral curves are circles centered at the origin.

We can find the integral curve that passes through a specified point by adjusting the constant C. For example, the integral curve that passes through the point $(3, 4)$ is the circle

$$x^2 + y^2 = 25. \quad \square$$

In the Leibniz notation equations with separated variables take the form

$$p(x) + q(y)\,\frac{dy}{dx} = 0.\dagger$$

PROBLEM. Find the integral curve of the equation

$$2x + \frac{1}{y^4}\frac{dy}{dx} = 0$$

that passes through the point $(0, 1)$.

Solution. The equation has the variables separated. The general solution

$$\int 2x\,dx + \int \frac{1}{y^4}\,dy = C$$

takes the form

$$x^2 - \frac{1}{3y^3} = C.$$

----

† This in turn is sometimes written

$$p(x)\,dx + q(y)\,dy = 0.$$

We want the integral curve for which $y = 1$ when $x = 0$. Substituting these values in the general solution, we find that $C = -\frac{1}{3}$. The integral curve we want can be written

$$x^2 - \frac{1}{3y^3} = -\frac{1}{3}.$$

This time we can solve explicitly for y. As you can check

$$y = \left(\frac{1}{3x^2 + 1}\right)^{1/3}. \quad \square$$

The equation

(1) $$\frac{x}{y} - y' = 0$$

does not have separated variables, but we can separate the variables by multiplying through by y:

(2) $$x - yy' = 0.$$

Now that the variables have been separated we can proceed as before:

$$\int x\,dx - \int y\,dy = C$$

$$\frac{1}{2}x^2 - \frac{1}{2}y^2 = C$$

$$x^2 - y^2 = 2C.$$

The integral curves of (2) are all the curves of the form

$$x^2 - y^2 = 2C, \qquad C \text{ arbitrary.}$$

These are hyperbolas for $C \neq 0$ and the lines $y = \pm x$ for $C = 0$. The integral curves of (1) are these same curves with the points at which $y = 0$ deleted. Reason for the deletion: Equation (1) has y in the denominator.

Any differential equation [such as (1)] for which we can separate the variables by algebraic means is called a *separable* equation.

PROBLEM. Find all the integral curves of the differential equation

$$\frac{dy}{dx} = x^2 y^3.$$

Solution. The equation is separable. We can separate the variables by writing

$$x^2 y^3 - \frac{dy}{dx} = 0$$

and then dividing by y^3:

(*) $$x^2 - \frac{1}{y^3}\frac{dy}{dx} = 0.$$

We can solve this equation by setting

$$\int x^2 \, dx - \int \frac{1}{y^3} \, dy = C.$$

Carrying out the integrations we have

$$\frac{1}{3} x^3 + \frac{1}{2y^2} = C.$$

This is the general solution of equation (∗) and gives all the integral curves of that equation. It does not, however, give all the integral curves of

$$\frac{dy}{dx} = x^2 y^3.$$

This equation is also satisfied by the constant function $y = 0$. This solution was lost to us when we divided through by y^3 to separate the variables. The integral curves of

$$\frac{dy}{dx} = x^2 y^3$$

are all the curves of the form

$$\frac{1}{3} x^3 + \frac{1}{2y^2} = C$$

and the x-axis, $y = 0$.   □

SOME REMARKS ON THE ARBITRARY CONSTANT. In one of the examples we arrived at the general solution

$$x^2 - y^2 = 2C.$$

Obviously, we could have replaced $2C$ by C and written

$$x^2 - y^2 = C$$

justifying the change in "C" by noting that in this context $2C$ and C both represent arbitrary real numbers. Sometimes the changes are more subtle. For example, the solution

(1) $e^{2x} = Ce^{-y}$

implies that C is positive. Therefore we can replace C by e^C. Equation (1) then becomes

$$e^{2x} = e^C e^{-y},$$

which we can write as

$$e^{2x} = e^{C-y}, \qquad 2x = C - y, \qquad \text{and finally,} \qquad 2x + y = C.$$

The family of curves

$$e^{2x} = Ce^{-y}$$

is the family of all straight lines

$$2x + y = C. \quad \square$$

A Second Population Model

Earlier for the population $P(t)$ with intrinsic growth rate k we considered the model based on the differential equation

(1) $$P'(t) = kP(t).$$

We found

$$P(t) = P_0 e^{kt},$$

where P_0 is the population at time $t = 0$.

Very few populations are able to sustain growth in this fashion for very long. Overcrowding, food shortages, and various other limiting factors tend to dampen the growth. A simple alternative model includes the concept of a *carrying capacity* in the environment. If we assume that the maximum population that the environment can support is M, we revise Equation (1) to read

(8.4.3) $$P'(t) = kP(t)\left(\frac{M - P(t)}{M}\right).$$

Implicit in this model is the assumption that, as the population P nears the carrying capacity M, the birth and death rates approach equality. The reasonableness of this assumption has been repeatedly confirmed by statistical data.

Equation (8.4.3) can be solved by separating the variables. As you are asked to show in Exercise 21,

$$P(t) = \frac{M}{1 + Ce^{-kt}}.$$

Notice that $P(t) \to M$ as $t \to \infty$. The graph of P, sketched in Figure 8.4.1, is called the logistic growth curve. The model reflects astonishingly well the population growth in the United States during years 1780 to 1930. During the 1930s the model breaks down. The severe economic problems of those years eroded the carrying capacity M.

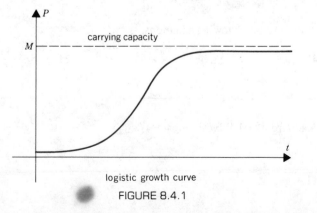

FIGURE 8.4.1

EXERCISES

Find the general solution.

1. $y' = y \sin (2x + 3)$. **2.** $y' = xe^y$. **3.** $\sec y + \csc x \dfrac{dy}{dx} = 0$.

4. $y^2 - x^2 \dfrac{dy}{dx} = 0$. **5.** $y' = (xy)^3$. **6.** $y' = 3x^2(1 + y^2)$.

7. $x^2 e^{y^2} - yy' = 0$. **8.** $(x^2y + y)y' + \dfrac{2x}{\sqrt{1 - y^2}} = 0$. **9.** $y' = \dfrac{y^2 + 1}{y + yx}$.

10. $y' = -\dfrac{\sin (1/x)}{x^2 \cos y}$. **11.** $\dfrac{dy}{dx} = \dfrac{1}{xy}$. **12.** $\dfrac{dy}{dx} = x\sqrt{1 - y^2}$.

13. $\dfrac{dy}{dx} = \dfrac{4 - y^2}{2xy - 3y}$. **14.** $\dfrac{dy}{dx} = -\dfrac{\sqrt{1 - y^2}}{\sqrt{1 - x^2}}$.

Solve the initial-value problem.

15. $y' = \dfrac{xy^2}{\sqrt{1 - x^2}}$, $y(0) = 2$. **16.** $y' = \dfrac{e^{x-y}}{1 + e^x}$, $y(1) = 0$.

17. $y' = e^x(1 + y^2)$, $y(0) = 0$. **18.** $y' = xe^{x^2-y}$, $y(1) = 1$.

19. $y^2 \dfrac{dy}{dx} - x^2(1 + y^3) = 0$, $y(0) = 2$. **20.** $(1 + x)\dfrac{dy}{dx} - y(1 + y) = 0$, $y(0) = 1.†$

21. Show that the general solution of Equation (8.4.3) can be written

$$P(t) = \frac{M}{1 + Ce^{-kt}}.$$ HINT: $\dfrac{M}{P(t)[M - P(t)]} = \dfrac{1}{P(t)} + \dfrac{1}{M - P(t)}$.

A first-order differential equation of the form

(8.4.4)
$$y' = g\left(\frac{y}{x}\right)$$

is said to be *homogeneous*. Here g is some continuous function of one variable. By setting $v = y/x$, we can transform (8.4.4) into the separable equation

(8.4.5)
$$\frac{1}{x} + \frac{1}{v - g(v)} v' = 0.$$

Use this result to solve the following equations.

22. $y' = \dfrac{x^2 + y^2}{2xy}$. **23.** $y' = \dfrac{y^2}{xy + x^2}$. **24.** $y' = \dfrac{x - y}{x + y}$.

25. $y' = \dfrac{x + y}{x - y}$. **26.** $y' = \dfrac{3x^2 + y^2}{xy}$. **27.** $y' = \dfrac{x^2 + 3y^2}{4xy}$.

28. Derive (8.4.5) from (8.4.4) by setting $v = y/x$.

_____

† HINT: $\dfrac{1}{y(1 + y)} = \dfrac{1}{y} - \dfrac{1}{1 + y}$.

(*Orthogonal trajectories*) If two curves intersect at right angles, one with slope m_1 and the other with slope m_2, then $m_1 m_2 = -1$. A curve that intersects every member of a family of curves at right angles is called an *orthogonal trajectory* for that family of curves. Suppose now that $f(x, y)$ is some expression in x and y. A differential equation of the form

$$y' = f(x, y)$$

generates a family of curves: all the integral curves of that particular equation. The orthogonal trajectories of this family are the integral curves of the differential equation.

$$y' = -\frac{1}{f(x, y)}.$$

Figure 8.4.2 shows the parabolas $y = Cx^2$. The orthogonal trajectories of this family of parabolas are ellipses.

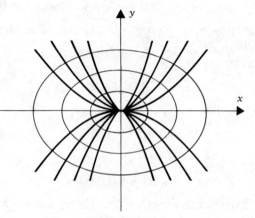

FIGURE 8.4.2

We can establish this by starting with the equation

$$y = Cx^2$$

and differentiating. Differentiation gives

$$y' = 2Cx.$$

Since $y = Cx^2$, we have $C = y/x^2$, and thus

$$y' = 2\left(\frac{y}{x^2}\right) x = \frac{2y}{x}.$$

The orthogonal trajectories are the integral curves of the differential equation

$$y' = -\frac{x}{2y}.$$

As you can check, the solutions of this equation are all of the form

$$x^2 + 2y^2 = K.$$

Find the orthogonal trajectories for the following families of curves. In each case draw several of the curves and several of the orthogonal trajectories.

29. $y = Cx$.   **30.** $2x + 3y = C$.   **31.** $xy = C$.

32. $x = Cy^4$.   **33.** $y = Ce^x$.   **34.** $y = Cx^3$.

8.5 ······SIMPLE HARMONIC MOTION

An object moves along a straight line. Instead of continuing in one direction, it moves back and forth, oscillating about a central point. Now call the central point $x = 0$ and denote by $x(t)$ the displacement at time t. If, throughout the motion, the acceleration is a constant negative multiple of the displacement, if at each time t

$$a(t) = -kx(t) \qquad \text{with } k > 0,$$

then the object is said to be in *simple harmonic motion*. The purpose of this section is to analyze such motion.

Since, by definition,

$$a(t) = x''(t),$$

in simple harmonic motion

$$x''(t) = -kx(t).$$

This gives

$$x''(t) + kx(t) = 0.$$

To emphasize that k is positive, we set $k = \beta^2$. The equation of motion then takes the form

(8.5.1) $$x''(t) + \beta^2 x(t) = 0.$$

It is easy to show that any function of the form

$$x(t) = C_1 \sin(\beta t + C_2)$$

satisfies this differential equation:

$$x'(t) = C_1 \beta \cos(\beta t + C_2)$$
$$x''(t) = -C_1 \beta^2 \sin(\beta t + C_2) = -\beta^2 x(t)$$

and thus

$$x''(t) + \beta^2 x(t) = 0.$$

What is not easy to see, but equally true, is that every solution of Equation (8.5.1) can be written in the form

(8.5.2) $$x(t) = C_1 \sin(\beta t + C_2).$$

We'll support this claim in the supplement to Section 8.6.

Now let's go on with (8.5.2) measuring t in seconds. Observe first that

$$x(t + 2\pi/\beta) = C_1 \sin [\beta(t + 2\pi/\beta) + C_2] = C_1 \sin (\beta t + C_2) = x(t).$$

This shows that the motion is *periodic* and the *period* is $2\pi/\beta$:

$$p = \frac{2\pi}{\beta}.$$

A complete oscillation takes $2\pi/\beta$ seconds. The reciprocal of the period gives the number of complete oscillations per second. This is called the *frequency*:

$$f = \frac{\beta}{2\pi}.$$

Since $\sin (\beta t + C_2)$ oscillates between -1 and 1, the product

$$x(t) = C_1 \sin (\beta t + C_2)$$

oscillates between $-|C_1|$ and $|C_1|$. The number $|C_1|$ is called the *amplitude* of the motion:

$$a = |C_1|.$$

In Figure 8.5.1 we have plotted x against t. The oscillations along the x-axis are now waves in the xt-plane. The period of the motion, $2\pi/\beta$, is the t distance (the time separation) between consecutive wave crests. The amplitude of the motion, $|C_1|$, is the height of the waves measured in x units from $x = 0$.

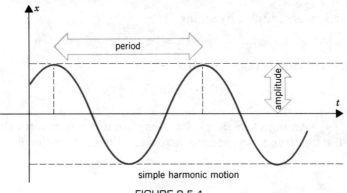

simple harmonic motion

FIGURE 8.5.1

PROBLEM. Find an equation for the oscillatory motion given that the period is $2\pi/3$ and, at time $t = 0$, $x = 1$ and $v = 3$.

Solution. We begin by setting

$$x(t) = C_1 \sin (\beta t + C_2).$$

Without loss of generality we take $C_1 \geq 0$ and $0 \leq C_2 < 2\pi.†$ In general the period is

---

† In the exercises you are asked to justify this step.

$2\pi/\beta$, so that here

$$\frac{2\pi}{\beta} = \frac{2\pi}{3} \quad \text{and thus} \quad \beta = 3.$$

The equation of motion takes the form

$$x(t) = C_1 \sin (3t + C_2).$$

By differentiation

$$v(t) = 3C_1 \cos (3t + C_2).$$

The conditions at $t = 0$ give

$$1 = x(0) = C_1 \sin C_2, \qquad 3 = v(0) = 3C_1 \cos C_2$$

and therefore

$$1 = C_1 \sin C_2, \qquad 1 = C_1 \cos C_2.$$

Adding the squares, we have

$$2 = C_1^2 \sin^2 C_2 + C_1^2 \cos^2 C_2 = C_1^2$$

and therefore, since we decided to take $C_1 \geq 0$,

$$C_1 = \sqrt{2}.$$

To find C_2 we note that

$$1 = \sqrt{2} \sin C_2, \qquad 1 = \sqrt{2} \cos C_2.$$

These equations are satisfied by setting

$$C_2 = \tfrac{1}{4}\pi.$$

The equation of motion can be written

$$x(t) = \sqrt{2} \sin (3t + \tfrac{1}{4}\pi). \quad \square$$

PROBLEM.   An object in simple harmonic motion passes through the central point $x = 0$ at time 0 and every second thereafter.   Find an equation for the motion if $v(0) = -4$.

Solution

$$x(t) = C_1 \sin (\beta t + C_2).$$

On each complete cycle the object must pass through the central point twice — once going one way, once going the other way.   The period is thus 2 seconds:

$$\frac{2\pi}{\beta} = 2 \quad \text{and therefore} \quad \beta = \pi.$$

We now know that

$$x(t) = C_1 \sin (\pi t + C_2)$$

and consequently

$$v(t) = \pi C_1 \cos (\pi t + C_2).$$

The initial conditions can be written

$$0 = x(0) = C_1 \sin C_2, \qquad -4 = v(0) = \pi C_1 \cos C_2$$

so that

$$0 = C_1 \sin C_2, \qquad -\frac{4}{\pi} = C_1 \cos C_2.$$

Taking $C_1 \geq 0$ and $0 \leq C_2 < 2\pi$, we have

$$C_1 = \frac{4}{\pi}, \qquad C_2 = \pi. \qquad\qquad \text{(check this out)}$$

The equation of motion can be written

$$x(t) = \frac{4}{\pi} \sin (\pi t + \pi). \quad \square$$

PROBLEM.   A coil spring hangs naturally to a length l_0. When a mass m is attached to it, the spring stretches l_1 inches.   The mass is later pulled down by hand an additional x_0 inches and then released.   What is the resulting motion?

Solution.   Throughout we refer to Figure 8.5.2, taking the downward direction as positive.

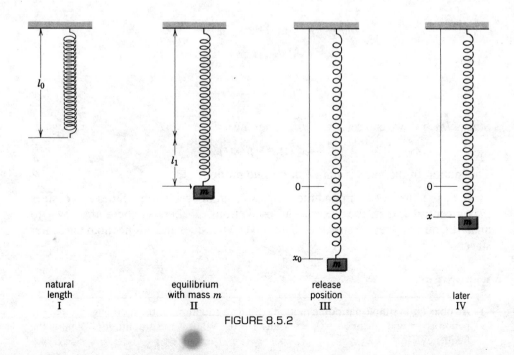

FIGURE 8.5.2

We begin by analyzing the forces acting on the mass at general position x (stage IV). First there is the weight of the object:

$$F_1 = mg.$$

This is a downward force, and by our choice of coordinate system, positive. Then there is the restoring force of the spring. This force, by Hooke's law, is proportional to the total displacement $l_1 + x$ and acts in the opposite direction:

$$F_2 = -k(l_1 + x) \qquad \text{with } k > 0.$$

If we neglect resistance, then these are the only forces acting on the object. Under these conditions the total force is

$$F = F_1 + F_2 = mg - k(l_1 + x),$$

which we rewrite as

(1) $$F = (mg - kl_1) - kx.$$

At stage II (Figure 8.5.2) there was equilibrium. The force of gravity, mg, plus the force of the spring, $-kl_1$, must have been 0:

$$mg - kl_1 = 0.$$

Equation (1) can therefore be simplified to

$$F = -kx.$$

Using Newton's

$$F = ma \qquad \text{(force = mass} \times \text{acceleration)}$$

we have

$$ma = -kx \quad \text{and thus} \quad a = -\frac{k}{m}x.$$

At any time t,

$$x''(t) = -\frac{k}{m}x(t).$$

Since $k/m > 0$, we can set $\beta = \sqrt{k/m}$ and write

$$x''(t) = -\beta^2 x(t).$$

The motion of the mass is simple harmonic motion. $\square$

In this section we examined the simplest form of oscillation. Sines and cosines play a central role in the study of all oscillations. Wherever there are waves to analyze (sound waves, radio waves, light waves, etc.) sines and cosines hold the center stage.

EXERCISES

1. An object is in simple harmonic motion. Find an equation for the motion given that the period is $\frac{1}{4}\pi$ and, at time $t = 0$, $x = 1$ and $v = 0$. What is the amplitude? What is the frequency?

2. An object is in simple harmonic motion. Find an equation for the motion given that the frequency is $1/\pi$ and, at time $t = 0$, $x = 0$ and $v = -2$. What is the amplitude? What is the period?

3. An object is in simple harmonic motion with period p and amplitude a. What is the velocity at the central point $x = 0$?

4. An object is in simple harmonic motion with period p. Find the amplitude given that $v = \pm v_0$ at $x = x_0$.

5. An object in simple harmonic motion passes through the central point $x = 0$ at time $t = 0$ and every 3 seconds thereafter. Find the equation of motion given that $v(0) = 5$.

6. Find the position at which an object in simple harmonic motion

$$x(t) = C_1 \sin (\beta t + C_2)$$

attains (a) maximum speed, (b) zero speed, (c) maximum acceleration, (d) zero acceleration.

7. Where does the object of Exercise 6 take on half of its maximum speed?

8. Show that in setting $x(t) = C_1 \sin (\beta t + C_2)$ there is no loss of generality in taking $C_1 \geq 0$ and $C_2 \in [0, 2\pi)$.†

9. What is $x(t)$ for the object of mass m discussed in the spring problem?

10. Show that the equation of harmonic motion

$$x(t) = C_1 \sin (\beta t + C_2)$$

can be written

$$x(t) = C_3 \cos (\beta t + C_4)$$

and also

$$x(t) = C_5 \cos \beta t + C_6 \sin \beta t.$$

11. Given that $x''(t) = 8 - 4x(t)$ with $x(0) = 0$ and $x'(0) = 0$, show that the motion is simple harmonic motion with the center at $x = 2$. Find the amplitude and the period.

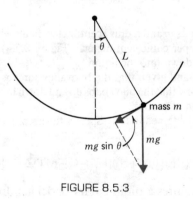

FIGURE 8.5.3

12. Figure 8.5.3 shows a pendulum of mass m swinging on an arm of length L. The angle θ is measured counterclockwise. Neglecting friction and the weight of the arm, we can de-

---

† Namely, show that every expression of the form $C_1 \sin (\beta t + C_2)$ can be written in the form $A \sin (\beta t + B)$ with $A \geq 0$ and $B \in [0, 2\pi)$.

scribe the motion by the equation

$$mL\theta''(t) = -mg \sin \theta(t)$$

which reduces to

$$\theta''(t) = -\frac{g}{L} \sin \theta(t).$$

(a) For small angles we replace $\sin \theta$ by θ and write

$$\theta''(t) \cong -\frac{g}{L} \theta(t).$$

Justify this step.

(b) Solve the approximate equation in (a) given that the pendulum
  (i) is held at an angle $\theta_0 > 0$ and released at time $t = 0$.
  (ii) passes through the vertical position at time $t = 0$ and

$$\theta'(0) = -\sqrt{\frac{g}{L}} \; \theta_0.$$

(c) Find L given that the motion repeats itself every 2 seconds.

FIGURE 8.5.4

13. A cylindrical buoy of mass m and radius r centimeters floats with its axis vertical in a liquid of density ρ kilograms per cubic centimeter. (Figure 8.5.4) Suppose that the buoy is pushed x_0 centimeters down into the liquid.
  (a) Neglecting friction and given that the buoyancy force is equal to the weight of the liquid displaced, show that the buoy bobs up and down in simple harmonic motion by finding the equation of motion.
  (b) Solve the equation obtained in (a). Specify the amplitude and the period.

8.6 ······SECOND-ORDER LINEAR DIFFERENTIAL EQUATIONS

Some of this material requires a rudimentary understanding of complex numbers. Complex numbers are explained in Appendix A.4.

A differential equation of the form

$$y'' + ay' + by = \phi(x) \qquad (a, b \text{ real}; \phi \text{ continuous})$$

is *a second-order linear differential equation with constant coefficients.* By a solution of such an equation we mean a function $y = y(x)$ that satisfies the equation for all x in the domain of ϕ.

The Reduced Equation

We begin by setting $\phi(x)$ identically zero and considering the *reduced equation*

(8.6.1)
$$y'' + ay' + by = 0. \quad †$$

Observe, first of all, that *if y_1 and y_2 are both solutions of the reduced equation, then every linear combination*

$$C_1 y_1 + C_2 y_2$$

is also a solution.

Proof. Set

$$y = C_1 y_1 + C_2 y_2$$

and observe that

$$y' = C_1 y_1' + C_2 y_2' \quad \text{and} \quad y'' = C_1 y_1'' + C_2 y_2''.$$

If

$$y_1'' + ay_1' + by_1 = 0 \quad \text{and} \quad y_2'' + ay_2' + by_2 = 0,$$

then

$$
\begin{aligned}
y'' + ay' + by &= (C_1 y_1'' + C_2 y_2'') + a(C_1 y_1' + C_2 y_2') + b(C_1 y_1 + C_2 y_2) \\
&= C_1(y_1'' + ay_1' + by_1) + C_2(y_2'' + ay_2' + by_2) \\
&= C_1(0) + C_2(0) = 0. \quad \square
\end{aligned}
$$

Two solutions y_1, y_2 of the reduced equation are said to be *fundamental* if and only if their Wronskian††

(8.6.2)
$$W(x) = y_1(x)y_2'(x) - y_1'(x)y_2(x)$$

is never zero. It can be shown that if y_1, y_2 are fundamental solutions, then every solution is a linear combination of y_1, y_2. *The general solution of the reduced equation can thus be written*

$$y = C_1 y_1 + C_2 y_2$$

where y_1, y_2 *are fundamental solutions and C_1, C_2 are arbitrary constants.*
Earlier you saw that the function $y = e^{-ax}$ satisfies the differential equation

$$y' + ay = 0.$$

Let's see if the equation

$$y'' + ay' + by = 0$$

also has solutions of the form $y = e^{rx}$.

---

† Often called the *homogeneous case.*

†† Named in honor of Count Hoëné-Wronski, a Polish mathematician (1778–1853).

If $y = e^{rx}$, then

$$y' = re^{rx} \quad \text{and} \quad y'' = r^2 e^{rx}.$$

Substitution into the differential equation gives

$$r^2 e^{rx} + are^{rx} + be^{rx} = 0$$

and, since $e^{rx} \neq 0$,

$$r^2 + ar + b = 0.$$

This shows that $y = e^{rx}$ satisfies *the differential equation provided that*

$$r^2 + ar + b = 0.$$

This quadratic in r is called the *characteristic equation.*

The roots of the characteristic equation are given by the general quadratic formula:

$$r = \frac{-a \pm \sqrt{a^2 - 4b}}{2}.$$

The nature of the solutions of the differential equation

$$y'' + ay' + by = 0$$

depends on the nature of these roots.

THEOREM 8.6.3

Given the reduced equation

(1) $$y'' + ay' + by = 0,$$

we form the characteristic equation

$$r^2 + ar + b = 0.$$

I. If the characteristic equation has two real roots r_1 and r_2, then the general solution of (1) takes the form

$$y = C_1 e^{r_1 x} + C_2 e^{r_2 x}.$$

II. If the characteristic equation has only one real root r_1, then the general solution takes the form

$$y = C_1 e^{r_1 x} + C_2 x e^{r_1 x} = (C_1 + C_2 x)e^{r_1 x}.$$

III. If the characteristic equation has two complex roots

$$r_1 = \alpha + i\beta \quad \text{and} \quad r_2 = \alpha - i\beta,$$

then the general solution takes the form

$$y = C_1 e^{\alpha x} \cos \beta x + C_2 e^{\alpha x} \sin \beta x = e^{\alpha x}(C_1 \cos \beta x + C_2 \sin \beta x).$$

We'll sketch a proof of III and leave the proofs of I and II to you.

Proof of III: By the general quadratic formula

$$\alpha = -\tfrac{1}{2}a \quad \text{and} \quad \beta = \tfrac{1}{2}\sqrt{4b - a^2}.$$

First we have to verify that the functions

$$y_1 = e^{\alpha x}\cos\beta x \quad \text{and} \quad y_2 = e^{\alpha x}\sin\beta x$$

satisfy the differential equation. Then we have to show that the pair y_1, y_2 has a nonzero Wronskian.

Routine differentiation of $y_1 = e^{\alpha x}\cos\beta x$ shows that

$$y_1' = e^{\alpha x}(\alpha \cos\beta x - \beta \sin\beta x),$$
$$y_1'' = e^{\alpha x}[(\alpha^2 - \beta^2)\cos\beta x - 2\alpha\beta \sin\beta x].$$

It follows that

$$y_1'' + ay_1' + by_1 = e^{\alpha x}[(\alpha^2 - \beta^2)\cos\beta x - 2\alpha\beta \sin\beta x + a\alpha \cos\beta x$$
$$- a\beta \sin\beta x + b \cos\beta x]$$
$$= e^{\alpha x}[(\alpha^2 - \beta^2 + a\alpha + b)\cos\beta x - \beta(2\alpha + a)\sin\beta x].$$

We have $y_1'' + ay_1' + by_1 = 0$ because

$$\alpha^2 - \beta^2 + a\alpha + b = (-\tfrac{1}{2}a)^2 - (\tfrac{1}{2}\sqrt{4b - a^2})^2 + a(-\tfrac{1}{2}a) + b$$
$$= \tfrac{1}{4}a^2 - b + \tfrac{1}{4}a^2 - \tfrac{1}{2}a^2 + b = 0$$

and

$$\beta(2\alpha + a) = 0 \quad \text{since} \quad 2\alpha + a = 2(-\tfrac{1}{2}a) + a = 0.$$

In a similar way one can show that y_2 also satisfies the differential equation. Now we show that the Wronskian of y_1, y_2 is never zero:

$$W(x) = y_1(x)y_2'(x) - y_1'(x)y_2(x)$$
$$= e^{\alpha x}\cos\beta x\,(\beta e^{\alpha x}\cos\beta x + \alpha e^{\alpha x}\sin\beta x)$$
$$- (-\beta e^{\alpha x}\sin\beta x + \alpha e^{\alpha x}\cos\beta x)e^{\alpha x}\sin\beta x$$
$$= \beta e^{2\alpha x}\cos^2\beta x + \beta e^{2\alpha x}\sin^2\beta x$$
$$= \beta e^{2\alpha x}(\cos^2\beta x + \sin^2\beta x) = \beta e^{2\alpha x} \neq 0. \quad \Box$$

It's time to look at specific equations.

PROBLEM. Find the general solution of the equation

$$y'' + 2y' - 15y = 0.$$

Then find the particular solution that satisfies the initial conditions

$$y(0) = 0, \qquad y'(0) = -1.$$

Solution. The characteristic equation is the quadratic

$$r^2 + 2r - 15 = 0.$$

Factoring the left side, we have

$$(r + 5)(r - 3) = 0.$$

There are two real roots: -5 and 3. The general solution takes the form

$$y = C_1 e^{-5x} + C_2 e^{3x}.$$

Differentiating the general solution, we have

$$y' = -5C_1 e^{-5x} + 3C_2 e^{3x}.$$

The conditions

$$y(0) = 0, \qquad y'(0) = -1$$

are satisfied iff

$$C_1 + C_2 = 0 \quad \text{and} \quad -5C_1 + 3C_2 = -1.$$

Solving these two equations simultaneously, we find that

$$C_1 = \tfrac{1}{8}, \qquad C_2 = -\tfrac{1}{8}.$$

The solution that satisfies the prescribed initial conditions is the function

$$y = \tfrac{1}{8}e^{-5x} - \tfrac{1}{8}e^{3x}.$$

Checking:

$$y = \tfrac{1}{8}e^{-5x} - \tfrac{1}{8}e^{3x}; \qquad y(0) = \tfrac{1}{8} - \tfrac{1}{8} = 0.\checkmark$$
$$y' = -\tfrac{5}{8}e^{-5x} - \tfrac{3}{8}e^{3x}; \qquad y'(0) = -\tfrac{5}{8} - \tfrac{3}{8} = -1.\checkmark$$
$$y'' + 2y' - 15y = (\tfrac{25}{8}e^{-5x} - \tfrac{9}{8}e^{3x}) + 2(-\tfrac{5}{8}e^{-5x} - \tfrac{3}{8}e^{3x}) - 15(\tfrac{1}{8}e^{-5x} - \tfrac{1}{8}e^{3x})$$
$$= e^{-5x}(\tfrac{25}{8} - \tfrac{10}{8} - \tfrac{15}{8}) + e^{3x}(-\tfrac{9}{8} - \tfrac{6}{8} + \tfrac{15}{8}) = 0.\checkmark \quad \square$$

PROBLEM. Find the general solution of the equation

$$y'' + 4y' + 4y = 0.$$

Then find the particular solution that satisfies the initial conditions

$$y(1) = 1, \qquad y'(1) = 2.$$

Solution. The characteristic equation takes the form

$$r^2 + 4r + 4 = 0,$$

which can be written

$$(r + 2)^2 = 0.$$

The number -2 is the only root. The general solution can be written

$$y = C_1 e^{-2x} + C_2 x e^{-2x}.$$

Differentiating the general solution, we have

$$y' = -2C_1 e^{-2x} - 2C_2 x e^{-2x} + C_2 e^{-2x} = -2C_1 e^{-2x} + C_2(1 - 2x)e^{-2x}.$$

The conditions

$$y(1) = 1, \qquad y'(1) = 2$$

require that

$$C_1 e^{-2} + C_2 e^{-2} = 1 \quad \text{and} \quad -2C_1 e^{-2} - C_2 e^{-2} = 2.$$

Solve these equations simultaneously for C_1, C_2 and you'll find that

$$C_1 = -3e^2, \qquad C_2 = 4e^2.$$

The solution that satisfies the prescribed initial conditions is the function

$$y = -3e^2 e^{-2x} + 4e^2 x e^{-2x} = -3e^{2(1-x)} + 4xe^{2(1-x)}.$$

We leave the checking to you. $\square$

PROBLEM. Find the general solution of the equation

$$y'' + y' + 3y = 0.$$

Solution. The characteristic equation is

$$r^2 + r + 3 = 0.$$

The general quadratic formula shows that there are two complex roots:

$$r_1 = -\tfrac{1}{2} + i \tfrac{1}{2} \sqrt{11}, \qquad r_2 = -\tfrac{1}{2} - i \tfrac{1}{2} \sqrt{11}.$$

The general solution takes the form

$$y = e^{-\tfrac{1}{2}x} [C_1 \cos (\tfrac{1}{2} \sqrt{11}\, x) + C_2 \sin (\tfrac{1}{2} \sqrt{11}\, x)]. \quad \square$$

The Complete Equation

Now we go on to the *complete equation*

(8.6.4) $$y'' + ay' + by = \phi(x). \quad \dagger$$

The function $\phi = \phi(x)$ appearing on the right is by assumption continuous. We begin by proving two simple but important results.

(8.6.5)   If both y_1 and y_2 are solutions of the complete equation, then their difference $u = y_1 - y_2$ is a solution of the reduced equation.

Proof. If

$$y_1'' + ay_1' + by_1 = \phi(x) \qquad \text{and} \qquad y_2'' + ay_2' + by_2 = \phi(x),$$

$\dagger$ Sometimes called the *nonhomogeneous case.*

then

$$u'' + au' + bu = (y_1'' - y_2'') + a(y_1' - y_2') + b(y_1 - y_2)$$
$$= (y_1'' + ay_1' + by_1) - (y_2'' + ay_2' + by_2)$$
$$= \phi(x) - \phi(x) = 0. \quad \square$$

> **(8.6.6)**   If y_p is a particular solution of the complete equation, then every solution of the complete equation can be written as a solution of the reduced equation plus y_p.

Proof. Let y_p be a particular solution of the complete equation. If y is also a solution of the complete equation, then [by (8.6.5)] $y - y_p$ is a solution of the reduced equation. Obviously

$$y = (y - y_p) + y_p. \quad \square$$

It follows from (8.6.6) that we can obtain *the general solution* of the complete equation by starting with the general solution of the reduced equation and adding a particular solution of the complete equation. The general solution of the complete equation can thus be written

(8.6.7)
$$\boxed{y = C_1 u_1 + C_2 u_2 + y_p}$$

where u_1, u_2 are any two fundamental solutions of the reduced equation and y_p is any particular solution of the complete equation.

There are many ways of searching for a particular solution y_p. We'll describe one of them: the *method of undetermined coefficients*. This method could also be called the method of educated guesses since we try particular solutions based on the right side of the equation and on our prior experience. For example, if the right side of the equation is a polynomial, we look for a particular solution in the form of a polynomial.

EXAMPLE. For the equation

$$y'' - y' - 2y = x^2 + 2x - 1$$

we try a solution of the form

$$y_p = d_2 x^2 + d_1 x + d_0.$$

Differentiation gives

$$y_p' = 2d_2 x + d_1, \qquad y_p'' = 2d_2.$$

Substituting y_p into the differential equation, we obtain

$$2d_2 - (2d_2 x + d_1) - 2(d_2 x^2 + d_1 x + d_0) = x^2 + 2x - 1,$$
$$-2d_2 x^2 - 2(d_2 + d_1)x + (2d_2 - d_1 - 2d_0) = x^2 + 2x - 1.$$

Comparing coefficients, we have

$$-2d_2 = 1, \qquad -2(d_2 + d_1) = 2, \qquad 2d_2 - d_1 - 2d_0 = -1.$$

These equations give

$$d_2 = -\tfrac{1}{2}, \qquad d_1 = -\tfrac{1}{2}, \qquad d_0 = \tfrac{1}{4}.$$

The polynomial

$$y_p = -\tfrac{1}{2}x^2 - \tfrac{1}{2}x + \tfrac{1}{4}$$

is a particular solution of the complete equation. You can verify this by substitution. Since the general solution of the reduced equation is

$$y = C_1 e^{2x} + C_2 e^{-x}, \qquad\qquad \text{(check this out)}$$

we know from (8.6.7) that the general solution of the complete equation can be written

$$y = C_1 e^{2x} + C_2 e^{-x} - \tfrac{1}{2}x^2 - \tfrac{1}{2}x + \tfrac{1}{4}. \quad \square$$

EXAMPLE. For the equation

$$y'' - y' - 2y = \sin 2x$$

we try a particular solution of the form

$$y_p = A \sin 2x + B \cos 2x.$$

Differentiation gives

$$y_p' = 2A \cos 2x - 2B \sin 2x, \qquad y_p'' = -4A \sin 2x - 4B \cos 2x.$$

Substituting y_p into the differential equation, we obtain

$$(-4A \sin 2x - 4B \cos 2x)$$
$$- (2A \cos 2x - 2B \sin 2x) - 2(A \sin 2x + B \cos 2x) = \sin 2x,$$
$$(-6A + 2B) \sin 2x + (-6B - 2A) \cos 2x = \sin 2x.$$

Comparing coefficients, we have

$$-6A + 2B = 1, \qquad -6B - 2A = 0.$$

These equations give

$$A = -\tfrac{3}{20}, \qquad B = \tfrac{1}{20}.$$

As you can verify by substitution,

$$y_p = -\tfrac{3}{20} \sin 2x + \tfrac{1}{20} \cos 2x$$

is a particular solution of the complete equation. $\square$

EXERCISES

Find the general solution of each of the following equations.

1. $y'' + 2y' - 15y = 0.$ 2. $y'' - 13y' + 42y = 0.$ 3. $y'' + 8y' + 16y = 0.$
4. $y'' + 7y' + 3y = 0.$ 5. $y'' + 2y' + 5y = 0.$ 6. $y'' - 3y' + 8y = 0.$
7. $3y'' - 4y' = 0.$ 8. $y'' - 12y = 0.$ 9. $y'' + 12y = 0.$
10. $y'' - 3y' + \tfrac{9}{4}y = 0.$ 11. $2y'' + 5y' - 3y = 0.$ 12. $2y'' + 3y' = 0.$

Solve the following initial value problems.

13. $y'' - 5y' + 6y = 0$, $y(0) = 1$, $y'(0) = 1$.
14. $y'' + 2y' + y = 0$, $y(2) = 1$, $y'(2) = 2$.
15. $y'' + \frac{1}{4}y = 0$, $y(\pi) = 1$, $y'(\pi) = -1$.
16. $y'' - 2y' + 2y = 0$, $y(0) = -1$, $y'(0) = -1$.

17. Find all solutions of the equation $y'' - y' - 2y = 0$ that satisfy the given initial conditions:
    (a) $y(0) = 1$.   (b) $y'(0) = 1$.   (c) $y(0) = 1$, $y'(0) = 1$.
18. Find all solutions of the equation $y'' + 2y' - 3y = 0$ that satisfy the given initial conditions:
    (a) $y(0) = 2$.   (b) $y'(0) = 6$.   (c) $y(0) = 2$, $y'(0) = 6$.

Find a particular solution.

19. $y'' + 5y' + 6y = 3x + 4$.   20. $y'' - 3y' - 10y = 5$.
21. $y'' + 2y' + 5y = x^2 - 1$.   22. $y'' + y' - 2y = x^3 + x$.
23. $y'' - y' - 12y = \cos x$.   24. $y'' - y' - 12y = \sin x$.
25. $y'' + 7y' + 6y = 3 \cos 2x$.   26. $y'' + y' + 3y = \sin 3x$.
27. $y'' + 6y' + 9y = e^{3x}$.   28. $y'' + 2y' + 2y = e^x$.

Find the general solution.

29. $y'' + y = e^x$.   30. $y'' - 2y' + y = -25 \sin 2x$.
31. $y'' - 3y' - 10y = -x - 1$.   32. $y'' + 4y = x$.

33. Show that, if

$$y_1 \text{ is a solution of } y'' + ay' + by = \phi_1(x)$$

and

$$y_2 \text{ is a solution of } y'' + ay' + by = \phi_2(x),$$

then

$$y_p = y_1 + y_2 \text{ is a solution of } y'' + ay' + by = \phi_1(x) + \phi_2(x).$$

Use Exercise 33 to find a particular solution.

34. $y'' + 2y' - 15y = x + e^{2x}$.   35. $y'' + y' - 6y = x + \sin x$.
36. $y'' - 7y' + 12y = e^{-x} + \sin 2x$.

37. Prove Part II of Theorem 8.6.3 by showing that

$$y_1 = e^{r_1 x}, \qquad y_2 = xe^{r_1 x}$$

are fundamental solutions. (First show that they are solutions; then show that their Wronskian is never zero.)
38. Let y_1, y_2 be two solutions of the reduced equation, y_2 never zero. Show that the Wronskian of y_1, y_2 is zero iff y_1 is a constant multiple of y_2.
39. In the absence of any external electromotive force, the current i in a simple electrical circuit varies with time t according to the formula

$$L \frac{d^2 i}{dt^2} + R \frac{di}{dt} + \frac{1}{C} i = 0. \qquad\qquad (L, R, C \text{ constants})\dagger$$

---

† L is inductance, R is resistance, and C is capacitance. If L is given in henrys, R in ohms, C in farads, and t in seconds, then the current i is given in amperes.

Find the general solution of this equation given that $L = 1$, $R = 10^3$, and
(a) $C = 5 \times 10^{-6}$.   (b) $C = 4 \times 10^{-6}$.   (c) $C = 2 \times 10^{-6}$.

40. In the presence of an external electromotive force $F(t)$, the equation in Exercise 39 takes the form

$$L \frac{d^2i}{dt^2} + R \frac{di}{dt} + \frac{1}{C} i = F(t).$$

Find the current i given that $F(t) = F_0$, $i(0) = 0$, $i'(0) = F_0/L$ and
(a) $CR^2 = 4L$.   (b) $CR^2 < 4L$.

41. Show that the change of variable $y = ve^{kx}$ transforms the equation

$$y'' + ay' + by = (c_n x^n + \cdots + c_1 x + c_0)e^{kx}$$

into

$$v'' + (2k + a)v' + (k^2 + ak + b)v = c_n x^n + \cdots + c_1 x + c_0.$$

42. Use Exercise 41 to find a particular solution of

$$y'' - y' - 12y = xe^{2x}.$$

43. Show that the general solution of the differential equation

$$y'' - \beta^2 y = 0 \qquad\qquad\qquad (\beta > 0)$$

can be written

$$y = C_1 \cosh \beta x + C_2 \sinh \beta x.$$

44. Find the general solution of the equation

$$y'' + 4y' + 3y = \cosh x.$$

Supplement to Section 8.6

In Section 8.5 we claimed that the general solution of

(1) $x''(t) + \beta^2 x(t) = 0$

could be written

$$x(t) = C_1 \sin (\beta t + C_2).$$

We will now support that claim.
    It's easy to see that the functions

$$x_1(t) = \cos \beta t, \qquad x_2(t) = \sin \beta t$$

satisfy the differential equation. Also they have a nonzero Wronskian:

$$W(t) = \cos \beta t \frac{d}{dt} (\sin \beta t) - \sin \beta t \frac{d}{dt} (\cos \beta t)$$

$$= \cos^2 \beta t + \sin^2 \beta t = 1.$$

Therefore the general solution of (1) can be written

$$x(t) = D_1 \cos \beta t + D_2 \sin \beta t.$$

(We use D_1, D_2 because C_1, C_2 are already being used.) All we have to show now is that every expression of the form

$$D_1 \cos \beta t + D_2 \sin \beta t \qquad \text{can be written} \qquad C_1 \sin (\beta t + C_2).$$

If $D_2 = 0$, we have

$$D_1 \cos \beta t + D_2 \sin \beta t = D_1 \cos \beta t = D_1 \sin (\beta t + \tfrac{1}{2}\pi).$$

This is in the desired form: set

$$C_1 = D_1, \qquad C_2 = \tfrac{1}{2}\pi.$$

If $D_2 \neq 0$, we have

$$D_1 \cos \beta t + D_2 \sin \beta t = \sqrt{D_1^2 + D_2^2} \left(\frac{D_1}{\sqrt{D_1^2 + D_2^2}} \cos \beta t + \frac{D_2}{\sqrt{D_1^2 + D_2^2}} \sin \beta t \right)$$

$$= \sqrt{D_1^2 + D_2^2} \left[\sin \left(\tan^{-1} \left(\frac{D_1}{D_2} \right) \right) \cos \beta t \right.$$

$$\left. + \cos \left(\tan^{-1} \left(\frac{D_1}{D_2} \right) \right) \sin \beta t \right]$$

$$= \sqrt{D_1^2 + D_2^2} \sin \left(\beta t + \tan^{-1} \left(\frac{D_1}{D_2} \right) \right).$$

This is also in the desired form: set

$$C_1 = \sqrt{D_1^2 + D_2^2}, \qquad C_2 = \tan^{-1} \left(\frac{D_1}{D_2} \right). \quad \square$$

8.7 ·····MECHANICAL VIBRATIONS

In Section 8.5 you saw that, in the absence of friction or any resistance, an object suspended from a coil spring vibrates about the point of equilibrium $x = 0$ in simple harmonic motion. At each time t the displacement $x = x(t)$ satisfies the equation

(8.7.1)
$$x'' + \frac{k}{m} x = 0.$$

The constants k and m are both positive; k is the constant of proportionality in Hooke's law and m is the mass of the suspended object.

Damped Vibrations

We derived the equation of motion (8.7.1) from the force equation

$$F = -kx.$$

Unless the spring is frictionless and the motion takes place in a vacuum, there is a resistance to the motion that tends to dampen the vibrations. Experiment shows that the resistance force is usually proportional to the velocity x':

$$R = -cx'. \qquad\qquad (c > 0)$$

Taking this resistance term into account, the force equation reads

$$F = -kx - cx'.$$

Newton's $F = ma = mx''$ then gives

$$mx'' = -cx' - kx,$$

which we can write as

(8.7.2)
$$x'' + \frac{c}{m} x' + \frac{k}{m} x = 0.$$

This is the equation of motion in the presence of a *damping* factor. To study the motion we will analyze this equation.

The characteristic equation

$$r^2 + \frac{c}{m} r + \frac{k}{m} = 0$$

has roots

$$r = \frac{-c \pm \sqrt{c^2 - 4km}}{2m}.$$

There are three possibilities:

$$c^2 - 4km < 0, \qquad c^2 - 4km > 0, \qquad c^2 - 4km = 0.$$

Case 1. $c^2 - 4km < 0$
In this case the characteristic equation has two complex conjugate roots:

$$r_1 = -\frac{c}{2m} + i\omega, \qquad r_2 = -\frac{c}{2m} - i\omega \qquad \text{where} \quad \omega = \frac{\sqrt{4km - c^2}}{2m}.$$

The general solution of (8.7.2),

$$x = e^{-(c/2m)t}(c_1 \cos \omega t + c_2 \sin \omega t),$$

can be written

(8.7.3)
$$x = C_1 e^{-(c/2m)t} (\sin \omega t + C_2).$$

This is called the *underdamped case*. The motion is similar to simple harmonic motion, except that the damping term $e^{-(c/2m)t}$ ensures that $x \to 0$ as $t \to \infty$. The vibrations continue indefinitely with constant frequency $\omega/2\pi$ but diminishing amplitude $|C_1| e^{-(c/2m)t}$. As $t \to \infty$, the amplitude of the vibrations tends to zero. The vibrations die down. The motion is illustrated in Figure 8.7.1.

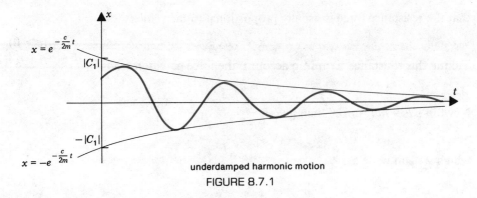

underdamped harmonic motion

FIGURE 8.7.1

Case 2. $c^2 - 4km > 0$

In this case the characteristic equation has two distinct real roots:

$$r_1 = \frac{-c + \sqrt{c^2 - 4km}}{2m}, \qquad r_2 = \frac{-c - \sqrt{c^2 - 4km}}{2m}.$$

The general solution takes the form

(8.7.4)
$$x = C_1 e^{r_1 t} + C_2 e^{r_2 t}.$$

This is called the *overdamped case*. The motion is nonoscillatory. Since $\sqrt{c^2 - 4km} < \sqrt{c^2} = c$, both r_1 and r_2 are negative. As $t \to \infty$, $x \to 0$. See Figure 8.7.2.

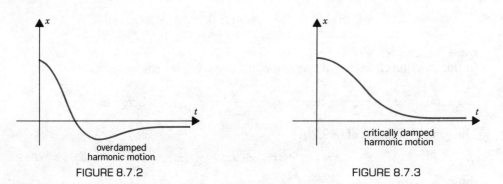

overdamped
harmonic motion

FIGURE 8.7.2

critically damped
harmonic motion

FIGURE 8.7.3

Case 3. $c^2 - 4km = 0$

In this case the characteristic equation has one double root

$$r_1 = -\frac{c}{2m}$$

and the general solution takes the form

(8.7.5)
$$x = C_1 e^{-(c/2m)t} + C_2 t e^{-(c/2m)t}.$$

This is called the *critically damped case*. Once again the motion is nonoscillatory. Moreover, as $t \to \infty$, $x \to 0$. See Figure 8.7.3.

For an example of damped vibrations consider the spring-loaded two-way door one might find in a restaurant kitchen, a door that can be pushed open in either direction. In the underdamped case the door flaps back and forth quite a bit when released before coming to rest. In the overdamped case the released door swings once past its resting position before coming to rest. This is usually the desired setting. In the critically damped case the released door slowly returns to its resting position without overswinging.

Forced Vibrations

The vibrations that we have been considering result from the interplay of three forces: the force of gravity, the elastic force of the spring, the retarding force of the surrounding medium. Such vibrations are called *free vibrations*.

The application of an external force to a freely vibrating system modifies the vibrations and results in what are called *forced vibrations*. In what follows we examine the effect of a pulsating force $F_0 \cos \gamma t$. Without loss of generality we can take both F_0 and γ as positive.

In an undamped system the force equation reads

$$F = -kx + F_0 \cos \gamma t$$

and the equation of motion takes the form

(8.7.6)
$$x'' + \frac{k}{m} x = \frac{F_0}{m} \cos \gamma t.$$

As usual we set $\beta = \sqrt{k/m}$ and write

(8.7.7)
$$x'' + \beta^2 x = \frac{F_0}{m} \cos \gamma t.$$

As you'll see, the nature of the vibrations depends on the relation between the *applied frequency*, $\gamma/2\pi$, and the *natural frequency* of the system, $\beta/2\pi$.

Case 1. $\gamma \neq \beta$

In this case the method of undetermined coefficients gives the particular solution

$$x_p = \frac{F_0/m}{\beta^2 - \gamma^2} \cos \gamma t. \qquad \text{(Exercise 4)}$$

The general equation of motion can thus be written

(8.7.8)
$$x = C_1 \sin (\beta t + C_2) + \frac{F_0/m}{\beta^2 - \gamma^2} \cos \gamma t.$$

If β/γ is rational, the vibrations are periodic (Exercise 5). If, on the other hand, β/γ is not rational, then the vibrations are not periodic and the motion, though bounded by

$$|C_1| + \left| \frac{F_0/m}{\beta^2 - \gamma^2} \right|,$$

can be highly irregular. □

Case 2. $\gamma = \beta$
In this case the method of undetermined coefficients gives

$$x_p = \frac{F_0}{2\beta m} t \sin \beta t \qquad\qquad \text{(Exercise 6)}$$

and the general solution takes the form

(8.7.9)
$$x = C_1 \sin (\beta t + C_2) + \frac{F_0}{2\beta m} t \sin \beta t.$$

The undamped system is said to be in *resonance*. The motion is oscillatory, but, because of the extra t present in the second summand, it is far from periodic. As $t \to \infty$, the amplitude of vibration increases without bound. □

Undamped systems and unbounded vibrations are mathematical fictions. No real mechanical system is totally undamped, and unbounded vibrations do not occur in nature. Nevertheless, a form of resonance can occur in a real mechanical system. (See Exercises 8 – 12.) A periodic external force applied to a mechanical system that is insufficiently damped can set up vibrations of very large amplitude. Such vibrations have caused the destruction of some formidable manmade structures. In 1850 the suspension bridge at Angers, France, was destroyed by vibrations set up by the unified step of a column of marching soldiers. More than two hundred French soldiers were killed in that catastrophe. (Soldiers today are told to break ranks before crossing a bridge.) The collapse of the bridge at Tacoma, Washington, is a more recent event. Slender in construction and graceful in design, the Tacoma bridge was opened to traffic on July 1, 1940. The third longest suspension bridge in the world, with a main span of 2800 feet, the bridge attracted many admirers. On November 1 of that same year, after less than five months of service, the main span of the bridge broke loose from its cables and crashed into the water below. (Luckily only one person was on the bridge at the time, and he was able to crawl to safety.) A driving wind had set up vibrations in resonance with the natural vibrations of the roadway, and the stiffening girders of the bridge had not provided sufficient damping to keep the vibrations from reaching destructive magnitude.

EXERCISES

1. What is the effect of an increase in the resistance constant c on the amplitude and frequency of the vibrations given by Equation (8.7.3)?

2. How many times can the motion given by (8.7.4) pass through the equilibrium point? How many times can the motion change directions?

3. How many times can the motion given by (8.7.5) pass through the equilibrium point? How many times can the motion change directions?

4. Show that, if $\gamma \neq \beta$, then the method of undetermined coefficients applied to (8.7.7) gives

$$x_p = \frac{F_0/m}{\beta^2 - \gamma^2} \cos \gamma t.$$

5. Show that, if β/γ is rational, then the vibrations given by (8.7.8) are periodic.

6. Show that, if $\gamma = \beta$, then the method of undetermined coefficients applied to (8.7.7) gives

$$x_p = \frac{F_0}{2\beta m} t \sin \beta t.$$

(*Forced vibrations in a damped system*) Write the equation

(8.7.10)
$$x'' + \frac{c}{m} x' + \frac{k}{m} x = \frac{F_0}{m} \cos \gamma t$$

as

(8.7.11)
$$x'' + 2\alpha x' + \beta^2 x = \frac{F_0}{m} \cos \gamma t.$$

We will assume throughout that $0 < \alpha < \beta$. (For large α the resistance is large and the motion is not as interesting.)

7. Find the general solution of the reduced equation $x'' + 2\alpha x' + \beta^2 x = 0$.
8. Verify that the function

(8.7.12)
$$x_p = \frac{F_0/m}{(\beta^2 - \gamma^2)^2 + 4\alpha^2\gamma^2} [(\beta^2 - \gamma^2) \cos \gamma t + 2\alpha\gamma \sin \gamma t]$$

is a particular solution of (8.7.11).

9. Determine x_p if $\beta = \gamma$. Show that the amplitude of the vibrations is very large if the resistance constant c is very small.

10. Show that (8.7.12) can be written

(8.7.13)
$$x_p = \frac{F_0/m}{\sqrt{(\beta^2 - \gamma^2)^2 + 4\alpha^2\gamma^2}} \sin (\gamma t + \phi).$$

HINT: For $D_2 \neq 0$,

$$D_1 \cos \gamma t + D_2 \sin \gamma t = \sqrt{D_1^2 + D_2^2} \sin \left(\gamma t + \tan^{-1}\left(\frac{D_1}{D_2}\right)\right).$$

11. Show that, if $2\alpha^2 \geq \beta^2$, then the amplitude of vibration in (8.7.13) decreases as γ increases.
12. Suppose now that $2\alpha^2 \leq \beta^2$.
    (a) Find the value of γ that maximizes the amplitude in (8.7.13).
    (b) Determine the frequency that corresponds to this value of γ. (This is called the *resonant frequency* of the damped system.)
    (c) What is the *resonant amplitude* of the system? (In other words, what is the amplitude

of vibration when the applied force is at resonant frequency?)

(d) Show that, if c, the constant of resistance, is very small, then the resonant amplitude is very large.

8.8 ······A PREDATOR–PREY MODEL

We consider the situation of two species, one of which serves as food for the other. For the sake of discussion we talk about foxes and rabbits. We assume that the size of the two populations is affected only by their numbers and that the influence of other factors such as water supply and weather remains constant.

We begin by describing the likely scenario, a description borne out by empirical evidence. Suppose that the rabbit population increases. The foxes have an easier time finding food and, as the foxes kill the rabbits, the foxes flourish. After a while the increased fox population causes the rabbit population to dwindle. But, then, the fox population starts to decline due to a lack of food (rabbits). The shrinking fox population reduces the threat to the rabbits, and thus, the rabbits begin to flourish again. The increasing rabbit population means a more accessible food source for the foxes. Again the fox population flourishes. The whole process is apparently cyclical.

To see if we can make this more precise, we let x be the number of foxes and y the number of rabbits at time t. We consider the species independently. If there are no foxes ($x = 0$) and the rabbit population grows unchecked, then by our work in Section 8.3 an exponential growth model is realistic:

$$(1) \qquad \frac{dy}{dt} = ay, \qquad a > 0.$$

On the other hand, if there are no rabbits, the foxes die off for lack of food and an exponential decline model is realistic:

$$(2) \qquad \frac{dx}{dt} = -bx, \qquad b > 0.$$

Suppose now that both foxes and rabbits abound. To account for the interaction of the two species, we assume that the rate at which foxes kill rabbits is proportional to the product xy. This means we subtract a term proportional to xy from (1) to allow for the decrease in the rabbit population, and we add such a term to (2) to allow for the increase in the fox population:

$$(8.8.1) \qquad \frac{dy}{dt} = ay - sxy, \qquad \frac{dx}{dt} = rxy - bx; \quad a, b, r, s > 0.$$

We use the term xy rather than some other expression like $x + y$ since the quantity xy is greatest when x and y are nearly equal; presumably the greatest number of kills will occur when there are relatively neither too many foxes looking for food nor too few rabbits to be found.

The pair of differential equations in (8.8.1) is an example of a *system*. Since the variable t does not appear on the right side of either equation, we can use the relation

$$\frac{dy}{dx} = \frac{dy/dt}{dx/dt}†$$

to solve the system.   We have

(8.8.2)
$$\frac{dy}{dx} = \frac{y(a - sx)}{x(ry - b)},$$

which we can solve by separating the variables:

$$\frac{ry - b}{y} \frac{dy}{dx} - \frac{a - sx}{x} = 0,$$

$$ry - b \ln y - a \ln x + sx = C,$$

$$ry + sx - C = \ln (y^b x^a),$$

$$e^{ry+sx-C} = y^b x^a,$$

$$e^{-C} = \frac{y^b x^a}{e^{ry} e^{sx}}.$$

Replacing the constant e^{-C} by $K > 0$, we have

(8.8.3)
$$K = \frac{y^b}{e^{ry}} \frac{x^a}{e^{sx}}.$$

A particular value of K may be found by substituting initial values x_0, y_0 for the two populations.   Notice that K does not depend on time t.

To analyze the behavior of this solution we observe that the right side of Equation (8.8.3) is composed of two similar factors each of the form

(8.8.4)
$$f(z) = \frac{z^p}{e^{mz}}, \qquad p, m > 0.$$

The graph of (8.8.4) for any positive values of p and m looks like the one shown in Figure 8.8.1.   Verification of this is left to you in the exercises.   Therefore, if we fix a particular value of x in (8.8.3) and solve the equation for y, we will ordinarily get two values.   This means that vertical lines that intersect the graph of (8.8.3) do so in two places.   The exception occurs when $y = b/r$ (that is, $z = p/m$); at that value of y, x takes on its maximum or minimum value.   Similarly, horizontal lines that intersect

---

† Here we are assuming that, at least over a short x-interval, y depends differentiably on x. Then, by the chain rule,

$$\frac{dy}{dt} = \frac{dy}{dx} \frac{dx}{dt} \qquad \text{and,} \qquad \text{if } \frac{dx}{dt} \neq 0, \quad \frac{dy}{dx} = \frac{dy/dt}{dx/dt}.$$

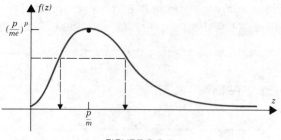

FIGURE 8.8.1

the graph of (8.8.3) ordinarily do so twice; y takes on its maximum and minimum values when $x = a/s$.   The graph of (8.8.3) is thus a simple closed curve, known in this context as a *trajectory*.   Trajectories for two values of K and fixed choices of a, b, r, s are displayed in Figure 8.8.2.

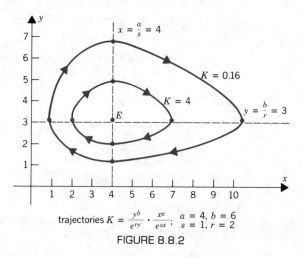

trajectories $K = \dfrac{y^b}{e^{ry}} \cdot \dfrac{x^a}{e^{sx}}$; $\begin{array}{l} a = 4, b = 6 \\ s = 1, r = 2 \end{array}$

FIGURE 8.8.2

To determine the direction in which the trajectories are traced out (indicated by the arrowheads in the figure), we note that

$$\frac{dx}{dt} = x(ry - b) > 0 \qquad \text{iff} \qquad y > \frac{b}{r}.$$

The motion is clockwise.   The point $(a/s, b/r)$ labeled E in Figure 8.8.2 is significant.   It represents a state of equilibrium in which the two populations are in perfect balance undergoing no change in number.   In practical terms this does not happen. The cyclical behavior displayed by a trajectory represents the true case.

To reinforce this notion of cycle, we consider the activity within each of the four regions determined by the lines $x = a/s$ and $y = b/r$.   (See Figure 8.8.3.)   Notice how this representation mirrors our original thoughts about the situation.

The numbers used for the trajectories sketched in Figure 8.8.2 are unrealistic.   In particular, whenever either population is less than 1, it does not recover according to the cycle but is extinct!   This observation raises an important point to be considered when we reexamine the assumptions that underly the model.

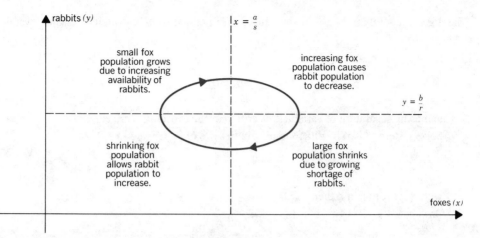

FIGURE 8.8.3

Recall that we assumed that all the other factors, which might influence the populations, remain constant. If any of these factors were to undergo sustained change, this change would have to be built into the model. On the other hand, if a factor changed suddenly and then remained constant, the cyclic behavior would be restored in time, but along a different trajectory. Such factors might include short-term diseases, a change in hunting laws, or a stretch of unseasonable weather. In this case anyone monitoring the situation would need to determine the new trajectory and examine the altered prospects of extinction for either species.

EXERCISES

Sketch trajectory (8.8.3) for the given values.

1. $a = b = 1$; $r = s = 2$; $K = 0.02$.
2. $a = b = 1$; $r = s = 2$; $K = 0.03$.
3. $a = b = 2$; $r = s = 1$; $K = 0.2$.
4. $a = b = 2$; $r = s = 1$; $K = 0.02$.

5. Verify that the graph given in Figure 8.8.1 for function (8.8.4) is correct.
6. Show that there are no "points of inflection" on the graph of (8.8.3).   HINT: Use (8.8.2) to find d^2y/dx^2 and conclude that the trajectory is concave down for $y > b/r$ and concave up for $y < b/r$.
7. Show that the average value of x is a/s.   HINT: Let T be the length (in time, of course) of one cycle so that $y(T) = y(0)$; integrate both sides of the equation

$$\frac{1}{y}\frac{dy}{dt} = a - sx$$

from $t = 0$ to $t = T$.

If we "linearize" the predator–prey model (8.8.1) by setting $y = b/r$ in the first equation and $x = a/s$ in the second equation, the resulting linear system

(8.8.5)
$$\frac{dy}{dt} = \frac{b}{r}(a - sx), \qquad \frac{dx}{dt} = \frac{a}{s}(ry - b)$$

has a general solution that, near the equilibrium point $(a/s, b/r)$, exhibits the same overall behavior as (8.8.3).

8. Solve system (8.8.5) by writing

$$\frac{dy}{dx} = \frac{dy/dt}{dx/dt}$$

and using separation of variables. Verify that the trajectories are ellipses.†

9. Solve system (8.8.5) by differentiating both sides of

$$\frac{dy}{dt} = \frac{b}{r}(a - sx)$$

with respect to t, and then use

$$\frac{dx}{dt} = \frac{a}{s}(ry - b)$$

to obtain a second-order linear differential equation with constant coefficients.

10. The system of differential equations

$$(8.8.6) \qquad \frac{dy}{dt} = ay - sxy, \qquad \frac{dx}{dt} = bx - rxy, \quad a, b, r, s > 0$$

is an effective model for the "predator–predator" situation for two competing species. (Note the revision in dx/dt.) Solve system (8.8.6) and show that the trajectories are not cyclic. In particular, one species must approach extinction except in the impractical case of equilibrium.

11. The "linear approximation" of system (8.8.6) is the system

$$(8.8.7) \qquad \frac{dy}{dt} = \frac{b}{r}(a - sx), \qquad \frac{dx}{dt} = \frac{a}{s}(b - ry), \quad a, b, r, s > 0.$$

Show that the trajectories are hyperbolas.††

8.9 ······NUMERICAL METHODS

As indicated earlier, the differential equations that occur most frequently in applications are of order one or two. In this chapter we have shown you some techniques for solving some of these equations. There are other techniques, one of which is explained in Chapter 13. However, many of the differential equations that arise in the study of physical phenomena cannot be solved exactly. Accordingly, we need effective numerical methods for making approximations. In this section we present two numerical methods for solving first-order differential equations. The methods are applicable to initial-value problems.

---

† For information on ellipses, see Section 10.4.

†† For information on hyperbolas, see Section 10.5.

To illustrate the accuracy of the approximations, we will work with an initial-value problem for which an exact solution is available. As you can check, the initial-value problem

(8.9.1) $y' = x + 2y,$ $y(0) = 1$

has the exact solution

(8.9.2) $y = \frac{1}{4}(5e^{2x} - 2x - 1).$

We will use our numerical methods to estimate $y(1)$; the actual value is

$$y(1) = \tfrac{1}{4}(5e^2 - 3) \cong 8.4864.$$

To simplify the discussion, we need the notation for a function of two variables. The evaluation of a function such as

$$F(x, y) = x^2 - 3xy$$

is carried out much as you would expect:

$$F(2, 5) = 2^2 - 3(2)(5) = -26, \qquad F(a, t) = a^2 - 3at.$$

The Euler Method

Figure 8.9.1 shows the graph of a differentiable function f. Given $f(x_0)$, we can estimate $f(x_0 + h)$ by proceeding along the tangent line, the line with slope $f'(x_0)$:

$$f(x_0 + h) \cong f(x_0) + h\,f'(x_0).$$

Using this estimate for $f(x_0 + h)$ we can go on to estimate $f(x_0 + 2h)$ by proceeding along the line with slope $f'(x_0 + h)$. We can then go on to estimate $f(x_0 + 3h)$, $f(x_0 + 4h)$, etc. We illustrate the process in Figure 8.9.2. Presumably, if h is taken small enough, the path of line segments stays fairly close to the graph of f. This way of approximating a curve by line segments is the basis of the Euler method for solving initial-value problems.

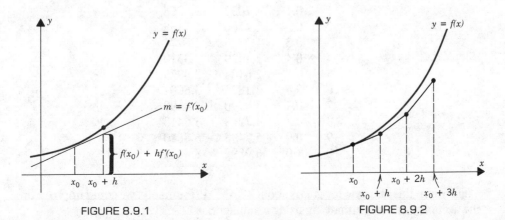

FIGURE 8.9.1   FIGURE 8.9.2

Consider the initial-value problem

(8.9.3)
$$y' = F(x, y), \qquad y(x_0) = y_0.$$

The point (x_0, y_0) lies on the solution curve. The point on the curve with x-coordinate $x_1 = x_0 + h$ has approximate y-coordinate

$$y_1 = y_0 + h\, y'(x_0) = y_0 + h\, F(x_0\ y_0).$$

The point on the curve with x-coordinate $x_2 = x_0 + 2h$ has approximate y-coordinate

$$y_2 = y_1 + h\, y'(x_1) = y_1 + h\, F(x_1, y_1).$$

Successive steps of h units (to the right when $h > 0$ and to the left when $h < 0$) produce a succession of points near the graph of the solution curve:

(8.9.4)
$$(x_n, y_n): \quad x_n = x_0 + nh, \quad y_n = y_{n-1} + h\, F(x_{n-1}, y_{n-1}), \qquad (n \geq 1).$$

EXAMPLE. Now let's return to the initial-value problem (8.9.1):

$$y' = x + 2y, \qquad y(0) = 1.$$

In the notation of (8.9.3)

$$F(x, y) = x + 2y, \qquad x_0 = 0, \quad y_0 = 1.$$

We want to estimate $y(1)$. Setting $h = 0.1$, we will need 10 iterations.
By (8.9.4)

$$x_n = (0.1)n \quad \text{and} \quad y_n = y_{n-1} + 0.1(x_{n-1} + 2y_{n-1}), \qquad 1 \leq n \leq 10.$$

The computations are given in the chart that follows. The numbers in the last column represent the actual values as calculated from the exact solution (8.9.2).

n	x_n	y_n	$y(x_n)$
0	0	1	1.0000
1	0.1	1.2000	1.2268
2	0.2	1.4500	1.5148
3	0.3	1.7600	1.8776
4	0.4	2.1420	2.3319
5	0.5	2.6104	2.8979
6	0.6	3.1825	3.6001
7	0.7	3.8790	4.4690
8	0.8	4.7248	5.5413
9	0.9	5.7498	6.8620
10	1.0	6.9897	8.4864

The error in this estimate for $y(1)$ is about 17.6%. Presumably, we could improve on the accuracy of our estimate by using a smaller h. □

Computational errors arise in several ways. With each iteration of the procedure we introduce the inherent error in the approximation method, and this error is compounded by the errors introduced in the previous steps. To reduce this contribution to the error, we can use smaller values of h. However, this improvement is made at the expense of increased round-off error. Each calculation produces an error in the last decimal place carried. Increasing the number of times the procedure is iterated by using smaller h values increases the number of times this round-off error is made and, thus, tends to increase the total error.

The Runge-Kutta Method

This is one of the oldest methods for generating numerical solutions of differential equations. And it remains one of the most accurate methods known. In the Euler method we estimated the value of $y(x_n)$ from our estimate for $y(x_{n-1})$ by using the slope of y at x_{n-1}. The idea behind the Runge-Kutta method is to select a slope more representative of the derivative of y on the interval $[x_{n-1}, x_n]$. This is done by selecting intermediate points in the interval and then forming a weighted average of the slopes at these points. Details of the development of the formulas used below may be found in any text on numerical analysis or differential equations.

Successive points of approximation for the initial-value problem

$$(1) \qquad\qquad y' = F(x, y), \qquad y(x_0) = y_0$$

are given by

$$(2) \qquad (x_n, y_n): \quad x_n = x_0 + nh, \quad y_n = y_{n-1} + hK \qquad (n \geq 1)$$

where

$$K_1 = F(x_{n-1}, y_{n-1})$$
$$K_2 = F(x_{n-1} + \tfrac{1}{2}h, y_{n-1} + \tfrac{1}{2}hK_1)$$
$$K_3 = F(x_{n-1} + \tfrac{1}{2}h, y_{n-1} + \tfrac{1}{2}hK_2)$$
$$K_4 = F(x_{n-1} + h, y_{n-1} + hK_3)$$

and

$$K = \tfrac{1}{6}(K_1 + 2K_2 + 2K_3 + K_4).$$

Notice that, in light of (1), the numbers K_1, K_2, K_3, K_4 represent slopes; K is the weighted average mentioned above. As you can see from (2), K represents the slope of the line segment that joins the approximation (x_{n-1}, y_{n-1}) to the approximation (x_n, y_n).

EXAMPLE. We go back once more to the initial-value problem (8.9.1):

$$y' = x + 2y, \qquad y(0) = 1$$

and this time we estimate $y(1)$ by the Runge-Kutta method. Again we have $F(x, y) = x + 2y$ and we take $h = 0.1$.

The results of the computations (these can be verified rather quickly on a computer or even a hand-held programmable calculator) are tabulated below. Again, (8.9.2) was used to calculate the actual values $y(x_n)$.

n	x_n	y_n	$y(x_n)$
0	0	1	1.0000
1	0.1	1.2268	1.2268
2	0.2	1.5148	1.5148
3	0.3	1.8777	1.8776
4	0.4	2.3320	2.3319
5	0.5	2.8979	2.8979
6	0.6	3.6002	3.6001
7	0.7	4.4691	4.4690
8	0.8	5.5414	5.5413
9	0.9	6.8622	6.8620
10	1.0	8.4865	8.4864

The error in this approximation of $y(1)$ is about 0.001%.   □

EXERCISES

A calculator is needed to work most of these exercises. Solve the following problems using (a) the Euler method, (b) the Runge-Kutta method.   Then, solve the initial-value problem and estimate the accuracy of your numerical estimate using

$$\text{relative percentage error} = \frac{y_{\text{actual}} - y_{\text{approx}}}{y_{\text{actual}}} \times 100\%.$$

1. Setting $h = 0.2$, estimate $y(1)$ if $y' = y$ and $y(0) = 1$.
2. Setting $h = 0.2$, estimate $y(1)$ if $y' = x + y$ and $y(0) = 2$.
3. Exercise 1 setting $h = 0.1$.
4. Exercise 2 setting $h = 0.1$.
5. Setting $h = 0.1$, estimate $y(1)$ if $y' = 2x$ and $y(2) = 5$.
6. Setting $h = 0.1$, estimate $y(0)$ if $y' = 3x^2$ and $y(1) = 2$.
7. Setting $h = 0.1$, estimate $y(2)$ if $y' = 1/2y$ and $y(1) = 1$.
8. Setting $h = 0.1$, estimate $y(2)$ if $y' = 1/3y^2$ and $y(1) = 1$.
9. Exercise 1 setting $h = 0.05$.
10. Exercise 2 setting $h = 0.05$.

8.10 CHAPTER SUMMARY

8.1 A Note on Mathematical Modeling

8.2 First-Order Linear Differential Equations

order of a differential equation (p. 398)
integrating factor (p. 400)

The key step in solving the first-order linear differential equation $y' + p(x)y = q(x)$ is multiplication by the integrating factor $e^{\int p(x)\,dx}$.

8.3 Applications

8.4 Separable Equations

8.5 Simple Harmonic Motion

8.6 Second-Order Linear Differential Equations

8.7 Mechanical Vibrations

8.8 A Predator – Prey Model

8.9 Numerical Methods

9

Techniques of Integration

9.1 ······REVIEW

We begin by listing a few integrals with which you are already familiar. A more extended table of integrals appears on the inside covers of the book.

1. $\displaystyle\int \alpha\, dx = \alpha x + C.$

2. $\displaystyle\int x^n\, dx = \frac{1}{n+1} x^{n+1} + C, \qquad n \neq -1.$

3. $\displaystyle\int \frac{dx}{x} = \ln |x| + C.$

4. $\displaystyle\int e^x\, dx = e^x + C.$

5. $\displaystyle\int p^x\, dx = \frac{p^x}{\ln p} + C.$

6. $\displaystyle\int \cos x\, dx = \sin x + C.$

7. $\displaystyle\int \sin x\, dx = -\cos x + C.$

8. $\displaystyle\int \sec^2 x\, dx = \tan x + C.$

9. $\displaystyle\int \csc^2 x\, dx = -\cot x + C.$

10. $\displaystyle\int \sec x \tan x\, dx = \sec x + C.$

11. $\displaystyle\int \csc x \cot x\, dx = -\csc x + C.$

12. $\displaystyle\int \tan x\, dx = \ln |\sec x| + C.$

13. $\displaystyle\int \cot x\, dx = \ln |\sin x| + C.$

14. $\displaystyle\int \sec x\, dx = \ln |\sec x + \tan x| + C.$

15. $\displaystyle\int \csc x\, dx = \ln |\csc x - \cot x| + C.$

____

16. $\displaystyle\int \frac{dx}{\sqrt{1 - x^2}} = \sin^{-1} x + C.$

17. $\displaystyle\int \frac{dx}{1 + x^2} = \tan^{-1} x + C.$

18. $\displaystyle\int \frac{dx}{|x| \sqrt{x^2 - 1}} = \sec^{-1} x + C.$

____

19. $\displaystyle\int \cosh x\, dx = \sinh x + C.$

20. $\displaystyle\int \sinh x\, dx = \cosh x + C.$

In the spirit of review we work out a few integrals.

PROBLEM. Find

$$\int x \tan x^2\, dx.$$

Solution. Set

$$u = x^2, \qquad du = 2x\, dx.$$

Then

$$\int x \tan x^2 \, dx = \tfrac{1}{2} \int \tan u \, du = \tfrac{1}{2} \ln |\sec u| + C = \tfrac{1}{2} \ln |\sec x^2| + C. \quad \square$$

PROBLEM. Compute

$$\int_0^1 \frac{e^x}{e^x + 2} \, dx.$$

Solution. First we calculate the indefinite integral

$$\int \frac{e^x}{e^x + 2} \, dx.$$

Set

$$u = e^x + 2, \qquad du = e^x \, dx.$$

Then

$$\int \frac{e^x}{e^x + 2} \, dx = \int \frac{du}{u} = \ln |u| + C = \ln |e^x + 2| + C$$

and thus

$$\int_0^1 \frac{e^x}{e^x + 2} \, dx = \left[\ln |e^x + 2| \right]_0^1 = \ln (e + 2) - \ln 3 = \ln [\tfrac{1}{3}(e + 2)]. \quad \square$$

The final problem involves a little algebra.

PROBLEM. Find

$$\int \frac{dx}{x^2 + 2x + 5}.$$

Solution. First we complete the square in the denominator:

$$\int \frac{dx}{x^2 + 2x + 5} = \int \frac{dx}{(x^2 + 2x + 1) + 4} = \int \frac{dx}{(x + 1)^2 + 2^2} = *.$$

We know that

$$\int \frac{du}{u^2 + 1} = \tan^{-1} u + C.$$

Setting

$$2u = x + 1, \qquad 2du = dx,$$

we have

$$* = \int \frac{2du}{4u^2 + 4} = \tfrac{1}{2} \int \frac{du}{u^2 + 1} = \tfrac{1}{2} \tan^{-1} u + C = \tfrac{1}{2} \tan^{-1} [\tfrac{1}{2} (x + 1)] + C. \quad \square$$

EXERCISES

Work out the following integrals.

1. $\displaystyle\int e^{2-x}\,dx.$

2. $\displaystyle\int \cos \tfrac{2}{3}x\,dx.$

3. $\displaystyle\int_0^1 \sin \pi x\,dx.$

4. $\displaystyle\int_0^t \sec \pi x \tan \pi x\,dx.$

5. $\displaystyle\int \sec^2 (1-x)\,dx.$

6. $\displaystyle\int \frac{dx}{5^x}.$

7. $\displaystyle\int_{\pi/6}^{\pi/3} \cot x\,dx.$

8. $\displaystyle\int_0^1 \frac{x^3}{1+x^4}\,dx.$

9. $\displaystyle\int \frac{x}{\sqrt{1-x^2}}\,dx.$

10. $\displaystyle\int_{-\pi/4}^{\pi/4} \frac{dx}{\cos^2 x}.$

11. $\displaystyle\int_{-\pi/4}^{\pi/4} \frac{\sin x}{\cos^2 x}\,dx.$

12. $\displaystyle\int \frac{e^{\sqrt{x}}}{\sqrt{x}}\,dx.$

13. $\displaystyle\int_1^2 \frac{e^{1/x}}{x^2}\,dx.$

14. $\displaystyle\int_{\pi/6}^{\pi/3} \csc x\,dx.$

15. $\displaystyle\int \frac{x}{x^2+1}\,dx.$

16. $\displaystyle\int \frac{x^3}{\sqrt{1-x^4}}\,dx.$

17. $\displaystyle\int_0^c \frac{dx}{x^2+c^2}.$

18. $\displaystyle\int a^x e^x\,dx.$

19. $\displaystyle\int \frac{\sec^2 \theta}{\sqrt{3\tan \theta + 1}}\,d\theta.$

20. $\displaystyle\int \frac{\sin \phi}{3-2\cos \phi}\,d\phi.$

21. $\displaystyle\int \frac{e^x}{ae^x - b}\,dx.$

22. $\displaystyle\int_0^{\pi/4} \frac{\sec^2 x \tan x}{\sqrt{2+\sec^2 x}}\,dx.$

23. $\displaystyle\int \frac{1+\cos 2x}{\sin^2 2x}\,dx.$

24. $\displaystyle\int \frac{dx}{x^2-4x+13}.$

25. $\displaystyle\int \frac{x}{(x+1)^2+4}\,dx.$

26. $\displaystyle\int \frac{\ln x}{x}\,dx.$

27. $\displaystyle\int \frac{x}{\sqrt{1-x^4}}\,dx.$

28. $\displaystyle\int \frac{e^x}{1+e^{2x}}\,dx.$

29. $\displaystyle\int \frac{dx}{x^2+6x+10}.$

30. $\displaystyle\int e^x \tan e^x\,dx.$

31. $\displaystyle\int x \sin x^2\,dx.$

32. $\displaystyle\int \frac{x+1}{\sqrt{1-x^2}}\,dx.$

33. $\displaystyle\int \sinh^2 x\,dx.$

34. $\displaystyle\int \tanh^2 2x\,dx.$

35. $\displaystyle\int \sinh^3 x\,dx.$

36. $\displaystyle\int \tanh^3 x\,dx.$

9.2 ······INTEGRATION BY PARTS

We begin with the differentiation formula

$$f(x)g'(x) + f'(x)g(x) = (f \cdot g)'(x).$$

Integrating both sides, we get

$$\int f(x)g'(x)\,dx + \int f'(x)g(x)\,dx = \int (f \cdot g)'(x)\,dx.$$

Since

$$\int (f \cdot g)'(x)\,dx = f(x)g(x) + C,$$

we have

$$\int f(x)g'(x)\, dx + \int f'(x)g(x)\, dx = f(x)g(x) + C$$

and therefore

$$\int f(x)g'(x)\, dx = f(x)g(x) - \int f'(x)g(x)\, dx + C.$$

Since the computation of

$$\int f'(x)g(x)\, dx$$

will yield its own arbitrary constant, there is no reason to keep the constant C. We therefore drop it and write

(9.2.1)
$$\int f(x)g'(x)\, dx = f(x)g(x) - \int f'(x)g(x)\, dx.$$

This formula, called the formula for *integration by parts,* enables us to find

$$\int f(x)g'(x)\, dx$$

by computing

$$\int f'(x)g(x)\, dx$$

instead. It is, of course, of practical use only if the second integral is easier to compute than the first.

In practice we usually set

$$u = f(x), \qquad dv = g'(x)\, dx$$

and compute

$$du = f'(x)\, dx, \qquad v = g(x).$$

The formula for integration by parts then takes the form

(9.2.2)
$$\int u\, dv = uv - \int v\, du.$$

Success with this formula depends on choosing u and dv so that

$$\int v\, du \quad \text{is easier to calculate than} \quad \int u\, dv.$$

PROBLEM. Calculate

$$\int xe^x\, dx.$$

Solution. We want to separate x from e^x. Setting

$$u = x, \qquad dv = e^x \, dx,$$

we have

$$du = dx, \qquad v = e^x.$$

Accordingly,

$$\int xe^x \, dx = \int u \, dv = uv - \int v \, du = xe^x - \int e^x \, dx = xe^x - e^x + C.$$

Our choice of u and dv worked out very well. Had we set

$$u = e^x, \qquad dv = x \, dx,$$

we would have had

$$du = e^x, \qquad v = \tfrac{1}{2}x^2.$$

Integration by parts would then have given

$$\int xe^x \, dx = \int u \, dv = uv - \int v \, du = \tfrac{1}{2}x^2 e^x - \tfrac{1}{2} \int x^2 e^x \, dx,$$

an integral more complicated than the one we started with. A shrewd choice of u and dv is crucial. □

As the next problem shows, effective choices of u and dv are not unique.

PROBLEM. Calculate

$$\int x \ln x \, dx.$$

Solution. Setting

$$u = \ln x, \qquad dv = x \, dx,$$

we have

$$du = \frac{1}{x} \, dx, \qquad v = \frac{x^2}{2}.$$

Then

$$\int x \ln x \, dx = \int u \, dv = uv - \int v \, du$$

$$= \frac{x^2}{2} \ln x - \int \frac{1}{x} \frac{x^2}{2} \, dx = \frac{1}{2} x^2 \ln x - \frac{1}{4} x^2 + C.$$

Alternative Solution. This time we set

$$u = x \ln x, \qquad\qquad dv = dx,$$

so that

$$du = (1 + \ln x)\, dx, \qquad v = x.$$

Substituting these selections in

$$\int u\, dv = uv - \int v\, du,$$

we find that

(1) $$\int x \ln x\, dx = x^2 \ln x - \int x(1 + \ln x)\, dx.$$

It may seem that the integral on the right is more complicated than the one we started with. However, we can rewrite equation (1) as

$$\int x \ln x\, dx = x^2 \ln x - \int x\, dx - \int x \ln x\, dx.$$

It follows that

$$2 \int x \ln x\, dx = x^2 \ln x - \int x\, dx$$

and thus

$$\int x \ln x\, dx = \frac{1}{2} x^2 \ln x - \frac{1}{4} x^2 + C$$

as before. □

PROBLEM. Calculate

$$\int x \sin x\, dx.$$

Solution. Setting

$$u = x, \qquad dv = \sin x\, dx,$$

we have

$$du = dx, \qquad v = -\cos x.$$

Therefore

$$\int x \sin x\, dx = -x \cos x - \int -\cos x\, dx = -x \cos x + \sin x + C. \quad \square$$

Integration by parts is often used to calculate integrals where the integrand is a mixture of function types; for example, polynomials and exponentials, or polynomials and trigonometric functions, etc. Some integrands, however, are better left as mixtures; for example, it is easy to see that

$$\int 2xe^{x^2}\, dx = e^{x^2} + C \qquad \text{and} \qquad \int 3x^2 \cos x^3\, dx = \sin x^3 + C.$$

Any attempt to separate these integrands by integration by parts is counterproductive. The mixtures in these integrands arise from the chain rule and we need these mixtures to calculate the integrals.

PROBLEM. Calculate

$$\int x^5 e^{x^3} \, dx.$$

Solution. To integrate e^{x^3} we need an x^2 factor. So we'll keep x^2 together with e^{x^3}. Setting

$$u = x^3, \qquad dv = x^2 e^{x^3} \, dx,$$

we have

$$du = 3x^2 \, dx, \qquad v = \tfrac{1}{3} e^{x^3}.$$

Thus

$$\int x^5 e^{x^3} \, dx = \int u \, dv = uv - \int v \, du$$

$$= \tfrac{1}{3} x^3 e^{x^3} - \int x^2 e^{x^3} \, dx$$

$$= \tfrac{1}{3} x^3 e^{x^3} - \tfrac{1}{3} e^{x^3} + C = \tfrac{1}{3}(x^3 - 1) e^{x^3} + C. \quad \square$$

To calculate some integrals you may have to integrate by parts more than once.

PROBLEM. Evaluate

$$\int_0^1 x^2 e^x \, dx.$$

Solution. First we calculate the indefinite integral

$$\int x^2 e^x \, dx$$

by separating x^2 from e^x. Setting

$$u = x^2, \qquad dv = e^x \, dx,$$

we have

$$du = 2x \, dx, \qquad v = e^x,$$

and thus

$$\int x^2 e^x \, dx = \int u \, dv = uv - \int v \, du = x^2 e^x - \int 2x e^x \, dx.$$

We now compute the integral on the right again by parts. This time we set

$$u = 2x, \qquad dv = e^x \, dx.$$

This gives

$$du = 2\,dx, \qquad v = e^x$$

and thus

$$\int 2xe^x\,dx = \int u\,dv = uv - \int v\,du = 2xe^x - \int 2e^x\,dx = 2xe^x - 2e^x + C.$$

This together with our earlier calculations gives

$$\int x^2 e^x\,dx = x^2 e^x - 2xe^x + 2e^x + C.$$

It follows now that

$$\int_0^1 x^2 e^x\,dx = \left[x^2 e^x - 2xe^x + 2e^x \right]_0^1 = (e - 2e + 2e) - 2 = e - 2. \quad \square$$

PROBLEM. Find

$$\int e^x \cos x\,dx.$$

Solution. Here we integrate by parts twice. First we write

$$u = e^x, \qquad dv = \cos x\,dx,$$
$$du = e^x\,dx, \qquad v = \sin x.$$

This gives

(1) $$\int e^x \cos x\,dx = \int u\,dv = uv - \int v\,du = e^x \sin x - \int e^x \sin x\,dx.$$

Now we work with the integral on the right. Setting

$$u = e^x, \qquad dv = \sin x\,dx,$$
$$du = e^x\,dx, \qquad v = -\cos x,$$

we have

(2) $$\int e^x \sin x\,dx = \int u\,dv = uv - \int v\,du = -e^x \cos x + \int e^x \cos x\,dx.$$

Substituting (2) in (1), we get

$$\int e^x \cos x\,dx = e^x \sin x + e^x \cos x - \int e^x \cos x\,dx,$$

$$2 \int e^x \cos x\,dx = e^x(\sin x + \cos x),$$

$$\int e^x \cos x\,dx = \tfrac{1}{2} e^x(\sin x + \cos x).$$

Since this integral is an indefinite integral, we add an arbitrary constant C:

$$\int e^x \cos x \, dx = \tfrac{1}{2}e^x(\sin x + \cos x) + C. \quad \Box$$

Finally, we give three basic formulas that can be readily derived by integration by parts. The derivations are left for you as exercises.

(9.2.3)
$$\int \ln x \, dx = x \ln x - x + C.$$

(9.2.4)
$$\int \sin^{-1} x \, dx = x \sin^{-1} x + \sqrt{1 - x^2} + C.$$

(9.2.5)
$$\int \tan^{-1} x \, dx = x \tan^{-1} x - \tfrac{1}{2}\ln(1 + x^2) + C.$$

EXERCISES

Work out the following integrals and check your results by differentiation.

1. $\displaystyle\int xe^{-x} \, dx.$

2. $\displaystyle\int \ln(-x) \, dx.$

3. $\displaystyle\int x^2 \ln x \, dx.$

4. $\displaystyle\int x2^x \, dx.$

5. $\displaystyle\int x^2 e^{-x^3} \, dx.$

6. $\displaystyle\int x \ln x^2 \, dx.$

7. $\displaystyle\int x^2 e^{-x} \, dx.$

8. $\displaystyle\int x^3 e^{-x^2} \, dx.$

9. $\displaystyle\int \frac{x^2}{\sqrt{1 - x}} \, dx.$

10. $\displaystyle\int \frac{dx}{x(\ln x)^3}.$

11. $\displaystyle\int x \ln \sqrt{x} \, dx.$

12. $\displaystyle\int x\sqrt{x + 1} \, dx.$

13. $\displaystyle\int \frac{\ln (x + 1)}{\sqrt{x + 1}} \, dx.$

14. $\displaystyle\int x^2(e^x - 1) \, dx.$

15. $\displaystyle\int (\ln x)^2 \, dx.$

16. $\displaystyle\int x(x + 5)^{-14} \, dx.$

17. $\displaystyle\int x^3 3^x \, dx.$

18. $\displaystyle\int \sqrt{x} \ln x \, dx.$

19. $\displaystyle\int x(x + 5)^{14} \, dx.$

20. $\displaystyle\int (2^x + x^2)^2 \, dx.$

21. $\displaystyle\int x \cos x \, dx.$

22. $\displaystyle\int x^2 \sin x \, dx.$

23. $\displaystyle\int x^2(x + 1)^9 \, dx.$

24. $\displaystyle\int x^2(2x - 1)^{-7} \, dx.$

25. $\displaystyle\int e^x \sin x \, dx.$

26. $\displaystyle\int (e^x + 2x)^2 \, dx.$

27. $\displaystyle\int \ln (1 + x^2) \, dx.$

28. $\displaystyle\int x \ln (x + 1) \, dx.$

29. $\displaystyle\int x \tan^{-1} x \, dx.$

30. $\displaystyle\int e^{3x} \cos 2x \, dx.$

31. $\int x^n \ln x \, dx. \ (n \neq -1)$ **32.** $\int x \sin^{-1} 2x^2 \, dx.$ **33.** $\int e^{2x} \sin 3x \, dx.$

34. $\int x \sinh x \, dx.$ **35.** $\int x \cosh x \, dx.$ **36.** $\int e^x \cosh x \, dx.$

37. $\int x^3 \sin x^2 \, dx.$ **38.** $\int x^3 \sin x \, dx.$ **39.** $\int x^4 e^x \, dx.$

40. Verify (9.2.3).   **41.** Verify (9.2.4).   **42.** Verify (9.2.5).

(*Revenue streams*) In Section 8.3 we talked about continuous compounding and you saw that the present value of A dollars t years from now is given by the formula

$$P.V. = Ae^{-rt}$$

where r is the annual rate of continuous compounding.

   Suppose now that revenue flows continually at a constant rate of R dollars per year for n years. What is the present value of such a revenue stream? It's not hard to show that the present value of such a revenue stream is given by the formula

(9.2.6)
$$P.V. = \int_0^n Re^{-rt} \, dt.$$

Let S be a constant revenue stream of 1000 dollars per year.

43. What is the present value of the first 4 years of revenue? Assume continuous compounding (a) at 4%. (b) at 8%.

44. What is the present value of the fifth year of revenue with continuous compounding (a) at 4%? (b) at 8%?

   Revenues usually do not flow at a constant rate R but rather at a time-dependent rate $R(t)$. In general, $R(t)$ tends to increase when business is good and tends to decrease when business is poor. "Growth companies" are so dubbed because of their continually increasing $R(t)$. The "cyclical companies" owe their appellation to a fluctuating $R(t)$; $R(t)$ increases for awhile, then decreases for awhile, and then the cycle is supposedly repeated.

   If we postulate a varying $R(t)$, then the present value of an n-year stream is given by the formula

(9.2.7)
$$P.V. = \int_0^n R(t)e^{-rt} \, dt.$$

Here, as before, r is the rate of continuous compounding used to discount future dollars.

Let S be a revenue stream with $R(t) = 1000 + 60t$ dollars per year.

45. What is the present value of the first 2 years of revenue? Assume continuous compounding (a) at 5%. (b) at 10%.

46. What is the present value of the third year of revenue with continuous compounding (a) at 5%? (b) at 10%?

Let S be a revenue stream with $R(t) = 1000 + 80t$ dollars per year.

47. What is the present value of the fourth year of revenue with continuous compounding (a) at 6%? (b) at 8%?

48. What is the present value of the first 4 years of revenue? Assume continuous compounding (a) at 6%. (b) at 8%.

Let S be a revenue stream with $R(t) = 1000 + 100 \sin t$ dollars per year.

49. What is the present value of the first 3 years of revenue? Assume continuous compounding (a) at 5%. (b) at 10%.

50. What is the present value of the third year of revenue with continuous compounding (a) at 5%? (b) at 10%?

9.3 ······PARTIAL FRACTIONS

A rational function is by definition the quotient of two polynomials. Thus, for example,

$$\frac{1}{x^2 - 4}, \quad \frac{2x^2 + 3}{x(x-1)^2}, \quad \frac{-2x}{(x+1)(x^2+1)}, \quad \frac{1}{x(x^2+x+1)},$$

$$\frac{3x^4 + x^3 + 20x^2 + 3x + 31}{(x+1)(x^2+4)^2}, \quad \frac{x^5}{x^2 - 1}$$

are all rational functions, but

$$\frac{1}{\sqrt{x}}, \quad \ln x, \quad \frac{|x-2|}{x^2}$$

are not rational functions.

To integrate a rational function it's usually necessary to first rewrite it as a polynomial (which may be identically 0) plus fractions of the form

(9.3.1)
$$\boxed{\frac{A}{(x-\alpha)^k} \quad \text{and} \quad \frac{Bx+C}{(x^2+\beta x+\gamma)^k}}$$

with the quadratic $x^2 + \beta x + \gamma$ irreducible (i.e., not factorable into linear terms with real coefficients).† Such fractions are called *partial fractions.*

It is shown in algebra that every rational function can be written in such a way. Here are some examples.

EXAMPLE 1. (*The denominator splits into distinct linear factors.*) For

$$\frac{1}{x^2 - 4} = \frac{1}{(x-2)(x+2)},$$

we write

$$\frac{1}{x^2 - 4} = \frac{A}{x-2} + \frac{B}{x+2}.$$

_____

† $\beta^2 - 4\gamma < 0$.

Clearing fractions, we have

(1) $1 = A(x + 2) + B(x - 2).$

To find A and B we substitute numbers for x:

setting $x = 2$, we get $1 = 4A$ and therefore $A = \frac{1}{4}$;

setting $x = -2$, we get $1 = -4B$ and therefore $B = -\frac{1}{4}$.†

The desired decomposition reads

$$\frac{1}{x^2 - 4} = \frac{1}{4(x - 2)} - \frac{1}{4(x + 2)}.$$

You can check this by carrying out the subtraction on the right.   □

> In general, each distinct linear factor $x - c$ in the denominator gives rise to a term of the form
>
> $$\frac{A}{x - c}$$
>
> in the decomposition.

EXAMPLE 2. (*The denominator has a repeated linear factor.*) For

$$\frac{2x^2 + 3}{x(x - 1)^2},$$

we write

$$\frac{2x^2 + 3}{x(x - 1)^2} = \frac{A}{x} + \frac{B}{x - 1} + \frac{C}{(x - 1)^2}.$$

This leads to

$$2x^2 + 3 = A(x - 1)^2 + Bx(x - 1) + Cx.$$

To determine the three coefficients A, B, C we need to substitute three values for x. We select 0 and 1 because for those values of x several terms on the right side will drop out. As a third value of x, any other number will do; we select 2 just to keep the arithmetic simple.

---

† Another way of finding A and B consists of rewriting (1) as

$$1 = (A + B)x + 2A - 2B$$

and then equating coefficients to produce the system of equations

$$A + B = 0$$
$$2A - 2B = 1.$$

We can then get A and B by solving these equations simultaneously. Usually this approach involves more algebra. We'll use the method of substituting *well-chosen* values of x.

Setting $x = 0$, we get $3 = A$.

Setting $x = 1$, we get $5 = C$.

Setting $x = 2$, we get $11 = A + 2B + 2C$

which, with $A = 3$ and $C = 5$, gives $B = -1$.

The decomposition is therefore

$$\frac{2x^2 + 3}{x(x - 1)^2} = \frac{3}{x} - \frac{1}{x - 1} + \frac{5}{(x - 1)^2}. \quad \Box$$

> In general, each factor of the form $(x - c)^k$ in the denominator gives rise to an expression of the form
>
> $$\frac{A_1}{x - c} + \frac{A_2}{(x - c)^2} + \cdots + \frac{A_k}{(x - c)^k}$$
>
> in the decomposition.

EXAMPLE 3. (*The denominator has an irreducible quadratic factor.*) For

$$\frac{-2x}{(x + 1)(x^2 + 1)},$$

we write

$$\frac{-2x}{(x + 1)(x^2 + 1)} = \frac{A}{x + 1} + \frac{Bx + C}{x^2 + 1}$$

and obtain

$$-2x = A(x^2 + 1) + (Bx + C)(x + 1).$$

This time we use $-1, 0$, and 1.

Setting $x = -1$, we get $2 = 2A$ so that $A = 1$.

Setting $x = 0$, we get $0 = A + C$ and thus $C = -1$.

Setting $x = 1$, we get $-2 = 2A + 2B + 2C$

which, with $A = 1$ and $C = -1$, gives $B = -1$.

The decomposition reads

$$\frac{-2x}{(x + 1)(x^2 + 1)} = \frac{1}{x + 1} - \frac{x + 1}{x^2 + 1}. \quad \Box$$

EXAMPLE 4. (*The denominator has an irreducible quadratic factor.*) For

$$\frac{1}{x(x^2 + x + 1)}$$

we write

$$\frac{1}{x(x^2 + x + 1)} = \frac{A}{x} + \frac{Bx + C}{x^2 + x + 1}$$

and obtain

$$1 = A(x^2 + x + 1) + (Bx + C)x.$$

Again we select values of x that produce zeros or simple arithmetic on the right side.

$$1 = A \qquad\qquad\qquad (x = 0),$$
$$1 = 3A + B + C \qquad (x = 1),$$
$$1 = A + B - C \qquad (x = -1).$$

From this we find that

$$A = 1, \quad B = -1, \quad C = -1,$$

and therefore

$$\frac{1}{x(x^2 + x + 1)} = \frac{1}{x} - \frac{x + 1}{x^2 + x + 1}. \quad \square$$

In general, each irreducible quadratic factor $x^2 + \beta x + \gamma$ in the denominator gives rise to a term of the form

$$\frac{Ax + B}{x^2 + \beta x + \gamma}$$

in the decomposition.

EXAMPLE 5. (*The denominator has a repeated irreducible quadratic factor.*) For

$$\frac{3x^4 + x^3 + 20x^2 + 3x + 31}{(x + 1)(x^2 + 4)^2}$$

we write

$$\frac{3x^4 + x^3 + 20x^2 + 3x + 31}{(x + 1)(x^2 + 4)^2} = \frac{A}{x + 1} + \frac{Bx + C}{x^2 + 4} + \frac{Dx + E}{(x^2 + 4)^2}.$$

This gives

$$3x^4 + x^3 + 20x^2 + 3x + 31$$
$$= A(x^2 + 4)^2 + (Bx + C)(x + 1)(x^2 + 4) + (Dx + E)(x + 1).$$

This time we use $-1, 0, 1, 2,$ and -2.

$$50 = 25A \qquad\qquad\qquad\qquad\qquad\qquad (x = -1),$$
$$31 = 16A \qquad\quad + 4C \qquad\quad + E \qquad (x = 0),$$
$$58 = 25A + 10B + 10C + 2D + 2E \qquad (x = 1),$$
$$173 = 64A + 48B + 24C + 6D + 3E \qquad (x = 2),$$
$$145 = 64A + 16B - 8C + 2D - E \qquad (x = -2).$$

With a little patience you can see that

$$A = 2, \quad B = 1, \quad C = 0, \quad D = 0, \quad \text{and} \quad E = -1.$$

This gives the decomposition

$$\frac{3x^4 + x^3 + 20x^2 + 3x + 31}{(x + 1)(x^2 + 4)^2} = \frac{2}{x + 1} + \frac{x}{x^2 + 4} - \frac{1}{(x^2 + 4)^2}. \quad \square$$

> In general, each multiple irreducible quadratic factor $(x^2 + \beta x + \gamma)^k$ in the denominator gives rise to an expression of the form
>
> $$\frac{A_1 x + B_1}{x^2 + \beta x + \gamma} + \frac{A_2 x + B_2}{(x^2 + \beta x + \gamma)^2} + \cdots + \frac{A_k x + B_k}{(x^2 + \beta x + \gamma)^k}$$
>
> in the decomposition.

A polynomial appears in the decomposition when the degree of the numerator is greater than or equal to that of the denominator.

EXAMPLE 6. (*The decomposition contains a polynomial.*) For

$$\frac{x^5 + 2}{x^2 - 1},$$

first carry out the suggested division:

$$
\begin{array}{r}
x^3 + x \\
x^2 - 1 \overline{)x^5 + 2} \\
\underline{x^5 - x^3 } \\
x^3 \\
\underline{x^3 - x} \\
x + 2.
\end{array}
$$

This gives

$$\frac{x^5 + 2}{x^2 - 1} = x^3 + x + \frac{x + 2}{x^2 - 1}.$$

Since the denominator of the fraction splits into linear factors, we write

$$\frac{x + 2}{x^2 - 1} = \frac{A}{x + 1} + \frac{B}{x - 1}.$$

This gives

$$x + 2 = A(x - 1) + B(x + 1).$$

Substitution of $x = 1$ gives $B = \frac{3}{2}$; substitution of $x = -1$ gives $A = -\frac{1}{2}$. The decomposition takes the form

$$\frac{x^5 + 2}{x^2 - 1} = x^3 + x - \frac{1}{2(x + 1)} + \frac{3}{2(x - 1)}. \quad \square$$

We have been decomposing rational functions into partial fractions so as to be able to integrate them. Here we carry out the integrations leaving some of the details to you.

EXAMPLE 1'

$$\int \frac{dx}{x^2 - 4} = \frac{1}{4} \int \left(\frac{1}{x-2} - \frac{1}{x+2} \right) dx$$

$$= \frac{1}{4} \left(\ln |x - 2| - \ln |x + 2| \right) + C = \frac{1}{4} \ln \left| \frac{x-2}{x+2} \right| + C. \quad \square$$

EXAMPLE 2'

$$\int \frac{2x^2 + 3}{x(x-1)^2} \, dx = \int \left[\frac{3}{x} - \frac{1}{x-1} + \frac{5}{(x-1)^2} \right] dx$$

$$= 3 \ln |x| - \ln |x - 1| - \frac{5}{x-1} + C. \quad \square$$

EXAMPLE 3'

$$\int \frac{-2x}{(x+1)(x^2+1)} \, dx = \int \left(\frac{1}{x+1} - \frac{x+1}{x^2+1} \right) dx.$$

Since

$$\int \frac{dx}{x+1} = \ln |x+1| + C_1$$

and

$$\int \frac{x+1}{x^2+1} \, dx = \frac{1}{2} \int \frac{2x}{x^2+1} \, dx + \int \frac{dx}{x^2+1} = \frac{1}{2} \ln (x^2+1) + \tan^{-1} x + C_2,$$

we have

$$\int \frac{-2x}{(x+1)(x^2+1)} \, dx = \ln |x+1| - \frac{1}{2} \ln (x^2+1) - \tan^{-1} x + C. \quad \square$$

EXAMPLE 4'.

$$\int \frac{dx}{x(x^2+x+1)} = \int \left(\frac{1}{x} - \frac{x+1}{x^2+x+1} \right) dx = \ln |x| - \int \frac{x+1}{x^2+x+1} \, dx = *.$$

To compute the remaining integral, note that

$$\int \frac{x+1}{x^2+x+1} \, dx = \frac{1}{2} \int \frac{2x+1}{x^2+x+1} \, dx + \frac{1}{2} \int \frac{dx}{x^2+x+1}.$$

The first integral is a logarithm:

$$\frac{1}{2} \int \frac{2x+1}{x^2+x+1} \, dx = \frac{1}{2} \ln (x^2+x+1) + C_1;$$

the second integral is an inverse tangent:

$$\frac{1}{2} \int \frac{dx}{x^2+x+1} = \frac{1}{2} \int \frac{dx}{(x+\frac{1}{2})^2 + (\sqrt{3}/2)^2} = \frac{1}{\sqrt{3}} \tan^{-1} \left[\frac{2}{\sqrt{3}} \left(x + \frac{1}{2} \right) \right] + C_2.$$

Combining results, we have

$$* = \ln |x| - \frac{1}{2} \ln (x^2 + x + 1) - \frac{1}{\sqrt{3}} \tan^{-1} \left[\frac{2}{\sqrt{3}} \left(x + \frac{1}{2} \right) \right] + C. \quad \square$$

EXAMPLE 5′

$$\int \frac{3x^4 + x^3 + 20x^2 + 3x + 31}{(x + 1)(x^2 + 4)^2} \, dx = \int \left[\frac{2}{x + 1} + \frac{x}{x^2 + 4} - \frac{1}{(x^2 + 4)^2} \right] dx.$$

The first two fractions are easy to integrate:

$$\int \frac{2}{x + 1} \, dx = 2 \ln |x + 1| + C_1,$$

$$\int \frac{x}{x^2 + 4} \, dx = \frac{1}{2} \int \frac{2x}{x^2 + 4} \, dx = \frac{1}{2} \ln (x^2 + 4) + C_2.$$

The integral of the last fraction is of the form

$$\int \frac{dx}{(x^2 + c^2)^n}.$$

All such integrals can be calculated by setting $c \tan u = x$:

(9.3.2) $$\boxed{\int \frac{dx}{(x^2 + c^2)^n} = \frac{1}{c^{2n-1}} \int \cos^{2(n-1)} u \, du.}$$ †
$$\underset{c \tan u = x}{}$$

The integration of such trigonometric powers is discussed in detail in the next section. Here we have

$$\int \frac{dx}{(x^2 + 4)^2} = \frac{1}{8} \int \cos^2 u \, du$$
$$\underset{2 \tan u = x}{}$$

$$= \frac{1}{16} \int (1 + \cos 2u) \, du$$

half-angle formula $$= \frac{1}{16} u + \frac{1}{32} \sin 2u + C_3$$

$$= \frac{1}{16} u + \frac{1}{16} \sin u \cos u + C_3$$

$\sin 2u = 2 \sin u \cos u$ $$= \frac{1}{16} \tan^{-1} \frac{x}{2} + \frac{1}{16} \left(\frac{x}{\sqrt{x^2 + 4}} \right) \left(\frac{2}{\sqrt{x^2 + 4}} \right) + C_3$$

$$= \frac{1}{16} \tan^{-1} \frac{x}{2} + \frac{1}{8} \left(\frac{x}{x^2 + 4} \right) + C_3.$$

---

† The proof of this reduction formula is left to you in the exercises.

The integral we want is therefore

$$2 \ln |x + 1| + \frac{1}{2} \ln (x^2 + 4) - \frac{1}{8} \left(\frac{x}{x^2 + 4} \right) - \frac{1}{16} \tan^{-1} \frac{x}{2} + C. \quad \square$$

EXAMPLE 6'

$$\int \frac{x^5 + 2}{x^2 - 1} \, dx = \int \left[x^3 + x - \frac{1}{2(x + 1)} + \frac{3}{2(x - 1)} \right] dx$$

$$= \tfrac{1}{4} x^4 + \tfrac{1}{2} x^2 - \tfrac{1}{2} \ln |x + 1| + \tfrac{3}{2} \ln |x - 1| + C. \quad \square$$

EXERCISES

Work out the following integrals.

1. $\displaystyle\int \frac{7}{(x - 2)(x + 5)} \, dx.$ **2.** $\displaystyle\int \frac{x}{(x + 1)(x + 2)(x + 3)} \, dx.$ **3.** $\displaystyle\int \frac{2x^2 + 3}{x^2(x - 1)} \, dx.$

4. $\displaystyle\int \frac{x^2 + 1}{x(x^2 - 1)} \, dx.$ **5.** $\displaystyle\int \frac{x^5}{(x - 2)^2} \, dx.$ **6.** $\displaystyle\int \frac{x^5}{x - 2} \, dx.$

7. $\displaystyle\int \frac{x + 3}{x^2 - 3x + 2} \, dx.$ **8.** $\displaystyle\int \frac{x^2 + 3}{x^2 - 3x + 2} \, dx.$ **9.** $\displaystyle\int \frac{dx}{(x - 1)^3}.$

10. $\displaystyle\int \frac{dx}{x^2 + 2x + 2}.$ **11.** $\displaystyle\int \frac{x^2}{(x - 1)^2(x + 1)} \, dx.$ **12.** $\displaystyle\int \frac{2x - 1}{(x + 1)^2(x - 2)} \, dx.$

13. $\displaystyle\int \frac{dx}{x^4 - 16}.$ **14.** $\displaystyle\int \frac{x}{x^3 - 1} \, dx.$ **15.** $\displaystyle\int \frac{x^3 + 4x^2 - 4x - 1}{(x^2 + 1)^2} \, dx.$

16. $\displaystyle\int \frac{dx}{(x^2 + 16)^2}.$ **17.** $\displaystyle\int \frac{dx}{x^4 + 4}.^\dagger$ **18.** $\displaystyle\int \frac{dx}{x^2 + 16}.^\dagger$

19. Show that

$$\text{if} \quad y = \frac{1}{x^2 - 1} \quad \text{then} \quad \frac{d^n y}{dx^n} = \frac{1}{2} (-1)^n \, n! \left[\frac{1}{(x - 1)^{n+1}} - \frac{1}{(x + 1)^{n+1}} \right].$$

20. Verify reduction formula 9.3.2.

21. It is known that m parts of chemical A combine with n parts of chemical B to produce a compound C. Suppose that the rate at which C is produced varies directly with the product of the amounts of A and B present at that instant. Find the amount of C produced in t minutes from an initial mixing of A_0 pounds of A with B_0 pounds of B, given that
   (a) $n = m$, $A_0 = B_0$, and A_0 pounds of C are produced in the first minute.
   (b) $n = m$, $A_0 = \frac{1}{2} B_0$, and A_0 pounds of C are produced in the first minute.
   (c) $n \neq m$, $A_0 = B_0$, and A_0 pounds of C are produced in the first minute.
   HINT: Denote by $A(t)$, $B(t)$, and $C(t)$ the amounts of A, B, and C present at time t. Observe that

$$C'(t) = k A(t) B(t).$$

Note that

$\dagger$ HINT: With $a > 0$, $x^4 + a^2 = (x^2 + \sqrt{2a} x + a)(x^2 - \sqrt{2a} x + a).$

$$A_0 - A(t) = \frac{m}{m+n} C(t) \quad \text{and} \quad B_0 - B(t) = \frac{n}{m+n} C(t)$$

and thus

$$C'(t) = k \left[A_0 - \frac{m}{m+n} C(t) \right] \left[B_0 - \frac{n}{m+n} C(t) \right].$$

9.4 ·····POWERS AND PRODUCTS OF SINES AND COSINES

I. We begin by explaining how to calculate integrals of the form

$$\int \sin^m x \cos^n x \, dx \qquad \text{with } m \text{ or } n \text{ odd.}$$

Suppose that n is odd. If $n = 1$, the integral is of the form

$$(1) \qquad \int \sin^m x \cos x \, dx = \frac{1}{m+1} \sin^{m+1} x + C.$$

If $n > 1$, write

$$\cos^n x = \cos^{n-1} x \cos x.$$

Since $n - 1$ is even, $\cos^{n-1} x$ can be expressed in powers of $\sin^2 x$ by noting that

$$\cos^2 x = 1 - \sin^2 x.$$

The integral then takes the form

$$\int (\text{sum of powers of } \sin x) \cdot \cos x \, dx,$$

which can be broken up into integrals of form (1).

Similarly if m is odd, write

$$\sin^m x = \sin^{m-1} x \sin x$$

and use the substitution

$$\sin^2 x = 1 - \cos^2 x.$$

EXAMPLE

$$\int \sin^2 x \cos^5 x \, dx = \int \sin^2 x \cos^4 x \cos x \, dx$$

$$= \int \sin^2 x \, (1 - \sin^2 x)^2 \cos x \, dx$$

$$= \int (\sin^2 x - 2 \sin^4 x + \sin^6 x) \cos x \, dx$$

$$= \int \sin^2 x \cos x \, dx - 2 \int \sin^4 x \cos x \, dx + \int \sin^6 x \cos x \, dx$$

$$= \tfrac{1}{3} \sin^3 x - \tfrac{2}{5} \sin^5 x + \tfrac{1}{7} \sin^7 x + C. \quad \square$$

EXAMPLE

$$\int \sin^5 x \, dx = \int \sin^4 x \sin x \, dx$$

$$= \int (1 - \cos^2 x)^2 \sin x \, dx$$

$$= \int (1 - 2 \cos^2 x + \cos^4 x) \sin x \, dx$$

$$= \int \sin x \, dx - 2 \int \cos^2 x \sin x \, dx + \int \cos^4 x \sin x \, dx$$

$$= -\cos x + \tfrac{2}{3} \cos^3 x - \tfrac{1}{5} \cos^5 x + C. \quad \square$$

II. To calculate integrals of the form

$$\int \sin^m x \cos^n x \, dx \qquad \text{with } m \text{ and } n \text{ both even}$$

use the following identities:

$$\sin x \cos x = \tfrac{1}{2} \sin 2x, \qquad \sin^2 x = \tfrac{1}{2} - \tfrac{1}{2} \cos 2x, \qquad \cos^2 x = \tfrac{1}{2} + \tfrac{1}{2} \cos 2x.$$

EXAMPLE

$$\int \cos^2 x \, dx = \int (\tfrac{1}{2} + \tfrac{1}{2} \cos 2x) \, dx$$

$$= \tfrac{1}{2} \int dx + \tfrac{1}{2} \int \cos 2x \, dx = \tfrac{1}{2} x + \tfrac{1}{4} \sin 2x + C. \quad \square$$

EXAMPLE

$$\int \sin^2 x \cos^2 x \, dx = \tfrac{1}{4} \int \sin^2 2x \, dx$$

$$= \tfrac{1}{4} \int (\tfrac{1}{2} - \tfrac{1}{2} \cos 4x) \, dx$$

$$= \tfrac{1}{8} \int dx - \tfrac{1}{8} \int \cos 4x \, dx = \tfrac{1}{8} x - \tfrac{1}{32} \sin 4x + C. \quad \square$$

EXAMPLE

$$\int \sin^4 x \cos^2 x \, dx = \int (\sin x \cos x)^2 \sin^2 x \, dx$$

$$= \int \tfrac{1}{4} \sin^2 2x \, (\tfrac{1}{2} - \tfrac{1}{2} \cos 2x) \, dx$$

$$= \tfrac{1}{8} \int \sin^2 2x \, dx - \tfrac{1}{8} \int \sin^2 2x \cos 2x \, dx$$

$$= \tfrac{1}{8} \int (\tfrac{1}{2} - \tfrac{1}{2} \cos 4x) \, dx - \tfrac{1}{8} \int \sin^2 2x \cos 2x \, dx$$

$$= \tfrac{1}{16} x - \tfrac{1}{64} \sin 4x - \tfrac{1}{48} \sin^3 2x + C. \quad \square$$

III. Finally we come to integrals of the form

$$\int \sin mx \cos nx \, dx, \qquad \int \sin mx \sin nx \, dx, \qquad \int \cos mx \cos nx \, dx.$$

If $m = n$, there is no difficulty. Suppose that $m \neq n$. For the first integral use the identity

(1) $$\sin mx \cos nx = \tfrac{1}{2} \sin [(m + n)x] + \tfrac{1}{2} \sin [(m - n)x].$$

You can confirm this identity by using the usual expansions for $\sin (\theta_1 + \theta_2)$ and $\sin (\theta_1 - \theta_2)$.† Set

$$\theta_1 = mx \quad \text{and} \quad \theta_2 = nx,$$

and you'll find that

$$\sin [(m + n)x] = \sin mx \cos nx + \cos mx \sin nx,$$
$$\sin [(m - n)x] = \sin mx \cos nx - \cos mx \sin nx.$$

Add these two equations, divide by 2, and you'll get identity (1).
   Integration of (1) gives

$$\int \sin mx \cos nx \, dx = \frac{1}{2} \int \sin [(m + n)x] \, dx + \frac{1}{2} \int \sin [(m - n)x] \, dx$$

$$= -\frac{\cos [(m + n)x]}{2(m + n)} - \frac{\cos [(m - n)x]}{2(m - n)} + C.$$

Similarly,

$$\int \sin mx \sin nx \, dx = -\frac{\sin [(m + n)x]}{2(m + n)} + \frac{\sin [(m - n)x]}{2(m - n)} + C,$$

$$\int \cos mx \cos nx \, dx = \frac{\sin [(m + n)x]}{2(m + n)} + \frac{\sin [(m - n)x]}{2(m - n)} + C.$$

---

† These are given in Section 1.2.

EXERCISES

Work out the following integrals.

1. $\int \sin^3 x \, dx.$ **2.** $\int \cos^2 4x \, dx.$ **3.** $\int \sin^2 3x \, dx.$

4. $\int_0^\pi \sin^3 x \, dx.$ **5.** $\int_0^{\pi/2} \cos^3 x \, dx.$ **6.** $\int \sin^3 x \cos^2 x \, dx.$

7. $\int \cos^4 x \sin^3 x \, dx.$ **8.** $\int \cos^3 x \, dx.$ **9.** $\int \sin^3 x \cos^3 x \, dx.$

10. $\int \sin^2 x \cos^4 x \, dx.$ **11.** $\int \sin^2 x \cos^3 x \, dx.$ **12.** $\int \sin^4 x \cos^3 x \, dx.$

13. $\int_0^\pi \sin^4 x \, dx.$ **14.** $\int \cos^3 x \cos 2x \, dx.$ **15.** $\int \sin 2x \cos 3x \, dx.$

16. $\int \cos 2x \sin 3x \, dx.$ **17.** $\int \sin^2 x \sin 2x \, dx.$ **18.** $\int_0^{\pi/2} \cos^4 x \, dx.$

19. $\int \sin^4 x \cos^4 x \, dx.$ **20.** $\int_0^{\pi/2} \sin^5 x \, dx.$ **21.** $\int_0^{\pi/2} \cos^5 x \, dx.$

22. $\int \cos^5 x \sin^5 x \, dx.$ **23.** $\int \cos 2x \cos 3x \, dx.$ **24.** $\int \sin 2x \sin 3x \, dx.$

Calculate the following integrals by a trigonometric substitution.

25. $\int \dfrac{dx}{(x^2 + 1)^3}.$ [set $x = \tan u$]   **26.** $\int \dfrac{dx}{(x^2 + 4)^3}.$

27. $\int \dfrac{dx}{[(x + 1)^2 + 1]^2}.$ **28.** $\int \dfrac{dx}{[(2x + 1)^2 + 9]^2}.$

Evaluate the following integrals. They are important in applied mathematics.

29. $\dfrac{1}{\pi} \int_0^{2\pi} \cos^2 nx \, dx.$ **30.** $\dfrac{1}{\pi} \int_0^{2\pi} \sin^2 nx \, dx.$

31. $\int_0^{2\pi} \sin mx \cos nx \, dx, \quad m \neq n.$ **32.** $\int_0^{2\pi} \sin mx \sin nx \, dx, \quad m \neq n.$

33. $\int_0^{2\pi} \cos mx \cos nx \, dx, \quad m \neq n.$

34. (a) Use integration by parts to derive the reduction formula:

$$\int \sin^{n+2} x \, dx = -\frac{\sin^{n+1} x \cos x}{n + 2} + \frac{n + 1}{n + 2} \int \sin^n x \, dx.$$

(b) Using (a), verify that

$$\int_0^{\pi/2} \sin^{n+2} x \, dx = \frac{n + 1}{n + 2} \int_0^{\pi/2} \sin^n x \, dx.$$

(c) Show that

$$\int_0^{\pi/2} \sin^m x \, dx = \begin{cases} \left(\dfrac{(m-1)\cdots 5\cdot 3\cdot 1}{m\cdots 6\cdot 4\cdot 2}\right)\dfrac{\pi}{2}, & m \text{ even, } m \geq 2 \\[3mm] \dfrac{(m-1)\cdots 4\cdot 2}{m\cdots 5\cdot 3}, & m \text{ odd, } m \geq 3 \end{cases}.$$

(d) Show that

$$\int_0^{\pi/2} \cos^m x \, dx = \int_0^{\pi/2} \sin^m x \, dx.$$

9.5 ······OTHER TRIGONOMETRIC POWERS

I. First we take up integrals of the form

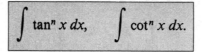

$$\int \tan^n x \, dx, \qquad \int \cot^n x \, dx.$$

To integrate $\tan^n x$, set

$$\tan^n x = \tan^{n-2} x \tan^2 x = (\tan^{n-2} x)(\sec^2 x - 1) = \tan^{n-2} x \sec^2 x - \tan^{n-2} x.$$

To integrate $\cot^n x$, set

$$\cot^n x = \cot^{n-2} x \cot^2 x = (\cot^{n-2} x)(\csc^2 x - 1) = \cot^{n-2} x \csc^2 x - \cot^{n-2} x.$$

EXAMPLE

$$\begin{aligned}
\int \tan^6 x \, dx &= \int (\tan^4 x \sec^2 x - \tan^4 x) \, dx \\
&= \int (\tan^4 x \sec^2 x - \tan^2 x \sec^2 x + \tan^2 x) \, dx \\
&= \int (\tan^4 x \sec^2 x - \tan^2 x \sec^2 x + \sec^2 x - 1) \, dx \\
&= \int \tan^4 x \sec^2 x \, dx - \int \tan^2 x \sec^2 x \, dx + \int \sec^2 x \, dx - \int dx \\
&= \tfrac{1}{5} \tan^5 x - \tfrac{1}{3} \tan^3 x + \tan x - x + C. \quad \square
\end{aligned}$$

II. Now consider the integrals

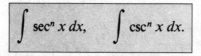

$$\int \sec^n x \, dx, \qquad \int \csc^n x \, dx.$$

For even powers write

$$\sec^n x = \sec^{n-2} x \sec^2 x = (\tan^2 x + 1)^{(n-2)/2} \sec^2 x$$

and

$$\csc^n x = \csc^{n-2} x \csc^2 x = (\cot^2 x + 1)^{(n-2)/2} \csc^2 x.$$

EXAMPLE

$$\int \sec^4 x \, dx = \int \sec^2 x \sec^2 x \, dx = \int (\tan^2 x + 1) \sec^2 x \, dx$$

$$= \int \tan^2 x \sec^2 x \, dx + \int \sec^2 x \, dx = \tfrac{1}{3} \tan^3 x + \tan x + C. \quad \square$$

The odd powers you can integrate by parts. For $\sec^n x$ set

$$u = \sec^{n-2} x, \quad dv = \sec^2 x \, dx$$

and, when $\tan^2 x$ appears, use the identity

$$\tan^2 x = \sec^2 x - 1.$$

You can handle $\csc^n x$ in a similar manner.

EXAMPLE. For

$$\int \sec^3 x \, dx$$

write

$$u = \sec x, \qquad\qquad dv = \sec^2 x \, dx,$$
$$du = \sec x \tan x \, dx, \qquad v = \tan x.$$

$$\int \sec^3 x \, dx = \int \sec x \sec^2 x \, dx$$

$$= \int u \, dv = uv - \int v \, du$$

$$= \sec x \tan x - \int \tan^2 x \sec x \, dx$$

$$= \sec x \tan x - \int (\sec^2 x - 1) \sec x \, dx$$

$$= \sec x \tan x - \int \sec^3 x \, dx + \int \sec x \, dx$$

$$= \sec x \tan x - \int \sec^3 x \, dx + \ln |\sec x + \tan x|.$$

$$2 \int \sec^3 x \, dx = \sec x \tan x + \ln |\sec x + \tan x|,$$

$$\int \sec^3 x \, dx = \tfrac{1}{2} \sec x \tan x + \tfrac{1}{2} \ln |\sec x + \tan x|.$$

Now add the arbitrary constant:

$$\int \sec^3 x \, dx = \tfrac{1}{2} \sec x \tan x + \tfrac{1}{2} \ln |\sec x + \tan x| + C. \quad \square$$

III. Finally we come to integrals of the form

$$\int \tan^m x \sec^n x \, dx, \qquad \int \cot^m x \csc^n x \, dx.$$

When n is even, write

$$\tan^m x \sec^n x = \tan^m x \sec^{n-2} x \sec^2 x$$

and express $\sec^{n-2} x$ entirely in terms of $\tan^2 x$ using

$$\sec^2 x = \tan^2 x + 1.$$

EXAMPLE

$$\int \tan^5 x \sec^4 x \, dx = \int \tan^5 x \sec^2 x \sec^2 x \, dx$$

$$= \int \tan^5 x \, (\tan^2 x + 1) \sec^2 x \, dx$$

$$= \int \tan^7 x \sec^2 x \, dx + \int \tan^5 x \sec^2 x \, dx$$

$$= \tfrac{1}{8} \tan^8 x + \tfrac{1}{6} \tan^6 x + C. \quad \square$$

When n and m are both odd, write

$$\tan^m x \sec^n x = \tan^{m-1} x \sec^{n-1} x \sec x \tan x$$

and express $\tan^{m-1} x$ entirely in terms of $\sec^2 x$ using

$$\tan^2 x = \sec^2 x - 1.$$

EXAMPLE

$$\int \tan^5 x \sec^3 x \, dx = \int \tan^4 x \sec^2 x \sec x \tan x \, dx$$

$$= \int (\sec^2 x - 1)^2 \sec^2 x \sec x \tan x \, dx$$

$$= \int (\sec^6 x - 2 \sec^4 x + \sec^2 x) \sec x \tan x \, dx$$

$$= \tfrac{1}{7} \sec^7 x - \tfrac{2}{5} \sec^5 x + \tfrac{1}{3} \sec^3 x + C. \quad \square$$

Finally, if n is odd and m is even, write the product entirely in terms of $\sec x$ and integrate by parts.

EXAMPLE

$$\int \tan^2 x \sec x \, dx = \int (\sec^2 x - 1) \sec x \, dx$$

$$= \int (\sec^3 x - \sec x) \, dx = \int \sec^3 x \, dx - \int \sec x \, dx.$$

We have calculated each of these integrals before:

$$\int \sec^3 x \, dx = \tfrac{1}{2} \sec x \tan x + \tfrac{1}{2} \ln |\sec x + \tan x| + C$$

and

$$\int \sec x \, dx = \ln |\sec x + \tan x| + C.$$

It follows that

$$\int \tan^2 x \sec x \, dx = \tfrac{1}{2} \sec x \tan x - \tfrac{1}{2} \ln |\sec x + \tan x| + C. \quad \square$$

You can handle integrals of $\cot^m x \csc^n x$ in a similar manner.

EXERCISES

Calculate

1. $\int \tan^2 3x \, dx.$ **2.** $\int \cot^2 5x \, dx.$ **3.** $\int \sec^2 \pi x \, dx.$

4. $\int \csc^2 2x \, dx.$ **5.** $\int \tan^3 x \, dx.$ **6.** $\int \cot^3 x \, dx.$

7. $\int \tan^2 x \sec^2 x \, dx.$ **8.** $\int \cot^2 x \csc^2 x \, dx.$ **9.** $\int \csc^3 x \, dx.$

10. $\int \sec^3 \pi x \, dx.$ **11.** $\int \cot^4 x \, dx.$ **12.** $\int \tan^4 x \, dx.$

13. $\int \cot^3 x \csc^3 x \, dx.$ **14.** $\int \tan^3 x \sec^3 x \, dx.$ **15.** $\int \csc^4 2x \, dx.$

16. $\int \sec^4 3x \, dx.$ **17.** $\int \cot^2 x \csc x \, dx.$ **18.** $\int \csc^3 \tfrac{1}{2}x \, dx.$

19. $\int \tan^5 3x \, dx.$ **20.** $\int \cot^5 2x \, dx.$ **21.** $\int \sec^5 x \, dx.$

22. $\int \csc^5 x \, dx.$ **23.** $\int \tan^4 x \sec^4 x \, dx.$ **24.** $\int \cot^4 x \csc^4 x \, dx.$

9.6 ······INTEGRALS INVOLVING $\sqrt{a^2 \pm x^2}$ AND $\sqrt{x^2 \pm a^2}$

Such integrals can usually be calculated by a trigonometric substitution:

$$\text{for} \quad \sqrt{a^2 - x^2} \quad \text{set} \quad a \sin u = x,$$
$$\text{for} \quad \sqrt{a^2 + x^2} \quad \text{set} \quad a \tan u = x,$$
$$\text{for} \quad \sqrt{x^2 - a^2} \quad \text{set} \quad a \sec u = x.$$

In each case take $a > 0$.

PROBLEM. Find

$$\int \frac{dx}{(a^2 - x^2)^{3/2}}.$$

Solution. Set

$$a \sin u = x, \qquad a \cos u\, du = dx.$$

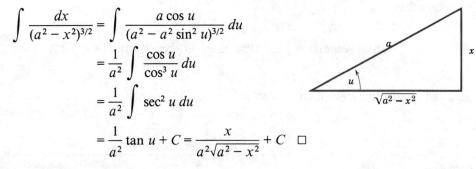

$$\int \frac{dx}{(a^2 - x^2)^{3/2}} = \int \frac{a \cos u}{(a^2 - a^2 \sin^2 u)^{3/2}}\, du$$

$$= \frac{1}{a^2} \int \frac{\cos u}{\cos^3 u}\, du$$

$$= \frac{1}{a^2} \int \sec^2 u\, du$$

$$= \frac{1}{a^2} \tan u + C = \frac{x}{a^2\sqrt{a^2 - x^2}} + C \quad \square$$

PROBLEM. Find

$$\int \sqrt{a^2 + x^2}\, dx.$$

Solution. Set

$$a \tan u = x, \qquad a \sec^2 u\, du = dx.$$

$$\int \sqrt{a^2 + x^2}\, dx = \int \sqrt{a^2 + a^2 \tan^2 u}\; a \sec^2 u\, du$$

$$= a^2 \int \sqrt{1 + \tan^2 u}\; \sec^2 u\, du$$

$$= a^2 \int \sec u \cdot \sec^2 u\, du$$

$$= a^2 \int \sec^3 u\, du$$

by Section 9.5 $\longrightarrow$

$$= \frac{a^2}{2} (\sec u \tan u + \ln |\sec u + \tan u|) + C$$

$$= \frac{a^2}{2}\left[\frac{\sqrt{a^2+x^2}}{a}\left(\frac{x}{a}\right) + \ln\left|\frac{\sqrt{a^2+x^2}}{a} + \frac{x}{a}\right|\right] + C$$

$$= \tfrac{1}{2}x\sqrt{a^2+x^2} + \tfrac{1}{2}a^2 \ln(x + \sqrt{a^2+x^2}) - \tfrac{1}{2}a^2 \ln a + C.$$

We can absorb the constant $-\tfrac{1}{2}a^2 \ln a$ in C and write

(9.6.1) $$\int \sqrt{a^2+x^2}\, dx = \tfrac{1}{2}x\sqrt{a^2+x^2} + \tfrac{1}{2}a^2 \ln(x + \sqrt{a^2+x^2}) + C.$$

This is one of the standard formulas. $\square$

Now a slight variation.

PROBLEM. Find

$$\int \frac{dx}{x\sqrt{4x^2+9}}.$$

Solution. Set

$$3 \tan u = 2x, \qquad 3 \sec^2 u\, du = 2\, dx.$$

$$\int \frac{dx}{x\sqrt{4x^2+9}} = \int \frac{\tfrac{3}{2}\sec^2 u}{\tfrac{3}{2}\tan u \cdot 3 \sec u}\, du$$

$$= \frac{1}{3}\int \frac{\sec u}{\tan u}\, du$$

$$= \frac{1}{3}\int \csc u\, du$$

$$= \frac{1}{3}\ln|\csc u - \cot u| + C$$

$$= \frac{1}{3}\ln\left|\frac{\sqrt{4x^2+9}-3}{2x}\right| + C. \quad \square$$

The next problem requires that we first complete the square under the radical.

PROBLEM. Find

$$\int \frac{x}{\sqrt{x^2+2x-3}}\, dx.$$

Solution. First note that

$$\int \frac{x}{\sqrt{x^2+2x-3}}\, dx = \int \frac{x}{\sqrt{(x+1)^2-4}}\, dx.$$

Now set

$$2 \sec u = x + 1, \qquad 2 \sec u \tan u = dx.$$

Then

$$\int \frac{x}{\sqrt{(x+1)^2 - 4}}\, dx = \int \frac{(2 \sec u - 1)2 \sec u \tan u}{2 \tan u}\, du$$

$$= \int (2 \sec^2 u - \sec u)\, du$$

$$= 2 \tan u - \ln |\sec u + \tan u| + C$$

$$= \sqrt{x^2 + 2x - 3} - \ln \left| \frac{x + 1 + \sqrt{x^2 + 2x - 3}}{2} \right| + C. \quad \square$$

Finally, we note that a trigonometric substitution may also be effective in cases where the quadratic in the integrand is not under a radical. For example, see reduction formula (9.3.2).

EXERCISES

Work out the following integrals.

1. $\displaystyle \int \frac{dx}{\sqrt{a^2 - x^2}}.$

2. $\displaystyle \int \frac{dx}{(x^2 + 2)^{3/2}}.$

3. $\displaystyle \int \frac{dx}{(5 - x^2)^{3/2}}.$

4. $\displaystyle \int \frac{x}{\sqrt{x^2 - 4}}\, dx.$

5. $\displaystyle \int_1^2 \sqrt{x^2 - 1}\, dx.$

6. $\displaystyle \int \frac{x}{\sqrt{4 - x^2}}\, dx.$

7. $\displaystyle \int \frac{x^2}{\sqrt{4 - x^2}}\, dx.$

8. $\displaystyle \int \frac{x^2}{\sqrt{x^2 - 4}}\, dx.$

9. $\displaystyle \int \frac{x}{(1 - x^2)^{3/2}}\, dx.$

10. $\displaystyle \int \frac{x^2}{\sqrt{4 + x^2}}\, dx.$

11. $\displaystyle \int \frac{x^2}{(1 - x^2)^{3/2}}\, dx.$

12. $\displaystyle \int \frac{x}{a^2 + x^2}\, dx.$

13. $\displaystyle \int x \sqrt{4 - x^2}\, dx.$

14. $\displaystyle \int \frac{e^x}{\sqrt{9 - e^{2x}}}\, dx.$

15. $\displaystyle \int \frac{x^2}{(x^2 + 8)^{3/2}}\, dx.$

16. $\displaystyle \int \frac{\sqrt{1 - x^2}}{x^4}\, dx.$

17. $\displaystyle \int \frac{dx}{x\sqrt{a^2 - x^2}}.$

18. $\displaystyle \int \frac{dx}{\sqrt{x^2 + a^2}}.$

19. $\displaystyle \int \frac{dx}{\sqrt{x^2 - a^2}}.$

20. $\displaystyle \int \sqrt{a^2 - x^2}\, dx.$

21. $\displaystyle \int e^x \sqrt{e^{2x} - 1}\, dx.$

22. $\displaystyle \int \frac{\sqrt{x^2 - 1}}{x}\, dx.$

23. $\displaystyle \int \frac{dx}{x^2 \sqrt{a^2 + x^2}}.$

24. $\displaystyle \int \frac{dx}{x^2 \sqrt{a^2 - x^2}}.$

25. $\displaystyle \int \frac{dx}{x^2 \sqrt{x^2 - a^2}}.$

26. $\displaystyle \int \frac{dx}{e^x \sqrt{4 + e^{2x}}}.$

27. $\displaystyle \int \frac{dx}{e^x \sqrt{e^{2x} - 9}}.$

28. $\displaystyle \int \frac{dx}{\sqrt{x^2 - 2x - 3}}.$

29. $\displaystyle \int \frac{dx}{(x^2 - 4x + 4)^{3/2}}.$

30. $\displaystyle \int \frac{x}{\sqrt{6x - x^2}}\, dx.$

31. $\displaystyle \int x\sqrt{6x - x^2 - 8}\, dx.$

32. $\displaystyle \int \frac{x + 2}{\sqrt{x^2 + 4x + 13}}\, dx.$

33. $\displaystyle \int \frac{x}{(x^2 + 2x + 5)^2}\, dx.$

34. $\int \dfrac{x}{\sqrt{x^2 - 2x - 3}}\, dx.$ **35.** $\int \dfrac{x + 3}{\sqrt{x^2 + 4x + 13}}\, dx.$ **36.** $\int x\sqrt{x^2 + 6x}\, dx.$

37. $\int \sqrt{6x - x^2 - 8}\, dx.$ **38.** $\int \dfrac{dx}{(4 - x^2)^2}.$ **39.** $\int x(8 - 2x - x^2)^{3/2}\, dx.$

Integrals involving $\sqrt{a^2 + x^2}$ and $\sqrt{x^2 - a^2}$ can also be calculated by using hyperbolic functions.

40. Derive (9.6.1) by setting $a \sinh u = x$.

41. Show that

$$\int \sqrt{x^2 - a^2}\, dx = \frac{1}{2}x\sqrt{x^2 - a^2} - \frac{a^2}{2} \cosh^{-1} \frac{x}{a} + C$$

$$= \frac{1}{2}x\sqrt{x^2 - a^2} - \frac{a^2}{2} \ln |x + \sqrt{x^2 - a^2}| + C$$

by setting $a \cosh u = x$.

42. Calculate

$$\int x^2 \sqrt{x^2 + 1}\, dx.$$

9.7 ⋯⋯RATIONAL EXPRESSIONS IN sin x AND cos x

There is a substitution that makes it possible to integrate all rational expressions in $\sin x$ and $\cos x$. The result is significant enough to be cast as a theorem.

THEOREM 9.7.1

If $f(x)$ is a rational expression in $\sin x$ and $\cos x$, then the substitution

$$2 \tan^{-1} u = x$$

transforms the integral

$$\int f(x)\, dx$$

into the integral of a rational function of u.

Proof. Set

$$2 \tan^{-1} u = x, \qquad \frac{2}{1 + u^2}\, du = dx$$

and observe that $u = \tan \frac{1}{2}x$. The substitution gives

$$\int f(x)\, dx = 2 \int \frac{f(2 \tan^{-1} u)}{1 + u^2}\, du.$$

Let's assume now that $f(x)$ is rational in $\cos x$ and $\sin x$. To prove the theorem, we need to show that $f(2 \tan^{-1} u)$ is rational in u. This we can do by showing that $\sin(2 \tan^{-1} u)$ and $\cos(2 \tan^{-1} u)$ are both rational in u. This follows directly:

$$\sin(2 \tan^{-1} u) = \sin x = 2 \sin \tfrac{1}{2}x \cos \tfrac{1}{2}x$$

$$= 2 \left(\frac{u}{\sqrt{1 + u^2}} \right) \left(\frac{1}{\sqrt{1 + u^2}} \right)$$

$$= 2 \left(\frac{u}{1 + u^2} \right),$$

$$\cos(2 \tan^{-1} u) = \cos x = \cos^2 \tfrac{1}{2}x - \sin^2 \tfrac{1}{2}x$$

$$= \frac{1}{1 + u^2} - \frac{u^2}{1 + u^2}$$

$$= \frac{1 - u^2}{1 + u^2}. \quad \Box$$

In proving the theorem we showed that

(9.7.2) $$\sin(2 \tan^{-1} u) = \frac{2u}{1 + u^2}, \qquad \cos(2 \tan^{-1} u) = \frac{1 - u^2}{1 + u^2}.$$

Keep this in mind as you work the problems.

PROBLEM. Find

$$\int \frac{dx}{1 + 2 \cos x}.$$

Solution. Set

$$2 \tan^{-1} u = x, \qquad \frac{2}{1 + u^2} \, du = dx.$$

With $u = \tan \tfrac{1}{2}x$,

$$\int \frac{dx}{1 + 2 \cos x} = \int \frac{2}{1 + u^2} \left[\frac{1}{1 + 2 \cos(2 \tan^{-1} u)} \right] du$$

$$= \int \frac{2}{1 + u^2} \left[\frac{1}{1 + 2 \left(\frac{1 - u^2}{1 + u^2} \right)} \right] du = -2 \int \frac{du}{u^2 - 3}$$

$$= \frac{1}{\sqrt{3}} \int \left(\frac{1}{u + \sqrt{3}} - \frac{1}{u - \sqrt{3}} \right) du$$

$$= \frac{1}{\sqrt{3}} (\ln |u + \sqrt{3}| - \ln |u - \sqrt{3}|) + C$$

$$= \frac{1}{\sqrt{3}} \ln \left| \frac{u + \sqrt{3}}{u - \sqrt{3}} \right| + C = \frac{1}{\sqrt{3}} \ln \left| \frac{\tan \tfrac{1}{2}x + \sqrt{3}}{\tan \tfrac{1}{2}x - \sqrt{3}} \right| + C. \quad \Box$$

Since the other trigonometric functions — tan x, cot x, sec x, csc x — are all rational combinations of sin x and cos x, the substitution $2 \tan^{-1} u = x$ also works for rational expressions involving these functions.

PROBLEM. Find

$$\int \frac{\sec x}{2 \tan x + \sec x - 1}\, dx.$$

Solution. Set

$$2 \tan^{-1} u = x, \qquad \frac{2}{1 + u^2}\, du = dx.$$

With $u = \tan \frac{1}{2} x$,

$$\int \frac{\sec x}{2 \tan x + \sec x - 1}\, dx = \int \frac{\dfrac{1}{\cos x}}{2 \dfrac{\sin x}{\cos x} + \dfrac{1}{\cos x} - 1}\, dx$$

$$= \int \frac{dx}{2 \sin x - \cos x + 1}$$

$$= \int \frac{\dfrac{2}{1 + u^2}}{2 \sin (2 \tan^{-1} u) - \cos (2 \tan^{-1} u) + 1}\, du$$

$$= \int \frac{\dfrac{2}{1 + u^2}}{2 \cdot \dfrac{2u}{1 + u^2} - \dfrac{1 - u^2}{1 + u^2} + 1}\, du = \int \frac{du}{u(u + 2)}$$

$$= \frac{1}{2} \int \left(\frac{1}{u} - \frac{1}{u + 2} \right) du = \frac{1}{2} \ln \left| \frac{u}{u + 2} \right| + C$$

$$= \frac{1}{2} \ln \left| \frac{\tan \frac{1}{2} x}{\tan \frac{1}{2} x + 2} \right| + C. \quad \square$$

EXERCISES

Work out the following integrals.

1. $\displaystyle\int \frac{dx}{1 + \cos x}$.

2. $\displaystyle\int \frac{dx}{1 - \cos x}$.

3. $\displaystyle\int \frac{dx}{1 - \sin x}$.

4. $\displaystyle\int_0^{\pi/2} \frac{dx}{3 + 2 \cos x}$.

5. $\displaystyle\int_0^{\pi/2} \frac{dx}{3 + \cos x}$.

6. $\displaystyle\int \frac{\sin x}{2 - \sin x}\, dx$.

7. $\displaystyle\int \frac{dx}{5 \sec x - 3}$.   **8.** $\displaystyle\int \frac{dx}{5 + 4 \cos x}$.   **9.** $\displaystyle\int \frac{dx}{1 + \tan x}$.

10. $\displaystyle\int \frac{\cos x}{1 - \cos x}\, dx$.   **11.** $\displaystyle\int \frac{1 + \sin x}{1 + \cos x}\, dx$.   **12.** $\displaystyle\int \frac{1 - \cos x}{1 + \sin x}\, dx$.

9.8 ······SOME RATIONALIZING SUBSTITUTIONS

PROBLEM. Find

$$\int \frac{dx}{1 + \sqrt{x}}.$$

Solution. To rationalize the integrand we set

$$u^2 = x, \qquad 2u\, du = dx.$$

With $u = \sqrt{x}$,

$$\int \frac{dx}{1 + \sqrt{x}} = \int \frac{2u}{1 + u}\, du = \int \left(2 - \frac{2}{1 + u}\right) du$$
$$= 2u - 2\ln|1 + u| + C$$
$$= 2\sqrt{x} - 2\ln|1 + \sqrt{x}| + C. \quad \square$$

PROBLEM. Find

$$\int \frac{x^{1/2}}{4(1 + x^{3/4})}\, dx.$$

Solution. Here we set

$$u^4 = x, \qquad 4u^3\, du = dx.$$

With $u = x^{1/4}$,

$$\int \frac{x^{1/2}}{4(1 + x^{3/4})}\, dx = \int \frac{(u^2)(4u^3)}{4(1 + u^3)}\, du$$
$$= \int \frac{u^5}{1 + u^3}\, du$$
$$= \int \left(u^2 - \frac{u^2}{1 + u^3}\right) du$$
$$= \tfrac{1}{3}u^3 - \tfrac{1}{3}\ln|1 + u^3| + C$$
$$= \tfrac{1}{3}x^{3/4} - \tfrac{1}{3}\ln|1 + x^{3/4}| + C. \quad \square$$

PROBLEM. Find

$$\int \sqrt{1 - e^x}\, dx.$$

Solution. To rationalize the integrand we set

$$u^2 = 1 - e^x.$$

To find dx in terms of u and du we solve the equation for x:

$$1 - u^2 = e^x, \qquad \ln(1 - u^2) = x, \qquad -\frac{2u}{1 - u^2}\, du = dx.$$

The rest is straightforward:

$$\int \sqrt{1 - e^x}\, dx = \int u\left(-\frac{2u}{1 - u^2}\right) du$$

$$= \int \frac{2u^2}{u^2 - 1}\, du$$

$$= \int \left(2 + \frac{1}{u - 1} - \frac{1}{u + 1}\right) du$$

$$= 2u + \ln|u - 1| - \ln|u + 1| + C$$

$$= 2u + \ln\left|\frac{u - 1}{u + 1}\right| + C$$

$$= 2\sqrt{1 - e^x} + \ln\left|\frac{\sqrt{1 - e^x} - 1}{\sqrt{1 - e^x} + 1}\right| + C. \quad \square$$

EXERCISES

Work out the following integrals.

1. $\displaystyle\int \frac{dx}{1 - \sqrt{x}}.$ **2.** $\displaystyle\int \frac{\sqrt{x}}{1 + x}\, dx.$ **3.** $\displaystyle\int \sqrt{1 + e^x}\, dx.$

4. $\displaystyle\int \frac{dx}{x(x^{1/3} - 1)}.$ **5.** $\displaystyle\int x\sqrt{1 + x}\, dx.$ [(a) set $u^2 = 1 + x$; (b) set $u = 1 + x$]

6. $\displaystyle\int x^2\sqrt{1 + x}\, dx.$ [(a) set $u^2 = 1 + x$; (b) set $u = 1 + x$]   **7.** $\displaystyle\int (x + 2)\sqrt{x - 1}\, dx.$

8. $\displaystyle\int (x - 1)\sqrt{x + 2}\, dx.$ **9.** $\displaystyle\int \frac{x^3}{(1 + x^2)^3}\, dx.$ **10.** $\displaystyle\int x(1 + x)^{1/3}\, dx.$

11. $\displaystyle\int \frac{\sqrt{x}}{\sqrt{x} - 1}\, dx.$ **12.** $\displaystyle\int \frac{x}{\sqrt{x} + 1}\, dx.$ **13.** $\displaystyle\int \frac{\sqrt{x - 1} + 1}{\sqrt{x - 1} - 1}\, dx.$

14. $\displaystyle\int \frac{1 - e^x}{1 + e^x}\, dx.$ **15.** $\displaystyle\int \frac{dx}{\sqrt{1 + e^x}}.$ **16.** $\displaystyle\int \frac{dx}{1 + e^{-x}}.$

17. $\displaystyle\int \frac{x}{\sqrt{x + 4}}\, dx.$ **18.** $\displaystyle\int \frac{x + 1}{x\sqrt{x - 2}}\, dx.$ **19.** $\displaystyle\int 2x^2(4x + 1)^{-5/2}\, dx.$

20. $\displaystyle\int x^2\sqrt{x - 1}\, dx.$ **21.** $\displaystyle\int \frac{x}{(ax + b)^{3/2}}\, dx.$ **22.** $\displaystyle\int \frac{x}{\sqrt{ax + b}}\, dx.$

9.9 ······NUMERICAL INTEGRATION

To evaluate a definite integral by the formula

$$\int_a^b f(x)\,dx = F(b) - F(a)$$

we must be able to find an antiderivative F and we must be able to evaluate this antiderivative both at a and at b. When this is not possible, the method fails.

The method fails even for such simple-looking integrals as

$$\int_0^1 \sqrt{x}\,\sin x\,dx \quad\text{and}\quad \int_0^1 e^{-x^2}\,dx.$$

There are no *elementary functions* with derivatives $\sqrt{x}\,\sin x$ and e^{-x^2}.

Here we take up some simple numerical methods for estimating definite integrals —methods that you can use whether or not you can find an antiderivative. All the methods we describe involve only simple arithmetic and are ideally suited to the computer.

We focus now on

$$\int_a^b f(x)\,dx.$$

As usual, we suppose that f is continuous on $[a, b]$ and, for pictorial convenience, assume that f is positive. We begin by subdividing $[a, b]$ into n nonoverlapping subintervals each of length $(b - a)/n$:

$$[a, b] = [x_0, x_1] \cup \cdots \cup [x_{i-1}, x_i] \cup \cdots \cup [x_{n-1}, x_n],$$

with

$$\Delta x_i = \frac{b - a}{n}.$$

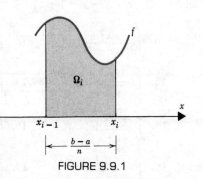

FIGURE 9.9.1

The region Ω_i pictured in Figure 9.9.1 can be approximated in many ways.

(1) By the left-endpoint rectangle (Figure 9.9.2):

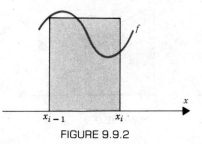

FIGURE 9.9.2

$$\text{area} = f(x_{i-1})\,\Delta x_i = f(x_{i-1})\left(\frac{b-a}{n}\right).$$

(2) By the right-endpoint rectangle (Figure 9.9.3):

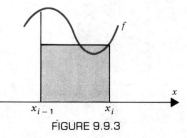

FIGURE 9.9.3

$$\text{area} = f(x_i)\,\Delta x_i = f(x_i)\left(\frac{b-a}{n}\right).$$

(3) By the midpoint rectangle (Figure 9.9.4):

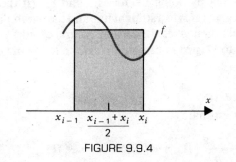

FIGURE 9.9.4

$$\text{area} = f\left(\frac{x_{i-1}+x_i}{2}\right)\Delta x_i = f\left(\frac{x_{i-1}+x_i}{2}\right)\left(\frac{b-a}{n}\right).$$

(4) By a trapezoid (Figure 9.9.5):

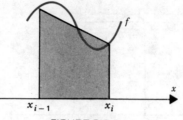

FIGURE 9.9.5

$$\text{area} = \frac{1}{2}[f(x_{i-1}) + f(x_i)]\,\Delta x_i = \frac{1}{2}[f(x_{i-1}) + f(x_i)]\left(\frac{b-a}{n}\right).$$

(5) By a parabolic region (Figure 9.9.6): take the parabola $y = Ax^2 + Bx + C$ that passes through the three points indicated.

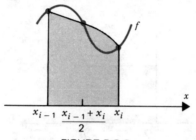

FIGURE 9.9.6

$$\text{area} = \frac{1}{6}\left[f(x_{i-1}) + 4f\left(\frac{x_{i-1} + x_i}{2}\right) + f(x_i)\right]\Delta x_i$$

$$= \left[f(x_{i-1}) + 4f\left(\frac{x_{i-1} + x_i}{2}\right) + f(x_i)\right]\left(\frac{b-a}{6n}\right).$$

You can verify this formula by doing Exercises 7 and 8. (If the three points are collinear, the parabola degenerates to a straight line and the parabolic region becomes a trapezoid. The formula then gives the area of the trapezoid.)

The approximations to Ω_i just considered yield the following estimates for

$$\int_a^b f(x)\,dx.$$

(1) The left-endpoint estimate:

$$L_n = \frac{b-a}{n}[f(x_0) + f(x_1) + \cdots + f(x_{n-1})].$$

(2) The right-endpoint estimate:

$$R_n = \frac{b-a}{n}[f(x_1) + f(x_2) + \cdots + f(x_n)].$$

(3) The midpoint estimate:

$$M_n = \frac{b-a}{n}\left[f\left(\frac{x_0+x_1}{2}\right) + \cdots + f\left(\frac{x_{n-1}+x_n}{2}\right)\right].$$

(4) The trapezoidal estimate (*trapezoidal rule*):

$$T_n = \frac{b-a}{n}\left[\frac{f(x_0)+f(x_1)}{2} + \frac{f(x_1)+f(x_2)}{2} + \cdots + \frac{f(x_{n-1})+f(x_n)}{2}\right]$$

$$= \frac{b-a}{2n}[f(x_0) + 2f(x_1) + \cdots + 2f(x_{n-1}) + f(x_n)].$$

(5) The parabolic estimate (*Simpson's rule*):

$$S_n = \frac{b-a}{6n}\left\{ f(x_0) + f(x_n) + 2[f(x_1) + \cdots + f(x_{n-1})]\right.$$

$$\left. + 4\left[f\left(\frac{x_0+x_1}{2}\right) + \cdots + f\left(\frac{x_{n-1}+x_n}{2}\right)\right]\right\}.$$

The first three estimates, L_n, R_n, M_n, are Riemann sums (Section 5.13). T_n and S_n, although not explicitly defined as Riemann sums, can be written as Riemann sums. (See Exercise 19.) It follows from (5.13.1) that any one of these estimates can be used to approximate the integral as closely as we may wish. All we have to do is take n sufficiently large.

As an example, we will find the approximate value of

$$\ln 2 = \int_1^2 \frac{dx}{x}$$

by applying each of the five estimates. Here

$$f(x) = \frac{1}{x}, \qquad [a, b] = [1, 2].$$

Taking $n = 5$, we have

$$\frac{b-a}{n} = \frac{2-1}{5} = \frac{1}{5}.$$

The partition points are

$$x_0 = \tfrac{5}{5}, \quad x_1 = \tfrac{6}{5}, \quad x_2 = \tfrac{7}{5}, \quad x_3 = \tfrac{8}{5}, \quad x_4 = \tfrac{9}{5}, \quad x_5 = \tfrac{10}{5}.$$

The five estimates then run as follows:

$$L_5 = \tfrac{1}{5}(\tfrac{5}{5} + \tfrac{5}{6} + \tfrac{5}{7} + \tfrac{5}{8} + \tfrac{5}{9}) = (\tfrac{1}{5} + \tfrac{1}{6} + \tfrac{1}{7} + \tfrac{1}{8} + \tfrac{1}{9}) \cong 0.75,$$

$$R_5 = \tfrac{1}{5}(\tfrac{5}{6} + \tfrac{5}{7} + \tfrac{5}{8} + \tfrac{5}{9} + \tfrac{5}{10}) = (\tfrac{1}{6} + \tfrac{1}{7} + \tfrac{1}{8} + \tfrac{1}{9} + \tfrac{1}{10}) \cong 0.65,$$

$$M_5 = \tfrac{1}{5}(\tfrac{10}{11} + \tfrac{10}{13} + \tfrac{10}{15} + \tfrac{10}{17} + \tfrac{10}{19}) = 2(\tfrac{1}{11} + \tfrac{1}{13} + \tfrac{1}{15} + \tfrac{1}{17} + \tfrac{1}{19}) \cong 0.69,$$

$$T_5 = \tfrac{1}{10}(\tfrac{5}{5} + \tfrac{10}{6} + \tfrac{10}{7} + \tfrac{10}{8} + \tfrac{10}{9} + \tfrac{5}{10}) = (\tfrac{1}{10} + \tfrac{1}{6} + \tfrac{1}{7} + \tfrac{1}{8} + \tfrac{1}{9} + \tfrac{1}{20}) \cong 0.70,$$

$$S_5 = \tfrac{1}{30}[\tfrac{5}{5} + \tfrac{5}{10} + 2(\tfrac{5}{6} + \tfrac{5}{7} + \tfrac{5}{8} + \tfrac{5}{9}) + 4(\tfrac{10}{11} + \tfrac{10}{13} + \tfrac{10}{15} + \tfrac{10}{17} + \tfrac{10}{19})] \cong 0.69.$$

Since the integrand $1/x$ decreases throughout the interval $[1, 2]$, you can expect the left-endpoint estimate, 0.75, to be too large and you can expect the right-endpoint estimate, 0.65, to be too small.   The other estimates should be better.

Table 1 at the end of the book gives $\ln 2 \cong 0.693$.   The estimate 0.69 is correct to the nearest hundredth.

PROBLEM.   Find the approximate value of

$$\int_0^2 \sqrt{4 + x^3}\, dx$$

by the trapezoidal rule.   Take $n = 4$.

Solution.   Each subinterval has length

$$\frac{b - a}{n} = \frac{2 - 0}{4} = \frac{1}{2}.$$

The partition points are

$$x_0 = 0, \quad x_1 = \tfrac{1}{2}, \quad x_2 = 1, \quad x_3 = \tfrac{3}{2}, \quad x_4 = 2.$$

Consequently

$$T_4 = \tfrac{1}{4}[f(0) + 2f(\tfrac{1}{2}) + 2f(1) + 2f(\tfrac{3}{2}) + f(2)].$$

With

$$f(0) = 2.000,$$
$$f(\tfrac{1}{2}) = \sqrt{4 + \tfrac{1}{8}} = \sqrt{4.125} \cong 2.031,$$
$$f(1) = \sqrt{5} \cong 2.236,$$
$$f(\tfrac{3}{2}) = \sqrt{4 + \tfrac{27}{8}} = \sqrt{7.375} \cong 2.716,$$
$$f(2) = \sqrt{12} \cong 3.464,$$

we have

$$T_4 \cong \tfrac{1}{4}(2.000 + 4.062 + 4.472 + 5.432 + 3.464) \cong 4.858. \quad \square$$

PROBLEM.   Find the approximate value of

$$\int_0^2 \sqrt{4 + x^3}\, dx$$

by Simpson's rule.   Take $n = 2$.

Solution.   There are two intervals each of length

$$\frac{b - a}{n} = \frac{2 - 0}{2} = 1.$$

We have

$$x_0 = 0, \quad x_1 = 1, \quad x_2 = 2.$$
$$\frac{x_0 + x_1}{2} = \frac{1}{2}, \quad \frac{x_1 + x_2}{2} = \frac{3}{2}.$$

Simpson's rule yields

$$S_2 = \tfrac{1}{6}[f(0) + f(2) + 2f(1) + 4f(\tfrac{1}{2}) + 4f(\tfrac{3}{2})],$$

which, in light of the square-root estimates given in the last problem, gives

$$S_2 \cong \tfrac{1}{6}(2.000 + 3.464 + 4.472 + 8.124 + 10.864) \cong 4.821. \quad \square$$

Error Estimates

A numerical estimate is useful only to the extent that we can gauge its accuracy. When we use any kind of approximation method, we face two forms of error: the error inherent in the method we use (we call this the *theoretical error*) and the error that accumulates from rounding off the decimals that arise during the course of computation (we call this the *round-off error*). The nature of round-off error is obvious. We'll speak first about theoretical error.

We begin with a function f continuous and increasing on $[a, b]$. We subdivide $[a, b]$ into n nonoverlapping intervals, each of length $(b - a)/n$. We want to estimate

$$\int_a^b f(x)\, dx$$

by the left-endpoint method. What is the theoretical error? It should be clear from Figure 9.9.7 that the theoretical error does not exceed

(1) $$[f(b) - f(a)]\left(\frac{b - a}{n}\right).$$

The error is represented by the sum of the areas of the shaded regions. These regions, when shifted to the right, all fit together within a rectangle of height $f(b) - f(a)$ and base $(b - a)/n$.

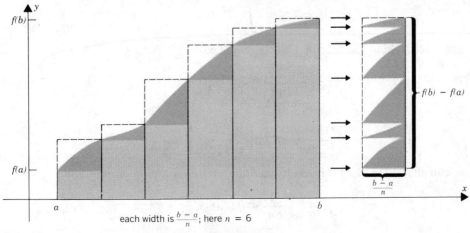

each width is $\dfrac{b - a}{n}$; here $n = 6$

FIGURE 9.9.7

Similar reasoning shows that, under the same circumstances, the theoretical error associated with the trapezoidal method does not exceed

(2) $$\frac{1}{2}[f(b) - f(a)]\left(\frac{b - a}{n}\right).$$

In this setting at least, the trapezoidal estimate does a better job.

We can improve on (2) considerably, even dropping the requirement that f be increasing. It is shown in texts on numerical analysis that, if f is twice differentiable, then the theoretical error of the trapezoidal rule can be written

(9.9.1) $$\boxed{\frac{(b - a)^3}{12n^2}f''(c)}$$

with c between a and b. Usually we can't pinpoint c any further. Nevertheless, as we show below, (9.9.1) is a powerful tool.

Recall the trapezoidal-rule estimate

$$\int_1^2 \frac{dx}{x} \cong 0.70.$$

We arrived at this taking $n = 5$. We will apply (9.9.1) to find the theoretical error. Here

$$f(x) = \frac{1}{x}, \qquad f'(x) = -\frac{1}{x^2}, \qquad f''(x) = \frac{2}{x^3}.$$

With $a = 1$ and $b = 2$, we have c between 1 and 2. Since $n = 5$,

$$\left|\frac{(b - a)^3}{12n^2}f''(c)\right| = \frac{1}{300}\frac{2}{c^3} < \frac{1}{150} < 0.007.$$
$$\underset{c > 1}{\underline{\qquad\qquad\qquad\qquad}}$$

The estimate 0.70 is in theoretical error by less than 0.007.

To obtain an estimate for

$$\int_1^2 \frac{dx}{x}$$

that is accurate to four decimal places, we need

(3) $$\left|\frac{(b - a)^3}{12n^2}f''(c)\right| < 0.00005.$$

Since

$$\left|\frac{(b - a)^3}{12n^2}f''(c)\right| \le \frac{1}{12n^2}\frac{2}{c^3} < \frac{1}{6n^2},$$

we can guarantee that (3) holds by having

$$\frac{1}{6n^2} < 0.00005.$$

As you can check, this requires that n be greater than 57.

In the exercises you'll be asked to estimate the theoretical error inherent in Simpson's rule. The formula for that error can be written

(9.9.2)
$$\frac{(b-a)^5}{180n^4} f^{(4)}(c)$$

where, as before, c is some number between a and b. Note that this estimate requires that f be 4-times differentiable.

Finally, a word about round-off error. For large n any numerical procedure requires careful consideration of round-off error. For example, suppose that 1, 2, 3, 4, 5 are estimates, each accurate to the nearest integer. This means that each estimate may be in error by as much as 0.5. The sum of these estimates, 15, may be in error by as much as 2.5, a 20% relative error. Sometimes cumulative round-off error can render theoretical error bounds and the entire calculation meaningless.

As an illustration we rework our trapezoidal estimate for

$$\int_1^2 \frac{dx}{x},$$

again taking $n = 5$, and assume our computer or calculator can store only two significant digits. As before,

(3)
$$\int_1^2 \frac{dx}{x} \cong \tfrac{1}{10}[\tfrac{1}{1} + 2\,(\tfrac{5}{6}) + 2\,(\tfrac{5}{7}) + 2\,(\tfrac{5}{8}) + 2\,(\tfrac{5}{9}) + (\tfrac{1}{2})].$$

Now our limited round-off machine goes to work:

$$\int_1^2 \frac{dx}{x} \cong (0.10)[(1.0) + 2(0.83) + 2(0.71) + 2(0.62) + 2(0.44) + (0.50)]$$

$$\text{``=''} \ (0.10)[(1.0) + (1.7) + (1.4) + (1.2) + (0.88) + (0.50)]$$

$$= (0.10)[6.7] = 0.67.$$

Earlier we used (9.9.1) to show that estimate (3) is in error by no more than 0.007 and found 0.70 as the approximation. Now with our limited round-off machine, we simplified (3) in a different way and obtained 0.67 as the approximation. The apparent error due to crude round off, $0.70 - 0.67 = 0.03$, exceeds the error of the approximation method itself. The lesson should be clear: round-off error is important.

EXERCISES

(In each of the numerical computations below round off your final answer to the nearest hundredth. The use of a calculator may be necessary.)

1. Estimate

$$\int_0^{12} x^2 \, dx.$$

(a) Use the left-endpoint estimate, $n = 12$.
(b) Use the right-endpoint estimate, $n = 12$.

(c) Use the midpoint estimate, $n = 6$.
(d) Use the trapezoidal rule, $n = 12$.
(e) Use Simpson's rule, $n = 6$.
Check your results by performing the integration.

2. Estimate

$$\int_0^1 \sin^2 \pi x \, dx.$$

(a) Use the midpoint estimate, $n = 3$.
(b) Use the trapezoidal rule, $n = 6$.
(c) Use Simpson's rule, $n = 3$.
Check your results by performing the integration.

3. Estimate

$$\int_0^3 \frac{dx}{1 + x^3}.$$

(a) Use the left-endpoint estimate, $n = 6$.
(b) Use the right-endpoint estimate, $n = 6$.
(c) Use the midpoint estimate, $n = 3$.
(d) Use the trapezoidal rule, $n = 6$.
(e) Use Simpson's rule, $n = 3$.

4. Estimate

$$\int_0^\pi \frac{\sin x}{\pi + x} \, dx.$$

(a) Use the trapezoidal rule, $n = 6$.   (b) Use Simpson's rule, $n = 3$.

5. Find the approximate value of π by estimating the integral

$$\frac{\pi}{4} = \tan^{-1} 1 = \int_0^1 \frac{dx}{1 + x^2}.$$

(a) Use the trapezoidal rule, $n = 4$.   (b) Use Simpson's rule, $n = 4$.

6. Estimate

$$\int_0^2 \frac{dx}{\sqrt{4 + x^3}}.$$

(a) Use the trapezoidal rule, $n = 4$.   (b) Use Simpson's rule, $n = 2$.

7. Show that there is one and only one curve of the form $y = Ax^2 + Bx + C$ through three distinct points with different x-coordinates.

8. Show that the function $g(x) = Ax^2 + Bx + C$ satisfies the condition

$$\int_a^b g(x) \, dx = \frac{b - a}{6} \left[g(a) + 4g\left(\frac{a + b}{2}\right) + g(b) \right]$$

for every interval $[a, b]$.

Determine the values of n for which a theoretical error less than ϵ can be guaranteed if the integral is estimated using (a) the trapezoidal rule. (b) Simpson's rule.

9. $\displaystyle\int_1^4 \sqrt{x} \, dx$; $\epsilon = 0.01$.

10. $\displaystyle\int_1^3 x^5 \, dx$; $\epsilon = 0.01$.

11. $\displaystyle\int_1^4 \sqrt{x} \, dx$; $\epsilon = 0.00001$.

12. $\displaystyle\int_1^3 x^5 \, dx$; $\epsilon = 0.00001$.

13. $\int_0^\pi \sin x \, dx$; $\epsilon = 0.001$

14. $\int_0^\pi \cos x \, dx$; $\epsilon = 0.001$.

15. $\int_1^3 e^x \, dx$; $\epsilon = 0.01$.

16. $\int_1^e \ln x \, dx$; $\epsilon = 0.01$.

17. Give an example of a function f for which the Simpson's rule estimate of $\int_a^b f(x) \, dx$ is exact (no theoretical error).

18. Give an example of a function f for which the trapezoidal rule estimate of $\int_a^b f(x) \, dx$ is exact (no theoretical error).

19. Show that, if f is continuous, then T_n and S_n can both be written as Riemann sums. HINT: Both

$$\frac{1}{2}[f(x_{i-1}) + f(x_i)] \quad \text{and} \quad \frac{1}{6}\left[f(x_{i-1}) + 4f\left(\frac{x_{i-1} + x_i}{2}\right) + f(x_i)\right]$$

lie between m_i and M_i, the minimum and maximum values of f on $[x_{i-1}, x_i]$.

9.10····ADDITIONAL EXERCISES

Work out the following integrals and check your answers by differentiation.

1. $\int 10^{nx} \, dx$.

2. $\int \tan\left(\frac{\pi}{n} x\right) dx$.

3. $\int \sqrt{2x + 1} \, dx$.

4. $\int x\sqrt{2x + 1} \, dx$.

5. $\int e^x \tan e^x \, dx$.

6. $\int \frac{\sin \sqrt{x}}{\sqrt{x}} \, dx$.

7. $\int \frac{dx}{a^2 x^2 + b^2}$.

8. $\int \sin 2x \cos x \, dx$.

9. $\int \ln (x\sqrt{x}) \, dx$.

10. $\int \sec 2x \, dx$.

11. $\int \frac{x^3}{\sqrt{1 + x^2}} \, dx$.

12. $\int x 2^x \, dx$.

13. $\int \sin^2\left(\frac{\pi}{n} x\right) dx$.

14. $\int \frac{dx}{x^3 - 1}$.

15. $\int \frac{dx}{a\sqrt{x} + b}$.

16. $\int (1 - \sec x)^2 \, dx$.

17. $\int \frac{\sin 3x}{2 + \cos 3x} \, dx$.

18. $\int \frac{\sqrt{a - x}}{\sqrt{a + x}} \, dx$. $(a > 0)$

19. $\int \frac{\sin x}{\cos^3 x} \, dx$.

20. $\int \frac{\cos x}{\sin^3 x} \, dx$.

21. $\int \frac{dx}{\cos x - \sin x}$.

22. $\int \frac{dx}{\sin x \cos x}$.

23. $\int \frac{\sqrt{a + x}}{\sqrt{a - x}} \, dx$.

24. $\int a^{2x} \, dx$.

25. $\int \frac{\sqrt{a^2 - x^2}}{x^2} \, dx$.

26. $\int \ln \sqrt{x + 1} \, dx$.

27. $\int \frac{x}{(x + 1)^2} \, dx$.

28. $\int \frac{\sin^5 x}{\cos^7 x} \, dx$.

29. $\int \frac{1 - \sin 2x}{1 + \sin 2x} \, dx$.

30. $\int \ln (ax + b) \, dx$.

31. $\int x \ln (ax + b) \, dx$.

32. $\int (\tan x + \cot x)^2 \, dx$.

33. $\int \frac{dx}{\sqrt{x + 1} - \sqrt{x}}$.

34. $\int \dfrac{e^{-\sqrt{x}}}{\sqrt{x}}\,dx.$

35. $\int \dfrac{x^2}{1+x^2}\,dx.$

36. $\int \sqrt{\dfrac{x^2}{9}-1}\,dx.$

37. $\int \dfrac{-x^2}{\sqrt{1-x^2}}\,dx.$

38. $\int e^x \sin \pi x\,dx.$

39. $\int \sinh^2 x\,dx.$

40. $\int 2x \sinh x\,dx.$

41. $\int e^{-x} \cosh x\,dx.$

42. $\int x \ln \sqrt{x^2+1}\,dx.$

43. $\int x \tan^{-1}(x-3)\,dx.$

44. $\int \dfrac{dx}{2-\sqrt{x}}.$

45. $\int \dfrac{2}{x(1+x^2)}\,dx.$

46. $\int \dfrac{dx}{\sqrt{2x-x^2}}.$

47. $\int \dfrac{\cos^4 x}{\sin^2 x}\,dx.$

48. $\int \dfrac{x-3}{x^2(x+1)}\,dx.$

49. $\int \dfrac{\sqrt{x^2+4}}{x}\,dx.$

50. $\int \dfrac{e^x}{\sqrt{e^x+1}}\,dx.$

51. $\int \dfrac{dx}{x\sqrt{9-x^2}}.$

52. $\int \dfrac{dx}{e^x-2e^{-x}}.$

53. $\int \dfrac{dx}{1+3\sin x}.$

54. $\int x \tan^2 \pi x\,dx.$

55. $\int \dfrac{dx}{\sqrt{1-e^{2x}}}.$

56. $\int \dfrac{\cos 2x}{\cos x}\,dx.$

57. $\int \dfrac{\sec^3 x}{\tan x}\,dx.$

58. $\int \sin^3 x \sec x\,dx.$

59. $\int \dfrac{\sin 4x}{\sin x}\,dx.$

60. $\int \dfrac{x^2+x}{\sqrt{1-x^2}}\,dx.$

61. $\int \sin^5 \left(\dfrac{x}{2}\right) dx.$

62. $\int \csc x \tan x\,dx.$

63. $\int \cot^2 x \sec x\,dx.$

64. $\int \sec^3 x \sin x\,dx.$

65. $\int \dfrac{\sin x}{\sin 2x}\,dx.$

66. $\int \dfrac{x^2}{\sqrt{3-2x-x^2}}\,dx.$

67. $\int x^2 \sin^{-1} x\,dx.$

68. $\int \dfrac{x+3}{\sqrt{x^2+2x-8}}\,dx.$

69. $\int x\sqrt{x^2+2x-8}\,dx.$

70. $\int x^2 \tan^{-1} x\,dx.$

71. $\int \dfrac{dx}{2x^2-2x+1}.$

72. $\int \sin 2x \cos 3x\,dx.$

73. $\int (\sin^2 x - \cos x)^2\,dx.$

74. $\int \ln(1-\sqrt{x})\,dx.$

75. $\int \dfrac{3}{\sqrt{2-3x-4x^2}}\,dx.$

76. $\int \dfrac{\sin x}{\cos^2 x - 2\cos x + 3}\,dx.$

77. $\int \left[\dfrac{x}{\sqrt{a^2-x^2}} - \sin^{-1}\left(\dfrac{x}{a}\right)\right] dx.$

9.11 CHAPTER SUMMARY

9.1 Review

A table of integrals appears on the inside covers.

9.2 Integration by Parts

$$\int u\,dv = uv - \int v\,du \qquad \text{revenue streams (p. 463)}$$

Success with the technique depends on choosing u and dv so that $\int v\,du$ is easier to integrate than $\int u\,dv$.

Integration by parts is often used to calculate integrals where the integrand is a mixture of function types; for example, polynomials and exponentials, or polynomials and trigonometric functions.

To calculate some integrals you may have to integrate by parts more than once.

9.3 Partial Fractions

We can integrate any rational function by writing it as a polynomial (that may be identically zero) plus fractions of the form

$$\frac{A}{(x - \alpha)^k} \qquad \text{and} \qquad \frac{Bx + C}{(x^2 + \beta x + \gamma)^k}.$$

9.4 Powers and Products of Sines and Cosines

Integrals of the form

$$\int \sin^n x \cos^m x \, dx$$

can be calculated by using the basic identity $\sin^2 x + \cos^2 x = 1$ and the double angle formulas

$$\sin x \cos x = \tfrac{1}{2} \sin 2x, \qquad \sin^2 x = \tfrac{1}{2} - \tfrac{1}{2} \cos 2x, \qquad \cos^2 x = \tfrac{1}{2} + \tfrac{1}{2} \cos 2x.$$

9.5 Other Trigonometric Powers

Evaluation of integrals involving $\tan x$, $\sec x$, $\cot x$, or $\csc x$ is sometimes facilitated by using the identities $1 + \tan^2 x = \sec^2 x$ and $1 + \cot^2 x = \csc^2 x$.

Sometimes it helps to rewrite the integrand in terms of $\sin x$ and $\cos x$ instead of $\tan x$ and $\sec x$ or $\cot x$ and $\csc x$.

9.6 Integrals Involving $\sqrt{a^2 \pm x^2}$ and $\sqrt{x^2 \pm a^2}$

Such integrals can usually be calculated by a trigonometric substitution:

$$\text{for } \sqrt{a^2 - x^2} \quad \text{set} \quad a \sin u = x,$$
$$\text{for } \sqrt{a^2 + x^2} \quad \text{set} \quad a \tan u = x,$$
$$\text{for } \sqrt{x^2 - a^2} \quad \text{set} \quad a \sec u = x,$$

Sometimes it is necessary to first complete the square under the radical. (p. 481)

A trigonometric substitution may also be effective in cases where the quadratic in the integrand is not under a radical.

9.7 Rational Expressions in sin x and cos x

If $f(x)$ is a rational expression in $\sin x$ and $\cos x$, then the substitution $2 \tan^{-1} u = x$ transforms the integral $\int f(x) \, dx$ into the integral of a rational function of u for then

$$\sin x = \frac{2u}{1 + u^2}, \qquad \cos x = \frac{1 - u^2}{1 + u^2}, \qquad \text{and} \qquad dx = \frac{2}{1 + u^2} \, du.$$

9.8 Some Rationalizing Substitutions

9.9 Numerical Integration

left-endpoint, right-endpoint and midpoint estimates; trapezoidal rule; Simpson's rule (p. 490–491)

theoretical error in trapezoidal rule: $\dfrac{(b - a)^3}{12n^2} f''(c)$

theoretical error in Simpson's rule: $\dfrac{(b - a)^5}{180n^4} f^{(4)}(c)$

round-off error (p. 493)

9.10 Additional Exercises

10

The Conic Sections

10.1 ···· INTRODUCTION

If a "double right circular cone" is cut by a plane, the resulting intersection is called a *conic section* or, more briefly, a *conic*. In Figure 10.1.1 we depict three important cases.

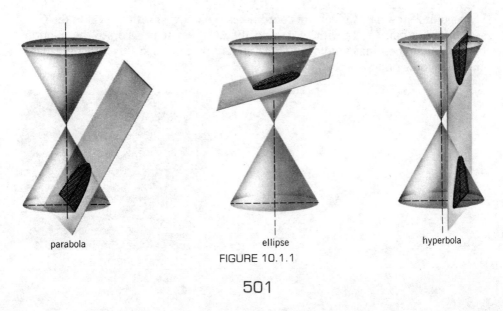

parabola　　　　ellipse　　　　hyperbola

FIGURE 10.1.1

By choosing a plane perpendicular to the axis of the cone, we can obtain a circle. The other possibilities are: a point, a line, or a pair of lines. Try to visualize this.

This three-dimensional approach to the conic sections goes back to Apollonius of Perga, a Greek of the third century B.C. He wrote eight books on the subject.

We will take a different approach. We will define parabola, ellipse, and hyperbola entirely in terms of plane geometry. But first some preliminary considerations.

10.2····TRANSLATIONS; THE DISTANCE BETWEEN A POINT AND A LINE

In Figure 10.2.1 we have drawn a rectangular coordinate system and marked a point $O'(x_0, y_0)$. Think of the Oxy system as a rigid frame and in your mind slide it along the plane, without letting it turn, so that the origin O falls on the point O'. (Figure 10.2.2) Such a motion, called a *translation*, produces a new coordinate system $O'XY$.

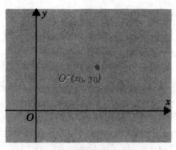

FIGURE 10.2.1

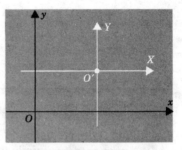

FIGURE 10.2.2

A point P now has two pairs of coordinates: a pair (x, y) with respect to the Oxy system and a pair (X, Y) with respect to the $O'XY$ system. To see the relation between these coordinates, note that, starting at O, we can reach P by first going to O' and then going on to P; thus

$$x = x_0 + X, \qquad y = y_0 + Y.$$

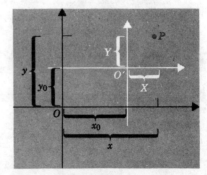

FIGURE 10.2.3

Translations are often used to simplify geometric arguments. If you carried out part (c) of Exercise 57 in Section 1.3, you found that the distance between a line l: $Ax + By + C = 0$ and the origin is given by the formula

(10.2.1)

$$d(O, l) = \frac{|C|}{\sqrt{A^2 + B^2}}.$$

We will derive the formula for the distance between a line and an arbitrary point by translating the coordinate system.

THEOREM 10.2.2

This distance between the line l: $Ax + By + C = 0$ and the point $P_1(x_1, y_1)$ is given by the formula

$$d(P_1, l) = \frac{|Ax_1 + By_1 + C|}{\sqrt{A^2 + B^2}}.$$

Proof. We translate the Oxy coordinate system to obtain a new system $O'XY$ with O' falling on the point P_1. The new coordinates are now related to the old coordinates as follows:

$$x = x_1 + X, \qquad y = y_1 + Y.$$

In the xy-system, l has equation

$$Ax + By + C = 0.$$

In the XY-system, l has equation

$$A(x_1 + X) + B(y_1 + Y) + C = 0.$$

We can write this last equation as

$$AX + BY + K = 0 \qquad \text{with} \quad K = Ax_1 + By_1 + C.$$

The distance we want is the distance between the line $AX + BY + K = 0$ and the new origin O'. By (10.2.1), this distance is

$$\frac{|K|}{\sqrt{A^2 + B^2}}.$$

Since $K = Ax_1 + By_1 + C$, we have

$$d(P_1, l) = \frac{|Ax_1 + By_1 + C|}{\sqrt{A^2 + B^2}}. \quad \square$$

PROBLEM.   Find the distance between the line

$$l: 3x + 4y - 5 = 0$$

and (a) the origin, (b) the point $P(-6, 2)$.

Solution

(a) $d(O, l) = \dfrac{|C|}{\sqrt{A^2 + B^2}} = \dfrac{|-5|}{\sqrt{3^2 + 4^2}} = \dfrac{5}{\sqrt{25}} = 1.$

(b) $d(P, l) = \dfrac{|Ax_1 + By_1 + C|}{\sqrt{A^2 + B^2}} = \dfrac{|3(-6) + 4(2) - 5|}{\sqrt{3^2 + 4^2}} = \dfrac{15}{\sqrt{25}} = 3.$ $\square$

If a curve has an equation in x and y, then that equation can be written in the form $f(x, y) = K$ with K a constant:

$$2y = 3x - 5 \qquad \text{can be written} \quad 3x - 2y = 5,$$
$$y^2 = x^2 + x + 1 \quad \text{can be written} \quad x^2 - y^2 + x = -1,$$
$$y^2 = x^3 \qquad \text{can be written} \quad x^3 - y^2 = 0, \text{ etc.}$$

Now let's start with a curve

$$C: \ f(x, y) = K.$$

The curve

$$C_1: \ f(x - 2, y - 3) = K$$

is a translation of C; set

$$x = 2 + X, \qquad y = 3 + Y$$

and the equation of C_1 takes the form

$$f(X, Y) = K.$$

The curve C_1 is the curve C displaced 2 units right and 3 units up. The curves

$$C_2: \ f(x + 2, y + 3) = K,$$
$$C_3: \ f(x - 2, y + 3) = K,$$
$$C_4: \ f(x + 2, y - 3) = K,$$

are also translations of C. C_2 is C displaced 2 units left and 3 units down; C_3 is C displaced 2 units right and 3 units down; C_4 is C displaced 2 units left, 3 units up.

EXERCISES

1. Find the distance between the line $5x + 12y + 2 = 0$ and
   (a) the origin.   (b) the point $P(1, -3)$.
2. Find the distance between the line $2x - 3y + 1 = 0$ and
   (a) the origin.   (b) the point $P(-2, 5)$.
3. Which of the points $(0, 1)$, $(1, 0)$, and $(-1, 1)$ is closest to $l: 8x + 7y - 6 = 0$? Which is farthest from l?

4. Consider the triangle with vertices $A(2, 0)$, $B(4, 3)$, $C(5, -1)$. Which of these vertices is furthest from the opposite side?

5. Find the area of the triangle with vertices $(1, -2)$, $(-1, 3)$, $(2, 4)$.

6. Find the area of the triangle with vertices $(-1, 1)$, $(3, \sqrt{2})$, $(\sqrt{2}, -1)$.

7. Write the equation of a line $Ax + By + C = 0$ in *normal form*:

$$x \cos \alpha + y \sin \alpha = p \qquad \text{with } p \geq 0.$$

What is the geometric signifixance of p? of α?

8. Find an expression for the distance between the parallel lines $Ax + By + C = 0$ and $Ax + By + C' = 0$.

9. Write an equation in x and y for the line l: $4x + 5y + 3 = 0$ displaced
   (a) 1 unit left, 2 units up.   (b) 1 unit right, 2 units up.
   (c) 1 unit left, 2 units down.   (d) 1 unit right, 2 units down.

10. Exercise 9 with l: $3x - 2y + 7 = 0$.

11. Write an equation in x and y for the curve C: $x^2 = y^3$ displaced
    (a) 3 units right, 4 units up.   (b) 3 units left, 4 units up.
    (c) 4 units right, 3 units down.   (d) 4 units left, 3 units down.

12. Exercise 11 with C: $x^2 + y^2 = 1$.

13. A ray l is rotating clockwise about the point $Q(-b^2, 0)$ at the rate of 1 revolution per minute. How fast is the distance between l and the origin changing at the moment that l has slope $\frac{3}{4}$?

14. A ray l is rotating counterclockwise about the point $Q(-b^2, 0)$ at the rate of $\frac{1}{2}$ revolution per minute. What is the slope of l at the moment that l is receding most quickly from the point $P(b^2, -1)$?

10.3····THE PARABOLA

We begin with a line l and a point F not on l. (Figure 10.3.1)

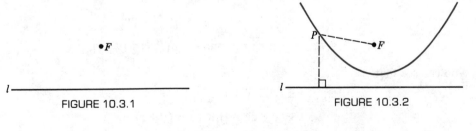

FIGURE 10.3.1   FIGURE 10.3.2

(10.3.1)   The set of points P equidistant from F and l is called a *parabola*.

See Figure 10.3.2.

The line l is called the *directrix* of the parabola, and the point F is called the *focus*. (You will see why later on.) The line through F perpendicular to l is called the *axis* of the parabola. (It is the axis of symmetry.) The point at which the axis intersects the parabola is called the *vertex*. (See Figure 10.3.3.)

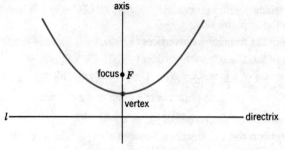

FIGURE 10.3.3

The equation of a parabola is particularly simple if we place the vertex at the origin and the focus on one of the coordinate axes. Suppose for the moment that the focus F is on the y-axis. Then F has coordinates of the form $(0, c)$. With the vertex at the origin, the directrix has equation $y = -c$. (See Figure 10.3.4.)

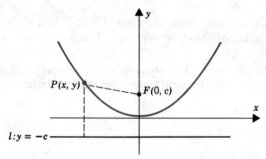

FIGURE 10.3.4

Every point $P(x, y)$ that lies on this parabola has the property that

$$d(P, F) = d(P, l).$$

Since

$$d(P, F) = \sqrt{x^2 + (y - c)^2} \qquad \text{and} \qquad d(P, l) = |y + c|,$$

you can see that

$$\sqrt{x^2 + (y - c)^2} = |y + c|,$$
$$x^2 + (y - c)^2 = |y + c|^2 = (y + c)^2,$$
$$x^2 + y^2 - 2cy + c^2 = y^2 + 2cy + c^2,$$
$$x^2 = 4cy. \quad \square$$

You have just seen that the equation

(10.3.2) $\boxed{x^2 = 4cy}$ (Figure 10.3.5)

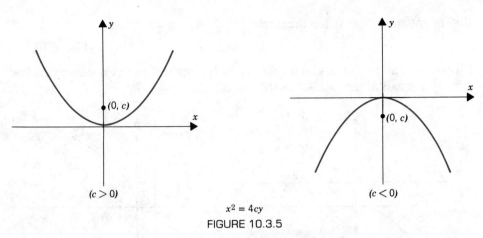

$x^2 = 4cy$

FIGURE 10.3.5

represents a parabola with vertex at the origin and focus at $(0, c)$. By interchanging the roles of x and y, you can see that the equation

(10.3.3) $y^2 = 4cx$ (Figure 10.3.6)

represents a parabola with vertex at the origin and focus at $(c, 0)$.

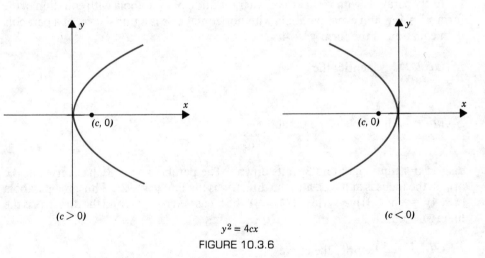

$y^2 = 4cx$

FIGURE 10.3.6

PROBLEM. Sketch the parabola specifying the vertex, focus, directrix, and axis:

(a) $x^2 = -4y$.   (b) $y^2 = 3x$.

Solution. (a) The equation $x^2 = -4y$ has the form

$$x^2 = 4cy \quad \text{with} \quad c = -1. \qquad \text{(Figure 10.3.7)}$$

The vertex is at the origin, and the focus is at $(0, -1)$; the directrix is the horizontal line $y = 1$; the axis of the parabola is the y-axis.

(b) The equation $y^2 = 3x$ has the form

$$y^2 = 4cx \qquad \text{with} \quad c = \tfrac{3}{4}. \qquad\qquad \text{(Figure 10.3.7)}$$

The vertex is at the origin, and the focus is at $(\tfrac{3}{4}, 0)$; the directrix is the vertical line $x = -\tfrac{3}{4}$; the axis of the parabola is the x-axis. $\square$

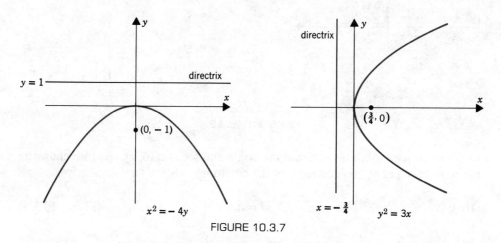

FIGURE 10.3.7

Every parabola with vertical axis is a translation of a parabola with equation of the form $x^2 = 4cy$, and every parabola with horizontal axis is a translation of a parabola with equation of the form $y^2 = 4cx$.

PROBLEM.   Identify the curve

$$(x - 4)^2 = 8(y + 3).$$

Solution.   The curve is the parabola

$$x^2 = 8y \qquad\qquad\qquad\qquad (c = 2)$$

displaced 4 units right and 3 units down.   The parabola $x^2 = 8y$ has vertex at the origin; the focus is at $(0, 2)$, and the directrix is the line $y = -2$.   Thus, the parabola $(x - 4)^2 = 8(y + 3)$ has vertex at $(4, -3)$; the focus is at $(4, -1)$, and the directrix is the line $y = -5$. $\square$

PROBLEM.   Identify the curve

$$(y - 1)^2 = 8(x + 3).$$

Solution.   This is the parabola

$$y^2 = 8x \qquad\qquad\qquad\qquad (c = 2)$$

displaced 3 units left, 1 unit up.   The parabola $y^2 = 8x$ has vertex at the origin; the focus is at $(2, 0)$, and the directrix is the vertical line $x = -2$.   Thus, the parabola $(y - 1)^2 = 8(x + 3)$ has vertex at $(-3, 1)$; the focus is at $(-1, 1)$, and the directrix is the line $x = -5$. $\square$

PROBLEM. Identify the curve

$$y = x^2 + 2x - 2.$$

Solution. We first complete the square on the right by adding 3 to both sides of the equation:

$$y + 3 = x^2 + 2x + 1 = (x + 1)^2.$$

This gives

$$(x + 1)^2 = y + 3.$$

This is the parabola

$$x^2 = y \qquad\qquad (c = \tfrac{1}{4})$$

displaced 1 unit left, 3 units down. The parabola $x^2 = y$ has vertex at the origin; the focus is at the point $(0, \tfrac{1}{4})$ and the directrix is the line $y = -\tfrac{1}{4}$. Thus, the parabola $(x + 1)^2 = y + 3$ has vertex at $(-1, -3)$; the focus is at $(-1, -\tfrac{11}{4})$ and the directrix is the line $y = -\tfrac{13}{4}$. $\square$

By the method of the last problem one can show that every quadratic

$$y = Ax^2 + Bx + C$$

represents a parabola with vertical axis. It looks like $\vee$ if A is positive and like $\wedge$ if A is negative.

Parabolic Mirrors

Parabolas are used in the design of mirrors for searchlights and telescopes. To explain the reason for this, we take a parabola and choose the coordinate system so that the equation takes the form $x^2 = 4cy$ with $c > 0$. We can express y in terms of x by writing

$$y = \frac{x^2}{4c}.$$

Since

$$\frac{dy}{dx} = \frac{2x}{4c} = \frac{x}{2c},$$

the tangent line at the point $P(x_0, y_0)$ has slope $m = x_0/2c$ and equation

(1) $$(y - y_0) = \frac{x_0}{2c}(x - x_0).$$

For the rest we refer to Figure 10.3.8. In the figure we have drawn a ray (a half-line) l parallel to the axis of the parabola, the y-axis. We want to show that the angles marked β and γ are equal.

Setting $x = 0$ in Equation (1), we find that

$$y = y_0 - \frac{x_0^2}{2c}.$$

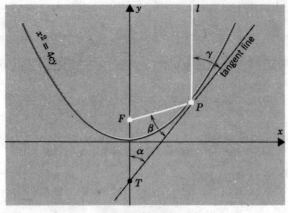

FIGURE 10.3.8

Since the point (x_0, y_0) lies on the parabola, we have $x_0^2 = 4cy_0$, and thus

$$y_0 - \frac{x_0^2}{2c} = y_0 - \frac{4cy_0}{2c} = -y_0.$$

The y-coordinate of the point marked T is $-y_0$. Since the focus F is at $(0, c)$,

$$d(F, T) = y_0 + c.$$

The distance between F and P is also $y_0 + c$:

$$d(F, P) = \sqrt{x_0^2 + (y_0 - c)^2} = \sqrt{4cy_0 + (y_0 - c)^2} = \sqrt{(y_0 + c)^2} = y_0 + c.$$
$$x_0^2 = 4cy_0 \longrightarrow$$

Since $d(F, T) = d(F, P)$, the triangle TFP is isosceles and the angles marked α and β are equal. Since l is parallel to the y-axis, $\alpha = \gamma$ and thus (and this is what we wanted to show)

$$\beta = \gamma.$$

The fact that $\beta = \gamma$ has important optical consequences. It means that light emitted from a source at the focus of a parabolic mirror is reflected in a beam parallel

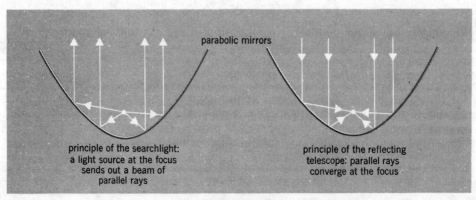

FIGURE 10.3.9

to the axis of the mirror;† this is the principle of the searchlight. It also means that light coming to a parabolic mirror in a beam parallel to the axis is reflected entirely to the focus; this is the principle of the reflecting telescope. (See Figure 10.3.9.)

Parabolic Trajectories

In the early part of the seventeenth century Galileo Galilei observed the motion of stones thrown from the tower of Pisa and noted that their trajectory was parabolic. By simple calculus, together with some simplifying physical assumptions, we obtain results that agree with Galileo's observations.

Consider a projectile fired at angle θ from a point (x_0, y_0) with initial velocity v_0 feet per second (Figure 10.3.10).

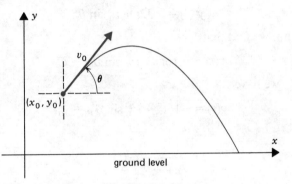

FIGURE 10.3.10

The horizontal component of v_0 is $v_0 \cos \theta$, and the vertical component is $v_0 \sin \theta$ (Figure 10.3.11).

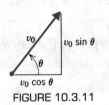

FIGURE 10.3.11

Let's neglect air resistance and the curvature of the earth. Under these circumstances there is no acceleration in the x-direction:

$$x''(t) = 0.$$

The only acceleration in the y-direction is due to gravity:

$$y''(t) = -32.$$

From the first equation, we have

$$x'(t) = C$$

---

† The angle of incidence equals the angle of reflection.

and, since $x'(0) = v_0 \cos \theta$,

$$x'(t) = v_0 \cos \theta.$$

Integrating again, we have

$$x(t) = (v_0 \cos \theta)t + C$$

and, since $x(0) = x_0$,

(1) $\qquad\qquad\qquad\qquad x(t) = (v_0 \cos \theta)t + x_0.$

The relation $y''(t) = -32$ gives

$$y'(t) = -32t + C,$$

and, since $y'(0) = v_0 \sin \theta$,

$$y'(t) = -32t + v_0 \sin \theta.$$

Integrating again, we find that

$$y(t) = -16t^2 + (v_0 \sin \theta)t + C.$$

Since $y(0) = y_0$, we have

(2) $\qquad\qquad\qquad\qquad y(t) = -16t^2 + (v_0 \sin \theta)t + y_0.$

From (1)

$$t = \frac{1}{v_0 \cos \theta}[x(t) - x_0].$$

Substitute this expression for t in (2) and you'll find that

$$y(t) = -\frac{16}{v_0^2} \sec^2 \theta \, [x(t) - x_0]^2 + \tan \theta \, [x(t) - x_0] + y_0.$$

The trajectory (the path followed by the projectile) is the curve

(10.3.4) $\qquad$ $\boxed{\; y = -\dfrac{16}{v_0^2} \sec^2 \theta \, [x - x_0]^2 + \tan \theta \, [x - x_0] + y_0. \;}$

This is a quadratic in x and therefore a parabola. $\square$

EXERCISES

Sketch the parabola and give an equation for it.

1. vertex $(0, 0)$, focus $(2, 0)$.
2. vertex $(0, 0)$, focus $(-2, 0)$.
3. vertex $(-1, 3)$, focus $(-1, 0)$.
4. vertex $(1, 2)$, focus $(1, 3)$.
5. focus $(1, 1)$, directrix $y = -1$.
6. focus $(2, -2)$, directrix $x = -5$.
7. focus $(1, 1)$, directrix $x = 2$.
8. focus $(2, 0)$, directrix $y = 3$.

Find the vertex, focus, axis, and directrix; then sketch the parabola.

9. $y^2 = 2x$.
10. $x^2 = -5y$.
11. $2y = 4x^2 - 1$.
12. $y^2 = 2(x - 1)$.
13. $(x + 2)^2 = 12 - 8y$.
14. $y - 3 = 2(x - 1)^2$.
15. $x = y^2 + y + 1$.
16. $y = x^2 + x + 1$.

Find an equation for the indicated parabola.

17. focus $(1, 2)$, directrix $x + y + 1 = 0$.   **18.** vertex $(2, 0)$, directrix $2x - y = 0$.

19. vertex $(2, 0)$, focus $(0, 2)$.   **20.** vertex $(3, 0)$, focus $(0, 1)$.

21. Show that every parabola has an equation of the form

$$(\alpha x + \beta y)^2 = \gamma x + \delta y + \epsilon \qquad \text{with} \quad \alpha^2 + \beta^2 \neq 0.$$

HINT: Take $l: Ax + By + C = 0$ as the directrix and $F(a, b)$ as the focus.

22. Show that not every equation of the form

$$(\alpha x + \beta y)^2 = \gamma x + \delta y + \epsilon \qquad \text{with} \quad \alpha^2 + \beta^2 \neq 0$$

represents a parabola.

23. A parabola intersects a rectangle of area A at two opposite vertices. Show that, if one side of the rectangle falls on the axis of the parabola, then the parabola subdivides the rectangle into two pieces, one of area $\frac{1}{3}A$, the other of area $\frac{2}{3}A$.

24. Show that every parabola with axis parallel to the y-axis has an equation of the form $y = Ax^2 + Bx + C$ with $A \neq 0$.

25. Find the vertex, the focus, and the directrix of the parabola

$$y = Ax^2 + Bx + C.$$

26. Identify the graph of $(x - y)^2 = b$ for different values of b.

27. Find an equation for the parabola which has directrix $y = 1$, axis $x = 2$, and passes through the point $(5, 6)$.

28. Find an equation for the parabola that has horizontal axis, vertex $(-1, 1)$, and passes through the point $(-6, 13)$.

In Exercises 29 through 34 we measure distances in feet and time in seconds. We neglect air resistance and the curvature of the earth. We take O as the origin, the x-axis as ground level, and consider a projectile fired from O at an angle θ with initial velocity v_0.

29. Find an equation for the trajectory.

30. What is the maximum height attained by the projectile?

31. Find the range of the projectile.

32. How many seconds after firing does the impact take place?

33. How should θ be chosen so as to maximize the range?

34. How should θ be chosen so that the range becomes r?

10.4 ···· THE ELLIPSE

Start with two points F_1, F_2 and a number k greater than the distance between them.

(10.4.1)

> The set of all points P such that
>
> $$d(P, F_1) + d(P, F_2) = k$$
>
> is called an *ellipse*. F_1 and F_2 are called the *foci*.

The idea is illustrated in Figure 10.4.1. A string is looped over tacks placed at the foci. The pencil placed in the loop traces out an ellipse.

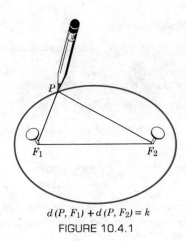

$$d(P, F_1) + d(P, F_2) = k$$

FIGURE 10.4.1

The *standard position* of an ellipse is with the foci along the *x*-axis at equal distances from the origin (Figure 10.4.2).

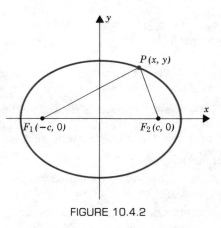

FIGURE 10.4.2

To find an equation for such an ellipse we set $k = 2a$. A point $P(x, y)$ will lie on the ellipse iff

$$d(P, F_1) + d(P, F_2) = 2a.$$

With F_1 at $(-c, 0)$ and F_2 at $(c, 0)$ we must have

$$\sqrt{(x + c)^2 + y^2} + \sqrt{(x - c)^2 + y^2} = 2a.$$

By transferring the second term to the right-hand side and squaring both sides, we obtain

$$(x + c)^2 + y^2 = 4a^2 + (x - c)^2 + y^2 - 4a\sqrt{(x - c)^2 + y^2}.$$

This reduces to

$$4a\sqrt{(x - c)^2 + y^2} = 4(a^2 - cx).$$

Canceling the factor 4 and squaring again, we obtain

$$a^2(x^2 - 2cx + c^2 + y^2) = a^4 - 2a^2cx + c^2x^2.$$

This in turn reduces to

$$(a^2 - c^2)x^2 + a^2y^2 = a^2(a^2 - c^2),$$

and thus to

$$\frac{x^2}{a^2} + \frac{y^2}{a^2 - c^2} = 1. \quad \square$$

It is customary to set

$$b = \sqrt{a^2 - c^2}.$$

The equation for an ellipse in standard position then takes the form

(10.4.2)
$$\frac{x^2}{a^2} + \frac{y^2}{b^2} = 1, \quad \text{with} \quad a > b.$$

The relation between a, b, and c is illustrated in Figure 10.4.3.

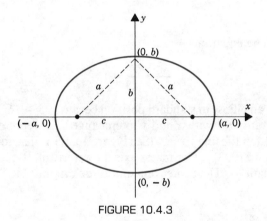

FIGURE 10.4.3

Every ellipse has four *vertices*. In Figure 10.4.3 these are marked $(a, 0), (-a, 0)$, $(0, b), (0, -b)$. The line segments that join opposite vertices are called the *axes* of the ellipse. The axis that contains the foci is called the *major axis*, the other the *minor axis*. In standard position the major axis is horizontal and has length $2a$; the minor axis is vertical and has length $2b$. The point at which the axes intersect is called the *center* of the ellipse. In standard position the center is at the origin.

EXAMPLE 1. The equation

$$16x^2 + 25y^2 = 400$$

can be written

$$\frac{x^2}{25} + \frac{y^2}{16} = 1. \qquad \qquad \text{(divide by 400)}$$

Here $a = 5$, $b = 4$, and $c = \sqrt{a^2 - b^2} = \sqrt{9} = 3$. The equation is in the form of (10.4.2). It is an ellipse in standard position with foci at $(-3, 0)$ and $(3, 0)$. The major axis has length $2a = 10$, and the minor axis has length $2b = 8$. The center is at the origin. The ellipse is sketched in Figure 10.4.4. □

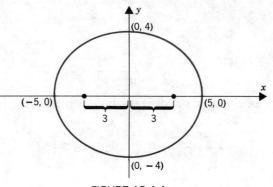

FIGURE 10.4.4

EXAMPLE 2. The equation

$$\frac{x^2}{16} + \frac{y^2}{25} = 1$$

does not represent an ellipse in standard position because $25 > 16$. This equation is the equation of Example 1 with x and y interchanged. It represents the ellipse of Example 1 reflected in the line $y = x$. (See Figure 10.4.5.) The foci are now on the y-axis, at $(0, -3)$ and $(0, 3)$. The major axis, now vertical, has length 10, and the minor axis has length 8. The center remains at the origin. □

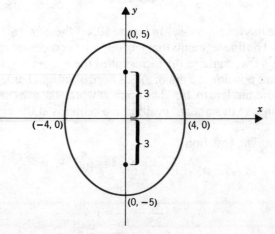

FIGURE 10.4.5

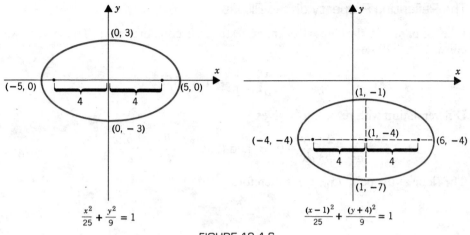

$$\frac{x^2}{25} + \frac{y^2}{9} = 1 \qquad\qquad \frac{(x-1)^2}{25} + \frac{(y+4)^2}{9} = 1$$

FIGURE 10.4.6

EXAMPLE 3. Figure 10.4.6 shows two ellipses:

$$\frac{x^2}{25} + \frac{y^2}{9} = 1 \quad\text{and}\quad \frac{(x-1)^2}{25} + \frac{(y+4)^2}{9} = 1.$$

The first ellipse is in standard position. Here $a = 5$, $b = 3$, $c = \sqrt{a^2 - b^2} = 4$. The foci are at $(-4, 0)$ and $(4, 0)$. The major axis has length 10, and the minor axis has length 6.

The second ellipse is the first ellipse displaced 1 unit right and 4 units down. The center is now at the point $(1, -4)$. The foci are at $(-3, -4)$ and $(5, -4)$. □

EXAMPLE 4. To identify the curve

$$4x^2 - 8x + y^2 + 4y - 8 = 0.$$

we write

$$4(x^2 - 2x + \quad) + (y^2 + 4y + \quad) = 8.$$

By completing the squares within the parentheses, we get

$$4(x^2 - 2x + 1) + (y^2 + 4y + 4) = 16,$$
$$4(x - 1)^2 + (y + 2)^2 = 16,$$

(∗)
$$\frac{(x-1)^2}{4} + \frac{(y+2)^2}{16} = 1.$$

This is the ellipse

(∗∗)
$$\frac{x^2}{16} + \frac{y^2}{4} = 1 \qquad (a = 4, b = 2, c = \sqrt{16 - 4} = 2\sqrt{3})$$

reflected in the line $y = x$ and then displaced 1 unit right and 2 units down. Since the foci of (∗∗) are at $(-2\sqrt{3}, 0)$ and $(2\sqrt{3}, 0)$, the foci of (∗) are at $(1, -2 - 2\sqrt{3})$ and $(1, -2 + 2\sqrt{3})$. The major axis, now vertical, has length 8; the minor axis has length 4. □

The Reflecting Property of the Ellipse

Like the parabola, the ellipse has an interesting reflecting property. To derive it, we consider the ellipse

$$\frac{x^2}{a^2} + \frac{y^2}{b^2} = 1.$$

Differentiation with respect to x gives

$$\frac{2x}{a^2} + \frac{2y}{b^2}\frac{dy}{dx} = 0 \quad \text{and thus} \quad \frac{dy}{dx} = -\frac{b^2 x}{a^2 y}.$$

The slope at the point (x_0, y_0) is therefore

$$-\frac{b^2 x_0}{a^2 y_0}$$

and the tangent line has equation

$$y - y_0 = -\frac{b^2 x_0}{a^2 y_0}(x - x_0).$$

We can rewrite this last equation as

$$(b^2 x_0)x + (a^2 y_0)y - a^2 b^2 = 0.$$

We can now show the following:

(10.4.3) | **At each point P of the ellipse, the focal radii $\overline{F_1 P}$ and $\overline{F_2 P}$ make equal angles with the tangent.**

Proof. If P lies on the x-axis, the focal radii are coincident and there is nothing to show. To visualize the argument for a point $P = P(x_0, y_0)$ not on the x-axis, see Figure 10.4.7. To show that $\overline{F_1 P}$ and $\overline{F_2 P}$ make equal angles with the tangent we need only show that the triangles $PT_1 F_1$ and $PT_2 F_2$ are similar. We can do this by showing that

$$\frac{d(T_1, F_1)}{d(F_1, P)} = \frac{d(T_2, F_2)}{d(F_2, P)}$$

or, equivalently, by showing that

$$\frac{|-b^2 x_0 c - a^2 b^2|}{\sqrt{(x_0 + c)^2 + y_0^2}} = \frac{|b^2 x_0 c - a^2 b^2|}{\sqrt{(x_0 - c)^2 + y_0^2}}.$$

The validity of this last equation can be seen by canceling the factor b^2 and then squaring. This gives

$$\frac{(x_0 c + a^2)^2}{(x_0 + c)^2 + y_0^2} = \frac{(x_0 c - a^2)^2}{(x_0 - c)^2 + y_0^2},$$

which can be simplified to

$$(a^2 - c^2)x_0^2 + a^2 y_0^2 = a^2(a^2 - c^2)$$

and thus to

$$\frac{x_0^2}{a^2} + \frac{y_0^2}{b^2} = 1.$$

This last equation holds since the point $P(x_0, y_0)$ is on the ellipse. □

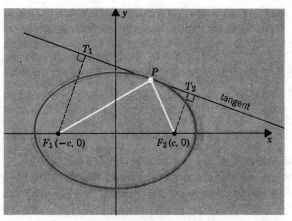

FIGURE 10.4.7

The result we just proved has the following physical consequence:

(10.4.4)   An elliptical mirror takes light or sound originating at one focus and converges it at the other focus.

EXERCISES

For each of the following ellipses find (a) the center, (b) the foci, (c) the length of the major axis, and (d) the length of the minor axis. Then sketch the figure.

1. $\dfrac{x^2}{9} + \dfrac{y^2}{4} = 1.$ **2.** $\dfrac{x^2}{4} + \dfrac{y^2}{9} = 1.$

3. $3x^2 + 2y^2 = 12.$ **4.** $3x^2 + 4y^2 - 12 = 0.$

5. $4x^2 + 9y^2 - 18y = 27.$ **6.** $4x^2 + y^2 - 6y + 5 = 0.$

7. $4(x - 1)^2 + y^2 = 64.$ **8.** $16(x - 2)^2 + 25(y - 3)^2 = 400.$

Find an equation for the ellipse that satisfies the given conditions.

9. Foci at $(-1, 0)$, $(1, 0)$; major axis 6.

10. Foci at $(0, -1)$, $(0, 1)$; major axis 6.

11. Foci at $(1, 3)$, $(1, 9)$; minor axis 8.

12. Foci at $(3, 1)$, $(9, 1)$; minor axis 10.

13. Focus at $(1, 1)$; center at $(1, 3)$; major axis 10.

14. Center at $(2, 1)$; vertices at $(2, 6)$ and $(1, 1)$.

15. Major axis 10; vertices at $(3, 2)$ and $(3, -4)$.

16. Focus at $(6, 2)$; vertices at $(1, 7)$, $(1, -3)$.

17. What is the length of the string in Figure 10.4.1?

18. Find the area enclosed by the ellipse

$$\frac{x^2}{a^2} + \frac{y^2}{b^2} = 1.$$

19. Show that in an ellipse the product of the distances between the foci and a tangent to the ellipse $[d(F_1, T_1) \, d(F_2, T_2)$ in Figure 10.4.7] is always the square of one-half the length of the minor axis.

The *eccentricity e* of an ellipse is the ratio of the distance between the foci to the length of the major axis:

(10.4.5)
$$e = \frac{c}{a}.$$

20. What happens to the ellipse if a remains constant but e tends to 0?

21. What happens to the ellipse if a remains constant but e tends to 1?

22. Find an equation for the ellipse in standard position that has major axis 10 and eccentricity $\frac{1}{2}$.

23. Find an equation for the ellipse in standard position that has minor axis $2\sqrt{3}$ and eccentricity $\frac{1}{2}$.

24. Like the parabola the ellipse can be defined in terms of one focus F and a directrix line l. Show that the ellipse

$$\frac{x^2}{a^2} + \frac{y^2}{a^2 - c^2} = 1$$

is the set of points $P(x, y)$ such that

$$d(P, F) = e \, d(P, l),$$

where F is $(c, 0)$, $e = c/a$, and $l: x = a^2/c$. Note that $0 < e < 1$.

10.5····THE HYPERBOLA

Start with two points F_1, F_2 and take a positive number k less than the distance between them.

(10.5.1)

The set of all points P such that
$$|d(P, F_1) - d(P, F_2)| = k$$
is called a *hyperbola*. F_1 and F_2 are called the *foci*.

The *standard position* of a hyperbola is with the foci along the *x*-axis at equal distances from the origin (Figure 10.5.1).

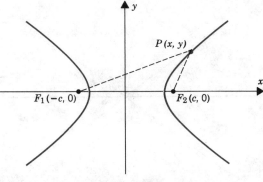

FIGURE 10.5.1

To find an equation for such a hyperbola we set $k = 2a$. A point $P(x, y)$ will lie on the hyperbola iff

$$|d(P, F_1) - d(P, F_2)| = 2a.$$

With F_1 at $(-c, 0)$ and F_2 at $(c, 0)$ we must have

$$\sqrt{(x + c)^2 + y^2} - \sqrt{(x - c)^2 + y^2} = \pm 2a. \qquad \text{(explain)}$$

Transferring the second term to the right and squaring both sides, we obtain

$$(x + c)^2 + y^2 = 4a^2 \pm 4a\sqrt{(x - c)^2 + y^2} + (x - c)^2 + y^2.$$

This equation reduces to

$$xc - a^2 = \pm a\sqrt{(x - c)^2 + y^2}.$$

Squaring once more, we obtain

$$x^2c^2 - 2a^2xc + a^4 = a^2(x^2 - 2xc + c^2 + y^2),$$

which reduces to

$$(c^2 - a^2)x^2 - a^2y^2 = a^2(c^2 - a^2),$$

and thus to

$$\frac{x^2}{a^2} - \frac{y^2}{c^2 - a^2} = 1. \quad \square$$

In this setting it is customary to set

$$b = \sqrt{c^2 - a^2}.$$

The equation for a hyperbola in standard position then takes the form

(10.5.2)
$$\frac{x^2}{a^2} - \frac{y^2}{b^2} = 1.$$

The hyperbola together with the relation between a, b, and c is illustrated in Figure 10.5.2.

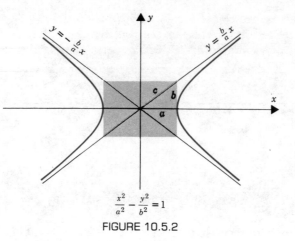

$$\frac{x^2}{a^2} - \frac{y^2}{b^2} = 1$$

FIGURE 10.5.2

As the figure suggests, the hyperbola remains between the lines

$$y = \frac{b}{a} x \quad \text{and} \quad y = -\frac{b}{a} x.$$

These lines are called the *asymptotes* of the hyperbola. They can be obtained from Equation (10.5.2) by replacing the 1 on the right-hand side by 0:

$$\frac{x^2}{a^2} - \frac{y^2}{b^2} = 0 \qquad \text{gives} \qquad y = \pm \frac{b}{a} x.$$

As $x \to \pm \infty$, the vertical separation between the hyperbola and the asymptotes tends to zero. To see this, solve the equation

$$\frac{x^2}{a^2} - \frac{y^2}{b^2} = 1$$

for y. This gives

$$y = \pm \sqrt{\frac{b^2}{a^2} x^2 - b^2}.$$

In all four quadrants the vertical separation between the hyperbola and the asymptotes can be written

$$\left| \frac{b}{a} |x| - \sqrt{\frac{b^2}{a^2} x^2 - b^2} \right|.$$ (check this)

As $x \to \pm \infty$,

$$\left| \frac{b}{a} |x| - \sqrt{\frac{b^2}{a^2} x^2 - b^2} \right| = \left| \frac{b}{a} |x| - \sqrt{\frac{b^2}{a^2} x^2 - b^2} \right| \frac{\left| \frac{b}{a} |x| + \sqrt{\frac{b^2}{a^2} x^2 - b^2} \right|}{\left| \frac{b}{a} |x| + \sqrt{\frac{b^2}{a^2} x^2 - b^2} \right|}$$

$$= \frac{b^2}{\left| \frac{b}{a} |x| + \sqrt{\frac{b^2}{a^2} x^2 - b^2} \right|} \to 0. \quad \square$$

The line determined by the foci of a hyperbola intersects the hyperbola at two points, called the *vertices*. The line segment that joins the vertices is called the *transverse axis*. The midpoint of the transverse axis is called the *center* of the hyperbola.

In standard position (Figure 10.5.2), the vertices are $(\pm a, 0)$, the transverse axis has length $2a$, and the center is at the origin.

EXAMPLE 1. The equation

$$\frac{x^2}{1} - \frac{y^2}{3} = 1 \qquad\qquad \text{(Figure 10.5.3)}$$

represents a hyperbola in standard position; here $a = 1, b = \sqrt{3}, c = \sqrt{1 + 3} = 2$. The center is at the origin. The foci are at $(-2, 0)$ and $(2, 0)$. The vertices are at $(-1, 0)$ and $(1, 0)$. The transverse axis has length 2. We can obtain the asymptotes by setting

$$\frac{x^2}{1} - \frac{y^2}{3} = 0.$$

The asymptotes are the lines

$$y = \pm\sqrt{3}x. \quad \square$$

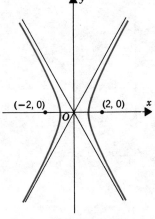

FIGURE 10.5.3

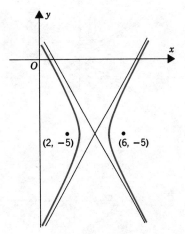

FIGURE 10.5.4

EXAMPLE 2. The hyperbola

$$\frac{(x - 4)^2}{1} - \frac{(y + 5)^2}{3} = 1 \qquad\qquad \text{(Figure 10.5.4)}$$

is the hyperbola

$$\frac{x^2}{1} - \frac{y^2}{3} = 1$$

of Example 1 displaced 4 units right and 5 units down. The center of the hyperbola is now at the point $(4, -5)$. The foci are at $(2, -5)$ and $(6, -5)$. The vertices are at $(3, -5)$ and $(5, -5)$. The new asymptotes are the lines

$$y + 5 = \pm \sqrt{3}(x - 4). \quad \square$$

EXAMPLE 3. The hyperbola

$$\frac{y^2}{1} - \frac{x^2}{3} = 1 \qquad\qquad \text{(Figure 10.5.5)}$$

is the hyperbola

$$\frac{x^2}{1} - \frac{y^2}{3} = 1$$

of Example 1 reflected in the line $y = x$. The center is still at the origin. The foci are now at $(0, -2)$ and $(0, 2)$. The vertices are at $(0, -1)$ and $(0, 1)$. The asymptotes are the lines

$$x = \pm \sqrt{3}y. \quad \square$$

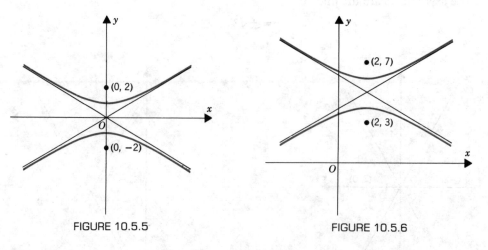

FIGURE 10.5.5   FIGURE 10.5.6

EXAMPLE 4. The hyperbola

$$\frac{(y - 5)^2}{1} - \frac{(x - 2)^2}{3} = 1 \qquad\qquad \text{(Figure 10.5.6)}$$

is the hyperbola of Example 3 displaced 2 units right and 5 units up. $\square$

The Tangent to a Hyperbola

Proceeding as in the case of the ellipse, one can show that, if a point (x_0, y_0) with $y_0 \neq 0$ lies on the hyperbola

$$\frac{x^2}{a^2} - \frac{y^2}{b^2} = 1,$$

then the slope at that point is given by the formula

$$m = \frac{b^2 x_0}{a^2 y_0}$$ (Exercise 21)

and the tangent line has equation

$$(b^2 x_0)x - (a^2 y_0)y - a^2 b^2 = 0.$$ (Exercise 22)

With this information, one can show that

(10.5.3)   *at each point P of a hyperbola, the tangent line bisects the angle between the focal radii $\overline{F_1 P}$ and $\overline{F_2 P}$.*   (Exercise 23)

An Application to Range Finding

There is a simple application of the hyperbola to range finding. If observers, located at two listening posts at a known distance apart, time the firing of a gun, the time difference multiplied by the velocity of sound gives the value of $2a$ and hence determines a hyperbola on which the gun must be located. The third listening post gives two more hyperbolas. The gun is found where the hyperbolas intersect.

EXERCISES

Find an equation for the indicated hyperbola.

1. Foci at $(-5, 0)$, $(5, 0)$; transverse axis 6.
2. Foci at $(-13, 0)$, $(13, 0)$; transverse axis 10.
3. Foci at $(0, -13)$, $(0, 13)$; transverse axis 10.
4. Foci at $(0, -13)$, $(0, 13)$; transverse axis 24.
5. Foci at $(-5, 1)$, $(5, 1)$; transverse axis 6.
6. Foci at $(-3, 1)$, $(7, 1)$; transverse axis 6.
7. Foci at $(-1, -1)$, $(-1, 1)$; transverse axis $\frac{1}{2}$.
8. Foci at $(2, 1)$, $(2, 5)$; transverse axis 3.

For each of the following hyperbolas find the center, the vertices, the foci, the asymptotes, and the length of the transverse axis. Then sketch the figure.

9. $x^2 - y^2 = 1.$

10. $y^2 - x^2 = 1.$

11. $\dfrac{x^2}{9} - \dfrac{y^2}{16} = 1.$

12. $\dfrac{x^2}{16} - \dfrac{y^2}{9} = 1.$

13. $\dfrac{y^2}{16} - \dfrac{x^2}{9} = 1.$

14. $\dfrac{y^2}{9} - \dfrac{x^2}{16} = 1.$

15. $\dfrac{(x-1)^2}{9} - \dfrac{(y-3)^2}{16} = 1.$

16. $\dfrac{(x-1)^2}{16} - \dfrac{(y-3)^2}{9} = 1.$

17. $4x^2 - 8x - y^2 + 6y - 1 = 0.$ **18.** $-3x^2 + y^2 - 6x = 0.$

19. Find the center, the vertices, the foci, the asymptotes, and the length of the transverse axis of the hyperbola with equation $xy = 1$.   HINT: Define new XY-coordinates by setting $x = X + Y$ and $y = X - Y$.

20. Find the area of the region that lies between the right-hand branch of the hyperbola

$$\frac{x^2}{a^2} - \frac{y^2}{b^2} = 1$$

and the vertical line $x = 2a$.

21. Show that, if $y_0 \neq 0$, then the slope of the hyperbola

$$\frac{x^2}{a^2} - \frac{y^2}{b^2} = 1$$

at the point (x_0, y_0) is given by

$$m = \frac{b^2 x_0}{a^2 y_0}.$$

22. Show that the tangent line at (x_0, y_0) has equation

$$(b^2 x_0)x - (a^2 y_0)y - a^2 b^2 = 0.$$

23. Show that the tangent to the hyperbola at the point P bisects the angle between the focal radii $\overline{F_1 P}$ and $\overline{F_2 P}$.

24. Like the parabola and the ellipse, the hyperbola can be defined in terms of one focus F and a directrix line l. Show that the hyperbola

$$\frac{x^2}{a^2} - \frac{y^2}{c^2 - a^2} = 1$$

is the set of all points $P(x, y)$ such that

$$d(P, F) = e\, d(P, l),$$

where F is $(c, 0)$, $e = c/a$, and $l: x = a^2/c$. Note that $e > 1$.

10.6····ADDITIONAL EXERCISES

Describe the following curves in detail.

1. $x^2 - 4y - 4 = 0.$

2. $3x^2 + 2y^2 - 6 = 0.$

3. $x^2 - 4y^2 - 10x + 41 = 0.$

4. $9x^2 - 4y^2 - 18x - 8y - 31 = 0.$

5. $x^2 + 3y^2 + 6x + 8 = 0.$

6. $x^2 - 10x - 8y + 41 = 0.$

7. $y^2 + 4y + 2x + 1 = 0.$

8. $9x^2 + 4y^2 - 18x - 8y - 23 = 0.$

9. $9x^2 + 25y^2 + 100y + 99 = 0.$

10. $7x^2 - y^2 + 42x + 14y + 21 = 0.$

11. $7x^2 - 5y^2 + 14x - 40y = 118.$

12. $2x^2 - 3y^2 + 4\sqrt{3}x - 6\sqrt{3}y = 9.$

13. $(x^2 - 4y)(4x^2 + 9y^2 - 36) = 0.$

14. $(x^2 - 4y)(x^2 - 4y^2) = 0.$

10.7····ROTATIONS; ELIMINATING THE *xy*-TERM

We begin by referring to Figure 10.7.1:

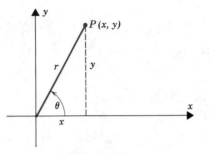

FIGURE 10.7.1

From the figure

$$\cos \theta = \frac{x}{r} \quad \text{and} \quad \sin \theta = \frac{y}{r}.$$

Thus

(10.7.1) $x = r \cos \theta \quad \text{and} \quad y = r \sin \theta.$

These equations come up repeatedly in calculus. We will consider them in more detail in Section 11.1 when we take up polar coordinates.

Consider now a rectangular coordinate system *Oxy*. If we rotate this system counterclockwise α radians about the origin, we obtain a new coordinate system *OXY*. See Figure 10.7.2.

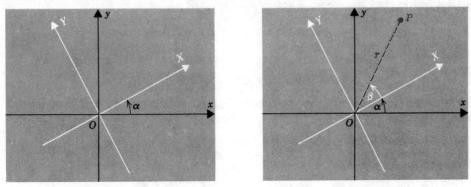

FIGURE 10.7.2   FIGURE 10.7.3

A point *P* will now have two pairs of rectangular coordinates:

(x, y) in the *Oxy* system   and (X, Y) in the *OXY* system.

Here we investigate the relation between (x, y) and (X, Y). With *P* as in Figure 10.7.3,

$$x = r \cos (\alpha + \beta), \qquad y = r \sin (\alpha + \beta)$$

and

$$X = r \cos \beta, \qquad Y = r \sin \beta.$$

Since

$$\cos (\alpha + \beta) = \cos \alpha \cos \beta - \sin \alpha \sin \beta,$$
$$\sin (\alpha + \beta) = \sin \alpha \cos \beta + \cos \alpha \sin \beta,$$

we have

$$x = r \cos (\alpha + \beta) = (\cos \alpha) r \cos \beta - (\sin \alpha) r \sin \beta,$$
$$y = r \sin (\alpha + \beta) = (\sin \alpha) r \cos \beta + (\cos \alpha) r \sin \beta,$$

and therefore

(10.7.2) $\qquad x = (\cos \alpha)X - (\sin \alpha)Y \qquad \text{and} \qquad y = (\sin \alpha)X + (\cos \alpha)Y.$

These formulas give the algebraic consequences of a counterclockwise rotation of α radians.

Eliminating the xy-Term

Rotations of the coordinate system enable us to simplify equations of the second degree by eliminating the xy-term; that is, if in the Oxy system, S has an equation of the form

(1) $\qquad\qquad ax^2 + bxy + cy^2 + dx + ey + f = 0 \qquad \text{with} \quad b \neq 0,$

then there exists a coordinate system $OXY,$ differing from Oxy by a rotation, such that in the OXY system S has an equation of the form

$$AX^2 + CY^2 + DX + EY + F = 0.$$

To see this, substitute

$$x = (\cos \alpha)X - (\sin \alpha)Y, \qquad y = (\sin \alpha)X + (\cos \alpha)Y$$

in Equation (1). This will give you a second-degree equation in X and Y in which the coefficient of XY is

$$-2a \cos \alpha \sin \alpha + b(\cos^2 \alpha - \sin^2 \alpha) + 2c \cos \alpha \sin \alpha.$$

This can be simplified to

$$(c - a) \sin 2\alpha + b \cos 2\alpha.$$

To eliminate the XY term we must have this coefficient equal to zero, that is, we must have

$$(a - c) \sin 2\alpha = b \cos 2\alpha.$$

There are two possibilities here: $a = c, a \neq c$.

I. If $a = c$, then

$$\cos 2\alpha = 0,$$
$$2\alpha = \tfrac{1}{2}\pi + n\pi, \qquad \text{(}n\text{ an arbitrary integer)}$$
$$\alpha = \tfrac{1}{4}\pi + \tfrac{1}{2}n\pi.$$

Thus, if $a = c$, we can eliminate the XY term by setting

(10.7.3) $\boxed{\alpha = \tfrac{1}{4}\pi.}$ (choose $n = 0$)

II. If $a \neq c$, then

$$\tan 2\alpha = \frac{b}{a - c},$$

$$2\alpha = \tan^{-1}\left(\frac{b}{a - c}\right) + n\pi,$$

$$\alpha = \tfrac{1}{2}\tan^{-1}\left(\frac{b}{a - c}\right) + \tfrac{1}{2}n\pi.$$

Thus, if $a \neq c$, we can eliminate the XY term by setting

(10.7.4) $\boxed{\alpha = \tfrac{1}{2}\tan^{-1}\left(\dfrac{b}{a - c}\right).}$ (choose $n = 0$)

EXAMPLE. In the case of

$$xy - 2 = 0,$$

we have $a = c$ and thus can choose $\alpha = \tfrac{1}{4}\pi$. Setting

$$x = (\cos \tfrac{1}{4}\pi)X - (\sin \tfrac{1}{4}\pi)Y = \tfrac{1}{2}\sqrt{2}\,(X - Y),$$
$$y = (\sin \tfrac{1}{4}\pi)X + (\cos \tfrac{1}{4}\pi)Y = \tfrac{1}{2}\sqrt{2}\,(X + Y),$$

we find that $xy - 2 = 0$ becomes

$$\tfrac{1}{2}(X^2 - Y^2) - 2 = 0,$$

which can be written

$$\frac{X^2}{4} - \frac{Y^2}{4} = 1.$$

This is the equation of a hyperbola in standard position in the OXY system. The hyperbola is shown in Figure 10.7.4. $\square$

EXAMPLE. In the case of

$$11x^2 + 4\sqrt{3}xy + 7y^2 - 1 = 0,$$

we have $a = 11$, $b = 4\sqrt{3}$, and $c = 7$. Thus we can choose

$$\alpha = \tfrac{1}{2}\tan^{-1}\left(\frac{b}{a - c}\right) = \tfrac{1}{2}\tan^{-1}\sqrt{3} = \tfrac{1}{6}\pi.$$

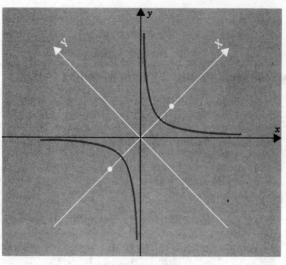

FIGURE 10.7.4

Setting

$$x = (\cos \tfrac{1}{6}\pi)X - (\sin \tfrac{1}{6}\pi)Y = \tfrac{1}{2}(\sqrt{3}X - Y),$$
$$y = (\sin \tfrac{1}{6}\pi)X + (\cos \tfrac{1}{6}\pi)Y = \tfrac{1}{2}(X + \sqrt{3}Y),$$

we find after simplification that our initial equation becomes

$$13X^2 + 5Y^2 - 1 = 0,$$

which we can write as

$$\frac{X^2}{(1/\sqrt{13})^2} + \frac{Y^2}{(1/\sqrt{5})^2} = 1.$$

This is the equation of an ellipse.   The ellipse is pictured in Figure 10.7.5   □

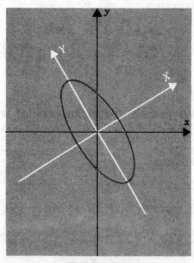

FIGURE 10.7.5

EXERCISES

For each of the equations below, (a) find a rotation $\alpha \in (-\frac{1}{4}\pi, \frac{1}{4}\pi]$ that eliminates the *xy*-term; (b) rewrite the equation in terms of the new coordinate system; (c) sketch the curve displaying both coordinate systems.

1. $xy = 1$.

2. $xy - y + x = 1$.

3. $11x^2 + 10\sqrt{3}xy + y^2 - 4 = 0$.

4. $52x^2 - 72xy + 73y^2 - 100 = 0$.

5. $x^2 - 2xy + y^2 + x + y = 0$.

6. $3x^2 + 2\sqrt{3}xy + y^2 - 2x + 2\sqrt{3}y = 0$.

7. $x^2 + 2\sqrt{3}xy + 3y^2 + 2\sqrt{3}x - 2y = 0$.

8. $2x^2 + 4\sqrt{3}xy + 6y^2 + (8 - \sqrt{3})x + (8\sqrt{3} + 1)y + 8 = 0$.

For each of the equations below, find a rotation $\alpha \in (-\frac{1}{4}\pi, \frac{1}{4}\pi]$ that eliminates the *xy*-term. Then find $\cos \alpha$ and $\sin \alpha$.

9. $x^2 + xy + Kx + Ly + M = 0$.

10. $5x^2 + 24xy + 12y^2 + Kx + Ly + M = 0$.

Supplement to Section 10.7

The Second-Degree Equation

It is possible to draw general conclusions about the graph of a second-degree equation

$$ax^2 + bxy + cy^2 + dx + ey + f = 0, \qquad a, b, c \text{ not all } 0,$$

just from the *discriminant*

$$\Delta = b^2 - 4ac.$$

There are three cases.

Case 1. If $\Delta < 0$, the graph is an ellipse, a circle, a point, or empty.

Case 2. If $\Delta > 0$, the graph is a hyperbola or a pair of intersecting lines.

Case 3. If $\Delta = 0$, the graph is a parabola, a line, a pair of lines, or empty.

Below we outline how these assertions can be verified. A useful first step is to rotate the coordinate system so that the equation takes the form

(1) $$AX^2 + CY^2 + DX + EY + F = 0.$$

An elementary but time-consuming computation shows that the discriminant is unchanged by a rotation, so that in this instance we have

$$\Delta = b^2 - 4ac = -4AC.$$

Moreover, A and C cannot both be zero. If $\Delta < 0$, then $AC > 0$ and we can rewrite (1) as

$$\frac{X^2}{C} + \frac{D}{AC}X + \frac{Y^2}{A} + \frac{EY}{AC} + \frac{F}{AC} = 0.$$

By completing the squares, we obtain an equation of the form

$$\frac{(X - \alpha)^2}{(\sqrt{|C|})^2} + \frac{(Y - \beta)^2}{(\sqrt{|A|})^2} = K.$$

If $K > 0$, we have an ellipse or a circle. If $K = 0$, we have the point (α, β). If $K < 0$, the set is empty.

If $\Delta > 0$, then $AC < 0$. Proceeding as before, we obtain an equation of the form

$$\frac{(X - \alpha)^2}{(\sqrt{|C|})^2} - \frac{(Y - \beta)^2}{(\sqrt{|A|})^2} = K.$$

If $K \neq 0$, we have a hyperbola. If $K = 0$, the equation becomes

$$\left(\frac{X - \alpha}{\sqrt{|C|}} - \frac{Y - \beta}{\sqrt{|A|}}\right)\left(\frac{X - \alpha}{\sqrt{|C|}} + \frac{Y - \beta}{\sqrt{|A|}}\right) = 0,$$

so that we have a pair of lines intersecting at the point (α, β).

If $\Delta = 0$, then $AC = 0$, so that either $A = 0$ or $C = 0$. Since A and C are not both zero, there is no loss in generality in assuming that $A \neq 0$ and $C = 0$. In this case Equation (1) reduces to

$$AX^2 + DX + EY + F = 0.$$

Dividing by A, we obtain an equation of the form

$$X^2 + HX + IY + J = 0.$$

Completion of the square gives us

$$(X - \alpha)^2 = \beta Y + K.$$

If $\beta \neq 0$, we have a parabola. If $\beta = 0$ and $K = 0$, we have a line. If $\beta = 0$ and $K > 0$, we have a pair of parallel lines. If $\beta = 0$ and $K < 0$, the set is empty. $\square$

10.8 CHAPTER SUMMARY

10.1 Introduction

conic section (p. 501)

10.2 Translations; The Distance Between a Point and a Line

translation (p. 502) $d(P_1, l) = \dfrac{|Ax_1 + By_1 + C|}{\sqrt{A^2 + B^2}}$

10.3 The Parabola

directrix, focus, axis, vertex (p. 505)   reflecting property (p. 510)
parabolic trajectories (p. 511)

A parabola is the set of points equidistant from a fixed line and a fixed point not on that line.

10.4 The Ellipse

foci, standard position (p. 514)   vertices, axes, center (p. 515)
reflecting property (p. 518)   eccentricity (p. 520)

An ellipse is the set of points the sum of whose distances from two fixed points is constant.

10.5 The Hyperbola

foci, standard position (p. 520)   asymptotes (p. 522)
vertices, transverse axis, center (p. 523)

A hyperbola is the set of points the difference of whose distances from two fixed points is constant.

10.6 Additional Exercises

10.7 Rotations; Eliminating the *xy*-Term

discriminant (p. 531)

11

Polar Coordinates; Parametric Equations

11.1····POLAR COORDINATES

The purpose of coordinates is to fix position with respect to a frame of reference. When we use rectangular coordinates, our frame of reference is a pair of lines that intersect at right angles. For a *polar coordinate system,* the frame of reference is a point O that we call the *pole* and a ray that emanates from it that we call the *polar axis* (Figure 11.1.1).

In Figure 11.1.2 we have drawn two more rays from the pole. One lies at an angle of θ radians from the polar axis; we call it *ray θ.* The opposite ray lies at an angle of $\theta + \pi$ radians; we call it *ray $\theta + \pi$.*

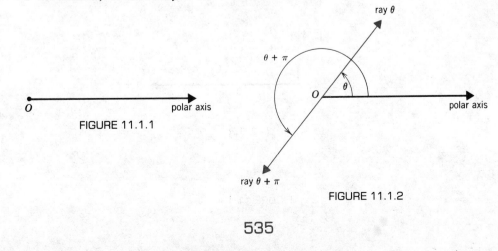

FIGURE 11.1.1

FIGURE 11.1.2

Figure 11.1.3 shows some points along these same rays, labeled with *polar coordinates*.

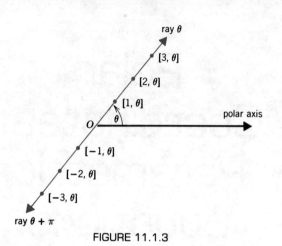

FIGURE 11.1.3

(11.1.1)   In general, a point is given *polar coordinates* $[r, \theta]$ iff it lies at a distance $|r|$ from the pole

along the ray θ, if $r \geq 0$,   and   along the ray $\theta + \pi$, if $r < 0$.

Figure 11.1.4 shows the point $[2, \frac{2}{3}\pi]$ at a distance of 2 units from the pole along the ray $\frac{2}{3}\pi$. The point $[-2, \frac{2}{3}\pi]$ also lies 2 units from the pole, not along the ray $\frac{2}{3}\pi$, but along the opposite ray.

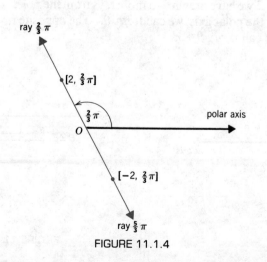

FIGURE 11.1.4

Polar coordinates are not unique.   Many pairs $[r, \theta]$ can represent the same point.

1. If $r = 0$, it does not matter how we choose θ.   The resulting point is still the pole:

(11.1.2) $$O = [0, \theta] \qquad \text{for all } \theta.$$

2. Geometrically there is no distinction between angles that differ by an integral multiple of 2π.   Consequently, as suggested in Figure 11.1.5,

(11.1.3) $$[r, \theta] = [r, \theta + 2n\pi] \qquad \text{for all integers } n.$$

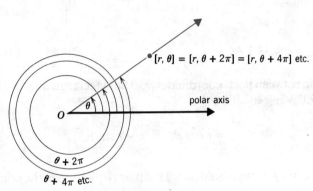

FIGURE 11.1.5

3. Adding π to the second coordinate is equivalent to changing the sign of the first coordinate:

(11.1.4) $$[r, \theta + \pi] = [-r, \theta].$$ (Figure 11.1.6)

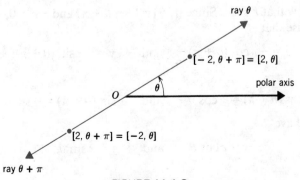

FIGURE 11.1.6

Relation to Rectangular Coordinates

In Figure 11.1.7 we have superimposed a polar coordinate system on a rectangular coordinate system. We have placed the pole at the origin and the polar axis along the positive x-axis.

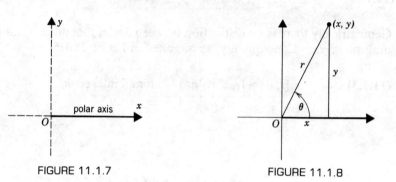

FIGURE 11.1.7   FIGURE 11.1.8

The relation between polar coordinates $[r, \theta]$ and rectangular coordinates (x, y) is given by the following equations:

(11.1.5)

$$x = r \cos \theta, \qquad y = r \sin \theta.$$

Proof. If $r = 0$, the formulas hold, since the point $[r, \theta]$ is then the origin and both x and y are 0:

$$0 = 0 \cos \theta, \qquad 0 = 0 \sin \theta.$$

For $r > 0$, we refer to Figure 11.1.8.† From the figure,

$$\cos \theta = \frac{x}{r}, \qquad \sin \theta = \frac{y}{r}$$

and therefore

$$x = r \cos \theta, \qquad y = r \sin \theta.$$

Suppose now that $r < 0$. Since $[r, \theta] = [-r, \theta + \pi]$ and $-r > 0$, we know from the previous case that

$$x = -r \cos (\theta + \pi) \qquad \text{and} \qquad y = -r \sin (\theta + \pi).$$

Since

$$\cos (\theta + \pi) = -\cos \theta \qquad \text{and} \qquad \sin (\theta + \pi) = -\sin \theta,$$

once again we have

$$x = r \cos \theta \qquad \text{and} \qquad y = r \sin \theta. \quad \square$$

---

† For simplicity we have placed (x, y) in the first quadrant. A similar argument works in each of the other quadrants.

From the relations we just proved you can see that, unless $x = 0$,

(11.1.6)
$$\tan \theta = \frac{y}{x}$$

and, under all circumstances,

(11.1.7)
$$x^2 + y^2 = r^2.$$ (check this out)

PROBLEM. Find the rectangular coordinates of the point P with polar coordinates $[-2, \frac{1}{3}\pi]$.

Solution. The relations
$$x = r \cos \theta, \qquad y = r \sin \theta$$

give
$$x = -2 \cos \tfrac{1}{3}\pi = -2(\tfrac{1}{2}) = -1$$

and
$$y = -2 \sin \tfrac{1}{3}\pi = -2(\tfrac{1}{2}\sqrt{3}) = -\sqrt{3}.$$

The point P has rectangular coordinates $(-1, -\sqrt{3})$. □

PROBLEM. Find all possible polar coordinates for the point P that has rectangular coordinates $(-2, 2\sqrt{3})$.

Solution. We know that
$$r \cos \theta = -2, \qquad r \sin \theta = 2\sqrt{3}.$$

We can get the possible values of r by squaring these expressions and then adding them:
$$r^2 = r^2 \cos^2 \theta + r^2 \sin^2 \theta = (-2)^2 + (2\sqrt{3})^2 = 16,$$

so that $r = \pm 4$.

Taking $r = 4$, we have
$$4 \cos \theta = -2, \qquad 4 \sin \theta = 2\sqrt{3}$$
$$\cos \theta = -\tfrac{1}{2}, \qquad \sin \theta = \tfrac{1}{2}\sqrt{3}.$$

These equations are satisfied by setting $\theta = \frac{2}{3}\pi$, or more generally, by setting
$$\theta = \tfrac{2}{3}\pi + 2n\pi.$$

The polar coordinates of P with first coordinate $r = 4$ are all pairs of the form
$$[4, \tfrac{2}{3}\pi + 2n\pi]$$

where n ranges over the set of all integers.

We could go through the same process again, this time taking $r = -4$, but there is no need to do so. Since $[r, \theta] = [-r, \theta + \pi]$, we know that

$$[4, \tfrac{2}{3}\pi + 2n\pi] = [-4, (\tfrac{2}{3}\pi + \pi) + 2n\pi].$$

The polar coordinates of P with first coordinate $r = -4$ are thus all pairs of the form

$$[-4, \tfrac{5}{3}\pi + 2n\pi]$$

where n again ranges over the set of all integers. ☐

Let's specify some simple sets in polar coordinates.

1. In rectangular coordinates the circle of radius a centered at the origin has equation

$$x^2 + y^2 = a^2.$$

The equation for this circle in polar coordinates is simply

$$r = a.$$

The interior of the circle is given by

$$0 \le r < a$$

and the exterior by

$$r > a.$$

2. The line through the origin with inclination α is given by the polar equation

$$\theta = \alpha.$$

3. The vertical line $x = a$ becomes

$$r \cos \theta = a$$

and the horizontal line $y = b$ becomes

$$r \sin \theta = b.$$

4. The line $Ax + By + C = 0$ can be written

$$r(A \cos \theta + B \sin \theta) + C = 0.$$

PROBLEM. Find an equation in polar coordinates for the equilateral hyperbola
$$x^2 - y^2 = a^2.$$

Solution. Setting

$$x = r \cos \theta, \qquad y = r \sin \theta$$

we have

$$r^2 \cos^2 \theta - r^2 \sin^2 \theta = a^2,$$
$$r^2(\cos^2 \theta - \sin^2 \theta) = a^2,$$
$$r^2 \cos 2\theta = a^2. \quad \square$$

PROBLEM. Show that the equation

$$r = 2a \cos \theta$$

represents a circle.

Solution. Multiplication by r gives

$$r^2 = 2ar \cos \theta,$$
$$x^2 + y^2 = 2ax,$$
$$x^2 - 2ax + y^2 = 0,$$
$$x^2 - 2ax + a^2 + y^2 = a^2,$$
$$(x - a)^2 + y^2 = a^2.$$

This is a circle of radius a centered at the point with rectangular coordinates $(a, 0)$. □

Symmetry

Symmetry with respect to each of the coordinate axes and with respect to the origin is illustrated in Figure 11.1.9. The coordinates marked are, of course, not the only ones possible.†

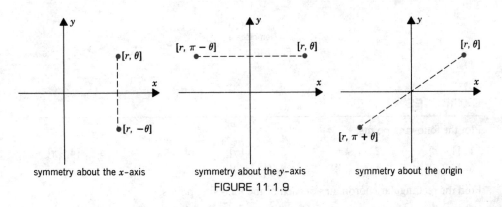

symmetry about the x-axis   symmetry about the y-axis   symmetry about the origin

FIGURE 11.1.9

PROBLEM. Test the lemniscate

$$r^2 = \cos 2\theta$$

for symmetry.

Solution. Since

$$\cos [2(-\theta)] = \cos (-2\theta) = \cos 2\theta,$$

you can see that, if $[r, \theta]$ is on the curve, then so is $[r, -\theta]$. This says that the curve is symmetric about the x-axis.

---

† The difficulties that this can cause are explained at the end of Section 11.3.

Since

$$\cos\,[2(\pi - \theta)] = \cos\,(2\pi -2\theta) = \cos\,(-2\theta) = \cos\,2\theta,$$

you can see that, if $[r, \theta]$ is on the curve, then so is $[r, \pi - \theta]$. The curve is therefore symmetric about the y-axis.

Being symmetric about both axes, the curve must also be symmetric about the origin. You can verify this directly by noting that

$$\cos\,[2(\pi + \theta)] = \cos\,(2\pi + 2\theta) = \cos\,2\theta,$$

so that, if $[r, \theta]$ lies on the curve, then so does $[r, \pi + \theta]$. A sketch of the lemniscate appears in Figure 11.1.10. □

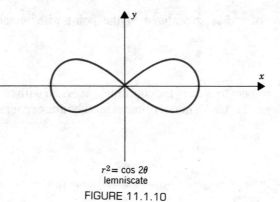

$r^2 = \cos 2\theta$
lemniscate
FIGURE 11.1.10

EXERCISES

Plot the following points:

1. $[1, \frac{1}{3}\pi]$.   2. $[1, \frac{1}{2}\pi]$.   3. $[-1, \frac{1}{3}\pi]$.   4. $[-1, -\frac{1}{3}\pi]$.   5. $[4, \frac{5}{4}\pi]$.
6. $[-2, 0]$.   7. $[-\frac{1}{2}, \pi]$.   8. $[\frac{1}{3}, \frac{2}{3}\pi]$.

Find the rectangular coordinates of each of the following points:

9. $[3, \frac{1}{2}\pi]$.   10. $[4, \frac{1}{6}\pi]$.   11. $[-1, -\pi]$.   12. $[-1, \frac{1}{4}\pi]$.   13. $[-3, -\frac{1}{3}\pi]$.
14. $[2, 0]$.   15. $[3, -\frac{1}{2}\pi]$.   16. $[2, 3\pi]$.

The following points are given in rectangular coordinates. Find all possible polar coordinates for each point.

17. $(0, 1)$.   18. $(1, 0)$.   19. $(-3, 0)$.   20. $(4, 4)$.   21. $(2, -2)$.
22. $(3, -3\sqrt{3})$.   23. $(4\sqrt{3}, 4)$.   24. $(\sqrt{3}, -1)$.   25. $(-1, \sqrt{3})$.

26. (a) Show that the distance between $[r_1, \theta_1]$ and $[r_2, \theta_2]$ is

$$\sqrt{r_1^2 + r_2^2 - 2r_1r_2 \cos\,(\theta_1 - \theta_2)}.$$

   HINT: Change to rectangular coordinates.
   (b) Show that for $r_1 > 0, r_2 > 0, |\theta_1 - \theta_2| < \pi$ the distance formula in part (a) is just the law of cosines.

Find the point $[r, \theta]$ symmetric to the given point about (a) the x-axis, (b) the y-axis, (c) the origin. Express your answer with $r > 0$ and $\theta \in [0, 2\pi)$.

27. $[\frac{1}{2}, \frac{1}{6}\pi]$.   **28.** $[3, -\frac{5}{4}\pi]$.   **29.** $[-2, \frac{1}{3}\pi]$.   **30.** $[-3, -\frac{7}{4}\pi]$.

Test these curves for symmetry about the coordinate axes and the origin.

31. $r = 2 + \cos\theta$.   **32.** $r = \cos 2\theta$.   **33.** $r(\sin\theta + \cos\theta) = 1$.

34. $r\sin\theta = 1$.   **35.** $r^2 \sin 2\theta = 1$.   **36.** $r^2 \cos 2\theta = 1$.

Write the equation in polar coordinates.

37. $x = 2$.   **38.** $y = 3$.   **39.** $2xy = 1$.

40. $x^2 + y^2 = 9$.   **41.** $x^2 + (y - 2)^2 = 4$.   **42.** $(x - a)^2 + y^2 = a^2$.

43. $y = x$.   **44.** $x^2 - y^2 = 4$.   **45.** $x^2 + y^2 + x = \sqrt{x^2 + y^2}$.

46. $y = mx$.   **47.** $(x^2 + y^2)^2 = 2xy$.   **48.** $(x^2 + y^2)^2 = x^2 - y^2$.

Identify the curve and write the equation in rectangular coordinates.

49. $r\sin\theta = 4$.   **50.** $r\cos\theta = 4$.   **51.** $\theta = \frac{1}{3}\pi$.

52. $\theta^2 = \frac{1}{9}\pi^2$.   **53.** $r = 2(1 - \cos\theta)^{-1}$.   **54.** $r = 4\sin(\theta + \pi)$.

55. $r = 3\cos\theta$.   **56.** $\theta = -\frac{1}{2}\pi$.   **57.** $\tan\theta = 2$.

58. $r = 2\sin\theta$.   **59.** $\theta^2 = \frac{1}{4}\pi^2$.   **60.** $r = (2 - \cos\theta)^{-1}$.

11.2···· GRAPHING IN POLAR COORDINATES

We begin with the equation

$$r = \theta, \qquad \theta \geq 0.$$

The graph is a nonending spiral, part of the famous *spiral of Archimedes*. The curve is shown in detail from $\theta = 0$ to $\theta = 2\pi$ in Figure 11.2.1. At $\theta = 0$, $r = 0$; at $\theta = \frac{1}{4}\pi$, $r = \frac{1}{4}\pi$; at $\theta = \frac{1}{2}\pi$, $r = \frac{1}{2}\pi$; etc. □

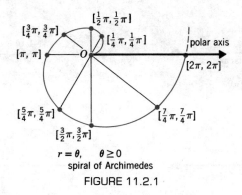

$$r = \theta, \qquad \theta \geq 0$$
spiral of Archimedes
FIGURE 11.2.1

The next examples involve trigonometric functions.

EXAMPLE. To sketch the curve

$$r = 1 - 2 \cos \theta$$

we refer to the graph of the cosine function in rectangular coordinates (Figure 11.2.2).

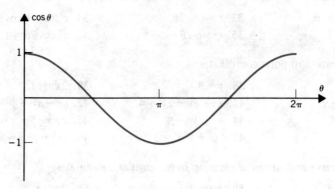

FIGURE 11.2.2

Since the cosine function is periodic, the curve $r = 1 - 2 \cos \theta$ is a closed curve. We will draw it from 0 to 2π. Outside that interval the curve repeats itself.

To begin the sketch of

$$r = 1 - 2 \cos \theta,$$

we first find the values of θ for which $r = 0$ or $|r|$ is a local maximum:

$$r = 0 \text{ at } \theta = \tfrac{1}{3}\pi, \tfrac{5}{3}\pi \quad \text{for then } \cos \theta = \tfrac{1}{2};$$
$$|r| \text{ is a local maximum at } \theta = 0, \pi, 2\pi.$$

These five values of θ generate four intervals:

$$[0, \tfrac{1}{3}\pi], \quad [\tfrac{1}{3}\pi, \pi], \quad [\pi, \tfrac{5}{3}\pi], \quad [\tfrac{5}{3}\pi, 2\pi].$$

We sketch the curve in four stages. These stages are shown in Figure 11.2.3.

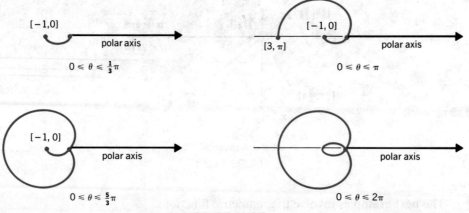

FIGURE 11.2.3

As θ increases from 0 to $\frac{1}{3}\pi$, $\cos\theta$ decreases from 1 to $\frac{1}{2}$ and $r = 1 - 2\cos\theta$ increases
   from -1 to 0.

As θ increases from $\frac{1}{3}\pi$ to π, $\cos\theta$ decreases from $\frac{1}{2}$ to -1 and r increases from 0 to 3.

As θ increases from π to $\frac{4}{3}\pi$, $\cos\theta$ increases from -1 to $\frac{1}{2}$ and r decreases from 3 to 0.

Finally, as θ increases from $\frac{5}{3}\pi$ to 2π, $\cos\theta$ increases from $\frac{1}{2}$ to 1 and r decreases from
   0 to -1.

As we could have read from the equation, the curve is symmetric about the x-axis.   □

EXAMPLE.   To sketch the curve

$$r = \cos 2\theta$$

we refer to the graph of $\cos 2\theta$ in rectangular coordinates (Figure 11.2.4).

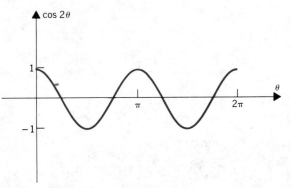

FIGURE 11.2.4

The values of θ for which $r = 0$ or $|r|$ is a local maximum are as follows:

$$\theta = \frac{n}{4}\pi, \qquad n = 0, 1, \ldots, 8.$$

The curve drawn in the corresponding eight stages is shown in Figure 11.2.5.   □

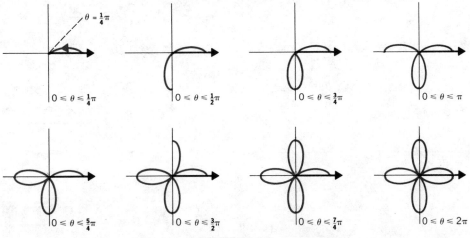

FIGURE 11.2.5

At this point we'll try to give you an overview of some of the basic polar curves. Figure 11.2.6 shows four *cardioids,* heart-shaped curves.

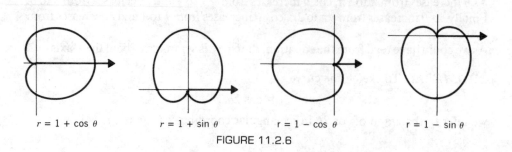

$r = 1 + \cos\theta$ $\qquad$ $r = 1 + \sin\theta$ $\qquad$ $r = 1 - \cos\theta$ $\qquad$ $r = 1 - \sin\theta$

FIGURE 11.2.6

Rotation of $r = 1 + \cos\theta$ by $\frac{1}{2}\pi$ radians gives

$$r = 1 + \cos\left(\theta - \tfrac{1}{2}\pi\right) = 1 + \sin\theta.$$

Rotation by another $\frac{1}{2}\pi$ radians gives

$$r = 1 + \cos\left(\theta - \pi\right) = 1 - \cos\theta.$$

Rotation by yet another $\frac{1}{2}\pi$ radians gives

$$r = 1 + \cos\left(\theta - \tfrac{3}{2}\pi\right) = 1 - \sin\theta.$$

Notice how easy it is to rotate axes in polar coordinates: each change

$$\cos\theta \rightarrow \sin\theta \rightarrow -\cos\theta \rightarrow -\sin\theta$$

represents a rotation by $\frac{1}{2}\pi$ radians. In the figures that follow you'll see evidence of such rotations.

The numbers a and b that appear below are to be interpreted as nonzero constants.

Lines: $\quad \theta = a \quad$ or $\quad r = \dfrac{a}{\cos\theta} = a\sec\theta$ $\qquad\qquad$ (Figure 11.2.7)

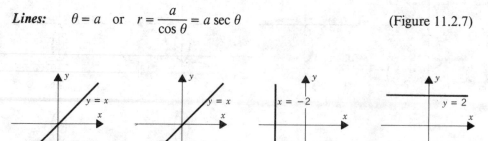

$\theta = \frac{1}{4}\pi$ $\qquad\qquad$ $\theta = \frac{5}{4}\pi$ $\qquad\qquad$ $r = -2\sec\theta$ $\qquad\qquad$ $r = 2\csc\theta$

FIGURE 11.2.7

Circles: $r = a$ or $r = a \cos \theta$ (Figure 11.2.8)

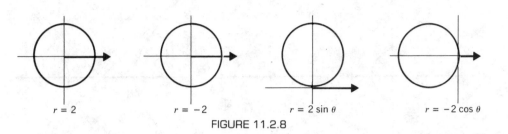

| $r = 2$ | $r = -2$ | $r = 2 \sin \theta$ | $r = -2 \cos \theta$ |

FIGURE 11.2.8

Limaçons:† $r = a + b \cos \theta$ (Figure 11.2.9)

If r is *never* zero on $[0, 2\pi)$, the limaçon is

$$\text{convex if } \left| \frac{a}{b} \right| \geq 2, \quad \text{dimpled if } 1 < \left| \frac{a}{b} \right| < 2.$$

If r is zero *once* on $[0, 2\pi)$, the limaçon has a cusp and is a cardioid.
If r is zero *twice* on $[0, 2\pi)$, the limaçon has an inner loop.

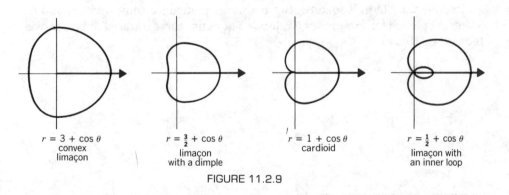

| $r = 3 + \cos \theta$ | $r = \frac{3}{2} + \cos \theta$ | $r = 1 + \cos \theta$ | $r = \frac{1}{2} + \cos \theta$ |
| convex limaçon | limaçon with a dimple | cardioid | limaçon with an inner loop |

FIGURE 11.2.9

Conics: $r = \dfrac{1}{a + b \cos \theta}$ (Figure 11.2.10)

If $a + b \cos \theta$ is *never* zero on $[0, 2\pi)$, we have an ellipse.   One of the foci is at the pole.

If $a + b \cos \theta$ is zero *once* on $[0, 2\pi)$, we have a parabola.   The focus is at the pole.

If $a + b \cos \theta$ is zero *twice* on $[0, 2\pi)$, we have a hyperbola.   One of the foci is at the pole.

---

† From the French term for snail.   The word is pronounced with a soft *c*.

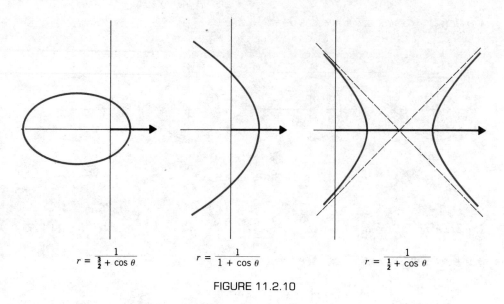

$$r = \frac{1}{\frac{3}{2} + \cos \theta} \qquad r = \frac{1}{1 + \cos \theta} \qquad r = \frac{1}{\frac{1}{2} + \cos \theta}$$

FIGURE 11.2.10

***Lemniscates*†** (of Bernoulli): $r^2 = a \cos 2\theta$ (Figure 11.2.11)

Because the *r* term is squared, two points are plotted for some θ values and no points are plotted for some other θ values.   The entire curve is traced out twice over the interval $[0, 2\pi)$.

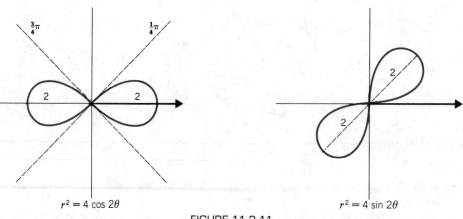

$$r^2 = 4 \cos 2\theta \qquad\qquad\qquad r^2 = 4 \sin 2\theta$$

FIGURE 11.2.11

---

† From the Latin *lemniscatus*, meaning "adorned with pendent ribbons."

Petal Curves: $r = a \cos n\theta$ with n an integer.   (Figure 11.2.12)

If n is *odd*, there are n petals.   If n is *even,* there are $2n$ petals.

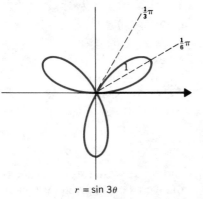

$r = \sin 3\theta$

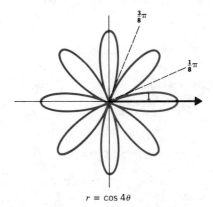

$r = \cos 4\theta$

FIGURE 11.2.12

Spirals: $r = a\theta$, spiral of Archimedes.   (Figure 11.2.13)

$r = e^{a\theta},$ $\ln r = a\theta$ logarithmic spiral.   (Figure 11.2.14)

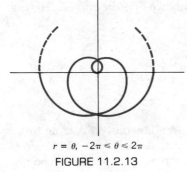

$r = \theta, \; -2\pi \leqslant \theta \leqslant 2\pi$

FIGURE 11.2.13

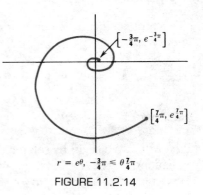

$\left[-\tfrac{3}{4}\pi, \, e^{-\tfrac{3}{4}\pi}\right]$

$\left[\tfrac{7}{4}\pi, \, e^{\tfrac{7}{4}\pi}\right]$

$r = e^{\theta}, \; -\tfrac{3}{4}\pi \leqslant \theta \, \tfrac{7}{4}\pi$

FIGURE 11.2.14

EXERCISES

Sketch the following polar curves.

1. $\theta = -\tfrac{1}{4}\pi.$ 2. $r = -3.$ 3. $r = 4.$

4. $r = 3 \cos \theta.$ 5. $r = -2 \sin \theta.$ 6. $\theta = \tfrac{2}{3}\pi.$

7. $r \csc \theta = 3.$ 8. $r + \cos \theta = 1.$ 9. $r = 1 - 2 \sin \theta.$

10. $r \sec \theta = -2.$ 11. $r = \sin 3\theta.$ 12. $r^2 = \cos 2\theta.$

13. $r = (1 - 2 \sin \theta)^{-1}.$ 14. $r = (1 - \cos \theta)^{-1}.$ 15. $r^2 = \sin 2\theta.$

16. $r = \cos 2\theta.$ 17. $r^2 = 4, \quad 0 < \theta < \tfrac{3}{4}\pi.$ 18. $r = (-1 + 2 \cos \theta)^{-1}.$

19. $\theta = \frac{2}{3}\pi, \quad -1 \le r < 2$.

20. $r = \sin\theta, \quad 0 \le \theta < \frac{1}{2}\pi$.

21. $r = 2 - \cos\theta, \quad 0 \le \theta \le \pi$.

22. $r^3 = 9r$.

23. $r = \cos 5\theta, \quad 0 \le \theta \le \frac{1}{2}\pi$.

24. $\theta = -\frac{1}{4}\pi, \quad -2 \le r < 1$.

25. $r = (2 - \cos\theta)^{-1}, \quad \frac{1}{2}\pi \le \theta \le \pi$.

26. $r = 2 + \sin\theta$.

27. $r^2 = 4r$.

28. $r = -1 + 2\cos\theta$.

29. $r = -1 + \sin\theta$.

30. $r = \cos 3\theta, \quad 0 \le \theta \le \frac{1}{2}\pi$.

31. $r = \theta, \quad -\frac{1}{2}\pi \le \theta \le \pi$.

32. $r = (2 + \sin\theta)^{-1}$.

33. $r = -1 + \sin\theta, \quad 0 \le \theta \le \frac{3}{2}\pi$.

34. $r = 2\sin\theta\cos\theta$.

35. $r = \tan\theta$.   36. $r = \cot\theta$.   37. $r = 2 + \sec\theta$.

38. $r = e^\theta, \quad -\pi \le \theta \le \pi$.   39. $r = \cos^2\theta - \sin^2\theta$.   40. $r = 3 - \csc\theta$.

11.3····THE INTERSECTION OF POLAR CURVES

The fact that a single point has many pairs of polar coordinates can cause complications. In particular, it means that a point $[r_1, \theta_1]$ can lie on a curve given by a polar equation although the coordinates r_1 and θ_1 do not satisfy the equation. For example, the coordinates of $[2, \pi]$ do not satisfy the equation $r^2 = 4\cos\theta$:

$$r^2 = 2^2 = 4 \quad \text{but} \quad 4\cos\theta = 4\cos\pi = -4.$$

Nevertheless the point $[2, \pi]$ does lie on the curve $r^2 = 4\cos\theta$. It lies on the curve because $[2, \pi] = [-2, 0]$ and the coordinates of $[-2, 0]$ satisfy the equation:

$$r^2 = (-2)^2 = 4, \qquad 4\cos\theta = 4\cos 0 = 4.$$

The difficulties are compounded when we deal with two or more curves. Here is an example.

PROBLEM. Find the points where the cardioids

$$r = a(1 - \cos\theta) \quad \text{and} \quad r = a(1 + \cos\theta) \qquad (a > 0)$$

intersect.

Solution. We begin by solving the two equations simultaneously. Adding these equations, we get $2r = 2a$ and thus $r = a$. This tells us that $\cos\theta = 0$ and therefore $\theta = \frac{1}{2}\pi + n\pi$. The points $[a, \frac{1}{2}\pi + n\pi]$ all lie on both curves. Not all of these points are distinct:

for n even, $[a, \frac{1}{2}\pi + n\pi] = [a, \frac{1}{2}\pi]$;   for n odd, $[a, \frac{1}{2}\pi + n\pi] = [a, \frac{3}{2}\pi]$.

In short, by solving the two equations simultaneously we have arrived at two common points:

$$[a, \tfrac{1}{2}\pi] = (0, a) \quad \text{and} \quad [a, \tfrac{3}{2}\pi] = (0, -a).$$

There is, however, a third point at which the curves intersect, and that is the origin O. (Figure 11.3.1)

The origin clearly lies on both curves:

for $r = a(1 - \cos\theta)$ take $\theta = 0, 2\pi$, etc.

for $r = a(1 + \cos\theta)$ take $\theta = \pi, 3\pi$, etc.

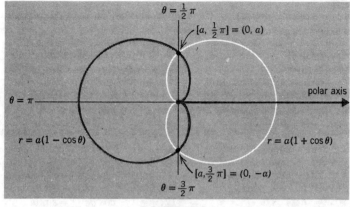

FIGURE 11.3.1

The reason that the origin does not appear when we solve the two equations simultaneously is that the curves do not pass through the origin "simultaneously"; that is, they do not pass through the origin for the same values of θ. Think of each of the equations

$$r = a(1 - \cos \theta) \quad \text{and} \quad r = a(1 + \cos \theta)$$

as giving the position of an object at time θ. At the points we found by solving the two equations simultaneously, the objects collide. (They both arrive there at the same time.) At the origin the situation is different. Both objects pass through the origin, but no collision takes place because the objects pass through the origin at *different* times. □

REMARK. Problems of incidence (does such and such a point lie on the curve with the following polar equation?) and problems of intersection (where do such and such polar curves intersect?) are usually handled more easily by first changing to rectangular coordinates. So it is with symmetry. For example, the curve

$$C: \quad r^2 = \sin \theta$$

is symmetric about the x-axis:

(1)   if $[r, \theta] \in C$,   then $[r, -\theta] \in C$.

But this is not easy to see from the polar equation because, in general, if the coordinates of the first point satisfy the equation, the coordinates of the second point do not. One way to see that (1) is valid is to note that

$$[r, -\theta] = [-r, \pi - \theta]$$

and then verify that, if the coordinates of $[r, \theta]$ satisfy the equation, then so do the coordinates of $[-r, \pi - \theta]$. But all this is very cumbersome. The easiest way to see that the curve $r^2 = \sin \theta$ is symmetric about the x-axis is to write it as

$$(x^2 + y^2)^3 = y^2.$$

The other symmetries are then also clear. □

EXERCISES

Determine whether the point lies on the curve.

1. $r^2 \cos \theta = 1$; $[1, \pi]$.
2. $r^2 = \cos 2\theta$; $[1, \frac{1}{4}\pi]$.
3. $r = \sin \frac{1}{3}\theta$; $[\frac{1}{2}, \frac{1}{2}\pi]$.
4. $r^2 = \sin 3\theta$; $[1, -\frac{5}{6}\pi]$.

5. Show that the point $[2, \pi]$ lies on both $r^2 = 4 \cos \theta$ and $r = 3 + \cos \theta$.

6. Show that the point $[2, \frac{1}{2}\pi]$ lies on both $r^2 \sin 2\theta = 4$ and $r = 2 \cos \theta$.

Find the points at which the curves intersect. Express your answers in rectangular coordinates.

7. $r = \sin \theta$, $r = -\cos \theta$.
8. $r^2 = \sin \theta$, $r = 2 - \sin \theta$.
9. $r = \cos^2 \theta$, $r = -1$.
10. $r = 2 \sin \theta$, $r = 2 \cos \theta$.
11. $r = 1 - \cos \theta$, $r = \cos \theta$.
12. $r = 1 - \cos \theta$, $r = \sin \theta$.

13. $r = \dfrac{1}{1 - \cos \theta}$, $r \sin \theta = 2$.
14. $r = \dfrac{1}{2 - \cos \theta}$, $r \cos \theta = 1$.

15. $r = \cos 3\theta$, $r = \cos \theta$.
16. $r = \sin 2\theta$, $r = \sin \theta$.

11.4····AREA IN POLAR COORDINATES

Here we develop a technique for calculating the area of a region the boundary of which is given in polar coordinates.

As a start, we suppose that α and β are two real numbers with $\alpha < \beta \le \alpha + 2\pi$. We take ρ as a function that is continuous on $[\alpha, \beta]$ and keeps a constant sign on that interval. We want the area of the polar region Γ generated by the curve

$$r = \rho(\theta), \qquad \alpha \le \theta \le \beta.$$

Such a region is portrayed in Figure 11.4.1.

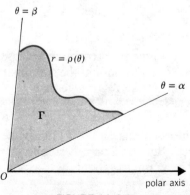

FIGURE 11.4.1

In the figure $\rho(\theta)$ remains nonnegative.   If $\rho(\theta)$ were negative, the region Γ would appear on the opposite side of the pole.   In either case, the area of Γ is given by the formula

(11.4.1)
$$A = \int_\alpha^\beta \tfrac{1}{2}[\rho(\theta)]^2 \, d\theta.$$

Proof.   We consider the case where $\rho(\theta) \geq 0$.   We take $P = \{\theta_0, \theta_1, \ldots, \theta_n\}$ as a partition of $[\alpha, \beta]$ and direct our attention to what happens between θ_{i-1} and θ_i.

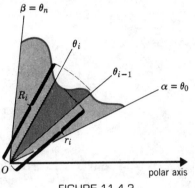

FIGURE 11.4.2

We set

$$r_i = \text{min value of } \rho \text{ on } [\theta_{i-1}, \theta_i] \quad \text{and} \quad R_i = \text{max value of } \rho \text{ on } [\theta_{i-1}, \theta_i].$$

The part of Γ that lies between θ_{i-1} and θ_i contains a circular sector of radius r_i and central angle $\Delta\theta_i = \theta_i - \theta_{i-1}$ and is contained in a circular sector of radius R_i and central angle $\Delta\theta_i = \theta_i - \theta_{i-1}$.   (See Figure 11.4.2.)   Its area A_i must therefore satisfy the inequality

$$\tfrac{1}{2} r_i^2 \, \Delta\theta_i \leq A_i \leq \tfrac{1}{2} R_i^2 \, \Delta\theta_i.†$$

By summing these inequalities from $i = 1$ to $i = n$, you can see that the total area A must satisfy the inequality

(1)
$$L_f(P) \leq A \leq U_f(P)$$

where

$$f(\theta) = \tfrac{1}{2}[\rho(\theta)]^2.$$

Since f is continuous and (1) holds for every partition P of $[a, b]$, we must have

$$A = \int_\alpha^\beta f(\theta) \, d\theta = \int_\alpha^\beta \tfrac{1}{2}[\rho(\theta)]^2 \, d\theta. \quad \square$$

---

† The area of a circular sector of radius r and central angle α is $\tfrac{1}{2}r^2\alpha$.

REMARK. If ρ is constant, Γ is a circular sector and

the area of Γ = (the constant value of $\frac{1}{2}\rho^2$ on $[\alpha, \beta]$) $\cdot$ $(\beta - \alpha)$.

If ρ varies continuously,

(11.4.2)   the area of Γ = (the average value of $\frac{1}{2}\rho^2$ on $[\alpha, \beta]$) $\cdot$ $(\beta - \alpha)$. $\square$

PROBLEM. Calculate the area enclosed by the cardioid

$$r = 1 - \cos \theta. \qquad\qquad \text{(Figure 11.2.6)}$$

Solution

$$\text{area} = \int_0^{2\pi} \tfrac{1}{2}(1 - \cos \theta)^2 \, d\theta = \frac{1}{2} \int_0^{2\pi} (1 - 2\cos\theta + \cos^2\theta) \, d\theta$$

$$= \frac{1}{2} \int_0^{2\pi} (\tfrac{3}{2} - 2\cos\theta + \cos 2\theta) \, d\theta.$$

half-angle formula: $\cos^2 \theta = \frac{1}{2} + \frac{1}{2}\cos 2\theta$

Since

$$\int_0^{2\pi} \cos\theta \, d\theta = 0 \qquad \text{and} \qquad \int_0^{2\pi} \cos 2\theta \, d\theta = 0,$$

we have

$$\text{area} = \frac{1}{2} \int_0^{2\pi} \tfrac{3}{2} \, d\theta = \tfrac{3}{4} \int_0^{2\pi} d\theta = \tfrac{3}{2}\pi. \quad \square$$

A slightly more complicated type of region is pictured in Figure 11.4.3. We can calculate the area of such a region Ω by taking the area out to $r = \rho_2(\theta)$ and subtracting from it the area out to $r = \rho_1(\theta)$. This gives the formula

(11.4.3) $$\text{area of } \Omega = \int_\alpha^\beta \tfrac{1}{2}([\rho_2(\theta)]^2 - [\rho_1(\theta)]^2) \, d\theta.$$

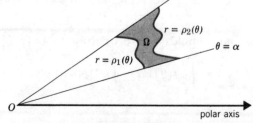

FIGURE 11.4.3

PROBLEM. Find the area of the region that consists of all points that lie within the circle $r = 2 \cos \theta$ but outside the circle $r = 1$.

Solution. The region is shown in Figure 11.4.4. Our first step is to find values of θ for the two points where the circles intersect:

$$2 \cos \theta = 1, \quad \cos \theta = \tfrac{1}{2}, \quad \theta = \tfrac{1}{3}\pi, \tfrac{5}{3}\pi.$$

Since the region is symmetric about the polar axis, the area below the polar axis equals the area above the polar axis. Thus

$$A = 2 \int_0^{\pi/3} \tfrac{1}{2}([2 \cos \theta]^2 - [1]^2) \, d\theta.$$

Carry out the integration and you'll see that

$$A = \tfrac{1}{3}\pi + \tfrac{1}{2}\sqrt{3}. \quad \square$$

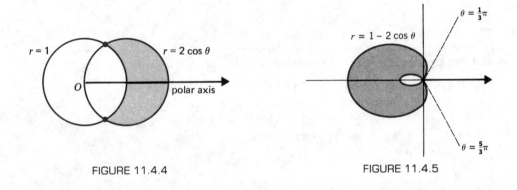

FIGURE 11.4.4   FIGURE 11.4.5

To find the area between two polar curves, we first determine the curves that serve as outer and inner boundaries of the region and the intervals of θ values over which these boundaries are traced out. Since the polar coordinates of a point are not unique, extra care is needed to determine these intervals of θ values.

EXAMPLE. The area of the region between the inner and outer loops of the limaçon

$$r = 1 - 2 \cos \theta \qquad \text{(Figure 11.4.5)}$$

can be computed as the difference between

$$\text{area within outer loop} = \int_{\pi/3}^{5\pi/3} \tfrac{1}{2}[1 - 2 \cos \theta]^2 \, d\theta$$

and

$$\text{area within inner loop} = \int_0^{\pi/3} \tfrac{1}{2}[1 - 2 \cos \theta]^2 \, d\theta + \int_{5\pi/3}^{2\pi} \tfrac{1}{2}[1 - 2 \cos \theta]^2 \, d\theta \quad \square$$

EXAMPLE. The area of the region marked Ω in Figure 11.4.6 can be represented as follows:

$$\text{area of region } \Omega = \int_{\pi/3}^{\pi} \tfrac{1}{2}[2 - \cos\theta]^2 \, d\theta - \int_{\pi/3}^{\pi/2} \tfrac{1}{2}[3\cos\theta]^2 \, d\theta. \quad \square$$

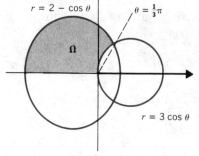

FIGURE 11.4.6

EXERCISES

Calculate the area enclosed by the following curves. Take $a > 0$.

1. $r = a\cos\theta$ from $\theta = -\tfrac{1}{2}\pi$ to $\theta = \tfrac{1}{2}\pi$.

2. $r = a\cos 3\theta$ from $\theta = -\tfrac{1}{6}\pi$ to $\theta = \tfrac{1}{6}\pi$.

3. $r = a\sqrt{\cos 2\theta}$ from $\theta = -\tfrac{1}{4}\pi$ to $\theta = \tfrac{1}{4}\pi$.

4. $r = a(1 + \cos 3\theta)$ from $\theta = -\tfrac{1}{3}\pi$ to $\theta = \tfrac{1}{3}\pi$.

5. $r^2 = a^2 \sin^2\theta$.

6. $r^2 = a^2 \sin^2 2\theta$.

Calculate the area of the region bounded by the following.

7. $r = \tan 2\theta$ and the rays $\theta = 0$, $\theta = \tfrac{1}{8}\pi$.

8. $r = \cos\theta$, $r = \sin\theta$, and the rays $\theta = 0$, $\theta = \tfrac{1}{4}\pi$.

9. $r = 2\cos\theta$, $r = \cos\theta$, and the rays $\theta = 0$, $\theta = \tfrac{1}{4}\pi$.

10. $r = 1 + \cos\theta$, $r = \cos\theta$, and the rays $\theta = 0$, $\theta = \tfrac{1}{2}\pi$.

11. $r = a(4\cos\theta - \sec\theta)$ and the rays $\theta = 0$, $\theta = \tfrac{1}{4}\pi$.

12. $r = \tfrac{1}{2}\sec^2\tfrac{1}{2}\theta$ and the vertical line through the origin.

Find the area of the region bounded by the following.

13. $r = e^\theta$, $0 \le \theta \le \pi$; $r = \theta$, $0 \le \theta \le \pi$;   the rays $\theta = 0$, $\theta = \pi$

14. $r = e^\theta$, $2\pi \le \theta \le 3\pi$; $r = \theta$, $0 \le \theta \le \pi$;   the rays $\theta = 0$, $\theta = \pi$.

15. $r = e^\theta$, $0 \le \theta \le \pi$; $r = e^{\theta/2}$, $0 \le \theta \le \pi$;   the rays $\theta = 2\pi$, $\theta = 3\pi$.

16. $r = e^\theta$, $0 \le \theta \le \pi$; $r = e^\theta$, $2\pi \le \theta \le 3\pi$;   the rays $\theta = 0$, $\theta = \pi$.

Represent the area by one or more integrals.

17. Outside $r = 2$, but inside $r = 4\sin\theta$.

18. Outside $r = 1 - \cos\theta$, but inside $r = 1 + \cos\theta$.

19. Inside $r = 4$, and to the right of $r = 2\sec\theta$.

20. Inside $r = 2$, but outside $r = 4 \cos \theta$.

21. Inside $r = 4$, and between the lines $\theta = \frac{1}{2}\pi$ and $r = 2 \sec \theta$.

22. Inside the inner loop of $r = 1 - 2 \sin \theta$.

23. Inside one petal of $r = 2 \sin 3\theta$.

24. Outside $r = 1 + \cos \theta$, but inside $r = 2 - \cos \theta$.

25. Interior to both $r = 1 - \sin \theta$ and $r = \sin \theta$.

26. Inside one petal of $r = 5 \cos 6\theta$.

27. Bounded by $r = 1/(1 - \cos \theta)$ and $r = \sec \theta$.

28. Inside $r^2 = 3$, and between the lines $\theta = 0$ and $r = \csc \theta$.

29. Inside $r^2 = 4$, and below $r(\sin \theta + \cos \theta) = -1 + \sqrt{3}$.

30. Between $r = \cos \theta$ and $r = 4/(2 - \cos \theta)$.

11.5····CURVES GIVEN PARAMETRICALLY

We begin with a pair of functions $x = x(t)$, $y = y(t)$ differentiable on the interior of an interval I. At the endpoints of I (if any) we require only continuity.

For each number t in I we can interpret $(x(t), y(t))$ as the point with x-coordinate $x(t)$ and y-coordinate $y(t)$. Then, as t ranges over I, the point $(x(t), y(t))$ traces out a path in the xy-plane. We call such a path a *parametrized curve* and refer to t as the *parameter*.

PROBLEM. Identify the curve parametrized by the functions

$$x(t) = t + 1, \quad y(t) = 2t - 5 \qquad t \text{ real}.$$

Solution. We can express $y(t)$ in term of $x(t)$:

$$y(t) = 2[x(t) - 1] - 5 = 2x(t) - 7.$$

The functions parametrize the line $y = 2x - 7$: as t ranges over the set of real numbers, the point $(x(t), y(t))$ traces out the line $y = 2x - 7$.   □

PROBLEM. Identify the curve parametrized by the functions

$$x(t) = 2t, \quad y(t) = t^2 \qquad t \text{ real}.$$

Solution. You can see that for all t

$$y(t) = \tfrac{1}{4}[x(t)]^2.$$

The functions parametrize the parabola $y = \frac{1}{4}x^2$: as t ranges over the set of real numbers, the point $(x(t), y(t))$ traces out the parabola $y = \frac{1}{4}x^2$.   □

PROBLEM. Identify the curve parametrized by the functions

$$x(t) = \sin^2 t, \quad y(t) = \cos t \qquad t \in [0, \pi].$$

Solution. Note first that

$$x(t) = \sin^2 t = 1 - \cos^2 t = 1 - [y(t)]^2.$$

The points $(x(t), y(t))$ all lie on the parabola

$$x = 1 - y^2.$$ (Figure 11.5.1)

At $t = 0$, $x = 0$ and $y = 1$; at $t = \pi$, $x = 0$ and $y = -1$. As t ranges from 0 to π, the point $(x(t), y(t))$ traverses the parabolic arc

$$x = 1 - y^2, \qquad -1 \le y \le 1$$

from the point $(0, 1)$ to the point $(0, -1)$. □

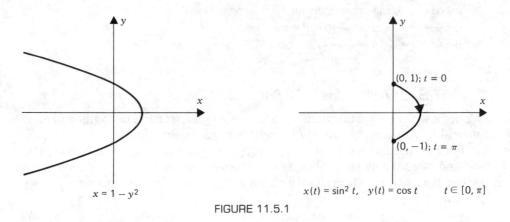

$$x = 1 - y^2 \qquad\qquad\qquad x(t) = \sin^2 t, \quad y(t) = \cos t \qquad t \in [0, \pi]$$

FIGURE 11.5.1

REMARK. Changing the domain in the previous problem to all real t does *not* give us any more of the parabola. For any given t we still have

$$0 \le x(t) \le 1 \qquad \text{and} \qquad -1 \le y(t) \le 1.$$

As t ranges over the set of real numbers, the point $(x(t), y(t))$ traces out that same parabolic arc back and forth an infinite number of times. □

The functions

(11.5.1) $\boxed{\; x(t) = x_0 + t(x_1 - x_0), \quad y(t) = y_0 + t(y_1 - y_0) \qquad t \text{ real} \;}$

parametrize the line that passes through (x_0, y_0) and (x_1, y_1).

Proof. If $x_1 = x_0$, then we have

$$x(t) = x_0, \quad y(t) = y_0 + t(y_1 - y_0).$$

As t ranges over the set of real numbers, $x(t)$ remains constantly x_0 and $y(t)$ ranges over the set of real numbers. The functions parametrize the vertical line $x = x_0$. Since $x_1 = x_0$, both (x_0, y_0) and (x_1, y_1) lie on this vertical line.

If $x_1 \ne x_0$, then we can solve the first equation for t:

$$t = \frac{x(t) - x_0}{x_1 - x_0}.$$

Substituting this into the second equation we obtain the identity

$$y(t) - y_0 = \frac{y_1 - y_0}{x_1 - x_0} [x(t) - x_0].$$

The functions parametrize the line with equation

$$y - y_0 = \frac{y_1 - y_0}{x_1 - x_0} (x - x_0).$$

This is the line determined by (x_0, y_0) and (x_1, y_1).   □

The functions

$$x(t) = a \cos t, \quad y(t) = b \sin t$$

satisfy the identity

$$\frac{[x(t)]^2}{a^2} + \frac{[y(t)]^2}{b^2} = 1.$$

As t ranges over any interval of length 2π, the point $(x(t), y(t))$ traces out the ellipse

$$\frac{x^2}{a^2} + \frac{y^2}{b^2} = 1.$$

Usually we let t range from 0 to 2π and parametrize the ellipse by setting

(11.5.2) $\quad\boxed{x(t) = a \cos t, \quad y(t) = b \sin t \qquad t \in [0, 2\pi].}$

If $b = a$, we have a circle. We can parametrize the circle

$$x^2 + y^2 = a^2$$

by setting

(11.5.3) $\quad\boxed{x(t) = a \cos t, \quad y(t) = a \sin t \qquad t \in [0, 2\pi].}$

Interpreting the parameter t as time measured in seconds, we can think of a pair of parametric equations, $x = x(t)$ and $y = y(t)$, as describing the motion of a particle in the xy-plane. Different parametrizations of the same curve represent different ways of traversing that curve.

EXAMPLE. The line that passes through the points (1, 2) and (3, 6) has equation $y = 2x$. The line segment that joins these same points is given by

$$y = 2x, \qquad 1 \leq x \leq 3.$$

We will parametrize this line segment in different ways and interpret each parametrization as the motion of a particle.
We begin by setting

$$x(t) = t, \quad y(t) = 2t \qquad t \in [1, 3].$$

At time $t = 1$, the particle is at the point $(1, 2)$. It traverses the line segment and arrives at the point $(3, 6)$ at time $t = 3$.

Now we set

$$x(t) = t + 1, \quad y(t) = 2t + 2 \qquad t \in [0, 2].$$

At time $t = 0$, the particle is at the point $(1, 2)$. It traverses the line segment and arrives at the point $(3, 6)$ at time $t = 2$.

The equations

$$x(t) = 3 - t, \quad y(t) = 6 - 2t \qquad t \in [0, 2]$$

represent a traversal of that same line segment in the opposite direction. At time $t = 0$, the particle is at $(3, 6)$. It arrives at $(1, 2)$ at time $t = 2$.

Set

$$x(t) = 3 - 4t, \quad y(t) = 6 - 8t \qquad t \in [0, \tfrac{1}{2}].$$

Now the particle traverses the same line segment in only half a second. At time $t = 0$, the particle is at $(3, 6)$. It arrives at $(1, 2)$ at time $t = \tfrac{1}{2}$.

Finally we set

$$x(t) = 2 - \cos t, \quad y(t) = 4 - 2 \cos t \qquad t \in [0, 4\pi].$$

In this instance the particle begins and ends its motion at the point $(1, 2)$, having traced and retraced the line segment twice during a span of 4π seconds. See Figure 11.5.2. □

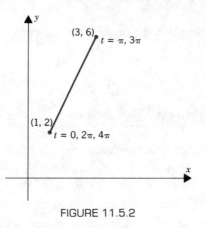

FIGURE 11.5.2

REMARK. When we eliminate the parameter t to describe a curve by an equation in x and y, we lose some of the information provided by the parameter. This loss occurs because parametric equations tell us *when* (t values) as well as *where* (x and y values). For example, all the motions described in the previous example lead to the same thing when we eliminate the parameter:

$$y = 2x, \qquad 1 \le x \le 3. \quad \square$$

EXAMPLE. We return to the ellipse

$$\frac{x^2}{a^2} + \frac{y^2}{b^2} = 1.$$

A particle with position given by the equations

$$x(t) = a \cos t, \quad y(t) = b \sin t \qquad \text{with } t \in [0, 2\pi]$$

traverses the ellipse in a counterclockwise manner. It begins at the point $(a, 0)$ and makes a full circuit in 2π seconds. If the equations of motion are

$$x(t) = a \cos 2\pi t, \quad y(t) = -b \sin 2\pi t \qquad \text{with } t \in [0, 1],$$

the particle still travels the same ellipse, but in a different manner. Once again it starts at $(a, 0)$, but this time it moves clockwise and makes the full circuit in only one second. If the equations of motion are

$$x(t) = a \sin 4\pi t, \quad y(t) = b \cos 4\pi t \qquad \text{with } t \in [0, \infty),$$

the motion begins at $(0, b)$ and goes on in perpetuity. The motion is clockwise, a complete circuit taking place every half second. □

Intersections and Collisions

PROBLEM. Two particles start at the same instant, the first along the linear path

$$x_1(t) = \tfrac{16}{3} - \tfrac{8}{3}t, \quad y_1(t) = 4t - 5 \qquad t \geq 0$$

and the second along the elliptical path

$$x_2(t) = 2 \sin \tfrac{1}{2}\pi t, \quad y_2(t) = -3 \cos \tfrac{1}{2}\pi t \qquad t \geq 0.$$

(i) At what points, if any, do the paths intersect?

(ii) At what points, if any, do the particles collide?

Solution. To see where the paths intersect, we find equations for them in x and y. The linear path can be written

$$3x + 2y - 6 = 0, \qquad x \leq \tfrac{16}{3}$$

and the elliptical path

$$\frac{x^2}{4} + \frac{y^2}{9} = 1.$$

Solving the two equations simultaneously, we get

$$x = 2, \quad y = 0 \qquad \text{and} \qquad x = 0, \quad y = 3.$$

This means that the paths intersect at the points $(2, 0)$ and $(0, 3)$. This answers part (i).

Now for part (ii). The first particle passes through $(2, 0)$ only when

$$x_1(t) = \tfrac{16}{3} - \tfrac{8}{3}t = 2 \qquad \text{and} \qquad y_1(t) = 4t - 5 = 0.$$

As you can check, this happens only when $t = \frac{5}{4}$. When $t = \frac{5}{4}$, the second particle is elsewhere. Hence no collision takes place at $(2, 0)$. There is however a collision at $(0, 3)$ because both particles get there at exactly the same time, $t = 2$:

$$x_1(2) = 0 = x_2(2), \qquad y_1(2) = 3 = y_2(2). \quad \square$$

EXERCISES

Express the curve by an equation in x and y.

1. $x(t) = t^2, \quad y(t) = 2t + 1$.
2. $x(t) = 3t - 1, \quad y(t) = 5 - 2t$.
3. $x(t) = t^2, \quad y(t) = 4t^4 + 1$.
4. $x(t) = 2t - 1, \quad y(t) = 8t^3 - 5$.
5. $x(t) = 2 \cos t, \quad y(t) = 3 \sin t$.
6. $x(t) = \sec^2 t, \quad y(t) = 2 + \tan t$.
7. $x(t) = \tan t, \quad y(t) = \sec t$.
8. $x(t) = 2 - \sin t, \quad y(t) = \cos t$.
9. $x(t) = \sin t, \quad y(t) = 1 + \cos^2 t$.
10. $x(t) = e^t, \quad y(t) = 4 - e^{2t}$.
11. $x(t) = 4 \sin t, \quad y(t) = 3 + 2 \sin t$.
12. $x(t) = \csc t, \quad y(t) = \cot t$.

Express the curve by an equation in x and y; then sketch the curve.

13. $x(t) = e^{2t}, \quad y(t) = e^{2t} - 1, \quad t \leq 0$.
14. $x(t) = 3 \cos t, \quad y(t) = 2 - \cos t, \quad 0 \leq t \leq \pi$.
15. $x(t) = \sin t, \quad y(t) = \csc t, \quad 0 < t \leq \frac{1}{4}\pi$.
16. $x(t) = 1/t, \quad y(t) = 1/t^2, \quad 0 < t < 3$.
17. $x(t) = 3 + 2t, \quad y(t) = 5 - 4t, \quad -1 \leq t \leq 2$.
18. $x(t) = \sec t, \quad y(t) = \tan t, \quad 0 \leq t \leq \frac{1}{4}\pi$.
19. $x(t) = \sin \pi t, \quad y(t) = 2t, \quad 0 \leq t \leq 4$.
20. $x(t) = t^3 - 4t, \quad y(t) = 4t - t^3, \quad -1 \leq t \leq 3$.
21. $x(t) = t^2 - 1, \quad y(t) = t^2, \quad -3 \leq t \leq 4$.
22. $x(t) = 2 \sin t, \quad y(t) = \cos t, \quad 0 \leq t \leq \frac{1}{2}\pi$.
23. $x(t) = \cot t, \quad y(t) = \csc t, \quad \frac{1}{4}\pi \leq t < \frac{1}{2}\pi$.
24. $x(t) = \sec t, \quad y(t) = \cos t, \quad 0 < t \leq \frac{1}{3}\pi$.

25. A particle with position given by the equations

$$x(t) = \sin 2\pi t, \quad y(t) = \cos 2\pi t \qquad t \in [0, 1]$$

starts at the point $(0, 1)$ and traverses the unit circle $x^2 + y^2 = 1$ once in a clockwise manner. Write equations of the form

$$x(t) = f(t), \quad y(t) = g(t) \qquad t \in [0, 1]$$

so that the particle
(a) begins at $(0, 1)$ and traverses the circle once in a counterclockwise manner;
(b) begins at $(0, 1)$ and traverses the circle twice in a clockwise manner;
(c) traverses the quarter circle from $(1, 0)$ to $(0, 1)$;
(d) traverses the three-quarter circle from $(1, 0)$ to $(0, 1)$.

26. A particle with position given by the equations

$$x(t) = 3 \cos 2\pi t, \quad y(t) = 4 \sin 2\pi t \qquad t \in [0, 1]$$

starts at the point $(3, 0)$ and traverses the ellipse $16x^2 + 9y^2 = 144$ once in a counterclock-wise manner. Write equations of the form

$$x(t) = f(t), \quad y(t) = g(t) \qquad t \in [0, 1]$$

so that the particle
(a) begins at $(3, 0)$ and traverses the ellipse once in a clockwise manner;
(b) begins at $(0, 4)$ and traverses the ellipse once in a clockwise manner;
(c) begins at $(-3, 0)$ and traverses the ellipse twice in a counterclockwise manner;
(d) traverses the upper half of the ellipse from $(3, 0)$ to $(0, 3)$.

27. Find a parametrization

$$x = x(t), \quad y = y(t) \qquad t \in (-1, 1)$$

for the horizontal line $y = 2$.

28. Find a parametrization

$$x(t) = \sin f(t), \quad y(t) = \cos f(t) \qquad t \in (0, 1)$$

which traces out the unit circle infinitely often.

Find a parametrization

$$x = x(t), \quad y = y(t) \qquad t \in [0, 1]$$

for the given curve.

29. The line segment from $(3, 7)$ to $(8, 5)$.
30. The line segment from $(2, 6)$ to $(6, 3)$.
31. The parabolic arc $x = 1 - y^2$ from $(0, -1)$ to $(0, 1)$.
32. The parabolic arc $x = y^2$ from $(4, 2)$ to $(0, 0)$.
33. The curve $y^2 = x^3$ from $(4, 8)$ to $(1, 1)$.
34. The curve $y^3 = x^2$ from $(1, 1)$ to $(8, 4)$.
35. The curve $y = f(x)$, $x \in [a, b]$.
36. The curve $x = g(y)$, $y \in [c, d]$.

37. Two particles start at the same instant, the first along the ray

$$x(t) = 2t + 6, \quad y(t) = 5 - 4t \qquad t \geq 0$$

and the second along the circular path

$$x(t) = 3 - 5 \cos \pi t, \quad y(t) = 1 + 5 \sin \pi t \qquad t \geq 0.$$

(a) At what points, if any, do these paths intersect?
(b) At what points, if any, will the particles collide?

38. Two particles start at the same instant, the first along the elliptical path

$$x_1(t) = 2 - 3 \cos \pi t, \quad y_1(t) = 3 + 7 \sin \pi t \qquad t \geq 0$$

and the second along the parabolic path

$$x_2(t) = 3t + 2, \quad y_2(t) = -\tfrac{7}{15}(3t + 1)^2 + \tfrac{157}{15} \qquad t \geq 0.$$

(a) At what points, if any, do these paths intersect?
(b) At what points, if any, will the particles collide?

To determine those points, if any, where a parametrized curve

$$C: \quad x = x(t), \quad y = y(t) \qquad t \in I$$

intersects itself, we can solve the system of equations

$$x(r) = x(s), \quad y(r) = y(s) \qquad \text{with } r \neq s.$$

Use this idea to identify the point(s) where the following curve intersects itself.

39. $x(t) = t^2 - 2t, \quad y(t) = t^3 - 3t^2 + 2t, \quad \text{real } t.$
40. $x(t) = \cos t \, (1 - 2 \sin t), \quad y(t) = \sin t \, (1 - 2 \sin t), \quad t \in [0, \pi].$
41. $x(t) = \sin 2\pi t, \quad y(t) = 2t - t^2, \quad t \in [0, 4].$
42. $x(t) = t^3 - 4t, \quad y(t) = t^3 - 3t^2 + 2t, \quad \text{real } t.$

11.6····TANGENTS TO CURVES GIVEN PARAMETRICALLY

A parametrized curve

$$C: \quad x = x(t), \quad y = y(t) \qquad \text{with } t \in I$$

can intersect itself. Thus, at any given point, it can have

(i) one tangent,   (ii) two or more tangents,   or   (iii) no tangent at all.

We illustrate these possibilities in Figure 11.6.1.

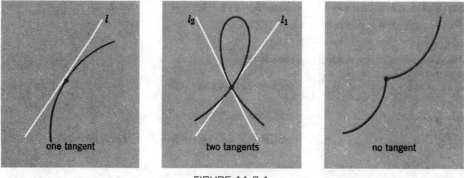

one tangent   two tangents   no tangent

FIGURE 11.6.1

As before, we are assuming that $x'(t)$ and $y'(t)$ exist, at least on the interior of I. To make sure that at least one tangent line exists at each point of c, we will make the additional *assumption* that

(11.6.1)
$$[x'(t)]^2 + [y'(t)]^2 \neq 0.$$

(Without this assumption most anything can happen. Some possibilities are considered in the exercises.)

Now choose a point (x_0, y_0) on the curve C and a time t_0 at which

$$x(t_0) = x_0 \quad \text{and} \quad y(t_0) = y_0.$$

We want the slope of the curve as it passes through the point (x_0, y_0) at time t_0.† To find this slope, we assume that $x'(t_0) \neq 0$. With $x'(t_0) \neq 0$, we can be sure that, for h sufficiently small,

$$x(t_0 + h) - x(t_0) \neq 0. \qquad \text{(explain)}$$

For such h we can form the quotient

$$\frac{y(t_0 + h) - y(t_0)}{x(t_0 + h) - x(t_0)}.$$

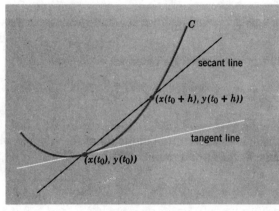

FIGURE 11.6.2

This quotient is the slope of the secant line pictured in Figure 11.6.2. The limit of this quotient as h tends to zero is the slope of the tangent line and thus the slope of the curve. Since

$$\frac{y(t_0 + h) - y(t_0)}{x(t_0 + h) - x(t_0)} = \frac{(1/h)[y(t_0 + h) - y(t_0)]}{(1/h)[x(t_0 + h) - x(t_0)]} \rightarrow \frac{y'(t_0)}{x'(t_0)} \qquad \text{as } h \rightarrow 0,$$

you can see that

(11.6.2)
$$m = \frac{y'(t_0)}{x'(t_0)}.$$

The equation for the tangent line can be written

$$y - y(t_0) = \frac{y'(t_0)}{x'(t_0)} [x - x(t_0)].$$

Multiplication by $x'(t_0)$ gives

$$y'(t_0)[x - x(t_0)] - x'(t_0)[y - y(t_0)] = 0,$$

---

† It could pass through the point (x_0, y_0) at other times also.

and thus

(11.6.3)
$$y'(t_0)[x - x_0] - x'(t_0)[y - y_0] = 0.$$

We derived this equation under the assumption that $x'(t_0) \neq 0$. If $x'(t_0) = 0$, Equation (11.6.3) still makes sense. It is simply $y'(t_0)[x - x_0] = 0$, which, since $y'(t_0) \neq 0$,† can be simplified to read

(11.6.4)
$$x = x_0.$$

In this instance the line is vertical, and we say that the curve has a *vertical tangent*.

PROBLEM. Find the tangent(s) to the curve

$$x(t) = t^3, \quad y(t) = 1 - t$$

at the point $(8, -1)$.

Solution. Since the curve passes through the point $(8, -1)$ only when $t = 2$, there can be only one tangent line at that point. With

$$x(t) = t^3, \quad y(t) = 1 - t$$

we have

$$x'(t) = 3t^2, \quad y'(t) = -1$$

and therefore

$$x'(2) = 12, \quad y'(2) = -1.$$

The tangent line has equation

$$(-1)[x - 8] - (12)[y - (-1)] = 0. \tag{11.6.3}$$

This reduces to

$$x + 12y + 4 = 0. \quad \square$$

PROBLEM. Find the points of the curve

$$x(t) = 3 - 4 \sin t, \quad y(t) = 4 + 3 \cos t$$

at which there is (i) a horizontal tangent, (ii) a vertical tangent.

Solution. Observe first of all that the derivatives

$$x'(t) = -4 \cos t \quad \text{and} \quad y'(t) = -3 \sin t$$

are never 0 simultaneously.

---

† We are assuming that $[x'(t)]^2 + [y'(t)]^2$ is never 0. Since $x'(t_0) = 0$, $y'(t_0) \neq 0$.

To find the points at which there is a horizontal tangent, we set $y'(t) = 0$. This gives $t = n\pi$. Horizontal tangents occur at all points of the form $(x(n\pi), y(n\pi))$. Since

$$x(n\pi) = 3 - 4 \sin n\pi = 3 \quad \text{and} \quad y(n\pi) = 4 + 3 \cos n\pi = \begin{cases} 7, & n \text{ even} \\ 1, & n \text{ odd} \end{cases},$$

there are horizontal tangents at $(3, 7)$ and $(3, 1)$.

To find the vertical tangents, we set $x'(t) = 0$. This gives $t = \frac{1}{2}\pi + n\pi$. Vertical tangents occur at all points of the form $(x(\frac{1}{2}\pi + n\pi), y(\frac{1}{2}\pi + n\pi))$. Since

$$x(\tfrac{1}{2}\pi + n\pi) = 3 - 4 \sin (\tfrac{1}{2}\pi + n\pi) = \begin{cases} -1, & n \text{ even} \\ 7, & n \text{ odd} \end{cases}$$

and

$$y(\tfrac{1}{2}\pi + n\pi) = 4 + 3 \cos (\tfrac{1}{2}\pi + n\pi) = 4,$$

there are vertical tangents at $(-1, 4)$ and $(7, 4)$. $\square$

PROBLEM. Find the tangent(s) to the curve

$$x(t) = t^2 - 2t + 1, \quad y(t) = t^4 - 4t^2 + 4$$

at the point $(1, 4)$.

Solution. The curve passes through the point $(1, 4)$ when $t = 0$ and when $t = 2$. (Check this out.) Differentiation gives

$$x'(t) = 2t - 2, \quad y'(t) = 4t^3 - 8t.$$

When $t = 0$,

$$x'(t) \neq 0 \quad \text{and} \quad y'(t) = 0;$$

the tangent line is horizontal and its equation can be written $y = 4$. When $t = 2$,

$$x'(t) = 2 \quad \text{and} \quad y'(t) = 16;$$

the equation for the tangent line can therefore be written

$$16(x - 1) - 2(y - 4) = 0, \tag{11.6.3}$$

or, more simply,

$$y - 4 = 8(x - 1). \quad \square$$

We can apply these ideas to a curve given in polar coordinates by an equation of the form $r = f(\theta)$. The coordinate transformations

$$x = r \cos \theta, \quad y = r \sin \theta$$

enable us to parametrize such a curve by setting

$$x(\theta) = f(\theta) \cos \theta, \quad y(\theta) = f(\theta) \sin \theta.$$

PROBLEM. Find the slope of the spiral

$$r = a\theta \quad \text{at } \theta = \tfrac{1}{2}\pi.$$

Solution. We write

$$x(\theta) = r\cos\theta = a\theta\cos\theta, \quad y(\theta) = r\sin\theta = a\theta\sin\theta.$$

Now we differentiate:

$$x'(\theta) = -a\theta\sin\theta + a\cos\theta, \quad y'(\theta) = a\theta\cos\theta + a\sin\theta.$$

Since

$$x'(\tfrac{1}{2}\pi) = -\tfrac{1}{2}\pi a \quad \text{and} \quad y'(\tfrac{1}{2}\pi) = a,$$

the slope of the curve at $\theta = \tfrac{1}{2}\pi$ is

$$\frac{y'(\tfrac{1}{2}\pi)}{x'(\tfrac{1}{2}\pi)} = -\frac{2}{\pi}. \quad \square$$

PROBLEM. Find the points of the cardioid

$$r = 1 - \cos\theta$$

at which the tangent line is vertical.

Solution. Since the cosine function has period 2π, we need only concern ourselves with θ in $[0, 2\pi)$. Parametrically we have

$$x(\theta) = (1 - \cos\theta)\cos\theta, \quad y(\theta) = (1 - \cos\theta)\sin\theta.$$

Differentiating and simplifying, we find that

$$x'(\theta) = (2\cos\theta - 1)\sin\theta, \quad y'(\theta) = (1 - \cos\theta)(1 + 2\cos\theta).$$

The only numbers in the interval $[0, 2\pi)$ at which x' is zero and y' is not zero are $\tfrac{1}{3}\pi$, π, and $\tfrac{5}{3}\pi$. The tangent line is vertical at

$$[\tfrac{1}{2}, \tfrac{1}{3}\pi], \quad [2, \pi], \quad [\tfrac{1}{2}, \tfrac{5}{3}\pi].$$

These points have rectangular coordinates

$$(\tfrac{1}{4}, \tfrac{1}{4}\sqrt{3}), \quad (-2, 0), \quad (\tfrac{1}{4}, -\tfrac{1}{4}\sqrt{3}). \quad \square$$

EXERCISES

Find an equation in x and y for the line tangent to the curve.

1. $x(t) = t$, $y(t) = t^3 - 1$; $t = 1$.
2. $x(t) = t^2$, $y(t) = t + 5$; $t = 2$.
3. $x(t) = 2t$, $y(t) = \cos\pi t$; $t = 0$.
4. $x(t) = 2t - 1$, $y(t) = t^4$; $t = 1$.
5. $x(t) = t^2$, $y(t) = (2 - t)^2$; $t = \tfrac{1}{2}$.
6. $x(t) = 1/t$, $y(t) = t^2 + 1$; $t = 1$.
7. $x(t) = \cos^3 t$, $y(t) = \sin^3 t$; $t = \tfrac{1}{4}\pi$.
8. $x(t) = e^t$, $y(t) = 3e^{-t}$; $t = 0$.

Find an equation in x and y for the line tangent to the polar curve.

9. $r = 4 - 2\sin\theta$, $\theta = 0$.
10. $r = 4\cos 2\theta$, $\theta = \tfrac{1}{4}\pi$.

11. $r = \dfrac{4}{5 - \cos\theta}$, $\theta = \tfrac{1}{2}\pi$.
12. $r = \dfrac{5}{4 - \cos\theta}$, $\theta = \tfrac{1}{6}\pi$.

13. $r = \dfrac{\sin\theta - \cos\theta}{\sin\theta + \cos\theta}$, $\theta = 0$.
14. $r = \dfrac{\sin\theta + \cos\theta}{\sin\theta - \cos\theta}$, $\theta = \tfrac{1}{2}\pi$.

Parametrize the curve by a pair of differentiable functions

$$x = x(t), \quad y = y(t) \qquad \text{with } [x'(t)]^2 + [y'(t)]^2 \neq 0.$$

Sketch the curve and determine the tangent line at the origin by the method of this section.

15. $y = x^3$.   **16.** $x = y^3$.   **17.** $y^5 = x^3$.   **18.** $y^3 = x^5$.

Find the points (x, y) at which the curve has (a) a horizontal tangent, (b) a vertical tangent. Then sketch the curve

19. $x(t) = 3t - t^3, \quad y(t) = t + 1$.   **20.** $x(t) = t^2 - 2t, \quad y(t) = t^3 - 12t$.

21. $x(t) = 3 - 4 \sin t, \quad y(t) = 4 + 3 \cos t$.   **22.** $x(t) = \sin 2t, \quad y(t) = \sin t$.

23. $x(t) = t^2 - 2t, \quad y(t) = t^3 - 3t^2 + 2t$.   **24.** $x(t) = 2 - 5 \cos t, \quad y(t) = 3 + \sin t$.

25. $x(t) = \cos t, \, y(t) = \sin 2t$.   **26.** $x(t) = 3 + 2 \sin t, \quad y(t) = 2 + 5 \sin t$.

27. Find the tangent(s) to the curve

$$x(t) = -t + 2 \cos \tfrac{1}{4}\pi t, \quad y(t) = t^4 - 4t^2$$

at the point $(2, 0)$.

28. Find the tangent(s) to the curve

$$x(t) = t^3 - t, \quad y(t) = t \sin \frac{\pi}{2} t$$

at the point $(0, 1)$.

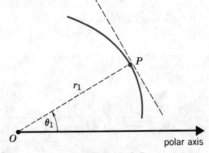

FIGURE 11.6.3

29. Let $P = [r_1, \theta_1]$ be a point on a polar curve $r = f(\theta)$ as in Figure 11.6.3. Show that, if $f'(\theta_1) = 0$ but $f(\theta_1) \neq 0$, then the tangent line at P is perpendicular to the line segment $\overline{OP}$.

30. If $0 < a < 1$, the polar curve $r = a - \cos \theta$ is a limaçon with an inner loop. Choose a so that the curve will intersect itself at the pole in a right angle.

Verify that $x'(0) = y'(0) = 0$ and that the given description holds at the point where $t = 0$. Sketch the graph.

31. $x(t) = t^3, \quad y(t) = t^2; \quad$ cusp.

32. $x(t) = t^3, \quad y(t) = t^5; \quad$ horizontal tangent.

33. $x(t) = t^5, \quad y(t) = t^3; \quad$ vertical tangent.

34. $x(t) = t^3 - 1, \quad y(t) = 2t^3; \quad$ tangent with slope 2.

35. $x(t) = t^2, \quad y(t) = t^2 + 1; \quad$ no tangent line.

36. Suppose $x(t)$ and $y(t)$ are twice differentiable.

(a) Show by example that $\dfrac{d^2y}{dx^2}$ is not $\dfrac{y''(t)}{x''(t)}$.

(b) Verify that, if $x'(t) \neq 0$, then

(11.6.5)

$$\frac{d^2y}{dx^2} = \frac{x'(t)y''(t) - y'(t)x''(t)}{[x'(t)]^3}.$$

Compute $\dfrac{d^2y}{dx^2}$ at the indicated point without eliminating the parameter.

37. $x(t) = \cos t, \quad y(t) = \sin t; \quad t = \frac{1}{6}\pi.$ **38.** $x(t) = t^3, \quad y(t) = t - 2; \quad t = 1.$

39. $x(t) = e^t, \quad y(t) = e^{-t}; \quad t = 0.$ **40.** $x(t) = \sin^2 t, \quad y(t) = \cos t; \quad t = \frac{1}{4}\pi.$

11.7 ···· THE CYCLOID AND SOME OTHER CLASSIC CURVES; A NOTE ON AREA

This section is set as a collection of exercises.

The Cycloid

Take a wheel of radius r and choose a point P on the rim of the wheel. Set the wheel on the x-axis so that P is at the origin. Now roll the wheel along the x-axis. The path described by the point P is called a *cycloid*.

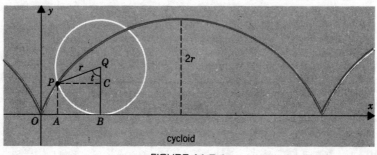

cycloid

FIGURE 11.7.1

Figure 11.7.1 shows the position of P after a turn of t radians.

1. Show that the cycloid can be parametrized by the functions

$$x(t) = r(t - \sin t), \quad y(t) = r(1 - \cos t).$$

HINT: Length of $\overline{OB}$ = length of arc $PB = rt$.

2. At the end of each arch the cycloid comes to a cusp and there is no tangent line. Verify that x' and y' are both 0 at the end of each arch.

3. Show that the line tangent to the cycloid at P (a) passes through the top of the circle and (b) intersects the x-axis at an angle of $\frac{1}{2}(\pi - t)$ radians.

4. Express the cycloid from $t = 0$ to $t = \pi$ by an equation in x and y.

The cycloid has other interesting properties. Attach a "frictionless" wire between two points as in Figure 11.7.2. What should be the shape of the wire so that a bead slides from top to bottom in the least amount of time? Answer: half of one arch of an inverted cycloid. For this reason the cycloid is called *the curve of quickest descent*.†

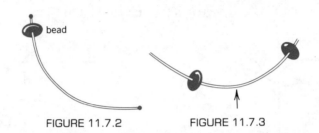

bead

FIGURE 11.7.2   FIGURE 11.7.3

Figure 11.7.3 represents a wire in the shape of an arch of an inverted cycloid. If two beads are released at the same time from different positions, which will get to the bottom first? Answer: neither; they will both get there at exactly the same time. In fact, it doesn't matter where a bead begins; it always takes exactly the same amount of time to reach bottom.††

The Trochoid

Let's return to the wheel of Figure 11.7.1. Choose a point S between P and Q (a point along the spoke $\overline{QP}$). As the wheel rolls along the axis, the point S describes a curve. Such a curve is called a *trochoid*.

Figure 11.7.4 shows the position of S after a turn of t radians.

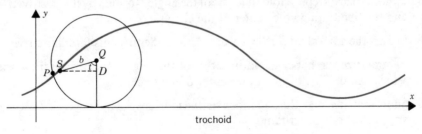

trochoid

FIGURE 11.7.4

---

† This was discovered in 1697 by Jacob Bernoulli and his brother Johann, members of the most celebrated family in the history of mathematics. From the mid-seventeenth century through the end of the eighteenth century, no fewer than eight Bernoullis made major contributions to mathematics and physics.

†† This was discovered in 1673 by Christian Huygens, who applied it to improve his invention, the pendulum clock.

5. Parametrize the trochoid in terms of angle t taking b as the length of $\overline{QS}$.

6. Draw a figure showing the path traced by a point T that is outside the wheel along an extension of the spoke $\overline{QP}$.

The Epicycloid and Hypocycloid

Let C be the circle $x^2 + y^2 = r^2$. We consider the motion of a point P on the circumference of a second circle C' of radius a as circle C' rolls around circle C. We take the point $(r, 0)$ as the initial position of point P. If C' is exterior to C, the curve traced out by P is called an *epicycloid*.† See Figure 11.7.5. If C' is interior to C, the curve traced out is called a *hypocycloid* (See Figure 11.7.6).

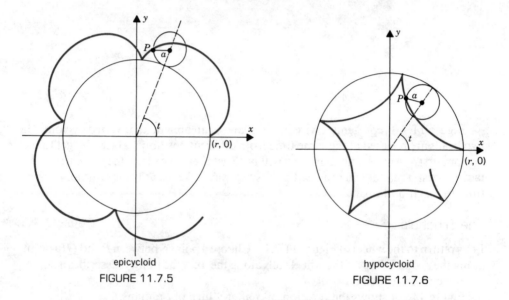

epicycloid

FIGURE 11.7.5

hypocycloid

FIGURE 11.7.6

7. Parametrize the epicycloid in terms of the angle t formed by the positive x-axis and the line through the center of the circles.

8. Sketch the epicycloid for the case $a = r$ and identify this familiar curve.

9. Parametrize the hypocycloid in terms of the angle t formed by the positive x-axis and the line through the center of the circles.

10. Show that, if $a = \frac{1}{4}r$, the equations for the four-cusped hypocycloid (also called an *astroid*) can be written

$$x(t) = r \cos^3 t, \quad y(t) = r \sin^3 t. \qquad \text{(Figure 11.7.7)}$$

Show that the equation in rectangular coordinates for an astroid is

$$x^{2/3} + y^{2/3} = r^{2/3}.$$

---

† Discovery of epicycloids is usually attributed to the Danish astronomer Ole Roemer (1644–1710). He worked with these curves in attempting to design teeth for geared wheels.

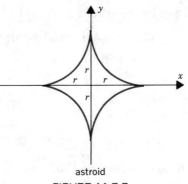

astroid

FIGURE 11.7.7

A Note on Area

Begin with the graph C of a nonnegative function f defined on an interval $[a, b]$. Suppose that C is also given parametrically by the functions

$$x = x(t), \quad y = y(t) \qquad \text{with } t \in [c, d].$$

Assume that x' and y are continuous and that $x(c) = a$ and $x(d) = b$.

11. Show that

(11.7.1)

$$\text{the area below } C = \int_c^d y(t)x'(t)\, dt.$$

HINT: $f(x(t)) = y(t)$.

12. Show that the area below one arch of the cycloid is three times the area of the rolling circle.

13. Sketch the curve

$$x(t) = rt, \quad y(t) = r(1 - \cos t) \qquad t \in [0, 2\pi].$$

and find the area below it.

14. Calculate the area of an ellipse $\dfrac{x^2}{a^2} + \dfrac{y^2}{b^2} = 1$ using

$$x(t) = -a \cos t, \quad y(t) = b \sin t \qquad t \in [0, \pi]$$

as a parametrization for the upper half

$$y = \frac{b}{a}\sqrt{a^2 - x^2}, \qquad x \in [-a, a].$$

What difficulty arises if we use the parametrization

$$x(t) = a \cos t, \quad y(t) = b \sin t \qquad t \in [0, \pi]?$$

15. Find the area enclosed by the astroid

$$x(t) = r \cos^3 t, \quad y(t) = r \sin^3 t. \qquad \text{(Figure 11.7.7)}$$

11.8····THE LEAST UPPER BOUND AXIOM

In Section 11.9 we'll be talking about the *length* of a curve. To be able to do that with precision we first need to look a little deeper into the real number system.

We begin with a set S of real numbers. As indicated in Chapter 1, a number M is called an *upper bound* for S iff

$$x \leq M \qquad \text{for all } x \in S.$$

Of course, not all sets of real numbers have upper bounds. Those that do are said to be *bounded above*.

It's obvious that every set that has a greatest element has an upper bound: if b is the greatest element of S, then

$$x \leq b \qquad \text{for all } x \in S;$$

this makes b an upper bound for S. The converse is false: the sets

$$(-\infty, 0) \quad \text{and} \quad \left\{ \frac{1}{2}, \frac{2}{3}, \frac{3}{4}, \cdots, \frac{n}{n+1}, \cdots \right\}$$

both have upper bounds (2 for instance), but neither has a greatest element.

Let's return to the first set, $(-\infty, 0)$. While $(-\infty, 0)$ does not have a greatest element, the set of its upper bounds, $[0, \infty)$, does have a least element, 0. We call 0 the *least upper bound of* $(-\infty, 0)$.

Now let's reexamine the second set. While the set of quotients

$$\frac{n}{n+1} = 1 - \frac{1}{n+1}$$

does not have a greatest element, the set of its upper bounds, $[1, \infty)$, does have a least element, 1. We call 1 the *least upper bound* of that set of quotients.

We are ready now to make explicit one of the key *assumptions* that we make about the real number system. It is called the *least upper bound axiom*.

AXIOM 11.8.1   THE LEAST UPPER BOUND AXIOM

Every nonempty set of real numbers that has an upper bound has a *least* upper bound.

To indicate the least upper bound of a set S, we will write lub S. Here are some examples:

1. $\text{lub}\,(-\infty, 0) = 0,$ $\text{lub}\,(-\infty, 0] = 0.$

2. $\text{lub}\,(-4, -1) = -1,$ $\text{lub}\,(-4, -1] = -1.$

3. $\text{lub}\left\{\dfrac{1}{2}, \dfrac{2}{3}, \dfrac{3}{4}, \cdots, \dfrac{n}{n+1}, \cdots\right\} = 1.$

4. $\text{lub}\left\{-\dfrac{1}{2}, -\dfrac{1}{8}, -\dfrac{1}{27}, \cdots, -\dfrac{1}{n^3}, \cdots\right\} = 0.$

5. $\text{lub}\,\{x: x^2 < 3\} = \text{lub}\,\{x: -\sqrt{3} < x < \sqrt{3}\} = \sqrt{3}.$ $\square$

The least upper bound of a set has a special property that deserves particular attention. The idea is this: the fact that M is the least upper bound of the set S does not tell us that M is in S (it need not be), but it does tell us that we can approximate M as closely as we may wish by elements of S. We state this as a theorem.

THEOREM 11.8.2

If M is the least upper bound of the set S and ϵ is a positive number, then there is at least one number s in S such that

$$M - \epsilon < s \leq M.$$

Proof. Let $\epsilon > 0$. Since M is an upper bound for S, the condition $s \leq M$ is satisfied by all numbers s in S. All we have to show therefore is that there is some number s in S such that

$$M - \epsilon < s.$$

Suppose on the contrary that there is no such number in S. We then have

$$x \leq M - \epsilon \qquad \text{for all } x \in S,$$

so that $M - \epsilon$ becomes an upper bound for S. But this cannot happen, for it makes $M - \epsilon$ an upper bound that is *less* than the least upper bound M. $\square$

The theorem we just proved is illustrated in Figure 11.8.1. Take S as the set of points marked in the figure. If $M = \text{lub}\,S$, then S has at least one element in every half-open interval of the form $(M - \epsilon, M]$.

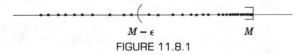

$M - \epsilon$ M

FIGURE 11.8.1

EXAMPLES

1. Let

$$S = \left\{\frac{1}{2}, \frac{2}{3}, \frac{3}{4}, \cdots, \frac{n}{n+1}, \cdots\right\}$$

and take

$$\epsilon = 0.0001.$$

Since 1 is the least upper bound of S, there must be a number s in S such that

$$1 - 0.0001 < s \leq 1.$$

There is: take, for example, $s = \frac{99999}{100000}$.   □

2. Let

$$S = \{1, 2, 3\}$$

and take

$$\epsilon = 0.000001.$$

Since 3 is the least upper bound of S, there must be a number s in S such that

$$3 - 0.000001 < s \leq 3.$$

There is: $s = 3$.   □

We come now to lower bounds. In the first place, a number m is called a *lower bound* for S iff

$$m \leq x \quad \text{for all } x \in S.$$

Sets that have lower bounds are said to be *bounded below*. Not all sets have lower bounds; those that do have *greatest lower bounds*. This need not be taken as an axiom. Using the least upper bound axiom, we can prove it as a theorem.

THEOREM 11.8.3

Every nonempty set of real numbers that has a lower bound has a *greatest lower bound*.

Proof. Suppose that S is nonempty and that it has a lower bound x. Then

$$x \leq s \quad \text{for all } s \in S.$$

It follows that

$$-s \leq -x \quad \text{for all } s \in S;$$

that is,

$$\{-s : s \in S\} \quad \text{has an upper bound } -x.$$

From the least upper bound axiom we conclude that $\{-s : s \in S\}$ has a least upper bound; call it x_0. Since

$$-s \leq x_0 \quad \text{for all } s \in S,$$

you can see that

$$-x_0 \leq s \quad \text{for all } s \in S,$$

and thus $-x_0$ is a lower bound for S. We now assert that $-x_0$ is the greatest lower bound of the set S. To see this, note that, if there existed a number x_1 satisfying

$$-x_0 < x_1 \leq s \qquad \text{for all } s \in S,$$

then we would have

$$-s \leq -x_1 < x_0 \qquad \text{for all } s \in S,$$

and thus x_0 would not be the *least* upper bound of $\{-s : s \in S\}$.† □

As in the case of the least upper bound, the greatest lower bound of a set need not be in the set but can be approximated as closely as we wish by members of the set. In short, we have the following theorem, the proof of which is left as an exercise.

THEOREM 11.8.4

If m is the greatest lower bound of the set S and ϵ is a positive number, then there is at least one number s in S such that

$$m \leq s < m + \epsilon.$$

The theorem is illustrated in Figure 11.8.2. If $m = \text{glb } S$ (that is, if m is the greatest lower bound of the set S), then S has at least one element in every half-open interval of the form $[m, m + \epsilon)$.

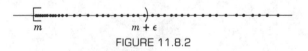

m $\qquad\qquad\qquad\qquad$ $m + \epsilon$

FIGURE 11.8.2

EXERCISES

Find the least upper bound (if it exists) and the greatest lower bound (if it exists) for each of the following sets.

1. $(0, 2)$.
2. $[0, 2]$.
3. $(0, \infty)$.
4. $(-\infty, 1)$.
5. $\{x : x^2 < 4\}$.
6. $\{x : |x - 1| < 2\}$.
7. $\{x : x^3 \geq 8\}$.
8. $\{x : x^4 \leq 16\}$.
9. $\{2\frac{1}{2}, 2\frac{1}{3}, 2\frac{1}{4}, \ldots\}$.
10. $\{-1, -\frac{1}{2}, -\frac{1}{3}, -\frac{1}{4}, \ldots\}$.
11. $\{0.9, 0.99, 0.999, \ldots\}$.
12. $\{-2, 2, -2.1, 2.1, -2.11, 2.11, \ldots\}$.
13. $\{x : \ln x < 1\}$.
14. $\{x : \ln x > 0\}$.
15. $\{x : x^2 + x - 1 < 0\}$.
16. $\{x : x^2 + x + 2 \geq 0\}$.
17. $\{x : x^2 > 4\}$.
18. $\{x : |x - 1| > 2\}$.
19. $\{x : \sin x \geq -1\}$.
20. $\{x : e^x < 1\}$.

---

† We proved Theorem 11.8.3 by assuming the least upper bound axiom. We could have proceeded the other way. We could have set Theorem 11.8.3 as an axiom, and then proved the least upper bound axiom as a theorem.

Illustrate the validity of Theorem 11.8.4 taking S and ϵ as given below.

21. $S = \{\frac{1}{11}, (\frac{1}{11})^2, (\frac{1}{11})^3, \ldots, (\frac{1}{11})^n, \ldots\}$, $\epsilon = 0.001$.

22. $S = \{1, 2, 3, 4\}$, $\epsilon = 0.0001$.

23. $S = \left\{\dfrac{1}{10}, \dfrac{1}{1000}, \dfrac{1}{100000}, \cdots, \dfrac{1}{10^{2n-1}}, \cdots\right\}$, $\epsilon = \dfrac{1}{10^k}$ $(k \geq 1)$.

24. $S = \left\{\dfrac{1}{2}, \dfrac{1}{4}, \dfrac{1}{8}, \cdots, \dfrac{1}{2^n}, \cdots,\right\}$, $\epsilon = \dfrac{1}{4^k}$ $(k \geq 1)$.

25. Prove Theorem 11.8.4 by imitating the proof of Theorem 11.8.2.

11.9····THE LENGTH OF A PARAMETRIZED CURVE

Definition of Arc Length

We come now to the notion of arc length. In Figure 11.9.1 we have sketched a curve C, which we assume is parametrized by a pair of *continuously differentiable* functions†

$$x = x(t), \quad y = y(t) \qquad t \in [a, b].$$

What we want to do is assign a length to this curve C.

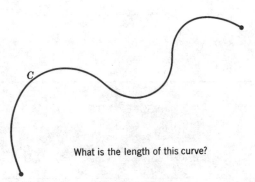

What is the length of this curve?

FIGURE 11.9.1

Here our experience in Chapter 5 can be used as a model. To decide what should be meant by the area of a region Ω, we approximated Ω by the union of a finite number of rectangles. To decide what should be meant by the length of C, we will approximate C by the union of a finite number of line segments.

Each point t in $[a, b]$ gives rise to a point $P = P(x(t), y(t))$ that lies on C. By choosing a finite number of points in $[a, b]$,

$$a = t_0 < t_1 < \cdots < t_{i-1} < t_i < \cdots < t_{n-1} < t_n = b,$$

we obtain a finite number of points on C,

$$P_0, P_1, \ldots, P_{i-1}, P_i, \ldots, P_{n-1}, P_n.$$

---

† By this we mean functions that have continuous first derivatives.

We join these points consecutively by line segments and call the resulting path,

$$L = \overline{P_0 P_1} \cup \cdots \cup \overline{P_{i-1} P_i} \cup \cdots \cup \overline{P_{n-1} P_n},$$

a *polygonal path* inscribed in C. (See Figure 11.9.2.)

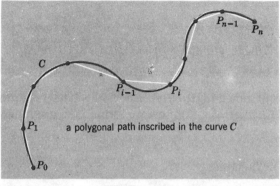

a polygonal path inscribed in the curve C

FIGURE 11.9.2

The length of such a polygonal path is the sum of the distances between consecutive vertices:

$$\text{length of } L = l(L) = d(P_0, P_1) + \cdots + d(P_{i-1}, P_i) + \cdots + d(P_{n-1}, P_n).$$

The path L serves as an approximation to the curve C, but obviously a better approximation can be obtained by adding more vertices to L. At this point let's ask ourselves exactly what it is we require of the number that we shall call the length of C. Certainly we require that

$$l(L) \le \text{the length of } C \qquad \text{for each } L \text{ inscribed in } C.$$

But that is not enough. There is another requirement that seems reasonable. If we can choose L to approximate C as closely as we wish, then we should be able to choose L so that $l(L)$ approximates the length of C as closely as we wish; namely, for each positive number ϵ there should exist a polygonal path L such that

$$(\text{length of } C) - \epsilon < l(L) \le \text{length of } C.$$

Theorem 11.8.2 tells us that we can achieve this result by defining the length of C as the least upper bound of all the $l(L)$. This in fact is what we do.

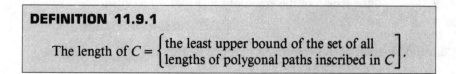

DEFINITION 11.9.1

$$\text{The length of } C = \left\{ \begin{array}{l} \text{the least upper bound of the set of all} \\ \text{lengths of polygonal paths inscribed in } C \end{array} \right\}.$$

Arc-Length Formulas

Now that we have explained what we mean by the length of a parametrized curve, it's time to describe a practical way to compute it. The basic result is easy to state. If C is parametrized by a pair of continuously differentiable functions

$$x = x(t), \quad y = y(t) \qquad t \in [a, b],$$

then

(11.9.2) $$\text{the length of } C = \int_a^b \sqrt{[x'(t)]^2 + [y'(t)]^2}\, dt.$$

Obviously, this is not something to be taken on faith. It has to be proved. We will do so, but not until Chapter 15. For now we assume the result and carry out some computations.

EXAMPLE.   The functions

$$x(t) = r \cos t, \quad y(t) = r \sin t \qquad t \in [0, 2\pi]$$

parametrize a circle C of radius r. Formula (11.9.2) gives

$$l(C) = \int_0^{2\pi} \sqrt{r^2 \sin^2 t + r^2 \cos^2 t}\, dt = \int_0^{2\pi} r\, dt = 2\pi r,$$

which is reassuring.   □

Suppose now that C is the graph of a continuously differentiable function

$$y = f(x), \qquad x \in [a, b].$$

Then we can parametrize C by setting

$$x(t) = t, \quad y(t) = f(t) \qquad t \in [a, b].$$

Since

$$x'(t) = 1 \qquad \text{and} \qquad y'(t) = f'(t),$$

Formula (11.9.2) gives

$$l(C) = \int_a^b \sqrt{1 + [f'(t)]^2}\, dt.$$

Replacing t by x we can write

(11.9.3) $$\text{the length of the graph of } f = \int_a^b \sqrt{1 + [f'(x)]^2}\, dx.$$

A direct derivation of this formula is outlined in Exercise 30.

EXAMPLE. If

$$f(x) = \frac{x^3}{6} + \frac{1}{2x},$$

then

$$f'(x) = \frac{3x^2}{6} - \frac{1}{2x^2} = \frac{x^2}{2} - \frac{1}{2x^2}$$

and

$$1 + [f'(x)]^2 = 1 + \left(\frac{x^4}{4} - \frac{1}{2} + \frac{1}{4x^4}\right) = \frac{x^4}{4} + \frac{1}{2} + \frac{1}{4x^4} = \left(\frac{x^2}{2} + \frac{1}{2x^2}\right)^2.$$

The length of the graph of f from $x = 1$ to $x = 3$ is

$$\int_1^3 \sqrt{1 + [f'(x)]^2}\, dx = \int_1^3 \sqrt{\left(\frac{x^2}{2} + \frac{1}{2x^2}\right)^2}\, dx$$

$$= \int_1^3 \left(\frac{x^2}{2} + \frac{1}{2x^2}\right) dx = \left[\frac{x^3}{6} - \frac{1}{2x}\right]_1^3 = \frac{26}{6} - \left(-\frac{1}{3}\right) = \frac{14}{3}. \quad \square$$

EXAMPLE. The graph of the function

$$f(x) = x^2, \qquad x \in [0, 1]$$

is a parabolic arc. The length of this arc is given by

$$\int_0^1 \sqrt{1 + [f'(x)]^2}\, dx = \int_0^1 \sqrt{1 + 4x^2}\, dx = 2 \int_0^1 \sqrt{(\tfrac{1}{2})^2 + x^2}\, dx$$

$$= \left[x\sqrt{(\tfrac{1}{2})^2 + x^2} + (\tfrac{1}{2})^2 \ln\left(x + \sqrt{(\tfrac{1}{2})^2 + x^2}\right)\right]_0^1$$

by 9.6.1

$$= \tfrac{1}{2}\sqrt{5} + \tfrac{1}{4} \ln(2 + \sqrt{5}). \quad \square$$

Suppose now that C is the graph of a polar function

$$r = \rho(\theta), \qquad \alpha \le \theta \le \beta.$$

We can parametrize C by setting

$$x(\theta) = \rho(\theta) \cos \theta, \quad y(\theta) = \rho(\theta) \sin \theta \qquad \theta \in [\alpha, \beta].$$

A straightforward calculation that we leave to you shows that

$$[x'(\theta)]^2 + [y'(\theta)]^2 = [\rho(\theta)]^2 + [\rho'(\theta)]^2.$$

The arc-length formula now reads

(11.9.4)
$$l(C) = \int_\alpha^\beta \sqrt{[\rho(\theta)]^2 + [\rho'(\theta)]^2}\, d\theta.$$

EXAMPLE. For fixed $a > 0$ the equation

$$r = a$$

represents a circle of radius a. Here

$$\rho(\theta) = a \quad \text{and} \quad \rho'(\theta) = 0.$$

The circumference of this circle is

$$\int_0^{2\pi} \sqrt{[\rho(\theta)]^2 + [\rho'(\theta)]^2}\, d\theta = \int_0^{2\pi} \sqrt{a^2 + 0^2}\, d\theta = \int_0^{2\pi} a\, d\theta = 2\pi a. \quad \square$$

EXAMPLE. In the case of the cardioid

$$r = 1 - \cos\theta,$$

we have

$$\rho(\theta) = 1 - \cos\theta, \quad \rho'(\theta) = \sin\theta.$$

Here

$$[\rho(\theta)]^2 + [\rho'(\theta)]^2 = 1 - 2\cos\theta + \cos^2\theta + \sin^2\theta = 2(1 - \cos\theta).$$

The identity

$$\tfrac{1}{2}(1 - \cos\theta) = \sin^2 \tfrac{1}{2}\theta$$

gives

$$[\rho(\theta)]^2 + [\rho'(\theta)]^2 = 4\sin^2 \tfrac{1}{2}\theta.$$

The length of this cardioid is 8:

$$\int_0^{2\pi} \sqrt{[\rho(\theta)]^2 + [\rho'(\theta)]^2}\, d\theta = \int_0^{2\pi} 2\sin \tfrac{1}{2}\theta\, d\theta = 4\left[-\cos \tfrac{1}{2}\theta \right]_0^{2\pi} = 8. \quad \square$$

EXERCISES

Find the length of the graph.

1. $f(x) = mx + b$ from $x = c$ to $x = d$.
2. $f(x) = x^{3/2}$ from $x = 0$ to $x = 44$.
3. $f(x) = \tfrac{1}{3}\sqrt{x}(x - 3)$ from $x = 0$ to $x = 3$.
4. $f(x) = \tfrac{2}{3}(x - 1)^{3/2}$ from $x = 1$ to $x = 2$.
5. $f(x) = \tfrac{1}{3}(x^2 + 2)^{3/2}$ from $x = 0$ to $x = 1$.
6. $f(x) = \tfrac{1}{8}x^2 - \ln x$ from $x = 1$ to $x = 4$.
7. $f(x) = \ln(\sec x)$ from $x = -\tfrac{1}{4}\pi$ to $x = \tfrac{1}{4}\pi$.
8. $f(x) = \tfrac{1}{2}x^2$ from $x = 0$ to $x = 1$.
9. $f(x) = \tfrac{1}{2}x\sqrt{3 - x^2} + \tfrac{3}{2}\sin^{-1}(\tfrac{1}{3}\sqrt{3}x)$ from $x = 0$ to $x = 1$.
10. $f(x) = \ln(\sin x)$ from $x = \tfrac{1}{6}\pi$ to $x = \tfrac{1}{2}\pi$.
11. $f(x) = \ln x$ from $x = 1$ to $x = \sqrt{3}$.
12. $f(x) = 2e^{x/2}$ from $x = 0$ to $x = \ln 8$.
13. $f(x) = e^x$ from $x = 0$ to $x = \tfrac{1}{2}\ln 3$.
14. $f(x) = \cosh x$ from $x = 0$ to $x = \ln 2$.

Find the length of the parametrized curve.

15. $x(t) = t^2$, $y(t) = 2t$ from $t = 0$ to $t = \sqrt{3}$.
16. $x(t) = t - 1$, $y(t) = \tfrac{1}{2}t^2$ from $t = 0$ to $t = 1$.

17. $x(t) = t^2$, $y(t) = t^3$ from $t = 0$ to $t = 1$.

18. $x(t) = \frac{1}{2}t^2$, $y(t) = \frac{2}{3}t^{3/2}$ from $t = 1$ to $t = 4$.

19. $x(t) = e^t \sin t$, $y(t) = e^t \cos t$ from $t = 0$ to $t = \pi$.

20. $x(t) = \cos t + t \sin t$, $y(t) = \sin t - t \cos t$ from $t = 0$ to $t = \pi$.

Find the length of the polar curve.

21. $r = e^\theta$ from $\theta = 0$ to $\theta = 4\pi$.   (logarithmic spiral)

22. $r = ae^\theta$ from $\theta = -2\pi$ to $\theta = 2\pi$.

23. $r = e^{2\theta}$ from $\theta = 0$ to $\theta = 2\pi$.

24. $r = 1 + \cos \theta$ from $\theta = 0$ to $\theta = 2\pi$.

25. $r = a\theta$ from $\theta = 0$ to $\theta = 2\pi$.   (spiral of Archimedes)

26. $r = 2a \sec \theta$ from $\theta = 0$ to $\theta = \frac{1}{4}\pi$.

27. At time t a particle has position

$$x(t) = 1 + \tan^{-1} t, \quad y(t) = 1 - \ln \sqrt{1 + t^2}.$$

Find the total distance traveled from time $t = 0$ to time $t = 1$.

28. At time t a particle has position

$$x(t) = 1 - \cos t, \quad y(t) = t - \sin t.$$

Find the total distance traveled from time $t = 0$ to time $t = 2\pi$.

29. Let f be a positive nonconstant function with the property that for every interval $[a, b]$ the length of the graph equals the area of the region under the graph. Find f, given that $f(0) = 1$.

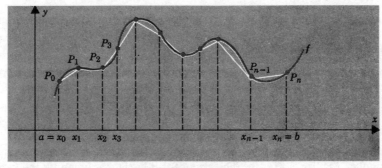

FIGURE 11.9.3

30. Figure 11.9.3 shows the graph of a continuously differentiable function f from $x = a$ to $x = b$ together with a polygonal approximation. Show that the length of this polygonal approximation can be written as the following Riemann sum:

$$\sqrt{1 + [f'(x_1^*)]^2}\, \Delta x_1 + \sqrt{1 + [f'(x_2^*)]^2}\, \Delta x_2 + \cdots + \sqrt{1 + [f'(x_n^*)]^2}\, \Delta x_n.$$

As $\|P\| = \max \Delta x_i$ tends to 0, such Riemann sums tend to

$$\int_a^b \sqrt{1 + [f'(x)]^2}\, dx.$$

31. Show that a homogeneous, flexible, inelastic rope hanging from two fixed points assumes the shape of a *catenary*:

$$f(x) = a \cosh\left(\frac{x}{a}\right) = \frac{a}{2}\left(e^{x/a} + e^{-x/a}\right).$$

HINT: Refer to Figure 11.9.4.   That part of the rope that corresponds to the interval $[0, x]$ is subject to the following forces:

(1) its weight, which is proportional to its length;
(2) a horizontal pull at 0, $p(0)$;
(3) a tangential pull at x, $p(x)$.

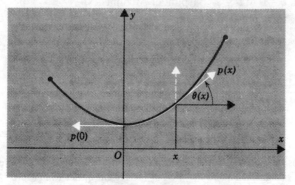

FIGURE 11.9.4

Balancing the vertical forces, we have

$$k \int_0^x \sqrt{1 + [f'(t)]^2} \, dt = p(x) \sin \theta. \qquad \text{(weight = vertical pull at } x\text{)}$$

Balancing the horizontal forces, we have

$$p(0) = p(x) \cos \theta. \qquad \text{(pull at 0 = horizontal pull at } x\text{)}$$

11.10··AREA OF A SURFACE OF REVOLUTION

Let f be a nonnegative function with derivative f' continuous on $[a, b]$.   By revolving the graph of f from $x = a$ to $x = b$ about the x-axis, we obtain a surface of revolution (see Figure 11.10.1.).   The area of this surface is given by the formula

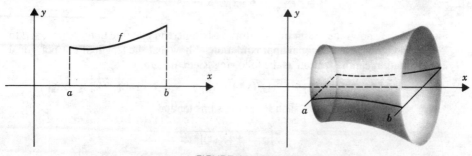

FIGURE 11.10.1

(11.10.1)
$$S = \int_a^b 2\pi f(x) \sqrt{1 + [f'(x)]^2}\, dx.$$

Idea of the Proof. We take a polygonal path as an approximation of the curve and revolve it about the x-axis to approximate the surface (see Figure 11.10.2). Each line segment in the path generates a frustum of a cone whose lateral surface area is given by the formula

(11.10.2) $S = \pi(r + R)l.$ (Exercise 17)

See Figure 11.10.3. We can approximate the area of the surface by summing quantities of this form.

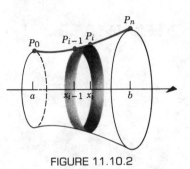

FIGURE 11.10.2

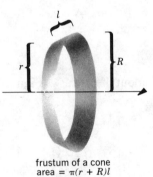

frustum of a cone
area $= \pi(r + R)l$

FIGURE 11.10.3

Proof. We begin with a partition $P = \{x_0, x_1, \ldots, x_n\}$ of $[a, b]$ and focus our attention on the part of the surface generated by the ith subinterval $[x_{i-1}, x_i]$. The line segment that joins P_{i-1} to P_i has length

$$\sqrt{[x_i - x_{i-1}]^2 + [f(x_i) - f(x_{i-1})]^2} = \sqrt{1 + \left(\frac{f(x_i) - f(x_{i-1})}{x_i - x_{i-1}}\right)^2}\, \Delta x_i.$$

Thus, by Formula (11.10.2) the approximating surface has area

(1) $\pi[f(x_{i-1}) + f(x_i)] \sqrt{1 + \left(\dfrac{f(x_i) - f(x_{i-1})}{x_i - x_{i-1}}\right)^2}\, \Delta x_i.$

By the mean-value theorem (4.1.1) there exists x_i^* between x_{i-1} and x_i such that

(2) $f'(x_i^*) = \dfrac{f(x_i) - f(x_{i-1})}{x_i - x_{i-1}}.$

We know that the average of two numbers, say $f(x_i)$ and $f(x_{i-1})$, lies between the two numbers. It follows by the intermediate-value theorem (2.6.1) that there exists x_i^{**} between x_{i-1} and x_i such that

(3) $f(x_i^{**}) = \tfrac{1}{2}[f(x_{i-1}) + f(x_i)].$

We use (2) and (3) to rewrite (1) as

(4) $$2\pi f(x_i^{**}) \sqrt{1 + [f'(x_i^*)]^2}\, \Delta x_i.$$

Summing (4) from $i = 1$ to $i = n$, we do *not* produce a Riemann sum since we cannot guarantee that $x_i^* = x_i^{**}$. Nevertheless, as is shown in advanced calculus, the limit of this sum as $\|P\| \to 0$ is the integral

$$\int_a^b 2\pi f(x) \sqrt{1 + [f'(x)]^2}\, dx$$

as long as f' is continuous.†   □

PROBLEM. Use (11.10.1) to derive the formula for the lateral area of a cone

$$S = \pi r \sqrt{h^2 + r^2}.$$

Solution. A cone of base radius r and height h can be generated by revolving the graph of

$$f(x) = \frac{r}{h} x \qquad \text{from } x = 0 \text{ to } x = h$$

about the x-axis. (Figure 11.10.4)

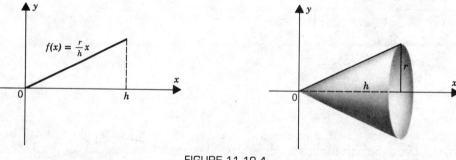

FIGURE 11.10.4

According to (11.10.1)

$$\text{lateral area} = \int_0^h 2\pi f(x) \sqrt{1 + [f'(x)]^2}\, dx$$

$$= 2\pi \int_0^h \frac{r}{h} x \sqrt{1 + \frac{r^2}{h^2}}\, dx$$

$$= \frac{2\pi r \sqrt{h^2 + r^2}}{h^2} \int_0^h x\, dx = \pi r \sqrt{h^2 + r^2}.\quad \square$$

PROBLEM. Find the area of the surface generated by revolving the graph of

$$f(x) = \sin x \qquad \text{from } x = 0 \text{ to } x = \tfrac{1}{2}\pi$$

about the x-axis.

† The advanced result needed here is known as Bliss's Theorem.

Solution. In this case we have

$$f(x) = \sin x, \qquad f'(x) = \cos x$$

and thus

$$\text{surface area} = \int_0^{\pi/2} 2\pi \sin x \sqrt{1 + \cos^2 x}\; dx.$$

To calculate this integral, set

$$u = \cos x, \qquad du = -\sin x\; dx.$$

At $x = 0$, $u = 1$; at $x = \tfrac{1}{2}\pi$, $u = 0$. Therefore

$$\int_0^{\pi/2} 2\pi \sin x \sqrt{1 + \cos^2 x}\; dx = -2\pi \int_1^0 \sqrt{1 + u^2}\; du$$

$$= 2\pi \int_0^1 \sqrt{1 + u^2}\; du$$

$$= 2\pi \left[\tfrac{1}{2} u \sqrt{1 + u^2} + \tfrac{1}{2} \ln\left(u + \sqrt{1 + u^2}\right) \right]_0^1$$

by 9.6.1 ⟶

$$= \pi[\sqrt{2} + \ln(1 + \sqrt{2})]. \quad \square$$

Suppose now that C is a curve in the upper half-plane parametrized by a pair of continuously differentiable functions

$$x = x(t), \quad y = y(t) \qquad t \in [c, d].$$

If C is *simple* (that is, if no two values of t between c and d give rise to the same point of C), then the area of the surface generated by revolving C about the x-axis is given by the formula

(11.10.3)
$$S = \int_c^d 2\pi y(t) \sqrt{[x'(t)]^2 + [y'(t)]^2}\; dt.$$

We will derive this formula only for a special case. We will assume that C is the graph of a continuously differentiable function f and that x' does not change signs between c and d. Under these conditions

$$f(x(t)) = y(t) \qquad \text{for all } t \in [c, d]$$

and by the chain rule

$$f'(x(t))\, x'(t) = y(t).$$

If $x' > 0$ between c and d, then $x = x(t)$ increases on $[c, d]$, and thus f is defined on $[x(c), x(d)]$. Then by (11.10.1)

$$S = \int_{x(c)}^{x(d)} 2\pi f(u) \sqrt{1 + [f'(u)]^2}\; du.$$

The substitution

$$u = x(t), \qquad du = x'(t)\, dt$$

gives

$$S = \int_c^d 2\pi f(x(t)) \sqrt{1 + [f'(x(t))]^2}\, x'(t)\, dt$$

$$= \int_c^d 2\pi f(x(t)) \sqrt{1 + [f'(x(t))]^2} \cdot \sqrt{[x'(t)]^2}\, dt$$

$$= \int_c^d 2\pi f(x(t)) \sqrt{[x'(t)]^2 + [f'(x(t))x'(t)]^2}\, dt$$

$$= \int_c^d 2\pi y(t) \sqrt{[x'(t)]^2 + [y'(t)]^2}\, dt.$$

If $x' < 0$ between c and d, then $x = x(t)$ decreases on $[c, d]$, and thus f is defined on $[x(d), x(c)]$. Then, again by (11.10.1),

$$S = \int_{x(d)}^{x(c)} 2\pi f(u) \sqrt{1 + [f'(u)]^2}\, du.$$

The substitution

$$u = x(t), \qquad du = x'(t)\, dt$$

gives

$$S = \int_d^c 2\pi f(x(t)) \sqrt{1 + [f'(x(t))]^2}\, x'(t)\, dt$$

$$= \int_d^c 2\pi f(x(t)) \sqrt{1 + [f'(x(t))]^2} \cdot (-\sqrt{[x'(t)]^2})\, dt\dagger$$

$$= \int_c^d 2\pi f(x(t)) \sqrt{[x'(t)]^2 + [f'(x(t))\, x'(t)]^2}\, dt$$

$$= \int_c^d 2\pi y(t) \sqrt{[x'(t)]^2 + [y'(t)]^2}\, dt. \quad \square$$

PROBLEM. Derive a formula for the surface area of a sphere.

Solution. We can generate a sphere of radius r by revolving the arc

$$x(t) = r \cos t, \quad y(t) = r \sin t \qquad t \in [0, \pi]$$

about the x-axis. Differentiation gives

$$x'(t) = -r \sin t, \quad y'(t) = r \cos t.$$

By Formula (11.10.3)

$$S = 2\pi \int_0^\pi r \sin t \sqrt{r^2(\sin^2 t + \cos^2 t)}\, dt$$

$$= 2\pi r^2 \int_0^\pi \sin t\, dt = 2\pi r^2 \left[-\cos t \right]_0^\pi = 4\pi r^2. \quad \square$$

---

† For $a < 0$, $a = -|a| = -\sqrt{a^2}$.

PROBLEM. Find the area of the surface generated by revolving the curve

$$y^2 - 2 \ln y = 4x \qquad \text{from } y = 1 \text{ to } y = 2$$

about the *x*-axis.

Solution. We can represent the curve parametrically by setting

$$x(t) = \tfrac{1}{4}(t^2 - 2 \ln t), \quad y(t) = t \qquad t \in [1, 2].$$

Here

$$x'(t) = \tfrac{1}{2}(t - t^{-1}), \quad y'(t) = 1$$

and

$$[x'(t)]^2 + [y'(t)]^2 = [\tfrac{1}{2}(t + t^{-1})]^2. \qquad \text{(check this)}$$

It follows that

$$S = \int_1^2 2\pi t[\tfrac{1}{2}(t + t^{-1})] \, dt = \int_1^2 \pi(t^2 + 1) \, dt = \pi \left[\tfrac{1}{3}t^3 + t \right]_1^2 = \tfrac{10}{3} \pi. \quad \square$$

EXERCISES

Find the area of the surface generated by revolving the curve about the *x*-axis.

1. $f(x) = r, \quad x \in [0, 1].$
2. $f(x) = \sqrt{x}, \quad x \in [1, 2].$
3. $y = \cos x, \quad x \in [-\tfrac{1}{2}\pi, \tfrac{1}{2}\pi].$
4. $f(x) = 2\sqrt{1 - x}, \quad x \in [-1, 0].$
5. $f(x) = \tfrac{1}{3}x^3, \quad x \in [0, 2].$
6. $f(x) = |x - 3|, \quad x \in [0, 6].$
7. $4y = x^3, \quad x \in [0, 1].$
8. $y^2 = 9x, \quad x \in [0, 4].$
9. $x(t) = 2t, \quad y(t) = 3t \text{ with } t \in [0, 1].$
10. $x(t) = t^2, \quad y(t) = 2t \text{ with } t \in [0, \sqrt{3}].$
11. $x^2 + y^2 = r^2, \quad x \in [-\tfrac{1}{2}r, \tfrac{1}{2}r].$
12. $y = \cosh x, \quad x \in [0, 1].$
13. $x(t) = a \cos^3 t, \quad y(t) = a \sin^3 t \text{ with } t \in [0, \tfrac{1}{2}\pi].$
14. $x(t) = e^t \sin t, \quad y(t) = e^t \cos t \text{ with } t \in [0, \tfrac{1}{2}\pi].$
15. $r = e^\theta, \quad \theta \in [0, \tfrac{1}{2}\pi].$
16. $r = 1 + \cos \theta, \quad \theta \in [0, \pi].$

17. By cutting a cone of slant height *l* and base radius *r* along a lateral edge and laying the surface flat we can form a sector of a circle of radius *l*. (See Figure 11.10.5.) Use this idea to verify Formula (11.10.2).

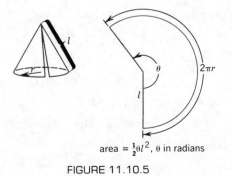

area $= \tfrac{1}{2}\theta l^2$, θ in radians

FIGURE 11.10.5

18. Find the area of the surface generated by revolving the curve
$$2x = y\sqrt{y^2 - 1} + \ln|y - \sqrt{y^2 - 1}| \quad \text{from } y = 2 \text{ to } y = 5$$
about the x-axis.

19. Find the area of the surface generated by revolving the curve
$$6a^2xy = y^4 + 3a^4 \quad \text{from } y = a \text{ to } y = 3a$$
about the x-axis.

20. Find the surface area of the *torus* generated by revolving the circle
$$x^2 + (y - b)^2 = a^2 \qquad\qquad (0 < a \le b)$$
about the x-axis.

21. Find the surface area of the ellipsoid obtained by revolving the ellipse
$$\frac{x^2}{a^2} + \frac{y^2}{b^2} = 1 \qquad\qquad (0 < b < a)$$
(a) about its major axis; (b) about its minor axis.

22. Verify that Formula (11.10.2) applied to
$$C: \quad x(t) = \cos t, \quad y(t) = r \quad \text{with } t \in [0, 2\pi]$$
gives $S = 8\pi r$. Note that the surface obtained by revolving C about the x-axis is a cylinder of base radius r and height h, and therefore S should be $4\pi r$. What's wrong?

11.11··ADDITIONAL EXERCISES

1. Sketch the curve $r^2 = 4 \sin 2\theta$ and find the area it encloses.

2. Sketch the curve $r = 2 + \sin \theta$ and find the area it encloses.

3. Sketch the curve $r = 2 + \sin 3\theta$ and find the area it encloses.

4. Sketch the region bounded by the curve $r = \sec \theta + \tan \theta$, the polar axis, and the ray $\theta = \frac{1}{4}\pi$. Then find the area of the region.

Find the length of the curve.

5. $y^2 = x^3$ from $x = 0$ to $x = \frac{5}{9}$. (upper branch)

6. $9y^2 = 4(1 + x^2)^3$ from $x = 0$ to $x = 3$. (upper branch)

7. $ay^2 = x^3$ from $x = 0$ to $x = 5a$. (upper branch)

8. $y = \ln(1 - x^2)$ from $x = 0$ to $x = \frac{1}{2}$.

9. Find the length of the parabolic arc
$$r = 2(1 + \cos \theta)^{-1}, \qquad \theta \in [0, \tfrac{1}{2}\pi].$$

10. Find the length of the parabolic arc
$$x(t) = \cos t, \quad y(t) = \sin^2 t \qquad t \in [0, \pi].$$

11. Find the length of the first arch of the cycloid:
$$x(t) = r(t - \sin t), \quad y(t) = r(1 - \cos t) \qquad t \in [0, 2\pi].$$

12. Find the length of the curve
$$r = a \sin^3 \tfrac{1}{3}\theta, \qquad \theta \in [0, 3\pi].$$

Find the area of the surface generated by revolving the curve about the x-axis.

13. $y^2 = 2px$ from $x = 0$ to $x = 4p$.

14. $y^2 = 4x$ from $x = 0$ to $x = 24$.

15. $6a^2xy = x^4 + 3a^4$ from $x = a$ to $x = 2a$.

16. $3x^2 + 4y^2 = 3a^2$.

17. $x(t) = r(t - \sin t)$, $y(t) = r(1 - \cos t)$ $t \in [0, 2\pi]$.

18. $x(t) = \frac{2}{3}t^{3/2}$, $y(t) = t$ $t \in [3, 8]$.

19. Part of the curve

$$(x/a)^{2/3} + (y/b)^{2/3} = 1 \qquad\qquad (a > 0, b > 0)$$

lies in the first quadrant. Find the length of that part (a) if $a = b$; (b) if $a \neq b$.

20. Show that, if f is continuously differentiable on $[a, b]$ and f' is never zero, then

the length of the graph of f^{-1} = the length of the graph of f.

11.12 CHAPTER SUMMARY

11.1 Polar Coordinates

The rectangular coordinates (x, y) and polar coordinates $[r, \theta]$ of a point are related by the following formulas:

$$x = r \cos \theta, \quad y = r \sin \theta \qquad \tan \theta = \frac{y}{x}, \quad x^2 + y^2 = r^2.$$

11.2 Graphing in Polar Coordinates

cardioids (p. 546)	lines (p. 546)	circles (p. 547)
limaçons (p. 547)	conics (p. 547)	lemniscates (p. 548)
petal curves (p. 549)	spirals (p. 549)	

11.3 The Intersection of Polar Curves

If we think of each of two polar equations as giving the position of an object at time θ, then simultaneous solution of the two equations gives us the points where the objects collide. To identify the points where two polar curves intersect, but do not collide, we usually need to convert the equations to rectangular coordinates.

11.4 Area in Polar Coordinates

Suppose that ρ_1 and ρ_2 are continuous positive functions with $\rho_1(\theta) \leq \rho_2(\theta)$ for all θ in $[\alpha, \beta]$. The area of the polar region between the graphs of ρ_1 and ρ_2 over $[\alpha, \beta]$ is given by the integral

$$\int_\alpha^\beta \tfrac{1}{2}([\rho_2(\theta)]^2 - [\rho_1(\theta)]^2) \, d\theta.$$

11.5 Curves Given Parametrically

Interpreting the parameter t as time measured in seconds, we can think of a pair of parametric equations, $x = x(t)$ and $y = y(t)$, as describing the motion of a particle in the xy-plane. [By $(x(t), y(t))$ we mean the position of the particle at time t.] Different parametrizations of the same curve represent different ways of traversing that curve.

Parametric equations tell us when (t values) as well as where (x and y values).

11.6 Tangents to Curves Given Parametrically

To make sure that a parametrized curve C: $x = x(t)$, $y = y(t)$ with $t \in I$ has at least one tangent line at each of its points, we assume, not only that $x'(t)$ and $y'(t)$ exist throughout I, but also that $[x'(t)]^2 + [y'(t)]^2 \neq 0$. Without this second assumption most anything can happen.

11.7 The Cycloid and Some Other Classic Curves; A Note on Area

11.8 The Least Upper Bound Axiom

11.9 The Length of a Parametrized Curve

length of a parametrized curve C: $\displaystyle\int_a^b \sqrt{[x'(t)]^2 + [y'(t)]^2}\, dt$

length of the graph of f: $\displaystyle\int_a^b \sqrt{1 + [f'(x)]^2}\, dx$

11.10 Area of a Surface of Revolution

revolution of the graph of f: $\displaystyle\int_a^b 2\pi f(x) \sqrt{1 + [f'(x)]^2}\, dx$

revolution of a parametrized curve C: $\displaystyle\int_c^d 2\pi y(t) \sqrt{[x'(t)]^2 + [y'(t)]^2}\, dt$

11.11 Additional Exercises

12

Sequences; Indeterminate Forms; Improper Integrals

12.1 ···· SEQUENCES OF REAL NUMBERS

So far our attention has been fixed on functions defined on an interval or on the union of intervals. Here we study functions defined on the set of positive integers.

> **DEFINITION 12.1.1**
>
> A function that takes on real values and is defined on the set of positive integers is called a *sequence of real numbers*.

The functions defined on the set of positive integers by setting

$$a(n) = n^2, \qquad b(n) = \frac{n}{n+1}, \qquad c(n) = \sqrt{\ln n}, \qquad d(n) = \frac{e^n}{n}$$

are all sequences of real numbers.

The notions developed for functions in general carry over to sequences. For example, a sequence is said to be bounded (bounded above, bounded below) iff its range is bounded (bounded above, bounded below). If a and b are sequences, then their linear combination $\alpha a + \beta b$ and their product ab are also sequences:

$$(\alpha a + \beta b)(n) = \alpha a(n) + \beta b(n) \qquad \text{and} \qquad (ab)(n) = a(n) \cdot b(n).$$

If the sequence b does not take on the value 0, then the reciprocal $1/b$ is a sequence and so is the quotient a/b:

$$\frac{1}{b}(n) = \frac{1}{b(n)} \qquad \text{and} \qquad \frac{a}{b}(n) = \frac{a(n)}{b(n)}.$$

The number $a(n)$, called *the nth term of the sequence a,* is usually written a_n and the sequence itself is written

$$\{a_1, a_2, a_3, \ldots\}$$

or, even more simply,

$$\{a_n\}.$$

For example, the sequence of reciprocals defined by setting

$$a_n = 1/n \qquad \text{for all } n$$

can be written

$$\{1, \tfrac{1}{2}, \tfrac{1}{3}, \ldots\} \quad \text{or} \quad \{1/n\}.$$

The sequence defined by setting

$$a_n = 10^{1/n} \qquad \text{for all } n$$

can be written

$$\{10, 10^{1/2}, 10^{1/3}, \ldots\} \quad \text{or} \quad \{10^{1/n}\}.$$

In this notation, we can write

$$\alpha\{a_n\} + \beta\{b_n\} = \{\alpha a_n + \beta b_n\}, \qquad \{a_n\}\{b_n\} = \{a_n b_n\}$$

and, provided that none of the b_n are zero,

$$\frac{1}{\{b_n\}} = \{1/b_n\} \qquad \text{and} \qquad \frac{\{a_n\}}{\{b_n\}} = \{a_n/b_n\}.$$

The following assertions will serve to illustrate the notation further.

(1) The sequence $\{1/2^n\}$ multiplied by 5 is the sequence $\{5/2^n\}$:

$$5\{1/2^n\} = \{5/2^n\}.$$

We can also write

$$5\{\tfrac{1}{2}, \tfrac{1}{4}, \tfrac{1}{8}, \tfrac{1}{16}, \ldots\} = \{\tfrac{5}{2}, \tfrac{5}{4}, \tfrac{5}{8}, \tfrac{5}{16}, \ldots\}.$$

(2) The sequence $\{n\}$ plus the sequence $\{1/n\}$ is the sequence $\{n + 1/n\}$:

$$\{n\} + \{1/n\} = \{n + 1/n\}.$$

In expanded form

$$\{1, 2, 3, \ldots\} + \{1, \tfrac{1}{2}, \tfrac{1}{3}, \ldots\} = \{2, 2\tfrac{1}{2}, 3\tfrac{1}{3}, \ldots\}.$$

(3) The sequence $\{n\}$ times the sequence $\{\sqrt{n}\}$ is the sequence $\{n\sqrt{n}\}$:

$$\{n\}\{\sqrt{n}\} = \{n\sqrt{n}\};$$

the sequence $\{2^n\}$ divided by the sequence $\{n\}$ is the sequence $\{2^n/n\}$:

$$\frac{\{2^n\}}{\{n\}} = \{2^n/n\}.$$

(4) The sequence $\{1/n\}$ is bounded below by 0 and bounded above by 1:

$$0 \le 1/n \le 1 \qquad \text{for all } n.$$

(5) The sequence $\{2^n\}$ is bounded below by 2:

$$2 \le 2^n \qquad \text{for all } n.$$

It is not bounded above: there is no fixed number M that satisfies

$$2^n \le M \qquad \text{for all } n.$$

(6) The sequence

$$a_n = (-1)^n 2^n$$

can be written

$$\{-2, 4, -8, 16, -32, 64, \ldots\}.$$

It is unbounded below and unbounded above. ☐

DEFINITION 12.1.2

A sequence $\{a_n\}$ is said to be

    (i) *increasing*   iff $a_n < a_{n+1}$ for each positive integer n,

    (ii) *nondecreasing*   iff $a_n \le a_{n+1}$ for each positive integer n,

    (iii) *decreasing*   iff $a_n > a_{n+1}$ for each positive integer n,

    (iv) *nonincreasing*   iff $a_n \ge a_{n+1}$ for each positive integer n.

If any of these four properties holds, the sequence is said to be *monotonic*.

The sequences

$$\{1, \tfrac{1}{2}, \tfrac{1}{3}, \ldots\}, \qquad \{2, 4, 8, 16, \ldots\}, \qquad \{2, 2, 4, 4, 8, 8, 16, 16, \ldots\}$$

are all monotonic, but the sequence

$$\{1, \tfrac{1}{2}, 1, \tfrac{1}{3}, 1, \tfrac{1}{4}, \ldots\}$$

is not monotonic.

The following examples are less trivial.

EXAMPLE. The sequence

$$a_n = \frac{n}{n+1}$$

is increasing. It is bounded below by $\tfrac{1}{2}$ and above by 1.

Proof. Since

$$\frac{a_{n+1}}{a_n} = \frac{n+1}{n+2} \cdot \frac{n+1}{n} = \frac{n^2 + 2n + 1}{n^2 + 2n} > 1,$$

we have

$$a_n < a_{n+1}.$$

This confirms that the sequence is increasing. Since the sequence can be written

$$\{\tfrac{1}{2}, \tfrac{2}{3}, \tfrac{3}{4}, \tfrac{4}{5}, \tfrac{5}{6}, \ldots\},$$

the bounds are obvious. $\square$

EXAMPLE. The sequence

$$a_n = \frac{2^n}{n!}$$

is nonincreasing. It decreases for $n \geq 2$.

Proof. The first two terms are equal:

$$a_1 = \frac{2^1}{1!} = 2 = \frac{2^2}{2!} = a_2.$$

for $n \geq 2$ the sequence decreases:

$$\frac{a_{n+1}}{a_n} = \frac{2^{n+1}}{(n+1)!} \cdot \frac{n!}{2^n} = \frac{2}{n+1} < 1 \qquad \text{if } n \geq 2. \quad \square$$

EXAMPLE. If $|c| > 1$, the sequence

$$a_n = |c|^n$$

increases without bound.

Proof. Assume that $|c| > 1$. Then

$$\frac{a_{n+1}}{a_n} = \frac{|c|^{n+1}}{|c|^n} = |c| > 1.$$

This shows that the sequence increases. To show the unboundedness, we take an arbitrary positive number M and show that there exists a positive integer k for which

$$|c|^k \geq M.$$

A suitable k is one such that

$$k \geq \frac{\ln M}{\ln |c|},$$

for then

$$k \ln |c| \geq \ln M, \qquad \ln |c|^k \geq \ln M, \qquad \text{and thus} \qquad |c|^k \geq M. \quad \square$$

Since sequences are defined on the set of positive integers and not on an interval, they are not directly susceptible to the methods of calculus. Fortunately, we can often circumvent this difficulty by dealing initially, not with the sequence itself, but with a function of a real variable x that agrees with the given sequence for all positive integers n.

We illustrate this idea in the next two examples. In the first example, we study the sequence

$$a_n = \frac{n}{e^n}$$

by examining the function

$$f(x) = \frac{x}{e^x}.$$

EXAMPLE. The sequence

$$a_n = \frac{n}{e^n}$$

decreases. It is bounded above by $1/e$ and below by 0.

Proof. We begin by setting

$$f(x) = \frac{x}{e^x}.$$

Differentiation gives

$$f'(x) = \frac{e^x - xe^x}{e^{2x}} = \frac{1 - x}{e^x}.$$

Since $f'(x)$ is 0 at $x = 1$ and negative for $x > 1$, f decreases on $[1, \infty)$. Obviously, then, the sequence $a_n = n/e^n$ decreases.

Since the sequence decreases, its first term $a_1 = 1/e$ is the greatest term. Thus $1/e$ is certainly an upper bound. Since all the terms of the sequence are positive, the number 0 is a lower bound. □

EXAMPLE. The sequence

$$a_n = n^{1/n}$$

decreases for $n \geq 3$.

Proof. We could compare a_n with a_{n+1} directly, but it is easier to consider the function

$$f(x) = x^{1/x}$$

instead. Since

$$f(x) = e^{(1/x)\ln x},$$

we have

$$f'(x) = e^{(1/x)\ln x} \frac{d}{dx}\left(\frac{1}{x}\ln x\right) = x^{1/x}\left(\frac{1 - \ln x}{x^2}\right).$$

For $x > e$, $f'(x) < 0$. This shows that f decreases on $[e, \infty)$. Since $3 > e$, f decreases on $[3, \infty)$. It follows that $\{a_n\}$ decreases for $n \geq 3$. $\square$

REMARK. We must be careful when we examine a function of a real variable x in order to analyze the behavior of a sequence. The function $y = f(x)$ and the sequence $y_n = f(n)$ may behave differently. For example, the sequence

$$f(n) = \frac{1}{n - 11.5}$$

is bounded (by 2 and -2) even though the function

$$f(x) = \frac{1}{x - 11.5}$$

is not bounded. Also, the sequence $f(n) = \sin n\pi$ is identically zero and thus monotonic even though the function $f(x) = \sin \pi x$ is not monotonic. $\square$

EXERCISES

Determine the boundedness and monotonicity of the indicated sequence.

1. $\dfrac{2}{n}$.

2. $\dfrac{(-1)^n}{n}$.

3. $\sqrt{n}$.

4. $(1.001)^n$.

5. $\dfrac{n + (-1)^n}{n}$.

6. $\dfrac{n - 1}{n}$.

7. $(0.9)^n$.

8. $\sqrt{n^2 + 1}$.

9. $\dfrac{n^2}{n + 1}$.

10. $\dfrac{2^n}{4^n + 1}$.

11. $\dfrac{4n}{\sqrt{4n^2 + 1}}$.

12. $\dfrac{n + 1}{n^2}$.

13. $\dfrac{4^n}{2^n + 100}$.

14. $\dfrac{n^2}{\sqrt{n^3 + 1}}$.

15. $\dfrac{10^{10}\sqrt{n}}{n + 1}$.

16. $\dfrac{n^2 + 1}{3n + 2}$.

17. $\ln\left(\dfrac{2n}{n + 1}\right)$.

18. $\dfrac{n + 2}{3^{10}\sqrt{n}}$.

19. $\dfrac{(n + 1)^2}{n^2}$.

20. $(-1)^n\sqrt{n}$.

21. $\sqrt{4 - \dfrac{1}{n}}$.

22. $\ln\left(\dfrac{n + 1}{n}\right)$.

23. $(-1)^{2n+1}\sqrt{n}$.

24. $\dfrac{\sqrt{n + 1}}{\sqrt{n}}$.

25. $\dfrac{2^n - 1}{2^n}$.

26. $\dfrac{1}{2n} - \dfrac{1}{2n + 3}$.

27. $\sin\dfrac{\pi}{n + 1}$.

28. $(-\frac{1}{2})^n$.

29. $(1.2)^{-n}$.

30. $\dfrac{n + 3}{\ln(n + 3)}$.

31. $\dfrac{1}{n} - \dfrac{1}{n + 1}$.

32. $\cos n\pi$.

33. $\dfrac{\ln(n + 2)}{n + 2}$.

34. $\dfrac{(-2)^n}{n^{10}}$.

35. $\dfrac{3^n}{(n + 1)^2}$.

36. $\dfrac{1 - (\frac{1}{2})^n}{(\frac{1}{2})^n}$.

37. Show that the sequence $\{5^n/n!\}$ decreases for $n \geq 5$. Is the sequence nonincreasing?

38. Let M be a positive integer. Show that $\{M^n/n!\}$ decreases for $n \geq M$.

39. Show that, if $0 < c < d$, then the sequence

$$a_n = (c^n + d^n)^{1/n}$$

is bounded and monotonic.

40. Show that linear combinations and products of bounded sequences are bounded.

A sequence $\{a_n\}$ is said to be defined *recursively* if, for some $k \geq 1$, the terms $a_1, a_2, \ldots, a_k$ are given and a_n is specified in terms of $a_1, a_2, \ldots, a_{n-1}$ for each $n \geq k$. The formula specifying a_n for $n \geq k$ in terms of some (or all) of its predecessors is called a *recurrence relation*. Identify the first six terms and the nth term of the following sequences defined recursively.

41. $a_1 = 1$ and   for $n \geq 1$ $a_{n+1} = \dfrac{1}{n+1} a_n$.

42. $a_1 = 1$ and   for $n \geq 1$ $a_{n+1} = a_n + 3n(n+1) + 1$.

43. $a_1 = 1$ and   for $n \geq 1$ $a_{n+1} = \frac{1}{2}(a_n + 1)$.

44. $a_1 = 1$ and   for $n \geq 1$ $a_{n+1} = \frac{1}{2}a_n + 1$.

45. $a_1 = 1$ and   for $n \geq 1$ $a_{n+1} = a_n + 2$.

46. $a_1 = 1$ and   for $n \geq 1$ $a_{n+1} = \dfrac{n}{n+1} a_n$.

47. $a_1 = 1$ and   for $n \geq 1$ $a_{n+1} = 3a_n + 1$.

48. $a_1 = 1$ and   for $n \geq 1$ $a_{n+1} = 4a_n + 3$.

49. $a_1 = 1$ and   for $n \geq 1$ $a_{n+1} = a_n + 2n + 1$.

50. $a_1 = 1$ and   for $n \geq 1$ $a_{n+1} = 2a_n + 1$.

51. $a_1 = 1, a_2 = 3$ and   for $n \geq 2$ $a_{n+1} = a_n + \cdots + a_1$.

52. $a_1 = 3$ and   for $n \geq 1$ $a_{n+1} = 4 - a_n$.

53. $a_1 = 2, a_2 = 1, a_3 = 2$ and   for $n \geq 3$ $a_{n+1} = 6 - (a_n + a_{n-1} + a_{n-2})$.

54. $a_1 = 1, a_2 = 2$ and   for $n \geq 2$ $a_{n+1} = 2a_n - a_{n-1}$.

55. $a_1 = 1, a_2 = 3$ and   for $n \geq 2$ $a_{n+1} = 2a_n - a_{n-1}$.

56. $a_1 = 1, a_2 = 3$ and   for $n \geq 2$ $a_{n+1} = 3a_n - 2n - 1$.

The formula for the nth term of a sequence $\{a_n\}$ defined recursively may be proved using mathematical induction.

57. Prove that $a_n = 2^n - 1$ given that $a_1 = 1$ and, for $n \geq 1$, $a_{n+1} = 2a_n + 1$.

58. Prove that $a_n = 5n - 2$ given that $a_1 = 3$ and, for $n \geq 1$, $a_{n+1} = a_n + 5$.

59. Prove that $a_n = \dfrac{n}{2^{n-1}}$ given that $a_1 = 1$ and, for $n \geq 1$, $a_{n+1} = \dfrac{n+1}{2n} a_n$.

60. Prove that $a_n = \dfrac{1}{n}$ given that $a_1 = 1$ and, for $n \geq 1$, $a_{n+1} = a_n - \dfrac{1}{n(n+1)}$.

12.2···· THE LIMIT OF A SEQUENCE

The gist of

$$\lim_{x \to c} f(x) = l$$

is that we can make $f(x)$ as close as we wish to the number l simply by requiring that x

be sufficiently close to c.   The gist of

$$\lim_{n\to\infty} a_n = l$$

(read "the limit of a_n as n tends to infinity is l") is that we can make a_n as close as we wish to the number l simply by requiring that n be sufficiently large.

DEFINITION 12.2.1   LIMIT

$$\lim_{n\to\infty} a_n = l \quad \text{iff} \quad \begin{cases} \text{for each } \epsilon > 0 \text{ there exists an integer } k > 0 \text{ such that} \\ \quad\quad \text{if } n \geq k, \quad\quad \text{then } |a_n - l| < \epsilon. \end{cases}$$

EXAMPLE

$$\lim_{n\to\infty} \frac{1}{n} = 0.$$

Proof.   Take $\epsilon > 0$ and choose an integer $k > 1/\epsilon$.   Then $1/k < \epsilon$, and, if $n \geq k$,

$$0 < \frac{1}{n} \leq \frac{1}{k} < \epsilon \quad \text{and thus} \quad \left|\frac{1}{n} - 0\right| < \epsilon. \quad \square$$

EXAMPLE

$$\lim_{n\to\infty} \frac{2n-1}{n} = 2.$$

Proof.   Let $\epsilon > 0$.   We must show that there exists an integer k such that

$$\left|\frac{2n-1}{n} - 2\right| < \epsilon \quad\quad \text{for all } n \geq k.$$

Since

$$\left|\frac{2n-1}{n} - 2\right| = \left|\frac{2n-1-2n}{n}\right| = \left|-\frac{1}{n}\right| = \frac{1}{n},$$

again we need only choose $k > 1/\epsilon$. $\square$

   The next example justifies the familiar statement

$$\tfrac{1}{3} = 0.333 \cdots.$$

EXAMPLE.   The decimal fractions

$$a_n = 0.\overbrace{33 \cdots 3}^{n}$$

tend to $\tfrac{1}{3}$ as a limit:

$$\lim_{n\to\infty} a_n = \tfrac{1}{3}.$$

Proof.   Let $\epsilon > 0$.   In the first place

(1) $$\left| a_n - \frac{1}{3} \right| = \left| 0.\overset{n}{\overbrace{33 \, \cdots \, 3}} - \frac{1}{3} \right| = \left| \frac{0.\overset{n}{\overbrace{99 \, \cdots \, 9}} - 1}{3} \right| = \frac{1}{3} \cdot \frac{1}{10^n} < \frac{1}{10^n}.$$

Now choose k so that $1/10^k < \epsilon$.   If $n \geq k$, then by (1)

$$\left| a_n - \frac{1}{3} \right| < \frac{1}{10^n} \leq \frac{1}{10^k} < \epsilon. \quad \square$$

Limit Theorems

The limit process for sequences is so similar to the limit process you've already studied that you may find you can prove many of the limit theorems yourself.   In any case, try to come up with your own proofs and refer to these only if necessary.

THEOREM 12.2.2   UNIQUENESS OF LIMIT

If

$$\lim_{n \to \infty} a_n = l \quad \text{and} \quad \lim_{n \to \infty} a_n = m,$$

then

$$l = m.$$

A proof, similar to the proof of Theorem 2.3.1, is given in the supplement at the end of this section.

DEFINITION 12.2.3

A sequence that has a limit is said to be *convergent*.   A sequence that has no limit is said to be *divergent*.

Instead of writing

$$\lim_{n \to \infty} a_n = l,$$

we'll often write

$$a_n \to l \qquad\qquad \text{(read "}a_n \text{ converges to } l\text{")}$$

or more fully

$$a_n \to l \quad \text{as} \quad n \to \infty.$$

THEOREM 12.2.4

Every convergent sequence is bounded.

Proof.   Assume that

$$a_n \to l$$

and choose any positive number: 1, for instance.   Using 1 as ϵ, you can see that there must exist k such that

$$|a_n - l| < 1 \qquad \text{for all } n \geq k.$$

This means that

$$|a_n| < 1 + |l| \qquad \text{for all } n \geq k$$

and, consequently,

$$|a_n| \leq \max \{|a_1|, |a_2|, \ldots, |a_{k-1}|, 1 + |l|\} \qquad \text{for all } n.$$

This proves that $\{a_n\}$ is bounded. $\square$

Since every convergent sequence is bounded, a sequence that is not bounded cannot be convergent; namely,

(12.2.5)   every unbounded sequence is divergent.

The sequences

$$a_n = \tfrac{1}{2}n, \qquad b_n = \frac{n^2}{n+1}, \qquad c_n = n \ln n$$

are all unbounded.   Each of these sequences is therefore divergent.

Boundedness does not imply convergence.   As a counterexample, consider the oscillating sequence

$$\{1, 0, 1, 0, \ldots\}.$$

This sequence is certainly bounded (above by 1 and below by 0), but obviously it does not converge: the limit would have to be arbitrarily close to both 0 and 1 simultaneously.

Boundedness together with monotonicity does imply convergence.

THEOREM 12.2.6

A bounded nondecreasing sequence converges to the least upper bound of its range; a bounded nonincreasing sequence converges to the greatest lower bound of its range.

Proof.   Suppose that $\{a_n\}$ is bounded and nondecreasing.   If l is the least upper bound of the range of this sequence, then

$$a_n \leq l \qquad \text{for all } n.$$

Now let ϵ be an arbitrary positive number.   By Theorem 11.8.2 there exists a_k such that

$$l - \epsilon < a_k.$$

Since the sequence is nondecreasing,

$$a_k \leq a_n \qquad \text{for all } n \geq k.$$

It follows that

$$l - \epsilon < a_n \leq l \qquad \text{for all } n \geq k.$$

This shows that

$$|a_n - l| < \epsilon \qquad \text{for all } n \geq k$$

and proves that

$$a_n \to l.$$

The nonincreasing case can be handled in a similar manner. □

EXAMPLE. Take the sequence

$$\{(3^n + 4^n)^{1/n}\}.$$

Since

$$3 = (3^n)^{1/n} < (3^n + 4^n)^{1/n} < (2 \cdot 4^n)^{1/n} = 2^{1/n} \cdot 4 \leq 8,$$

the sequence is bounded. Note that

$$(3^n + 4^n)^{(n+1)/n} = (3^n + 4^n)^{1/n}(3^n + 4^n)$$
$$= (3^n + 4^n)^{1/n} 3^n + (3^n + 4^n)^{1/n} 4^n$$
$$> (3^n)^{1/n} 3^n + (4^n)^{1/n} 4^n = 3 \cdot 3^n + 4 \cdot 4^n = 3^{n+1} + 4^{n+1}.$$

Taking the $(n + 1)$st root of both extremes, we find that

$$(3^n + 4^n)^{1/n} > (3^{n+1} + 4^{n+1})^{1/(n+1)}.$$

The sequence is decreasing. Being bounded, it must be convergent. (Later you will be asked to show that the limit is 4.) □

THEOREM 12.2.7

Let α be a real number. If $a_n \to l$ and $b_n \to m$, then

$\quad$ (i) $a_n + b_n \to l + m$, $\quad$ (ii) $\alpha a_n \to \alpha l$, $\quad$ (iii) $a_n b_n \to lm$.

If, in addition, $m \neq 0$ and b_n is never 0, then

$$\text{(iv)} \ \frac{1}{b_n} \to \frac{1}{m} \qquad \text{and} \qquad \text{(v)} \ \frac{a_n}{b_n} \to \frac{l}{m}.$$

Proofs of parts (i) and (ii) are left as exercises. For proofs of parts (iii)–(v), see the supplement at the end of this section.

We are now in a position to handle any rational sequence

$$a_n = \frac{\alpha_k n^k + \alpha_{k-1} n^{k-1} + \cdots + \alpha_0}{\beta_j n^j + \beta_{j-1} n^{j-1} + \cdots + \beta_0}.$$

To determine the behavior of such a sequence we need only divide both numerator and denominator by the highest power of n that occurs.

EXAMPLE

$$\frac{3n^4 - 2n^2 + 1}{n^5 - 3n^3} = \frac{3/n - 2/n^3 + 1/n^5}{1 - 3/n^2} \to \frac{0}{1} = 0. \quad \square$$

EXAMPLE

$$\frac{1 - 4n^7}{n^7 + 12n} = \frac{1/n^7 - 4}{1 + 12/n^6} \to \frac{-4}{1} = -4. \quad \square$$

EXAMPLE

$$\frac{n^4 - 3n^2 + n + 2}{n^3 + 7n} = \frac{1 - 3/n^2 + 1/n^3 + 2/n^4}{1/n + 7/n^3}.$$

Since the numerator tends to 1 and the denominator tends to 0, the sequence is unbounded. Therefore it cannot converge. $\square$

THEOREM 12.2.8

$$a_n \to l \quad \text{iff} \quad a_n - l \to 0 \quad \text{iff} \quad |a_n - l| \to 0.$$

We leave the proof to you.

THEOREM 12.2.9   THE PINCHING THEOREM FOR SEQUENCES

Suppose that for all n sufficiently large

$$a_n \le b_n \le c_n.$$

If $a_n \to l$ and $c_n \to l$, then $b_n \to l$.

Once again the proof is left to you.

As an immediate and obvious consequence of the pinching theorem we have the following corollary.

(12.2.10)

Suppose that for all n sufficiently large

$$|b_n| \le |c_n|.$$

If $|c_n| \to 0$, then $|b_n| \to 0$.

EXAMPLE

$$\frac{\cos n}{n} \to 0 \qquad \text{since} \qquad \left|\frac{\cos n}{n}\right| \le \frac{1}{n} \quad \text{and} \quad \frac{1}{n} \to 0. \quad \square$$

EXAMPLE

$$\sqrt{4 + \left(\frac{1}{n}\right)^2} \to 2$$

since

$$2 \le \sqrt{4 + \left(\frac{1}{n}\right)^2} \le \sqrt{4 + 4\left(\frac{1}{n}\right) + \left(\frac{1}{n}\right)^2} = 2 + \frac{1}{n} \quad \text{and} \quad 2 + \frac{1}{n} \to 2. \quad \square$$

EXAMPLE

(12.2.11)
$$\lim_{n \to \infty} \left(1 + \frac{1}{n}\right)^n = e.$$

Proof. You have already seen that, for all positive integers n,

$$\left(1 + \frac{1}{n}\right)^n \le e \le \left(1 + \frac{1}{n}\right)^{n+1}. \qquad \text{(Theorem 7.5.12)}$$

Dividing the right-hand inequality by $1 + 1/n$, we have

$$\frac{e}{1 + 1/n} \le \left(1 + \frac{1}{n}\right)^n.$$

Combining this with the left-hand inequality, we can write

$$\frac{e}{1 + 1/n} \le \left(1 + \frac{1}{n}\right)^n \le e.$$

Since

$$\frac{e}{1 + 1/n} \to \frac{e}{1} = e,$$

we can conclude from the pinching theorem that

$$\left(1 + \frac{1}{n}\right)^n \to e. \quad \square$$

The sequences

$$\left\{\cos \frac{\pi}{n}\right\}, \quad \left\{\ln\left(\frac{n}{n+1}\right)\right\}, \quad \{e^{1/n}\}, \quad \left\{\tan\left(\sqrt{\frac{\pi^2 n^2 - 8}{16n^2}}\right)\right\}$$

are all of the form $\{f(c_n)\}$ with f a continuous function. Such sequences are frequently easy to deal with. The basic idea is this: when a continuous function is applied to a convergent sequence, the result is itself a convergent sequence. More precisely, we have the following theorem.

> ## THEOREM 12.2.12
>
> Suppose that
>
> $$c_n \to c$$
>
> and that, for each n, c_n is in the domain of f. If f is continuous at c, then
>
> $$f(c_n) \to f(c).$$

Proof.   We assume that f is continuous at c and take $\epsilon > 0$. From the continuity of f at c we know that there exists $\delta > 0$ such that

$$\text{if}\quad |x - c| < \delta, \qquad \text{then}\quad |f(x) - f(c)| < \epsilon.$$

Since $c_n \to c$, we know that there exists a positive integer k such that

$$\text{if}\quad n \geq k, \qquad \text{then}\quad |c_n - c| < \delta.$$

It follows therefore that

$$\text{if}\quad n \geq k, \qquad \text{then}\quad |f(c_n) - f(c)| < \epsilon. \quad \square$$

EXAMPLES

1. Since

$$\frac{\pi}{n} \to 0$$

and the cosine function is continuous at 0, we have

$$\cos \frac{\pi}{n} \to \cos 0 = 1. \quad \square$$

2. Since

$$\frac{n}{n + 1} = \frac{1}{1 + 1/n} \to 1$$

and the logarithm function is continuous at 1,

$$\ln \left(\frac{n}{n + 1} \right) \to \ln 1 = 0. \quad \square$$

3. Since

$$\frac{1}{n} \to 0$$

and the exponential function is continuous at 0,

$$e^{1/n} \to e^0 = 1. \quad \square$$

4. Since

$$\frac{\pi^2 n^2 - 8}{16 n^2} = \frac{\pi^2 - 8/n^2}{16} \to \frac{\pi^2}{16}$$

and the function $f(x) = \tan \sqrt{x}$ is continuous at $\pi^2/16$,

$$\tan \left(\sqrt{\frac{\pi^2 n^2 - 8}{16 n^2}} \right) \to \tan \left(\sqrt{\frac{\pi^2}{16}} \right) = \tan \frac{\pi}{4} = 1. \quad \square$$

5. Since

$$\frac{2n + 1}{n} + \left(5 - \frac{1}{n^2} \right) \to 7$$

and the square-root function is continuous at 7,

$$\sqrt{\frac{2n + 1}{n} + \left(5 - \frac{1}{n^2} \right)} \to \sqrt{7}. \quad \square$$

6. Since the absolute-value function is everywhere continuous,

$$\text{if} \quad a_n \to l, \quad \text{then} \quad |a_n| \to |l|. \quad \square$$

EXERCISES

State whether or not the sequence converges and, if it does, find the limit.

1. 2^n.

2. $\dfrac{2}{n}$.

3. $\dfrac{(-1)^n}{n}$.

4. $\sqrt{n}$.

5. $\dfrac{n - 1}{n}$.

6. $\dfrac{n + (-1)^n}{n}$.

7. $\dfrac{n + 1}{n^2}$.

8. $\sin \dfrac{\pi}{2n}$.

9. $\dfrac{2^n}{4^n + 1}$.

10. $\dfrac{n^2}{n + 1}$.

11. $(-1)^n \sqrt{n}$.

12. $\dfrac{4n}{\sqrt{n^2 + 1}}$.

13. $(-\tfrac{1}{2})^n$.

14. $\dfrac{4^n}{2^n + 10^6}$.

15. $\tan \dfrac{n\pi}{4n + 1}$.

16. $\dfrac{10^{10} \sqrt{n}}{n + 1}$.

17. $\dfrac{(2n + 1)^2}{(3n - 1)^2}$.

18. $\ln \left(\dfrac{2n}{n + 1} \right)$.

19. $\dfrac{n^2}{\sqrt{2n^4 + 1}}$.

20. $\dfrac{n^4 - 1}{n^4 + n - 6}$.

21. $\cos n\pi$.

22. $\dfrac{n^5}{17 n^4 + 12}$.

23. $e^{1/\sqrt{n}}$.

24. $\sqrt{4 - \dfrac{1}{n}}$.

25. $(0.9)^{-n}$.

26. $\dfrac{2^n - 1}{2^n}$.

27. $\ln n - \ln (n + 1)$.

28. $\dfrac{1}{n} - \dfrac{1}{n+1}$.

29. $\dfrac{\sqrt{n+1}}{2\sqrt{n}}$.

30. $(0.9)^n$.

31. $\left(1 + \dfrac{1}{n}\right)^{2n}$.

32. $2\ln 3n - \ln(n^2 + 1)$.

33. $\dfrac{2^n}{n^2}$.

34. $\dfrac{(n+1)\cos\sqrt{n}}{n(1+\sqrt{n})}$.

35. $\dfrac{\sqrt{n}\sin(e^n\pi)}{n+1}$.

36. $\left(1 + \dfrac{1}{n}\right)^{n/2}$.

37. Prove that, if $a_n \to l$ and $b_n \to m$, then $a_n + b_n \to l + m$.

38. Let α be a real number. Prove that, if $a_n \to l$, then $\alpha a_n \to \alpha l$.

39. Prove that

$$\left(1 + \frac{1}{n}\right)^{n+1} \to e \quad \text{given that} \quad \left(1 + \frac{1}{n}\right)^{n} \to e.$$

40. Determine the convergence or divergence of a rational sequence

$$a_n = \frac{\alpha_k n^k + \alpha_{k-1} n^{k-1} + \cdots + \alpha_0}{\beta_j n^j + \beta_{j-1} n^{j-1} + \cdots + \beta_0} \quad \text{with } \alpha_k \neq 0, \beta_j \neq 0,$$

given that (a) $k = j$.   (b) $k < j$.   (c) $k > j$.

41. Prove that a bounded nonincreasing sequence converges to the greatest lower bound of its range.

42. Let $\{a_n\}$ be a sequence of real numbers. Let $\{e_n\}$ be the sequence of even terms:

$$e_n = a_{2n}$$

and let $\{o_n\}$ be the sequence of odd terms:

$$o_n = a_{2n-1}.$$

Show that

$$a_n \to l \quad \text{iff} \quad e_n \to l \text{ and } o_n \to l.$$

43. Prove the pinching theorem for sequences.

44. Show that

$$\frac{2^n}{n!} \to 0.$$

HINT: First show that

$$\frac{2^n}{n!} = \frac{2}{1} \cdot \frac{2}{2} \cdot \frac{2}{3} \cdot \quad \cdots \quad \cdot \frac{2}{n} \le \frac{4}{n}.$$

45. Prove that $(1/n)^{1/p} \to 0$ for all odd positive integers p.

46. Prove Theorem 12.2.8.

The following sequences are defined recursively.† Determine in each case whether the sequence converges and, if so, find the limit.

47. $a_1 = 1$ and   for $n \ge 1$ $a_{n+1} = \dfrac{1}{e} a_n$.

48. $a_1 = 1$ and   for $n \ge 1$ $a_{n+1} = 2^{n+1} a_n$.

---

† The notion was introduced in the exercises at the end of Section 12.1.

49. $a_1 = 1$ and   for $n \geq 1$ $a_{n+1} = \dfrac{1}{n+1} a_n$.

50. $a_1 = 1$ and   for $n \geq 1$ $a_{n+1} = \dfrac{n}{n+1} a_n$.

51. $a_1 = 1$ and   for $n \geq 1$ $a_{n+1} = 1 - a_n$.
52. $a_1 = 1$ and   for $n \geq 1$ $a_{n+1} = -a_n$.
53. $a_1 = 1$ and   for $n \geq 1$ $a_{n+1} = \frac{1}{2} a_n + 1$.
54. $a_1 = 1$ and   for $n \geq 1$ $a_{n+1} = \frac{1}{3} a_n + 1$.

Supplement to Section 12.2

Proof of Theorem 12.2.2.   If $l \neq m$, then

$$\tfrac{1}{2} |l - m| > 0.$$

The assumption that

$$\lim_{n \to \infty} a_n = l \quad \text{and} \quad \lim_{n \to \infty} a_n = m$$

gives the existence of k_1 such that

$$\text{if} \quad n \geq k_1, \quad \text{then} \quad |a_n - l| < \tfrac{1}{2} |l - m|$$

and the existence of k_2 such that

$$\text{if} \quad n \geq k_2, \quad \text{then} \quad |a_n - m| < \tfrac{1}{2} |l - m|.\dagger$$

For $n \geq \max \{k_1, k_2\}$ we have

$$|a_n - l| + |a_n - m| < |l - m|.$$

By the triangle inequality we have

$$|l - m| = |(l - a_n) + (a_n - m)| \leq |l - a_n| + |a_n - m| = |a_n - l| + |a_n - m|.$$

Combining the last two statements, we have

$$|l - m| < |l - m|.$$

The hypothesis $l \neq m$ has led to an absurdity.   We conclude that $l = m$. $\square$

Proof of Theorem 12.2.7(iii)–(v).   To prove (iii), we set $\epsilon > 0$.   For each n,

$$|a_n b_n - lm| = |(a_n b_n - a_n m) + (a_n m - lm)|$$
$$\leq |a_n| |b_n - m| + |m| |a_n - l|.$$

Since $\{a_n\}$ is convergent, $\{a_n\}$ is bounded; that is, there exists $M > 0$ such that

$$|a_n| \leq M \qquad \text{for all } n.$$

---

† We can reach these conclusions from Definition 12.2.1 by taking $\frac{1}{2} |l - m|$ as ϵ.

Since $|m| < |m| + 1$, we have

(1) $$|a_n b_n - lm| \le M|b_n - m| + (|m| + 1)|a_n - l|.\dagger$$

Since $b_n \to m$, we know that there exists k_1 such that

$$\text{if} \quad n \ge k_1, \quad \text{then} \quad |b_n - m| < \frac{\epsilon}{2M}.$$

Since $a_n \to l$, we know that there exists k_2 such that

$$\text{if} \quad n \ge k_2, \quad \text{then} \quad |a_n - l| < \frac{\epsilon}{2(|m| + 1)}.$$

For $n \ge \max \{k_1, k_2\}$ both conditions hold, and consequently

$$M|b_n - m| + (|m| + 1)|a_n - l| < \frac{\epsilon}{2} + \frac{\epsilon}{2} = \epsilon.$$

In view of (1), we can conclude that

$$\text{if} \quad n \ge \max \{k_1, k_2\}, \quad \text{then} \quad |a_n b_n - lm| < \epsilon.$$

This proves that

$$a_n b_n \to lm. \quad \square$$

To prove (iv), once again we set $\epsilon > 0$. In the first place

$$\left| \frac{1}{b_n} - \frac{1}{m} \right| = \left| \frac{m - b_n}{b_n m} \right| = \frac{|b_n - m|}{|b_n||m|}.$$

Since $b_n \to m$ and $|m|/2 > 0$, there exists k_1 such that

$$\text{if} \quad n \ge k_1, \quad \text{then} \quad |b_n - m| < \frac{|m|}{2}.$$

This tells us that for $n \ge k_1$ we have

$$|b_n| > \frac{|m|}{2} \quad \text{and thus} \quad \frac{1}{|b_n|} < \frac{2}{|m|}.$$

Thus for $n \ge k_1$ we have

(2) $$\left| \frac{1}{b_n} - \frac{1}{m} \right| \le \frac{2}{|m|^2} |b_n - m|.$$

Since $b_n \to m$, there exists k_2 such that

$$\text{if} \quad n \ge k_2, \quad \text{then} \quad |b_n - m| < \frac{\epsilon|m|^2}{2}.$$

---

† Soon we'll want to divide by the coefficient of $|a_n - l|$. We have replaced $|m|$ by $|m| + 1$ because $|m|$ can be zero.

Thus for $n \geq k_2$ we have

$$\frac{2}{|m|^2} |b_n - m| < \epsilon.$$

In view of (2), we can be sure that

$$\text{if} \quad n \geq \max \{k_1, k_2\}, \qquad \text{then} \quad \left| \frac{1}{b_n} - \frac{1}{m} \right| < \epsilon.$$

This proves that

$$\frac{1}{b_n} \rightarrow \frac{1}{m}. \quad \square$$

The proof of (v) is now easy:

$$\frac{a_n}{b_n} = a_n \cdot \frac{1}{b_n} \rightarrow l \cdot \frac{1}{m} = \frac{l}{m}. \quad \square$$

12.3····SOME IMPORTANT LIMITS

Our purpose here is to familiarize you with some limits that are particularly important in calculus and to give you more experience with limit arguments.

(12.3.1)

> **If $x > 0$, then**
>
> $$x^{1/n} \rightarrow 1 \qquad \text{as} \quad n \rightarrow \infty.$$

Proof.   Note that

$$\ln (x^{1/n}) = \frac{1}{n} \ln x \rightarrow 0.$$

Since the exponential function is continuous at 0, it follows from Theorem 12.2.12 that

$$x^{1/n} = e^{(1/n)\ln x} \rightarrow e^0 = 1. \quad \square$$

(12.3.2)

> **If $|x| < 1$, then**
>
> $$x^n \rightarrow 0 \qquad \text{as} \quad n \rightarrow \infty.$$

Proof.   Take $|x| < 1$ and observe that $\{|x|^n\}$ is a decreasing sequence:

$$|x|^{n+1} = |x| |x|^n < |x|^n.$$

Now let $\epsilon > 0$.   By (12.3.1)

$$\epsilon^{1/n} \rightarrow 1 \qquad \text{as} \quad n \rightarrow \infty.$$

Thus there exists an integer $k > 0$ such that

$$|x| < \epsilon^{1/k}. \qquad \text{(explain)}$$

Obviously, then, $|x|^k < \epsilon$. Since $\{|x|^n\}$ is a decreasing sequence,

$$|x^n| = |x|^n < \epsilon \qquad \text{for all } n \geq k. \quad \square$$

(12.3.3)

> **For each real x**
>
> $$\dfrac{x^n}{n!} \to 0 \qquad \text{as} \quad n \to \infty.$$

Proof. Choose an integer k such that $k > |x|$. For $n > k$,

$$\frac{k^n}{n!} = \left(\frac{k^k}{k!}\right)\left[\frac{k}{k+1}\frac{k}{k+2} \cdots \frac{k}{n-1}\right]\left(\frac{k}{n}\right) < \left(\frac{k^{k+1}}{k!}\right)\left(\frac{1}{n}\right).$$

the middle term is less than 1

Since $k > |x|$, we have

$$0 < \frac{|x|^n}{n!} < \frac{k^n}{n!} < \left(\frac{k^{k+1}}{k!}\right)\left(\frac{1}{n}\right).$$

Since k is fixed and $1/n \to 0$, it follows from the pinching theorem that

$$\frac{|x|^n}{n!} \to 0 \qquad \text{and thus} \qquad \frac{x^n}{n!} \to 0. \quad \square$$

(12.3.4)

> **For each $\alpha > 0$**
>
> $$\dfrac{1}{n^\alpha} \to 0 \qquad \text{as} \quad n \to \infty.$$

Proof. Since $\alpha > 0$, there exists an odd positive integer p such that $\dfrac{1}{p} < \alpha$. As $\dfrac{1}{n} \leq 1$, we conclude that

$$0 < \frac{1}{n^\alpha} = \left(\frac{1}{n}\right)^\alpha \leq \left(\frac{1}{n}\right)^{1/p}.$$

Since $1/n \to 0$ and $f(x) = x^{1/p}$ is continuous at 0, we have

$$\left(\frac{1}{n}\right)^{1/p} \to 0 \quad \text{and thus by the pinching theorem} \quad \frac{1}{n^\alpha} \to 0. \quad \square$$

(12.3.5)

$$\frac{\ln n}{n} \to 0 \quad \text{as} \quad n \to \infty.$$

Proof. A routine proof can be based on L'Hospital's rule (12.6.3), but that is not available to us yet. We will appeal to the pinching theorem and base our argument on the integral representation of the logarithm:

$$0 \le \frac{\ln n}{n} = \frac{1}{n} \int_1^n \frac{dt}{t} \le \frac{1}{n} \int_1^n \frac{dt}{\sqrt{t}} = \frac{2}{n} (\sqrt{n} - 1) = 2 \left(\frac{1}{\sqrt{n}} - \frac{1}{n} \right) \to 0. \quad \square$$

(12.3.6)

$$n^{1/n} \to 1 \quad \text{as} \quad n \to \infty.$$

Proof. We have

$$n^{1/n} = e^{(1/n)\ln n}.$$

Since

$$(1/n) \ln n \to 0 \qquad\qquad (12.3.5)$$

and the exponential function is continuous at 0, it follows from (12.2.12) that

$$n^{1/n} \to e^0 = 1. \quad \square$$

(12.3.7)

> **For each real x**
>
> $$\left(1 + \frac{x}{n}\right)^n \to e^x \quad \text{as} \quad n \to \infty.$$

Proof. For $x = 0$, the result is obvious. For $x \ne 0$,

$$\ln\left(1 + \frac{x}{n}\right)^n = n \ln\left(1 + \frac{x}{n}\right) = x \left[\frac{\ln(1 + x/n) - \ln 1}{x/n} \right].$$

The crux here is to recognize that the bracketed expression is a difference quotient for the logarithm function. Once we see this, we can write

$$\lim_{n \to \infty} \left[\frac{\ln(1 + x/n) - \ln 1}{x/n} \right] = \lim_{h \to 0} \left[\frac{\ln(1 + h) - \ln 1}{h} \right] = 1.\dagger$$

---

† For each $t > 0$

$$\lim_{h \to 0} \frac{\ln(t + h) - \ln t}{h} = \frac{d}{dt}(\ln t) = \frac{1}{t}.$$

It follows that

$$\ln\left(1 + \frac{x}{n}\right)^n \to x,$$

and consequently

$$\left(1 + \frac{x}{n}\right)^n = e^{\ln(1+x/n)^n} \to e^x. \quad \square$$

EXERCISES

State whether or not the sequence converges as $n \to \infty$; if it does, find the limit.

1. $2^{2/n}$.

2. $e^{-\alpha/n}$.

3. $\left(\dfrac{2}{n}\right)^n$.

4. $\dfrac{\log_{10} n}{n}$.

5. $\dfrac{\ln(n+1)}{n}$.

6. $\dfrac{3^n}{4^n}$.

7. $\dfrac{x^{100n}}{n!}$.

8. $n^{1/(n+2)}$.

9. $n^{\alpha/n}, \ \alpha > 0$.

10. $\ln\left(\dfrac{n+1}{n}\right)$.

11. $\dfrac{3^{n+1}}{4^{n-1}}$.

12. $\displaystyle\int_{-n}^{0} e^{2x} \, dx$.

13. $(n+2)^{1/n}$.

14. $\left(1 - \dfrac{1}{n}\right)^n$.

15. $\displaystyle\int_{0}^{n} e^{-x} \, dx$.

16. $\dfrac{2^{3n-1}}{7^{n+2}}$.

17. $\displaystyle\int_{-n}^{n} \dfrac{dx}{1+x^2}$.

18. $\displaystyle\int_{0}^{n} e^{-nx} \, dx$.

19. $(n+2)^{1/(n+2)}$.

20. $n^2 \sin n\pi$.

21. $\dfrac{\ln n^2}{n}$.

22. $\displaystyle\int_{-1+1/n}^{1-1/n} \dfrac{dx}{\sqrt{1-x^2}}$.

23. $n^2 \sin \dfrac{\pi}{n}$.

24. $\dfrac{n!}{2^n}$.

25. $\dfrac{5^{n+1}}{4^{2n-1}}$.

26. $\left(1 + \dfrac{x}{n}\right)^{3n}$.

27. $\left(\dfrac{n+1}{n+2}\right)^n$.

28. $\displaystyle\int_{1/n}^{1} \dfrac{dx}{\sqrt{x}}$.

29. $\displaystyle\int_{n}^{n+1} e^{-x^2} \, dx$.

30. $\left(1 + \dfrac{1}{n^2}\right)^n$.

31. $\dfrac{n^n}{2^{n^2}}$.

32. $\displaystyle\int_{0}^{1/n} \cos e^x \, dx$.

33. $\left(1 + \dfrac{x}{2n}\right)^{2n}$.

34. $\left(1 + \dfrac{1}{n}\right)^{n^2}$.

35. $\displaystyle\int_{-1/n}^{1/n} \sin x^2 \, dx$.

36. $\left(t + \dfrac{x}{n}\right)^n, \quad t > 0, x > 0$.

37. Show that $\lim\limits_{n\to\infty} (\sqrt{n+1} - \sqrt{n}) = 0$.

38. Show that $\lim\limits_{n\to\infty} \sqrt{n^2+n} - n = \frac{1}{2}$.

39. Find $\lim\limits_{n\to\infty} [2n \sin (\pi/n)]$. What is the geometric significance of this limit?

HINT: Think of a regular polygon of n sides inscribed in the unit circle.

40. Show that

$$\text{if} \quad 0 < c < d, \quad \text{then} \quad (c^n + d^n)^{1/n} \to d.$$

Find the following limits.

41. $\lim\limits_{n\to\infty} \dfrac{1 + 2 + \cdots + n}{n^2}$.   HINT: $1 + 2 + \cdots + n = \dfrac{n(n + 1)}{2}$.

42. $\lim\limits_{n\to\infty} \dfrac{1^2 + 2^2 + \cdots + n^2}{(1 + n)(2 + n)}$.   HINT: $1^2 + 2^2 + \cdots + n^2 = \dfrac{n(n + 1)(2n + 1)}{6}$.

43. $\lim\limits_{n\to\infty} \dfrac{1^3 + 2^3 + \cdots + n^3}{2n^4 + n - 1}$.   HINT: $1^3 + 2^3 + \cdots + n^3 = \dfrac{n^2(n + 1)^2}{4}$.

44. A sequence $\{a_n\}$ is said to be a *Cauchy sequence*† iff

(12.3.8)
> for each $\epsilon > 0$ there exists a positive integer k such that
> $$|a_n - a_m| < \epsilon \qquad \text{for all } m, n \ge k.$$

Show that

(12.3.9)
> every convergent sequence is a Cauchy sequence.

It is also true that every Cauchy sequence is convergent, but this is more difficult to prove.

45. (*Arithmetic means*) Let

$$m_n = \frac{1}{n}(a_1 + a_2 + \cdots + a_n).$$

(a) Prove that if $\{a_n\}$ is increasing, then $\{m_n\}$ is increasing.

(b) Prove that if $a_n \to 0$, then $m_n \to 0$.

HINT: Choose an integer $j > 0$ such that, if $n \ge j$, then $a_n < \epsilon/2$. Then for $n \ge j$,

$$|m_n| < \frac{|a_1 + a_2 + \cdots + a_j|}{n} + \frac{\epsilon}{2}\left(\frac{n - j}{n}\right).$$

12.4 ···· LIMITS AS $x \to \pm\infty$

(Much of the material that appears in this section was introduced informally in Section 4.8.)

To say that

$$\lim_{x\to\infty} f(x) = l$$

---

† After the French baron Augustin Louis Cauchy (1789–1857), one of the most prolific mathematicians of all time.

[in Section 4.8 we wrote "as $x \to \infty$, $f(x) \to l$"] is to say that we can make the difference between $f(x)$ and l as small as we wish simply by requiring that x be sufficiently large. More precisely,

$$(12.4.1) \qquad \lim_{x\to\infty} f(x) = l \quad \text{iff} \quad \begin{cases} \text{for each } \epsilon > 0 \text{ there exists } K > 0 \text{ such that} \\ \quad \text{if } \ x \geq K, \qquad \text{then} \quad |f(x) - l| < \epsilon. \end{cases}$$

Here are some simple examples:

$$\lim_{x\to\infty} \frac{1}{x} = 0, \qquad \lim_{x\to\infty} \frac{x^2 - 1}{2x^2 + 5} = \lim_{x\to\infty} \frac{1 - 1/x^2}{2 + 5/x^2} = \frac{1}{2}, \qquad \lim_{x\to\infty} e^{1/x} = 1. \quad \square$$

It is easy to interpret this idea geometrically. To say that $\lim_{x\to\infty} f(x) = A$ (see Figure 12.4.1) is to say that, as x becomes arbitrarily large, the graph of f approaches the horizontal line $y = A$. The line is called a *horizontal asymptote*.

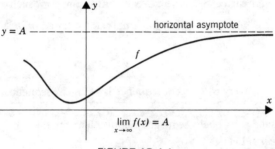

FIGURE 12.4.1

Limits as $x \to \infty$ (if they exist) are unique, and the usual rules for computation hold. For example, if

$$\lim_{x\to\infty} f(x) = l \quad \text{and} \quad \lim_{x\to\infty} g(x) = m,$$

then

$$\lim_{x\to\infty} [\alpha f(x) + \beta g(x)] = \alpha l + \beta m, \qquad \lim_{x\to\infty} [f(x)g(x)] = lm,$$

and if $m \neq 0$

$$\lim_{x\to\infty} \frac{f(x)}{g(x)} = \frac{l}{m}.$$

Moreover, the pinching theorem is valid. Suppose that for all x sufficiently large

$$h(x) \leq f(x) \leq g(x).$$

If $\quad \lim_{x\to\infty} h(x) = l = \lim_{x\to\infty} g(x), \qquad$ then $\quad \lim_{x\to\infty} f(x) = l.$

We illustrate these ideas by carrying out some computations.

PROBLEM. Find

$$\lim_{x \to \infty} \frac{\sin^2 x}{x^2}.$$

Solution. For $x \neq 0$,

$$0 \le \frac{\sin^2 x}{x^2} \le \frac{1}{x^2}. \qquad \text{(since } |\sin x| \le 1\text{)}$$

Since obviously

$$\lim_{x \to \infty} \frac{1}{x^2} = 0,$$

we have

$$\lim_{x \to \infty} \frac{\sin^2 x}{x^2} = 0. \quad \square$$

PROBLEM. Find

$$\lim_{x \to \infty} \frac{x(e^{-x} + 1)}{2x - 1}.$$

Solution. For x different from 0 and $\frac{1}{2}$,

$$\frac{x(e^{-x} + 1)}{2x - 1} = \frac{e^{-x} + 1}{2 - 1/x}.$$

Since

$$\lim_{x \to \infty} (e^{-x} + 1) = 1 \qquad \text{and} \qquad \lim_{x \to \infty} (2 - 1/x) = 2,$$

we have

$$\lim_{x \to \infty} \frac{x(e^{-x} + 1)}{2x - 1} = \frac{1}{2}. \quad \square$$

PROBLEM. Find

$$\lim_{x \to \infty} \frac{x + \ln x}{x \ln x}.$$

Solution. For x different from 0 and 1,

$$\frac{x + \ln x}{x \ln x} = \frac{x}{x \ln x} + \frac{\ln x}{x \ln x} = \frac{1}{\ln x} + \frac{1}{x}.$$

Since

$$\lim_{x \to \infty} \frac{1}{\ln x} = 0 \qquad \text{and} \qquad \lim_{x \to \infty} \frac{1}{x} = 0,$$

you can see that

$$\lim_{x \to \infty} \frac{x + \ln x}{x \ln x} = 0. \quad \square$$

There is a simple relation between limits at ∞ and right-hand limits at 0. Set $x = 1/t$, and you'll see that

(12.4.2)
$$\lim_{x \to \infty} f(x) = l \quad \text{iff} \quad \lim_{t \to 0^+} f(1/t) = l.$$

We'll use this idea in the next section.

Limits as $x \to -\infty$ are defined by setting

(12.4.3)
$$\lim_{x \to -\infty} f(x) = l \quad \text{iff} \quad \begin{cases} \text{for each } \epsilon > 0 \text{ there exists } K < 0 \text{ such that} \\ \text{if } x \le K, \quad \text{then } |f(x) - l| < \epsilon. \end{cases}$$

The behavior of such limits is entirely analogous to the case $x \to \infty$. Here are some examples:

$$\lim_{x \to -\infty} e^x = 0 \quad \text{and} \quad \lim_{x \to -\infty} \frac{3 - x}{2 + x} = \lim_{x \to -\infty} \frac{3/x - 1}{2/x + 1} = -1.$$

For the function

$$h(x) = \begin{cases} -1, & x < 0 \\ 1, & x > 0 \end{cases},$$

we have

$$\lim_{x \to \infty} h(x) = 1 \quad \text{and} \quad \lim_{x \to -\infty} h(x) = -1.$$

If

$$P(x) = a_n x^n + a_{n-1} x^{n-1} + \cdots + a_0 \quad \text{and} \quad Q(x) = b_n x^n + b_{n-1} x^{n-1} + \cdots + b_0$$

are both polynomials of the same degree n, then

$$\lim_{x \to \infty} \frac{P(x)}{Q(x)} = \frac{a_n}{b_n} = \lim_{x \to -\infty} \frac{P(x)}{Q(x)}.$$

To see this, divide both numerator and denominator by x^n:

$$\frac{P(x)}{Q(x)} = \frac{a_n + a_{n-1}/x + \cdots + a_0/x^n}{b_n + b_{n-1}/x + \cdots + b_0/x^n}.$$

As $x \to \pm\infty$, the numerator tends to a_n and the denominator to b_n.

EXERCISES

Find the following limits.

1. $\lim_{x \to \infty} \dfrac{3}{x}$.

2. $\lim_{x \to \infty} \dfrac{x}{x^2 + 1}$.

3. $\lim_{x \to \infty} \dfrac{x^2 + x + 1}{x^3 + 2x + 1}$.

4. $\displaystyle\lim_{x\to\infty} \frac{x-1}{x+1}$.

5. $\displaystyle\lim_{x\to\infty} \frac{2\sin x}{x}$.

6. $\displaystyle\lim_{x\to\infty} \ln\left(\frac{2x}{x+1}\right)$.

7. $\displaystyle\lim_{x\to\infty} \frac{(ax-b)^2}{(a-x)(b-x)}$.

8. $\displaystyle\lim_{x\to\infty} \frac{(x-a)(x-b)}{(ax+b)^2}$.

9. $\displaystyle\lim_{x\to\infty} 10^{1/x}$.

10. $\displaystyle\lim_{x\to\infty} \frac{x^{3/2}+2}{5x^{3/2}+1}$.

11. $\displaystyle\lim_{x\to\infty} \sin\frac{1}{x}$.

12. $\displaystyle\lim_{x\to\infty} e^{-x}\cos^2 x$.

13. $\displaystyle\lim_{x\to\infty} \left(x\sin\frac{1}{x}\right)$.

14. $\displaystyle\lim_{x\to\infty} \left(1-\sin\frac{1}{x}\right)^2$.

15. $\displaystyle\lim_{x\to-\infty} e^x\sin x$.

16. $\displaystyle\lim_{x\to\infty} e^{-x}\sin x$.

17. $\displaystyle\lim_{x\to\infty} \int_e^x \frac{dt}{t(\ln t)^2}$.

18. $\displaystyle\lim_{x\to\infty} \int_0^x \frac{dt}{1+t^2}$.

19. $\displaystyle\lim_{x\to-\infty} \frac{\sqrt{x^2+1}}{2x}$.

20. $\displaystyle\lim_{x\to\infty} \frac{x^2 e^{-x}}{2-x^2}$.

21. $\displaystyle\lim_{x\to\infty} \left(x-x\cos\frac{1}{x}\right)$.

22. $\displaystyle\lim_{x\to\infty} \int_0^x te^{-t}\,dt$.

23. $\displaystyle\lim_{x\to-\infty} \frac{(2x^2+3)^2}{(1+x^2)(1-x^3)}$.

24. $\displaystyle\lim_{x\to\infty} \left(x^2-x^2\cos\frac{2}{x}\right)$.

25. $\displaystyle\lim_{x\to\infty} [2\ln x - \ln(3x^2+1)]$.

26. $\displaystyle\lim_{x\to-\infty} \frac{x^3-1}{(x+1)(x^2+x+1)}$.

27. $\displaystyle\lim_{x\to\infty} (\sqrt{x^2+x}-\sqrt{x^2+1})$.

28. $\displaystyle\lim_{x\to\infty} (\sqrt{x+1}-\sqrt{x})$.

29. Show that

$$\lim_{x\to\infty} \frac{\ln x}{\sqrt{x}} = 0$$

by showing first that $\ln x < 3x^{1/3}$ for $x \ge 1$.

30. Given that P is a polynomial of degree n and Q is a polynomial of degree $m > n$, determine

$$\lim_{x\to\infty} \frac{P(x)}{Q(x)} \quad\text{and}\quad \lim_{x\to-\infty} \frac{P(x)}{Q(x)}.$$

31. Prove that, if f is continuous on $[a, \infty)$ and has a finite limit as x tends to ∞, then f is bounded on $[a, \infty)$.

32. (a) Prove that, if f is increasing and bounded on $[a, \infty)$, then f has a limit as x tends to ∞.
(b) Prove that, if f is decreasing and bounded on $[a, \infty)$, then f has a limit as x tends to ∞.

12.5····THE INDETERMINATE FORM (0/0)

Here we are concerned with limits of quotients

$$\frac{f(x)}{g(x)}$$

where the numerator and denominator both tend to 0 and elementary methods fail or are difficult to apply. For convenience we will dispense with the formality of writing

$$\lim_{x\to c} f(x) = 0, \qquad \lim_{x\to\infty} f(x) = 0, \qquad \text{etc.}$$

and use the notation introduced in Section 4.8:

$$\text{as} \quad x \to c, \qquad f(x) \to 0,$$
$$\text{as} \quad x \to \infty, \qquad f(x) \to 0, \quad \text{etc.}$$

THEOREM 12.5.1   L'HOSPITAL'S RULE (0/0)†

Suppose that

$$f(x) \to 0 \quad \text{and} \quad g(x) \to 0$$

as $\quad x \to c^+, x \to c^-, x \to c, x \to \infty, \text{ or } x \to -\infty.$

If $\quad \dfrac{f'(x)}{g'(x)} \to l, \quad$ then $\quad \dfrac{f(x)}{g(x)} \to l.$

We will prove the validity of L'Hospital's rule a little later. First we demonstrate its usefulness.

PROBLEM. Find

$$\lim_{x \to \pi/2} \frac{\cos x}{\pi - 2x}.$$

Solution. As $x \to \pi/2$, both the numerator $f(x) = \cos x$ and the denominator $g(x) = \pi - 2x$ tend to zero, but it's not at all obvious what happens to the quotient

$$\frac{f(x)}{g(x)} = \frac{\cos x}{\pi - 2x}.$$

Therefore we test the quotient of derivatives:

$$\frac{f'(x)}{g'(x)} = \frac{-\sin x}{-2} = \frac{\sin x}{2} \to \frac{1}{2} \quad \text{as} \quad x \to \pi/2.$$

It follows from L'Hospital's rule that

$$\frac{\cos x}{\pi - 2x} \to \frac{1}{2} \quad \text{as} \quad x \to \pi/2.$$

We can express all this on just one line using * to indicate the differentiation of numerator and denominator:

$$\lim_{x \to \pi/2} \frac{\cos x}{\pi - 2x} \overset{*}{=} \lim_{x \to \pi/2} \frac{-\sin x}{-2} = \lim_{x \to \pi/2} \frac{\sin x}{2} = \frac{1}{2}. \quad \square$$

---

† Named after a Frenchman G. F. A. L'Hospital (1661–1704). The result was actually discovered by his teacher, Jakob Bernoulli (1654–1705).

PROBLEM. Find

$$\lim_{x \to 0^+} \frac{x}{\sin \sqrt{x}}.$$

Solution. As $x \to 0^+$, both numerator and denominator tend to 0. Since

$$\frac{f'(x)}{g'(x)} = \frac{1}{(\cos \sqrt{x})(1/2\sqrt{x})} = \frac{2\sqrt{x}}{\cos \sqrt{x}} \to 0 \qquad \text{as} \quad x \to 0^+,$$

it follows from L'Hospital's rule that

$$\frac{x}{\sin \sqrt{x}} \to 0 \qquad \text{as} \quad x \to 0^+.$$

For short we can write

$$\lim_{x \to 0^+} \frac{x}{\sin \sqrt{x}} \overset{*}{=} \lim_{x \to 0^+} \frac{2\sqrt{x}}{\cos \sqrt{x}} = 0. \quad \square$$

Sometimes it's necessary to differentiate numerator and denominator more than once. The next problem gives such an instance.

PROBLEM. Find

$$\lim_{x \to 0} \frac{e^x - x - 1}{x^2}.$$

Solution. As $x \to 0$, both numerator and denominator tend to 0. Here

$$\frac{f'(x)}{g'(x)} = \frac{e^x - 1}{2x}.$$

Since both numerator and denominator still tend to 0, we differentiate again:

$$\frac{f''(x)}{g''(x)} = \frac{e^x}{2}.$$

Since this last quotient tends to $\frac{1}{2}$, we can conclude that

$$\frac{e^x - 1}{2x} \to \frac{1}{2} \qquad \text{and therefore} \qquad \frac{e^x - x - 1}{x^2} \to \frac{1}{2}.$$

For short we can write

$$\lim_{x \to 0} \frac{e^x - x - 1}{x^2} \overset{*}{=} \lim_{x \to 0} \frac{e^x - 1}{2x} \overset{*}{=} \lim_{x \to 0} \frac{e^x}{2} = \frac{1}{2}. \quad \square$$

PROBLEM. Find

$$\lim_{x \to 0^+} (1 + x)^{1/x}.$$

Solution. Here we are dealing with an indeterminate of the form 1^∞: as $x \to 0^+$, $1 + x \to 0$ and $1/x$ increases without bound.

As the expression stands, it is not amenable to L'Hospital's rule. To make it so, we take its logarithm. This gives

$$\lim_{x \to 0^+} \ln (1 + x)^{1/x} = \lim_{x \to 0^+} \frac{\ln (1 + x)}{x} \overset{*}{=} \lim_{x \to 0^+} \frac{1}{1 + x} = 1.$$

Since $\ln (1 + x)^{1/x}$ tends to 1, $(1 + x)^{1/x}$ itself tends to e. □†

PROBLEM. Find

$$\lim_{n \to \infty} (\cos \pi/n)^n.$$

Solution. This again is an indeterminate of the form 1^∞. To apply the methods of this section we replace the integer variable n by the real variable x and examine the behavior of

$$(\cos \pi/x)^x \qquad \text{as} \quad x \to \infty.$$

Taking the logarithm of this expression, we have

$$\ln (\cos \pi/x)^x = x \ln (\cos \pi/x).$$

The right side is an indeterminate of the form $\infty \cdot 0$. To apply L'Hospital's rule, we express it as an indeterminate of the form $0/0$:

$$x \ln (\cos \pi/x) = \frac{\ln (\cos \pi/x)}{1/x}.$$

We then have

$$\lim_{x \to \infty} \ln (\cos \pi/x)^x = \lim_{x \to \infty} \frac{\ln (\cos \pi/x)}{1/x}$$

$$\overset{*}{=} \lim_{x \to \infty} \frac{(-\sin \pi/x)(-\pi/x^2)}{(\cos \pi/x)(-1/x^2)} = \lim_{x \to \infty} (-\pi \tan \pi/x) = 0.$$

This shows that $(\cos \pi/x)^x$ tends to 1 and thus that $(\cos \pi/n)^n$ tends to 1. □

To derive L'Hospital's rule, we need a generalization of the mean-value theorem.

THEOREM 12.5.2   THE CAUCHY MEAN-VALUE THEOREM††

Suppose that f and g are differentiable on (a, b) and continuous on $[a, b]$. If g' is never 0 in (a, b), then there is a number c in (a, b) for which

$$\frac{f'(c)}{g'(c)} = \frac{f(b) - f(a)}{g(b) - g(a)}.$$

---

† Setting $x = 1/n$, we have the familiar result

$$\left(1 + \frac{1}{n}\right)^n \to e.$$

†† Another contribution of A. L. Cauchy, after whom Cauchy sequences were named.

Proof. We can prove this by applying the mean-value theorem (4.1.1) to the function

$$G(x) = [g(b) - g(a)][f(x) - f(a)] - [g(x) - g(a)][f(b) - f(a)].$$

Since

$$G(a) = 0 \quad \text{and} \quad G(b) = 0,$$

there exists (by the mean-value theorem) a number c in (a, b) for which

$$G'(c) = 0.$$

Since, in general,

$$G'(x) = [g(b) - g(a)]f'(x) - g'(x)[f(b) - f(a)],$$

we must have

$$[g(b) - g(a)]f'(c) - g'(c)[f(b) - f(a)] = 0,$$

and thus

$$[g(b) - g(a)]f'(c) = g'(c)[f(b) - f(a)].$$

Since g' is never 0 in (a, b),

$$g'(c) \neq 0 \quad \text{and} \quad g(b) - g(a) \neq 0.$$
$$\underset{\qquad\qquad\text{explain}}{\uparrow\!\_\_\_}$$

We can therefore divide by these numbers and obtain

$$\frac{f'(c)}{g'(c)} = \frac{f(b) - f(a)}{g(b) - g(a)}. \qquad \square$$

Now we prove L'Hospital's rule for the case $x \to c^+$. We assume that, as $x \to c^+$,

$$f(x) \to 0, \quad g(x) \to 0, \quad \text{and} \quad \frac{f'(x)}{g'(x)} \to l$$

and show that

$$\frac{f(x)}{g(x)} \to l.$$

Proof. The fact that

$$\frac{f'(x)}{g'(x)} \to l \qquad \text{as} \quad x \to c^+$$

assures us that both f' and g' exist on a set of the form $(c, c + h]$ and that g' is not zero there. By setting $f(c) = 0$ and $g(c) = 0$, we ensure that f and g are both continuous on $[c, c + h]$. We can now apply the Cauchy mean-value theorem and conclude that there exists a number c_h between c and $c + h$ such that

$$\frac{f'(c_h)}{g'(c_h)} = \frac{f(c + h) - f(c)}{g(c + h) - g(c)} = \frac{f(c + h)}{g(c + h)}.$$

The result is now obtained by letting $h \to 0^+$. Since the left side tends to l, the right side tends to l. □

Here is a proof of L'Hospital's rule for the case $x \to \infty$.

Proof.   The key here is to set $x = 1/t$:

$$\lim_{x \to \infty} \frac{f'(x)}{g'(x)} = \lim_{t \to 0^+} \frac{f'(1/t)}{g'(1/t)} = \lim_{t \to 0^+} \frac{-t^{-2}f'(1/t)}{-t^{-2}g'(1/t)} \underset{\uparrow}{=} \lim_{t \to 0^+} \frac{f(1/t)}{g(1/t)} = \lim_{x \to \infty} \frac{f(x)}{g(x)}. \quad \square$$

by L'Hospital's rule for the case $t \to 0^+$

CAUTION.   L'Hospital's rule does not apply when the numerator or the denominator has a finite nonzero limit.   For example,

$$\lim_{x \to 0} \frac{x}{x + \cos x} = \frac{0}{1} = 0.$$

A blind application of L'Hospital's rule would lead to

$$\lim_{x \to 0} \frac{x}{x + \cos x} \overset{*}{=} \lim_{x \to 0} \frac{1}{1 - \sin x} = 1.$$

This is wrong.   □

EXERCISES

Find the indicated limit.

1. $\lim\limits_{x \to 0^+} \dfrac{\sin x}{\sqrt{x}}$.

2. $\lim\limits_{x \to 1} \dfrac{\ln x}{1 - x}$.

3. $\lim\limits_{x \to 0} \dfrac{e^x - 1}{\ln (1 + x)}$.

4. $\lim\limits_{x \to 4} \dfrac{\sqrt{x} - 2}{x - 4}$.

5. $\lim\limits_{x \to \pi/2} \dfrac{\cos x}{\sin 2x}$.

6. $\lim\limits_{x \to a} \dfrac{x - a}{x^n - a^n}$.

7. $\lim\limits_{x \to 0} \dfrac{2^x - 1}{x}$.

8. $\lim\limits_{x \to 0} \dfrac{\tan^{-1} x}{x}$.

9. $\lim\limits_{x \to 1} \dfrac{x^{1/2} - x^{1/4}}{x - 1}$.

10. $\lim\limits_{x \to 0} \dfrac{e^x - 1}{x(1 + x)}$.

11. $\lim\limits_{x \to 0} \dfrac{e^x - e^{-x}}{\sin x}$.

12. $\lim\limits_{x \to 0} \dfrac{1 - \cos x}{3x}$.

13. $\lim\limits_{x \to 0} \dfrac{x + \sin \pi x}{x - \sin \pi x}$.

14. $\lim\limits_{x \to 0} \dfrac{a^x - (a + 1)^x}{x}$.

15. $\lim\limits_{x \to 0} (e^x + x)^{1/x}$.

16. $\lim\limits_{x \to \infty} \left(1 + \dfrac{1}{x}\right)^x$.

17. $\lim\limits_{x \to 0} \dfrac{\tan \pi x}{e^x - 1}$.

18. $\lim\limits_{x \to 0} (e^x + 3x)^{1/x}$.

19. $\lim\limits_{x \to 0} \dfrac{1 + x - e^x}{x(e^x - 1)}$.

20. $\lim\limits_{x \to 0} \dfrac{\ln (\sec x)}{x^2}$.

21. $\lim\limits_{x \to 0} \dfrac{x - \tan x}{x - \sin x}$.

22. $\lim\limits_{x \to 0} \dfrac{xe^{nx} - x}{1 - \cos nx}$.

23. $\lim\limits_{x \to 1^-} \dfrac{\sqrt{1 - x^2}}{\sqrt{1 - x^3}}$.

24. $\lim\limits_{x \to 0} \left(\dfrac{1}{\sin x} - \dfrac{1}{x}\right)$.

25. $\lim\limits_{x\to\pi/2} \dfrac{\ln(\sin x)}{(\pi-2x)^2}$.

26. $\lim\limits_{x\to 0^+} \dfrac{\sqrt{x}}{\sqrt{x}+\sin\sqrt{x}}$.

27. $\lim\limits_{x\to 1}\left(\dfrac{1}{\ln x}-\dfrac{x}{x-1}\right)$.

28. $\lim\limits_{x\to 0} \dfrac{\sqrt{a+x}-\sqrt{a-x}}{x}$.

29. $\lim\limits_{x\to\pi/4} \dfrac{\sec^2 x - 2\tan x}{1+\cos 4x}$.

30. $\lim\limits_{x\to 0} \dfrac{x-\sin^{-1} x}{\sin^3 x}$.

Find the limit of the sequence.

31. $\lim\limits_{n\to\infty} n(\pi/2 - \tan^{-1} n)$.

32. $\lim\limits_{n\to\infty} [\ln(1-1/n)\csc 1/n]$.

33. $\lim\limits_{n\to\infty} \dfrac{1}{n[\ln(n+1)-\ln n]}$.

34. $\lim\limits_{n\to\infty} \dfrac{\sinh \pi/n - \sin \pi/n}{\sin^3 \pi/n}$.

35. Find the fallacy:

$$\lim_{x\to 0}\frac{2+x+\sin x}{x^3+x-\cos x} \overset{*}{=} \lim_{x\to 0}\frac{1+\cos x}{3x^2+1+\sin x} \overset{*}{=} \lim_{x\to 0}\frac{-\sin x}{6x+\cos x} = \frac{0}{1} = 0.$$

36. Show that, if $a > 0$, then

$$\lim_{n\to\infty} n(a^{1/n}-1) = \ln a.$$

37. Given that f is continuous, use L'Hospital's rule to determine

$$\lim_{x\to 0}\left(\frac{1}{x}\int_0^x f(t)\,dt\right).$$

12.6···INFINITE LIMITS; THE INDETERMINATE FORM (∞/∞)

(Some of this material was introduced informally in Section 4.8.)
     We write

$$\lim_{x\to c} f(x) = \infty$$

[in Section 4.8 we wrote "as $x\to c, f(x)\to\infty$"] iff we can make $f(x)$ as large as we wish simply by requiring that x be sufficiently close to c. More precisely,

(12.6.1) $\lim\limits_{x\to c} f(x) = \infty$ iff $\begin{cases}\text{for each } M > 0 \text{ there exists } \delta > 0 \text{ such that,}\\ \text{if } 0 < |x-c| < \delta, \quad\text{then}\quad f(x)\ge M.\end{cases}$

EXAMPLES

$$\lim_{x\to c}\frac{1}{|x-c|} = \infty, \qquad \lim_{x\to c}\frac{1}{(\sqrt{x}-\sqrt{c})^2} = \infty, \qquad \lim_{x\to c}\frac{1}{\sin^2(x-c)} = \infty. \quad\square$$

One-sided infinite limits

$$\lim_{x\to c^+} f(x) = \infty \quad\text{and}\quad \lim_{x\to c^-} f(x) = \infty$$

are defined in a similar manner. We won't take time to spell out the details since the idea must be clear from Section 4.8. It must also be clear how all these notions can be extended to allow for a limit of $-\infty$.

Geometrically, limits of the form

$$\lim_{x \to c} f(x) = \pm \infty, \qquad \lim_{x \to c^+} f(x) = \pm \infty, \qquad \lim_{x \to c^-} f(x) = \pm \infty$$

signal the presence of a *vertical asymptote.* See Figures 12.6.1 – 12.6.4.

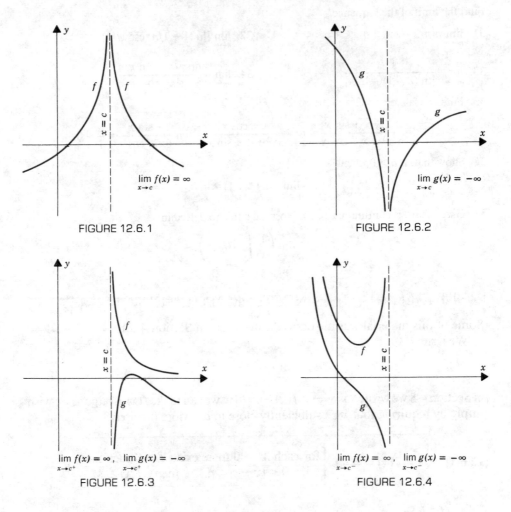

FIGURE 12.6.1

FIGURE 12.6.2

FIGURE 12.6.3

FIGURE 12.6.4

We have yet to introduce limits of the form

$$\lim_{x \to \pm \infty} f(x) = \pm \infty.$$

There are four possibilities here. We will spell out details for only one of them. By writing

$$\lim_{x \to \infty} f(x) = \infty$$

we mean that we can make $f(x)$ as large as we wish simply by requiring that x be sufficiently large:

$$(12.6.2) \qquad \lim_{x\to\infty} f(x) = \infty \text{ iff } \begin{cases} \text{for each } M > 0 \text{ there exists } K > 0 \text{ such that,} \\ \text{if } x \geq K, \quad \text{then } f(x) \geq M. \end{cases}$$

Some simple examples:

$$\lim_{x\to\infty} \sqrt{x} = \infty, \qquad \lim_{x\to\infty} e^x = \infty, \qquad \lim_{x\to\infty} \ln x = \infty, \qquad \lim_{x\to\infty} (x + 1/x) = \infty.$$

To illustrate these ideas further we will calculate some limits that are not quite so obvious.

PROBLEM. Find

$$\lim_{x\to\infty} x(2 + \sin x).$$

Solution. Since $-1 \leq \sin x$, we have

$$1 \leq 2 + \sin x$$

and thus for $x > 0$

$$x \leq x(2 + \sin x).$$

Since $\lim_{x\to\infty} x = \infty$, it's clear that

$$\lim_{x\to\infty} x(2 + \sin x) = \infty. \quad \square$$

PROBLEM. Find

$$\lim_{x\to\infty} \frac{1 - x^2}{2x + 1}.$$

Solution

$$\lim_{x\to\infty} \frac{1 - x^2}{2x + 1} = \lim_{x\to\infty} \frac{1/x^2 - 1}{2/x + 1/x^2} = -\infty. \quad \square$$

PROBLEM. Find

$$\lim_{x\to\infty} \ln \left(\frac{x}{x^2 + 1} \right).$$

Solution. Note first that

$$\lim_{x\to\infty} \frac{x}{x^2 + 1} = \lim_{x\to\infty} \frac{1}{x + 1/x} = 0.$$

It follows that

$$\lim_{x\to\infty} \ln \left(\frac{x}{x^2 + 1} \right) = -\infty. \quad \square$$

PROBLEM. Find

$$\lim_{x \to \infty} \left(x \sin \frac{1}{x} \right).$$

Solution

$$\lim_{x \to \infty} \left(x \sin \frac{1}{x} \right) = \lim_{x \to \infty} \frac{\sin 1/x}{1/x} = \lim_{t \to 0^+} \frac{\sin t}{t} = 1. \quad \square$$

PROBLEM. Find

$$\lim_{x \to 0} \left(\frac{1}{x} - \frac{1}{x^2} \right).$$

Solution

$$\lim_{x \to 0} \left(\frac{1}{x} - \frac{1}{x^2} \right) = \lim_{x \to 0} \frac{x - 1}{x^2} = -\infty. \quad \square$$

We come now to limits of quotients

$$\frac{f(x)}{g(x)}$$

where numerator and denominator both tend to ∞. We take l as a fixed real number.

THEOREM 12.6.3   L'HOSPITAL'S RULE (∞/∞)

Suppose that

$$f(x) \to \pm\infty \quad \text{and} \quad g(x) \to \pm\infty$$

as $x \to c^-, x \to c^+, x \to c, x \to \infty$, or $x \to -\infty$.

If $\dfrac{f'(x)}{g'(x)} \to l,$ then $\dfrac{f(x)}{g(x)} \to l.$

While the proof of L'Hospital's rule in this setting is a little more complicated than it was in the (0/0) case,† the application of the rule is much the same.

PROBLEM. Show that

(12.6.4)

$$\lim_{x \to \infty} \frac{\ln x}{x} = 0.$$

---
† We omit the proof.

Solution. Both numerator and denominator tend to ∞ with x. L'Hospital's rule gives

$$\lim_{x\to\infty} \frac{\ln x}{x} \overset{*}{=} \lim_{x\to\infty} \frac{1}{x} = 0. \quad \square$$

PROBLEM. Show that

(12.6.5)
$$\lim_{x\to\infty} \frac{x^k}{e^x} = 0.$$

Solution. Here we differentiate numerator and denominator k times:

$$\lim_{x\to\infty} \frac{x^k}{e^x} \overset{*}{=} \lim_{x\to\infty} \frac{kx^{k-1}}{e^x} \overset{*}{=} \lim_{x\to\infty} \frac{k(k-1)x^{k-2}}{e^x} \overset{*}{=} \cdots \overset{*}{=} \lim_{x\to\infty} \frac{k!}{e^x} = 0. \quad \square$$

PROBLEM. Show that

(12.6.6)
$$\lim_{x\to 0^+} x^x = 1.$$

Solution. Here we are dealing with an indeterminate of the form 0^0. Our first step is to take the logarithm of x^x. Then we apply L'Hospital's rule:

$$\lim_{x\to 0^+} \ln x^x = \lim_{x\to 0^+} (x \ln x) = \lim_{x\to 0^+} \frac{\ln x}{1/x} \overset{*}{=} \lim_{x\to 0^+} \frac{1/x}{-1/x^2} = \lim_{x\to 0^+} (-x) = 0.$$

Since $\ln x^x$ tends to 0, x^x must tend to 1. $\quad \square$

PROBLEM. Show that

$$\lim_{x\to\infty} (x^2 + 1)^{1/\ln x} = e^2.$$

Solution. Here we have an indeterminate of the form ∞^0. Taking the logarithm and then applying L'Hospital's rule, we find that

$$\lim_{x\to\infty} \ln (x^2 + 1)^{1/\ln x} = \lim_{x\to\infty} \frac{\ln (x^2 + 1)}{\ln x} \overset{*}{=} \lim_{x\to\infty} \frac{2x/(x^2 + 1)}{1/x} = \lim_{x\to\infty} \frac{2x^2}{x^2 + 1} = 2.$$

It follows that

$$\lim_{x\to\infty} (x^2 + 1)^{1/\ln x} = e^2. \quad \square$$

PROBLEM. Find the limit as $n \to \infty$ of the sequence

$$a_n = \frac{\ln n}{\sqrt{n}}.$$

Solution. To bring into play the methods of calculus we investigate

$$\lim_{x \to \infty} \frac{\ln x}{\sqrt{x}}$$

instead. Since both numerator and denominator tend to ∞ with x, we try L'Hospital's rule:

$$\lim_{x \to \infty} \frac{\ln x}{\sqrt{x}} \overset{*}{=} \lim_{x \to \infty} \frac{1/x}{1/2\sqrt{x}} = \lim_{x \to \infty} \frac{2}{\sqrt{x}} = 0.$$

The limit of the sequence must also be 0. □

CAUTION. L'Hospital's rule does not apply when the numerator or denominator has a finite nonzero limit. While

$$\lim_{x \to 0^+} \frac{1 + x}{\sin x} = \infty,$$

a misapplication of L'Hospital's rule can lead to the *incorrect conclusion* that

$$\lim_{x \to 0^+} \frac{1 + x}{\sin x} \overset{*}{=} \lim_{x \to 0^+} \frac{1}{-\cos x} = -1. □$$

EXERCISES

Find the indicated limit.

1. $\displaystyle\lim_{x \to \pi/2^-} \tan x.$

2. $\displaystyle\lim_{x \to 0^+} \ln \frac{1}{x}.$

3. $\displaystyle\lim_{x \to \infty} \frac{x^3}{1 - x^3}.$

4. $\displaystyle\lim_{x \to \infty} \frac{x^3 - 1}{2 - x}.$

5. $\displaystyle\lim_{x \to \infty} \left(x^2 \sin \frac{1}{x} \right).$

6. $\displaystyle\lim_{x \to \infty} \frac{\ln x^k}{x}.$

7. $\displaystyle\lim_{x \to \pi/2^-} \frac{\tan 5x}{\tan x}.$

8. $\displaystyle\lim_{x \to 0} (x \ln |\sin x|).$

9. $\displaystyle\lim_{x \to 0^+} x^{2x}.$

10. $\displaystyle\lim_{x \to \infty} \left(x \sin \frac{\pi}{x} \right).$

11. $\displaystyle\lim_{x \to 0} [x (\ln |x|)^2].$

12. $\displaystyle\lim_{x \to 0^+} \frac{\ln x}{\cot x}.$

13. $\displaystyle\lim_{x \to \infty} \left(\frac{1}{x} \int_0^x e^{t^2} \, dt \right).$

14. $\displaystyle\lim_{x \to \infty} \frac{\sqrt{1 + x^2}}{x}.$

15. $\displaystyle\lim_{x \to 0} \left[\frac{1}{\sin^2 x} - \frac{1}{x^2} \right].$

16. $\displaystyle\lim_{x \to 0} |\sin x|^x.$

17. $\displaystyle\lim_{x \to 1} x^{1/(x-1)}.$

18. $\displaystyle\lim_{x \to 0^+} x^{\sin x}.$

19. $\displaystyle\lim_{x \to \infty} \left(\cos \frac{1}{x} \right)^x.$

20. $\displaystyle\lim_{x \to \pi/2} |\sec x|^{\cos x}.$

21. $\displaystyle\lim_{x \to 0} \left[\frac{1}{\ln (1 + x)} - \frac{1}{x} \right].$

22. $\displaystyle\lim_{x \to \infty} (x^2 + a^2)^{(1/x)^2}.$

23. $\displaystyle\lim_{x \to 1} \left[\frac{x}{x - 1} - \frac{1}{\ln x} \right].$

24. $\displaystyle\lim_{x \to \infty} \ln \left(\frac{x^2 - 1}{x^2 + 1} \right)^3.$

25. $\displaystyle\lim_{x \to \infty} (\sqrt{x^2 + 2x} - x).$

26. $\displaystyle\lim_{x \to \infty} \frac{1}{x} \int_0^x \sin \left(\frac{1}{t + 1} \right) dt.$

27. $\displaystyle\lim_{x \to \infty} (x^3 + 1)^{1/\ln x}.$

28. $\displaystyle\lim_{x \to \infty} (e^x + 1)^{1/x}.$

29. $\displaystyle\lim_{x \to \infty} (\cosh x)^{1/x}.$

30. $\displaystyle\lim_{x \to \infty} (x^4 + 1)^{1/\ln x}.$

Find the limit of the sequence.

31. $\lim\limits_{n\to\infty} \left(\dfrac{1}{n}\ln\dfrac{1}{n}\right).$

32. $\lim\limits_{n\to\infty} \dfrac{n^k}{2^n}.$

33. $\lim\limits_{n\to\infty} (\ln n)^{1/n}.$

34. $\lim\limits_{n\to\infty} \dfrac{\ln n}{n^p},$ given that $p > 0.$

35. $\lim\limits_{n\to\infty} (n^2 + n)^{1/n}.$

36. $\lim\limits_{n\to\infty} n^{\sin(\pi/n)}.$

37. $\lim\limits_{n\to\infty} \dfrac{n^2 \ln n}{e^n}.$

38. $\lim\limits_{n\to\infty} (\sqrt{n} - 1)^{1/\sqrt{n}}.$

Sketch the following curves specifying all vertical and horizontal asymptotes.

39. $y = x^2 - \dfrac{1}{x^3}.$

40. $y = \sqrt{\dfrac{x}{x-1}}.$

41. $y = xe^x.$

42. $y = xe^{-x}.$

43. $y = x^2 e^{-x}.$

44. $y = \dfrac{\ln x}{x}.$

The graphs of two functions $y = f(x)$ and $y = g(x)$ are said to be *asymptotic as $x \to \infty$* iff

$$\lim_{x\to\infty} [f(x) - g(x)] = 0;$$

they are said to be *asymptotic as $x \to -\infty$* iff

$$\lim_{x\to-\infty} [f(x) - g(x)] = 0.$$

45. Show that the hyperbolic arc $y = (b/a)\sqrt{x^2 - a^2}$ is asymptotic to the line $y = (b/a)x$ as $x \to \infty.$

46. Show that the graphs of $y = \cosh x$ and $y = \sinh x$ are asymptotic.

47. Give an example of a function the graph of which is asymptotic to the cubing function $y = x^3$ as $x \to \infty.$

48. Give an example of a function the graph of which is asymptotic to the parabola $y = x^2$ as $x \to \infty$ and crosses the graph of the parabola twice.

49. Give an example of a function the graph of which is asymptotic to the line $y = x$ as $x \to \infty$ and crosses the graph of the line infinitely often.

50. Let P be a polynomial of degree n: $P(x) = a_n x^n + a_{n-1}x^{n-1} + \cdots + a_0.$ Let Q be a polynomial of degree $m < n$: $Q(x) = b_m x^m + b_{m-1}x^{m-1} + \cdots + b_0.$ Find

$$\lim_{x\to\infty} \frac{P(x)}{Q(x)}$$

given that a_n and b_m have (a) the same sign, (b) opposite signs.

51. Find the fallacy:

$$\lim_{x\to 0^+} \frac{x^2}{\sin x} \overset{*}{=} \lim_{x\to 0^+} \frac{2x}{\cos x} \overset{*}{=} \lim_{x\to 0^+} \frac{2}{-\sin x} = -\infty.$$

52. Show that, for each positive integer k,

$$\lim_{n\to\infty} \frac{(\ln n)^k}{n} = 0.$$

HINT: Use induction.

53. Show that, for each positive integer k,

$$\lim_{n\to\infty} \frac{n^k \ln n}{e^n} = 0.$$

12.7 ···· IMPROPER INTEGRALS

We begin with a function f continuous on an unbounded interval $[a, \infty)$. For each number $b > a$ we can form the integral

$$\int_a^b f(x)\,dx.$$

If, as b tends to ∞, this integral tends to a finite limit l,

$$\lim_{b \to \infty} \int_a^b f(x)\,dx = l,$$

then we write

$$\int_a^\infty f(x)\,dx = l$$

and say that the *improper integral*

$$\int_a^\infty f(x)\,dx$$

converges to l. Otherwise, we say that the *improper integral*

$$\int_a^\infty f(x)\,dx$$

diverges.

In a similar manner, improper integrals

$$\int_{-\infty}^b f(x)\,dx$$

arise as limits of the form

$$\lim_{a \to -\infty} \int_a^b f(x)\,dx.$$

EXAMPLES

(1) $\displaystyle\int_1^\infty e^{-x}\,dx = \frac{1}{e}.$ (2) $\displaystyle\int_1^\infty \frac{dx}{x}$ diverges.

(3) $\displaystyle\int_1^\infty \frac{dx}{x^2} = 1.$ (4) $\displaystyle\int_{-\infty}^1 \cos \pi x\,dx$ diverges.

Verification

(1) $\displaystyle\int_1^\infty e^{-x}\,dx = \lim_{b \to \infty} \int_1^b e^{-x}\,dx = \lim_{b \to \infty} \left[-e^{-x} \right]_1^b = \lim_{b \to \infty} \left(\frac{1}{e} - \frac{1}{e^b} \right) = \frac{1}{e}.$

(2) $\displaystyle\int_1^\infty \frac{dx}{x} = \lim_{b \to \infty} \int_1^b \frac{dx}{x} = \lim_{b \to \infty} \ln b = \infty.$

(3) $\displaystyle\int_1^\infty \frac{dx}{x^2} = \lim_{b\to\infty} \int_1^b \frac{dx}{x^2} = \lim_{b\to\infty}\left[-\frac{1}{x}\right]_1^b = \lim_{b\to\infty}\left(1 - \frac{1}{b}\right) = 1.$

(4)   Note first that

$$\int_a^1 \cos \pi x\, dx = \left[\frac{1}{\pi}\sin \pi x\right]_a^1 = -\frac{1}{\pi}\sin \pi a.$$

As a tends to $-\infty$, $\sin \pi a$ oscillates between -1 and 1. Therefore the integral

$$\int_a^1 \cos \pi x\, dx$$

oscillates between $1/\pi$ and $-1/\pi$ and does not converge. □

The usual formulas for area and volume are extended to the unbounded case by means of improper integrals.

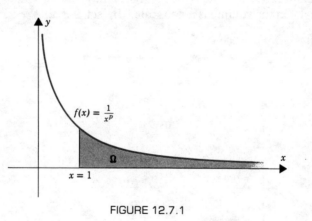

$f(x) = \dfrac{1}{x^p}$

Ω

$x = 1$

FIGURE 12.7.1

EXAMPLE. If Ω is the region below the graph of

$$f(x) = \frac{1}{x^p}, \qquad x \geq 1 \qquad\qquad \text{(Figure 12.7.1)}$$

then

$$\text{the area of }\Omega = \left\{\begin{array}{ll} \dfrac{1}{p-1}, & \text{if } p > 1 \\[2mm] \infty, & \text{if } p \leq 1 \end{array}\right].$$

This comes about from setting

$$\text{area of }\Omega = \lim_{b\to\infty} \int_1^b \frac{dx}{x^p} = \int_1^\infty \frac{dx}{x^p}.$$

For $p \neq 1$,

$$\int_1^\infty \frac{dx}{x^p} = \lim_{b \to \infty} \int_1^b \frac{dx}{x^p} = \lim_{b \to \infty} \frac{1}{1-p}(b^{1-p} - 1) = \left\{ \begin{array}{ll} \frac{1}{p-1}, & \text{if } p > 1 \\ \infty, & \text{if } p < 1 \end{array} \right].$$

For $p = 1$,

$$\int_1^\infty \frac{dx}{x^p} = \int_1^\infty \frac{dx}{x} = \infty,$$

as you have seen already. $\square$

EXAMPLE. From the last example you know that the region below the graph of

$$f(x) = \frac{1}{x}, \qquad x \geq 1$$

has infinite area. Suppose that this region with infinite area is revolved about the x-axis (see Figure 12.7.2). What is the volume of the resulting solid? It may surprise you somewhat, but the volume is not infinite. In fact, it is π. We can see this by the disc method:

$$V = \pi \int_1^\infty \frac{dx}{x^2} = \pi \cdot 1 = \pi. \quad \square$$

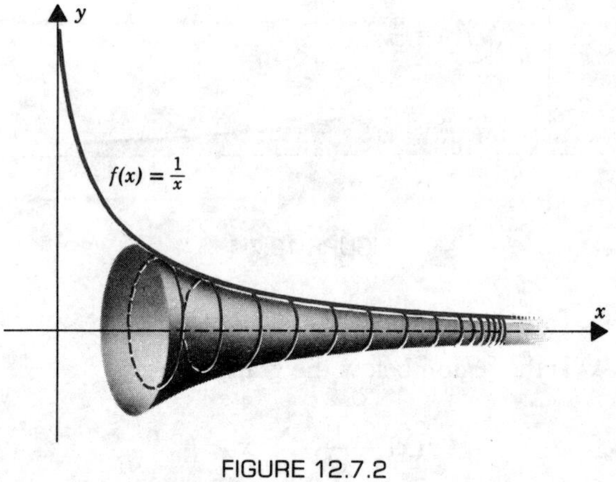

FIGURE 12.7.2

For future reference we record the following:

(12.7.1) $\qquad \int_1^\infty \frac{dx}{x^p}$ converges for $p > 1$ and   diverges for $p \leq 1$.

It's often difficult to determine the convergence or divergence of a given integral by direct methods, but we can usually gain some information by comparison with integrals of known behavior.

(12.7.2)

> (*A comparison test*) Suppose that f and g are continuous and
> $$0 \le f(x) \le g(x) \qquad \text{for all } x \in [a, \infty).$$
> (i) If $\displaystyle\int_a^\infty g(x)\,dx$ converges   then $\displaystyle\int_a^\infty f(x)\,dx$ converges.
> (ii) If $\displaystyle\int_a^\infty f(x)\,dx$ diverges,   then $\displaystyle\int_a^\infty g(x)\,dx$ diverges.

A similar test holds for integrals from $-\infty$ to b. The proof of (12.7.2) is left as an exercise.

EXAMPLE. The improper integral

$$\int_1^\infty \frac{dx}{\sqrt{1+x^3}}$$

converges since

$$\frac{1}{\sqrt{1+x^3}} < \frac{1}{x^{3/2}} \quad \text{for } x \in [1, \infty) \quad \text{and} \quad \int_1^\infty \frac{dx}{x^{3/2}} \text{ converges.} \quad \square$$

EXAMPLE. The improper integral

$$\int_1^\infty \frac{dx}{\sqrt{1+x^2}}$$

diverges since

$$\frac{1}{1+x} \le \frac{1}{\sqrt{1+x^2}} \quad \text{for } x \in [1, \infty) \quad \text{and} \quad \int_1^\infty \frac{dx}{1+x} \text{ diverges.} \quad \square$$

Suppose now that f is continuous on $(-\infty, \infty)$. The *improper integral*

$$\int_{-\infty}^\infty f(x)\,dx$$

is said to *converge* iff

$$\int_{-\infty}^0 f(x)\,dx \quad \text{and} \quad \int_0^\infty f(x)\,dx$$

both converge. We then set

$$\int_{-\infty}^\infty f(x)\,dx = l + m$$

where

$$\int_{-\infty}^0 f(x)\,dx = l \quad \text{and} \quad \int_0^\infty f(x)\,dx = m.$$

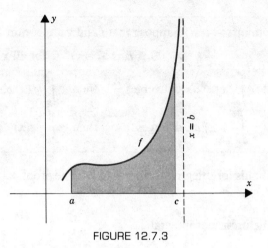

FIGURE 12.7.3

Improper integrals can also arise on bounded intervals. Suppose that f is continuous on the half-open interval $[a, b)$ but unbounded there. See Figure 12.7.3. If

$$\lim_{c \to b^-} \int_a^c f(x)\, dx = l \qquad (l \text{ finite}),$$

then we say that the *improper integral*

$$\int_a^b f(x)\, dx$$

converges to l. Otherwise, we say that the *improper integral diverges*. Similarly, functions continuous but unbounded on intervals of the form $(a, b]$ lead to limits of the form

$$\lim_{c \to a^+} \int_c^b f(x)\, dx$$

and thus to improper integrals

$$\int_a^b f(x)\, dx.$$

EXAMPLES

(1) $\displaystyle\int_0^1 (1 - x)^{-2/3}\, dx = 3.$ (2) $\displaystyle\int_0^1 \frac{dx}{x}$ diverges.

Verification

(1) $\displaystyle\int_0^1 (1 - x)^{-2/3}\, dx = \lim_{c \to 1^-} \int_0^c (1 - x)^{-2/3}\, dx$

$$= \lim_{c \to 1^-} \left[-3(1 - x)^{1/3} \right]_0^c = \lim_{c \to 1^-} [-3(1 - c)^{1/3} + 3] = 3.$$

(2) $\displaystyle\int_0^1 \frac{dx}{x} = \lim_{c\to 0^+} \int_c^1 \frac{dx}{x} = \lim_{c\to 0^+}(-\ln c) = \infty.$ $\square$

Now suppose that f is continuous on an interval $[a, b]$ except at some point c in (a, b) and that $f(x) \to \pm\infty$ as $x \to c^-$ or as $x \to c^+$. We say that the improper integral

$$\int_a^b f(x)\, dx$$

converges iff *both* of the improper integrals

$$\int_a^c f(x)\, dx \qquad \text{and} \qquad \int_c^b f(x)\, dx$$

converge.

EXAMPLE.   To evaluate

(3) $\displaystyle\int_1^4 \frac{dx}{(x-2)^2}$

we need to calculate

$$\lim_{c\to 2^-} \int_1^c \frac{dx}{(x-2)^2} \qquad \text{and} \qquad \lim_{c\to 2^+} \int_c^4 \frac{dx}{(x-2)^2}.$$

As you can verify, neither of these limits exists and thus improper integral (3) diverges.

Notice that, if we ignore the fact that integral (3) is improper, then we are led to the *incorrect conclusion* that

$$\int_1^4 \frac{dx}{(x-2)^2} = \left[\frac{-1}{x-2}\right]_1^4 = -\frac{3}{2}.$$ $\square$

EXERCISES

Evaluate the improper integrals that converge.

1. $\displaystyle\int_1^\infty \frac{dx}{x^2}.$ 2. $\displaystyle\int_0^\infty \frac{dx}{1+x^2}.$ 3. $\displaystyle\int_0^\infty \frac{dx}{4+x^2}.$

4. $\displaystyle\int_0^\infty e^{-px}\, dx, \quad p > 0.$ 5. $\displaystyle\int_0^\infty e^{px}\, dx, \quad p > 0.$ 6. $\displaystyle\int_0^1 \frac{dx}{\sqrt{x}}.$

7. $\displaystyle\int_0^8 \frac{dx}{x^{2/3}}.$ 8. $\displaystyle\int_0^1 \frac{dx}{x^2}.$ 9. $\displaystyle\int_0^1 \frac{dx}{\sqrt{1-x^2}}.$

10. $\displaystyle\int_0^1 \frac{dx}{\sqrt{1-x}}.$ 11. $\displaystyle\int_0^2 \frac{x}{\sqrt{4-x^2}}\, dx.$ 12. $\displaystyle\int_0^a \frac{dx}{\sqrt{a^2-x^2}}.$

13. $\displaystyle\int_e^\infty \frac{\ln x}{x}\, dx.$ 14. $\displaystyle\int_e^\infty \frac{dx}{x\ln x}.$ 15. $\displaystyle\int_0^1 x\ln x\, dx.$

16. $\displaystyle\int_e^\infty \frac{dx}{x(\ln x)^2}.$

17. $\displaystyle\int_{-\infty}^\infty \frac{dx}{1+x^2}.$

18. $\displaystyle\int_2^\infty \frac{dx}{x^2-1}.$

19. $\displaystyle\int_{-\infty}^\infty \frac{dx}{x^2}.$

20. $\displaystyle\int_{1/3}^3 \frac{dx}{\sqrt[3]{3x-1}}.$

21. $\displaystyle\int_1^\infty \frac{dx}{x(x+1)}.$

22. $\displaystyle\int_{-\infty}^0 xe^x\,dx.$

23. $\displaystyle\int_3^5 \frac{x}{\sqrt{x^2-9}}\,dx.$

24. $\displaystyle\int_1^4 \frac{dx}{x^2-4}.$

25. $\displaystyle\int_{-3}^3 \frac{dx}{x(x+1)}.$

26. $\displaystyle\int_1^\infty \frac{x}{(1+x^2)^2}\,dx.$

27. $\displaystyle\int_{-3}^1 \frac{dx}{x^2-4}.$

28. $\displaystyle\int_0^\infty \sinh x\,dx.$

29. $\displaystyle\int_0^\infty \cosh x\,dx.$

30. $\displaystyle\int_1^4 \frac{dx}{x^2-5x+6}.$

31. Let Ω be the region under the curve $y=e^{-x}, x\ge 0$. (a) Sketch Ω. (b) Find the area of Ω. (c) Find the volume of the solid obtained by revolving Ω about the x-axis. (d) Find the volume obtained by revolving Ω about the y-axis. (e) Find the lateral surface area of the solid in part (c).

32. Find the area of the region bounded below by $y(x^2+1)=x$, above by $xy=1$, and to the left by $x=1$.

33. Let Ω be the region below the curve $y=x^{-1/4}, 0<x\le 1$. (a) Sketch Ω. (b) Find the area of Ω. (c) Find the volume of the solid obtained by revolving Ω about the x-axis. (d) Find the volume of the solid obtained by revolving Ω about the y-axis.

34. Prove the validity of the comparison test (12.7.2).

Use the comparison test (12.7.2) to determine which of the following integrals converge.

35. $\displaystyle\int_1^\infty \frac{x}{\sqrt{1+x^5}}\,dx.$

36. $\displaystyle\int_1^\infty e^{-x^2}\,dx.$

37. $\displaystyle\int_0^\infty (1+x^5)^{-1/6}\,dx.$

38. $\displaystyle\int_\pi^\infty \frac{\sin^2 2x}{x^2}\,dx.$

39. $\displaystyle\int_1^\infty \frac{\ln x}{x^2}\,dx.$

40. $\displaystyle\int_e^\infty \frac{dx}{\sqrt{x+1}\,\ln x}.$

12.8···ADDITIONAL EXERCISES

State whether the indicated sequence converges, and if it does, find the limit.

1. $3^{1/n}.$

2. $n2^{1/n}.$

3. $\cos n\pi \sin n\pi.$

4. $\dfrac{(n+1)(n+2)}{(n+3)(n+4)}.$

5. $\left(\dfrac{n}{1+n}\right)^{1/n}.$

6. $\dfrac{n^2+5n+1}{n^3+1}.$

7. $\cos\dfrac{\pi}{n}\sin\dfrac{\pi}{n}.$

8. $\dfrac{n^\pi}{1-n^\pi}.$

9. $\left(2+\dfrac{1}{n}\right)^n.$

10. $\dfrac{\pi}{n}\cos\dfrac{\pi}{n}.$

11. $\dfrac{\ln[n(n+1)]}{n}.$

12. $\left[\ln\left(1+\dfrac{1}{n}\right)\right]^n.$

13. $\dfrac{\pi}{n}\ln\dfrac{n}{\pi}.$

14. $\dfrac{\pi}{n}e^{\pi/n}.$

15. $\dfrac{n}{\pi}\sin n\pi.$

16. $3\ln 2n-\ln(n^3+1).$

17. $\displaystyle\int_n^{n+1} e^{-x}\,dx.$

18. $\displaystyle\int_1^n \frac{dx}{\sqrt{x}}.$

19. The function

$$f(x) = \frac{1}{\sqrt{2\pi}} \int_{-\infty}^{x} e^{-t^2/2} \, dt$$

is important in statistics. Prove that the integral on the right converges for all real x.

20. Evaluate

$$\int_{0}^{a} \ln \frac{1}{x} \, dx \qquad \text{for } a > 0.$$

21. (*Useful later*) Let f be a function, continuous, decreasing, and positive on $[1, \infty)$. Show that

$$\int_{1}^{\infty} f(x) \, dx \quad \text{converges} \quad \text{iff} \quad \text{the sequence} \quad \left\{ \int_{1}^{n} f(x) \, dx \right\} \quad \text{converges.}$$

22. Find the length of the curve

$$y = (a^{2/3} - x^{2/3})^{3/2} \qquad\qquad (a > 0)$$

from $x = 0$ to $x = a$.

23. Let f be a function continuous on $(-\infty, \infty)$ and L a real number.
   (a) Show that

$$\text{if} \quad \int_{-\infty}^{\infty} f(x) \, dx = L \quad \text{then} \quad \lim_{c \to \infty} \int_{-c}^{c} f(x) \, dx = L.$$

   (b) Show that the converse of (a) is false by showing that

$$\lim_{c \to \infty} \int_{-c}^{c} x \, dx = 0 \quad \text{but} \quad \int_{-\infty}^{\infty} x \, dx \quad \text{diverges.}$$

24. Show that

$$\int_{-\infty}^{\infty} f(x) \, dx = L \quad \text{iff} \quad \lim_{c \to \infty} \int_{-c}^{c} f(x) \, dx = L$$

in the event that f is (a) nonnegative or (b) even.

The present value of a perpetual stream of revenues that flows continually at the rate of $R(t)$ dollars per year is given by the formula

$$P.V. = \int_{0}^{\infty} R(t) \, e^{-rt} \, dt,$$

where r is the rate of continuous compounding.

25. What is the present value of such a stream if $R(t)$ is constantly \$100 per year and r is 5%?

26. What is the present value if $R(t) = 100 + 60t$ dollars per year and r is 10%?

12.9 CHAPTER SUMMARY

12.1 Sequences of Real Numbers

It is often possible to obtain useful information about a sequence $y_n = f(n)$ by applying the techniques of calculus to the function $y = f(x)$. However, in some respects, the function $y = f(x)$ and the sequence $y_n = f(n)$ may behave differently.

12.2 The Limit of a Sequence

limit of a sequence (p. 600)   convergent, divergent (p. 601)

pinching theorem (p. 604) $\displaystyle \lim_{n \to \infty} \left(1 + \frac{1}{n}\right)^n = e$

Every convergent sequence is bounded (p. 601); thus, every unbounded sequence is divergent.

A bounded, monotonic sequence converges. (p. 602).

Suppose $c_n \to c$ and that, for each n, c_n is in the domain of f. If f is continuous at c, then $f(c_n) \to f(c)$. (p. 606).

12.3 Some Important Limits

for $x > 0$, $\displaystyle \lim_{n \to \infty} x^{1/n} = 1$ for $|x| < 1$, $\displaystyle \lim_{n \to \infty} x^n = 0$

for each real x, $\displaystyle \lim_{n \to \infty} \frac{x^n}{n!} = 0$ for $\alpha > 0$, $\displaystyle \lim_{n \to \infty} \frac{1}{n^\alpha} = 0$

$\displaystyle \lim_{n \to \infty} \frac{\ln n}{n} = 0$ $\displaystyle \lim_{n \to \infty} n^{1/n} = 1$

for each real x, $\displaystyle \lim_{n \to \infty} \left(1 + \frac{x}{n}\right)^n = e^x$ Cauchy sequence (p. 615)

12.4 Limits as $x \to \pm \infty$

$$\lim_{x \to \infty} f(x) = l \quad \text{iff} \quad \lim_{t \to 0^+} f\left(\frac{1}{t}\right) = l$$

12.5 The Indeterminate Form (0/0)

L'Hospital's rule (0/0) (p. 620)
Cauchy mean-value theorem (p. 622)

If a product $f(x)g(x)$ gives rise to the indeterminate form $0 \cdot \infty$, then that same product written as $f(x)/(1/g(x))$ gives rise to the indeterminate form 0/0.

Suppose that $f(x)$ gives rise to the indeterminate form 1^∞. If $\ln f(x) \to A$, then $f(x) \to e^A$.

12.6 Infinite Limits; The Indeterminate Form (∞/∞)

L'Hospital's rule (∞/∞) (p. 628)   asymptotic graphs (p. 631)

$$\lim_{x\to\infty} \frac{\ln x}{x} = 0 \qquad \lim_{x\to\infty} \frac{x^k}{e^x} = 0 \qquad \lim_{x\to 0^+} x^x = 1$$

12.7 Improper Integrals

improper integrals (p. 632)   a comparison test (p. 635)

$$\int_1^\infty \frac{dx}{x^p} \text{ converges for } p > 1 \quad \text{and} \quad \text{diverges for } p \le 1$$

12.8 Additional Exercises

13

Infinite Series

13.1····SIGMA NOTATION

To indicate the sequence

$$\{1, \tfrac{1}{2}, \tfrac{1}{4}, \ldots\}$$

we can set $a_n = (\tfrac{1}{2})^{n-1}$ and write

$$\{a_1, a_2, a_3, \ldots\}.$$

We can also set $b_n = (\tfrac{1}{2})^n$ and write

$$\{b_0, b_1, b_2, \ldots\},$$

thereby beginning with the index 0. More generally, we can set $c_n = (\tfrac{1}{2})^{n-p}$ and write

$$\{c_p, c_{p+1}, c_{p+2}, \ldots\},$$

thereby beginning with the index p. In this chapter we often begin with an index other than 1.

The symbol Σ is the capital Greek letter "sigma." We write

(1)
$$\sum_{k=0}^{n} a_k$$

(read "the sum of the a sub k from k equals 0 to k equals n") to indicate the sum

$$a_0 + a_1 + \cdots + a_n.$$

More generally, if $n \geq m$, we write

(2)
$$\sum_{k=m}^{n} a_k$$

to indicate the sum

$$a_m + a_{m+1} + \cdots + a_n.$$

In (1) and (2) the letter "k" is being used as a "dummy" variable. That is, it can be replaced by any letter not already engaged. For instance,

$$\sum_{i=3}^{7} a_i, \qquad \sum_{j=3}^{7} a_j, \qquad \sum_{k=3}^{7} a_k$$

can all be used to indicate the sum

$$a_3 + a_4 + a_5 + a_6 + a_7.$$

Translating

$$(a_0 + \cdots + a_n) + (b_0 + \cdots + b_n) = (a_0 + b_0) + \cdots + (a_n + b_n),$$
$$\alpha(a_0 + \cdots + a_n) = \alpha a_0 + \cdots + \alpha a_n,$$
$$(a_0 + \cdots + a_m) + (a_{m+1} + \cdots + a_n) = a_0 + \cdots + a_n$$

into the Σ-notation, we have

$$\sum_{k=0}^{n} a_k + \sum_{k=0}^{n} b_k = \sum_{k=0}^{n} (a_k + b_k), \qquad \alpha \sum_{k=0}^{n} a_k = \sum_{k=0}^{n} \alpha a_k,$$
$$\sum_{k=0}^{m} a_k + \sum_{k=m+1}^{n} a_k = \sum_{k=0}^{n} a_k.$$

At times it's convenient to change indices. In this connection note that

$$\sum_{k=j}^{n} a_k = \sum_{i=0}^{n-j} a_{i+j}. \qquad \text{(set } i = k - j\text{)}$$

Both expressions are abbreviations for $a_j + a_{j+1} + \cdots + a_n$.

You can familiarize yourself further with this notation by doing the exercises below, but first one more remark. If all the a_k are equal to some fixed number x, then

$$\sum_{k=0}^{n} a_k \quad \text{can be written} \quad \sum_{k=0}^{n} x.$$

Obviously then

$$\sum_{k=0}^{n} x = \overbrace{x + x + \cdots + x}^{n+1} = (n+1)x.$$

In particular

$$\sum_{k=0}^{n} 1 = n + 1.$$

EXERCISES

Evaluate the following expressions.

1. $\sum_{k=0}^{2} (3k + 1)$.   2. $\sum_{k=1}^{4} (3k - 1)$.   3. $\sum_{k=0}^{3} 2^k$.   4. $\sum_{k=0}^{3} (-1)^k 2^k$.

5. $\sum_{k=0}^{3} (-1)^k 2^{k+1}$.   6. $\sum_{k=2}^{5} (-1)^{k+1} 2^{k-1}$.   7. $\sum_{k=1}^{4} \frac{1}{2^k}$.   8. $\sum_{k=2}^{5} \frac{1}{k!}$.

9. $\sum_{k=3}^{5} \frac{(-1)^k}{k!}$.   10. $\sum_{k=2}^{4} \frac{1}{3^{k-1}}$.   11. $\sum_{k=0}^{3} (\frac{1}{2})^{2k}$.   12. $\sum_{k=1}^{3} (-1)^{k+1} (\frac{1}{2})^{2k-1}$.

Express in sigma notation.

13. the lower sum $m_1 \Delta x_1 + m_2 \Delta x_2 + \cdots + m_n \Delta x_n$.
14. the upper sum $M_1 \Delta x_1 + M_2 \Delta x_2 + \cdots + M_n \Delta x_n$.
15. the Riemann sum $f(x_1^*) \Delta x_1 + f(x_2^*) \Delta x_2 + \cdots + f(x_n^*) \Delta x_n$.
16. $a^5 + a^4 b + a^3 b^2 + a^2 b^3 + ab^4 + b^5$.
17. $a^5 - a^4 b + a^3 b^2 - a^2 b^3 + ab^4 - b^5$.
18. $a^n + a^{n-1} b + \cdots + ab^{n-1} + b^n$.
19. $a_0 x^4 + a_1 x^3 + a_2 x^2 + a_3 x + a_4$.
20. $a_0 x^n + a_1 x^{n-1} + \cdots + a_{n-1} x + a_n$.
21. $1 - 2x + 3x^2 - 4x^3 + 5x^4$.
22. $3x - 4x^2 + 5x^3 - 6x^4$.

Write the following sums as

$$\sum_{k=3}^{10} a_k \quad \text{and} \quad \sum_{i=0}^{7} a_{i+3}:$$

23. $\frac{1}{2^3} + \frac{1}{2^4} + \cdots + \frac{1}{2^{10}}$.   24. $\frac{3^3}{3!} + \frac{4^4}{4!} + \cdots + \frac{10^{10}}{10!}$.

25. $\frac{3}{4} - \frac{4}{5} + \cdots - \frac{10}{11}$.   26. $\frac{1}{3} + \frac{1}{5} + \frac{1}{7} + \cdots + \frac{1}{17}$.

27. (a) (*Important*) Show that for $x \neq 1$

$$\sum_{k=0}^{n} x^k = \frac{1 - x^{n+1}}{1 - x}.$$

(b) Determine whether the sequence

$$a_n = \sum_{k=0}^{n} \frac{1}{3^k}$$

converges and, if it does, find the limit.

28. Express

$$\sum_{k=1}^{n} \frac{a_k}{10^k}$$

as a decimal fraction, given that each a_k is an integer from 0 to 9.

29. Let p be a positive integer. Show that, as $n \to \infty$,

$$a_n \to l \quad \text{iff} \quad a_{n-p} \to l.$$

30. Show that

$$\sum_{k=1}^{n} \frac{1}{\sqrt{k}} \geq \sqrt{n}.$$

Verify by induction.

31. $\displaystyle\sum_{k=1}^{n} k = \frac{1}{2}(n)(n+1)$.

32. $\displaystyle\sum_{k=1}^{n} (2k-1) = n^2$.

33. $\displaystyle\sum_{k=1}^{n} k^2 = \frac{1}{6}(n)(n+1)(2n+1)$.

34. $\displaystyle\sum_{k=1}^{n} k^3 = \left(\sum_{k=1}^{n} k\right)^2$.

13.2····INFINITE SERIES

Introduction; Definitions

While it's possible to add two numbers, three numbers, a hundred numbers, or even a million numbers, it's impossible to add an infinite number of numbers. The theory of *infinite series* arose from attempts to circumvent this impossibility.

To form an infinite series we begin with an infinite sequence of real numbers: a_0, $a_1, a_2, \ldots$. We can't form the sum of all the a_k (there is an infinite number of them), but we can form the *partial sums*

$$s_0 = a_0 = \sum_{k=0}^{0} a_k,$$

$$s_1 = a_0 + a_1 = \sum_{k=0}^{1} a_k,$$

$$s_2 = a_0 + a_1 + a_2 = \sum_{k=0}^{2} a_k,$$

$$s_3 = a_0 + a_1 + a_2 + a_3 = \sum_{k=0}^{3} a_k,$$

$$\vdots$$

$$s_n = a_0 + a_1 + a_2 + a_3 + \cdots + a_n = \sum_{k=0}^{n} a_k$$

$$\vdots$$

If the sequence $\{s_n\}$ of partial sums converges to a finite limit l, we write

$$\sum_{k=0}^{\infty} a_k = l$$

and say that

the *series* $\sum_{k=0}^{\infty} a_k$ *converges* to l.

We call l the *sum* of the series.   If the sequence of partial sums diverges, we say that

the *series* $\sum_{k=0}^{\infty} a_k$ *diverges.*

REMARK. It is important to note that the sum of a series is not a sum in the ordinary sense. It is a limit. □

Here are some examples.

EXAMPLE. We begin with the series

$$\sum_{k=0}^{\infty} \frac{1}{(k+1)(k+2)}.$$

To determine whether or not this series converges we must examine the partial sums.
Since

$$\frac{1}{(k+1)(k+2)} = \frac{1}{k+1} - \frac{1}{k+2},$$

you can see that

$$s_n = \frac{1}{1 \cdot 2} + \frac{1}{2 \cdot 3} + \cdots + \frac{1}{n(n+1)} + \frac{1}{(n+1)(n+2)}$$

$$= \left(\frac{1}{1} - \frac{1}{2}\right) + \left(\frac{1}{2} - \frac{1}{3}\right) + \cdots + \left(\frac{1}{n} - \frac{1}{n+1}\right) + \left(\frac{1}{n+1} - \frac{1}{n+2}\right)$$

$$= 1 - \frac{1}{2} + \frac{1}{2} - \frac{1}{3} + \cdots + \frac{1}{n} - \frac{1}{n+1} + \frac{1}{n+1} - \frac{1}{n+2}.$$

Since all but the first and last terms occur in pairs with opposite signs, the sum collapses to give

$$s_n = 1 - \frac{1}{n+2}.$$

Obviously, as $n \to \infty$, $s_n \to 1$. This means that the series converges to 1:

$$\sum_{k=0}^{\infty} \frac{1}{(k+1)(k+2)} = 1. \quad □$$

EXAMPLE. Here we examine two divergent series

$$\sum_{k=0}^{\infty} 2^k \quad \text{and} \quad \sum_{k=1}^{\infty} (-1)^k.$$

The partial sums of the first series take the form

$$s_n = \sum_{k=0}^{n} 2^k = 1 + 2 + \cdots + 2^n.$$

The sequence $\{s_n\}$ is unbounded and therefore divergent (12.2.5). This means that the series diverges.

For the second series we have

$$s_n = -1 \text{ if } n \text{ is odd} \quad \text{and} \quad s_n = 0 \text{ if } n \text{ is even.}$$

The sequence of partial sums looks like this:

$$-1, \quad 0, \quad -1, \quad 0, \quad -1, \quad 0, \quad \cdots .$$

The series diverges since the sequence of partial sums diverges. □

The Geometric Series

In school you probably studied geometric progression:

$$1, \quad x, \quad x^2, \quad x^3, \quad \cdots .$$

The sums

$$1, \quad 1 + x, \quad 1 + x + x^2, \quad 1 + x + x^2 + x^3, \quad \cdots$$

generated by numbers in geometric progression are the partial sums of what is known as the *geometric series*:

$$\sum_{k=0}^{\infty} x^k.$$

The geometric series arises in so many different contexts that it merits special attention.

The following result is fundamental:

(13.2.1)

$$\text{(i) if } |x| < 1, \quad \text{then } \sum_{k=0}^{\infty} x^k = \frac{1}{1-x};$$

$$\text{(ii) if } |x| \geq 1, \quad \text{then } \sum_{k=0}^{\infty} x^k \text{ diverges.}$$

Proof.   The nth partial sum of the geometric series

$$\sum_{k=0}^{\infty} x^k$$

takes the form

(1) $$s_n = 1 + x + \cdots + x^n.$$

Multiplication by x gives

$$xs_n = x + x^2 + \cdots + x^{n+1}.$$

Subtracting the second equation from the first, we find that

$$(1 - x)s_n = 1 - x^{n+1}.$$

For $x \neq 1$, this gives

(2) $$s_n = \frac{1 - x^{n+1}}{1 - x}.$$

If $|x| < 1$, then $x^{n+1} \to 0$ and thus, by equation (2),

$$s_n \to \frac{1}{1 - x}.$$

This proves (i).

Now let's prove (ii).   For $x = 1$, we use equation (1) and deduce that $s_n = n + 1$. Obviously, $\{s_n\}$ diverges.   For $x \neq 1$ with $|x| \geq 1$, we use equation (2).   Since in this instance $\{x^{n+1}\}$ diverges, $\{s_n\}$ diverges. $\square$

You may have seen (13.2.1) before written as

$$a + ar + ar^2 + \cdots + ar^n + \cdots = \begin{cases} \dfrac{a}{1 - r}, & |r| < 1 \\ \text{diverges}, & |r| \geq 1 \end{cases}.$$

Taking $a = 1$ and $r = \frac{1}{2}$, we have

$$\sum_{k=0}^{\infty} \frac{1}{2^k} = \frac{1}{1 - \frac{1}{2}} = 2.$$

Begin the summation at $k = 1$ instead of at $k = 0$, and you see that

(13.2.2) $$\sum_{k=1}^{\infty} \frac{1}{2^k} = 1.$$

The partial sums of this series

$$s_1 = \tfrac{1}{2},$$
$$s_2 = \tfrac{1}{2} + \tfrac{1}{4} = \tfrac{3}{4},$$
$$s_3 = \tfrac{1}{2} + \tfrac{1}{4} + \tfrac{1}{8} = \tfrac{7}{8},$$
$$s_4 = \tfrac{1}{2} + \tfrac{1}{4} + \tfrac{1}{8} + \tfrac{1}{16} = \tfrac{15}{16},$$
$$s_5 = \tfrac{1}{2} + \tfrac{1}{4} + \tfrac{1}{8} + \tfrac{1}{16} + \tfrac{1}{32} = \tfrac{31}{32},$$
etc.

are illustrated in Figure 13.2.1. Each new partial sum lies halfway between the previous partial sum and the number 1.

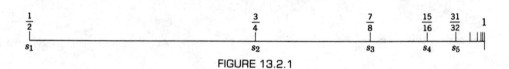

FIGURE 13.2.1

The convergence of the geometric series at $x = \tfrac{1}{10}$ enables us to assign a precise meaning to infinite decimals. Begin with the fact that

$$\sum_{k=0}^{\infty} \left(\frac{1}{10}\right)^k = \sum_{k=0}^{\infty} \frac{1}{10^k} = \frac{1}{1 - \tfrac{1}{10}} = \frac{10}{9}.$$

This gives

$$\sum_{k=1}^{\infty} \frac{1}{10^k} = \frac{1}{9}$$

and shows that the partial sums

$$s_n = \frac{1}{10} + \frac{1}{10^2} + \cdots + \frac{1}{10^n}$$

are all less than $\tfrac{1}{9}$. Now take a series of the form

$$\sum_{k=1}^{\infty} \frac{a_k}{10^k} \quad \text{with} \quad a_k = 0, 1, \ldots, \text{or } 9.$$

Its partial sums

$$t_n = \frac{a_1}{10} + \frac{a_2}{10^2} + \cdots + \frac{a_n}{10^n}$$

are all less than 1:

$$t_n = \frac{a_1}{10} + \frac{a_2}{10^2} + \cdots + \frac{a_n}{10^n} \le 9\left(\frac{1}{10} + \frac{1}{10^2} + \cdots + \frac{1}{10^n}\right) = 9s_n < 9\left(\frac{1}{9}\right) = 1.$$

Since $\{t_n\}$ is nondecreasing, as well as bounded above, $\{t_n\}$ is convergent; this means that the series

$$\sum_{k=1}^{\infty} \frac{a_k}{10^k}$$

is convergent.   The sum of this series is what we mean by the infinite decimal

$$0.a_1 a_2 a_3 \cdots a_n \cdots .$$

Below are two simple problems that lead naturally to the geometric series.   You'll find more in the exercises.

PROBLEM.   An electric fan is turned off, and the blades begin to lose speed. Given that the blades turn N times during the first second of no power and lose at least $\sigma\%$ of their speed with the passing of each ensuing second, show that the blades cannot turn more than $100N\sigma^{-1}$ times after power shutdown.

Solution.   The number of turns during the first second of no power is

$$N.$$

The number of turns during the first 2 seconds is at most

$$N + \left(1 - \frac{1}{100}\sigma\right) N;$$

during the first 3 seconds, at most

$$N + \left(1 - \frac{1}{100}\sigma\right) N + \left(1 - \frac{1}{100}\sigma\right)^2 N;$$

and, during the first $n + 1$ seconds, at most

$$N \sum_{k=0}^{n} \left(1 - \frac{1}{100}\sigma\right)^k.$$

The total number of turns after power shutdown cannot exceed the limiting value

$$N \sum_{k=0}^{\infty} \left(1 - \frac{1}{100}\sigma\right)^k = N \left[\frac{1}{1 - (1 - \frac{1}{100}\sigma)}\right] = \frac{100N}{\sigma} = 100N\sigma^{-1}. \quad \square$$

PROBLEM.   According to Figure 13.2.2, it is 2 o'clock.   At what time between 2 and 3 o'clock will the two hands coincide?

Solution.   We will solve the problem by setting up a geometric series.   We will then confirm our answer by approaching the problem from a different perspective.
    The hour hand travels one-twelfth as fast as the minute hand.   At 2 o'clock the minute hand points to 12 and the hour hand points to 2.   By the time the minute hand reaches 2, the hour hand points to $2 + \frac{1}{6}$.   By the time the minute hand reaches

FIGURE 13.2.2

$2 + \frac{1}{6}$, the hour hand points to

$$2 + \frac{1}{6} + \frac{1}{6 \cdot 12}.$$

By the time the minute hand reaches

$$2 + \frac{1}{6} + \frac{1}{6 \cdot 12},$$

the hour hand points to

$$2 + \frac{1}{6} + \frac{1}{6 \cdot 12} + \frac{1}{6 \cdot 12^2}$$

and so on. In general, by the time the minute hand reaches

$$2 + \frac{1}{6} + \frac{1}{6 \cdot 12} + \cdots + \frac{1}{6 \cdot 12^{n-1}} = 2 + \frac{1}{6} \sum_{k=0}^{n-1} \frac{1}{12^k},$$

the hour hand points to

$$2 + \frac{1}{6} + \frac{1}{6 \cdot 12} + \cdots + \frac{1}{6 \cdot 12^{n-1}} + \frac{1}{6 \cdot 12^n} = 2 + \frac{1}{6} \sum_{k=0}^{n} \frac{1}{12^k}.$$

The two hands coincide when they both point to the limiting value

$$2 + \frac{1}{6} \sum_{k=0}^{\infty} \frac{1}{12^k} = 2 + \frac{1}{6} \left(\frac{1}{1 - \frac{1}{12}} \right) = 2 + \frac{2}{11}.$$

This happens at $2 + \frac{2}{11}$ o'clock, approximately 10 minutes and 55 seconds after 2.

We can confirm this as follows. Suppose that the two hands meet at hour $2 + x$. The hour hand will have moved a distance x and the minute hand a distance $2 + x$. Since the minute hand moves 12 times as fast as the hour hand, we have

$$12x = 2 + x, \qquad 11x = 2, \qquad \text{and thus} \qquad x = \frac{2}{11}. \quad \square$$

We'll return to the geometric series later. Right now we turn our attention to series in general.

Some Basic Results

1. If

$$\sum_{k=0}^{\infty} a_k \quad \text{converges} \quad \text{and} \quad \sum_{k=0}^{\infty} b_k \text{ converges,}$$

then

$$\sum_{k=0}^{\infty} (a_k + b_k) \quad \text{converges.}$$

Moreover, if

$$\sum_{k=0}^{\infty} a_k = l \quad \text{and} \quad \sum_{k=0}^{\infty} b_k = m,$$

then

(13.2.3)

$$\sum_{k=0}^{\infty} (a_k + b_k) = l + m.$$

2. If

$$\sum_{k=0}^{\infty} a_k \quad \text{converges,}$$

then

$$\sum_{k=0}^{\infty} \alpha a_k \quad \text{converges for each real number } \alpha.$$

Moreover,

$$\text{if} \quad \sum_{k=0}^{\infty} a_k = l, \quad \text{then} \quad \sum_{k=0}^{\infty} \alpha a_k = \alpha l.$$

Proof. Let

$$s_n = \sum_{k=0}^{n} a_k, \qquad t_n = \sum_{k=0}^{n} b_k,$$

$$u_n = \sum_{k=0}^{n} (a_k + b_k), \qquad v_n = \sum_{k=0}^{n} \alpha a_k.$$

Note that

$$u_n = s_n + t_n \quad \text{and} \quad v_n = \alpha s_n.$$

If $s_n \to l$ and $t_n \to m$, we have

$$u_n \to l + m \quad \text{and} \quad v_n \to \alpha l. \quad \square$$

THEOREM 13.2.4

The *kth term* of a convergent series tends to 0; namely,

$$\text{if } \sum_{k=0}^{\infty} a_k \text{ converges,} \qquad \text{then } a_k \to 0.$$

Proof.   To say that the series converges is to say that the sequence of partial sums converges to some number l:

$$s_n = \sum_{k=0}^{n} a_k \to l.$$

Obviously, then, $s_{n-1} \to l$. Since $a_n = s_n - s_{n-1}$, we have $a_n \to l - l = 0$. A change in notation gives $a_k \to 0$.   □

The next result is an obvious, but important, consequence of Theorem 13.2.4.

THEOREM 13.2.5   A DIVERGENCE TEST

$$\text{If } a_k \not\to 0, \qquad \text{then } \sum_{k=0}^{\infty} a_k \text{ diverges.}$$

EXAMPLES. Since $\dfrac{k}{k+1} \not\to 0$, the series

$$\sum_{k=0}^{\infty} \frac{k}{k+1} = 0 + \frac{1}{2} + \frac{2}{3} + \frac{3}{4} + \frac{4}{5} + \cdots$$

diverges.   Since $\sin k \not\to 0$, the series

$$\sum_{k=0}^{\infty} \sin k = \sin 0 + \sin 1 + \sin 2 + \sin 3 + \cdots$$

also diverges.   □

CAUTION.   Theorem 13.2.4 does *not* say that, if $a_k \to 0$, then $\sum_{k=0}^{\infty} a_k$ converges. There are divergent series for which $a_k \to 0$.

EXAMPLE.   In the case of

$$\sum_{k=1}^{\infty} \frac{1}{\sqrt{k}} = \frac{1}{\sqrt{1}} + \frac{1}{\sqrt{2}} + \frac{1}{\sqrt{3}} + \frac{1}{\sqrt{4}} + \cdots$$

we have

$$a_k = \frac{1}{\sqrt{k}} \to 0,$$

but, since

$$S_n = \frac{1}{\sqrt{1}} + \frac{1}{\sqrt{2}} + \cdots + \frac{1}{\sqrt{n}} > \frac{n}{\sqrt{n}} = \sqrt{n},$$

the sequence of partial sums is unbounded, and therefore the series diverges.   □

EXERCISES

Find the sum of the series.

1. $\displaystyle\sum_{k=3}^{\infty} \frac{1}{(k+1)(k+2)}$.

2. $\displaystyle\sum_{k=0}^{\infty} \frac{1}{(k+3)(k+4)}$.

3. $\displaystyle\sum_{k=1}^{\infty} \frac{1}{2k(k+1)}$.

4. $\displaystyle\sum_{k=3}^{\infty} \frac{1}{k^2 - k}$.

5. $\displaystyle\sum_{k=1}^{\infty} \frac{1}{k(k+3)}$.

6. $\displaystyle\sum_{k=0}^{\infty} \frac{1}{(k+1)(k+3)}$.

7. $\displaystyle\sum_{k=0}^{\infty} \frac{3}{10^k}$.

8. $\displaystyle\sum_{k=0}^{\infty} \frac{12}{100^k}$.

9. $\displaystyle\sum_{k=0}^{\infty} \frac{67}{1000^k}$.

10. $\displaystyle\sum_{k=0}^{\infty} \frac{(-1)^k}{5^k}$.

11. $\displaystyle\sum_{k=0}^{\infty} \left(\frac{3}{4}\right)^k$.

12. $\displaystyle\sum_{k=0}^{\infty} \frac{3^k + 4^k}{5^k}$.

13. $\displaystyle\sum_{k=0}^{\infty} \frac{1 - 2^k}{3^k}$.

14. $\displaystyle\sum_{k=0}^{\infty} \left(\frac{25}{10^k} - \frac{6}{100^k}\right)$.

15. $\displaystyle\sum_{k=3}^{\infty} \frac{1}{2^{k-1}}$.

16. $\displaystyle\sum_{k=0}^{\infty} \frac{1}{2^{k+3}}$.

17. $\displaystyle\sum_{k=0}^{\infty} \frac{2^{k+3}}{3^k}$.

18. $\displaystyle\sum_{k=2}^{\infty} \frac{3^{k-1}}{4^{3k+1}}$.

Write the decimal fraction as an infinite series and express the sum as the quotient of two integers.

19. $0.777\cdots$.

20. $0.999\cdots$.

21. $0.\overparen{24}\overparen{24}\cdots$.

22. $0.8\overparen{98}\overparen{98}\cdots$.

23. $0.\overparen{112}\overparen{112}\overparen{112}\cdots$.

24. $0.\overparen{315}\overparen{315}\overparen{315}\cdots$.

25. $0.62\overparen{45}\overparen{45}\cdots$.

26. $0.112\overparen{019}\overparen{019}\cdots$.

27. Using series, show that every repeating decimal represents a rational number (the quotient of two integers).

28. Show that

$$\sum_{k=0}^{\infty} a_k = l \qquad \text{iff} \qquad \sum_{k=j+1}^{\infty} a_k = l - (a_0 + \cdots + a_j).$$

Derive these results from the geometric series.

29. $\displaystyle\sum_{k=0}^{\infty} (-1)^k x^k = \frac{1}{1+x}$, $|x| < 1$.

30. $\displaystyle\sum_{k=0}^{\infty} (-1)^k x^{2k} = \frac{1}{1+x^2}$, $|x| < 1$.

Find a series expansion for the given expression.

31. $\dfrac{x}{1-x}$ valid for $|x| < 1$.

32. $\dfrac{x}{1+x}$ valid for $|x| < 1$.

33. $\dfrac{x}{1+x^2}$ valid for $|x| < 1$.

34. $\dfrac{1}{4-x^2}$ valid for $|x| < 2$.

35. $\dfrac{1}{1+4x^2}$ valid for $|x| < \dfrac{1}{2}$.

36. $\dfrac{x^2}{1-x}$ valid for $|x| < 1$.

37. At some time between 4 and 5 o'clock the minute hand is directly above the hour hand. Express this time as a geometric series. What is the sum of this series?

38. Given that a ball dropped to the floor rebounds to a height proportional to the height from which it is dropped, find the total distance traveled by a ball dropped from a height of 6 feet if it rebounds initially to a height of 3 feet.

39. Exercise 38 under the supposition that the ball rebounds initially to a height of 2 feet.

40. In the setting of Exercise 38, to what height does the ball rebound initially if the total distance traveled by the ball is 21 feet?

41. How much money must you deposit at $r\%$ interest compounded annually to enable your descendants to withdraw n_1 dollars at the end of the first year, n_2 dollars at the end of the second year, n_3 dollars at the end of the third year, and so on in perpetuity? Assume that the sequence $\{n_k\}$ is bounded, $n_k \le N$ for all k, and express your answer as an infinite series.

42. Sum the series you obtained in Exercise 41 setting
    (a) $r = 5$, $n_k = 5000(\frac{1}{2})^{k-1}$.   (b) $r = 6$, $n_k = 1000(0.8)^{k-1}$.   (c) $r = 5$, $n_k = N$.

43. Show that the series

$$\sum_{k=1}^{\infty} \ln\left(\frac{k+1}{k}\right)$$

diverges even though $\lim\limits_{k \to \infty} \ln\left(\frac{k+1}{k}\right) = 0$.

44. Show that the series

$$\sum_{k=1}^{\infty} \left(\frac{k+1}{k}\right)^k$$

diverges.

45. Let $\{d_k\}$ be a sequence of real numbers that converges to 0.
    (a) Show that

$$\sum_{k=1}^{\infty} (d_k - d_{k+1}) = d_1.$$

    (b) Sum the following series:

    (i) $\displaystyle\sum_{k=1}^{\infty} \frac{\sqrt{k+1} - \sqrt{k}}{\sqrt{k(k+1)}}$.   (ii) $\displaystyle\sum_{k=1}^{\infty} \frac{2k+1}{2k^2(k+1)^2}$.

46. Show that

$$\sum_{k=1}^{\infty} kx^{k-1} = \frac{1}{(1-x)^2} \qquad \text{for } |x| < 1.$$

HINT: Verify that s_n, the nth partial sum, satisfies the identity

$$(1-x)^2 s_n = 1 - (n+1)x^n + nx^{n+1}.$$

13.3····THE INTEGRAL TEST; COMPARISON THEOREMS

Here and in the next section we direct our attention to *series with nonnegative terms*: $a_k \ge 0$ for all k. For such series the following theorem is fundamental.

> ## THEOREM 13.3.1
>
> A series with nonnegative terms converges iff the sequence of partial sums is bounded.

Proof. Assume that the series converges. Then the sequence of partial sums is convergent and therefore bounded (Theorem 12.2.4).

Suppose now that the sequence of partial sums is bounded. Since the terms are nonnegative, the sequence is nondecreasing. By being bounded and nondecreasing, the sequence of partial sums converges (Theorem 12.2.6). This means that the series converges. □

The convergence or divergence of a series can sometimes be deduced from the convergence or divergence of a closely related improper integral.

> ## THEOREM 13.3.2   THE INTEGRAL TEST
>
> If f is continuous, decreasing, and positive on $[1, \infty)$, then
>
> $$\sum_{k=1}^{\infty} f(k) \quad \text{converges} \quad \text{iff} \quad \int_{1}^{\infty} f(x)\,dx \quad \text{converges.}$$

Proof. In Exercise 21, Section 12.8, you were asked to show that with f continuous, decreasing, and positive on $[1, \infty)$

$$\int_{1}^{\infty} f(x)\,dx \quad \text{converges} \quad \text{iff} \quad \text{the sequence} \quad \left\{ \int_{1}^{n} f(x)\,dx \right\} \quad \text{converges.}$$

We assume this result and base our proof on the behavior of the sequence of integrals. To visualize our argument see Figure 13.3.1.

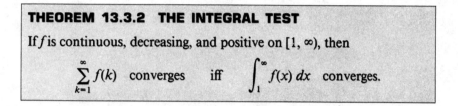

FIGURE 13.3.1

Since f decreases on the interval $[1, n]$,

$$f(2) + \cdots + f(n) \quad \text{is a lower sum for } f \text{ on } [1, n]$$

and

$$f(1) + \cdots + f(n-1) \quad \text{is an upper sum for } f \text{ on } [1, n].$$

Consequently

$$f(2) + \cdots + f(n) \le \int_1^n f(x)\, dx \quad \text{and} \quad \int_1^n f(x)\, dx \le f(1) + \cdots + f(n-1).$$

If the sequence of integrals converges, it is bounded. By the first inequality the sequence of partial sums is bounded and the series is therefore convergent.

Suppose now that the sequence of integrals diverges. Since f is positive, the sequence of integrals increases:

$$\int_1^n f(x)\, dx < \int_1^{n+1} f(x)\, dx.$$

Since this sequence diverges, it must be unbounded. By the second inequality, the sequence of partial sums must be unbounded and the series divergent. $\square$

Applying the Integral Test

EXAMPLE. (*The Harmonic Series*)

(13.3.3)
$$\sum_{k=1}^{\infty} \frac{1}{k} = 1 + \frac{1}{2} + \frac{1}{3} + \frac{1}{4} + \cdots \quad \textbf{diverges.}$$

Proof. The function $f(x) = 1/x$ is continuous, decreasing, and positive on $[1, \infty)$. We know that

$$\int_1^{\infty} \frac{dx}{x} \quad \text{diverges.} \qquad\qquad (12.7.1)$$

By the integral test

$$\sum_{k=1}^{\infty} \frac{1}{k} \quad \text{diverges.} \quad \square$$

The next example gives a more general result.

EXAMPLE. (*The p-series*)

(13.3.4)
$$\sum_{k=1}^{\infty} \frac{1}{k^p} = 1 + \frac{1}{2^p} + \frac{1}{3^p} + \frac{1}{4^p} + \cdots \quad \textbf{converges} \quad \textbf{iff} \quad p > 1.$$

Proof. If $p \le 0$, then each term of the series is greater than or equal to 1 and, by the divergence test (13.2.5), the series cannot converge. We assume therefore that $p > 0$. The function $f(x) = 1/x^p$ is then continuous, decreasing, and positive on $[1, \infty)$. Thus by the integral test

$$\sum_{k=1}^{\infty} \frac{1}{k^p} \quad \text{converges} \quad \text{iff} \quad \int_1^{\infty} \frac{dx}{x^p} \quad \text{converges.}$$

Earlier you saw that

$$\int_1^\infty \frac{dx}{x^p} \quad \text{converges} \quad \text{iff} \quad p > 1.$$ (12.7.1)

It follows that

$$\sum_{k=1}^\infty \frac{1}{k^p} \quad \text{converges} \quad \text{iff} \quad p > 1. \quad \square$$

EXAMPLE. Here we show that the series

$$\sum_{k=1}^\infty \frac{1}{k \ln (k + 1)} = \frac{1}{\ln 2} + \frac{1}{2 \ln 3} + \frac{1}{3 \ln 4} + \cdots$$

diverges. We begin by setting

$$f(x) = \frac{1}{x \ln (x + 1)}.$$

Since f is continuous, decreasing, and positive on $[1, \infty)$, we can use the integral test. Note that

$$\int_1^b \frac{dx}{x \ln (x + 1)} > \int_1^b \frac{dx}{(x + 1) \ln (x + 1)}$$

$$= \left[\ln (\ln (x + 1)) \right]_1^b = \ln (\ln (b + 1)) - \ln (\ln 2).$$

As $b \to \infty$, $\ln (\ln (b + 1)) \to \infty$. This shows that

$$\int_1^\infty \frac{dx}{x \ln (x + 1)} \quad \text{diverges}.$$

It follows that the series diverges. $\square$

REMARK ON NOTATION. You have seen that for each $j \geq 0$

$$\sum_{k=0}^\infty a_k \quad \text{converges} \quad \text{iff} \quad \sum_{k=j+1}^\infty a_k \quad \text{converges}$$

(Exercise 28, Section 13.2). This tells you that, in determining whether or not a series converges, it does not matter where we begin the summation.† Where detailed indexing would contribute nothing, we will omit it and write $\Sigma \, a_k$ without specifying where the summation begins. For instance, it makes sense to say that

$$\Sigma \frac{1}{k^2} \quad \text{converges} \quad \text{and} \quad \Sigma \frac{1}{k} \quad \text{diverges}$$

without specifying where we begin the summation. $\square$

---

† In the convergent case it does, however, affect the sum. Thus, for example,

$$\sum_{k=0}^\infty \frac{1}{2^k} = 2, \quad \sum_{k=1}^\infty \frac{1}{2^k} = 1, \quad \sum_{k=2}^\infty \frac{1}{2^k} = \frac{1}{2}, \quad \text{and so forth.}$$

The convergence or divergence of a series with nonnegative terms is usually deduced by comparison with a series of known behavior.

THEOREM 13.3.5   THE BASIC COMPARISON THEOREM

Let $\Sigma\, a_k$ be a series with nonnegative terms.

(i) $\Sigma\, a_k$ converges if there exists a convergent series $\Sigma\, c_k$ with nonnegative terms such that

$$a_k \le c_k \qquad \text{for all } k \text{ sufficiently large;}$$

(ii) $\Sigma\, a_k$ diverges if there exists a divergent series $\Sigma\, d_k$ with nonnegative terms such that

$$d_k \le a_k \qquad \text{for all } k \text{ sufficiently large.}$$

Proof. The proof is just a matter of noting that, in the first instance, the partial sums of $\Sigma\, a_k$ are bounded and, in the second instance, unbounded. The details are left to you. □

EXAMPLES

1. $\Sigma\, \dfrac{1}{2k^3 + 1}$ converges by comparison with $\Sigma\, \dfrac{1}{k^3}$:

$$\frac{1}{2k^3 + 1} < \frac{1}{k^3} \qquad \text{and} \qquad \Sigma\, \frac{1}{k^3} \quad \text{converges.} \quad \square$$

2. $\Sigma\, \dfrac{1}{3k + 1}$ diverges by comparison with $\Sigma\, \dfrac{1}{3(k + 1)}$:

$$\frac{1}{3(k + 1)} < \frac{1}{3k + 1} \qquad \text{and} \qquad \Sigma\, \frac{1}{3(k + 1)} = \frac{1}{3} \Sigma\, \frac{1}{k + 1} \quad \text{diverges.} \quad \square$$

3. $\Sigma\, \dfrac{k^3}{k^5 + 5k^4 + 7}$ converges by comparison with $\Sigma\, \dfrac{1}{k^2}$:

$$\frac{k^3}{k^5 + 5k^4 + 7} < \frac{k^3}{k^5} = \frac{1}{k^2} \qquad \text{and} \qquad \Sigma\, \frac{1}{k^2} \quad \text{converges.} \quad \square$$

PROBLEM. Show that

$$\Sigma\, \frac{1}{\ln (k + 6)} \quad \text{diverges.}$$

Solution. We know that as $k \to \infty$

$$\frac{\ln k}{k} \to 0. \qquad\qquad (12.3.5)$$

It follows that

$$\frac{\ln (k + 6)}{k + 6} \to 0$$

and thus that

$$\frac{\ln (k + 6)}{k} = \frac{\ln (k + 6)}{k + 6} \left(\frac{k + 6}{k} \right) \to 0.$$

Thus, for k sufficiently large,

$$\ln (k + 6) < k \qquad \text{and} \qquad \frac{1}{k} < \frac{1}{\ln (k + 6)}.$$

Since

$$\Sigma \frac{1}{k} \quad \text{diverges,}$$

we can conclude that

$$\Sigma \frac{1}{\ln (k + 6)} \quad \text{diverges.} \quad \square$$

REMARK.   Another way to show that

$$\ln (k + 6) < k \qquad \text{for large } k$$

is to examine the function

$$f(x) = x - \ln (x + 6).$$

At $x = 3$ the function is positive:

$$f(3) = 3 - \ln 9 \cong 3 - 2.197 > 0.$$

Since

$$f'(x) = 1 - \frac{1}{x + 6} > 0 \qquad \text{for all } x > 0,$$

$f(x) > 0$ for all $x \geq 3$.   It follows that

$$\ln (x + 6) < x \qquad \text{for all } x \geq 3. \quad \square$$

We come now to a somewhat more sophisticated comparison theorem.   Our proof relies on the basic comparison theorem.

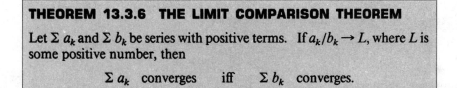

THEOREM 13.3.6   THE LIMIT COMPARISON THEOREM

Let $\Sigma\, a_k$ and $\Sigma\, b_k$ be series with positive terms.   If $a_k / b_k \to L$, where L is some positive number, then

$$\Sigma\, a_k \quad \text{converges} \qquad \text{iff} \qquad \Sigma\, b_k \quad \text{converges.}$$

Proof.   Choose ϵ between 0 and L. Since $a_k/b_k \to L$, we know that for all k sufficiently large (for all k greater than some k_0)

$$\left|\frac{a_k}{b_k} - L\right| < \epsilon.$$

For such k we have

$$L - \epsilon < \frac{a_k}{b_k} < L + \epsilon$$

and thus

$$(L - \epsilon)b_k < a_k < (L + \epsilon)b_k.$$

This last inequality is what we needed:

if $\Sigma\, a_k$ converges, then $\Sigma\, (L - \epsilon)b_k$ converges, and thus $\Sigma\, b_k$ converges;
if $\Sigma\, b_k$ converges, then $\Sigma\, (L + \epsilon)b_k$ converges, and thus $\Sigma\, a_k$ converges.   □

To apply the limit comparison theorem to a series $\Sigma\, a_k$, we must first find a series $\Sigma\, b_k$ of known behavior for which a_k/b_k converges to a positive number.

PROBLEM.   Determine whether the series

$$\Sigma\, \frac{3k^2 + 2k + 1}{k^3 + 1}$$

converges or diverges.

Solution.   For large values of k, the terms with the highest powers of k dominate. Here $3k^2$ dominates the numerator and k^3 dominates the denominator. Thus

$$\frac{3k^2 + 2k + 1}{k^3 + 1} \quad \text{differs little from} \quad \frac{3k^2}{k^3} = \frac{3}{k}.$$

Since

$$\frac{3k^2 + 2k + 1}{k^3 + 1} \div \frac{3}{k} = \frac{3k^3 + 2k^2 + k}{3k^3 + 3} = \frac{1 + 2/3k + 1/3k^2}{1 + 1/k^3} \to 1$$

and

$$\Sigma\, \frac{3}{k} = 3\Sigma\, \frac{1}{k} \quad \text{diverges,}$$

we know that the series diverges.   □

PROBLEM.   Determine whether the series

$$\Sigma\, \frac{5\sqrt{k} + 100}{2k^2\sqrt{k} + 9\sqrt{k}}$$

converges or diverges.

Solution. For large values of k, $5\sqrt{k}$ dominates the numerator and $2k^2\sqrt{k}$ dominates the denominator. Thus, for such k,

$$\frac{5\sqrt{k} + 100}{2k^2\sqrt{k} + 9\sqrt{k}} \quad \text{differs little from} \quad \frac{5\sqrt{k}}{2k^2\sqrt{k}} = \frac{5}{2k^2}.$$

Since

$$\frac{5\sqrt{k} + 100}{2k^2\sqrt{k} + 9\sqrt{k}} \div \frac{5}{2k^2} = \frac{10k^2\sqrt{k} + 200k^2}{10k^2\sqrt{k} + 45\sqrt{k}} = \frac{1 + 20/\sqrt{k}}{1 + 9/2k^2} \to 1$$

and

$$\Sigma \frac{5}{2k^2} = \frac{5}{2} \Sigma \frac{1}{k^2} \quad \text{converges,}$$

the series converges. ☐

PROBLEM. Determine whether the series

$$\Sigma \sin \frac{\pi}{k}$$

converges or diverges.

Solution. Recall that

$$\text{as } x \to 0, \quad \frac{\sin x}{x} \to 1. \qquad\qquad (2.5.3)$$

As $k \to \infty$, $\pi/k \to 0$ and thus

$$\frac{\sin \pi/k}{\pi/k} \to 1.$$

Since $\Sigma \pi/k$ diverges, $\Sigma \sin \pi/k$ diverges. ☐

REMARK. The question of what we can and cannot conclude by limit comparison if $a_k/b_k \to 0$ is taken up in Exercise 31. ☐

EXERCISES

Determine whether the series converges or diverges.

1. $\Sigma \dfrac{k}{k^3 + 1}$.

2. $\Sigma \dfrac{1}{3k + 2}$.

3. $\Sigma \dfrac{1}{(2k + 1)^2}$.

4. $\Sigma \dfrac{\ln k}{k}$.

5. $\Sigma \dfrac{1}{\sqrt{k + 1}}$.

6. $\Sigma \dfrac{1}{k^2 + 1}$.

7. $\Sigma \dfrac{1}{\sqrt{2k^2 - k}}$.

8. $\Sigma \left(\dfrac{5}{2}\right)^{-k}$.

9. $\Sigma \dfrac{\tan^{-1} k}{1 + k^2}$.

10. $\Sigma \dfrac{\ln k}{k^3}$.

11. $\Sigma \dfrac{1}{k^{2/3}}$.

12. $\Sigma \dfrac{1}{(k + 1)(k + 2)(k + 3)}$.

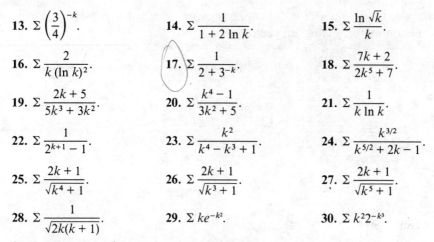

13. $\Sigma \left(\dfrac{3}{4}\right)^{-k}.$

14. $\Sigma \dfrac{1}{1 + 2 \ln k}.$

15. $\Sigma \dfrac{\ln \sqrt{k}}{k}.$

16. $\Sigma \dfrac{2}{k (\ln k)^2}.$

17. $\Sigma \dfrac{1}{2 + 3^{-k}}.$

18. $\Sigma \dfrac{7k + 2}{2k^5 + 7}.$

19. $\Sigma \dfrac{2k + 5}{5k^3 + 3k^2}.$

20. $\Sigma \dfrac{k^4 - 1}{3k^2 + 5}.$

21. $\Sigma \dfrac{1}{k \ln k}.$

22. $\Sigma \dfrac{1}{2^{k+1} - 1}.$

23. $\Sigma \dfrac{k^2}{k^4 - k^3 + 1}.$

24. $\Sigma \dfrac{k^{3/2}}{k^{5/2} + 2k - 1}.$

25. $\Sigma \dfrac{2k + 1}{\sqrt{k^4 + 1}}.$

26. $\Sigma \dfrac{2k + 1}{\sqrt{k^3 + 1}}.$

27. $\Sigma \dfrac{2k + 1}{\sqrt{k^5 + 1}}.$

28. $\Sigma \dfrac{1}{\sqrt{2k(k + 1)}}.$

29. $\Sigma k e^{-k^2}.$

30. $\Sigma k^2 2^{-k^3}.$

31. Let $\Sigma\, a_k$ and $\Sigma\, b_k$ be series with positive terms and suppose that $a_k / b_k \to 0$.
   (a) Show that, if $\Sigma\, b_k$ converges, then $\Sigma\, a_k$ converges.
   (b) Show that, if $\Sigma\, a_k$ diverges, then $\Sigma\, b_k$ diverges.
   (c) Show by example that, if $\Sigma\, a_k$ converges, then $\Sigma\, b_k$ may converge or diverge.
   (d) Show by example that, if $\Sigma\, b_k$ diverges, then $\Sigma\, a_k$ may converge or diverge.
   [Parts (c) and (d) explain why we stipulated $L > 0$ in Theorem 13.3.6.]

32. All the results of this section were stated for series with nonnegative terms. Corresponding results hold for *series with nonpositive terms*: $a_k \le 0$ for all k.
   (a) State a comparison theorem analogous to Theorem 13.3.5, this time for series with
       nonpositive terms.
   (b) As stated, the integral test (Theorem 13.3.2) applies only to series with positive terms.
       State the equivalent result for series with negative terms.

33. This exercise demonstrates that we cannot always use the same testing series for both the
   basic comparison test and the limit comparison test.
   (a) Show that

$$\Sigma \frac{\ln n}{n \sqrt{n}} \quad \text{converges by comparison with} \quad \Sigma \frac{1}{n^{5/4}}.$$

   (b) Show that the limit comparison test does not apply.

13.4···· THE ROOT TEST; THE RATIO TEST

The relative growth of successive terms in a geometric series

$$\Sigma\, a_k = \Sigma\, x^k$$

may be recorded in two ways:

$$(a_k)^{1/k} = x \quad \text{and} \quad \frac{a_{k+1}}{a_k} = x.$$

Only geometric series exhibit this type of behavior. But, there are many series that,
for large k, are "almost geometric":

$$(a_k)^{1/k} \to \text{a constant} \quad \text{and} \quad \frac{a_{k+1}}{a_k} \to \text{a constant}.$$

This generalization of geometric growth is the basis for two important convergence tests: the root test and the ratio test.

> ### THEOREM 13.4.1 THE ROOT TEST
>
> Let $\Sigma\, a_k$ be a series with nonnegative terms and suppose that
> $$(a_k)^{1/k} \to \rho.$$
> If $\rho < 1$, $\Sigma\, a_k$ converges. If $\rho > 1$, $\Sigma\, a_k$ diverges. If $\rho = 1$, the test is inconclusive.

Proof. We suppose first that $\rho < 1$ and choose μ so that

$$\rho < \mu < 1.$$

Since $(a_k)^{1/k} \to \rho$, we have

$$(a_k)^{1/k} < \mu \qquad \text{for all } k \text{ sufficiently large.} \qquad \text{(explain)}$$

Thus

$$a_k < \mu^k \qquad \text{for all } k \text{ sufficiently large.}$$

Since $\Sigma\, \mu^k$ converges (a geometric series with $0 < \mu < 1$), we know by the basic comparison theorem that $\Sigma\, a_k$ converges.

We suppose now that $\rho > 1$ and choose μ so that

$$\rho > \mu > 1.$$

Since $(a_k)^{1/k} \to \rho$, we have

$$(a_k)^{1/k} > \mu \qquad \text{for all } k \text{ sufficiently large.} \qquad \text{(explain)}$$

Thus

$$a_k > \mu^k \qquad \text{for all } k \text{ sufficiently large.}$$

Since $\Sigma\, \mu^k$ diverges (a geometric series with $\mu > 1$), the basic comparison theorem tells us that $\Sigma\, a_k$ diverges.

To see the inconclusiveness of the root test when $\rho = 1$, note that $(a_k)^{1/k} \to 1$ for both $\Sigma\, 1/k^2$ and $\Sigma\, 1/k.$† The first series converges, but the second diverges. $\square$

---

† In the first instance

$$(a_k)^{1/k} = \left(\frac{1}{k^2}\right)^{1/k} = \left(\frac{1}{k^{1/k}}\right)^2 \to 1^2 = 1;$$

in the second instance

$$(a_k)^{1/k} = \left(\frac{1}{k}\right)^{1/k} = \frac{1}{k^{1/k}} \to 1.$$

Applying the Root Test

EXAMPLE. For the series

$$\Sigma \frac{1}{(\ln k)^k}$$

we have

$$(a_k)^{1/k} = \frac{1}{\ln k} \to 0.$$

The series converges. □

EXAMPLE. For the series

$$\Sigma \frac{2^k}{k^3}$$

we have

$$(a_k)^{1/k} = 2 \left(\frac{1}{k}\right)^{3/k} = 2 \left[\left(\frac{1}{k}\right)^{1/k}\right]^3 \to 2 \cdot 1^3 = 2.$$

The series diverges. □

EXAMPLE. In the case of

$$\Sigma \left(1 - \frac{1}{k}\right)^k,$$

we have

$$(a_k)^{1/k} = 1 - \frac{1}{k} \to 1.$$

Here the root test is inconclusive. It is also unnecessary: since $a_k = (1 - 1/k)^k$ converges to $1/e$ and not to 0 (12.3.7), the series diverges (13.2.5). □

THEOREM 13.4.2 THE RATIO TEST

Let $\Sigma\, a_k$ be a series with positive terms and suppose that

$$\frac{a_{k+1}}{a_k} \to \lambda.$$

If $\lambda < 1$, $\Sigma\, a_k$ converges. If $\lambda > 1$, $\Sigma\, a_k$ diverges. If $\lambda = 1$, the test is inconclusive.

Proof. We suppose first that $\lambda < 1$ and choose μ so that

$$\lambda < \mu < 1.$$

Since

$$\frac{a_{k+1}}{a_k} \to \lambda,$$

we know that there exists $k_0 > 0$ such that

$$\text{if } k \geq k_0, \quad \text{then} \quad \frac{a_{k+1}}{a_k} < \mu. \qquad \text{(explain)}$$

This gives

$$a_{k_0+1} < \mu a_{k_0}, \qquad a_{k_0+2} < \mu a_{k_0+1} < \mu^2 a_{k_0},$$

and more generally,

$$a_{k_0+j} < \mu^j a_{k_0}.$$

For $k > k_0$ we have

(1)
$$a_k < \mu^{k-k_0} a_{k_0} = \frac{a_{k_0}}{\mu^{k_0}} \mu^k.$$

$$\text{set } j = k - k_0$$

Since $\mu < 1$,

$$\Sigma \frac{a_{k_0}}{\mu^{k_0}} \mu^k = \frac{a_{k_0}}{\mu^{k_0}} \Sigma \mu^k \quad \text{converges.}$$

Recalling (1), you can see by the basic comparison theorem that $\Sigma \, a_k$ converges. The proof of the rest of the theorem is left to the exercises. □

REMARK. Contrary to some people's intuition the root and ratio tests are *not* equivalent. See Exercise 36. □

Apply the Ratio Test

EXAMPLE. The ratio test shows that the series

$$\Sigma \frac{1}{k!}$$

converges:

$$\frac{a_{k+1}}{a_k} = \frac{1}{(k+1)!} \cdot \frac{k!}{1} = \frac{1}{k+1} \to 0. \quad □$$

EXAMPLE. For the series

$$\Sigma \frac{k}{10^k}$$

we have

$$\frac{a_{k+1}}{a_k} = \frac{k+1}{10^{k+1}} \cdot \frac{10^k}{k} = \frac{1}{10} \frac{k+1}{k} \to \frac{1}{10}.$$

The series converges.† □

_____

† This series can be summed explicitly. See Exercise 33.

EXAMPLE.   For the series

$$\Sigma \frac{k^k}{k!}$$

we have

$$\frac{a_{k+1}}{a_k} = \frac{(k+1)^{k+1}}{(k+1)!} \cdot \frac{k!}{k^k} = \left(\frac{k+1}{k}\right)^k = \left(1 + \frac{1}{k}\right)^k \to e.$$

Since $e > 1$, the series diverges.   □

EXAMPLE.   For the series

$$\Sigma \frac{1}{2k+1}$$

the ratio test is inconclusive:

$$\frac{a_{k+1}}{a_k} = \frac{1}{2(k+1)+1} \cdot \frac{2k+1}{1} = \frac{2k+1}{2k+3} = \frac{2+1/k}{2+3/k} \to 1.$$

Therefore, we have to look further.   Comparison with the harmonic series shows that the series diverges:

$$\frac{1}{2k+1} > \frac{1}{2(k+1)} \qquad \text{and} \qquad \Sigma \frac{1}{2(k+1)} \quad \text{diverges.}   □$$

Summary on Convergence Tests

In general, the root test is used only if powers are involved.   The ratio test is particularly effective with factorials and with combinations of powers and factorials.   If the terms are rational functions of k, the ratio test is inconclusive and the root test is difficult to apply.   Rational terms are most easily handled by comparison or limit comparison with a p-series, $\Sigma 1/k^p$.   If the terms have the configuration of a derivative, you may be able to apply the integral test.   Finally, keep in mind that, if $a_k \not\to 0$, then there is no reason to apply any special convergence test.   The series diverges (13.2.5).

EXERCISES

Determine whether the series converges or diverges.

1. $\Sigma \dfrac{10^k}{k!}$.

2. $\Sigma \dfrac{1}{k2^k}$.

3. $\Sigma \dfrac{1}{k^k}$.

4. $\Sigma \left(\dfrac{k}{2k+1}\right)^k$.

5. $\Sigma \dfrac{k!}{100^k}$.

6. $\Sigma \dfrac{(\ln k)^2}{k}$.

7. $\Sigma \dfrac{k^2+2}{k^3+6k}$.

8. $\Sigma \dfrac{1}{(\ln k)^k}$.

9. $\Sigma k \left(\dfrac{2}{3}\right)^k$.

10. $\Sigma \dfrac{1}{(\ln k)^{10}}$.

11. $\Sigma \dfrac{1}{1+\sqrt{k}}$.

12. $\Sigma \dfrac{2k+\sqrt{k}}{k^3+\sqrt{k}}$.

13. $\Sigma \dfrac{k!}{10^{4k}}$.

14. $\Sigma \dfrac{k^2}{e^k}$.

15. $\Sigma \dfrac{\sqrt{k}}{k^2+1}$.

16. $\Sigma \dfrac{2^k k!}{k^k}$.

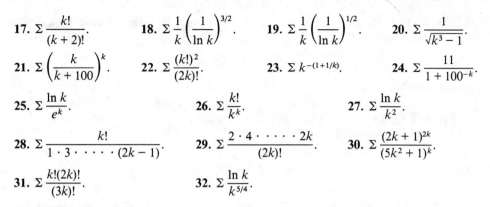

17. $\Sigma \dfrac{k!}{(k+2)!}.$ 18. $\Sigma \dfrac{1}{k}\left(\dfrac{1}{\ln k}\right)^{3/2}.$ 19. $\Sigma \dfrac{1}{k}\left(\dfrac{1}{\ln k}\right)^{1/2}.$ 20. $\Sigma \dfrac{1}{\sqrt{k^3-1}}.$

21. $\Sigma \left(\dfrac{k}{k+100}\right)^k.$ 22. $\Sigma \dfrac{(k!)^2}{(2k)!}.$ 23. $\Sigma\, k^{-(1+1/k)}.$ 24. $\Sigma \dfrac{11}{1+100^{-k}}.$

25. $\Sigma \dfrac{\ln k}{e^k}.$ 26. $\Sigma \dfrac{k!}{k^k}.$ 27. $\Sigma \dfrac{\ln k}{k^2}.$

28. $\Sigma \dfrac{k!}{1\cdot 3\cdot\,\cdots\,\cdot(2k-1)}.$ 29. $\Sigma \dfrac{2\cdot 4\cdot\,\cdots\,\cdot 2k}{(2k)!}.$ 30. $\Sigma \dfrac{(2k+1)^{2k}}{(5k^2+1)^k}.$

31. $\Sigma \dfrac{k!(2k)!}{(3k)!}.$ 32. $\Sigma \dfrac{\ln k}{k^{5/4}}.$

33. Find the sum of the series

$$\sum_{k=1}^{\infty} \frac{k}{10^k}.$$

HINT: Exercise 46 of Section 13.2.

34. Complete the proof of the ratio test.
   (a) Prove that, if $\lambda > 1$, then $\Sigma\, a_k$ diverges.
   (b) Prove that, if $\lambda = 1$, the ratio test is inconclusive.
      HINT: Consider $\Sigma\, 1/k$ and $\Sigma\, 1/k^2$.

35. Let $\{a_k\}$ be a sequence of positive numbers, and take $r > 0$. Use the root test to show that, if $(a_k)^{1/k} \to \rho$ and $\rho < 1/r$, then $\Sigma\, a_k r^k$ converges.

36. Consider the series

$$\frac{1}{2} + 1 + \frac{1}{8} + \frac{1}{4} + \frac{1}{32} + \frac{1}{16} + \frac{1}{128} + \frac{1}{64} + \cdots$$

formed by rearranging consecutive pairs of terms of a geometric series whose sum is 2.
(a) Use the root test to show that the series converges.   (b) Show that the ratio test does not apply.

13.5····ABSOLUTE AND CONDITIONAL CONVERGENCE; ALTERNATING SERIES

In this section we consider series that have both positive and negative terms.

Absolute and Conditional Convergence

Let $\Sigma\, a_k$ be a series with both positive and negative terms.   One way to show that $\Sigma\, a_k$ converges is to show that $\Sigma\, |a_k|$ converges.

THEOREM 13.5.1

If $\Sigma\, |a_k|$ converges,   then $\Sigma\, a_k$ converges.

Proof.   For each k,

$$-|a_k| \le a_k \le |a_k| \quad \text{and therefore} \quad 0 \le a_k + |a_k| \le 2|a_k|.$$

If $\Sigma\,|a_k|$ converges, then $\Sigma\,2|a_k| = 2\,\Sigma\,|a_k|$ converges, and therefore, by the basic comparison theorem, $\Sigma\,(a_k + |a_k|)$ converges. Since

$$a_k = (a_k + |a_k|) - |a_k|,$$

we can conclude that $\Sigma\,a_k$ converges. $\square$

Series $\Sigma\,a_k$ for which $\Sigma\,|a_k|$ converge are called *absolutely convergent*. The theorem we just proved says that

(13.5.2) | absolutely convergent series are convergent. |

As we'll show presently, the converse is false. There are convergent series that are not absolutely convergent. Such series are called *conditionally convergent*.

EXAMPLE

$$1 - \frac{1}{2^2} + \frac{1}{3^2} - \frac{1}{4^2} + \frac{1}{5^2} - \frac{1}{6^2} + \cdots.$$

If we replace each term by its absolute value, we obtain the series

$$1 + \frac{1}{2^2} + \frac{1}{3^2} + \frac{1}{4^2} + \frac{1}{5^2} + \frac{1}{6^2} + \cdots.$$

This is a *p*-series with $p = 2$. It is therefore convergent. This means that the initial series is absolutely convergent. $\square$

EXAMPLE

$$1 - \frac{1}{2} - \frac{1}{2^2} + \frac{1}{2^3} - \frac{1}{2^4} - \frac{1}{2^5} + \frac{1}{2^6} - \frac{1}{2^7} - \frac{1}{2^8} + \cdots.$$

If we replace each term by its absolute value, we obtain the series

$$1 + \frac{1}{2} + \frac{1}{2^2} + \frac{1}{2^3} + \frac{1}{2^4} + \frac{1}{2^5} + \frac{1}{2^6} + \frac{1}{2^7} + \frac{1}{2^8} + \cdots.$$

This is a convergent geometric series. The initial series is therefore absolutely convergent. $\square$

EXAMPLE

$$1 - \frac{1}{2} + \frac{1}{3} - \frac{1}{4} + \frac{1}{5} - \frac{1}{6} + \cdots.$$

This series is only conditionally convergent. It is convergent (see the next theorem), but it is not absolutely convergent: if we replace each term by its absolute value, we obtain the divergent harmonic series

$$1 + \frac{1}{2} + \frac{1}{3} + \frac{1}{4} + \frac{1}{5} + \frac{1}{6} + \cdots .† \quad \square$$

EXAMPLE

$$\frac{1}{2} - 1 + \frac{1}{3} - 1 + \frac{1}{4} - 1 + \frac{1}{5} - 1 + \cdots .$$

Here the terms do not tend to zero. The series is divergent. $\square$

Alternating Series

Series in which the consecutive terms have opposite signs are called *alternating series.* Here are some examples:

$$1 - \frac{1}{2} + \frac{1}{3} - \frac{1}{4} + \frac{1}{5} - \frac{1}{6} + \cdots ,$$

$$1 - \frac{1}{\sqrt{2}} + \frac{1}{\sqrt{3}} - \frac{1}{\sqrt{4}} + \frac{1}{\sqrt{5}} - \frac{1}{\sqrt{6}} + \cdots ,$$

$$1 - \frac{2}{\ln 2} + \frac{3}{\ln 3} - \frac{4}{\ln 4} + \frac{5}{\ln 5} - \frac{6}{\ln 6} + \cdots .$$

The series

$$1 - \frac{1}{2} - \frac{1}{3} + \frac{1}{4} - \frac{1}{5} - \frac{1}{6} + \cdots$$

is not an alternating series because there are consecutive terms with the same sign.

THEOREM 13.5.3 ALTERNATING SERIES††

Let $\{a_k\}$ be a decreasing sequence of positive numbers.

$$\text{If} \quad a_k \rightarrow 0, \quad \text{then} \quad \sum_{k=0}^{\infty} (-1)^k a_k \quad \text{converges.}$$

Proof. First we look at the even partial sums, s_{2m}. Since

$$s_{2m} = (a_0 - a_1) + (a_2 - a_3) + \cdots + (a_{2m-2} - a_{2m-1}) + a_{2m}$$

is the sum of positive numbers, the even partial sums are all positive. Since

$$s_{2m+2} = s_{2m} - (a_{2m+1} - a_{2m+2}) \qquad \text{and} \qquad a_{2m+1} - a_{2m+2} > 0,$$

---

† In Section 13.6 we'll show that the original series,

$$1 - \tfrac{1}{2} + \tfrac{1}{3} - \tfrac{1}{4} + \tfrac{1}{5} - \tfrac{1}{6} + \cdots ,$$

converges to ln 2.

†† This theorem dates back to Leibniz. He observed the result in 1705.

we have

$$s_{2m+2} < s_{2m}.$$

This means that the sequence of even partial sums is decreasing. Being bounded below by 0, it is convergent; say,

$$s_{2m} \to l.$$

Now

$$s_{2m+1} = s_{2m} - a_{2m+1}.$$

Since $a_{2m+1} \to 0$, we also have

$$s_{2m+1} \to l.$$

Since both the even and the odd partial sums tend to l, the sequence of all partial sums tends to l (Exercise 42, Section 12.2). □

From this theorem you can see that the following series all converge:

$$1 - \frac{1}{2} + \frac{1}{3} - \frac{1}{4} + \frac{1}{5} - \frac{1}{6} + \cdots,$$

$$1 - \frac{1}{\sqrt{2}} + \frac{1}{\sqrt{3}} - \frac{1}{\sqrt{4}} + \frac{1}{\sqrt{5}} - \frac{1}{\sqrt{6}} + \cdots,$$

$$1 - \frac{1}{2!} + \frac{1}{3!} - \frac{1}{4!} + \frac{1}{5!} - \frac{1}{6!} + \cdots.$$

The first two series converge only conditionally; the third converges absolutely.

An Estimate for Alternating Series You have seen that if $\{a_k\}$ is a decreasing sequence of positive numbers that tends to 0, then

$$\sum_{k=0}^{\infty} (-1)^k a_k \quad \text{converges to a sum } l.$$

(13.5.4)
> This sum l of an alternating series lies between consecutive partial sums s_n, s_{n+1}, and thus s_n approximates l to within a_{n+1}:
>
> $$|s_n - l| < a_{n+1}.$$

Proof. For all n

$$a_{n+1} > a_{n+2}.$$

If n is odd,

$$s_{n+2} = s_n + a_{n+1} - a_{n+2} > s_n;$$

if n is even,

$$s_{n+2} = s_n - a_{n+1} + a_{n+2} < s_n.$$

The odd partial sums increase toward l; the even partial sums decrease toward l. For odd n

$$s_n < l < s_{n+1} = s_n + a_{n+1},$$

and for even n

$$s_n - a_{n+1} = s_{n+1} < l < s_n.$$

Thus, for all n, l lies between s_n and s_{n+1}, and s_n approximates l to within a_{n+1}. $\square$

EXAMPLES. Both

$$1 - \frac{1}{2} + \frac{1}{3} - \frac{1}{4} + \frac{1}{5} - \frac{1}{6} + \cdots \quad \text{and} \quad 1 - \frac{1}{2^2} + \frac{1}{3^2} - \frac{1}{4^2} + \frac{1}{5^2} - \frac{1}{6^2} + \cdots$$

are convergent alternating series. The nth partial sum of the first series approximates the sum of that series within $1/(n+1)$; the nth partial sum of the second series approximates the sum of the second series within $1/(n+1)^2$. The second series converges more rapidly than the first series. $\square$

Rearrangements

A *rearrangement* of a series Σa_k is a series that has exactly the same terms but in a different order. Thus, for example,

$$1 + \frac{1}{3^3} - \frac{1}{2^2} + \frac{1}{5^5} - \frac{1}{4^4} + \frac{1}{7^7} - \frac{1}{6^6} + \cdots$$

and

$$1 + \frac{1}{3^3} + \frac{1}{5^5} - \frac{1}{2^2} - \frac{1}{4^4} + \frac{1}{7^7} + \frac{1}{9^9} - \cdots$$

are both rearrangements of

$$1 - \frac{1}{2^2} + \frac{1}{3^3} - \frac{1}{4^4} + \frac{1}{5^5} - \frac{1}{6^6} + \frac{1}{7^7} - \cdots.$$

In 1867 Riemann published a theorem on rearrangements of series that underscores the importance of distinguishing between absolute convergence and conditional convergence. According to this theorem all rearrangements of an absolutely convergent series converge absolutely to the same sum. In sharp contrast, a series that is only conditionally convergent can be rearranged to converge to any number we please. It can also be arranged to diverge to $+\infty$, or to diverge to $-\infty$, or even to oscillate between any two bounds we choose.[†]

----

† For a complete proof see pp. 138–139, 318–320 in Konrad Knopp's *Theory and Applications of Infinite Series* (Second English Edition), Blackie & Son Limited, London, 1951.

EXERCISES

Test these series for (a) absolute convergence, (b) conditional convergence.

1. $1 + (-1) + 1 + \cdots + (-1)^k + \cdots$.

2. $\dfrac{1}{4} - \dfrac{1}{6} + \dfrac{1}{8} - \dfrac{1}{10} + \cdots + \dfrac{(-1)^k}{2k} + \cdots$.

3. $\dfrac{1}{2} - \dfrac{2}{3} + \dfrac{3}{4} - \dfrac{4}{5} + \cdots + (-1)^k \dfrac{k}{k+1} + \cdots$.

4. $\dfrac{1}{2 \ln 2} - \dfrac{1}{3 \ln 3} + \dfrac{1}{4 \ln 4} - \dfrac{1}{5 \ln 5} + \cdots + (-1)^k \dfrac{1}{k \ln k} + \cdots$.

5. $\Sigma \, (-1)^k \dfrac{\ln k}{k}$.

6. $\Sigma \, (-1)^k \dfrac{k}{\ln k}$.

7. $\Sigma \left(\dfrac{1}{k} - \dfrac{1}{k!} \right)$.

8. $\Sigma \dfrac{k^3}{2^k}$.

9. $\Sigma \, (-1)^k \dfrac{1}{2k+1}$.

10. $\Sigma \, (-1)^k \dfrac{(k!)^2}{(2k)!}$.

11. $\Sigma \dfrac{k!}{(-2)^k}$.

12. $\Sigma \sin \left(\dfrac{k\pi}{4} \right)$.

13. $\Sigma \, (-1)^k (\sqrt{k+1} - \sqrt{k})$.

14. $\Sigma \, (-1)^k \dfrac{k}{k^2 + 1}$.

15. $\Sigma \sin \left(\dfrac{\pi}{4k^2} \right)$.

16. $\Sigma \dfrac{(-1)^k}{\sqrt{k(k+1)}}$.

17. $\Sigma \, (-1)^k \dfrac{k}{2^k}$.

18. $\Sigma \left(\dfrac{1}{\sqrt{k}} - \dfrac{1}{\sqrt{k+1}} \right)$.

19. $\Sigma \dfrac{(-1)^k}{k - 2\sqrt{k}}$.

20. $\dfrac{1}{2} - \dfrac{1}{3} - \dfrac{1}{4} + \dfrac{1}{5} - \dfrac{1}{6} - \dfrac{1}{7} + \cdots + \dfrac{1}{3k+2} - \dfrac{1}{3k+3} - \dfrac{1}{3k+4} + \cdots$.

21. $\dfrac{2 \cdot 3}{4 \cdot 5} - \dfrac{5 \cdot 6}{7 \cdot 8} + \cdots + (-1)^k \dfrac{(3k+2)(3k+3)}{(3k+4)(3k+5)} + \cdots$.

22. Let s_n be the nth partial sum of the series.

$$\sum_{k=0}^{\infty} (-1)^k \frac{1}{10^k}.$$

Find the least value of n for which s_n approximates the sum of the series within
(a) 0.001.   (b) 0.0001.

23. Find the sum of the series in Exercise 22.

24. Verify that the series

$$1 - \frac{1}{2} + \frac{1}{2} - \frac{1}{3} + \frac{1}{2} - \frac{1}{3} + \frac{1}{3} - \frac{1}{4} + \frac{1}{3} - \frac{1}{4} + \frac{1}{3} - \frac{1}{4} + \cdots$$

diverges and explain how this does not violate the theorem on alternating series.

25. Let l be the sum of the series

$$\sum_{k=0}^{\infty} (-1)^k \frac{1}{k!}$$

and let s_n be the nth partial sum. Find the least value of n for which s_n approximates l
within (a) 0.01.   (b) 0.001.

26. Let $\{a_k\}$ be a nonincreasing sequence of positive numbers that converges to 0. Does the
alternating series $\Sigma \, (-1)^k a_k$ necessarily converge?

27. Can the hypothesis of Theorem 13.5.3 be relaxed to require only that $\{a_{2k}\}$ and $\{a_{2k+1}\}$ be decreasing sequences of positive numbers with limit zero?

28. Indicate how a conditionally convergent series may be rearranged (a) to converge to an arbitrary real number l; (b) to diverge to $+\infty$; (c) to diverge to $-\infty$.
HINT: Collect the positive terms

$$p_1, p_2, p_3, \ldots, p_k, \ldots$$

and also the negative terms

$$n_1, n_2, n_3, \ldots, n_k, \ldots$$

in the order in which they appear in the original series.

29. In Section 13.8 we prove that, if $\Sigma\, a_k x_1^k$ converges, then $\Sigma\, a_k x^k$ converges absolutely for $|x| < |x_1|$.   Try to prove this now.

13.6····TAYLOR POLYNOMIALS IN x; TAYLOR SERIES IN x

Taylor Polynomials in x

We begin with a function f continuous at 0 and set $P_0(x) = f(0)$. If f is differentiable at 0, the linear function that best approximates f at points close to 0 is the linear function

$$P_1(x) = f(0) + f'(0)x;$$

P_1 has the same value as f at 0 and also the same first derivative (the same rate of change):

$$P_1(0) = f(0), \quad P_1'(0) = f'(0).$$

If f has two derivatives at 0, then we can get a better approximation to f by using the quadratic polynomial

$$P_2(x) = f(0) + f'(0)x + \frac{f''(0)}{2!} x^2;$$

P_2 has the same value as f at 0 and the same first two derivatives:

$$P_2(0) = f(0), \quad P_2'(0) = f'(0), \quad P_2''(0) = f''(0).$$

If f has three derivatives at 0, we can form the cubic polynomial

$$P_3(x) = f(0) + f'(0)x + \frac{f''(0)}{2!} x^2 + \frac{f'''(0)}{3!} x^3;$$

P_3 has the same value as f at 0 and the same first three derivatives:

$$P_3(0) = f(0), \quad P_3'(0) = f'(0), \quad P_3''(0) = f''(0), \quad P_3'''(0) = f'''(0).$$

More generally, if f has n derivatives at 0, we can form the polynomial

$$P_n(x) = f(0) + f'(0)x + \frac{f''(0)}{2!} x^2 + \cdots + \frac{f^{(n)}(0)}{n!} x^n;$$

P_n is the polynomial of degree n that has the same value as f at 0 and the same first n derivatives:

$$P_n(0) = f(0), \quad P_n'(0) = f'(0), \quad P_n''(0) = f''(0), \quad \dots, \quad P_n^{(n)}(0) = f^{(n)}(0).$$

These approximating polynomials $P_0(x), P_1(x), P_2(x), \dots, P_n(x)$ are called *Taylor polynomials* after the English mathematician Brook Taylor (1685–1731). Taylor introduced these polynomials in the year 1712.

EXAMPLE 1. The exponential function

$$f(x) = e^x$$

has derivatives

$$f'(x) = e^x, \quad f''(x) = e^x, \quad f'''(x) = e^x, \quad \text{etc.}$$

Thus

$$f(0) = 1, \quad f'(0) = 1, \quad f''(0) = 1, \quad f'''(0) = 1, \quad \dots, \quad f^{(n)}(0) = 1.$$

The nth Taylor polynomial takes the form

$$P_n(x) = 1 + x + \frac{x^2}{2!} + \frac{x^3}{3!} + \cdots + \frac{x^n}{n!}. \quad \square$$

EXAMPLE 2. To find the Taylor polynomials that approximate the sine function we write

$$f(x) = \sin x, \quad f'(x) = \cos x, \quad f''(x) = -\sin x, \quad f'''(x) = -\cos x.$$

The pattern now repeats itself:

$$f^{(4)}(x) = \sin x, \quad f^{(5)}(x) = \cos x, \quad f^{(6)}(x) = -\sin x, \quad f^{(7)}(x) = -\cos x.$$

At 0, the sine function and all its even derivatives are 0. The odd derivatives are alternately 1 and -1:

$$f'(0) = 1, \quad f'''(0) = -1, \quad f^{(5)}(0) = 1, \quad f^{(7)}(0) = -1, \quad \text{etc.}$$

The Taylor polynomials are therefore as follows:

$$P_0(x) = 0$$
$$P_1(x) = P_2(x) = x$$
$$P_3(x) = P_4(x) = x - \frac{x^3}{3!}$$
$$P_5(x) = P_6(x) = x - \frac{x^3}{3!} + \frac{x^5}{5!}$$
$$P_7(x) = P_8(x) = x - \frac{x^3}{3!} + \frac{x^5}{5!} - \frac{x^7}{7!}, \quad \text{etc.}$$

Only odd powers appear. $\square$

It is not enough to say that the Taylor polynomials

$$P_n(x) = f(0) + f'(0)x + \frac{f''(0)}{2!}x^2 + \cdots + \frac{f^{(n)}(0)}{n!}x^n$$

approximate $f(x)$. We must describe the accuracy of the approximation. Our first step is to prove a result known as Taylor's theorem.

> ### THEOREM 13.6.1 TAYLOR'S THEOREM
>
> If f has $n + 1$ continuous derivatives on the interval I that joins 0 to x, then
>
> $$f(x) = f(0) + f'(0)x + \frac{f''(0)}{2!}x^2 + \cdots + \frac{f^{(n)}(0)}{n!}x^n + R_{n+1}(x)$$
>
> where the *remainder* $R_{n+1}(x)$ is given by the formula
>
> $$R_{n+1}(x) = \frac{1}{n!}\int_0^x f^{(n+1)}(t)(x-t)^n\, dt.$$

Proof. Integration by parts (see Exercise 33) gives

$$f'(0)x = \int_0^x f'(t)\, dt - \int_0^x f''(t)(x-t)\, dt,$$

$$\frac{f''(0)}{2!}x^2 = \int_0^x f''(t)(x-t)\, dt - \frac{1}{2!}\int_0^x f'''(t)(x-t)^2\, dt,$$

$$\frac{f'''(0)}{3!}x^3 = \frac{1}{2!}\int_0^x f'''(t)(x-t)^2\, dt - \frac{1}{3!}\int_0^x f^{(4)}(t)(x-t)^3\, dt,$$

$$\vdots$$

$$\frac{f^{(n)}(0)}{n!}x^n = \frac{1}{(n-1)!}\int_0^x f^{(n)}(t)(x-t)^{n-1}\, dt - \frac{1}{n!}\int_0^x f^{(n+1)}(t)(x-t)^n\, dt.$$

We now add these equations. The sum on the left is simply

$$f'(0)x + \frac{f''(0)}{2!}x^2 + \frac{f'''(0)}{3!}x^3 + \cdots + \frac{f^{(n)}(0)}{n!}x^n = P_n(x) - f(0).$$

The sum on the right telescopes to give

$$\int_0^x f'(t)\, dt - \frac{1}{n!}\int_0^x f^{(n+1)}(t)(x-t)^n\, dt = f(x) - f(0) - \frac{1}{n!}\int_0^x f^{(n+1)}(t)(x-t)^n\, dt.$$

It follows that

$$f(x) = P_n(x) + \frac{1}{n!}\int_0^x f^{(n+1)}(t)(x-t)^n\, dt,$$

and thus

$$R_{n+1}(x) = \frac{1}{n!} \int_0^x f^{(n+1)}(t)(x-t)^n \, dt. \quad \square$$

We can now describe how closely

$$P_n(x) = f(0) + f'(0)x + \frac{f''(0)}{2!} x^2 + \cdots + \frac{f^{(n)}(0)}{n!} x^n$$

approximates $f(x)$ by giving an estimate for the remainder

$$R_{n+1}(x) = \frac{1}{n!} \int_0^x f^{(n+1)}(t)(x-t)^n \, dt.$$

Working with the integral on the right you can see that

(13.6.2)
$$|R_{n+1}(x)| \le \left(\max_{t \in I} |f^{(n+1)}(t)| \right) \frac{|x|^{n+1}}{(n+1)!}.$$

The derivation of this *remainder estimate* is left to you as an exercise.

EXAMPLE 3. The Taylor polynomials of the exponential function

$$f(x) = e^x$$

take the form

$$P_n(x) = 1 + x + \frac{x^2}{2!} + \cdots + \frac{x^n}{n!}. \qquad \text{(Example 1)}$$

We will show with our remainder estimate that for all real x

$$R_{n+1}(x) \to 0,$$

and therefore we can approximate e^x as closely as we wish by Taylor polynomials.

We begin by fixing x and letting M be the maximum value of the exponential function on the interval I that joins 0 to x. (If $x > 0$, then $M = e^x$ but, if $x < 0$, $M = e^0 = 1$.) Since

$$f^{(n+1)}(t) = e^t \qquad \text{for all } n,$$

we have

$$\max_{t \in I} |f^{(n+1)}(t)| = M \qquad \text{for all } n.$$

Thus by (13.6.2)

$$|R_{n+1}(x)| \le M \frac{|x|^{n+1}}{(n+1)!}.$$

By (12.3.3) we know that

$$\frac{|x|^{n+1}}{(n+1)!} \to 0.$$

It follows then that

$$R_{n+1}(x) \to 0$$

as asserted.   □

EXAMPLE 4.   We return to the sine function

$$f(x) = \sin x$$

and its Taylor polynomials

$$P_1(x) = P_2(x) = x$$

$$P_3(x) = P_4(x) = x - \frac{x^3}{3!}$$

$$P_5(x) = P_6(x) = x - \frac{x^3}{3!} + \frac{x^5}{5!}, \quad \text{etc.}$$

The pattern of derivatives was established in Example 2; namely, for all k,

$$f^{(4k)}(x) = \sin x, \quad f^{(4k+1)}(x) = \cos x, \quad f^{(4k+2)}(x) = -\sin x, \quad f^{(4k+3)}(x) = -\cos x.$$

Thus, for all n and all real t,

$$|f^{(n+1)}(t)| \leq 1.$$

It follows from our remainder estimate (13.6.2) that

$$|R_{n+1}(x)| \leq \frac{|x|^{n+1}}{(n+1)!}.$$

Since

$$\frac{|x|^{n+1}}{(n+1)!} \to 0 \qquad \text{for all real } x,$$

we have

$$R_{n+1}(x) \to 0 \qquad \text{for all real } x.$$

Thus the sequence of Taylor polynomials converges to the sine function and therefore can be used to approximate $\sin x$ as closely as we may wish.   □

Taylor Series in x

By definition $0! = 1$.   By adopting the convention that $f^{(0)} = f$, we can write Taylor polynomials

$$P_n(x) = f(0) + f'(0)x + \frac{f''(0)}{2!}x^2 + \cdots + \frac{f^{(n)}(0)}{n!}x^n$$

in Σ notation:

$$P_n(x) = \sum_{k=0}^{n} \frac{f^{(k)}(0)}{k!}x^k.$$

If f is infinitely differentiable at $x = 0$, then we have

$$f(x) = \sum_{k=0}^{n} \frac{f^{(k)}(0)}{k!} x^k + R_{n+1}(x)$$

for all positive integers n. If, as in the case of the exponential function and the sine function, $R_{n+1}(x) \to 0$, then

$$\sum_{k=0}^{n} \frac{f^{(k)}(0)}{k!} x^k \to f(x).$$

In this case, we say that $f(x)$ can be expanded as a *Taylor series in x* and write

(13.6.3)
$$f(x) = \sum_{k=0}^{\infty} \frac{f^{(k)}(0)}{k!} x^k.$$

[Taylor series in x are sometimes called Maclaurin series after Colin Maclaurin, a Scottish mathematician (1698–1746). In some circles the name Maclaurin remains attached to these series, although Taylor considered them some twenty years before Maclaurin.]

From Example 3 it is clear that

(13.6.4)
$$e^x = \sum_{k=0}^{\infty} \frac{x^k}{k!} = 1 + x + \frac{x^2}{2!} + \frac{x^3}{3!} + \cdots \quad \text{for all real } x.$$

From Example 4 we have

(13.6.5)
$$\sin x = \sum_{k=0}^{\infty} \frac{(-1)^k}{(2k+1)!} x^{2k+1} = x - \frac{x^3}{3!} + \frac{x^5}{5!} - \frac{x^7}{7!} + \cdots \quad \text{for all real } x.$$

We leave it to you as an exercise to show that

(13.6.6)
$$\cos x = \sum_{k=0}^{\infty} \frac{(-1)^k}{(2k)!} x^{2k} = 1 - \frac{x^2}{2!} + \frac{x^4}{4!} - \frac{x^6}{6!} + \cdots \quad \text{for all real } x.$$

We come now to the logarithm function. Since $\ln x$ is not defined at $x = 0$, we cannot expand $\ln x$ in powers of x. We will work instead with $\ln (1 + x)$.

(13.6.7)
$$\ln (1 + x) = \sum_{k=1}^{\infty} \frac{(-1)^{k+1}}{k} x^k = x - \frac{x^2}{2} + \frac{x^3}{3} - \cdots \quad \text{for } -1 < x \le 1.$$

Proof.† The function

$$f(x) = \ln (1 + x)$$

has derivatives

$$f'(x) = \frac{1}{1 + x}, \quad f''(x) = -\frac{1}{(1 + x)^2}, \quad f'''(x) = \frac{2}{(1 + x)^3},$$

$$f^{(4)}(x) = -\frac{3!}{(1 + x)^4}, \quad f^{(5)}(x) = \frac{4!}{(1 + x)^5}, \quad \text{and so on.}$$

For $k \geq 1$

$$f^{(k)}(x) = (-1)^{k+1} \frac{(k - 1)!}{(1 + x)^k}, \quad f^{(k)}(0) = (-1)^{k+1}(k - 1)!, \quad \frac{f^{(k)}(0)}{k!} = \frac{(-1)^{k+1}}{k}.$$

Since $f(0) = 0$, the nth Taylor polynomial takes the form

$$P_n(x) = \sum_{k=1}^{n} (-1)^{k+1} \frac{x^k}{k} = x - \frac{x^2}{2} + \cdots + (-1)^{n+1} \frac{x^n}{n}.$$

All we have to show therefore is that

$$R_{n+1}(x) \to 0 \quad \text{for } -1 < x \leq 1.$$

Instead of trying to apply our usual remainder estimate (in this case, that estimate is not delicate enough to show that $R_{n+1}(x) \to 0$ for $-1 < x < -\frac{1}{2}$), we write the remainder in its integral form. From Taylor's theorem

$$R_{n+1}(x) = \frac{1}{n!} \int_0^x f^{(n+1)}(t)(x - t)^n \, dt,$$

so that in this case

$$R_{n+1}(x) = \frac{1}{n!} \int_0^x (-1)^{n+2} \frac{n!}{(1 + t)^{n+1}} (x - t)^n \, dt = (-1)^n \int_0^x \frac{(x - t)^n}{(1 + t)^{n+1}} \, dt.$$

For $0 \leq x \leq 1$ we have

$$|R_{n+1}(x)| = \int_0^x \frac{(x - t)^n}{(1 + t)^{n+1}} \, dt \leq \int_0^x (x - t)^n \, dt = \frac{x^{n+1}}{n + 1} \to 0.$$

explain

For $-1 < x < 0$ we have

$$|R_{n+1}(x)| = \left| \int_0^x \frac{(x - t)^n}{(1 + t)^{n+1}} \, dt \right| = \int_x^0 \left(\frac{t - x}{1 + t} \right)^n \frac{1}{1 + t} \, dt.$$

---

† The proof we give here illustrates the methods of this section. Another, somewhat simpler way of obtaining this series expansion is given in Section 13.9.

By the mean-value for integrals (5.10.5) there exists a number x_n between x and 0 such that

$$\int_x^0 \left(\frac{t-x}{1+t}\right)^n \frac{1}{1+t}\, dt = \left(\frac{x_n - x}{1 + x_n}\right)^n \left(\frac{1}{1 + x_n}\right)(-x).$$

Since $-x = |x|$ and $0 < 1 + x < 1 + x_n$, we can conclude that

$$|R_{n+1}(x)| < \left(\frac{x_n + |x|}{1 + x_n}\right)^n \left(\frac{|x|}{1+x}\right).$$

Since $|x| < 1$ and $x_n < 0$, we have

$$x_n < |x|x_n, \qquad x_n + |x| < |x|x_n + |x| = |x|(1 + x_n)$$

and thus

$$\frac{x_n + |x|}{1 + x_n} < |x|.$$

It now follows that

$$|R_{n+1}(x)| < |x|^n \left(\frac{|x|}{1+x}\right)$$

and, since $|x| < 1$, that $R_{n+1}(x) \to 0$. □

REMARK. The series expansion for $\ln(1 + x)$ that we just verified for $-1 < x \le 1$ cannot be extended to other values of x. For $x \le -1$ neither side makes sense: $\ln(1 + x)$ is not defined, and the series on the right diverges. For $x \ge 1$, $\ln(1 + x)$ is defined, but the series on the right diverges and hence does not represent the function. At $x = 1$ the series gives an intriguing result:

$$\ln 2 = 1 - \tfrac{1}{2} + \tfrac{1}{3} - \tfrac{1}{4} + \cdots . \quad □$$

We want to emphasize again the role played by the remainder term $R_{n+1}(x)$. We can form a Taylor series

$$\sum_{k=0}^{\infty} \frac{f^{(k)}(0)}{k!} x^k$$

for any function f with derivatives of all orders at $x = 0$, but such a series need not converge at any number $x \ne 0$. Even if it does converge, the sum need not be $f(x)$. (See Exercise 35.) The Taylor series converges to $f(x)$ if and only if the remainder term $R_{n+1}(x)$ tends to 0.

Some Numerical Calculations

If the Taylor series converges to $f(x)$, we can use the partial sums (the Taylor polynomials) to calculate $f(x)$ as accurately as we wish. In what follows we show some sample calculations. For ready reference we list some values of $k!$ and $1/k!$

TABLE 13.6.1

$k!$
$2! = 2$
$3! = 6$
$4! = 24$
$5! = 120$
$6! = 720$
$7! = 5,040$
$8! = 40,320$

TABLE 13.6.2

$1/k!$	
$0.16666 < \dfrac{1}{3!} < 0.16667$	$0.00138 < \dfrac{1}{6!} < 0.00139$
$0.04166 < \dfrac{1}{4!} < 0.04167$	$0.00019 < \dfrac{1}{7!} < 0.00020$
$0.00833 < \dfrac{1}{5!} < 0.00834$	$0.00002 < \dfrac{1}{8!} < 0.00003$

PROBLEM. Estimate e within 0.001.

Solution. For all x

$$e^x = 1 + x + \frac{x^2}{2!} + \cdots + \frac{x^n}{n!} + \cdots .$$

Taking $x = 1$ we have

$$e = 1 + 1 + \frac{1}{2!} + \cdots + \frac{1}{n!} + \cdots .$$

From Example 3 we know that the nth partial sum of this series, the Taylor polynomial

$$P_n(1) = 1 + 1 + \frac{1}{2!} + \cdots + \frac{1}{n!},$$

approximates e within

$$|R_{n+1}(1)| \le e \frac{|1|^{n+1}}{(n+1)!} < \frac{3}{(n+1)!}.$$

here $M = e^1 = e$ $e < 3$

Since

$$\frac{3}{7!} = \frac{3}{5040} = \frac{1}{1680} < 0.001,$$

we can take $n = 6$ and be sure that

$$P_6(1) = 1 + 1 + \frac{1}{2!} + \frac{1}{3!} + \frac{1}{4!} + \frac{1}{5!} + \frac{1}{6!} = \frac{1957}{720}$$

differs from e by less than 0.001.

To turn this into a decimal estimate for e, note that

$$2.7180 < \frac{1957}{720} < 2.7181.$$

Within the prescribed limits of accuracy we can take $e \cong 2.718.$ $\square$

PROBLEM. Estimate $e^{0.2}$ within 0.001.

Solution. The exponential series at $x = 0.2$ gives

$$e^{0.2} = 1 + 0.2 + \frac{(0.2)^2}{2!} + \cdots + \frac{(0.2)^n}{n!} + \cdots .$$

From Example 3 we know that the nth partial sum of this series, the Taylor polynomial

$$P_n(0.2) = 1 + 0.2 + \frac{(0.2)^2}{2!} + \cdots + \frac{(0.2)^n}{n!},$$

approximates $e^{0.2}$ within

$$|R_{n+1}(0.2)| \leq e^{0.2} \frac{|0.2|^{n+1}}{(n+1)!} < 3 \frac{(0.2)^{n+1}}{(n+1)!}.$$

$$\text{here } M = e^{0.2}$$

Since

$$3 \frac{(0.2)^4}{4!} = \frac{(3)(16)}{240,000} < 0.001,$$

we can take $n = 3$ and be sure that

$$P_3(0.2) = 1 + 0.2 + \frac{(0.2)^2}{2!} + \frac{(0.2)^3}{3!} = \frac{7326}{6000} = 1.221$$

differs from $e^{0.2}$ by less than 0.001. □

PROBLEM. Estimate $\sin 0.5$ within 0.001.

Solution. At $x = 0.5$ the sine series gives

$$\sin 0.5 = 0.5 - \frac{(0.5)^3}{3!} + \frac{(0.5)^5}{5!} - \frac{(0.5)^7}{7!} + \cdots .$$

From Example 4 we know that the nth partial sum, the nth Taylor polynomial $P_n(0.5)$, approximates $\sin 0.5$ within

$$|R_{n+1}(0.5)| \leq \frac{(0.5)^{n+1}}{(n+1)!}.$$

Since

$$\frac{(0.5)^5}{5!} = \frac{1}{(2^5)(5!)} = \frac{1}{(32)(120)} = \frac{1}{3840} < 0.001,$$

we can be sure that

$$P_4(0.5) = P_3(0.5) = 0.5 - \frac{(0.5)^3}{3!} = \frac{23}{48}$$

the coefficient of x^4 is 0

approximates $\sin 0.5$ within 0.001.

To obtain a decimal estimate, note that

$$0.4791 < \frac{23}{48} < 0.4792.$$

Within the prescribed limits of accuracy we can take sin $0.5 \cong 0.479$.   □

REMARK. We could have solved the last problem without reference to the remainder estimate derived in Example 4.   The series for sin 0.5 is an alternating series of the type studied in Section 13.5.   By (13.5.4) we can conclude immediately that sin 0.5 lies between any two consecutive partial sums.   In particular

$$0.5 - \frac{(0.5)^3}{3!} < \sin 0.5 < 0.5 - \frac{(0.5)^3}{3!} + \frac{(0.5)^5}{5!}.\quad \square$$

PROBLEM.   Estimate ln 1.4 within 0.01 by using (13.6.7).†

Solution

$$\ln 1.4 = \ln (1 + 0.4) = 0.4 - \tfrac{1}{2}(0.4)^2 + \tfrac{1}{3}(0.4)^3 - \tfrac{1}{4}(0.4)^4 + \cdots .$$

Since this is an alternating series and the terms form a decreasing sequence, we know that ln 1.4 lies between consecutive partial sums.
      The first term less than 0.01 is

$$\tfrac{1}{4}(0.4)^4 = \tfrac{1}{4}(0.0256) = 0.0064.$$

The relation

$$0.4 - \tfrac{1}{2}(0.4)^2 + \tfrac{1}{3}(0.4)^3 - \tfrac{1}{4}(0.4)^4 < \ln 1.4 < 0.4 - \tfrac{1}{2}(0.4)^2 + \tfrac{1}{3}(0.4)^3$$

gives

$$0.335 < \ln 1.4 < 0.341.$$

Within the prescribed limits of accuracy we can take

$$\ln 1.4 \cong 0.34   \square$$

EXERCISES

Find the Taylor polynomial $P_4(x)$ for each of the following functions.

1. $x - \cos x.$ **2.** $\sqrt{1 + x}.$ **3.** ln cos $x.$ **4.** sec $x.$

Find the Taylor polynomial $P_5(x)$ for each of the following functions.

5. $(1 + x)^{-1}.$ **6.** $e^x \sin x.$ **7.** tan $x.$ **8.** $x \cos x^2.$

9. Determine $P_0(x)$, $P_1(x)$, $P_2(x)$, $P_3(x)$ for $1 - x + 3x^2 + 5x^3.$
10. Determine $P_0(x)$, $P_1(x)$, $P_2(x)$, $P_3(x)$ for $(x + 1)^3.$

Determine the nth Taylor polynomial $P_n(x)$.

11. $e^{-x}.$ **12.** sinh $x.$ **13.** cosh $x.$ **14.** ln $(1 - x).$

_____

† A much more effective tool for computing logarithms is given in the exercises.

Use Taylor polynomials to estimate the following within 0.01.

15. $\sqrt{e}$.   **16.** $\sin 0.3$.   **17.** $\sin 1$ **18.** $\ln 1.2$.   **19.** $\cos 1$.   **20.** $e^{-0.8}$.

21. Let $P_n(x)$ be the nth Taylor polynomial of

$$f(x) = \ln(1 + x).$$

Find the least integer n for which
(a) $P_n(0.5)$ approximates $\ln 1.5$ within 0.01.
(b) $P_n(0.3)$ approximates $\ln 1.3$ within 0.01.
(c) $P_n(1)$ approximates $\ln 2$ within 0.001.

22. Let $P_n(x)$ be the nth Taylor polynomial of

$$f(x) = \sin x.$$

Find the least integer n for which
(a) $P_n(1)$ approximates $\sin 1$ within 0.001.
(b) $P_n(2)$ approximates $\sin 2$ within 0.001.
(c) $P_n(3)$ approximates $\sin 3$ within 0.001.

23. Show that a polynomial

$$P(x) = a_0 + a_1 x + \cdots + a_n x^n$$

is its own Taylor series.

24. Show that

$$\cos x = \sum_{k=0}^{\infty} \frac{(-1)^k}{(2k)!} x^{2k} \qquad \text{for all real } x.$$

Derive a series expansion in x for each of the following and specify the numbers x for which the expansion is valid.   Take $a > 0$.

25. e^{ax}.   HINT: Set $t = ax$ and expand e^t in powers of t.

26. $\sin ax$.   **27.** $\cos ax$.   **28.** $\ln(1 - ax)$.

29. $\ln(a + x)$.   HINT: $\ln(a + x) = \ln[a(1 + x/a)]$.

30. The series we derived for $\ln(1 + x)$ converges too slowly to be of much practical use.   The following logarithm series converges much more quickly:

(13.6.8) $\boxed{\ln\left(\frac{1+x}{1-x}\right) = 2\left(x + \frac{x^3}{3} + \frac{x^5}{5} + \cdots\right) \quad \text{for } -1 < x < 1.}$

Derive this series expansion.

31. Set $x = \frac{1}{3}$ and use the first three nonzero terms of (13.6.8) to estimate $\ln 2$.   Check this estimate against the table in the back of the book.

32. Use the first two nonzero terms of (13.6.8) to estimate $\ln 1.4$.   Check this estimate against the table in the back of the book and compare it to the estimate we obtained earlier by using the first three terms of (13.6.7).

33. Verify the identity

$$\frac{f^{(k)}(0)}{k!} x^k = \frac{1}{(k-1)!} \int_0^x f^{(k)}(t)(x-t)^{k-1} - \frac{1}{k!} \int_0^x f^{(k+1)}(t)(x-t)^k \, dt$$

by computing the second integral by parts.

34. Derive the remainder estimate (13.6.2).

35. Show that for the function

$$f(x) = \left\{ \begin{array}{ll} e^{-1/x^2}, & x \neq 0 \\ 0, & x = 0 \end{array} \right\},$$

$f^{(k)}(0) = 0$, $k = 0, 1, 2$. Similar arguments show that $f^{(k)}(0) = 0$ for all k. The Taylor series in x is therefore identically 0 and does not represent the function except at $x = 0$.

36. Show that e is irrational by following these steps.
(1) Take the expansion

$$e = \sum_{k=0}^{\infty} \frac{1}{k!}$$

and show that the qth partial sum

$$s_q = \sum_{k=0}^{q} \frac{1}{k!}$$

satisfies the inequality

$$0 < q! \, (e - s_q) < \frac{1}{q}.$$

(2) Show that $q! s_q$ is an integer and argue that, if e were of the form p/q, then $q! \, (e - s_q)$ would be a positive integer less than 1.

13.7 ···· TAYLOR POLYNOMIALS IN $x - a$; TAYLOR SERIES IN $x - a$

So far we've considered series expansions only in powers of x. Here we generalize to expansions in powers of $x - a$ where a is an arbitrary real number. We begin with a more general version of Taylor's theorem.

THEOREM 13.7.1 TAYLOR'S THEOREM

If g has $n + 1$ continuous derivatives on the interval I that joins a to x, then

$$g(x) = g(a) + g'(a)(x - a) + \frac{g''(a)}{2!}(x - a)^2 + \cdots$$

$$+ \frac{g^{(n)}(a)}{n!}(x - a)^n + R_{n+1}(x)$$

where

$$R_{n+1}(x) = \frac{1}{n!} \int_a^x g^{(n+1)}(s)(x - s)^n \, ds.$$

In this more general setting the remainder estimate can be written

(13.7.2) $$|R_{n+1}(x)| \leq \left(\max_{s \in I} |g^{(n+1)}(s)| \right) \frac{|x - a|^{n+1}}{(n + 1)!}.$$

If $R_{n+1}(x) \to 0$, then we have

$$g(x) = g(a) + g'(a)(x - a) + \frac{g''(a)}{2!} (x - a)^2 + \cdots + \frac{g^{(n)}(a)}{n!} (x - a)^n + \cdots .$$

In sigma notation we have

(13.7.3)
$$g(x) = \sum_{k=0}^{\infty} \frac{g^{(k)}(a)}{k!} (x - a)^k .$$

This is known as the Taylor expansion of $g(x)$ in powers of $x - a$. The series on the right is called a *Taylor series in $x - a$.*

All this differs from what you saw before only by a translation. Define

$$f(t) = g(t + a).$$

Then obviously

$$f^{(k)}(t) = g^{(k)}(t + a) \quad \text{and} \quad f^{(k)}(0) = g^{(k)}(a).$$

The results of this section as stated for g can be derived by applying the results of Section 13.6 to the function f.

PROBLEM. Expand

$$g(x) = 4x^3 - 3x^2 + 5x - 1 \quad \text{in powers of } x - 2.$$

Solution. We want to evaluate g and its derivatives at $x = 2$.

$$g(x) = 4x^3 - 3x^2 + 5x - 1$$
$$g'(x) = 12x^2 - 6x + 5$$
$$g''(x) = 24x - 6$$
$$g'''(x) = 24.$$

All higher derivatives are identically 0.

Substitution gives

$$g(2) = 29, \quad g'(2) = 41, \quad g''(2) = 42, \quad g'''(2) = 24$$

and $g^{(k)}(2) = 0$ for all $k \geq 4$. Thus from (13.7.3)

$$g(x) = 29 + 41(x - 2) + \frac{42}{2!} (x - 2)^2 + \frac{24}{3!} (x - 2)^3$$

$$= 29 + 41(x - 2) + 21(x - 2)^2 + 4(x - 2)^3. \quad \square$$

PROBLEM. Expand

$$g(x) = x^2 \ln x \quad \text{in powers of } x - 1.$$

Solution. We want to evaluate g and its derivatives at $x = 1$.

$$g(x) = x^2 \ln x$$
$$g'(x) = x + 2x \ln x$$
$$g''(x) = 3 + 2 \ln x$$
$$g'''(x) = 2x^{-1}$$
$$g^{(4)}(x) = -2x^{-2}$$
$$g^{(5)}(x) = (2)(2)x^{-3}$$
$$g^{(6)}(x) = -(2)(2)(3)x^{-4} = -2(3!)x^{-4}$$
$$g^{(7)}(x) = (2)(2)(3)(4)x^{-5} = (2)(4!)x^{-5}, \quad \text{etc.}$$

The pattern is now clear: for $k \geq 3$

$$g^{(k)}(x) = (-1)^{k+1}2(k - 3)!\, x^{-k+2}.$$

Evaluation at $x = 1$ gives

$$g(1) = 0, \quad g'(1) = 1, \quad g''(1) = 3$$

and, for $k \geq 3$,

$$g^{(k)}(1) = (-1)^{k+1}2(k - 3)!.$$

The expansion in powers of $x - 1$ can be written

$$g(x) = (x - 1) + \frac{3}{2!}(x - 1)^2 + \sum_{k=3}^{\infty} \frac{(-1)^{k+1}2(k - 3)!}{k!}(x - 1)^k$$

$$= (x - 1) + \frac{3}{2}(x - 1)^2 + \sum_{k=3}^{\infty} \frac{(-1)^{k+1}2}{k(k - 1)(k - 2)}(x - 1)^k. \quad \square$$

Another way to expand $g(x)$ in powers of $x - a$ is to expand $g(t + a)$ in powers of t and then set $t = x - a$. This is the approach we take when the expansion in t is known to us, or, if not known to us, easily available.

EXAMPLE. We can expand

$$g(x) = e^{x/2} \qquad \text{in powers of } x - 3$$

by expanding

$$g(t + 3) = e^{(t+3)/2} \qquad \text{in powers of } t$$

and then setting $t = x - 3$.
    Note that

$$g(t + 3) = e^{3/2}e^{t/2} = e^{3/2} \sum_{k=0}^{\infty} \frac{(t/2)^k}{k!} = e^{3/2} \sum_{k=0}^{\infty} \frac{1}{2^k k!} t^k.$$

exponential series $\longrightarrow$

Setting $t = x - 3$, we have

$$g(x) = e^{3/2} \sum_{k=0}^{\infty} \frac{1}{2^k k!}(x - 3)^k.$$

Since the expansion of $g(t + 3)$ is valid for all real t, the expansion of $g(x)$ is valid for all real x. ☐

Taking this same approach, we can easily prove that

(13.7.4)

> for $0 < x \leq 2a$
>
> $$\ln x = \ln a + \frac{1}{a}(x - a) - \frac{1}{2a^2}(x - a)^2 + \frac{1}{3a^3}(x - a)^3 - \cdots .$$

Proof.   We'll expand $\ln (a + t)$ in powers of t and then set $t = x - a$.
   In the first place

$$\ln (a + t) = \ln \left[a \left(1 + \frac{t}{a} \right) \right] = \ln a + \ln \left(1 + \frac{t}{a} \right).$$

From (13.6.7) it's clear that

$$\ln \left(1 + \frac{t}{a} \right) = \frac{t}{a} - \frac{1}{2} \left(\frac{t}{a} \right)^2 + \frac{1}{3} \left(\frac{t}{a} \right)^3 - \cdots \qquad \text{for} -a < t \leq a.$$

Adding $\ln a$ to both sides, we have

$$\ln (a + t) = \ln a + \frac{1}{a}t - \frac{1}{2a^2}t^2 + \frac{1}{3a^3}t^3 - \cdots \qquad \text{for} -a < t \leq a.$$

Setting $t = x - a$, we find that

$$\ln x = \ln a + \frac{1}{a}(x - a) - \frac{1}{2a^2}(x - a)^2 + \frac{1}{3a^3}(x - a)^3 - \cdots$$

for all x such that $-a < x - a \leq a$; that is, for all x such that $0 < x \leq 2a$.   ☐

EXERCISES

Expand $g(x)$ as indicated and specify the values of x for which the expansion is valid.

1. $g(x) = 3x^3 - 2x^2 + 4x + 1$ in powers of $x - 1$.
2. $g(x) = x^4 - x^3 + x^2 - x + 1$ in powers of $x - 2$.
3. $g(x) = 2x^5 + x^2 - 3x - 5$ in powers of $x + 1$.
4. $g(x) = x^{-1}$ in powers of $x - 1$.
5. $g(x) = (1 + x)^{-1}$ in powers of $x - 1$.
6. $g(x) = (b + x)^{-1}$ in powers of $x - a$, $a \neq -b$.
7. $g(x) = (1 - 2x)^{-1}$ in powers of $x + 2$.
8. $g(x) = e^{-4x}$ in powers of $x + 1$.
9. $g(x) = \sin x$ in powers of $x - \pi$.
10. $g(x) = \sin x$ in powers of $x - \frac{1}{2}\pi$.
11. $g(x) = \cos x$ in powers of $x - \pi$.
12. $g(x) = \cos x$ in powers of $x - \frac{1}{2}\pi$.

13. $g(x) = \sin \frac{1}{2}\pi x$ in powers of $x - 1$.

14. $g(x) = \sin \pi x$ in powers of $x - 1$.

15. $g(x) = \ln(1 + 2x)$ in powers of $x - 1$.

16. $g(x) = \ln(2 + 3x)$ in powers of $x - 4$.

Expand $g(x)$ as indicated.

17. $g(x) = x \ln x$ in powers of $x - 2$.

18. $g(x) = x^2 + e^{3x}$ in powers of $x - 2$.

19. $g(x) = x \sin x$ in powers of x.

20. $g(x) = \ln(x^2)$ in powers of $x - 1$.

21. $g(x) = (1 - 2x)^{-3}$ in powers of $x + 2$.

22. $g(x) = \sin^2 x$ in powers of $x - \frac{1}{2}\pi$.

23. $g(x) = \cos^2 x$ in powers of $x - \pi$.

24. $g(x) = (1 + 2x)^{-4}$ in powers of $x - 2$.

25. $g(x) = x^n$ in powers of $x - 1$.

26. $g(x) = (x - 1)^n$ in powers of x.

27. (a) Expand e^x in powers of $x - a$.

 (b) Use the expansion to show that $e^{x_1 + x_2} = e^{x_1} e^{x_2}$.

 (c) Expand e^{-x} in powers of $x - a$.

28. (a) Expand $\sin x$ and $\cos x$ in powers of $x - a$.

 (b) Show that both series are absolutely convergent for all real x.

 (c) As noted earlier (Section 13.5), Riemann proved that the order of the terms of an absolutely convergent series may be changed without altering the sum of the series. Use Riemann's discovery and the Taylor expansions of part (a) to derive the addition formulas

$$\sin(x_1 + x_2) = \sin x_1 \cos x_2 + \cos x_1 \sin x_2,$$

$$\cos(x_1 + x_2) = \cos x_1 \cos x_2 - \sin x_1 \sin x_2.$$

13.8····POWER SERIES

You've become familiar with Taylor series

$$\sum_{k=0}^{\infty} \frac{f^{(k)}(a)}{k!} (x - a)^k \qquad \text{and} \qquad \sum_{k=0}^{\infty} \frac{f^{(k)}(0)}{k!} x^k.$$

Here we study series of the form

$$\sum_{k=0}^{\infty} a_k (x - a)^k \qquad \text{and} \qquad \sum_{k=0}^{\infty} a_k x^k$$

without regard to how the coefficients have been generated.   Such series are called *power series*.

Since a simple translation converts

$$\sum_{k=0}^{\infty} a_k (x - a)^k \qquad \text{into} \qquad \sum_{k=0}^{\infty} a_k x^k,$$

we can focus our attention on power series of the form

$$\sum_{k=0}^{\infty} a_k x^k.$$

When detailed indexing is unnecessary, we will omit it and write

$$\sum a_k x^k.$$

We begin the discussion with a definition.

DEFINITION 13.8.1

A power series $\Sigma\, a_k x^k$ is said to converge

   (i) at x_1 iff $\Sigma\, a_k x_1^k$ converges.

   (ii) on the set S iff $\Sigma\, a_k x^k$ converges for each x in S.

The following result is fundamental.

THEOREM 13.8.2

If $\Sigma\, a_k x^k$ converges at $x_1 \neq 0$, then it converges absolutely for $|x| < |x_1|$.
If $\Sigma\, a_k x^k$ diverges at x_1, then it diverges for $|x| > |x_1|$.

Proof. If $\Sigma\, a_k x_1^k$ converges, then $a_k x_1^k \to 0$. In particular, for k sufficiently large,

$$|a_k x_1^k| \leq 1$$

and thus

$$|a_k x^k| = |a_k x_1^k| \left|\frac{x}{x_1}\right|^k \leq \left|\frac{x}{x_1}\right|^k.$$

For $|x| < |x_1|$, we have

$$\left|\frac{x}{x_1}\right| < 1.$$

The convergence of $\Sigma\, |a_k x^k|$ follows by comparison with the geometric series. This proves the first statement.

Suppose now that $\Sigma\, a_k x_1^k$ diverges. By the previous argument, there cannot exist x with $|x| > |x_1|$ such that $\Sigma\, a_k x^k$ converges. The existence of such an x would imply the absolute convergence of $\Sigma\, a_k x_1^k$. This proves the second statement. $\square$

From the theorem we just proved you can see that there are exactly three possibilities for a power series:

Case I. *The series converges only at 0.* This is what happens with

$$\Sigma\, k^k x^k.$$

As you can tell from the root test, the kth term, $k^k x^k$, tends to 0 only if $x = 0$.

Case II. *The series converges everywhere absolutely.* This is what happens with the exponential series

$$\Sigma\, \frac{x^k}{k!}.$$

Case III. *There exists a positive number r such that the series converges absolutely for* $|x| < r$ *and diverges for* $|x| > r$. This is what happens with the geometric series

$$\Sigma\, x^k.$$

In this instance, there is absolute convergence for $|x| < 1$, divergence for $|x| > 1$.

Associated with each case is a *radius of convergence*:

In Case I, we say that the radius of convergence is 0.
In Case II, we say that the radius of convergence is ∞.
In Case III, we say that the radius of convergence is r.

The three cases are pictured in Figure 13.8.1.

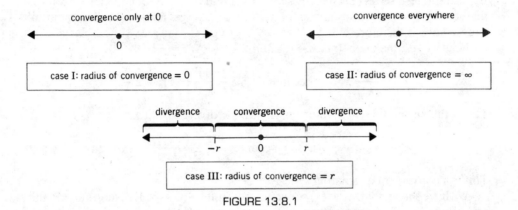

FIGURE 13.8.1

In general, the behavior of a power series at $-r$ and at r is not predictable. The series

$$\Sigma\, x^k, \qquad \Sigma\, \frac{1}{k}\, x^k, \qquad \Sigma\, \frac{(-1)^k}{k}\, x^k, \qquad \Sigma\, \frac{1}{k^2}\, x^k,$$

all have radius of convergence 1, but while the first series converges only on $(-1, 1)$, the second series converges on $[-1, 1)$, the third on $(-1, 1]$, and the fourth on $[-1, 1]$.

The maximal interval on which a power series converges is called the *interval of convergence*. For a series with infinite radius of convergence, the interval of convergence is $(-\infty, \infty)$. For a series with radius of convergence r, the interval of convergence can be $[-r, r]$, $(-r, r]$, $[-r, r)$, or $(-r, r)$. For a series with radius of convergence 0, the interval of convergence reduces to a point, $\{0\}$.

PROBLEM. Verify that the series

(1) $$\Sigma\, \frac{(-1)^k}{k}\, x^k$$

has interval of convergence $(-1, 1]$.

Solution. First we show that the radius of convergence is 1 (that the series converges absolutely for $|x| < 1$ and diverges for $|x| > 1$). We do this by forming the series

$$(2) \qquad \Sigma \left| \frac{(-1)^k}{k} x^k \right| = \Sigma \frac{1}{k} |x|^k$$

and applying the ratio test.

We set

$$b_k = \frac{1}{k} |x|^k$$

and note that

$$\frac{b_{k+1}}{b_k} = \frac{k}{k+1} \frac{|x|^{k+1}}{|x|^k} = \frac{k}{k+1} |x| \rightarrow |x|.$$

By the ratio test, series (2) converges for $|x| < 1$ and diverges for $|x| > 1$.[†] It follows that series (1) converges absolutely for $|x| < 1$ and diverges for $|x| > 1$. The radius of convergence is therefore 1.

Now we test the endpoints $x = -1$ and $x = 1$. At $x = -1$

$$\Sigma \frac{(-1)^k}{k} x^k \qquad \text{becomes} \qquad \Sigma \frac{(-1)^k}{k} (-1)^k = \Sigma \frac{1}{k}.$$

This is the harmonic series which, as you know, diverges. At $x = 1$,

$$\Sigma \frac{(-1)^k}{k} x^k \qquad \text{becomes} \qquad \Sigma \frac{(-1)^k}{k}.$$

This is a convergent alternating series.

We have shown that series (1) converges absolutely for $|x| < 1$, diverges at -1, and converges at 1. The interval of convergence is $(-1, 1]$. □

PROBLEM. Verify that the series

$$(1) \qquad \Sigma \frac{1}{k^2} x^k$$

has interval of convergence $[-1, 1]$.

Solution. First we examine the series

$$(2) \qquad \Sigma \left| \frac{1}{k^2} x^k \right| = \Sigma \frac{1}{k^2} |x|^k.$$

Here again we use the ratio test. We set

$$b_k = \frac{1}{k^2} |x|^k$$

---

† We could also have used the root test:

$$(b_k)^{1/k} = \left| \frac{1}{k} \right|^{1/k} |x| = \frac{1}{k^{1/k}} |x| \rightarrow |x|.$$

and note that

$$\frac{b_{k+1}}{b_k} = \frac{k^2}{(k+1)^2} \frac{|x|^{k+1}}{|x|^k} = \left(\frac{k}{k+1}\right)^2 |x| \to |x|.$$

By the ratio test, (2) converges for $|x| < 1$ and diverges for $|x| > 1$.† This shows that (1) converges absolutely for $|x| < 1$ and diverges for $|x| > 1$. The radius of convergence is therefore 1.

Now for the endpoints. At $x = -1$,

$$\Sigma \frac{1}{k^2} x^k \quad \text{takes the form} \quad \Sigma \frac{(-1)^k}{k^2} = -1 + \tfrac{1}{4} - \tfrac{1}{9} + \tfrac{1}{16} - \cdots .$$

This is a convergent alternating series. At $x = 1$,

$$\Sigma \frac{1}{k^2} x^k \quad \text{becomes} \quad \Sigma \frac{1}{k^2}.$$

This is a convergent p-series. The interval of convergence is therefore the entire closed interval $[-1, 1]$. □

PROBLEM. Find the interval of convergence of

(1) $$\Sigma \frac{k}{6^k} x^k.$$

Solution. We begin by examining the series

(2) $$\Sigma \left| \frac{k}{6^k} x^k \right| = \Sigma \frac{k}{6^k} |x|^k.$$

We set

$$b_k = \frac{k}{6^k} |x|^k$$

and apply the root test. (The ratio test will also work.) Since

$$b^{1/k} = \tfrac{1}{6} k^{1/k} |x| \to \tfrac{1}{6} |x|,$$

you can see that (2) converges

$$\text{for} \quad \tfrac{1}{6}|x| < 1 \qquad\qquad\qquad\qquad (\text{for } |x| < 6)$$

and diverges

$$\text{for} \quad \tfrac{1}{6}|x| > 1. \qquad\qquad\qquad\qquad (\text{for } |x| > 6)$$

This shows that (1) converges absolutely for $|x| < 6$ and diverges for $|x| > 6$. The radius of convergence is 6.

---

† Once again we could have used the root test:

$$(b_k)^{1/k} = \frac{1}{k^{2/k}} |x| \to |x|.$$

It is easy to see that (1) diverges both at -6 and at 6. The interval of convergence is therefore $(-6, 6)$. $\square$

PROBLEM. Find the interval of convergence of

(1) $$\Sigma \frac{(2k)!}{(3k)!} x^k.$$

Solution. We begin by examining the series

(2) $$\Sigma \left| \frac{(2k)!}{(3k)!} x^k \right| = \Sigma \frac{(2k)!}{(3k)!} |x|^k.$$

Set

$$b_k = \frac{(2k)!}{(3k)!} |x|^k.$$

Since factorials are involved, we will use the ratio test. Note that

$$\frac{b_{k+1}}{b_k} = \frac{[2(k+1)]!}{[3(k+1)]!} \frac{(3k)!}{(2k)!} \frac{|x|^{k+1}}{|x|^k} = \frac{(2k+2)(2k+1)}{(3k+3)(3k+2)(3k+1)} |x|.$$

Since

$$\frac{(2k+2)(2k+1)}{(3k+3)(3k+2)(3k+1)} \rightarrow 0 \qquad \text{as } k \rightarrow \infty$$

(the numerator is a quadratic in k, the denominator a cubic), the ratio b_{k+1}/b_k tends to 0 no matter what x is. By the ratio test, (2) converges for all x and therefore (1) converges absolutely for all x. The radius of convergence is ∞ and the interval of convergence is $(-\infty, \infty)$. $\square$

PROBLEM. Find the interval of convergence of

$$\Sigma (\tfrac{1}{2}k)^k x^k.$$

Solution. Since $(\tfrac{1}{2}k)^k x^k \rightarrow 0$ only if $x = 0$ (explain), there is no need to invoke the ratio test or the root test. By (13.2.5) the series can converge only at $x = 0$. There it converges trivially. $\square$

EXERCISES

Find the interval of convergence.

1. $\Sigma\, kx^k.$

2. $\Sigma \dfrac{1}{k} x^k.$

3. $\Sigma \dfrac{1}{(2k)!} x^k.$

4. $\Sigma \dfrac{2^k}{k^2} x^k.$

5. $\Sigma\, (-k)^{2k} x^{2k}.$

6. $\Sigma \dfrac{(-1)^k}{\sqrt{k}} x^k.$

7. $\Sigma \dfrac{1}{k2^k} x^k.$

8. $\Sigma \dfrac{1}{k^2 2^k} x^k.$

9. $\Sigma \left(\dfrac{k}{100} \right)^k x^k.$

10. $\Sigma \dfrac{k^2}{1+k^2} x^k.$

11. $\Sigma \dfrac{2^k}{\sqrt{k}} x^k.$

12. $\Sigma \dfrac{1}{\ln k} x^k.$

13. $\Sigma \dfrac{k-1}{k} x^k$.   **14.** $\Sigma\, ka^k x^k$.   **15.** $\Sigma \dfrac{k}{10^k} x^k$.   **16.** $\Sigma \dfrac{3^{k^2}}{e^k} x^k$.

17. $\Sigma \dfrac{x^k}{k^k}$.   **18.** $\Sigma \dfrac{7^k}{k!} x^k$.

19. $\Sigma \dfrac{(-1)^k}{k^k} (x-2)^k$.   **20.** $\Sigma \dfrac{(-1)^k a^k}{k^2} (x-a)^k$.

21. $\Sigma \dfrac{\ln k}{2^k} (x-2)^k$.   **22.** $\Sigma \dfrac{2^{1/k}\pi^k}{k(k+1)(k+2)} (x-2)^k$.

23. $\Sigma\, (-1)^k (\tfrac{2}{3})^k (x+1)^k$.   **24.** $\Sigma \dfrac{1}{(\ln k)^k} (x-1)^k$.

25. Let $\Sigma\, a_k x^k$ be a power series, and let r be its radius of convergence.
     (a) Given that $|a_k|^{1/k} \to \rho$, show that, if $\rho \neq 0$, then $r = 1/\rho$ and, if $\rho = 0$, then $r = \infty$.
     (b) Given that $|a_{k+1}/a_k| \to \lambda$, show that, if $\lambda \neq 0$, then $r = 1/\lambda$ and, if $\lambda = 0$, then $r = \infty$.

26. Find the interval of convergence of $\Sigma\, s_k x^k$ where s_k is the kth partial sum of $\displaystyle\sum_{n=1}^{\infty} 1/n$.

13.9···DIFFERENTIATION AND INTEGRATION OF POWER SERIES

We begin with a simple but important result.

THEOREM 13.9.1

If

$$\sum_{k=0}^{\infty} a_k x^k = a_0 + a_1 x + a_2 x^2 + \cdots + a_n x^n + \cdots$$

converges on $(-c, c)$, then

$$\sum_{k=0}^{\infty} \frac{d}{dx}(a_k x^k) = \sum_{k=1}^{\infty} k a_k x^{k-1} = a_1 + 2a_2 x + \cdots + na_n x^{n-1} + \cdots$$

also converges on $(-c, c)$.

Proof. Let's assume that

$$\sum_{k=0}^{\infty} a_k x^k \quad \text{converges on } (-c, c).$$

By Theorem 13.8.2 it converges there absolutely.
     Now let x be some fixed number in $(-c, c)$ and choose $\epsilon > 0$ such that

$$|x| < |x| + \epsilon < |c|.$$

Since $|x| + \epsilon$ lies within the interval of convergence,

$$\sum_{k=0}^{\infty} |a_k(|x| + \epsilon)^k| \quad \text{converges.}$$

In Exercise 32 you are asked to show that, for all k sufficiently large,

$$|kx^{k-1}| \leq (|x| + \epsilon)^k.$$

It follows that for all such k

$$|ka_k x^{k-1}| \leq |a_k(|x| + \epsilon)^k|.$$

Since

$$\sum_{k=0}^{\infty} |a_k(|x| + \epsilon)^k| \quad \text{converges,}$$

we can conclude that

$$\sum_{k=0}^{\infty} \left| \frac{d}{dx}(a_k x^k) \right| = \sum_{k=1}^{\infty} |ka_k x^{k-1}| \quad \text{converges,}$$

and thus that

$$\sum_{k=0}^{\infty} \frac{d}{dx}(a_k x^k) = \sum_{k=1}^{\infty} ka_k x^{k-1} \quad \text{converges.} \quad \square$$

Repeated application of the theorem shows that

$$\sum_{k=0}^{\infty} \frac{d^2}{dx^2}(a_k x^k), \quad \sum_{k=0}^{\infty} \frac{d^3}{dx^3}(a_k x^k), \quad \sum_{k=0}^{\infty} \frac{d^4}{dx^4}(a_k x^k), \quad \text{etc.}$$

all converge on $(-c, c)$.

EXAMPLE. Since the geometric series

$$\sum_{k=0}^{\infty} x^k = 1 + x + x^2 + x^3 + x^4 + x^5 + x^6 + \cdots$$

converges on $(-1, 1)$, the series

$$\sum_{k=0}^{\infty} \frac{d}{dx}(x^k) = \sum_{k=1}^{\infty} kx^{k-1} = 1 + 2x + 3x^2 + 4x^3 + 5x^4 + 6x^5 + \cdots,$$

$$\sum_{k=0}^{\infty} \frac{d^2}{dx^2}(x^k) = \sum_{k=2}^{\infty} k(k-1)x^{k-2} = 2 + 6x + 12x^2 + 20x^3 + 30x^4 + \cdots,$$

$$\sum_{k=0}^{\infty} \frac{d^3}{dx^3}(x^k) = \sum_{k=3}^{\infty} k(k-1)(k-2)x^{k-3} = 6 + 24x + 60x^2 + 120x^3 + \cdots,$$

$$\vdots$$

all converge on $(-1, 1)$. $\square$

Suppose now that

$$\sum_{k=0}^{\infty} a_k x^k \quad \text{converges on } (-c, c).$$

Then, as you just saw,

$$\sum_{k=0}^{\infty} \frac{d}{dx} (a_k x^k) \quad \text{also converges on } (-c, c).$$

Using the first series, we can define a function f on $(-c, c)$ by setting

$$f(x) = \sum_{k=0}^{\infty} a_k x^k.$$

Using the second series, we can define a function g on $(-c, c)$ by setting

$$g(x) = \sum_{k=0}^{\infty} \frac{d}{dx} (a_k x^k).$$

The crucial point is that

$$f'(x) = g(x).$$

THEOREM 13.9.2   THE DIFFERENTIABILITY THEOREM

If

$$f(x) = \sum_{k=0}^{\infty} a_k x^k \quad \text{for all } x \text{ in } (-c, c),$$

then f is differentiable on $(-c, c)$ and

$$f'(x) = \sum_{k=0}^{\infty} \frac{d}{dx} (a_k x^k) \quad \text{for all } x \text{ in } (-c, c).$$

By applying this theorem to f', you can see that f' is itself differentiable. This in turn implies that f'' is differentiable, and so on. In short, f has derivatives of all orders.

We can summarize as follows:

in the interior of its interval of convergence a power series defines an infinitely differentiable function, the derivatives of which can be obtained by differentiating term by term:

$$\frac{d^n}{dx^n} \left(\sum_{k=0}^{\infty} a_k x^k \right) = \sum_{k=0}^{\infty} \frac{d^n}{dx^n} (a_k x^k) \quad \text{for all } n.$$

For a detailed proof of the differentiability theorem see the supplement at the end of this section. We go on to examples.

EXAMPLE. You know that

$$\frac{d}{dx} (e^x) = e^x.$$

You can see this directly by differentiating the exponential series:

$$\frac{d}{dx}(e^x) = \frac{d}{dx}\left(\sum_{k=0}^{\infty}\frac{x^k}{k!}\right) = \sum_{k=0}^{\infty}\frac{d}{dx}\left(\frac{x^k}{k!}\right) = \sum_{k=1}^{\infty}\frac{x^{k-1}}{(k-1)!} \underset{\underset{\text{set } n = k - 1}{\uparrow}}{=} \sum_{n=0}^{\infty}\frac{x^n}{n!} = e^x. \quad \square$$

EXAMPLE. You have seen that

$$\sin x = x - \frac{x^3}{3!} + \frac{x^5}{5!} - \frac{x^7}{7!} + \frac{x^9}{9!} - \cdots$$

and

$$\cos x = 1 - \frac{x^2}{2!} + \frac{x^4}{4!} - \frac{x^6}{6!} + \frac{x^8}{8!} - \cdots .$$

The relations

$$\frac{d}{dx}(\sin x) = \cos x, \qquad \frac{d}{dx}(\cos x) = -\sin x$$

can be confirmed by differentiating the series term by term:

$$\frac{d}{dx}(\sin x) = 1 - \frac{3x^2}{3!} + \frac{5x^4}{5!} - \frac{7x^6}{7!} + \frac{9x^8}{9!} - \cdots$$

$$= 1 - \frac{x^2}{2!} + \frac{x^4}{4!} - \frac{x^6}{6!} + \frac{x^8}{8!} - \cdots = \cos x,$$

$$\frac{d}{dx}(\cos x) = -\frac{2x}{2!} + \frac{4x^3}{4!} - \frac{6x^5}{6!} + \frac{8x^7}{8!} - \cdots$$

$$= -x + \frac{x^3}{3!} - \frac{x^5}{5!} + \frac{x^7}{7!} - \cdots$$

$$= -\left(x - \frac{x^3}{3!} + \frac{x^5}{5!} - \frac{x^7}{7!} + \cdots\right) = -\sin x. \quad \square$$

EXAMPLE. We can sum the series

$$\sum_{k=1}^{\infty}\frac{x^k}{k} \qquad \text{for all } x \text{ in } (-1, 1)$$

by setting

$$g(x) = \sum_{k=1}^{\infty}\frac{x^k}{k} \qquad \text{for all } x \text{ in } (-1, 1)$$

and noting that

$$g'(x) = \sum_{k=1}^{\infty}\frac{kx^{k-1}}{k} = \sum_{k=1}^{\infty}x^{k-1} = \sum_{n=0}^{\infty}x^n \underset{\underset{\text{the geometric series}}{\uparrow}}{=} \frac{1}{1-x}.$$

With

$$g'(x) = \frac{1}{1-x} \quad \text{and} \quad g(0) = 0,$$

we can conclude that

$$g(x) = -\ln(1-x) = \ln\left(\frac{1}{1-x}\right).$$

It follows that

$$\sum_{k=1}^{\infty} \frac{x^k}{k} = \ln\left(\frac{1}{1-x}\right) \quad \text{for all } x \text{ in } (-1, 1). \quad \square$$

Power series can also be integrated term by term.

THEOREM 13.9.3   TERM-BY-TERM INTEGRATION

If

$$f(x) = \sum_{k=0}^{\infty} a_k x^k \quad \text{converges on } (-c, c),$$

then

$$g(x) = \sum_{k=0}^{\infty} \frac{a_k}{k+1} x^{k+1} \quad \text{converges on } (-c, c)$$

and

$$\int f(x)\, dx = g(x) + C.$$

Proof. If

$$\sum_{k=0}^{\infty} a_k x^k \quad \text{converges on } (-c, c),$$

then

$$\sum_{k=0}^{\infty} |a_k x^k| \quad \text{converges on } (-c, c).$$

Since

$$\left| \frac{a_k}{k+1} x^k \right| \le |a_k x^k| \quad \text{for all } k,$$

we know by comparison that

$$\sum_{k=0}^{\infty} \left| \frac{a_k}{k+1} x^k \right| \quad \text{also converges on } (-c, c).$$

It follows that

$$x \sum_{k=0}^{\infty} \frac{a_k}{k+1} x^k = \sum_{k=0}^{\infty} \frac{a_k}{k+1} x^{k+1} \quad \text{converges on } (-c, c).$$

With

$$f(x) = \sum_{k=0}^{\infty} a_k x^k \quad \text{and} \quad g(x) = \sum_{k=0}^{\infty} \frac{a_k}{k+1} x^{k+1},$$

we know from the differentiability theorem that

$$g'(x) = f(x) \quad \text{and therefore} \quad \int f(x) \, dx = g(x) + C. \quad \square$$

Term-by-term integration can be expressed as follows:

(13.9.4)

$$\int \left(\sum_{k=0}^{\infty} a_k x^k \right) dx = \left(\sum_{k=0}^{\infty} \frac{a_k}{k+1} x^{k+1} \right) + C.$$

If a power series converges at c and converges at d, then it converges at all numbers in between and

(13.9.5)

$$\int_c^d \left(\sum_{k=0}^{\infty} a_k x^k \right) dx = \sum_{k=0}^{\infty} \left(\int_c^d a_k x^k \, dx \right) = \sum_{k=0}^{\infty} \frac{a_k}{k+1} (d^{k+1} - c^{k+1}).$$

EXAMPLE. You are familiar with the series expansion

$$\frac{1}{1+x} = \frac{1}{1-(-x)} = \sum_{k=0}^{\infty} (-1)^k x^k.$$

It is valid for all x in $(-1, 1)$ and for no other x. Integrating term by term we have

$$\ln(1+x) = \int \left(\sum_{k=0}^{\infty} (-1)^k x^k \right) dx = \left(\sum_{k=0}^{\infty} \frac{(-1)^k}{k+1} x^{k+1} \right) + C$$

for all x in $(-1, 1)$. At $x = 0$ both $\ln(1+x)$ and the series on the right are 0. It follows that $C = 0$ and thus

$$\ln(1+x) = \sum_{k=0}^{\infty} \frac{(-1)^k}{k+1} x^{k+1} = x - \frac{x^2}{2} + \frac{x^3}{3} - \frac{x^4}{4} + \cdots$$

for all x in $(-1, 1)$. $\square$

In Section 13.6 we were able to prove that this expansion for $\ln(1+x)$ was valid on the half-closed interval $(-1, 1]$; this gave us an expansion for $\ln 2$. Term-by-term integration gives us only the open interval $(-1, 1)$. Well, you may say, it's easy to see that the logarithm series also converges at $x = 1$.† True enough, but why to $\ln 2$?

———————
† An alternating series with $a_k \to 0$.

This takes us back to consideration of the remainder term, the method of Section 13.6.

There is, however, another way to proceed. The great Norwegian mathematician Niels Henrik Abel (1802–1829) proved the following result: suppose that

$$\sum_{k=0}^{\infty} a_k x^k \quad \text{converges on } (-c, c)$$

and there represents $f(x)$. If f is continuous at one of the endpoints (c or $-c$) and the series converges at that endpoint, then the series represents the function at that endpoint.

Using Abel's theorem it is evident that the series does represent $\ln(1 + x)$ at $x = 1$.

We come now to another important series expansion:

(13.9.6)
$$\tan^{-1} x = x - \frac{x^3}{3} + \frac{x^5}{5} - \frac{x^7}{7} + \cdots \qquad \text{for } -1 \le x \le 1.$$

Proof.   For x in $(-1, 1)$

$$\frac{1}{1 + x^2} = \frac{1}{1 - (-x^2)} = \sum_{k=0}^{\infty} (-1)^k x^{2k}$$

so that, by integration,

$$\tan^{-1} x = \int \left(\sum_{k=0}^{\infty} (-1)^k x^{2k} \right) dx = \left(\sum_{k=0}^{\infty} \frac{(-1)^k}{2k + 1} x^{2k+1} \right) + C.$$

The constant C is 0 because the series on the right and the inverse tangent are both 0 at $x = 0$. Thus, for all x in $(-1, 1)$, we have

$$\tan^{-1} x = \sum_{k=0}^{\infty} \frac{(-1)^k}{2k + 1} x^{2k+1} = x - \frac{x^3}{3} + \frac{x^5}{5} - \frac{x^7}{7} + \cdots.$$

That the series also represents the function at $x = -1$ and $x = 1$ follows directly from Abel's theorem: at both these points $\tan^{-1} x$ is continuous, and at both of these points the series converges.   □

Since $\tan^{-1} 1 = \frac{1}{4}\pi$, we have

$$\tfrac{1}{4}\pi = 1 - \tfrac{1}{3} + \tfrac{1}{5} - \tfrac{1}{7} + \tfrac{1}{9} - \cdots.$$

This series was known to the Scottish mathematician James Gregory in 1671. It is an elegant formula for π, but it converges too slowly for computational purposes. A much more effective way of computing π is outlined in the supplement at the end of this section.

Term-by-term integration provides a method of calculating some (otherwise rather intractable) definite integrals. Suppose that you are trying to evaluate

$$\int_a^b f(x)\, dx$$

but cannot find an antiderivative. If you can expand $f(x)$ in a convergent power series, then you can evaluate this integral by forming the series and integrating term by term.

EXAMPLE. With the tools at our disposal, the only practical way to evaluate

$$\int_0^1 e^{-x^2}\, dx$$

is to expand the integrand in a power series and integrate the series term by term. Since

$$e^x = 1 + x + \frac{x^2}{2!} + \frac{x^3}{3!} + \frac{x^4}{4!} + \cdots,$$

we have

$$e^{-x^2} = 1 - x^2 + \frac{x^4}{2!} - \frac{x^6}{3!} + \frac{x^8}{4!} - \cdots.$$

Term-by-term integration gives

$$\int_0^1 e^{-x^2}\, dx = \left[x - \frac{x^3}{3} + \frac{x^5}{5\cdot 2!} - \frac{x^7}{7\cdot 3!} + \frac{x^9}{9\cdot 4!} - \cdots \right]_0^1$$

$$= 1 - \frac{1}{3} + \frac{1}{5\cdot 2!} - \frac{1}{7\cdot 3!} + \frac{1}{9\cdot 4!} - \cdots.$$

This is an alternating series of the type discussed in Section 13.5. Thus

$$1 - \frac{1}{3} + \frac{1}{5\cdot 2!} - \frac{1}{7\cdot 3!} \le \int_0^1 e^{-x^2}\, dx \le 1 - \frac{1}{3} + \frac{1}{5\cdot 2!} - \frac{1}{7\cdot 3!} + \frac{1}{9\cdot 4!}.$$

A little arithmetic shows that

$$0.742 < \int_0^1 e^{-x^2}\, dx < 0.748.$$

Obviously, we can obtain greater accuracy by using more terms. □

It's time to relate Taylor series

$$\sum_{k=0}^{\infty} \frac{f^{(k)}(0)}{k!} x^k$$

to power series in general. The relation is very simple:

> On its interval of convergence a power series is the Taylor series of its sum.

To see this, all you have to do is differentiate

$$f(x) = a_0 + a_1 x + a_2 x^2 + \cdots + a_k x^k + \cdots$$

term by term. Do this and you'll find that $f^{(k)}(0) = k!\, a_k$ and therefore

$$a_k = \frac{f^{(k)}(0)}{k!}.$$

The a_k are the Taylor coefficients of f.

We end this section by carrying out a few simple expansions.

PROBLEM. Expand $\cosh x$ and $\sinh x$ in powers of x.

Solution. There is no need to go through the labor of computing the Taylor coefficients

$$\frac{f^{(k)}(0)}{k!}$$

by differentiation. We know that

$$\cosh x = \tfrac{1}{2}(e^x + e^{-x}) \quad \text{and} \quad \sinh x = \tfrac{1}{2}(e^x - e^{-x}). \qquad (7.9.1)$$

Since

$$e^x = 1 + x + \frac{x^2}{2!} + \frac{x^3}{3!} + \frac{x^4}{4!} + \frac{x^5}{5!} + \cdots,$$

we have

$$e^{-x} = 1 - x + \frac{x^2}{2!} - \frac{x^3}{3!} + \frac{x^4}{4!} - \frac{x^5}{5!} + \cdots.$$

Thus

$$\cosh x = \frac{1}{2}\left(2 + 2\frac{x^2}{2!} + 2\frac{x^4}{4!} + \cdots\right)$$

$$= 1 + \frac{x^2}{2!} + \frac{x^4}{4!} + \cdots = \sum_{k=0}^{\infty} \frac{x^{2k}}{(2k)!}$$

and

$$\sinh x = \frac{1}{2}\left(2x + 2\frac{x^3}{3!} + 2\frac{x^5}{5!} + \cdots\right)$$

$$= x + \frac{x^3}{3!} + \frac{x^5}{5!} + \cdots = \sum_{k=0}^{\infty} \frac{x^{2k+1}}{(2k+1)!}.$$

Both expansions are valid for all real x, since the exponential expansions are valid for all real x. □

PROBLEM. Expand $x^2 \cos x^3$ in powers of x.

Solution

$$\cos x = 1 - \frac{x^2}{2!} + \frac{x^4}{4!} - \frac{x^6}{6!} + \cdots$$

Thus

$$\cos x^3 = 1 - \frac{(x^3)^2}{2!} + \frac{(x^3)^4}{4!} - \frac{(x^3)^6}{6!} + \cdots$$

$$= 1 - \frac{x^6}{2!} + \frac{x^{12}}{4!} - \frac{x^{18}}{6!} + \cdots,$$

and

$$x^2 \cos x^3 = x^2 - \frac{x^8}{2!} + \frac{x^{14}}{4!} - \frac{x^{20}}{6!} + \cdots.$$

This expansion is valid for all real x, since the expansion for $\cos x$ is valid for all real x. □

Alternative Solution. Since

$$x^2 \cos x^3 = \frac{d}{dx} \left(\frac{1}{3} \sin x^3 \right),$$

we can derive the expansion for $x^2 \cos x^3$ by expanding $\frac{1}{3} \sin x^3$ and then differentiating term by term. □

EXERCISES

Expand in powers of x, basing your calculations on the geometric series

$$\frac{1}{1-x} = 1 + x + x^2 + \cdots + x^n + \cdots.$$

1. $\dfrac{1}{(1-x)^2}$.

2. $\dfrac{1}{(1-x)^3}$.

3. $\dfrac{1}{(1-x)^k}$.

4. $\ln(1-x)$.

5. $\ln(1-x^2)$.

6. $\ln(2-3x)$.

Expand in powers of x, basing your calculations on

$$\tan x = x + \tfrac{1}{3}x^3 + \tfrac{2}{15}x^5 + \tfrac{17}{315}x^7 + \cdots.$$

7. $\sec^2 x$.

8. $\ln \cos x$.

Find $f^{(9)}(0)$.

9. $f(x) = x^2 \sin x$.

10. $f(x) = x \cos x^2$.

Expand in powers of x.

11. $\sin x^2$.

12. $x^2 \tan^{-1} x$.

13. e^{3x^3}.

14. $\dfrac{1-x}{1+x}$.

15. $\dfrac{2x}{1-x^2}$.

16. $x \sinh x^2$.

17. $\dfrac{1}{1-x} + e^x$.

18. $\cosh x \sinh x$.

19. $x \ln(1+x^3)$.

20. $(x^2 + x) \ln(1+x)$.

21. $x^3 e^{-x^3}$.

22. $x^5(\sin x + \cos 2x)$.

Estimate within 0.01.

23. $\displaystyle\int_0^1 e^{-x^3}\,dx.$ **24.** $\displaystyle\int_0^1 \sin x^2\,dx.$ **25.** $\displaystyle\int_0^1 \sin\sqrt{x}\,dx.$

26. $\displaystyle\int_0^1 x^4 e^{-x^2}\,dx.$ **27.** $\displaystyle\int_0^1 \tan^{-1} x^2\,dx.$ **28.** $\displaystyle\int_1^2 \frac{1-\cos x}{x}\,dx.$

29. $\displaystyle\int_0^{2/3} x\ln(1+x)\,dx.$ **30.** $\displaystyle\int_0^1 x\sin\sqrt{x}\,dx.$

31. Show that, if $\Sigma\, a_k x^k$ and $\Sigma\, b_k x^k$ both converge to the same sum on some interval, then $a_k = b_k$ for each k.

32. Show that, if $\epsilon > 0$, then

$$|kx^{k-1}| < (|x| + \epsilon)^k \qquad \text{for all } k \text{ sufficiently large.}$$

HINT: Take the kth root of the left side and let $k \to \infty$.

Sum the following series.

33. $\displaystyle\sum_{k=0}^{\infty} \frac{1}{k!} x^{3k}.$ **34.** $\displaystyle\sum_{k=0}^{\infty} \frac{1}{k!} x^{3k+1}.$ **35.** $\displaystyle\sum_{k=1}^{\infty} \frac{3k}{k!} x^{3k-1}.$

36. Deduce the differentiation formulas

$$\frac{d}{dx}(\sinh x) = \cosh x, \qquad \frac{d}{dx}(\cosh x) = \sinh x$$

from the expansions of $\sinh x$ and $\cosh x$ in powers of x.

37. Verify that all functions of the form

$$y(x) = x\left(C + \sum_{k=0}^{\infty} \frac{1}{(2k+1)k!} x^{2k+1}\right)$$

with C an arbitrary constant satisfy the differential equation

$$xy' - y = x^2 e^{x^2}.$$

Supplement to Section 13.9

Proof of Theorem 13.9.2

Set

$$f(x) = \sum_{k=0}^{\infty} a_k x^k \qquad \text{and} \qquad g(x) = \sum_{k=0}^{\infty} \frac{d}{dx}(a_k x^k) = \sum_{k=1}^{\infty} k a_k x^{k-1}.$$

Select x from $(-c, c)$. We want to show that

$$\lim_{h\to 0} \frac{f(x+h) - f(x)}{h} = g(x).$$

For $x + h$ in $(-c, c)$, $h \neq 0$, we have

$$\left| g(x) - \frac{f(x+h) - f(x)}{h} \right| = \left| \sum_{k=1}^{\infty} k a_k x^{k-1} - \sum_{k=0}^{\infty} \frac{a_k(x+h)^k - a_k x^k}{h} \right|$$

$$= \left| \sum_{k=1}^{\infty} k a_k x^{k-1} - \sum_{k=1}^{\infty} a_k \left[\frac{(x+h)^k - x^k}{h} \right] \right|.$$

By the mean-value theorem

$$\frac{(x+h)^k - x^k}{h} = kt_k^{k-1}$$

for some number t_k between x and $x + h$. Thus we can write

$$
\left| g(x) - \frac{f(x+h) - f(x)}{h} \right| = \left| \sum_{k=1}^{\infty} ka_k x^{k-1} - \sum_{k=1}^{\infty} ka_k t_k^{k-1} \right|
$$

$$
= \left| \sum_{k=1}^{\infty} ka_k(x^{k-1} - t_k^{k-1}) \right|
$$

$$
= \left| \sum_{k=2}^{\infty} ka_k(x^{k-1} - t_k^{k-1}) \right|.
$$

By the mean-value theorem

$$\frac{x^{k-1} - t_k^{k-1}}{x - t_k} = (k-1)p_{k-1}^{k-2}$$

for some number p_{k-1} between x and t_k. Obviously, then,

$$|x^{k-1} - t_k^{k-1}| = |x - t_k||(k-1)p_{k-1}^{k-2}|.$$

Since $|x - t_k| < |h|$ and $|p_{k-1}| \leq |\alpha|$ where $|\alpha| = \max\{|x|, |x + h|\}$,

$$|x^{k-1} - t_k^{k-1}| \leq |h||(k-1)\alpha^{k-2}|.$$

Thus

$$
\left| g(x) - \frac{f(x+h) - f(x)}{h} \right| \leq |h| \sum_{k=2}^{\infty} |k(k-1)a_k\alpha^{k-2}|.
$$

Since the series converges,

$$\lim_{h \to 0} \left(|h| \sum_{k=2}^{\infty} |k(k-1)a_k\alpha^{k-2}| \right) = 0.$$

This gives

$$\lim_{h \to 0} \left| g(x) - \frac{f(x+h) - f(x)}{h} \right| = 0$$

and thus

$$\lim_{h \to 0} \frac{f(x+h) - f(x)}{h} = g(x). \quad \square$$

Computing π

We base our computation of π on the inverse tangent series

$$\tan^{-1} x = x - \frac{x^3}{3} + \frac{x^5}{5} - \frac{x^7}{7} + \cdots \qquad \text{for } -1 \leq x \leq 1$$

and the relation

(13.9.7)
$$\tfrac{1}{4}\pi = 4\tan^{-1}\tfrac{1}{5} - \tan^{-1}\tfrac{1}{239}.\dagger$$

The inverse tangent series gives

$$\tan^{-1}\tfrac{1}{5} = \tfrac{1}{5} - \tfrac{1}{3}(\tfrac{1}{5})^3 + \tfrac{1}{5}(\tfrac{1}{5})^5 - \tfrac{1}{7}(\tfrac{1}{5})^7 + \cdots$$

and

$$\tan^{-1}\tfrac{1}{239} = \tfrac{1}{239} - \tfrac{1}{3}(\tfrac{1}{239})^3 + \tfrac{1}{5}(\tfrac{1}{239})^5 - \tfrac{1}{7}(\tfrac{1}{239})^7 + \cdots.$$

These are alternating series $\Sigma\,(-1)^k a_k$ with a_k decreasing toward 0. Thus we know that

$$\tfrac{1}{5} - \tfrac{1}{3}(\tfrac{1}{5})^3 \le \tan^{-1}\tfrac{1}{5} \le \tfrac{1}{5} - \tfrac{1}{3}(\tfrac{1}{5})^3 + \tfrac{1}{5}(\tfrac{1}{5})^5$$

and

$$\tfrac{1}{239} - \tfrac{1}{3}(\tfrac{1}{239})^3 \le \tan^{-1}\tfrac{1}{239} \le \tfrac{1}{239}.$$

With these inequalities together with relation (13.9.7), we can show that

$$3.14 < \pi < 3.147.$$

By using six terms of the series for $\tan^{-1}\tfrac{1}{5}$ and still only two of the series for $\tan^{-1}\tfrac{1}{239}$, we can show that

$$3.14159262 < \pi < 3.14159267.$$

Greater accuracy can be obtained by taking more terms into account. For instance, fifteen terms of the series for $\tan^{-1}\tfrac{1}{5}$ and just four terms of the series for $\tan^{-1}\tfrac{1}{239}$ determine π to twenty decimal places:

$$\pi \cong 3.14159\ 26535\ 89793\ 23846.$$

13.10··THE BINOMIAL SERIES

Through a collection of problems we invite you to derive for yourself the basic properties of one of the most celebrated series of all — *the binomial series.*

Start with the binomial $1 + x$ (2 terms). Choose a real number $\alpha \ne 0$ and form the function

$$f(x) = (1 + x)^\alpha.$$

---

† This relation was discovered in 1706 by John Machin, a Scotsman. It can be verified by repeated applications of the addition formula

$$\tan\,(A + B) = \frac{\tan A + \tan B}{1 - \tan A \tan B}.$$

First calculate $\tan\,(2\tan^{-1}\tfrac{1}{5})$, then $\tan\,(4\tan^{-1}\tfrac{1}{5})$, and finally $\tan\,(4\tan^{-1}\tfrac{1}{5} - \tan^{-1}\tfrac{1}{239})$.

PROBLEM 1. Show that

$$\frac{f^{(k)}(0)}{k!} = \frac{\alpha[\alpha - 1][\alpha - 2] \cdots [\alpha - (k - 1)]}{k!}.$$

The number you just obtained is the coefficient of x^k in the expansion of $(1 + x)^\alpha$. It is called *the kth binomial coefficient* and is usually denoted by $\binom{\alpha}{k}$:

$$\binom{\alpha}{k} = \frac{\alpha[\alpha - 1][\alpha - 2] \cdots [\alpha - (k - 1)]}{k!}.$$

PROBLEM 2. Show that the binomial series

$$\Sigma \binom{\alpha}{k} x^k$$

has radius of convergence 1.   HINT: Use the ratio test.

From Problem 2 you know that the binomial series converges on the open interval $(-1, 1)$ and defines there an infinitely differentiable function. The next thing to show is that this function (the one defined by the series) is actually $(1 + x)^\alpha$. To do this, you first need some other results.

PROBLEM 3. Verify the identity

$$(k + 1) \binom{\alpha}{k + 1} + k \binom{\alpha}{k} = \alpha \binom{\alpha}{k}.$$

PROBLEM 4. Use the identity of Problem 3 to show that the sum of the binomial series

$$\phi(x) = \sum_{k=0}^{\infty} \binom{\alpha}{k} x^k$$

satisfies the differential equation

$$(1 + x)\phi'(x) = \alpha\phi(x)   \quad \text{for all } x \text{ in } (-1, 1)$$

together with the side condition $\phi(0) = 1$.

You are now in a position to prove the main result.

PROBLEM 5. Show that

(13.10.1) $$(1 + x)^\alpha = \sum_{k=0}^{\infty} \binom{\alpha}{k} x^k   \quad \text{for all } x \text{ in } (-1, 1).$$

You can probably get a better feeling for the series by writing out the first few terms:

(13.10.2) $$(1 + x)^\alpha = 1 + \alpha x + \frac{\alpha(\alpha - 1)}{2!} x^2 + \frac{\alpha(\alpha - 1)(\alpha - 2)}{3!} x^3 + \cdots .$$

EXERCISES

Expand in powers of x up to x^4.

1. $\sqrt{1 + x}$.
2. $\sqrt{1 - x}$.
3. $\sqrt{1 + x^2}$.
4. $\sqrt{1 - x^2}$.

5. $\dfrac{1}{\sqrt{1 + x}}$.
6. $\dfrac{1}{\sqrt[3]{1 + x}}$.
7. $\sqrt[4]{1 - x}$.
8. $\dfrac{1}{\sqrt[4]{1 + x}}$.

Estimate within 0.01.

9. $\sqrt{98}$.　HINT: $\sqrt{98} = (100 - 2)^{1/2} = 10(1 - \frac{1}{50})^{1/2}$.　10. $\sqrt[5]{36}$.
11. $\sqrt[3]{9}$.　　　　12. $\sqrt[4]{620}$.　　　　13. $17^{-1/4}$.　　　14. $9^{-1/3}$.

13.11··SERIES SOLUTIONS OF DIFFERENTIAL EQUATIONS

You have seen that, on its interval of convergence, a power series represents an infinitely differentiable function and that the derivatives of that function can be obtained by differentiating the series term by term. Moreover, as you were asked to show in Exercise 31 of Section 13.9:

(13.11.1)

if
$$\sum_{k=0}^{\infty} a_k x^k \quad \text{and} \quad \sum_{k=0}^{\infty} b_k x^k$$
both converge to the same sum on some interval, then
$$a_k = b_k \quad \text{for all } k.\dagger$$

We can use these ideas to solve certain differential equations. The technique consists of postulating a series solution

$$y = \sum_{k=0}^{\infty} a_k x^k,$$

and then determining the coefficients from the conditions imposed by the differential equation.

EXAMPLE. We begin with the differential equation

(1) $$y' = 2y.$$

---

† Reason: both sets of coefficients must be the Taylor coefficients of the sum.

Our first step is to assume that the equation has a series solution

(2) $$y = a_0 + a_1 x + a_2 x^2 + \cdots + a_n x^n + \cdots .$$

Differentiating term by term, we have

(3) $$y' = a_1 + 2a_2 x + 3a_3 x^2 + \cdots + (n + 1)a_{n+1} x^n + \cdots .$$

Substituting (2) and (3) in (1), we have

$$a_1 + 2a_2 x + 3a_2 x^2 + \cdots + (n + 1)a_{n+1} x^n + \cdots$$
$$= 2(a_0 + a_1 x + a_2 x^2 + \cdots + a_n x^n + \cdots).$$

Equating coefficients [here we are using (13.11.1)], we find that

$$a_1 = 2a_0, \qquad 2a_2 = 2a_1, \qquad 3a_3 = 2a_2, \qquad \text{etc;}$$

In general

$$a_{n+1} = \frac{2}{n + 1} a_n.$$

We can use this last relation to express all the coefficients in terms of the first coefficient a_0:

$$a_1 = 2a_0,$$

$$a_2 = \frac{2}{2} a_1 = \frac{2^2}{2} a_0,$$

$$a_3 = \frac{2}{3} a_2 = \frac{2}{3} \frac{2^2}{2} a_0 = \frac{2^3}{3!} a_0,$$

$$a_4 = \frac{2}{4} a_3 = \frac{2}{4} \frac{2^3}{3!} a_0 = \frac{2^4}{4!} a_0,$$

$$\vdots$$

$$a_n = \frac{2}{n} a_{n-1} = \frac{2}{n} \frac{2^{n-1}}{(n - 1)!} a_0 = \frac{2^n}{n!} a_0 . \dagger$$

We then have

$$y = a_0 + a_1 x + a_2 x^2 + \cdots + a_n x^n + \cdots ,$$

$$= a_0 + 2a_0 x + \frac{2^2}{2!} a_0 x^2 + \cdots + \frac{2^n}{n!} a_0 x^n + \cdots ,$$

$$= a_0 \left(1 + (2x) + \frac{(2x)^2}{2!} + \cdots + \frac{(2x)^n}{n!} + \cdots \right),$$

$$= a_0 \sum_{k=0}^{\infty} \frac{(2x)^k}{k!} = a_0 e^{2x}.$$

---

† It seems evident that this formula for a_n is correct. A formal proof of this would require induction.

This, of course, is what we should expect from our work in Section 8.3. In this case, the undetermined coefficient a_0 plays the role of arbitrary constant. $\square$

EXAMPLE. Next we consider the differential equation

$$(1 + x)y'' + y' = 1.$$

Again we assume a solution of the form

$$y = a_0 + a_1x + a_2x^2 + \cdots + a_nx^n + \cdots = \sum_{k=0}^{\infty} a_kx^k.$$

Differentiating twice we find that

$$y' = \sum_{k=1}^{\infty} ka_kx^{k-1} \quad \text{and} \quad y'' = \sum_{k=2}^{\infty} k(k-1)a_kx^{k-2}.$$

Substituting these results in the differential equation, we see that

$$(1 + x) \sum_{k=2}^{\infty} k(k-1)a_kx^{k-2} + \sum_{k=1}^{\infty} ka_kx^{k-1} = 1$$

and therefore

$$\sum_{k=2}^{\infty} k(k-1)a_kx^{k-2} + \sum_{k=2}^{\infty} k(k-1)a_kx^{k-1} + \sum_{k=1}^{\infty} ka_kx^{k-1} = 1.$$

To collect all like powers of x, we want to replace the x^{k-2} in the first series by x^{k-1}. We can do this by noting that

$$\sum_{k=2}^{\infty} k(k-1)a_kx^{k-2} = \sum_{k=1}^{\infty} k(k+1)a_{k+1}x^{k-1}.$$

Now, we have

$$\sum_{k=1}^{\infty} k(k+1)a_{k+1}x^{k-1} + \sum_{k=2}^{\infty} k(k-1)a_kx^{k-1} + \sum_{k=1}^{\infty} ka_kx^{k-1} = 1.$$

Only the first and third summations begin with $k = 1$, so we record the $k = 1$ terms separately. This gives

$$(2a_2 + a_1) + \sum_{k=2}^{\infty} [k(k+1)a_{k+1} + k(k-1)a_k + ka_k]x^{k-1} = 1$$

and thus

$$(2a_2 + a_1) + \sum_{k=2}^{\infty} [k(k+1)a_{k+1} + k^2a_k]x^{k-1} = 1.$$

Equating the constant terms, we have

(∗) $2a_2 + a_1 = 1.$

Equating the remaining coefficients, we see that, for $k \geq 2$,

$$k(k+1)a_{k+1} + k^2a_k = 0$$

and therefore

(**)
$$a_{k+1} = -\frac{k}{k+1} a_k.$$

We notice first that a_0 is not involved; it plays the role of an arbitrary constant. Taking a_1 as a second arbitrary constant,† we use (*) to write

$$a_2 = \frac{1 - a_1}{2}.$$

Successive applications of (**) give

$$a_3 = -\frac{2}{3} a_2 = -\frac{2}{3}\left(\frac{1-a_1}{2}\right) = -\frac{1}{3}(1-a_1),$$

$$a_4 = -\frac{3}{4} a_3 = -\frac{3}{4}\left(-\frac{1}{3}\right)(1-a_1) = \frac{1}{4}(1-a_1),$$

$$a_5 = -\frac{4}{5} a_4 = -\frac{4}{5}\left(\frac{1}{4}\right)(1-a_1) = -\frac{1}{5}(1-a_1), \quad \text{etc.}$$

With a_0 and a_1 as arbitrary constants, we have

$$a_k = (-1)^k \frac{1}{k}(1-a_1), \qquad k \geq 2.$$

The general solution of the differential equation takes the form

$$y = a_0 + a_1 x + \sum_{k=2}^{\infty} a_k x^k,$$

$$= a_0 + a_1 x + \sum_{k=2}^{\infty} (-1)^k \frac{1}{k}(1-a_1)x^k,$$

$$= a_0 + a_1 x + (1-a_1) \sum_{k=2}^{\infty} \frac{(-1)^k}{k} x^k.$$

As you can verify, this series converges for $-1 < x \leq 1$.

In this instance, we can write the solution in closed form.†† Since

$$\ln(1+x) = \sum_{k=1}^{\infty} \frac{(-1)^{k+1}}{k} x^k = x - \sum_{k=2}^{\infty} \frac{(-1)^k}{k} x^k,$$

we have

$$y = a_0 + a_1 x + (1-a_1)[x - \ln(1+x)].$$

This simplifies to give

$$y = x + a_0 + (a_1 - 1)\ln(1+x). \quad \square$$

---

† Remember, the differential equation is of second order, so we can expect two arbitrary constants.

†† A *closed form* in this context is an expression that does not involve an infinite summation. For example, the closed form for $\sum_{k=0}^{\infty} \frac{x^k}{k!}$ is e^x.

We have found series solutions

$$y = a_0 + a_1 x + a_2 x^2 + \cdots + a_n x^n + \cdots$$

to two differential equations; one of the first order, the other of the second order. In the first-order case, a_0 was arbitrary. What does a_0 represent? It represents $y(0)$, the initial value of the solution. In the second-order case, we found two arbitrary constants, a_0 and a_1. While a_0 represents the initial value of the solution, a_1 represents the initial value of the first derivative of the solution:

$$a_0 = y(0), \qquad a_1 = y'(0).$$

FINAL REMARKS. When we assume that a differential equation has a power-series solution, we are assuming (among other things) that the differential equation has solutions that are infinitely differentiable. This is not always the case. Some differential equations have solutions with only a finite number of derivatives. Thus, the use of power series to solve differential equations is somewhat limited. Moreover, the surrounding theory of convergence is not simple. Even so, the polynomial approximations provided by series remain a useful tool, particularly where solutions in closed form are unobtainable. □

EXERCISES

Find the general series solution of the differential equation. Then find the solution by the methods of Chapter 8 and reconcile your answers.

1. $y' + 2y = 0$.   **2.** $y' - 3y = 0$.   **3.** $y' + 2y = 3$.   **4.** $y' - 3y = 4$.
5. $y' + 2y = x$.   **6.** $y' - 3y = 2x$.   **7.** $xy' - 3y = 0$.   **8.** $xy' - 2y = 0$.
9. $y'' + 2y' = 1$.   **10.** $y'' - 3y' = 2$.   **11.** $y'' - y = 0$.   **12.** $y'' + y = 0$.

Find the series solution to the initial-value problem. Then find the solution by the methods of Chapter 8 and reconcile your answers.

13. $y' + 2y = x$, $y(0) = -\frac{1}{4}$.
14. $y' - 3y = 2x$, $y(0) = -\frac{2}{9}$.
15. $y' + 2y = 3$, $y(0) = 2$.
16. $y' - 3y = 4$, $y(0) = -1$.
17. $y'' - 3y' + 2y = 0$, $y(0) = 1$, $y'(0) = 1$.
18. $y'' - y' - 2y = 0$, $y(0) = 1$, $y'(0) = -1$.
19. $y'' - 3y' + 2y = 2$, $y(0) = 0$, $y'(0) = -1$.
20. $y'' - y' - 2y = 4$, $y(0) = 0$, $y'(0) = -2$.

13.12··ADDITIONAL EXERCISES

Sum the following series.

1. $\displaystyle\sum_{k=0}^{\infty} \left(\frac{1}{4}\right)^k$.   **2.** $\displaystyle\sum_{k=0}^{\infty} \left(\frac{3}{4}\right)^{k+1}$.   **3.** $\displaystyle\sum_{k=0}^{\infty} (-1)^k \left(\frac{1}{2}\right)^k$.

4. $\displaystyle\sum_{k=0}^{\infty} \frac{(\ln 2)^k}{k!}$.   **5.** $\displaystyle\sum_{k=1}^{\infty} \left(\frac{1}{k} - \frac{1}{k+1}\right)$.   **6.** $\displaystyle\sum_{k=2}^{\infty} \left(\frac{1}{k^2} - \frac{1}{(k+1)^2}\right)$.

7. $\displaystyle\sum_{k=0}^{\infty} x^{5k+1}$.

8. $\displaystyle\sum_{k=0}^{\infty} 2x^{3k+2}$.

9. $\displaystyle\sum_{k=1}^{\infty} \frac{3}{2}x^{2k-1}$.

10. $\displaystyle\sum_{k=1}^{\infty} \frac{1}{(k-1)!} x^k$.

11. $\displaystyle\sum_{k=1}^{\infty} \frac{k^2}{k!}$.

12. $\displaystyle\sum_{k=1}^{\infty} \frac{1}{k(k+1)(k+2)}$.

Test for (a) absolute convergence, (b) conditional convergence.

13. $\displaystyle\sum_{k=0}^{\infty} \frac{1}{2k+1} = 1 + \frac{1}{3} + \frac{1}{5} + \cdots$.

14. $\displaystyle\sum_{k=0}^{\infty} \frac{1}{(2k+1)(2k+3)} = \frac{1}{1\cdot3} + \frac{1}{3\cdot5} + \frac{1}{5\cdot7} + \cdots$.

15. $\displaystyle\sum_{k=1}^{\infty} \frac{(-1)^{k+1}}{(k+1)(k+2)} = \frac{1}{2\cdot3} - \frac{1}{3\cdot4} + \frac{1}{4\cdot5} - \cdots$.

16. $\displaystyle\sum_{k=2}^{\infty} \frac{1}{k\ln k} = \frac{1}{2\ln 2} + \frac{1}{3\ln 3} + \frac{1}{4\ln 4} + \cdots$.

17. $\displaystyle\sum_{k=0}^{\infty} \frac{(-1)^k}{2k+1} = 1 - \frac{1}{3} + \frac{1}{5} - \cdots$.

18. $\displaystyle\sum_{k=1}^{\infty} (-1)^{k+1} \frac{100^k}{k!} = 100 - \frac{100^2}{2!} + \frac{100^3}{3!} - \cdots$.

19. $\displaystyle\sum_{k=1}^{\infty} (-1)^{k-1} \frac{k}{3^{k-1}} = 1 - \frac{2}{3} + \frac{3}{3^2} - \cdots$.

20. $\displaystyle\sum_{k=1}^{\infty} k\left(\frac{3}{4}\right)^k = \frac{3}{4} + 2\left(\frac{3}{4}\right)^2 + 3\left(\frac{3}{4}\right)^3 + \cdots$.

21. $\displaystyle\sum_{k=1}^{\infty} \frac{(-1)^{k-1}}{\sqrt{(k+1)(k+2)}} = \frac{1}{\sqrt{2\cdot3}} - \frac{1}{\sqrt{3\cdot4}} + \frac{1}{\sqrt{4\cdot5}} - \cdots$.

22. $\displaystyle\sum_{k=1}^{\infty} \frac{(-1)^{k-1}}{\sqrt[k]{5}} = \frac{1}{5} - \frac{1}{\sqrt{5}} + \frac{1}{\sqrt[3]{5}} - \cdots$.

Find the interval of convergence.

23. $\displaystyle\sum \frac{5^k}{k} (x-2)^k$.

24. $\displaystyle\sum \frac{(-1)^k}{3^k} x^{k+1}$.

25. $\displaystyle\sum (k+1)k(x-1)^{2k}$.

26. $\displaystyle\sum (-1)^k 4^k x^{2k}$.

27. $\displaystyle\sum \frac{k}{2k+1} x^{2k+1}$.

28. $\displaystyle\sum \frac{1}{2^{k!}} (x-2)^k$.

29. $\displaystyle\sum \frac{k!}{2} (x+1)^k$.

30. $\displaystyle\sum \frac{(-1)^k}{\sqrt{k}} (x+3)^k$.

31. $\displaystyle\sum \frac{(-1)^k k}{3^{2k}} x^k$.

32. $\displaystyle\sum \ln k\,(x-2)^k$.

33. $\displaystyle\sum \frac{(-1)^k}{5^{k+1}} (x-2)^k$.

34. $\displaystyle\sum \frac{2^k}{(2k)!} (x-1)^{2k}$.

Expand in powers of x.

35. xe^{5x^2}.

36. $\ln(1+x^2)$.

37. $\sqrt{x}\tan^{-1}\sqrt{x}$.

38. a^x.   **39.** $(x + x^2)(\sin x^2)$.   **40.** $x \ln \left(\dfrac{1 + x^2}{1 - x^2} \right)$.

41. Expand $e^{\sin x}$ in powers of x up to x^4.
42. Expand $e^{\sin x} \cos x$ in powers of x up to x^3.
43. Expand $(1 - x^2)^{-1/2}$ in powers of x up to x^4.
44. Expand $\sin^{-1} x$ in powers of x up to x^5.

Estimate within 0.01.

45. $\displaystyle\int_0^{1/2} \dfrac{dx}{1 + x^4}$.   **46.** $e^{2/3}$.   **47.** $\sqrt[3]{60}$.   **48.** $\displaystyle\int_0^1 x \sin x^4 \, dx$.

49. Find the sum of the series

$$\sum_{k=1}^{\infty} a_k \quad \text{given that} \quad a_k = \int_k^{k+1} x e^{-x} \, dx.$$

50. Show that

$$\sum_{k=1}^{\infty} \frac{1}{k^2} = 1 + \sum_{k=1}^{\infty} \frac{1}{k^2(k + 1)}.$$

51. Determine whether or not the series

$$\sum_{k=2}^{\infty} a_k$$

converges or diverges. If it converges, find the sum.

(a) $a_k = \displaystyle\sum_{n=0}^{\infty} \left(\dfrac{1}{k} \right)^n$.   (b) $a_k = \displaystyle\sum_{n=1}^{\infty} \left(\dfrac{1}{k} \right)^n$.   (c) $a_k = \displaystyle\sum_{n=2}^{\infty} \left(\dfrac{1}{k} \right)^n$.

52. (*The Lagrange form of the remainder*) Show that the remainder in Taylor's theorem (Theorem 13.6.1) can be written

$$R_{n+1}(x) = f^{(n+1)}(c_{n+1}) \frac{x^{n+1}}{(n + 1)!}$$

with c_{n+1} between 0 and x.   HINT: For $x > 0$

$$\frac{1}{n!} \int_0^x m_{n+1}(x - t)^n \, dt \le R_{n+1}(x) \le \frac{1}{n!} \int_0^x M_{n+1}(x - t)^n \, dt$$

where

$$m_{n+1} = \min_{t \in I} f^{(n+1)}(t) \quad \text{and} \quad M_{n+1} = \max_{t \in I} f^{(n+1)}(t).$$

53. Show that every sequence of real numbers can be covered by a sequence of open intervals of arbitrarily small total length; namely, show that if $\{x_1, x_2, x_3, \ldots\}$ is a sequence of real numbers and ϵ is positive, then there exists a sequence of open intervals (a_n, b_n) with $a_n < x_n < b_n$ such that

$$\sum_{n=1}^{\infty} (b_n - a_n) < \epsilon.$$

13.13 CHAPTER SUMMARY

13.1 Sigma Notation

13.2 Infinite Series

partial sums (p. 646)   convergence, divergence (p. 647)
sum of a series (p. 647)   a divergence test (p. 654)

$$\text{geometric series: } \sum_{k=0}^{\infty} x^k = \left\{ \begin{array}{ll} \dfrac{1}{1-x}, & |x| < 1 \\[2mm] \text{diverges}, & |x| \geq 1 \end{array} \right]$$

If $\sum\limits_{k=0}^{\infty} a_k$ converges, then $a_k \to 0$. (p. 654)   The converse is not true.

13.3 The Integral Test; Comparison Theorems

integral test (p. 657)   basic comparison (p. 660)
limit comparison (p. 661)

$$\text{harmonic series: } \sum_{k=1}^{\infty} \frac{1}{k} \text{ diverges} \qquad p\text{-series: } \sum_{k=1}^{\infty} \frac{1}{k^p} \text{ converges iff } p > 1$$

13.4 The Root Test; The Ratio Test

root test (p. 665)   ratio test (p. 666)
summary on convergence tests (p. 668)

13.5 Absolute and Conditional Convergence; Alternating Series

absolutely convergent, conditionally convergent (p. 670)
convergence test for alternating series (p. 671)
an estimate for alternating series (p. 672)

13.6 Taylor Polynomials in x; Taylor Series in x

Taylor polynomials in x (p. 675)   remainder term $R_{n+1}(x)$ (p. 677)
remainder estimate (p. 678)

$$\text{Taylor series in } x \text{ (Maclaurin series): } \sum_{k=0}^{\infty} \frac{f^{(k)}(0)}{k!} x^k$$

$$e^x = \sum_{k=0}^{\infty} \frac{x^k}{k!}, \quad \text{all real } x \qquad \sin x = \sum_{k=0}^{\infty} \frac{(-1)^k}{(2k+1)!} x^{2k+1}, \quad \text{all real } x$$

$$\cos x = \sum_{k=0}^{\infty} \frac{(-1)^k}{(2k)!} x^{2k}, \quad \text{all real } x$$

$$\ln(1+x) = \sum_{k=1}^{\infty} \frac{(-1)^{k+1}}{k} x^k, \quad -1 < x \leq 1$$

13.7 Taylor Polynomials in $x - a$; Taylor Series in $x - a$

Taylor series in $x - a$: $\displaystyle\sum_{k=0}^{\infty} \frac{g^{(k)}(a)}{k!} (x - a)^k$

13.8 Power Series

power series (p. 691)   radius of convergence (p. 693)
interval of convergence (p. 693)

If a power series converges at $x_1 \neq 0$, then it converges absolutely for $|x| < |x_1|$; if it diverges at x_1, then it diverges for $|x| > |x_1|$.

13.9 Differentiation and Integration of Power Series

$$\tan^{-1} x = \sum_{k=0}^{\infty} \frac{(-1)^k}{2k + 1} x^{2k+1}, \quad -1 \leq x \leq 1$$

$$\cosh x = \sum_{k=0}^{\infty} \frac{x^{2k}}{(2k)!}, \quad \text{all real } x \qquad \sinh x = \sum_{k=0}^{\infty} \frac{x^{2k+1}}{(2k + 1)!}$$

On the interior of its interval of convergence, a power series can be differentiated and integrated term-by-term.

On its interval of convergence a power series is the Taylor series of its sum.

13.10 The Binomial Series

$$(1 + x)^\alpha = \sum_{k=0}^{\infty} \binom{\alpha}{k} x^k = 1 + \alpha x + \frac{\alpha(\alpha - 1)}{2!} x^2 + \cdots, \quad -1 < x < 1$$

13.11 Series Solutions of Differential Equations

13.12 Additional Exercises

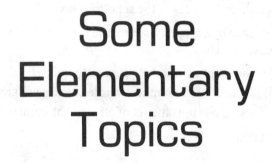

Some Elementary Topics

A.1 ······SETS

A *set* is a collection of objects. The objects in a set are called the *elements* (or *members*) of the set.

We might, for example, consider the set of capital letters appearing on this page, or the set of motorcycles licensed in Idaho, or the set of rational numbers. Suppose, however, that we wanted to find the set of rational people. Everybody might have a different collection. Which would be the right one? To avoid such problems we insist that sets be unambiguously defined. Collections based on highly subjective judgments — such as "all good football players" or "all likeable children" — are not sets.

Notation

To indicate that an object x is in the set A, we write

$$x \in A.$$

To indicate that x is not in A, we write

$$x \notin A.$$

Thus

$$\sqrt{2} \in \text{the set of real numbers} \quad \text{but} \quad \sqrt{2} \notin \text{the set of rational numbers.}$$

Sets are often denoted by braces. The set consisting of a alone is written $\{a\}$; that consisting of a, b is written $\{a, b\}$; that consisting of $a, b, c, \{a, b, c\}$; and so on. Thus

$$0 \in \{0, 1, 2\}, \quad 1 \in \{0, 1, 2\}, \quad 2 \in \{0, 1, 2\}, \quad \text{but} \quad 3 \notin \{0, 1, 2\}.$$

We can also use braces for infinite sets:

$\{1, 2, 3, \ldots\}$ is the set of positive integers,

$\{-1, -2, -3, \ldots\}$ is the set of negative integers,

$\{1, 2, 2^2, 2^3, \ldots\}$ is the set of powers of 2.

Sets are often defined by a property. We write $\{x:\ P\}$ to indicate *the set of all x for which property P holds*. Thus

$\{x:\ x > 2\}$ is the set of all numbers greater than 2;

$\{x:\ x^2 > 9\}$ is the set of all numbers whose squares are greater than 9;

$\{p/q:\ p, q \text{ integers}, q \neq 0\}$ is the set of all rational numbers.

If A is a set, then $\{x:\ x \in A\}$ is A itself.

Containment and Equality

If A and B are sets, then A is said to be *contained* in B, in symbols $A \subseteq B$, iff† every element of A is also an element of B. For example,

the set of equilateral triangles $\subseteq$ the set of all triangles,

the set of all college freshmen $\subseteq$ the set of all college students,

the set of rational numbers $\subseteq$ the set of real numbers.

If A is contained in B, then A is called a *subset* of B. Thus

the set of equilateral triangles is a subset of the set of all triangles,

the set of college freshmen is a subset of the set of all college students,

the set of rational numbers is a subset of the set of real numbers.

Two sets are said to be *equal* iff they have exactly the same membership. In symbols,

(A.1.1) $$A = B \quad \text{iff} \quad A \subseteq B \text{ and } B \subseteq A.$$

EXAMPLES

$\{x:\ x^2 = 4\} = \{-2, 2\},$

$\{x:\ x^2 < 4\} = \{x: -2 < x < 2\},$

$\{x:\ x^2 > 4\} = \{x: x < -2 \text{ or } x > 2\}.$ $\square$

---

† By "iff" we mean "if and only if". This expression is used so often in mathematics that it is convenient to have an abbreviation for it.

The Intersection of Two Sets

The set of elements common to two sets A and B is called the *intersection* of A and B and is denoted by $A \cap B$. The idea is illustrated in Figure A.1.1. In symbols,

(A.1.2) $\boxed{x \in A \cap B \quad \text{iff} \quad x \in A \quad \text{and} \quad x \in B.}$

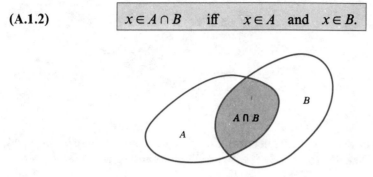

FIGURE A.1.1

EXAMPLES

1. If A is the set of all nonnegative numbers, and B is the set of all nonpositive numbers, then $A \cap B = \{0\}$.

2. If A is the set of all multiples of 3, and B is the set of all multiples of 4, then $A \cap B$ is the set of all multiples of 12.

3. If $A = \{a, b, c, d, e\}$, and $B = \{c, d, e, f\}$, then $A \cap B = \{c, d, e\}$.

4. If $A = \{x: \ x > 1\}$ and $B = \{x: \ x < 4\}$, then $A \cap B = \{x: \ 1 < x < 4\}$. $\square$

The Union of Two Sets

The *union* of two sets A and B, written $A \cup B$, is the set of elements that are either in A or in B. This does not exclude objects that are elements of both A and B. (See Figure A.1.2.) In symbols,

(A.1.3) $\boxed{x \in A \cup B \quad \text{iff} \quad x \in A \quad \text{or} \quad x \in B.}$

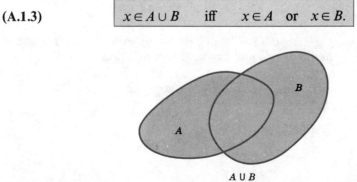

$A \cup B$

FIGURE A.1.2

EXAMPLES

1. If A is the set of all nonnegative numbers and B is the set of all nonpositive numbers, then $A \cup B$ is the set of all real numbers.

2. If $A = \{a, b, c, d, e\}$ and $B = \{c, d, e, f\}$, then $A \cup B = \{a, b, c, d, e, f\}$.

3. If $A = \{x: 0 < x < 1\}$ and $B = \{0, 1\}$, then $A \cup B = \{x: 0 \le x \le 1\}$.

4. If $A = \{x: x > 1\}$ and $B = \{x: x > 2\}$, then $A \cup B = \{x: x > 1\}$.   □

The Empty Set

If the sets A and B have no elements in common, we say that A and B are *disjoint* and write $A \cap B = \varnothing$. We regard $\varnothing$ as a set with no elements and refer to it as the *empty set*.

EXAMPLES

1. If A is the set of all positive numbers, and B is the set of all negative numbers, then $A \cap B = \varnothing$.

2. If $A = \{0, 1, 2, 3\}$ and $B = \{4, 5, 6, 7, 8\}$, then $A \cap B = \varnothing$.

3. The set of all irrational rational numbers is empty; so is the set of all even odd integers; so is the set of real numbers whose squares are negative.   □

The empty set $\varnothing$ plays a role in the theory of sets that is strikingly similar to the role played by 0 in the arithmetic of numbers. Without pursuing the matter very far, note that for numbers,

$$a + 0 = 0 + a = a, \qquad a \cdot 0 = 0 \cdot a = 0,$$

and for sets,

$$A \cup \varnothing = \varnothing \cup A = A, \qquad A \cap \varnothing = \varnothing \cap A = \varnothing.$$

Cartesian Products

If A and B are nonempty sets, then $A \times B$, the *Cartesian product* of A and B, is the set of all ordered pairs (a, b) with $a \in A$ and $b \in B$. In set notation

(A.1.4) $A \times B = \{(a, b): a \in A, b \in B\}.$

Notice that $A \times B = B \times A$ iff $A = B$.

EXAMPLES

1. For $A = \{0, 1\}, B = \{1, 2, 3\}, A \times B = \{(0, 1), (0, 2), (0, 3), (1, 1), (1, 2), (1, 3)\}$ and $B \times A = \{(1, 0), (1, 1) (2, 0), (2, 1), (3, 0), (3, 1)\}$.

2. If A is the set of rational numbers and B is the set of irrational numbers, then $A \times B$ is the set of all pairs (a, b) with a rational and b irrational.   □

The Cartesian product $A \times B \times C$ consists of all ordered triples (a, b, c) with $a \in A$, $b \in B$, $c \in C$:

(A.1.5) $A \times B \times C = \{(a, b, c):\ a \in A, b \in B, c \in C\}.$

EXERCISES†

For Exercises 1–20, take

$$A = \{0, 2\}, \qquad B = \{-1, 0, 1\}, \qquad C = \{1, 2, 3, 4\}, \qquad D = \{2, 4, 6, 8, \ldots\},$$

and determine the following sets:

1. $A \cup B$.	**2.** $B \cup C$.	**3.** $A \cap B$.	**4.** $B \cap C$.
5. $B \cup D$.	**6.** $A \cup D$.	**7.** $B \cap D$.	**8.** $A \cap D$.
9. $C \cup D$.	**10.** $C \cap D$.	**11.** $A \times B$.	**12.** $B \times C$.
13. $B \times A$.	**14.** $C \times B$.	**15.** $A \times A \times B$.	**16.** $A \times B \times A$.
17. $A \cap (C \cap D)$.	**18.** $A \cap (B \cup C)$.	**19.** $A \cup (C \cap D)$.	**20.** $A \cup (B \cap C)$.

For Exercises 21–28, take

$$A = \{x: x > 2\}, \qquad B = \{x: x \le 4\}, \qquad C = \{x: x > 3\},$$

and determine the following sets:

21. $A \cup B$.	**22.** $B \cup C$.	**23.** $A \cap B$.	**24.** $B \cap C$.
25. $A \cup C$.	**26.** $A \cap C$.	**27.** $B \cup A$.	**28.** $C \cap B$

29. Given that $A \subseteq B$, find (a) $A \cup B$. (b) $A \cap B$.

30. What can you conclude about A and B given that
  (a) $A \cup B = A$?   (b) $A \cap B = A$?   (c) $A \cup B = A$ and $A \cap B = A$?

31. List all the nonempty subsets of $\{0, 1, 2\}$.

32. Determine the number of nonempty subsets of a set A with n elements.

A.2 ·····RADIAN MEASURE

Degree measure, traditionally used to measure the angles of a geometric figure, has one serious drawback. It is artificial. There is no intrinsic connection between a degree and the geometry of a circle. Why 360 degrees for one revolution? Why not 400? or 100?

There is another way of measuring angles that is more natural and lends itself better to the methods of calculus: measuring angles in *radians*. Figure A.2.1 shows a central angle in a circle of radius R. Suppose you had never heard of degree measurement. How would you measure this angle? The most natural thing to do, it would seem, would be to measure the length of the arc from A to B and compare the length of

---

† The odd-numbered exercises have anwers at the back of the book.

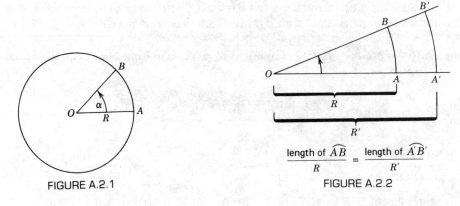

FIGURE A.2.1   FIGURE A.2.2

this arc to the radius R.   The *radian measure* of $\angle AOB$ is, by definition, *the length of $\widehat{AB}$ divided by R*:

(A.2.1) $\angle AOB$ measures α radians   iff $\dfrac{\text{length of } \widehat{AB}}{R} = \alpha.$

Figure A.2.2 shows an angle serving as a central angle for two different circles. Using the smaller circle we find that the angle measures

$$\frac{\text{length of } \widehat{AB}}{R} \text{ radians.}$$

Using the larger circle we find that the angle measures

$$\frac{\text{length of } \widehat{A'B'}}{R'} \text{ radians.}$$

For our definition of radian measure to make sense, it must be true that

$$\frac{\text{length of } \widehat{AB}}{R} = \frac{\text{length of } \widehat{A'B'}}{R'}.$$

You can verify this relation by noting that sectors AOB and $A'OB'$ are similar figures.

Since the circumference of a circle of radius R is $2\pi R$, a complete revolution comprises 2π radians; half a revolution (a straight angle) comprises π radians; a quarter revolution (a right angle) comprises $\frac{1}{2}\pi$ radians. See Figure A.2.3.

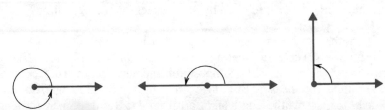

2π radians   π radians $\frac{1}{2}$π radians
a complete revolution   a straight angle   a right angle

FIGURE A.2.3

The conversion of radians to degrees and vice versa is made by noting that, if A is the measure of an angle in degrees and x is the measure of that same angle in radians, then

(A.2.1)

$$\frac{A}{360} = \frac{x}{2\pi}.$$

In particular

$$1 \text{ radian} = \frac{360}{2\pi} \text{ degrees} \cong 57.30 \text{ degrees}$$

and

$$1 \text{ degree} = \frac{2\pi}{360} \text{ radians} \cong 0.0175 \text{ radians}.$$

PROBLEM. Convert $\frac{1}{10}\pi$ radians to degree measure.

Solution. We set

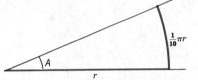

$$\frac{A}{360} = \frac{\frac{1}{10}\pi}{2\pi}$$

and find that $A = 360(\frac{1}{20}) = 18$. Therefore, $\frac{1}{10}\pi$ radians amounts to 18 degrees. □

Table A.2.1 gives some common angles measured both in degrees and in radians.

TABLE A.2.1									
degrees	0	30	45	60	90	120	135	150	180
radians	0	$\frac{1}{6}\pi$	$\frac{1}{4}\pi$	$\frac{1}{3}\pi$	$\frac{1}{2}\pi$	$\frac{2}{3}\pi$	$\frac{3}{4}\pi$	$\frac{5}{6}\pi$	π

The angles used most frequently in simple practice problems are those of a 30–60–90-degree triangle and those of a 45–45–90-degree triangle because at these angles we can evaluate the trigonometric functions without having to consult a table.

PROBLEM. Find $\sec \frac{1}{6}\pi$. (That is, find the secant of an angle of $\frac{1}{6}\pi$ radians.)

Solution. Since

$$\frac{1}{6}\pi \text{ radians} = 30 \text{ degrees},$$

we can use a 30–60–90-degree triangle:

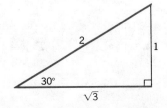

$$\sec \frac{1}{6}\pi = \frac{\text{hypotenuse}}{\text{adjacent}} = \frac{2}{\sqrt{3}}. \quad \square$$

PROBLEM.   A 12-inch arc on a circle is subtended by a central angle of 40°. What is the radius of the circle?

Solution.   Let r be the radius of the circle measured in inches. The radian measure of the 40° angle is $12/r$. Thus

$$\frac{40}{360} = \frac{12/r}{2\pi}.$$

Solving this equation for r, we find that the radius measures $54/\pi$ inches.   □

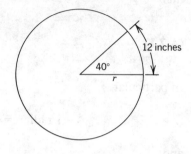

EXERCISES

Convert to radian measure.

1. 30°.   2. 135°.   3. 270°.   4. 120°.
5. 10°.   6. 210°.   7. 225°.   8. 300°.

Convert to degree measure.

9. $\frac{1}{4}\pi$.   10. $\frac{7}{4}\pi$.   11. $\frac{7}{12}\pi$.   12. $\frac{2}{3}\pi$.
13. $\frac{1}{3}\pi$.   14. $\frac{11}{6}\pi$.   15. $\frac{5}{6}\pi$.   16. $\frac{1}{12}\pi$.

17. A wheel makes 15 complete revolutions in one minute.
   (a) Through how many degrees does the wheel turn in one second?
   (b) Through how many radians does the wheel turn in 20 seconds?

18. A wheel with spokes 10 centimeters long rolls along the ground, the spokes spinning at a rate of 120° per second.
   (a) Through how many radians does the wheel turn in one minute?
   (b) How far does the wheel roll in one minute?

19. How many radians are there in a central angle that subtends an arc of 30 centimeters on a circle of radius one meter?

20. How many radians are there in a central angle that subtends a one foot arc on a circle of radius 5 inches?

21. An arc of a circle of radius 10 inches is subtended by a central angle of $\frac{1}{7}\pi$ radians. What is the length of the arc in inches?

22. An arc of a circle of radius 8 centimeters is subtended by a central angle of 60°. What is the length of the arc in centimeters?

23. A 10-inch arc on a circle is subtended by a central angle of $\frac{1}{3}\pi$ radians. What is the radius of the circle in inches?

Evaluate.

24. $\sin \frac{1}{4}\pi$ 25. $\cos \frac{1}{4}\pi$.   26. $\tan \frac{1}{6}\pi$.   27. $\csc \frac{1}{3}\pi$.
28. $\sec \frac{1}{6}\pi$.   29. $\sin \frac{1}{6}\pi$.   30. $\csc \frac{1}{4}\pi$.   31. $\tan \frac{1}{4}\pi$.
32. $\cos \frac{1}{4}\pi$.   33. $\sec \frac{1}{4}\pi$.   34. $\cos \frac{1}{3}\pi$.   35. $\cot \frac{1}{3}\pi$.

A.3 ······INDUCTION

Suppose that you were asked to show that a certain set S contains the set of positive integers. You could start by verifying that $1 \in S$, and $2 \in S$, and $3 \in S$, and so on, but even if each such step took you only one-hundredth of a second, you would still never finish.

To avoid such a bind, mathematicians use a special procedure called *induction*. That induction works is an *assumption* that we make.

AXIOM A.3.1   AXIOM OF INDUCTION

Let S be a set of integers.   If

      (A) $1 \in S$ and   (B) $k \in S$ implies $k + 1 \in S$,

then all the positive integers are in S.

You can think of the axiom of induction as a kind of "domino theory." If the first domino falls (Figure A.3.1), and if each domino that falls causes the next one to fall, then, according to the axiom of induction, all the dominoes will fall.

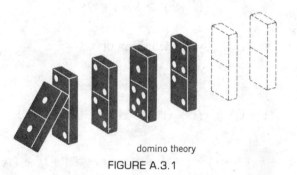

domino theory

FIGURE A.3.1

While we cannot prove that this axiom is valid (axioms are by their very nature assumptions and therefore not subject to proof), we can argue that it is *plausible*.

Let's assume that we have a set S that satisfies conditions (A) and (B). Now let's choose a positive integer m and "argue" that $m \in S$.

From (A) we know that $1 \in S$. Since $1 \in S$, we know from (B) that $1 + 1 \in S$, and thus that $(1 + 1) + 1 \in S$, and so on. Since m can be obtained from 1 by adding 1 successively $(m - 1)$ times, it *seems clear* that $m \in S$.   □

As an example of this procedure, note that

$$5 = \{[(1 + 1) + 1] + 1\} + 1$$

and thus $5 \in S$.

PROBLEM. Show that

      if $0 \le a < b$ then $a^n < b^n$ for all positive integers n.

Solution. Suppose that $0 \leq a < b$, and let S be the set of positive integers n for which $a^n < b^n$.

Obviously, $1 \in S$. Let's assume now that $k \in S$. This assures us that $a^k < b^k$. It follows that

$$a^{k+1} = a \cdot a^k < a \cdot b^k < b \cdot b^k = b^{k+1}$$

and thus that $k + 1 \in S$.

We have shown that

$$1 \in S \quad \text{and that} \quad k \in S \text{ implies } k + 1 \in S.$$

By the axiom of induction, we can conclude that all the positive integers are in S. □

PROBLEM. Show that, if $x \geq -1$, then

$$(1 + x)^n \geq 1 + nx \quad \text{for all positive integers } n.$$

Solution. Take $x \geq -1$ and let S be the set of positive integers n for which

$$(1 + x)^n \geq 1 + nx.$$

Since

$$(1 + x)^1 \geq 1 + 1 \cdot x,$$

you can see that $1 \in S$.

Assume now that $k \in S$. By the definition of S,

$$(1 + x)^k \geq 1 + kx.$$

Since

$$(1 + x)^{k+1} = (1 + x)^k (1 + x) \geq (1 + kx)(1 + x) \qquad \text{(explain)}$$

and

$$(1 + kx)(1 + x) = 1 + (k + 1)x + kx^2 \geq 1 + (k + 1)x,$$

it follows that

$$(1 + x)^{k+1} \geq 1 + (k + 1)x$$

and thus that $k + 1 \in S$.

We have shown that

$$1 \in S \quad \text{and that} \quad k \in S \text{ implies } k + 1 \in S.$$

By the axiom of induction, all the positive integers are in S. □

EXERCISES

For Exercises 1–12, show that the statement holds for all positive integers n.

1. $2n \leq 2^n$.   **2.** $1 + 2n \leq 3^n$.

3. $n(n + 1)$ is divisible by 2.   [HINT: $(k + 1)(k + 2) = k(k + 1) + 2(k + 1)$.]

4. $n(n + 1)(n + 2)$ is divisible by 6.

5. $1 + 2 + 3 + \cdots + n = \frac{1}{2}n(n + 1).$

6. $1 + 3 + 5 + \cdots + (2n - 1) = n^2.$

7. $1^2 + 2^2 + 3^2 + \cdots + n^2 = \frac{1}{6}n(n + 1)(2n + 1).$

8. $1^3 + 2^3 + 3^3 + \cdots + n^3 = (1 + 2 + 3 + \cdots + n)^2.$ [HINT: Use Exercise 5.]

9. $1^3 + 2^3 + \cdots + (n - 1)^3 < \frac{1}{4}n^4 < 1^3 + 2^3 + \cdots + n^3.$

10. $1^2 + 2^2 + \cdots + (n - 1)^2 < \frac{1}{3}n^3 < 1^2 + 2^2 + \cdots + n^2.$

11. $\dfrac{1}{\sqrt{1}} + \dfrac{1}{\sqrt{2}} + \dfrac{1}{\sqrt{3}} + \cdots + \dfrac{1}{\sqrt{n}} > \sqrt{n}.$

12. $\dfrac{1}{1 \cdot 2} + \dfrac{1}{2 \cdot 3} + \dfrac{1}{3 \cdot 4} + \cdots + \dfrac{1}{n(n + 1)} = \dfrac{n}{n + 1}$

13. For what integers n is $3^{2n+1} + 2^{n+2}$ divisible by 7? Prove that your answer is correct.

14. For what integers n is $9^n - 8n - 1$ divisible by 64? Prove that your answer is correct.

15. Find a simplifying expression for the product

$$\left(1 - \frac{1}{2}\right)\left(1 - \frac{1}{3}\right) \cdots \left(1 - \frac{1}{n}\right)$$

and verify its validity for all integers $n \geq 2$.

16. Find a simplifying expression for the product

$$\left(1 - \frac{1}{2^2}\right)\left(1 - \frac{1}{3^2}\right) \cdots \left(1 - \frac{1}{n^2}\right)$$

and verify its validity for all integers $n \geq 2$.

17. Prove that an N-sided convex polygon has $\frac{1}{2}N(N - 3)$ diagonals.

18. Prove that the sum of the angles in an N-sided convex polygon is $(N - 2)180°$.

19. Prove that all sets with n elements have 2^n subsets. Count the empty set $\varnothing$ as a subset.

A.4 ·······COMPLEX NUMBERS

While there are real numbers x with the property that

$$x^2 = 1,$$

there are no real numbers x such that

$$x^2 = -1.$$

More generally, while a quadratic

$$ax^2 + bx + c = 0$$

has real roots if $b^2 - 4ac \geq 0$, it has no real roots if $b^2 - 4ac < 0$. We can overcome this deficiency by using *complex numbers*.

Just as the real numbers can be thought of as points of the number line, the *complex numbers* can be thought of as points of the coordinate plane (see Figure A.4.1). For x-axis, write *real axis*. For y-axis, write *imaginary axis*. For the point (a, b), write $a + bi$.

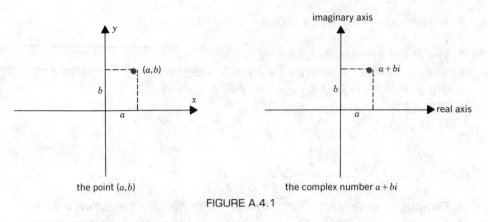

FIGURE A.4.1

If $b = 0$, then $a + bi$ reduces to $a + 0i$, which we write simply as a. In this sense the set of real numbers forms a subset of the set of complex numbers:

$$\text{if } x \text{ is real,} \quad \text{then } x = x + 0i.$$

If $a = 0$, then $a + bi$ reduces to $0 + bi$, which we write simply as bi. Complex numbers of the form bi are called *purely imaginary*.

A complex number $a + bi$ is said to have two parts: a *real part a* and a *purely imaginary part b*.

Some complex numbers are plotted in Figure A.4.2.

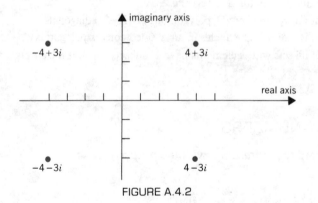

FIGURE A.4.2

To add or subtract complex numbers, we add the real and imaginary parts separately:

(A.4.1)
$$(a + bi) + (c + di) = (a + c) + (b + d)\,i,$$
$$(a + bi) - (c + di) = (a - c) + (b - d)\,i.$$

Thus, for example,

$$(2 + 3i) + (6 - 5i) = 8 - 2i,$$
$$(2 + 3i) - (6 - 5i) = -4 + 8i,$$
$$(2 + 3i) - (2 + 3i) = 0 + 0i = 0.$$

Multiplication is defined by setting

(A.4.2) $(a + bi)(c + di) = (ac - bd) + (ad + bc)\, i.$

Here are some routine multiplications carried out:

$$(2 + 3i)(6 + 5i) = [(2)(6) - (3)(5)] + [(2)(5) + (3)(6)]\, i$$
$$= -3 + 28\, i.$$
$$(2 + 3i)(6 - 5i) = [(2)(6) - (3)(-5)] + [(2)(-5) + (3)(6)]\, i$$
$$= 27 + 8\, i.$$
$$(2 - 3i)(6 - 5i) = [(2)(6) - (-3)(-5)] + [(2)(-5) + (-3)(6)]\, i$$
$$= -3 - 28\, i.$$

The special merit of multiplication according to the rule

$$(a + bi)(c + di) = (ac - bd) + (ad + bc)\, i$$

is that it gives us a square root of -1. In fact, it gives us two of them: $\pm i$.

(A.4.3) $i^2 = -1 \quad \text{and} \quad (-i)^2 = -1.$

Not only can we take the square root of -1, but we can take the square root of any negative number $-p$.

(A.4.4)   If $p > 0$, the equation $x^2 = -p$ has two purely imaginary roots
$$x = \pm \sqrt{p}\, i.$$

We leave it to you to verify this.

With complex numbers at our disposal, we can take the square root of every real number — positive, zero, or negative. We can therefore apply the general quadratic formula

$$x = \frac{-b \pm \sqrt{b^2 - 4ac}}{2a}$$

to all quadratic equations

$$ax^2 + bx + c = 0, \qquad a \neq 0.$$

We have solved equations with $b^2 - 4ac \geq 0$ before. Here we solve some where $b^2 - 4ac < 0$.

PROBLEM. Solve the equation

$$x^2 + x + 1 = 0.$$

Solution. According to the general quadratic formula,

$$x = \frac{-1 \pm \sqrt{1 - 4}}{2} = -\tfrac{1}{2} \pm \tfrac{1}{2}\sqrt{-3} = -\tfrac{1}{2} \pm \tfrac{1}{2}\sqrt{3}\, i. \quad \square$$

PROBLEM.   Solve the equation

$$2x^2 + 3x + 7 = 0.$$

Solution.   The general formula gives

$$x = \frac{-3 \pm \sqrt{9 - 56}}{4} = -\tfrac{3}{4} \pm \tfrac{1}{4}\sqrt{-47} = -\tfrac{3}{4} \pm \tfrac{1}{4}\sqrt{47}\ i. \quad \square$$

EXERCISES

1. Plot these complex numbers:
   (a) $1 + 2i$.   (b) $1 - 2i$.   (c) $-1 + 2i$.   (d) $-1 - 2i$.
   (e) $3i$.   (f) $-3i$.   (g) 1.   (h) -1.

Calculate:

2. $(5 + i) + (3 - 2i)$.   **3.** $(5 + i) - (3 - 2i)$.

4. $(6 - 4i) - (5 - 3i) + i$.   **5.** $(6 - 4i) + (5 - 3i) - i$.

6. $(5 + i)(3 - 2i)$.   **7.** $(5 + i)(3 + 2i)$.

8. $(6 - 4i)(5 - 3i)$.   **9.** $(6 - 4i)(-5 - 3i)$.

10. $i(5 + i)$.   **11.** $i(5 - i)$.

12. i^3.   **13.** i^4.

14. $(1 + i)^3$.   **15.** $(1 - i)^3$.

16. $(\tfrac{1}{2}\sqrt{2} + \tfrac{1}{2}\sqrt{2}\ i)^2$.   **17.** $(\tfrac{1}{2}\sqrt{2} + \tfrac{1}{2}\sqrt{2}\ i)^4$.

Solve the following quadratic equations:

18. $x^2 + 9 = 0$.   **19.** $x^2 + 2x + 9 = 0$.   **20.** $3x^2 + 2x + 1 = 0$.

21. $3x^2 + 2x + 10 = 0$.   **22.** $2x^2 + 2x + 1 = 0$.   **23.** $5x^2 - x + 7 = 0$.

24. Show that the addition of complex numbers is commutative:

$$(a + bi) + (c + di) = (c + di) + (a + bi).$$

25. Show that the multiplication of complex numbers is commutative:

$$(a + bi)(c + di) = (c + di)(a + bi).$$

26. Interpret the addition of complex numbers geometrically.

[The remaining exercises should be done in sequence.]

27. The *absolute value* of a complex number $z = a + bi$ is defined by setting

(A.4.5) $$|z| = \sqrt{a^2 + b^2}.$$

   (a) Interpret $|z|$ geometrically.
   (b) Show that the absolute value of the product of two complex numbers is the product of their absolute values:

(A.4.6) $$|z_1 z_2| = |z_1||z_2|.$$

   [HINT: Set $z_1 = a + bi$, $z_2 = c + di$ and carry out the calculations.]

28. The *complex conjugate* $\bar{z}$ of a complex number $z = a + bi$ is defined by setting

$$\bar{z} = a - bi.$$

(a) Draw a figure giving the relative positions of z and $\bar{z}$.
(b) Show that

(A.4.7)
$$\boxed{|\bar{z}| = |z| \quad \text{and} \quad z\bar{z} = |z|^2.}$$

29. Show that if $z \neq 0$, then

$$z w_1 = z w_2 \quad \text{implies} \quad w_1 = w_2.$$

(It follows that there can be at most one complex number w for which $zw = 1$.)

30. For $z \neq 0$, we define the reciprocal $1/z$ by setting

$$\frac{1}{z} = \frac{\bar{z}}{|z|^2}.$$

Show that

$$z \cdot \frac{1}{z} = 1.$$

Calculate the following reciprocals.

31. $\dfrac{1}{i}$.   **32.** $\dfrac{1}{1 + i}$.   **33.** $\dfrac{1}{1 - i}$.   **34.** $\dfrac{1}{2 + 3i}$.

We define the quotient z_1/z_2 for $z_2 \neq 0$ by setting

$$\frac{z_1}{z_2} = z_1 \cdot \frac{1}{z_2}.$$

It follows from Exercise 29 that

$$\frac{z_1}{z_2} \cdot z_2 = z_1.$$

Calculate the following quotients.

35. $\dfrac{i}{3 - 5i}$.   **36.** $\dfrac{3 + 2i}{2 + i}$.   **37.** $\dfrac{2 + 5i}{5 - 2i}$.   **38.** $\dfrac{6 - 7i}{4 + 5i}$.

Some Additional Proofs

In this appendix we present some proofs that many would consider too advanced for the main body of the text. Some details are omitted. These are left to you.

The arguments presented in Sections B.1, B.2, and B.4 require some familiarity with the *least upper bound axiom*. This is discussed in Section 11.8. In addition, Section B.4 requires some understanding of *sequences*, for which we refer you to Sections 12.1 and 12.2.

B.1 ······ THE INTERMEDIATE-VALUE THEOREM

> **LEMMA B.1.1**
>
> Let f be continuous on $[a, b]$. If $f(a) < 0 < f(b)$ or $f(b) < 0 < f(a)$, then there is a number c between a and b such that $f(c) = 0$.

Proof. Suppose that $f(a) < 0 < f(b)$. (The other case can be treated in a similar manner.) Since $f(a) < 0$, we know from the continuity of f that there exists a number ξ such that f is negative on $[a, \xi)$. Let

$$c = \text{lub } \{\xi: f \text{ is negative on } [a, \xi)\}.$$

Clearly, $c \leq b$. We cannot have $f(c) > 0$, for then f would be positive on some interval extending to the left of c, and we know that, to the left of c, f is negative. Incidentally this argument excludes the possibility $c = b$ and means that $c < b$. We cannot have $f(c) < 0$, for then there would be an interval $[a, t)$, with $t > c$, on which f is negative, and this would contradict the definition of c. It follows that $f(c) = 0$. ☐

THEOREM B.1.2   THE INTERMEDIATE-VALUE THEOREM

If f is continuous on $[a, b]$ and C is a number between $f(a)$ and $f(b)$, then there is at least one number c between a and b for which $f(c) = C$.

Proof. Suppose for example that

$$f(a) < C < f(b).$$

(The other possibility can be handled in a similar manner.)   The function

$$g(x) = f(x) - C$$

is continuous on $[a, b]$.   Since

$$g(a) = f(a) - C < 0 \quad \text{and} \quad g(b) = f(b) - C > 0,$$

we know from the lemma that there is a number c between a and b such that $g(c) = 0$. Obviously, then, $f(c) = C$. ☐

B.2 ······THE MAXIMUM-MINIMUM THEOREM

LEMMA B.2.1

If f is continuous on $[a, b]$, then f is bounded on $[a, b]$.

Proof. Consider

$$\{x: x \in [a, b] \text{ and } f \text{ is bounded on } [a, x]\}.$$

It is easy to see that this set is nonempty and bounded above by b. Thus we can set

$$c = \text{lub } \{x: f \text{ is bounded on } [a, x]\}.$$

Now we argue that $c = b$. To do so, we suppose that $c < b$. From the continuity of f at c, it is easy to see that f is bounded on $[c - \epsilon, c + \epsilon]$ for some $\epsilon > 0$. Being bounded on $[a, c - \epsilon]$ and on $[c - \epsilon, c + \epsilon]$, it is obviously bounded on $[a, c + \epsilon]$. This contradicts our choice of c. We can therefore conclude that $c = b$. This tells us that f is bounded on $[a, x]$ for all $x < b$. We are now almost through. From the continuity of f, we know that f is bounded on some interval of the form $[b - \epsilon, b]$. Since $b - \epsilon < b$, we know from what we have just proved that f is bounded on $[a, b - \epsilon]$. Being bounded on $[a, b - \epsilon]$ and $[b - \epsilon, b]$, it is bounded on $[a, b]$. ☐

THEOREM B.2.2   THE MAXIMUM-MINIMUM THEOREM

If f is continuous on $[a, b]$, then f takes on both a maximum value M and a minimum value m on $[a, b]$.

Proof.   By the lemma, f is bounded on $[a, b]$.   Set

$$M = \text{lub } \{f(x): \ x \in [a, b]\}.$$

We must show that there exists c in $[a, b]$ such that $f(c) = M$.   To do this, we set

$$g(x) = \frac{1}{M - f(x)}.$$

If f does not take on the value M, then g is continuous on $[a, b]$ and thus, by the lemma, bounded on $[a, b]$.   A look at the definition of g makes it clear that g cannot be bounded on $[a, b]$.   The assumption that f does not take on the value M has led to a contradiction.   (That f takes on a minimum value m can be proved in a similar manner.) $\square$

B.3 ······INVERSES

THEOREM B.3.1   CONTINUITY OF THE INVERSE

Let f be a one-to-one function defined on an interval (a, b).   If f is continuous, then its inverse f^{-1} is also continuous.

Proof.   If f is continuous, then, being one-to-one, f either increases throughout (a, b) or it decreases throughout (a, b).   The proof of this assertion we leave to you.

Let's suppose now that f increases throughout (a, b).   Let's take c in the domain of f^{-1} and show that f^{-1} is continuous at c.

We first observe that $f^{-1}(c)$ lies in (a, b) and choose $\epsilon > 0$ sufficiently small so that $f^{-1}(c) - \epsilon$ and $f^{-1}(c) + \epsilon$ also lie in (a, b).   We seek $\delta > 0$ such that

$$\text{if} \quad c - \delta < x < c + \delta \quad \text{then} \quad f^{-1}(c) - \epsilon < f^{-1}(x) < f^{-1}(c) + \epsilon.$$

This condition can be met by choosing δ to satisfy

$$f(f^{-1}(c) - \epsilon) < c - \delta \quad \text{and} \quad c + \delta < f(f^{-1}(c) + \epsilon)$$

for then, if $c - \delta < x < c + \delta$, then

$$f(f^{-1}(c) - \epsilon) < x < f(f^{-1}(c) + \epsilon)$$

and, since f^{-1} also increases,

$$f^{-1}(c) - \epsilon < f^{-1}(x) < f^{-1}(c) + \epsilon.$$

The case where f decreases throughout (a, b) can be handled in a similar manner. $\square$

THEOREM B.3.2   DIFFERENTIABILITY OF THE INVERSE

Let f be a one-to-one function defined on an interval (a, b). If f is differentiable and its derivative does not take on the value 0, then f^{-1} is differentiable and

$$(f^{-1})'(x) = \frac{1}{f'(f^{-1}(x))}.$$

Proof.   Let x be in the domain of f^{-1}. We take $\epsilon > 0$ and show that there exists $\delta > 0$ such that

$$\text{if }\ 0 < |t - x| < \delta \quad \text{then} \quad \left| \frac{f^{-1}(t) - f^{-1}(x)}{t - x} - \frac{1}{f'(f^{-1}(x))} \right| < \epsilon.$$

Since f is differentiable at $f^{-1}(x)$ and $f'(f^{-1}(x)) \neq 0$, there exists $\delta_1 > 0$ such that, if

$$0 < |y - f^{-1}(x)| < \delta_1,$$

then

$$\left| \frac{1}{\frac{f(y) - f(f^{-1}(x))}{y - f^{-1}(x)}} - \frac{1}{f'(f^{-1}(x))} \right| < \epsilon$$

and therefore

$$\left| \frac{y - f^{-1}(x)}{f(y) - f(f^{-1}(x))} - \frac{1}{f'(f^{-1}(x))} \right| < \epsilon.$$

By the previous theorem, f^{-1} is continuous at x and therefore there exists $\delta > 0$ such that

$$\text{if }\ 0 < |t - x| < \delta \quad \text{then} \quad 0 < |f^{-1}(t) - f^{-1}(x)| < \delta_1.$$

It follows from the special property of δ_1 that

$$\left| \frac{f^{-1}(t) - f^{-1}(x)}{t - x} - \frac{1}{f'(f^{-1}(x))} \right| < \epsilon. \quad \square$$

B.4 ······THE INTEGRABILITY OF CONTINUOUS FUNCTIONS

The aim here is to prove that, if f is continuous on $[a, b]$, then there is one and only one number I that satisfies the inequality

$$L_f(P) \leq I \leq U_f(P) \qquad \text{for all partitions } P \text{ of } [a, b].$$

DEFINITION B.4.1

A function f is said to be *uniformly continuous* on $[a, b]$ iff for each $\epsilon > 0$ there exists $\delta > 0$ such that,

$$\text{if}\quad x, y \in [a, b]\quad \text{and}\quad |x - y| < \delta, \qquad \text{then}\quad |f(x) - f(y)| < \epsilon.$$

For convenience, let's agree to say that *the interval* $[a, b]$ *has the property* P_ϵ iff there exist sequences $\{x_n\}$, $\{y_n\}$ satisfying

$$x_n, y_n \in [a, b], \qquad |x_n - y_n| < 1/n, \qquad |f(x_n) - f(y_n)| \geq \epsilon.$$

LEMMA B.4.2

If f is not uniformly continuous on $[a, b]$, then $[a, b]$ has the property P_ϵ for some $\epsilon > 0$.

The proof is easy.

LEMMA B.4.3

Let f be continuous on $[a, b]$. If $[a, b]$ has the property P_ϵ, then at least one of the subintervals $[a, \frac{1}{2}(a + b)]$, $[\frac{1}{2}(a + b), b]$ has the property P_ϵ.

Proof.　Let's suppose that the lemma is false. For convenience, we let

$$c = \tfrac{1}{2}(a + b),$$

so that the halves become $[a, c]$ and $[c, b]$. Since $[a, c]$ fails to have the property P_ϵ, there exists an integer p such that,

$$\text{if}\quad x, y \in [a, c]\quad \text{and}\quad |x - y| < 1/p, \qquad \text{then}\quad |f(x) - f(y)| < \epsilon.$$

Since $[c, b]$ fails to have the property P_ϵ, there exists an integer q such that,

$$\text{if}\quad x, y \in [c, b]\quad \text{and}\quad |x - y| < 1/q, \qquad \text{then}\quad |f(x) - f(y)| < \epsilon.$$

Since f is continuous at c, there exists an integer r such that, if $|x - c| < 1/r$, then $|f(x) - f(c)| < \frac{1}{2}\epsilon$. Set $s = \max\{p, q, r\}$ and suppose that

$$x, y \in [a, b], \qquad |x - y| < 1/s.$$

If x, y are both in $[a, c]$ or both in $[c, b]$, then

$$|f(x) - f(y)| < \epsilon.$$

The only other possibility is that $x \in [a, c]$ and $y \in [c, b]$. In this case we have

$$|x - c| < 1/r, \qquad |y - c| < 1/r,$$

and thus

$$|f(x) - f(c)| < \tfrac{1}{2}\epsilon, \qquad |f(y) - f(c)| < \tfrac{1}{2}\epsilon.$$

By the triangle inequality, we again have

$$|f(x) - f(y)| < \epsilon.$$

In summary, we have obtained the existence of an integer s with the property that

$$x, y \in [a, b], \quad |x - y| < 1/s \qquad \text{implies} \qquad |f(x) - f(y)| < \epsilon.$$

Hence $[a, b]$ does not have the property P_ϵ. This is a contradiction and proves the lemma. □

THEOREM B.4.4

If f is continuous on $[a, b]$, then f is uniformly continuous on $[a, b]$.

Proof. We suppose that f is not uniformly continuous on $[a, b]$ and base our argument on a mathematical version of the classical maxim "Divide and Conquer."

By the first lemma of this section, we know that $[a, b]$ has the property P_ϵ for some $\epsilon > 0$. We bisect $[a, b]$ and note by the second lemma that one of the halves, say $[a_1, b_1]$, has the property P_ϵ. We then bisect $[a_1, b_1]$ and note that one of the halves, say $[a_2, b_2]$, has the property P_ϵ. Continuing in this manner, we obtain a sequence of intervals $[a_n, b_n]$, each with the property P_ϵ. Then for each n, we can choose $x_n, y_n \in [a_n, b_n]$ such that

$$|x_n - y_n| < 1/n \qquad \text{and} \qquad |f(x_n) - f(y_n)| \geq \epsilon.$$

Since

$$a \leq a_n \leq a_{n+1} < b_{n+1} \leq b_n \leq b,$$

we see that the sequences $\{a_n\}$ and $\{b_n\}$ are both bounded and monotonic. Thus they are convergent. Since $b_n - a_n \to 0$, we see that $\{a_n\}$ and $\{b_n\}$ both converge to the same limit, say l. From the inequality

$$a_n \leq x_n \leq y_n \leq b_n,$$

we conclude that

$$x_n \to l \quad \text{and} \quad y_n \to l.$$

This tells us that

$$|f(x_n) - f(y_n)| \to |f(l) - f(l)| = 0,$$

which contradicts the statement that $|f(x_n) - f(y_n)| \geq \epsilon$ for all n. □

LEMMA B.4.5

If P and Q are partitions of $[a, b]$, then $L_f(P) \leq U_f(Q)$.

Proof. $P \cup Q$ is a partition of $[a, b]$ that contains both P and Q. It's obvious then that

$$L_f(P) \leq L_f(P \cup Q) \leq U_f(P \cup Q) \leq U_f(Q). \quad \square$$

From the last lemma it follows that the set of all lower sums is bounded above and has a least upper bound L. The number L satisfies the inequality

$$L_f(P) \leq L \leq U_f(P) \qquad \text{for all partitions } P$$

and is clearly the least of such numbers. Similarly, we find that the set of all upper sums is bounded below and has a greatest lower bound U. The number U satisfies the inequality

$$L_f(P) \leq U \leq U_f(P) \qquad \text{for all partitions } P$$

and is clearly the greatest of such numbers.

We are now ready to prove the basic theorem.

THEOREM B.4.6   THE INTEGRABILITY THEOREM

If f is continuous on $[a, b]$, then there exists one and only one number I that satisfies the inequality

$$L_f(P) \leq I \leq U_f(P) \qquad \text{for all partitions } P \text{ of } [a, b].$$

Proof. We know that

$$L_f(P) \leq L \leq U \leq U_f(P) \qquad \text{for all } P,$$

so that existence is no problem. We will have uniqueness if we can prove that

$$L = U.$$

To do this, we let $\epsilon > 0$ and note that f, being continuous on $[a, b]$, is uniformly continuous on $[a, b]$. Thus there exists $\delta > 0$ such that, if

$$x, y \in [a, b] \quad \text{and} \quad |x - y| < \delta, \qquad \text{then} \quad |f(x) - f(y)| < \frac{\epsilon}{b - a}.$$

We now choose a partition $P = \{x_0, x_1, \ldots, x_n\}$ for which $\max \Delta x_i < \delta$. For this partition P, we have

$$\begin{aligned}
U_f(P) - L_f(P) &= \sum_{i=1}^{n} M_i \, \Delta x_i - \sum_{i=1}^{n} m_i \, \Delta x_i \\
&= \sum_{i=1}^{n} (M_i - m_i) \, \Delta x_i \\
&< \sum_{i=1}^{n} \frac{\epsilon}{b - a} \Delta x_i \\
&= \frac{\epsilon}{b - a} \sum_{i=1}^{n} \Delta x_i = \frac{\epsilon}{b - a} (b - a) = \epsilon.
\end{aligned}$$

Since

$$U_f(P) - L_f(P) < \epsilon \qquad \text{and} \qquad 0 \le U - L \le U_f(P) - L_f(P),$$

you can see that

$$0 \le U - L < \epsilon.$$

Since ϵ was chosen arbitrarily, we must have $U - L = 0$ and $L = U$. $\square$

B.5 ······THE INTEGRAL AS THE LIMIT OF RIEMANN SUMS

For the notation we refer to Section 5.13.

THEOREM B.5.1

If f is continuous on $[a, b]$, then

$$\int_a^b f(x)\, dx = \lim_{\|P\| \to 0} S^*(P).$$

Proof. Let $\epsilon > 0$. We must show that there exists $\delta > 0$ such that

$$\text{if} \quad \|P\| < \delta \qquad \text{then} \quad \left| S^*(P) - \int_a^b f(x)\, dx \right| < \epsilon.$$

From the proof of Theorem B.4.6 we know that there exists $\delta > 0$ such that

$$\text{if} \quad \|P\| < \delta \qquad \text{then} \quad U_f(P) - L_f(P) < \epsilon.$$

For such P we have

$$U_f(P) - \epsilon < L_f(P) \le S^*(P) \le U_f(P) < L_f(P) + \epsilon.$$

This gives

$$\int_a^b f(x)\, dx - \epsilon < S^*(P) < \int_a^b f(x)\, dx + \epsilon$$

and therefore

$$\left| S^*(P) - \int_a^b f(x)\, dx \right| < \epsilon. \quad \square$$

APPENDIX C
Tables

TABLE 1.
Natural Logs

x	$\ln x$	x	$\ln x$	x	$\ln x$	x	$\ln x$
		3.0	1.099	6.0	1.792	9.0	2.197
0.1	−2.303	3.1	1.131	6.1	1.808	9.1	2.208
0.2	−1.609	3.2	1.163	6.2	1.825	9.2	2.219
0.3	−1.204	3.3	1.194	6.3	1.841	9.3	2.230
0.4	−0.916	3.4	1.224	6.4	1.856	9.4	2.241
0.5	−0.693	3.5	1.253	6.5	1.872	9.5	2.251
0.6	−0.511	3.6	1.281	6.6	1.887	9.6	2.262
0.7	−0.357	3.7	1.308	6.7	1.902	9.7	2.272
0.8	−0.223	3.8	1.335	6.8	1.917	9.8	2.282
0.9	−0.105	3.9	1.361	6.9	1.932	9.9	2.293
1.0	0.000	4.0	1.386	7.0	1.946	10	2.303
1.1	0.095	4.1	1.411	7.1	1.960	20	2.996
1.2	0.182	4.2	1.435	7.2	1.974	30	3.401
1.3	0.262	4.3	1.459	7.3	1.988	40	3.689
1.4	0.336	4.4	1.482	7.4	2.001	50	3.912
1.5	0.405	4.5	1.504	7.5	2.015	60	4.094
1.6	0.470	4.6	1.526	7.6	2.028	70	4.248
1.7	0.531	4.7	1.548	7.7	2.041	80	4.382
1.8	0.588	4.8	1.569	7.8	2.054	90	4.500
1.9	0.642	4.9	1.589	7.9	2.067	100	4.605
2.0	0.693	5.0	1.609	8.0	2.079		
2.1	0.742	5.1	1.629	8.1	2.092		
2.2	0.788	5.2	1.649	8.2	2.104		
2.3	0.833	5.3	1.668	8.3	2.116		
2.4	0.875	5.4	1.686	8.4	2.128		
2.5	0.916	5.5	1.705	8.5	2.140		
2.6	0.956	5.6	1.723	8.6	2.152		
2.7	0.993	5.7	1.740	8.7	2.163		
2.8	1.030	5.8	1.758	8.8	2.175		
2.9	1.065	5.9	1.775	8.9	2.186		

TABLE 2.
Exponentials (0.01 to 0.99)

x	e^x	e^{-x}	x	e^x	e^{-x}	x	e^x	e^{-x}
0.01	1.010	0.990	0.34	1.405	0.712	0.67	1.954	0.512
0.02	1.020	0.980	0.35	1.419	0.705	0.68	1.974	0.507
0.03	1.030	0.970	0.36	1.433	0.698	0.69	1.994	0.502
0.04	1.041	0.961	0.37	1.448	0.691	0.70	2.014	0.497
0.05	1.051	0.951	0.38	1.462	0.684	0.71	2.034	0.492
0.06	1.062	0.942	0.39	1.477	0.677	0.72	2.054	0.487
0.07	1.073	0.932	0.40	1.492	0.670	0.73	2.075	0.482
0.08	1.083	0.923	0.41	1.507	0.664	0.74	2.096	0.477
0.09	1.094	0.914	0.42	1.522	0.657	0.75	2.117	0.472
0.10	1.105	0.905	0.43	1.537	0.651	0.76	2.138	0.468
0.11	1.116	0.896	0.44	1.553	0.644	0.77	2.160	0.463
0.12	1.127	0.887	0.45	1.568	0.638	0.78	2.181	0.458
0.13	1.139	0.878	0.46	1.584	0.631	0.79	2.203	0.454
0.14	1.150	0.869	0.47	1.600	0.625	0.80	2.226	0.449
0.15	1.162	0.861	0.48	1.616	0.619	0.81	2.248	0.445
0.16	1.174	0.852	0.49	1.632	0.613	0.82	2.270	0.440
0.17	1.185	0.844	0.50	1.649	0.607	0.83	2.293	0.436
0.18	1.197	0.835	0.51	1.665	0.600	0.84	2.316	0.432
0.19	1.209	0.827	0.52	1.682	0.595	0.85	2.340	0.427
0.20	1.221	0.819	0.53	1.699	0.589	0.86	2.363	0.423
0.21	1.234	0.811	0.54	1.716	0.583	0.87	2.387	0.419
0.22	1.246	0.803	0.55	1.733	0.577	0.88	2.411	0.415
0.23	1.259	0.795	0.56	1.751	0.571	0.89	2.435	0.411
0.24	1.271	0.787	0.57	1.768	0.566	0.90	2.460	0.407
0.25	1.284	0.779	0.58	1.786	0.560	0.91	2.484	0.403
0.26	1.297	0.771	0.59	1.804	0.554	0.92	2.509	0.399
0.27	1.310	0.763	0.60	1.822	0.549	0.93	2.535	0.395
0.28	1.323	0.756	0.61	1.840	0.543	0.94	2.560	0.391
0.29	1.336	0.748	0.62	1.859	0.538	0.95	2.586	0.387
0.30	1.350	0.741	0.63	1.878	0.533	0.96	2.612	0.383
0.31	1.363	0.733	0.64	1.896	0.527	0.97	2.638	0.379
0.32	1.377	0.726	0.65	1.916	0.522	0.98	2.664	0.375
0.33	1.391	0.719	0.66	1.935	0.517	0.99	2.691	0.372

TABLE 3.
Exponentials (1.0 to 4.9)

x	e^x	e^{-x}	x	e^x	e^{-x}
1.0	2.718	0.368	3.0	20.086	0.050
1.1	3.004	0.333	3.1	22.198	0.045
1.2	3.320	0.301	3.2	24.533	0.041
1.3	3.669	0.273	3.3	27.113	0.037
1.4	4.055	0.247	3.4	29.964	0.033
1.5	4.482	0.223	3.5	33.115	0.030
1.6	4.953	0.202	3.6	·36.598	0.027
1.7	5.474	0.183	3.7	40.447	0.025
1.8	6.050	0.165	3.8	44.701	0.024
1.9	6.686	0.150	3.9	49.402	0.020
2.0	7.389	0.135	4.0	54.598	0.018
2.1	8.166	0.122	4.1	60.340	0.017
2.2	9.025	0.111	4.2	66.686	0.015
2.3	9.974	0.100	4.3	73.700	0.014
2.4	11.023	0.091	4.4	81.451	0.012
2.5	12.182	0.082	4.5	90.017	0.011
2.6	13.464	0.074	4.6	99.484	0.010
2.7	14.880	0.067	4.7	109.947	0.009
2.8	16.445	0.061	4.8	121.510	0.008
2.9	18.174	0.055	4.9	134.290	0.007

TABLE 4.
Sines, Cosines, Tangents (Radian Measure)

x	$\sin x$	$\cos x$	$\tan x$	x	$\sin x$	$\cos x$	$\tan x$
0.00	0.000	1.000	0.000	0.42	0.408	0.913	0.447
0.01	0.010	1.000	0.010	0.43	0.417	0.909	0.459
0.02	0.020	1.000	0.020	0.44	0.426	0.905	0.471
0.03	0.030	1.000	0.030	0.45	0.435	0.900	0.483
0.04	0.040	0.999	0.040	0.46	0.444	0.896	0.495
0.05	0.050	0.999	0.050	0.47	0.453	0.892	0.508
0.06	0.060	0.998	0.060	0.48	0.462	0.887	0.521
0.07	0.070	0.998	0.070	0.49	0.471	0.882	0.533
0.08	0.080	0.997	0.080	0.50	0.479	0.878	0.546
0.09	0.090	0.996	0.090	0.51	0.488	0.873	0.559
0.10	0.100	0.995	0.100	0.52	0.497	0.868	0.573
0.11	0.110	0.994	0.110	0.53	0.506	0.863	0.586
0.12	0.120	0.993	0.121	0.54	0.514	0.858	0.599
0.13	0.130	0.992	0.131	0.55	0.523	0.853	0.613
0.14	0.140	0.990	0.141	0.56	0.531	0.847	0.627
0.15	0.149	0.989	0.151	0.57	0.540	0.842	0.641
0.16	0.159	0.987	0.161	0.58	0.548	0.836	0.655
0.17	0.169	0.986	0.172	0.59	0.556	0.831	0.670
0.18	0.179	0.984	0.182	0.60	0.565	0.825	0.684
0.19	0.189	0.982	0.192	0.61	0.573	0.820	0.699
0.20	0.199	0.980	0.203	0.62	0.581	0.814	0.714
0.21	0.208	0.978	0.213	0.63	0.589	0.808	0.729
0.22	0.218	0.976	0.224	0.64	0.597	0.802	0.745
0.23	0.228	0.974	0.234	0.65	0.605	0.796	0.760
0.24	0.238	0.971	0.245	0.66	0.613	0.790	0.776
0.25	0.247	0.969	0.255	0.67	0.621	0.784	0.792
0.26	0.257	0.966	0.266	0.68	0.629	0.778	0.809
0.27	0.267	0.964	0.277	0.69	0.637	0.771	0.825
0.28	0.276	0.961	0.288	0.70	0.644	0.765	0.842
0.29	0.286	0.958	0.298	0.71	0.652	0.758	0.860
0.30	0.296	0.955	0.309	0.72	0.659	0.752	0.877
0.31	0.305	0.952	0.320	0.73	0.667	0.745	0.895
0.32	0.315	0.949	0.331	0.74	0.674	0.738	0.913
0.33	0.324	0.946	0.343	0.75	0.682	0.732	0.932
0.34	0.333	0.943	0.354	0.76	0.689	0.725	0.950
0.35	0.343	0.939	0.365	0.77	0.696	0.718	0.970
0.36	0.352	0.936	0.376	0.78	0.703	0.711	0.989
0.37	0.362	0.932	0.388	0.79	0.710	0.704	1.009
0.38	0.371	0.929	0.399	0.80	0.717	0.697	1.030
0.39	0.380	0.925	0.411	0.81	0.724	0.689	1.050
0.40	0.389	0.921	0.423	0.82	0.731	0.682	1.072
0.41	0.399	0.917	0.435	0.83	0.738	0.675	1.093

TABLE 4 (continued)

x	$\sin x$	$\cos x$	$\tan x$	x	$\sin x$	$\cos x$	$\tan x$
0.84	0.745	0.667	1.116	1.22	0.939	0.344	2.733
0.85	0.751	0.660	1.138	1.23	0.942	0.334	2.820
0.86	0.758	0.652	1.162	1.24	0.946	0.325	2.912
0.87	0.764	0.645	1.185	1.25	0.949	0.315	3.010
0.88	0.771	0.637	1.210	1.26	0.952	0.306	3.113
0.89	0.777	0.629	1.235	1.27	0.955	0.296	3.224
0.90	0.783	0.622	1.260	1.28	0.958	0.287	3.341
0.91	0.790	0.614	1.286	1.29	0.961	0.277	3.467
0.92	0.796	0.606	1.313	1.30	0.964	0.267	3.602
0.93	0.802	0.598	1.341	1.31	0.966	0.258	3.747
0.94	0.808	0.590	1.369	1.32	0.969	0.248	3.903
0.95	0.813	0.582	1.398	1.33	0.971	0.238	4.072
0.96	0.819	0.574	1.428	1.34	0.973	0.229	4.256
0.97	0.825	0.565	1.459	1.35	0.976	0.219	4.455
0.98	0.830	0.557	1.491	1.36	0.978	0.209	4.673
0.99	0.836	0.549	1.524	1.37	0.980	0.199	4.913
1.00	0.841	0.540	1.557	1.38	0.982	0.190	5.177
1.01	0.847	0.532	1.592	1.39	0.984	0.180	5.471
1.02	0.852	0.523	1.628	1.40	0.985	0.170	5.798
1.03	0.857	0.515	1.665	1.41	0.987	0.160	6.165
1.04	0.862	0.506	1.704	1.42	0.989	0.150	6.581
1.05	0.867	0.498	1.743	1.43	0.990	0.140	7.055
1.06	0.872	0.489	1.784	1.44	0.991	0.130	7.602
1.07	0.877	0.480	1.827	1.45	0.993	0.121	8.238
1.08	0.882	0.471	1.871	1.46	0.994	0.111	8.989
1.09	0.887	0.462	1.917	1.47	0.995	0.101	9.887
1.10	0.891	0.454	1.965	1.48	0.996	0.091	10.983
1.11	0.896	0.445	2.014	1.49	0.997	0.081	12.350
1.12	0.900	0.436	2.066	1.50	0.997	0.071	14.101
1.13	0.904	0.427	2.120	1.51	0.998	0.061	16.428
1.14	0.909	0.418	2.176	1.52	0.999	0.051	19.670
1.15	0.913	0.408	2.234	1.53	0.999	0.041	24.498
1.16	0.917	0.399	2.296	1.54	1.000	0.031	32.461
1.17	0.921	0.390	2.360	1.55	1.000	0.021	48.078
1.18	0.925	0.381	2.427	1.56	1.000	0.011	92.620
1.19	0.928	0.372	2.498	1.57	1.000	0.001	1255.770
1.20	0.932	0.362	2.572	1.58	1.000	-0.009	-108.649
1.21	0.936	0.353	2.650				

TABLE 5.
Sines, Cosines, Tangents (Degree Measure)

x	$\sin x$	$\cos x$	$\tan x$	x	$\sin x$	$\cos x$	$\tan x$
0°	0.00	1.00	0.00	23	0.39	0.92	0.42
1	0.02	1.00	0.02	24	0.41	0.91	0.45
2	0.03	1.00	0.03	25	0.42	0.91	0.47
3	0.05	1.00	0.05	26	0.44	0.90	0.49
4	0.07	1.00	0.07	27	0.45	0.89	0.51
5	0.09	1.00	0.09	28	0.47	0.88	0.53
6	0.10	0.99	0.11	29	0.48	0.87	0.55
7	0.12	0.99	0.12	30	0.50	0.87	0.58
8	0.14	0.99	0.14	31	0.52	0.86	0.60
9	0.16	0.99	0.16	32	0.53	0.85	0.62
10	0.17	0.98	0.18	33	0.54	0.84	0.65
11	0.19	0.98	0.19	34	0.56	0.83	0.67
12	0.21	0.98	0.21	35	0.57	0.82	0.70
13	0.22	0.97	0.23	36	0.59	0.81	0.73
14	0.24	0.97	0.25	37	0.60	0.80	0.75
15	0.26	0.97	0.27	38	0.62	0.79	0.78
16	0.28	0.96	0.29	39	0.63	0.78	0.81
17	0.29	0.96	0.31	40	0.64	0.77	0.84
18	0.31	0.95	0.32	41	0.66	0.75	0.87
19	0.33	0.95	0.34	42	0.67	0.74	0.90
20	0.34	0.94	0.36	43	0.68	0.73	0.93
21	0.36	0.93	0.38	44	0.69	0.72	0.97
22	0.37	0.93	0.40	45	0.71	0.71	1.00

TABLE 5   (continued)

x	$\sin x$	$\cos x$	$\tan x$	x	$\sin x$	$\cos x$	$\tan x$
45°	0.71	0.71	1.00	68	0.93	0.37	2.48
46	0.72	0.69	1.04	69	0.93	0.36	2.61
47	0.73	0.68	1.07	70	0.94	0.34	2.75
48	0.74	0.67	1.11	71	0.95	0.33	2.90
49	0.75	0.66	1.15	72	0.95	0.31	3.08
50	0.77	0.64	1.19	73	0.96	0.29	3.27
51	0.78	0.63	1.23	74	0.96	0.28	3.49
52	0.79	0.62	1.28	75	0.97	0.26	3.73
53	0.80	0.60	1.33	76	0.97	0.24	4.01
54	0.81	0.59	1.38	77	0.97	0.22	4.33
55	0.82	0.57	1.43	78	0.98	0.21	4.70
56	0.83	0.56	1.48	79	0.98	0.19	5.14
57	0.84	0.54	1.54	80	0.98	0.17	5.67
58	0.85	0.53	1.60	81	0.99	0.16	6.31
59	0.86	0.52	1.66	82	0.99	0.14	7.12
60	0.87	0.50	1.73	83	0.99	0.12	8.14
61	0.87	0.48	1.80	84	0.99	0.10	9.51
62	0.88	0.47	1.88	85	1.00	0.09	11.43
63	0.89	0.45	1.96	86	1.00	0.07	14.30
64	0.90	0.44	2.05	87	1.00	0.05	19.08
65	0.91	0.42	2.14	88	1.00	0.03	28.64
66	0.91	0.41	2.25	89	1.00	0.02	57.29
67	0.92	0.39	2.36	90	1.00	0.00	—

Answers to Odd-Numbered Exercises

SECTION 1.3

1. $-\frac{2}{3}$ **3.** 0 **5.** -1 **7.** $-y_0/x_0$

9. slope 2, y-intercept -4 **11.** slope $\frac{1}{3}$, y-intercept 2

13. slope undefined, no y-intercept   **15.** slope $\frac{7}{3}$, y-intercept $\frac{4}{3}$

17. slope 0, y-intercept $\frac{5}{7}$ **19.** $y = 5x + 2$ **21.** $y = -5x + 2$

23. $y = 3$ **25.** $x = -3$ **27.** $y = 7$

29. $3y - 2x - 17 = 0$ **31.** $2y + 3x - 20 = 0$ **33.** $y = -2x + 4$

35. $y - 2 = -2(x - 1)$ **37.** $\dfrac{x}{6} - \dfrac{y}{3} = 1$ **39.** $45°$

41. $90°$ **43.** approx. $153°$ **45.** $y = \frac{1}{3}\sqrt{3}\,x + 2$

47. $y = -\sqrt{3}\,x + 3$ **49.** $(\frac{3}{5}, -\frac{3}{5})$; approx. $23°$ **51.** $(-\frac{2}{23}, \frac{38}{23})$; approx. $17°$

53. $90°$, $45°$, $45°$ **55.** $16° - 17°$, $32° - 33°$, $130° - 131°$

57. (a) $Bx - Ay = 0$ (b) $Q = \left(-\dfrac{AC}{A^2 + B^2}, -\dfrac{BC}{A^2 + B^2} \right)$ (c) $d = \dfrac{|C|}{\sqrt{A^2 + B^2}}$

SECTION 1.4

1. $(-\infty, 1)$ **3.** $(-\infty, -3]$ **5.** $(-\infty, -\frac{1}{5})$

7. $(-1, 1)$ **9.** $(-\infty, 1) \cup (2, \infty)$ **11.** $(0, 1) \cup (2, \infty)$

13. $[0, \infty)$ **15.** $(-\infty, 2 - \sqrt{3}) \cup (2 + \sqrt{3}, \infty)$

17. $(-5 - 2\sqrt{6}, -5 + 2\sqrt{6})$ **19.** $(-\infty, 0) \cup (0, \infty)$ **21.** $(-1, 0) \cup (1, \infty)$

23. $(-\infty, 0] \cup (5, \infty)$ **25.** $(-\infty, -\frac{5}{3}) \cup (5, \infty)$ **27.** $(-3, -1) \cup (3, \infty)$

29. $(0, 2)$ **31.** $(-\infty, -6) \cup (2, \infty)$ **33.** $(-\infty, 0)$

35. $(-2, 0) \cup (2, \infty)$ **37.** $(-3, 1) \cup (3, \infty)$ **39.** $(1, 2) \cup (6, \infty)$

41. $(-\infty, 1) \cup (3, 5)$ **43.** $(-3, 0) \cup (0, 5)$ **45.** $(-\infty, 0) \cup (0, 1) \cup (3, \infty)$

47. (a) $\dfrac{1}{x} < \dfrac{1}{\sqrt{x}} < 1 < \sqrt{x} < x$ (b) $x < \sqrt{x} < 1 < \dfrac{1}{\sqrt{x}} < \dfrac{1}{x}$

49. obvious with hint since $b^2 > 0$ iff $b \neq 0$

51. With $0 \leq a \leq b$

$$a(1 + b) = a + ab \leq b + ab = b(1 + a).$$

Division by $(1 + b)(1 + a)$ gives

$$\frac{a}{1 + a} \leq \frac{b}{1 + b}.$$

SECTION 1.5

1. $(-2, 2)$ **3.** $(-\infty, -3) \cup (3, \infty)$ **5.** $(\frac{3}{2}, \frac{5}{2})$

7. $(-\frac{9}{4}, -\frac{7}{4})$ **9.** $(-1, 0) \cup (0, 1)$ **11.** $(\frac{3}{2}, 2) \cup (2, \frac{5}{2})$

13. $(-5, 3) \cup (3, 11)$ **15.** $(1, 2)$ **17.** $(-\frac{5}{8}, -\frac{3}{8})$

19. $(-\infty, -4) \cup (-1, \infty)$ **21.** $(-\infty, -\frac{8}{5}) \cup (2, \infty)$ **23.** $|x| < 3$

25. $|x - 2| < 5$ **27.** $|x + 2| < 5$ **29.** $A < \frac{3}{2}$

31. $A > 6$

33. $\big\|a| - |b\big\|^2 = (|a| - |b|)^2 = |a|^2 - 2|a||b| + |b|^2$
$$= a^2 - 2|a||b| + b^2 \leq a^2 - 2ab + b^2 = (a - b)^2$$

$\underset{\qquad (ab \leq |ab|)}{\uparrow\rule{2cm}{0.4pt}}$

Thus, $\big\|a| - |b\big\| \leq \sqrt{(a - b)^2} = |a - b|$.

SECTION 1.6

1. $x = 1, 3$ **3.** $x = -2$

5. $x = n\pi,$ n an integer   **7.** $x = n\pi,$ n an integer

9. dom $(f) = (-\infty, \infty)$; ran $(f) = [0, \infty)$

11. dom $(f) = (-\infty, \infty)$; ran $(f) = (-\infty, \infty)$

13. dom $(f) = (-\infty, 0) \cup (0, \infty)$; ran $(f) = (0, \infty)$

15. dom $(f) = (-\infty, 1]$; ran $(f) = [0, \infty)$ **17.** dom $(f) = (-\infty, 1]$; ran $(f) = [-1, \infty)$

19. dom $(f) = (-\infty, 1)$; ran $(f) = (0, \infty)$ **21.** dom $(f) = (-\infty, \infty)$; ran $(f) = [0, 1]$

23. dom $(f) = (-\infty, \infty)$; ran $(f) = [-2, 2]$

25. dom $(f) = \left\{ x : x \neq \dfrac{2n + 1}{2} \pi, n \text{ an integer} \right\}$; ran $(f) = [1, \infty)$

27. horizontal line one unit above the x-axis

29. line through the origin with slope 2

31. line through the origin with slope $\frac{1}{2}$ **33.** line through (0, 2) with slope $\frac{1}{2}$

35. upper semicircle of radius 2 centered at the origin

37. Figure A.1.6.1   **39.** Figure A.1.6.2   **41.** Figure A.1.6.3

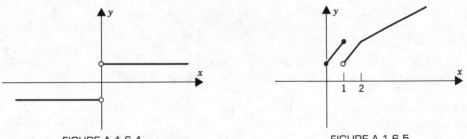

Note: $\sqrt{\sin^2 x} = |\sin x|$

FIGURE A.1.6.1   FIGURE A.1.6.2   FIGURE A.1.6.3

43. dom $(f) = (-\infty, 0) \cup (0, \infty)$; ran $(f) = \{-1, 1\}$; Figure A.1.6.4

45. dom $(f) = [0, \infty)$; ran $(f) = [1, \infty)$; Figure A.1.6.5

FIGURE A.1.6.4   FIGURE A.1.6.5

47. (a) $(6f + 3g)(x) = 9\sqrt{x}, \quad x > 0$ (b) $(fg)(x) = x - 2/x - 1, \quad x > 0$

(c) $(f/g)(x) = \dfrac{x+1}{x-2}, \quad 0 < x < 2 \ \text{ and } \ x > 2$

49. (a) $(f + g)(x) = \begin{cases} 1 - x, & x \le 1 \\ 2x - 1, & 1 < x < 2 \\ 2x - 2, & x \ge 2 \end{cases}$

(b) $(f - g)(x) = \begin{cases} 1 - x. & x \le 1 \\ 2x - 1, & 1 < x < 2 \\ 2x, & x \ge 2 \end{cases}$ (c) $(fg)(x) = \begin{cases} 0, & x < 2 \\ 1 - 2x, & x \ge 2 \end{cases}$

51. Figure A.1.6.6   **53.** Figure A.1.6.7

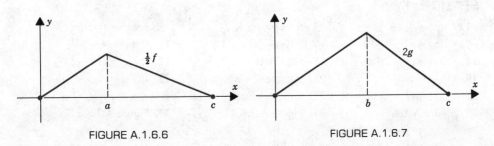

FIGURE A.1.6.6   FIGURE A.1.6.7

55. Figure A.1.6.8   **57.** Figure A.1.6.9

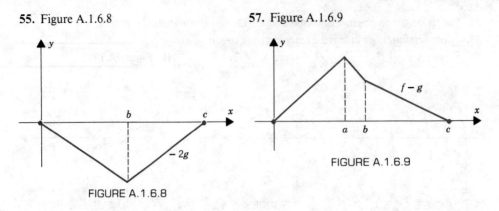

FIGURE A.1.6.8

FIGURE A.1.6.9

59. odd   **61.** neither   **63.** even   **65.** odd
67. even   **69.** even; $(fg)(-x) = f(-x)g(-x) = f(x)g(x) = (fg)(x)$
71. symmetry about the y-axis   **73.** $g(-x) = f(-x) + f(-(-x)) = f(-x) + f(x) = g(x)$

SECTION 1.7

1. $(f \circ g)(x) = 2x^2 + 5$ **3.** $(f \circ g)(x) = \sqrt{x^2 + 5}$
5. $(f \circ g)(x) = x, \quad x \neq 0$ **7.** $(f \circ g)(x) = 1/x - 1$

9. $(f \circ g)(x) = \dfrac{1}{x^2 + 1}$ **11.** $(f \circ g \circ h)(x) = 4(x^2 - 1)$

13. $(f \circ g \circ h)(x) = (x^4 - 1)^2$ **15.** $(f \circ g \circ h)(x) = 2x^2 + 1$

17. $f(x) = \dfrac{1}{x}$ **19.** $f(x) = 2 \sin x$

21. $g(x) = \left(1 - \dfrac{1}{x^4}\right)^{2/3}$ **23.** $g(x) = 2x^3 - 1; \quad g(x) = -(2x^3 - 1)$

25. $(f \circ g)(x) = |x|; \quad (g \circ f)(x) = x, \quad x \geq 0$
27. $(f \circ g)(x) = 2 \sin x; \quad (g \circ f)(x) = \sin 2x$

29. $(f \circ g)(x) = \begin{cases} x^2, & x < 0 \\ 1 + x, & 0 \leq x < 1 \\ (1 + x)^2, & x \geq 1 \end{cases}; \quad (g \circ f)(x) = \begin{cases} 2 - x, & x \leq 0 \\ -x^2, & 0 < x < 1 \\ 1 + x^2, & x \geq 1 \end{cases}$

SECTION 1.8

1. $f^{-1}(x) = \frac{1}{5}(x - 3)$ **3.** $f^{-1}(x) = \frac{1}{4}(x + 7)$ **5.** not one-to-one
7. $f^{-1}(x) = (x - 1)^{1/5}$ **9.** $f^{-1}(x) = [\frac{1}{3}(x - 1)]^{1/3}$ **11.** $f^{-1}(x) = 1 - x^{1/3}$
13. $f^{-1}(x) = (x - 2)^{1/3} - 1$ **15.** $f^{-1}(x) = x^{5/3}$ **17.** $f^{-1}(x) = \frac{1}{3}(2 - x^{1/3})$
19. $f^{-1}(x) = 1/x$ **21.** not one-to-one   **23.** $f^{-1}(x) = (1/x - 1)^{1/3}$
25. $f^{-1}(x) = (2 - x)/(x - 1)$ **27.** they are equal
29. Figure A.1.8.1   **31.** Figure A.1.8.2   **33.** Figure A.1.8.3

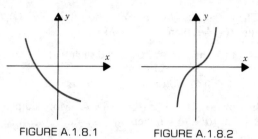

FIGURE A.1.8.1   FIGURE A.1.8.2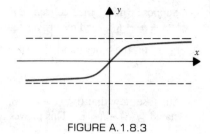

FIGURE A.1.8.3

SECTION 2.1

1. (a) 2   (b) -1 (c) does not exist   (d) -3

3. (a) does not exist   (b) -3 (c) does not exist   (d) -3

5. (a) does not exist   (b) does not exist   (c) does not exist   (d) 1

7. (a) 2   (b) 2   (c) 2   (d) -1

9. (a) -1 (b) -1 (c) -1 (d) undefined

11. (a) 0   (b) 0   (c) 0   (d) 0

13. $c = 0, 6$ **15.** -1 **17.** 4   **19.** 1

21. $\frac{3}{2}$ **23.** does not exist   **25.** 2   **27.** does not exist

29. 1   **31.** does not exist   **33.** 2   **35.** 2

37. does not exist   **39.** 3   **41.** 0   **43.** 2

45. 2   **47.** 0

SECTION 2.2

1. $\frac{1}{2}$ **3.** does not exist   **5.** $\frac{4}{5}\sqrt{5}$ **7.** 4

9. does not exist   **11.** -1 **13.** 1   **15.** 1

17. δ_1 and δ_2 **19.** $\frac{1}{2}\epsilon$ **21.** 2ϵ

23. Take $\delta = \frac{1}{2}\epsilon$. If $0 < |x - 4| < \frac{1}{2}\epsilon$, then $|(2x - 5) - 3| = 2|x - 4| < \epsilon$.

25. Take $\delta = \frac{1}{6}\epsilon$. If $0 < |x - 3| < \frac{1}{6}\epsilon$, then $|(6x - 7) - 11| = 6|x - 3| < \epsilon$.

27. Take $\delta = \frac{1}{3}\epsilon$. If $0 < |x - 2| < \frac{1}{3}\epsilon$, then $\big\|1 - 3x| - 5\big| \le 3|x - 2| < \epsilon$.

29. statements (b), (e), (g), and (i) are necessarily true

31. (i) $\displaystyle\lim_{x \to 3} \frac{1}{x - 1} = \frac{1}{2}$ (ii) $\displaystyle\lim_{x \to 3} \left(\frac{1}{x - 1} - \frac{1}{2} \right) = 0$

(iii) $\displaystyle\lim_{x \to 3} \left| \frac{1}{x - 1} - \frac{1}{2} \right| = 0$ (iv) $\displaystyle\lim_{h \to 0} \frac{1}{(3 + h) - 1} = \frac{1}{2}$

33. Let $\epsilon > 0$. If $\displaystyle\lim_{x \to c} f(x) = l$, then there exists $\delta > 0$ such that

$$\text{if} \quad 0 < |x - c| < \delta \quad \text{then} \quad |f(x) - l| < \epsilon.$$

Since $\big\||f(x)| - |l|\big\| \le |f(x) - l|$, the same number δ will work for the second limit.

35. Let $\epsilon > 0$. If $\displaystyle\lim_{x \to c} f(x) = l$, then there must exist $\delta > 0$ such that

(*) $\text{if} \quad 0 < |x - c| < \delta \quad \text{then} \quad |f(x) - l| < \epsilon.$

Suppose now that $0 < |h| < \delta$. Then $0 < |(c + h) - c| < \delta$, and thus by (*), $|f(c + h) - l| < \epsilon$. This proves that, if $\lim_{x \to c} f(x) = l$, then $\lim_{h \to 0} f(c + h) = l$.

If, on the other hand, $\lim_{h \to 0} f(c + h) = l$, then there must exist $\delta > 0$ such that

(**)   if $0 < |h| < \delta$ then $|f(c + h) - l| < \epsilon$.

Suppose now that $0 < |x - c| < \delta$. Then by (**), $|f(c + (x - c)) - l| < \epsilon$. More simply stated, $|f(x) - l| < \epsilon$. This proves that, if $\lim_{h \to 0} f(c + h) = l$, then $\lim_{x \to c} f(x) = l$.

37. (a) From the hint, for $x > 0$ and $c > 0$,

$$0 \leq |\sqrt{x} - \sqrt{c}| < \frac{1}{\sqrt{c}} |x - c|.$$

Since

$$\lim_{x \to c} 0 = 0 \quad \text{and} \quad \lim_{x \to c} \frac{1}{\sqrt{c}} |x - c| = 0,$$

we know from the pinching theorem that $\lim_{x \to c} |\sqrt{x} - \sqrt{c}| = 0$. It follows from (2.2.5) that

$\lim_{x \to c} \sqrt{x} = \sqrt{c}$.

(b) Take $\delta = $ minimum of ϵ and 1. If $0 < x < \delta$, then $|\sqrt{x} - 0| < x < \epsilon$.

39. Take $\delta = $ minimum of 1 and $\epsilon/7$. If $0 < |x - 1| < \delta$, then

$$|x^3 - 1| = |x - 1||x^2 + x + 1| < 7|x - 1| < 7(\epsilon/7) = \epsilon.$$

41. Take $\delta = $ minimum of ϵ and 1. If $3 - \delta < x < 3$, then $|\sqrt{3 - x} - 0| < |3 - x| < \epsilon$.

43. Suppose, on the contrary, that $\lim_{x \to c} f(x) = l$ for some particular c. Taking $\epsilon = \frac{1}{2}$, there must exist $\delta > 0$ such that,

if $0 < |x - c| < \delta$,   then $|f(x) - l| < \frac{1}{2}$.

Let x_1 be a rational number satisfying $0 < |x_1 - c| < \delta$, and x_2 an irrational number satisfying $0 < |x_2 - c| < \delta$. (That such numbers exist follows from the fact that every interval contains both rational and irrational numbers.) Now $f(x_1) = 1$ and $f(x_2) = 0$. Thus we must have both $|1 - l| < \frac{1}{2}$ and $|0 - l| < \frac{1}{2}$. From the first inequality we conclude that $l > \frac{1}{2}$. From the second, we conclude that $l < \frac{1}{2}$. Clearly no such number l exists.

45. We begin by assuming that $\lim_{x \to c^+} f(x) = l$ and showing that $\lim_{h \to 0} f(c + |h|) = l$. Let $\epsilon > 0$.

Since $\lim_{x \to c^+} f(x) = l$, there exists $\delta > 0$ such that

(*)   if $c < x < c + \delta$ then $|f(x) - l| < \epsilon$.

Suppose now that $0 < |h| < \delta$. Then $c < c + |h| < c + \delta$ and, by (*), $|f(c + |h|) - l| < \epsilon$. Thus $\lim_{h \to 0} f(c + |h|) = l$.

Conversely let's assume that $\lim_{h \to 0} f(c + |h|) = l$ and again take $\epsilon > 0$. Then there exists $\delta > 0$ such that

(**)   if $0 < |h| < \delta$ then $|f(c + |h|) - l| < \epsilon$.

Suppose now that $c < x < c + \delta$. Then $0 < x - c < \delta$ so that, by (**),

$$|f(c + (x - c)) - l| < \epsilon \quad \text{or} \quad |f(x) - l| < \epsilon.$$

Thus $\lim_{x \to c^+} f(x) = l$.

SECTION 2.3

1. (a) 3   (b) 4   (c) -2 (d) 0   (e) does not exist   (f) $\frac{1}{3}$

3. $\lim\limits_{x \to 4} \left[\left(\frac{1}{x} - \frac{1}{4}\right)\left(\frac{1}{x-4}\right)\right] = \lim\limits_{x \to 4} \left[\left(\frac{4-x}{4x}\right)\left(\frac{1}{x-4}\right)\right] = \lim\limits_{x \to 4} \frac{-1}{4x} = -\frac{1}{16};$

Theorem 2.3.2 does not apply since $\lim\limits_{x \to 4} \dfrac{1}{x-4}$ does not exist.

5. 3   7. -3 9. 5   11. 2

13. does not exist   15. $-\frac{23}{20}$ 17. 0   19. -1

21. $\frac{1}{4}$ 23. 0   25. 0   27. does not exist

29. does not exist   31. -1 33. 4   35. a/b

37. $\frac{5}{4}$ 39. does not exist   41. does not exist   43. does not exist

45. (a) 4   (b) -2 (c) 2   (d) does not exist

47. 0   49. 1   51. 0

53. Suppose on the contrary that the limit exists and is some number l: $\lim\limits_{x \to c} f(x) = l$. Since $\lim\limits_{x \to c} g(x) = 0$, we have

$$\lim\limits_{x \to c} [f(x)g(x)] = \left(\lim\limits_{x \to c} f(x)\right)\left(\lim\limits_{x \to c} g(x)\right) = l \cdot 0 = 0.$$

But since $f(x)g(x) = 1$ for all real x, we know that $\lim\limits_{x \to c} [f(x)g(x)] = 1$. This contradicts the uniqueness of limit.

55. set, for instance,

$$f(x) = \begin{cases} 0, & x < c \\ 1, & x > c \end{cases}, \qquad g(x) = \begin{cases} 1, & x < c \\ 0, & x > c \end{cases}$$

57. (a) If $f(x) \geq g(x)$, then

$$\max\{f(x), g(x)\} = f(x)$$

and, since $|f(x) - g(x)| = f(x) - g(x)$,

$$\tfrac{1}{2}\{[f(x) + g(x)] + |f(x) - g(x)|\} = \tfrac{1}{2}\{[f(x) + g(x)] + [f(x) - g(x)]\}$$
$$= \tfrac{1}{2}\{2f(x)\} = f(x).$$

The case $f(x) \leq g(x)$ is similar.

(b) $\min\{f(x), g(x)\} = \tfrac{1}{2}\{[f(x) + g(x)] - |f(x) - g(x)|\}$

59. Let $\epsilon = l > 0$. Since $\lim\limits_{x \to c} f(x) = l$, there exists $\delta > 0$ such that

$$\text{if} \quad 0 < |x - c| < \delta \qquad \text{then} \quad |f(x) - l| < l.$$

Thus $-l < f(x) - l < l$, so that $f(x) > 0$ on $(c - \delta, c) \cup (c, c + \delta)$.

61. Let $p > 0$. Suppose that, for all x such that $c < x < c + p$,

$$h(x) \leq f(x) \leq g(x).$$

If $\lim\limits_{x \to c^+} h(x) = l$ and $\lim\limits_{x \to c^+} g(x) = l$, then $\lim\limits_{x \to c^+} f(x) = l$.

For a proof use the proof of Theorem (2.3.10) with each $|x - c|$ replaced by $x - c$.

SECTION 2.4

1. continuous   3. continuous

5. continuous   7. removable discontinuity

9. essential discontinuity

11. continuous

13. essential discontinuity

15. removable discontinuity at 2

17. no discontinuities

19. essential discontinuity at 1

21. no discontinuities

23. no discontinuities

25. essential discontinuities at 0 and 2

27. removable discontinuity at -2; essential discontinuity at 3

29. $f(1) = 2$

31. impossible

33. 4

35. $A - B = 3$ with $B \neq 3$

37. set for instance

39. nowhere

$$f(x) = \begin{cases} 0, & x \leq \frac{1}{2} \\ 1, & x > \frac{1}{2} \end{cases}$$

41. $x = 0$, $x = 2$, and all nonintegral values of x

43. Refer to (2.2.5). Use the equivalence of (i) to (iv) setting $l = f(c)$.

SECTION 2.5

1. 3   3. $\frac{3}{5}$ 5. 0   7. does not exist

9. $\frac{9}{5}$ 11. $\frac{2}{3}$ 13. 1   15. $\frac{1}{2}$

17. -4 19. 1   21. $\frac{3}{5}$ 23. 0

25. $\dfrac{2}{\pi}\sqrt{2}$ 27. -1 29. 0

31. By the hint, $\lim\limits_{x\to 0} \cos x = \lim\limits_{x\to 0} [1 - 2\sin^2 \frac{1}{2}x] = 1$

33. Let $\epsilon > 0$ and suppose $a \neq 0$. Since $\lim\limits_{x\to 0} f(x) = l$, there exists $\delta_1 > 0$ such that

(*)   if $0 < |ax| < \delta_1$ then $|f(ax) - l| < \epsilon$.

Take $\delta = \delta_1/|a|$. By (*) we have

if $0 < |x| < \delta$ then $|f(ax) - l| < \epsilon$

so that $\lim\limits_{x\to 0} f(ax) = l$.

SECTION 2.6

1. $m_4 = 1.6875$ 3. $m_5 = 1.53125$ 5. $m_4 = 1.6875$ 7. $m_5 = -3.03125$

9. $m_5 = 0.9375$ 11. Figure A.2.6.1   13. Figure A.2.6.2   15. impossible

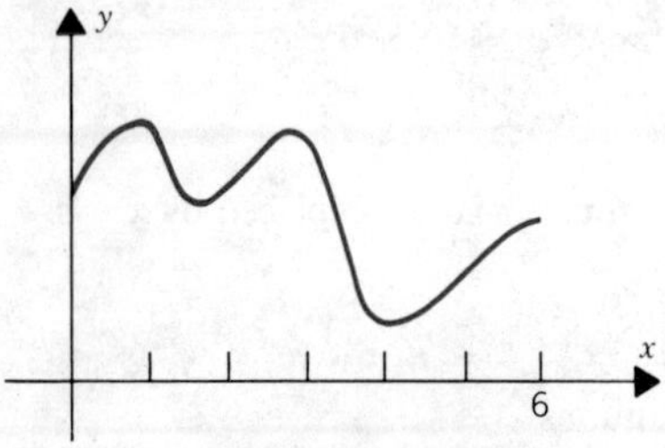

FIGURE A.2.6.1

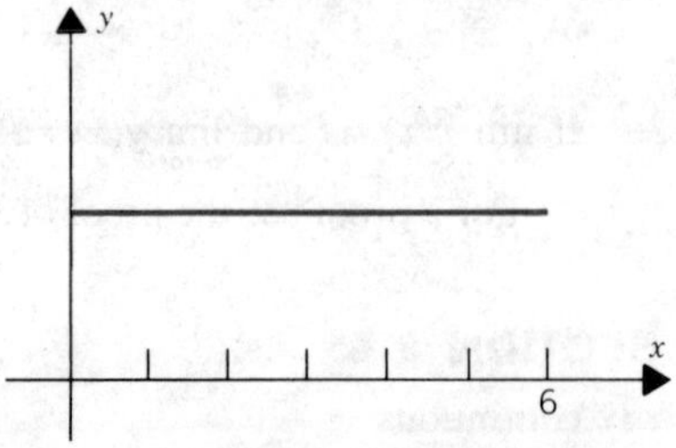

FIGURE A.2.6.2

17. $f(x) = x$ **19.** $f(x) = (2x - 1)^2$

21. Set $g(x) = x - f(x)$. Since g is continuous on $[0, 1]$ and $g(0) \le 0 \le g(1)$, there exists c in $[0, 1]$ such that $g(c) = c - f(c) = 0$.

23. Set $h(x) = f(x) - g(x)$. Since h is continuous on $[0, 1]$ and $h(0) < 0 < h(1)$, there exists c between 0 and 1 such that $h(c) = f(c) - g(c) = 0$.

25. $m_{10} = 1.7314$ **27.** $m_{10} = 0.6181$ **29.** $m_{12} = 1.9997$ **31.** $m_{10} = 0.7392$

SECTION 2.7

1. does not exist **3.** 0 **5.** 6 **7.** -1

9. 1 **11.** 0 **13.** 1 **15.** does not exist

17. does not exist **19.** 0 **21.** $-\frac{1}{2}$ **23.** 1

25. $-\frac{1}{16}$ **27.** does not exist **29.** 0 **31.** 0

33. $\frac{1}{6}$ **35.** $\frac{5}{2}$ **37.** $\frac{4}{9}$ **39.** -3

41. $-\frac{1}{2}$ **43.** $\frac{5}{2}$ **45.** $\frac{1}{3}$ **47.** does not exist

49. -3 **51.** 2 **53.** $\frac{1}{2}$ **55.** does not exist

57. $-\frac{3}{8}$ **59.** 6 **61.** 6 **63.** 1

65. (a) Figure A.2.7.1
   (b) (i) 1   (ii) 1   (iii) 1   (iv) 5
      (v) 5   (vi) 5   (vii) 9   (viii) 4
      (ix) does not exist
   (c) (i) at 1 and 2   (ii) at 1
      (iii) at 1   (iv) at 2

67. 0

69. Take $\delta = \frac{1}{5}\epsilon$. If $0 < |x - 2| < \frac{1}{5}\epsilon$, then $|(5x - 4) - 6| = 5|x - 2| < \epsilon$.

71. Take $\delta = \frac{1}{2}\epsilon$. If $0 < |x + 4| < \frac{1}{2}\epsilon$, then $\left||2x + 5| - 3\right| \le 2|x + 4| < \epsilon$.

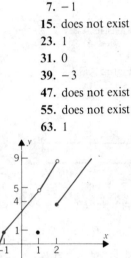

FIGURE A.2.7.1

73. Take $\delta = $ minimum of 4 and ϵ. If $0 < |x - 9| < \delta$, then $x - 5 > 0$ and $|x - 9| < \epsilon$. It follows that

$$|\sqrt{x - 5} - 2||\sqrt{x - 5} + 2| = |(x - 5) - 4| = |x - 9| < \epsilon$$

and, since $|\sqrt{x - 5} + 2| > 1$, that $|\sqrt{x - 5} - 2| < \epsilon$.

75. The polynomial $P(x) = x^5 - 4x + 1$ is continuous on $[0, 2]$. (Polynomials are everywhere continuous.) Since $P(0) < 7.21 < P(2)$, we know from the intermediate-value theorem that there is a number x_0 between 0 and 2 such that $P(x_0) = 7.21$.

77. $m_5 = 2.03$ **79.** $m_4 = 2.43$

SECTION 3.1

1. 0 **3.** -3 **5.** $5 - 2x$ **7.** $4x^3$

9. $\frac{1}{2}(x - 1)^{-1/2}$ **11.** $-2x^{-3}$ **13.** -6 **15.** $-\frac{1}{4}$

17. $\frac{3}{2}$

19. tangent $y - 4x + 4 = 0$; normal $4y + x - 18 = 0$

21. tangent $y + 3x - 16 = 0$; normal $3y - x - 8 = 0$

23. tangent $y + x = 0$; normal $y - x - 8 = 0$

25. tangent $y + x + 4 = 0$; normal $y - x - 2 = 0$

27. Figure A.3.1.1; $x = -1$ **29.** Figure A.3.1.2; $x = 0$ **31.** Figure A.3.1.3; $x = 1$

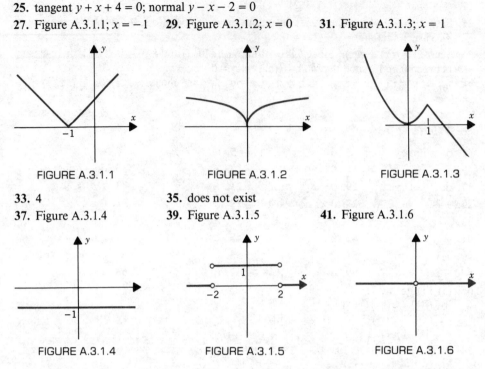

FIGURE A.3.1.1   FIGURE A.3.1.2   FIGURE A.3.1.3

33. 4   **35.** does not exist
37. Figure A.3.1.4   **39.** Figure A.3.1.5   **41.** Figure A.3.1.6

FIGURE A.3.1.4   FIGURE A.3.1.5   FIGURE A.3.1.6

43. Since $f(1) = 1$ and $\lim\limits_{x \to 1^+} f(x) = 2$, f is not continuous at 1 and thus, by (3.1.4), is not differentiable at 1.

45. (a) $f'(x) = \begin{cases} 2(x + 1), & x < 0 \\ 2(x - 1), & x > 0 \end{cases}$

(b) $\lim\limits_{h \to 0^-} \dfrac{f(0 + h) - f(0)}{h} = \lim\limits_{h \to 0^-} \dfrac{(h + 1)^2 - 1}{h} = \lim\limits_{h \to 0^-} (h + 2) = 2,$

$\lim\limits_{h \to 0^+} \dfrac{f(0 + h) - f(0)}{h} = \lim\limits_{h \to 0^+} \dfrac{(h - 1)^2 - 1}{h} = \lim\limits_{h \to 0^+} (h - 2) = -2$

In 47–53, there are many possible answers. Here are some.

47. $f(x) = c$, c any constant   **49.** $f(x) = |x + 1|$; $f(x) = \begin{cases} 0, & x \neq -1 \\ 1, & x = -1 \end{cases}$

51. $f(x) = 2x + 5$ **53.** $f(x) = \begin{cases} 0, & x \text{ rational} \\ 1, & x \text{ irrational} \end{cases}$

SECTION 3.2

1. -1 **3.** $55x^4 - 18x^2$ **5.** $2ax + b$

7. $\dfrac{2}{x^3}$ **9.** $3x^2 - 6x - 1$ **11.** $\dfrac{3x^2 - 2x^3}{(1 - x)^2}$

13. $2x - 3$ **15.** $\dfrac{2(x^2 + 3x + 1)}{(2x + 3)^2}$ **17.** $-\dfrac{2(3x^2 - x + 1)}{x^2(x - 2)^2}$

19. $-80x^9 + 81x^8 - 64x^7 + 63x^6$

21. $f'(0) = -\frac{1}{4}, \quad f'(1) = -1$

23. $f'(0) = 0, \quad f'(1) = -1$

25. $f'(0) = \dfrac{ad - bc}{d^2}, \quad f'(1) = \dfrac{ad - bc}{(c + d)^2}$

27. $f'(0) = 3$

29. $f'(0) = \frac{20}{9}$

31. $2y - x - 8 = 0$

33. $y - 4x + 12 = 0$

35. $9y + 4x - 18 = 0$

37. $(-1, 27), (3, -5)$

39. $(-1, -\frac{5}{2}), (1, \frac{5}{2})$

41. $(2, 3)$

43. $(-2, -10)$

45. $(-1, -2), (\frac{5}{3}, \frac{50}{27})$

47. $\frac{425}{8}$

49. $A = -1, B = 0, C = 4$

51. Since

$$\left(\frac{f}{g}\right)(x) = \frac{f(x)}{g(x)} = f(x) \cdot \frac{1}{g(x)};$$

it follows from the product and reciprocal rules that

$$\left(\frac{f}{g}\right)'(x) = \left(f \cdot \frac{1}{g}\right)'(x) = f(x)\left(-\frac{g'(x)}{[g(x)]^2}\right) + f'(x) \cdot \frac{1}{g(x)} = \frac{g(x)f'(x) - f(x)g'(x)}{[g(x)]^2}.$$

53. $g(x) = [f(x)]^2 = f(x) \cdot f(x)$

$g'(x) = f(x)f'(x) + f(x)f'(x) = 2f(x)f'(x).$

55. $A = -2, B = -8$

SECTION 3.3

1. $\dfrac{dy}{dx} = 12x^3 - 2x$

3. $\dfrac{dy}{dx} = 1 + \dfrac{1}{x^2}$

5. $\dfrac{dy}{dx} = \dfrac{1 - x^2}{(1 + x^2)^2}$

7. $\dfrac{dy}{dx} = \dfrac{2x - x^2}{(1 - x)^2}$

9. $\dfrac{dy}{dx} = \dfrac{-6x^2}{(x^3 - 1)^2}$

11. 2

13. $18x^2 + 30x + 5x^{-2}$

15. $\dfrac{-4t}{(t^2 - 1)^2}$

17. $\dfrac{2t^3(t^3 - 2)}{(2t^3 - 1)^2}$

19. $\dfrac{2}{(1 - 2u)^2}$

21. $-\left[\dfrac{1}{(u - 1)^2} + \dfrac{1}{(u + 1)^2}\right] = -2\left[\dfrac{u^2 + 1}{(u^2 - 1)^2}\right]$

23. $2x\left[\dfrac{1}{(1 - x^2)^2} + \dfrac{1}{x^4}\right]$

25. $\dfrac{-2}{(x - 1)^2}$

27. 47

29. $\frac{1}{4}$

31. $42x - 210x^3$

33. $-6x^{-3}$

35. $4 - 12x^{-4}$

37. 2

39. 0

41. $6 + 60x^{-6}$

43. $1 - 4x$

45. -24

47. -24

49. If $f(x) = g(x) = x$, then $(fg)(x) = x^2$, so that $(fg)''(x) = 2$, but

$$f(x)g''(x) + f''(x)g(x) = x \cdot 0 + 0 \cdot x = 0.$$

51. (a) $x = 0$ (b) $x > 0$ (c) $x < 0$

53. (a) $x = -2, x = 1$ (b) $x < -2, x > 1$ (c) $-2 < x < 1$

55. The result is true for $n = 1$:

$$\frac{d^1y}{dx^1} = \frac{dy}{dx} = -x^{-2} = (-1)^1 1! \, x^{-1-1}.$$

If the result is true for $n = k$:

$$\frac{d^k y}{dx^k} = (-1)^k k! \, x^{-k-1},$$

then the result is true for $n = k + 1$:

$$\frac{d^{k+1}y}{dx^{k+1}} = \frac{d}{dx}\left[\frac{d^k y}{dx^k}\right] = (-1)^k k! \, (-k - 1)x^{-k-2} = (-1)^{k+1}(k + 1)! \, x^{-(k+1)-1}.$$

SECTION 3.4

1. $\dfrac{dA}{dr} = 2\pi r, \quad 4\pi$ **3.** $\dfrac{dA}{dz} = z, \quad 4$ **5.** $-\frac{5}{36}$ **7.** $\dfrac{dV}{dr} = 4\pi r^2$

9. $x_0 = \frac{3}{4}$ **11.** (a) $\dfrac{3\sqrt{2}}{4}\, w^2$ (b) $\dfrac{\sqrt{3}}{3}\, z^2$

13. (a) $\frac{1}{2}r^2$ (b) $r\theta$ (c) $-4Ar^{-3} = -2\theta/r$ **15.** $x = \frac{1}{2}$

SECTION 3.5

1. $x(5) = -6, v(5) = -7, a(5) = -2$, speed $= 7$
3. $x(2) = -4, v(2) = 6, a(2) = 12$, speed $= 6$
5. $x(1) = 6, v(1) = -2, a(1) = \frac{4}{3}$, speed $= 2$
7. $x(1) = 0, v(1) = 18, a(1) = 54$, speed $= 18$
9. never   **11.** at $-2 + \sqrt{5}$ **13.** at $2\sqrt{2}$
15. A **17.** A **19.** A and B
21. A **23.** A and C **25.** $(0, 2), (7, \infty)$
27. $(0, 3), (4, \infty)$ **29.** $(2, 5)$ **31.** $(0, 2 - \frac{2}{3}\sqrt{3}), (4, \infty)$
33. 576 ft   **35.** 9 ft/sec
37. (a) 2 sec   (b) 16 ft   (c) 48 ft/sec
39. (a) $\frac{1625}{16}$ ft   (b) $\frac{6475}{64}$ ft   (c) 100 ft

SECTION 3.6

1. $2(1 - 2x)^{-2}$ **3.** $20(x^5 - x^{10})^{19}(5x^4 - 10x^9)$

5. $4\left(x - \dfrac{1}{x}\right)^3\left(1 + \dfrac{1}{x^2}\right)$ **7.** $4(x - x^3 - x^5)^3\,(1 - 3x^2 - 5x^4)$

9. $200t\,(t^2 - 1)^{99}$ **11.** $-4(t^{-1} + t^{-2})^3\,(t^{-2} + 2t^{-3})$

13. $324x^3\left[\dfrac{1 - x^2}{(x^2 + 1)^5}\right]$ **15.** $2(x^4 + x^2 + x)(4x^3 + 2x + 1)$

17. $-\left(\dfrac{x^3}{3} + \dfrac{x^2}{2} + \dfrac{x}{1}\right)^{-2}(x^2 + x + 1)$

19. $3\left(\dfrac{1}{x + 2} - \dfrac{1}{x - 2}\right)^2\left[\dfrac{-1}{(x + 2)^2} + \dfrac{1}{(x - 2)^2}\right] = \dfrac{384x}{(x + 2)^4(x - 2)^4}$

21. -1 **23.** 0

25. $\dfrac{dy}{dt} = \dfrac{dy}{du}\dfrac{du}{dx}\dfrac{dx}{dt} = \dfrac{7(2t-5)^4 + 12(2t-5)^2 - 2}{[(2t-5)^4 + 2(2t-5)^2 + 2]^2} [4(2t-5)]$

27. 16   **29.** 1   **31.** 1

33. 1   **35.** 2   **37.** 2

39. 0   **41.** $2x\,f'(x^2+1)$ **43.** $2\,f(x)f'(x)$

45. (a) $x = 0$ (b) $x < 0$ (c) $x > 0$

47. (a) $x = -1,\ x = 1$ (b) $-1 < x < 1$ (c) $x < -1,\ x > 1$

49. at 3   **51.** at 2 and $2\sqrt{3}$

53. If $p(x) = (x-a)^2 q(x)$, then $p'(x) = (x-a)[2q(x) + (x-a)q'(x)]$.

55. $2[(7x - x^{-1})^{-2} + 3x^2]^{-2}\,[(7x - x^{-1})^{-3}(7 + x^{-2}) - 3x]$

57. $3[(x + x^{-1})^2 - (x^2 + x^{-2})^{-1}]^2\,[2(x + x^{-1})(1 - x^{-2}) + (x^2 + x^{-2})^{-2}(2x - 2x^{-3})]$

SECTION 3.7

1. $\dfrac{dy}{dx} = -3\sin x - 4\sec x \tan x$ **3.** $\dfrac{dy}{dx} = 3x^2 \csc x - x^3 \csc x \cot x$

5. $\dfrac{dy}{dt} = -2\cos t \sin t$ **7.** $\dfrac{dy}{du} = 2u^{-1/2} \sin^3 \sqrt{u} \cos \sqrt{u}$

9. $\dfrac{dy}{dx} = 2x \sec^2 x^2$ **11.** $\dfrac{dy}{dx} = 4(1 - \pi \csc^2 \pi x)(x + \cot \pi x)^3$

13. $\dfrac{d^2y}{dx^2} = -\sin x$ **15.** $\dfrac{d^2y}{dx^2} = \cos x\,(1 + \sin x)^{-2}$

17. $\dfrac{d^2y}{du^2} = 12\cos 2u\,(2\sin^2 2u - \cos^2 2u)$ **19.** $\dfrac{d^2y}{dt^2} = 8\sec^2 2t \tan 2t$

21. $\dfrac{d^2y}{dx^2} = (2 - 9x^2)\sin 3x + 12x \cos 3x$ **23.** $\dfrac{d^2y}{dx^2} = 0$

25. $\sin x$ **27.** $(27t^3 - 12t)\sin 3t - 45t^2 \cos 3t$

29. $3\cos 3x\,f'(\sin 3x)$ **31.** $y = x$

33. $y - \sqrt{3} = -4(x - \tfrac{1}{6}\pi)$ **35.** $y - \sqrt{2} = \sqrt{2}(x - \tfrac{1}{4}\pi)$

37. at π **39.** at $\tfrac{1}{6}\pi,\ \tfrac{7}{6}\pi$

41. at $\tfrac{1}{2}\pi,\ \pi,\ \tfrac{3}{2}\pi$ **43.** at $\tfrac{1}{4}\pi,\ \tfrac{3}{4}\pi,\ \tfrac{5}{4}\pi,\ \tfrac{7}{4}\pi$

45. at $\tfrac{7}{6}\pi,\ \tfrac{11}{6}\pi$ **47.** at $\tfrac{1}{4}\pi,\ \tfrac{5}{4}\pi$

49. $(\tfrac{1}{2}\pi, \tfrac{2}{3}\pi),\ (\tfrac{7}{6}\pi, \tfrac{4}{3}\pi),\ (\tfrac{11}{6}\pi, 2\pi)$ **51.** $(0, \tfrac{1}{4}\pi),\ (\tfrac{7}{4}\pi, 2\pi)$

53. $(\tfrac{5}{6}\pi, \tfrac{3}{2}\pi)$

55. (a) $(2u)(\sec x \tan x)(\pi)$ (b) $2\pi \tan \pi t \sec^2 \pi t$

57. (a) $-2\left(\dfrac{1-u}{2}\right)^3 (-\sin x)(2)$ (b) $4\sin 2t \left(\dfrac{1 - \cos 2t}{2}\right)^3 = 8\sin^7 t \cos t$

59. $\dfrac{d^n}{dx^n}(\cos x) = \begin{cases} (-1)^{(n+1)/2} \sin x, & n\ \text{odd} \\ (-1)^{n/2} \cos x, & n\ \text{even} \end{cases}$

61. $\dfrac{d}{dx}(\sec x) = \dfrac{d}{dx}\left(\dfrac{1}{\cos x}\right) = \dfrac{\sin x}{\cos^2 x} = \sec x \tan x$

SECTION 3.8

1. $\frac{3}{2}x^2(x^3+1)^{-1/2}$

3. $\frac{2x^2+1}{\sqrt{x^2+1}}$

5. $\frac{x}{(\sqrt[4]{2x^2+1})^3}$

7. $\frac{x(2x^2-5)}{\sqrt{2-x^2}\,\sqrt{3-x^2}}$

9. $\frac{1}{2}\left(\frac{1}{\sqrt{x}}-\frac{1}{x\sqrt{x}}\right)$

11. $\frac{1}{(\sqrt{x^2+1})^3}$

13. $\frac{1}{3}\left[\frac{1}{(\sqrt[3]{x})^2}-\frac{1}{(\sqrt[3]{x})^4}\right]$

15. (a) Figure A.3.8.1   (b) Figure A.3.8.2   (c) Figure A.3.8.3

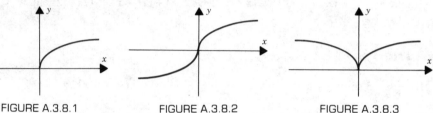

FIGURE A.3.8.1   FIGURE A.3.8.2   FIGURE A.3.8.3

17. $-\frac{2b^2}{9(\sqrt[3]{a+bx})^5}$

19. $-a^2(a^2-x^2)^{-3/2}$

21. $\frac{\sqrt{x}\cos\sqrt{x}-(x+1)\sin\sqrt{x}}{4x\sqrt{x}}$

23. $\frac{1}{2\sqrt{x}}f'(\sqrt{x}+1)$

25. $\frac{xf'(x^2+1)}{\sqrt{f(x^2+1)}}$

27. $\frac{1}{x}$

29. $\frac{1}{\sqrt{1-x^2}}$

31. unitary

33. inelastic for $0<P<500$, unitary at $P=500$, elastic for $500<P<1000$

35. inelastic for $0<P<200$, unitary at $P=200$, elastic for $200<P<300$

SECTION 3.9

1. $\frac{dy}{dx}=\frac{2}{3}x^{-1/3}$

3. $\frac{dy}{dx}=-\frac{a}{x^2}+c$

5. $\frac{dy}{dx}=\frac{\sqrt{a}}{2}\left(\frac{1}{\sqrt{x}}-\frac{1}{x\sqrt{x}}\right)$

7. $\frac{dr}{d\theta}=-\frac{1}{\sqrt{1-2\theta}}$

9. $f'(x)=\frac{x}{(\sqrt{a^2-x^2})^3}$

11. $\frac{dy}{dx}=-\frac{6b}{x^3}\left(a+\frac{b}{x^2}\right)^2$

13. $\frac{ds}{dt}=\frac{a^2+2t^2}{\sqrt{a^2+t^2}}$

15. $\frac{dy}{dx}=\frac{4a^2x}{(a^2-x^2)^2}$

17. $\frac{dy}{dx}=\frac{2x^2-8x-1}{(1+2x^2)^2}$

19. $\frac{dy}{dx}=\frac{2a-bx}{2(\sqrt{a-bx})^3}$

21. $\frac{dy}{dx}=-\frac{c}{(1+cx)^2}\sqrt{\frac{1+cx}{1-cx}}$

23. $\frac{dy}{dx}=\frac{2a^2x}{(a^2-x^2)^2}\sqrt{\frac{a^2-x^2}{a^2+x^2}}$

25. $\frac{dr}{d\theta}=-\frac{3a+2b\theta}{3\theta^2(\sqrt[3]{a+b\theta})^2}$

27. $\dfrac{dy}{dx} = -\dfrac{bx}{a\sqrt{a^2 - x^2}}$

29. $\dfrac{dy}{dx} = -x^{-1/3}(a^{2/3} - x^{2/3})^{1/2}$

31. $\dfrac{dy}{dx} = 2x \sec x^2 \tan x^2$

33. $\dfrac{dy}{dx} = -6 \csc^2 2x \cot^2 2x$

35. $\dfrac{dy}{dx} = -\sin x \cos (\cos x)$

37. 540   **39.** $\frac{1}{12}$ **41.** $\frac{5}{6}$ **43.** $\frac{3}{64}$

45. $-\frac{41}{90}$ **47.** 0   **49.** 20   **51.** 8

53. $-\frac{3}{2}\sqrt{3}$ **55.** $(1 - \frac{1}{4}\pi)\sqrt{2}$

SECTION 3.10

1. $-\dfrac{x}{y}$ **3.** $-\dfrac{4x}{9y}$ **5.** $-\dfrac{x^2(x + 3y)}{x^3 + y^3}$

7. $\dfrac{2(x - y)}{2(x - y) + 1}$ **9.** $\dfrac{y - \cos (x + y)}{\cos (x + y) - x}$ **11.** $\dfrac{16}{(x + y)^3}$

13. $\dfrac{90}{(2y + x)^3}$ **15.** $\dfrac{dy}{dx} = \dfrac{5}{8}, \ \dfrac{d^2y}{dx^2} = -\dfrac{9}{128}$ **17.** $\dfrac{dy}{dx} = -\dfrac{1}{2}, \ \dfrac{d^2y}{dx^2} = 0$

19. tangent $2x + 3y - 5 = 0$; normal $3x - 2y + 12 = 0$

21. tangent $x + 2y + 8 = 0$; normal $2x - y + 1 = 0$

23. Let (x_0, y_0) be a point of the circle. If $x_0 = 0$, the normal line is the y-axis; if $y_0 = 0$, the normal line is the x-axis. For all other choices of (x_0, y_0) the normal line takes the form

$$y - y_0 = \frac{y_0}{x_0} (x - x_0) \qquad \text{which reduces to} \qquad y = \frac{y_0}{x_0} x.$$

In each case the normal line passes through the origin.

25. at right angles

27. The hyperbola and the ellipse intersect at the four pts $(\pm 3, \pm 2)$. For the hyperbola, $\dfrac{dy}{dx} = \dfrac{x}{y}$. For the ellipse, $\dfrac{dy}{dx} = -\dfrac{4x}{9y}$. The product of these slopes is therefore $-\dfrac{4x^2}{9y^2}$. At each of the points of intersection this product is -1.

29. $y - 2x + 12 = 0, \quad y - 2x - 12 = 0$

SECTION 3.11

1. (a) -2 units/sec   (b) 4 units/sec

3. $\frac{2}{27}$ m/min, $\frac{8}{3}$ m²/min   **5.** $1/(50\pi)$ ft/min, $\frac{8}{5}$ ft²/min

7. 6 cm   **9.** decreasing 7 in²/min

11. boat A **13.** 10 ft³/hr

15. $\frac{1600}{3}$ ft/min   **17.** decreasing $\frac{5}{6}\pi$ in³/min

19. decreasing 0.04 radians/min   **21.** 5π mi/min

23. decreasing 0.12 radians/sec   **25.** increasing $\frac{4}{101}$ radians/min

SECTION 3.12

1. $\Delta V = (x + h)^3 - x^3$
    $= (x^3 + 3x^2h + 3xh^2 + h^3) - x^3$
    $= 3x^2h + 3xh^2 + h^3,$
    $dV = 3x^2h,$
    $\Delta V - dV = 3xh^2 + h^3$

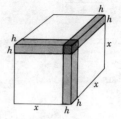

3. $10\frac{1}{30}$ taking $x = 1000$ 5. $1\frac{31}{32}$ taking $x = 16$ 7. 1.975 taking $x = 32$
9. 8.15 taking $x = 32$ 11. 0.719   13. 0.531
15. 1.6   17. $2\pi rht$ 19. error ≤ 0.01 ft
21. about 0.00153 sec   23. within $\frac{1}{2}\%$ 25. x_n is a root
27. For $x_1 \neq 0$ the root 0 is not found since $x_{n+1} = -2x_n = (-2)^n x_1$.
29. 4.69   31. -3.00 33. 2.50   35. 1.50
37. 3.14   39. (a) and (b)

41. $0 = \lim\limits_{h \to 0} \dfrac{g_1(h)}{h} + \lim\limits_{h \to 0} \dfrac{g_2(h)}{h} = \lim\limits_{h \to 0} \dfrac{g_1(h) + g_2(h)}{h}$,   so $g_1(h) + g_2(h) = o(h)$.

$\lim\limits_{h \to 0} \dfrac{g_1(h)g_2(h)}{h} = \lim\limits_{h \to 0} h\, \dfrac{g_1(h)g_2(h)}{h^2} = \left(\lim\limits_{h \to 0} h \right)\left(\lim\limits_{h \to 0} \dfrac{g_1(h)}{h} \right)\left(\lim\limits_{h \to 0} \dfrac{g_2(h)}{h} \right)$

$= 0 \cdot 0 \cdot 0 = 0,$ so $g_1(h)g_2(h) = o(h)$.

SECTION 3.13

1. (a) $x_0 = 2$ (b) $x_0 = \pm\sqrt{2}$ (c) $x_0 = \frac{1}{4}$
3. (a) $(1, \frac{2}{3})$ (b) $(3, 2\sqrt{3})$ (c) $(\frac{1}{3}, \frac{2}{27}\sqrt{3})$

5. $y = \dfrac{1}{m}(x - b) + a$ 7. $b^n n!$ 9. decreasing 4 units/sec

11. $y + x = 0$, $y - 26x - 54 = 0$ 13. decreasing 2.25 in/min
15. increasing 1.6 cm²/min   17. increasing $10/\pi$ in³/min
19. $(0, \frac{1}{6}\pi), (\frac{1}{2}\pi, \frac{5}{6}\pi), (\frac{3}{2}\pi, 2\pi)$

21. $\dfrac{dS}{S} = \dfrac{12xh}{6x^2} = 2\,\dfrac{h}{x} = 0.002,$ $\dfrac{dV}{V} = \dfrac{3x^2h}{x^3} = 0.003$

23. $\frac{1}{10}$ ft/min   25. $\frac{3}{2}a^2k$ units²/sec   27. 984 ft

29. $C = \dfrac{1 - 2\sqrt{AB}}{B}; \left(\dfrac{\sqrt{AB}}{A}, \dfrac{1 - \sqrt{AB}}{B} \right)$ is the equilibrium point.

31. $A = 1, B = -3, C = 5$ 33. at $\frac{1}{3}\pi, \pi, \frac{5}{3}\pi$
35. increasing 15 mph or $15\sqrt{3}$ mph
37. (a) about 0.0533 sec/in   (b) 0.0106 sec

SECTION 4.1

1. $c = \frac{3}{2}$　　　　　3. $c = \frac{1}{3}\sqrt{39}$　　　　5. $c = \frac{1}{2}\sqrt{2}$　　　　7. $c = 0$

9. $f'(x) = \begin{cases} 2, & x \leq -1 \\ 3x^2 - 1, & x > -1 \end{cases}$; $\quad -3 < c \leq -1$ and $c = 1$

11. $\dfrac{f(1) - f(-1)}{(1) - (-1)} = 0$ and $f'(x)$ is never zero; f is not differentiable at 0

13. Set $P(x) = 6x^4 - 7x + 1$. If there existed three numbers $a < b < c$ at which $P(x) = 0$, then by Rolle's theorem $P'(x)$ would have to be zero for some x in (a, b) and also for some x in (b, c). This is not the case: $P'(x) = 2\cdot x^3 - 7$ is zero only at $x = (\frac{7}{24})^{1/3}$.

15. Set $P(x) = x^3 + 9x^2 + 33x - 8$. Note that $P(0) < 0$ and $P(1) > 0$. Thus by the intermediate-value theorem there exists some number c between 0 and 1 at which $P(x) = 0$. If the equation $P(x) = 0$ had an additional real root, then by Rolle's theorem there would have to be some real number at which $P'(x) = 0$. This is not the case: $P'(x) = 3x^2 + 18x + 33$ is never 0 since the discriminant $b^2 - 4ac = (18)^2 - 12(33) < 0$.

17. Let c and d be two consecutive roots of the equation $P'(x) = 0$. The equation $P(x) = 0$ cannot have two or more roots between c and d, for then, by Rolle's theorem, $P'(x)$ would have to be zero somewhere between these two roots and thus between c and d. In this case, c and d would no longer be consecutive roots of $P'(x) = 0$.

19. If $x_1 = x_2$, then $|f(x_1) - f(x_2)|$ and $|x_1 - x_2|$ are both 0 and the inequality holds. If $x_1 \neq x_2$, then you know by the mean-value theorem that

$$\frac{f(x_1) - f(x_2)}{x_1 - x_2} = f'(c)$$

for some number c between x_1 and x_2. Since $|f'(c)| \leq 1$, you can conclude that

$$\left| \frac{f(x_1) - f(x_2)}{x_1 - x_2} \right| \leq 1 \quad \text{and thus that} \quad |f(x_1) - f(x_2)| \leq |x_1 - x_2|.$$

21. set, for instance, $f(x) = \begin{cases} 1, & a < x < b \\ 0, & x = a, b \end{cases}$

23. (a) Between any two times that the object is at the origin there is at least one instant when the velocity is zero. (b) On any time interval there is at least one instant when the instantaneous velocity equals the average velocity over the interval.

25. $f'(x_0) = \lim\limits_{y \to 0} \dfrac{f(x_0 + y) - f(x_0)}{y} = \lim\limits_{y \to 0} \dfrac{f'(x_0 + \theta y)y}{y} = \lim\limits_{y \to 0} f'(x_0 + \theta y) = \lim\limits_{x \to x_0} f'(x) = L$

$\quad\quad\quad\quad\quad\quad\quad\quad\quad\quad\quad\quad\quad$└──by the hint$\quad\quad\quad\quad\quad\quad\quad\quad\quad$└──by (2.2.5)

SECTION 4.2

1. increases on $(-\infty, -1]$ and $[1, \infty)$, decreases on $[-1, 1]$
3. increases on $(-\infty, -1]$ and $[1, \infty)$, decreases on $[-1, 0)$ and $(0, 1]$
5. increases on $[-\frac{3}{4}, \infty)$, decreases on $(-\infty, -\frac{3}{4}]$
7. increases on $[-1, \infty)$, decreases on $(-\infty, -1]$
9. increases on $(-\infty, 2)$, decreases on $(2, \infty)$

11. increases on $(-\infty, -1)$ and $(-1, 0]$, decreases on $[0, 1)$ and $(1, \infty)$

13. increases on $[-\sqrt{5}, 0]$ and $[\sqrt{5}, \infty)$, decreases on $(-\infty, -\sqrt{5}]$ and $[0, \sqrt{5}]$

15. increases on $(-\infty, -1)$ and $(-1, \infty)$

17. decreases on $[0, \infty)$

19. increases on $[0, \infty)$, decreases on $(-\infty, 0]$

21. decreases on $(0, 3]$

23. increases on $[0, 2\pi]$

25. increases on $[\frac{2}{3}\pi, \pi]$, decreases on $[0, \frac{2}{3}\pi]$

27. increases on $[0, \frac{2}{3}\pi]$ and $[\frac{5}{6}\pi, \pi]$, decreases on $[\frac{2}{3}\pi, \frac{5}{6}\pi]$

29. $f(x) = \frac{1}{3}x^3 - x + \frac{8}{3}$ 31. $f(x) = x^5 + x^4 + x^3 + x^2 + x + 5$

33. $f(x) = \frac{3}{4}x^{4/3} - \frac{2}{3}x^{3/2} + 1$, $x > 0$ 35. $f(x) = 2x - \cos x + 4$

37. increases on $(-\infty, -3)$ and $[-1, 1]$, decreases on $[-3, -1]$ and $[1, \infty)$

39. increases on $(-\infty, 0]$ and $[3, \infty)$, decreases on $[0, 1)$ and $[1, 3]$

41. (a) $M \le L \le N$ (b) none   (c) $M = L = N$

43. set, for instance, $f(x) = \begin{cases} 1, & x \text{ rational} \\ 0, & x \text{ irrational} \end{cases}$

45. Set $h(x) = f(x) - g(x)$. Since $h'(x) > 0$ for all x, h increases everywhere. Since $h(0) = 0$,

$$h(x) < 0 \quad \text{on } (-\infty, 0) \qquad \text{and} \qquad h(x) > 0 \quad \text{on } (0, \infty).$$

It follows that

     (a) $f(x) < g(x)$ on $(-\infty, 0)$ and   (b) $f(x) > g(x)$ on $(0, \infty)$.

SECTION 4.3

1. no critical pts; no local extreme values

3. critical pts ± 1; local max $f(-1) = -2$, local min $f(1) = 2$

5. critical pts 0, $\frac{2}{3}$; $f(0) = 0$ local min, $f(\frac{2}{3}) = \frac{4}{27}$ local max

7. no critical pts; no local extreme values

9. critical pt $-\frac{1}{2}$; local max $f(-\frac{1}{2}) = -8$

11. critical pts 0, $\frac{3}{5}$, 1; local max $f(\frac{3}{5}) = \dfrac{2^2 3^3}{5^5}$, local min $f(1) = 0$

13. critical pts $\frac{5}{8}$, 1; local max $f(\frac{5}{8}) = \frac{27}{2048}$

15. critical pts -2, 0; local max $f(-2) = 4$, local min $f(0) = 0$

17. critical pts -2, $-\frac{1}{2}$, 1; local max $f(-\frac{1}{2}) = \frac{9}{4}$, local min $f(-2) = f(1) = 0$

19. critical pts -2, $-\frac{12}{7}$, 0; local max $f(-\frac{12}{7}) = \frac{144}{49}(\frac{2}{7})^{1/3}$, local min $f(0) = 0$

21. critical pts $-\frac{1}{2}$, 3; local min $f(-\frac{1}{2}) = \frac{7}{2}$

23. critical pt 1; local min $f(1) = 3$

25. critical pts $\frac{1}{4}\pi$, $\frac{5}{4}\pi$; local max $f(\frac{1}{4}\pi) = \sqrt{2}$, local min $f(\frac{5}{4}\pi) = -\sqrt{2}$

27. critical pts $\frac{1}{3}\pi$, $\frac{1}{2}\pi$, $\frac{2}{3}\pi$; local max $f(\frac{1}{2}\pi) = 1 - \sqrt{3}$, local min $f(\frac{1}{3}\pi) = f(\frac{2}{3}\pi) = -\frac{3}{4}$

29. critical pts $\frac{1}{3}\pi$, $\frac{5}{3}\pi$; local max $f(\frac{5}{3}\pi) = \frac{5}{4}\sqrt{3} + \frac{10}{3}\pi$, local min $f(\frac{1}{3}\pi) = -\frac{5}{4}\sqrt{3} + \frac{2}{3}\pi$

31. (a) Theorem 4.2.2   (b) f continuous at c (c) Definition 4.2.1   (d) Definition 4.3.1

33. See answer for Exercise 31; f increases [decreases] on $(c - \delta, c + \delta)$ and thus has neither a maximum nor a minimum at c.

35. critical pts 1, 2, 3; local max $P(2) = -4$, local min $P(1) = P(3) = -5$

Since $P'(x) < 0$ for $x < 0$, P decreases on $(-\infty, 0]$. Since $P(0) > 0$, P does not take on the value 0 on $(-\infty, 0]$.

Since $P(0) > 0$ and $P(1) < 0$, P takes on the value 0 at least once on $(0, 1)$. Since $P'(x) < 0$ on $(0, 1)$, P decreases on $[0, 1]$. It follows that P takes on the value zero only once on $[0, 1]$.

Since $P'(x) > 0$ on $(1, 2)$ and $P'(x) < 0$ on $(2, 3)$, P increases on $[1, 2]$ and decreases on $[2, 3]$. Since $P(1), P(2), P(3)$ are all negative, P cannot take on the value 0 between 1 and 3.

Since $P(3) < 0$ and $P(100) > 0$, P takes on the value 0 at least once on $(3, 100)$. Since $P'(x) > 0$ on $(3, 100)$, P increases on $[3, 100]$. It follows that P takes on the value zero only once on $[3, 100]$.

Since $P'(x) > 0$ on $(100, \infty)$, P increases on $[100, \infty)$. Since $P(100) > 0$, P does not take on the value 0 on $[100, \infty)$.

SECTION 4.4

1. critical pt -2; $f(-2) = 0$ endpt min and absolute min

3. critical pts 0, 2, 3; $f(0) = 1$ endpt max and absolute max, $f(2) = -3$ local min and absolute min, $f(3) = -2$ endpt max

5. critical pt $2^{-1/3}$; $f(2^{-1/3}) = 3 \cdot 2^{-2/3}$ local min

7. critical pts $\frac{1}{10}$, $2^{-1/3}$, 2; $f(\frac{1}{10}) = 10\frac{1}{100}$ endpt max and absolute max; $f(2^{-1/3}) = 3 \cdot 2^{-2/3}$ local min and absolute min, $f(2) = 4\frac{1}{2}$ endpt max

9. critical pts 0, $\frac{3}{2}$, 2; $f(0) = 2$ endpt max and absolute max, $f(\frac{3}{2}) = -\frac{1}{4}$ local min and absolute min, $f(2) = 0$ endpt max

11. critical pts -3, -2, 1; $f(-3) = -\frac{3}{13}$ endpt max, $f(-2) = -\frac{1}{4}$ local min and absolute min, $f(1) = \frac{1}{5}$ endpt max and absolute max

13. critical pts 0, $\frac{1}{4}$, 1; $f(0) = 0$ endpt min and absolute min, $f(\frac{1}{4}) = \frac{1}{16}$ local max, $f(1) = 0$ local min and absolute min

15. critical pts 2, 3; $f(2) = 2$ local max and absolute max, $f(3) = 0$ endpt min

17. critical pt 1; no extreme values

19. critical pts 0, $\frac{5}{6}\pi$, π; $f(0) = -\sqrt{3}$ endpt min and absolute min, $f(\frac{5}{6}\pi) = \frac{7}{4}$ local max and absolute max, $f(\pi) = \sqrt{3}$ endpt min

21. critical pts 0, π; $f(0) = 5$ endpt max and absolute max, $f(\pi) = -5$ endpt min and absolute min

23. critical pts $-\frac{1}{3}\pi$, 0; $f(-\frac{1}{3}\pi) = \frac{1}{3}\pi - \sqrt{3}$ endpt min and absolute min, no absolute max

25. critical pts 0, 1, 4, 7; $f(0) = 0$ endpt min, $f(1) = -2$ local min and absolute min, $f(4) = 1$ local max and absolute max, $f(7) = -2$ endpt min and absolute min

27. critical pts -2, -1, 1, 3; $f(-2) = 5$ endpt max, $f(-1) = 2$ local min and absolute min, $f(1) = 6$ local max and absolute max, $f(3) = 2$ local min and absolute min

29. critical pts -3, -1, 0, 2; $f(-3) = 2$ endpt max and absolute max, $f(-1) = 0$ local min, $f(0) = 2$ local max and absolute max, $f(2) = -2$ local min and absolute min

31. By contradiction. If f is continuous at c, then $f(c)$ is not a local maximum by the first-derivative test (4.3.3).

33. If f is not differentiable on (a, b), then f has a critical point at each point c in (a, b) where $f'(c)$ does not exist.   If f is differentiable on (a, b), then by the mean-value theorem there exists c in (a, b) where $f'(c) = (f(b) - f(a))/(b - a)$.   With $f(b) = f(a)$, we have $f'(c) = 0$ and thus c is a critical point of f.

SECTION 4.5

1. 400   **3.** 20 by 10 ft   **5.** 32

7. 100 by 150 ft with the partition as 100 ft

9. radius of semicircle $\dfrac{90}{12 + 5\pi}$ ft; height of rectangle $\dfrac{90 + 30\pi}{12 + 5\pi}$ ft

11. $x = 2$, $y = \frac{3}{2}$ **13.** $-\frac{5}{2}$

15. $\frac{10}{3}\sqrt{3}$ in. by $\frac{5}{3}\sqrt{3}$ in.   **17.** equilateral triangle with side 4

19. $(1, 1)$

21. height of rectangle $\frac{15}{11}(5 - \sqrt{3})$ in.; side of triangle $\frac{10}{11}(6 + \sqrt{3})$ in.

23. $\frac{5}{3}$ **25.** $(0, \sqrt{3})$ **27.** $5\sqrt{5}$ ft   **29.** 54 by 72 in.

31. (a) use it all for the circle   (b) use $28\pi/(4 + \pi)$ in. for the circle

33. base radius $\frac{10}{3}$ and height $\frac{8}{3}$ **35.** 10 by 10 by 12.5 ft.

37. equilateral triangle with side $2r\sqrt{3}$ **39.** base radius $\frac{1}{3}R\sqrt{6}$ and height $\frac{2}{3}R\sqrt{3}$

41. base radius $\frac{2}{3}R\sqrt{2}$ and height $\frac{4}{3}R$

43. \$160,000   **45.** $\tan \theta = m$ **47.** $6\sqrt{6}$ ft

SECTION 4.6

1. concave down on $(-\infty, 0)$, concave up on $(0, \infty)$

3. concave down on $(-\infty, 0)$, concave up on $(0, \infty)$; pt of inflection $(0, 2)$

5. concave up on $(-\infty, -\frac{1}{3}\sqrt{3})$, concave down on $(-\frac{1}{3}\sqrt{3}, \frac{1}{3}\sqrt{3})$, concave up on $(\frac{1}{3}\sqrt{3}, \infty)$; pts of inflection $(-\frac{1}{3}\sqrt{3}, -\frac{5}{36})$, $(\frac{1}{3}\sqrt{3}, -\frac{5}{36})$

7. concave down on $(-\infty, -1)$ and on $(0, 1)$, concave up on $(-1, 0)$ and on $(1, \infty)$; pt of inflection $(0, 0)$

9. concave up on $(-\infty, -\frac{1}{3}\sqrt{3})$, concave down on $(-\frac{1}{3}\sqrt{3}, \frac{1}{3}\sqrt{3})$, concave up on $(\frac{1}{3}\sqrt{3}, \infty)$; pts of inflection $(-\frac{1}{3}\sqrt{3}, \frac{4}{9})$, $(\frac{1}{3}\sqrt{3}, \frac{4}{9})$

11. concave up on $(0, \infty)$

13. concave down on $(-\infty, -2)$, concave up on $(-2, \infty)$; pt of inflection $(-2, 0)$

15. concave up on $(0, \frac{1}{4}\pi)$, concave down on $(\frac{1}{4}\pi, \frac{3}{4}\pi)$, concave up on $(\frac{3}{4}\pi, \pi)$; pts of inflection $(\frac{1}{4}\pi, \frac{1}{2})$ and $(\frac{3}{4}\pi, \frac{1}{2})$

17. concave up on $(0, \frac{1}{12}\pi)$, concave down on $(\frac{1}{12}\pi, \frac{5}{12}\pi)$, concave up on $(\frac{5}{12}\pi, \pi)$; pts of inflection $\left(\dfrac{1}{12}\pi, \dfrac{72 + \pi^2}{144}\right)$ and $\left(\dfrac{5}{12}\pi, \dfrac{72 + 25\pi^2}{144}\right)$

19. $d = \frac{1}{3}(a + b + c)$ **21.** $a = -\frac{1}{2}$, $b = \frac{1}{2}$ **23.** $A = 18$, $B = -4$

SECTION 4.7   [Graphs not drawn to scale.]

1. Figure A.4.7.1

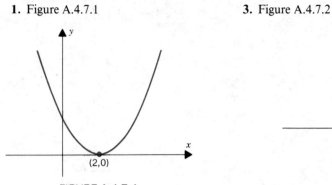

FIGURE A.4.7.1

3. Figure A.4.7.2

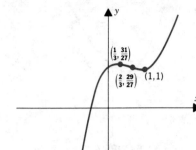

FIGURE A.4.7.2

5. Figure A.4.7.3

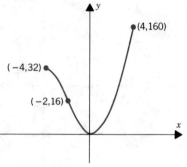

FIGURE A.4.7.3

7. Figure A.4.7.4

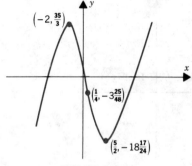

FIGURE A.4.7.4

9. Figure A.4.7.5

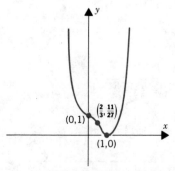

FIGURE A.4.7.5

11. Figure A.4.7.6

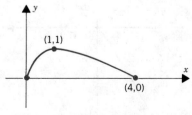

FIGURE A.4.7.6

13. Figure A.4.7.7

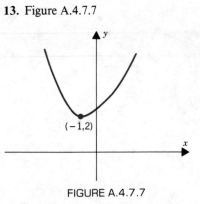

FIGURE A.4.7.7

15. Figure A.4.7.8

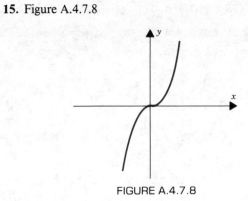

FIGURE A.4.7.8

17. Figure A.4.7.9

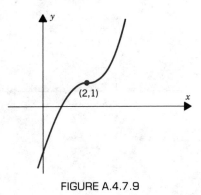

FIGURE A.4.7.9

19. Figure A.4.7.10

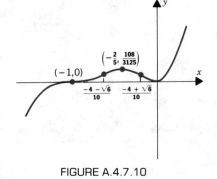

FIGURE A.4.7.10

21. Figure A.4.7.11

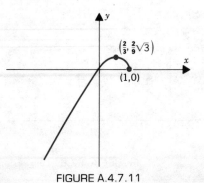

FIGURE A.4.7.11

23. Figure A.4.7.12

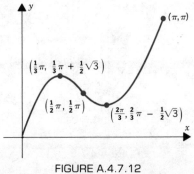

FIGURE A.4.7.12

25. Figure A.4.7.13

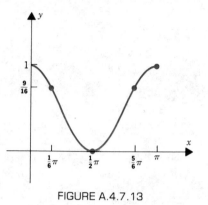

FIGURE A.4.7.13

27. Figure A.4.7.14

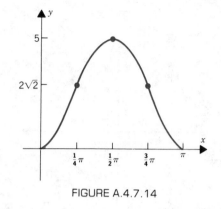

FIGURE A.4.7.14

SECTION 4.8

1. vertical: $x = \frac{1}{3}$; horizontal: $y = \frac{1}{3}$

3. vertical: $x = 2$; horizontal: none

5. vertical: $x = \pm 3$; horizontal: $y = 0$

7. vertical: $x = -\frac{4}{3}$; horizontal: $y = \frac{4}{9}$

9. vertical: $x = \frac{5}{2}$; horizontal: $y = 0$

11. vertical: none; horizontal: $y = \frac{3}{2}$

13. vertical: $x = 1$; horizontal: $y = 0$

15. vertical: none; horizontal: $y = 0$

17. vertical: $x = (2n + \frac{1}{2})\pi$; horizontal: none

19. neither   **21.** cusp   **23.** tangent   **25.** neither

27. cusp   **29.** cusp   **31.** tangent   **33.** neither

SECTION 4.9   [Graphs not drawn to scale.]

1. Figure A.4.9.1

3. Figure A.4.9.2

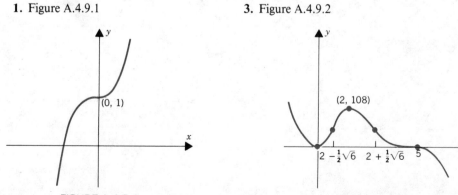

FIGURE A.4.9.1

FIGURE A.4.9.2

5. Figure A.4.9.3

7. Figure A.4.9.4

9. Figure A.4.9.5

11. Figure A.4.9.6

13. Figure A.4.9.7

15. Figure A.4.9.8

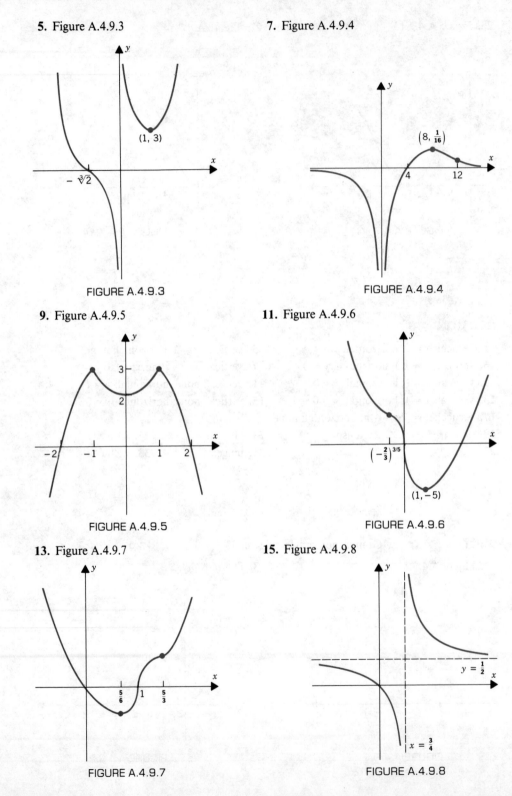

FIGURE A.4.9.3

FIGURE A.4.9.4

FIGURE A.4.9.5

FIGURE A.4.9.6

FIGURE A.4.9.7

FIGURE A.4.9.8

17. Figure A.4.9.9

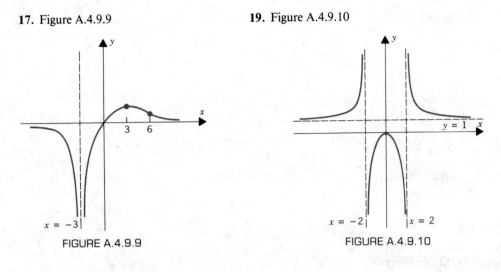

FIGURE A.4.9.9

19. Figure A.4.9.10

FIGURE A.4.9.10

21. Figure A.4.9.11

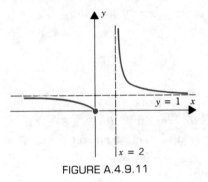

FIGURE A.4.9.11

23. Figure A.4.9.12

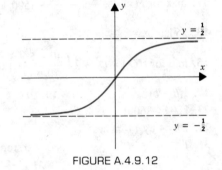

FIGURE A.4.9.12

25. Figure A.4.9.13

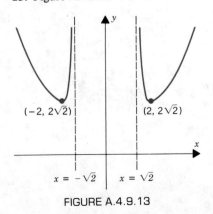

FIGURE A.4.9.13

27. Figure A.4.9.14

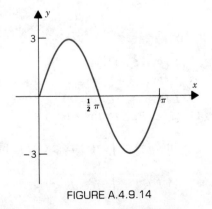

FIGURE A.4.9.14

29. Figure A.4.9.15   **31.** Figure A.4.9.16   **33.** Figure A.4.9.17

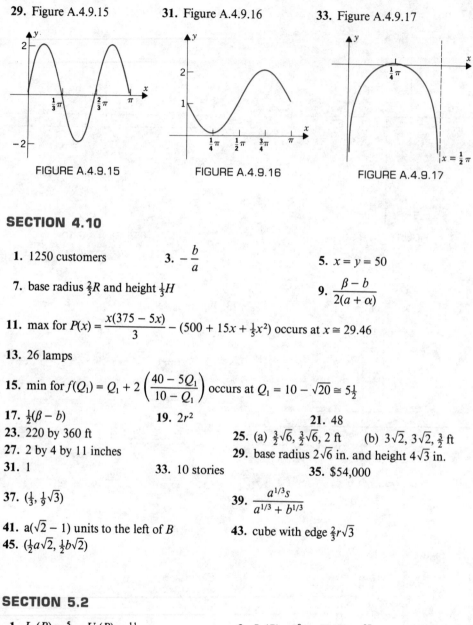

FIGURE A.4.9.15   FIGURE A.4.9.16   FIGURE A.4.9.17

SECTION 4.10

1. 1250 customers   **3.** $-\dfrac{b}{a}$ **5.** $x = y = 50$

7. base radius $\frac{2}{3}R$ and height $\frac{1}{3}H$ **9.** $\dfrac{\beta - b}{2(a + \alpha)}$

11. max for $P(x) = \dfrac{x(375 - 5x)}{3} - (500 + 15x + \frac{1}{5}x^2)$ occurs at $x \approx 29.46$

13. 26 lamps

15. min for $f(Q_1) = Q_1 + 2\left(\dfrac{40 - 5Q_1}{10 - Q_1}\right)$ occurs at $Q_1 = 10 - \sqrt{20} \approx 5\frac{1}{2}$

17. $\frac{1}{2}(\beta - b)$ **19.** $2r^2$ **21.** 48

23. 220 by 360 ft   **25.** (a) $\frac{3}{2}\sqrt{6}, \frac{3}{2}\sqrt{6}, 2$ ft   (b) $3\sqrt{2}, 3\sqrt{2}, \frac{3}{2}$ ft

27. 2 by 4 by 11 inches   **29.** base radius $2\sqrt{6}$ in. and height $4\sqrt{3}$ in.

31. 1   **33.** 10 stories   **35.** \$54,000

37. $(\frac{1}{3}, \frac{1}{9}\sqrt{3})$ **39.** $\dfrac{a^{1/3}s}{a^{1/3} + b^{1/3}}$

41. $a(\sqrt{2} - 1)$ units to the left of B **43.** cube with edge $\frac{2}{3}r\sqrt{3}$

45. $(\frac{1}{2}a\sqrt{2}, \frac{1}{2}b\sqrt{2})$

SECTION 5.2

1. $L_f(P) = \frac{5}{8}, \quad U_f(P) = \frac{11}{8}$ **3.** $L_f(P) = \frac{9}{64}, \quad U_f(P) = \frac{37}{64}$

5. $L_f(P) = \frac{17}{16}, \quad U_f(P) = \frac{25}{16}$ **7.** $L_f(P) = \frac{7}{16}, \quad U_f(P) = \frac{25}{16}$

9. $L_f(P) = \frac{3}{16}, \quad U_f(P) = \frac{43}{32}$ **11.** $L_f(P) = \frac{1}{6}\pi, \quad U_f(P) = \frac{11}{12}\pi$

13. (a) $L_f(P) \le U_f(P)$ but $3 \not\le 2$

(b) $L_f(P) \le \displaystyle\int_{-1}^{1} f(x)\,dx \le U_f(P)$ but $3 \not\le 2 \le 6$

(c) $L_f(P) \le \displaystyle\int_{-1}^{1} f(x)\,dx \le U_f(P)$ but $3 \le 10 \not\le 6$

Tutorial 12. Techniques of Integration: Parts and Rational Functions

pp 462/463. Q1, 3, 7, 9, 13, 15, 17, 29, 33, 35, 37.

p 471   Q1, 3, 5, 7, 11, 13, 15, 17, 19.

Tutorial 13. Techniques of Integration: Trigonometric Integrals + Substitution

pp 475/476. Q1, 3, 5, 7, 9, 13, 15, 19, 21, 25, 29, 31, 33, 34

p 482/483. Q3, 5, 7, 9, 13, 15, 21, 23, 27, 29, 31, 33, 35, 39, 41

pp 485/486. Q1, 3, 5, 7, 11

p 381   Q63, 65, 67

Tutorial 14. Differential Equations

p 418. Q1, 3, 7, 9, 13, 15, 19

pp 418/420. Q23, 25, 27, 31, 33

Questions A. Solve the following D.E's

(i) $\frac{dy}{dx} = \frac{y-x+1}{y+x+5}$ (ii) $\frac{dy}{dx} = \frac{y-x+1}{y-x+5}$

(iii) $(2x + 9y - 20)dx - (6x + 2y - 10)dy = 0$, $y(2) = 1$

(iv) $(3x - 4y - 2)dx - (3x - 4y - 3)dy = 0$

p 402.   Q3, 9, 12, 15, 17, 23, 25, 27, 29

pp 410/413   Q17, 27, 28, 29   (These are optional)

pp 433/434   Q1, 3, 5, 7, 12, 13, 15

             Q19, 21, 25, 27, 29, 31

Tutorial 15. Functions of Several Variables

See separate tutorial sheet

— # —

15. (a) $L_f(P) = -3x_1(x_1 - x_0) - 3x_2(x_2 - x_1) - \cdots - 3x_n(x_n - x_{n-1})$

$ U_f(P) = -3x_0(x_1 - x_0) - 3x_1(x_2 - x_1) - \cdots - 3x_{n-1}(x_n - x_{n-1})$

(b) $-\frac{3}{2}(b^2 - a^2)$

17. $L_f(P) = x_0^3(x_1 - x_0) + x_1^3(x_2 - x_1) + \cdots + x_{n-1}^3(x_n - x_{n-1})$

$ U_f(P) = x_1^3(x_1 - x_0) + x_2^3(x_2 - x_1) + \cdots + x_n^3(x_n - x_{n-1})$

For each index j

$$x_{j-1}^3 \leq \frac{x_j^3 + x_j^2 x_{j-1} + x_j x_{j-1}^2 + x_{j-1}^3}{4} \leq x_j^3$$

and thus by the hint

$$x_{j-1}^3(x_j - x_{j-1}) \leq \frac{x_j^4 - x_{j-1}^4}{4} \leq x_j^3(x_j - x_{j-1}).$$

Adding up these inequalities, we find that

$$L_f(P) \leq \frac{x_n^4 - x_0^4}{4} \leq U_f(P).$$

Since $x_n = 1$ and $x_0 = 0$, the middle term is $\frac{1}{4}$: $\displaystyle\int_0^1 x^3 \, dx = \frac{1}{4}$

19. Let $P = \{x_0, x_1, \ldots, x_n\}$ be a partition of $[0, 4]$. Clearly $L_f(P) = 8$ for all partitions P. Next, if $x_j = 3$ for some j, then $U_f(P) = 8 + 5(x_{j+1} - x_{j-1})$; and, if $x_j < 3 < x_{j+1}$ for some j, then $U_f(P) = 8 + 5(x_{j+1} - x_j)$. In either case the only number I that satisfies the inequality $L_f(P) \leq I \leq U_f(P)$ for all P is $I = 8$.

SECTION 5.3

1. (a) 5   (b) -2 (c) -1 (d) 0   (e) -4 (f) 1

3. With $P = \left\{1, \frac{3}{2}, 2\right\}$ and $f(x) = \frac{1}{x}$, we have

$$0.5 < \frac{7}{12} = L_f(P) \leq \int_1^2 \frac{dx}{x} \leq U_f(P) = \frac{5}{6} < 1.$$

5. (a) $F(0) = 0$ (b) $F'(x) = x\sqrt{x+1}$ (c) $F'(2) = 2\sqrt{3}$

(d) $F(2) = \displaystyle\int_0^2 t\sqrt{t+1}\, dt$ (e) $-F(x) = \displaystyle\int_x^0 t\sqrt{t+1}\, dt$

7. (a) $\frac{1}{10}$ (b) $\frac{1}{9}$ (c) $\frac{4}{37}$ (d) $\dfrac{-2x}{(x^2 + 9)^2}$

9. (a) $\sqrt{2}$ (b) 0   (c) $-\frac{1}{4}\sqrt{5}$ (d) $-\dfrac{2x^2 + 1}{\sqrt{x^2 + 1}}$

11. (a) -1 (b) 1   (c) 0   (d) $-\pi \sin \pi x$

13. (a) Since $P_1 \subseteq P_2$, $\ U_f(P_2) \leq U_f(P_1)$ but $5 \not\leq 4$.

(b) Since $P_1 \subseteq P_2$, $\ L_f(P_1) \leq L_f(P_2)$ but $5 \not\leq 4$.

15. By the hint $F(b) - F(a) = F'(c)(b - a)$ for some c in (a, b). The desired result follows by observing that

$$F(b) = \int_a^b f(t)\, dt, \qquad F(a) = 0, \qquad \text{and} \qquad F'(c) = f(c).$$

17. Set $G(x) = \displaystyle\int_a^x f(t)\, dt$. Then $F(x) = \displaystyle\int_c^a f(t)\, dt + G(x)$. By (5.3.5) G, and thus F, is continuous on $[a, b]$, is differentiable on (a, b), and $F'(x) = G'(x) = f(x)$ for all x in (a, b).

SECTION 5.4

1. -2 **3.** 1 **5.** $\frac{14}{3}$ **7.** $\frac{32}{3}$

9. $\frac{2}{3}$ **11.** 0 **13.** $\frac{5}{72}$ **15.** $\frac{13}{2}$

17. $-\frac{4}{15}$ **19.** $\dfrac{2^{18} - 1}{18}$ **21.** $\dfrac{a^2}{6}$ **23.** $\frac{7}{4}$

25. $-\frac{1}{12}$ **27.** $\frac{21}{2}$ **29.** 1 **31.** 1

33. $2 - \sqrt{2}$ **35.** 0 **37.** (a) $\displaystyle\int_2^x \frac{dt}{t}$ (b) $-3 + \displaystyle\int_2^x \frac{dt}{t}$

39. $f(x)$ and $f(x) - f(a)$, respectively

SECTION 5.5

1. $\frac{9}{4}$ **3.** $\frac{38}{3}$ **5.** $\frac{47}{15}$ **7.** $\frac{5}{3}$ **9.** $\frac{1}{2}$

11. Figure A.5.5.1, area $= \frac{1}{3}$ **13.** Figure A.5.5.2, area $= \frac{9}{2}$

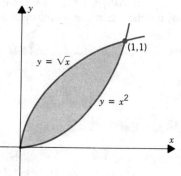

FIGURE A.5.5.1

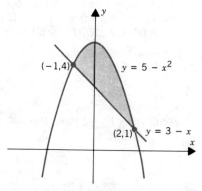

FIGURE A.5.5.2

15. Figure A.5.5.3, area $= \frac{64}{3}$ **17.** Figure A.5.5.4, area $= 10$

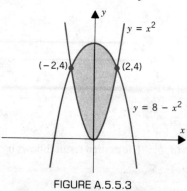

FIGURE A.5.5.3

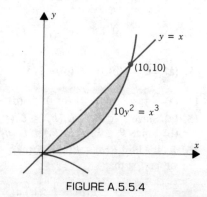

FIGURE A.5.5.4

19. Figure A.5.5.5, area = $\frac{32}{3}$

21. Figure A.5.5.6, area = 4

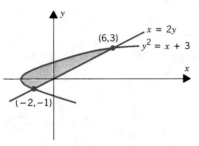

FIGURE A.5.5.5

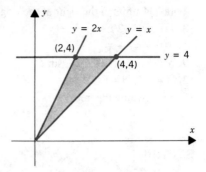

FIGURE A.5.5.6

23. Figure A.5.5.7, area = $2 + \frac{2}{3}\pi^3$

25. Figure A.5.5.8, area = $\frac{\pi^2}{8} - 1$

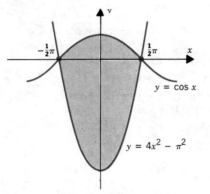

FIGURE A.5.5.7

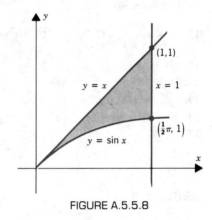

FIGURE A.5.5.8

SECTION 5.6

1. $-\dfrac{1}{3x^3} + C$

3. $\frac{1}{2}ax^2 + bx + C$

5. $2\sqrt{1+x} + C$

7. $\dfrac{1}{2}x^2 + \dfrac{1}{x} + C$

9. $\frac{1}{3}t^3 - \frac{1}{2}(a+b)t^2 + abt + C$

11. $-\dfrac{1}{g(x)} + C$

13. $f(x)g(x) + C$

15. $\sin t + C$

17. $\tan x + C$

19. $x^2 - x - 2$

21. $\dfrac{a}{2}x^2 + bx - 2a - 2b$

23. $3 - \cos x$

25. $x^3 - x^2 + x + 2$

27. $\frac{1}{12}(x^4 - 2x^3 + 2x + 23)$

29. $x - \cos x + 3$

31. $\frac{1}{3}x^3 - \frac{3}{2}x^2 - \frac{1}{3}x + 3$

33. $\dfrac{d}{dx}\left(\displaystyle\int f(x)\,dx\right) = f(x), \quad \displaystyle\int \dfrac{d}{dx}[f(x)]\,dx = f(x) + C$

SECTION 5.7

1. (a) 34 units to the right of the origin   (b) 44 units

3. (a) $v(t) = 2(t + 1)^{1/2} - 1$ (b) $x(t) = \frac{4}{3}(t + 1)^{3/2} - t - \frac{4}{3}$

5. $x(t) = v_0 t + x_0$ **7.** $x(t) = x_0 + v_0 t + At^2 + Bt^3$

9. $x(t) = x_0 + (v_0 + 1)t - \sin t$ **11.** at $(\frac{160}{3}, 50)$

13. $A = -\frac{5}{2}, B = 2$ **15.** (a) at $t = \frac{11}{6}\pi$ sec   (b) at $t = \frac{13}{6}\pi$ sec

17. mean-value theorem

SECTION 5.8

1. $\dfrac{1}{3(2 - 3x)} + C$ **3.** $\frac{1}{3}(2x + 1)^{3/2} + C$ **5.** $\dfrac{4}{7a}(ax + b)^{7/4} + C$

7. $-\dfrac{1}{8(4t^2 + 9)} + C$ **9.** $\frac{1}{75}(5t^3 + 9)^5 + C$ **11.** $\frac{4}{15}(1 + x^3)^{5/4} + C$

13. $-\dfrac{1}{4(1 + s^2)^2} + C$ **15.** $\sqrt{x^2 + 1} + C$ **17.** $-\dfrac{b^3}{2a^4}\sqrt{1 - a^4 x^4} + C$

19. $\frac{15}{8}$ **21.** $\frac{31}{2}$ **23.** 0

25. $\frac{1}{3}|a|^3$ **27.** $\frac{2}{5}(x + 1)^{5/2} - \frac{2}{3}(x + 1)^{3/2} + C$

29. $\frac{1}{10}(2x - 1)^{5/2} + \frac{1}{6}(2x - 1)^{3/2} + C$ **31.** $\frac{1}{14}(y + 1)^{14} - \frac{1}{13}(y + 1)^{13} + C$

33. $\frac{1}{8}(t - 2)^8 + \frac{4}{7}(t - 2)^7 + \frac{2}{3}(t - 2)^6 + C$ **35.** $\frac{16}{3}\sqrt{2} - \frac{14}{3}$

37. $-\frac{769}{112}$

SECTION 5.9

1. yes; $\displaystyle\int_a^b [f(x) - g(x)]\, dx = \int_a^b f(x)\, dx - \int_a^b g(x)\, dx > 0.$

3. yes; otherwise we would have $f(x) \le g(x)$ for all $x \in [a, b]$, and it would follow that

$$\int_a^b f(x)\, dx \le \int_a^b g(x)\, dx$$

5. no; take $f(x) = 0, g(x) = -1$ on $[0, 1]$

7. no; take, for example, any odd function on an interval of the form $[-c, c]$

9. no; $\displaystyle\int_{-1}^1 x\, dx = 0$ but $\displaystyle\int_{-1}^1 |x|\, dx \ne 0$

11. yes; $U_f(P) \ge \displaystyle\int_a^b f(x)\, dx = 0$ **13.** no; $L_f(P) \le \displaystyle\int_a^b f(x)\, dx = 0$

15. yes; $\displaystyle\int_a^b [f(x) + 1]\, dx = \int_a^b f(x)\, dx + \int_a^b 1\, dx = 0 + b - a = b - a$

17. $\dfrac{2x}{\sqrt{2x^2 + 7}}$ **19.** $-f(x)$ **21.** $\dfrac{1}{x}$

23. $\dfrac{3}{1 + (2 + 3x)^{3/2}} - \dfrac{1}{3x^{2/3}(1 + x^{1/2})}$

25. (a) With P a partition of $[a, b]$

$$L_f(P) \le \int_a^b f(x)\, dx.$$

If f is nonnegative on $[a, b]$, then $L_f(P)$ is nonnegative and, consequently, so is the integral. If f is positive on $[a, b]$, then $L_f(P)$ is positive and, consequently, so is the integral.

(b) Take F as an antiderivative of f on $[a, b]$. Observe that

$$F'(x) = f(x) \quad \text{on } (a, b) \qquad \text{and} \qquad \int_a^b f(x)\, dx = F(b) - F(a).$$

If $f(x) \ge 0$ on $[a, b]$, then F is nondecreasing on $[a, b]$ and $F(b) - F(a) \ge 0$.
If $f(x) > 0$ on $[a, b]$, then F is increasing on $[a, b]$ and $F(b) - F(a) > 0$.

27. For all $x \in [a, b]$

$$-f(x) \le |f(x)| \qquad \text{and} \qquad f(x) \le |f(x)|.$$

It follows from II that

$$\int_a^b -f(x)\, dx \le \int_a^b |f(x)|\, dx \qquad \text{and} \qquad \int_a^b f(x)\, dx \le \int_a^b |f(x)|\, dx,$$

and, consequently, that

$$\left| \int_a^b f(x)\, dx \right| \le \int_a^b |f(x)|\, dx.$$

29. $H(x) = \displaystyle\int_{2x}^{x^3 - 4} \dfrac{x\, dt}{1 + \sqrt{t}} = x \int_{2x}^{x^3 - 4} \dfrac{dt}{1 + \sqrt{t}}$

$H'(x) = x \cdot \left[\dfrac{3x^2}{1 + \sqrt{x^3 - 4}} - \dfrac{2}{1 + \sqrt{2x}} \right] + 1 \cdot \displaystyle\int_{2x}^{x^3 - 4} \dfrac{dt}{1 + \sqrt{t}}$

$H'(2) = 2 \left[\dfrac{12}{3} - \dfrac{2}{3} \right] + \underbrace{\displaystyle\int_4^4 \dfrac{dt}{1 + \sqrt{t}}}_{= 0} = \dfrac{20}{3}$

SECTION 5.10

1. $A.V. = \frac{1}{2}mc + b, \quad x = \frac{1}{2}c$

3. $A.V. = 0, \quad x = 0$

5. $A.V. = 1, \quad x = \pm 1$

7. $A.V. = \frac{2}{3}, \quad x = 1 \pm \frac{1}{3}\sqrt{3}$

9. $A.V. = 2, \quad x = 4$

11. $A.V. = 0, \quad x = 0, \pi, 2\pi$

13. A = average value of f on $[a, b] = \dfrac{1}{b - a} \displaystyle\int_a^b f(x)\, dx$

15. average of f' on $[a, b] = \dfrac{1}{b - a} \displaystyle\int_a^b f'(x)\, dx = \dfrac{1}{b - a} \Big[f(x) \Big]_a^b = \dfrac{f(b) - f(a)}{b - a}$

17. (a) 1   (b) $\frac{2}{3}\sqrt{3}$ (c) $\frac{7}{9}\sqrt{3}$

19. (a) The terminal velocity is twice the average velocity.
(b) The average velocity during the first $\frac{1}{2}x$ seconds is one-third of the average velocity during the next $\frac{1}{2}x$ seconds.

21. If f and g take on the same average value on every interval $[a, x]$, then

$$\frac{1}{x-a} \int_a^x f(t)\, dt = \frac{1}{x-a} \int_a^x g(t)\, dt.$$

Multiplication by $(x - a)$ gives

$$\int_a^x f(t)\, dt = \int_a^x g(t)\, dt.$$

Differentiation with respect to x gives $f(x) = g(x)$. This shows that, if the averages are everywhere the same, then the functions are everywhere the same.

SECTION 5.11

1. $\frac{2}{3}[(x-a)^{3/2} - (x-b)^{3/2}] + C$ **3.** $\frac{1}{2}(t^{2/3} - 1)^3 + C$

5. $x + \frac{8}{3}x^{3/2} + 2x^2 + C$ **7.** $\frac{2}{3b}(a + b\sqrt{y+1})^3 + C$ **9.** $-\dfrac{1}{2[g(x)]^2} + C$

11. $\frac{13}{3}$ **13.** $y = \frac{1}{3}(x^2 + 1)^{3/2} + \frac{2}{3}$

15. (a) $\displaystyle\int_0^{x_0} [g(x) - y_0]\, dx$ (b) $\displaystyle\int_0^{x_0} [y_0 - f(x)]\, dx$ (c) $\displaystyle\int_0^{x_0} f(x)\, dx + \int_{x_0}^a g(x)\, dx$

(d) $\displaystyle\int_0^{x_0} \left[\left(\frac{c-b}{a}x + b \right) - g(x) \right] dx + \int_{x_0}^a \left[\left(\frac{c-b}{a}x + b \right) - f(x) \right] dx$

(e) $\displaystyle\int_{x_0}^a [f(x) - g(x)]\, dx$

17. Figure A.5.11.1, area = 8   **19.** Figure A.5.11.2, area $= \frac{125}{6}$

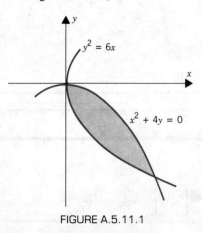

FIGURE A.5.11.1

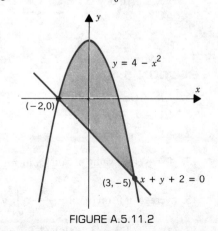

FIGURE A.5.11.2

21. Figure A.5.11.3, area $= \frac{3}{4}$

23. Figure A.5.11.4, area $= \dfrac{a}{2}$

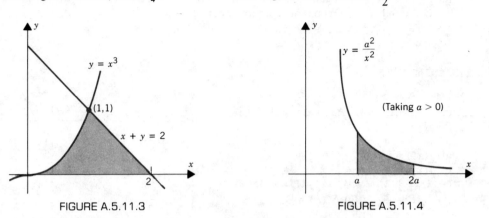

FIGURE A.5.11.3   FIGURE A.5.11.4

25. necessarily holds: $L_g(P) \leq \displaystyle\int_a^b g(x)\, dx < \int_a^b f(x)\, dx \leq U_f(P)$

27. necessarily holds: $L_g(P) \leq \displaystyle\int_a^b g(x)\, dx < \int_a^b f(x)\, dx$

29. necessarily holds: $U_f(P) \geq \displaystyle\int_a^b f(x)\, dx > \int_a^b g(x)\, dx$

31. $y = \dfrac{1}{1 + \sqrt{x}}$

33. $U_f(P) = 1(\frac{1}{25}) + \frac{5}{6}(\frac{3}{25}) + \frac{5}{7}(\frac{5}{25}) + \frac{5}{8}(\frac{7}{25}) + \frac{5}{9}(\frac{9}{25}) = \frac{921}{1400}$

$L_f(P) = \frac{5}{6}(\frac{1}{25}) + \frac{5}{7}(\frac{3}{25}) + \frac{5}{8}(\frac{5}{25}) + \frac{5}{9}(\frac{7}{25}) + \frac{1}{2}(\frac{9}{25}) = \frac{7303}{12600}$

$0.579 < \frac{7303}{12600} \leq$ area $\leq \frac{921}{1400} < 0.658.$

35. $\dfrac{2x}{1 + x^4}$

37. at $x = 1$

SECTION 5.12

1. $\frac{1}{3}\sin(3x - 1) + C$

3. $-\dfrac{1}{\pi}\cot \pi x + C$

5. $\frac{1}{2}\cos(3 - 2x) + C$

7. $-\frac{1}{5}\cos^5 x + C$

9. $\frac{2}{3}(1 + \sin x)^{3/2} + C$

11. $-2\cos x^{1/2} + C$

13. $\tan x + C$

15. $\frac{1}{8}\sin^4 x^2 + C$

17. $-\cot x - \frac{1}{3}\cot^3 x + C$

19. $\frac{1}{2}x - \frac{1}{12}\sin 6x + C$

21. $2(1 + \tan x)^{1/2} + C$

23. 0

25. $\dfrac{1}{\pi}(\sqrt{3} - 1)$

27. $\frac{1}{4}$

29. $2 - \sqrt{2}$

31. π

33. (a) $\frac{1}{2}\sec^2 x + C$ (b) $\frac{1}{2}\tan^2 x + C'$
(c) $\frac{1}{2}\sec^2 x + C = \frac{1}{2}(1 + \tan^2 x) + C = \frac{1}{2}\tan^2 x + (C + \frac{1}{2}) = \frac{1}{2}\tan^2 x + C'$,
$C + \frac{1}{2}$ and C' each represent an arbitrary constant

SECTION 5.13

1. Figure A.5.13.1
3. (a) $\Delta x_1 = \Delta x_2 = \frac{1}{8}$, $\Delta x_3 = \Delta x_4 = \Delta x_5 = \frac{1}{4}$
(b) $\|P\| = \frac{1}{4}$
(c) $m_1 = 0$, $m_2 = \frac{1}{4}$, $m_3 = \frac{1}{2}$, $m_4 = 1$, $m_5 = \frac{3}{2}$
(d) $f(x_1^*) = \frac{1}{8}$, $f(x_2^*) = \frac{3}{8}$, $f(x_3^*) = \frac{3}{4}$,
$f(x_4^*) = \frac{5}{4}$, $f(x_5^*) = \frac{7}{4}$
(e) $M_1 = \frac{1}{4}$, $M_2 = \frac{1}{2}$, $M_3 = 1$, $M_4 = \frac{3}{2}$, $M_5 = 2$
(f) $L_f(P) = \frac{25}{32}$ (g) $S^*(P) = \frac{15}{16}$

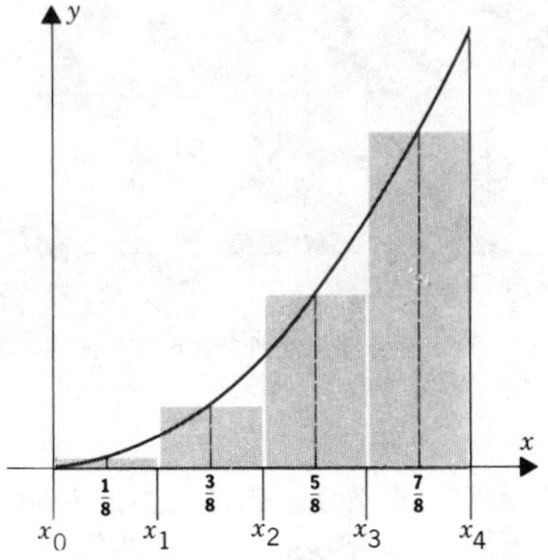

(h) $U_f(P) = \frac{39}{32}$ (i) $\displaystyle\int_a^b f(x)\, dx = 1$

5. (a) $\dfrac{1}{n^2}(1 + 2 + \cdots + n) = \dfrac{1}{n^2}\left[\dfrac{n(n+1)}{2}\right]$

$$= \frac{1}{2} + \frac{1}{2n}$$

(b) $S_n^* = \dfrac{1}{2} + \dfrac{1}{2n}$, $\displaystyle\int_0^1 x\, dx = \left[\frac{1}{2}x^2\right]_0^1 = \frac{1}{2}$

$\left| S_n^* - \displaystyle\int_0^1 x\, dx\right| = \dfrac{1}{2n} < \dfrac{1}{n} < \epsilon$ if $n > \dfrac{1}{\epsilon}$

7. (a) $\dfrac{1}{n^4}(1^3 + 2^3 + \cdots + n^3) = \dfrac{1}{n^4}\left[\dfrac{n^2(n+1)^2}{4}\right] = \dfrac{1}{4} + \dfrac{1}{2n} + \dfrac{1}{4n^2}$

(b) $S_n^* = \dfrac{1}{4} + \dfrac{1}{2n} + \dfrac{1}{4n^2}$, $\displaystyle\int_0^1 x^3\, dx = \left[\frac{1}{4}x^4\right]_0^1 = \frac{1}{4}$

$\left| S_n^* - \displaystyle\int_0^1 x^3\, dx\right| = \dfrac{1}{2n} + \dfrac{1}{4n^2} < \dfrac{1}{n} < \epsilon$ if $n > \dfrac{1}{\epsilon}$

FIGURE A.5.13.1

SECTION 6.1

1.

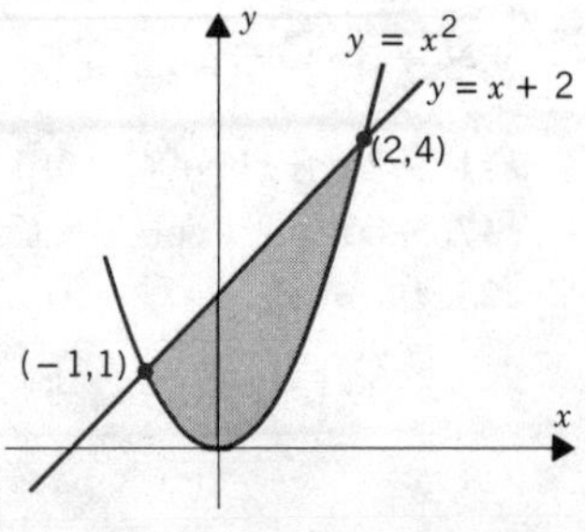

(a) $\displaystyle\int_{-1}^{2} [(x + 2) - x^2]\, dx$

(b) $\displaystyle\int_0^1 [\sqrt{y} - (-\sqrt{y})]\, dy + \int_1^4 [\sqrt{y} - (y - 2)]\, dy$

3.

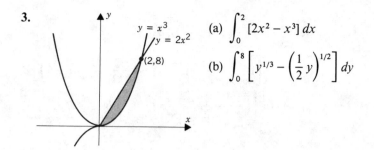

(a) $\displaystyle\int_0^2 [2x^2 - x^3]\, dx$

(b) $\displaystyle\int_0^8 \left[y^{1/3} - \left(\frac{1}{2} y \right)^{1/2} \right] dy$

5.

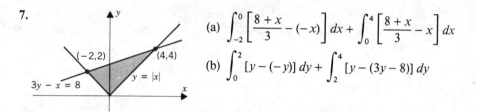

(a) $\displaystyle\int_0^4 [0 - (-\sqrt{x})]\, dx + \int_4^6 [0 - (x - 6)]\, dx$

(b) $\displaystyle\int_{-2}^0 [(y + 6) - y^2]\, dy$

7.

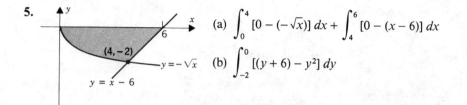

(a) $\displaystyle\int_{-2}^0 \left[\frac{8 + x}{3} - (-x) \right] dx + \int_0^4 \left[\frac{8 + x}{3} - x \right] dx$

(b) $\displaystyle\int_0^2 [y - (-y)]\, dy + \int_2^4 [y - (3y - 8)]\, dy$

9.

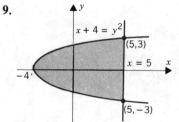

(a) $\displaystyle\int_{-4}^5 [\sqrt{4 + x} - (-\sqrt{4 + x})]\, dx$

(b) $\displaystyle\int_{-3}^3 [5 - (y^2 - 4)]\, dy$

11.

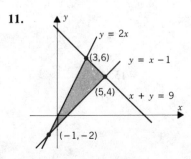

(a) $\displaystyle\int_{-1}^3 [2x - (x - 1)]\, dx + \int_3^5 [(9 - x) - (x - 1)]\, dx$

(b) $\displaystyle\int_{-2}^4 \left[(y + 1) - \frac{1}{2} y \right] dy + \int_4^6 \left[(9 - y) - \frac{1}{2} y \right] dy$

13.

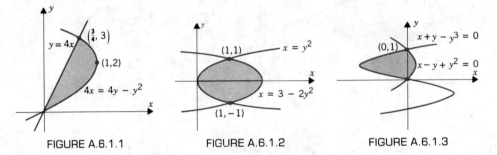

(a) $\int_{-1}^{1} [x^{1/3} - (x^2 + x - 1)]\, dx$

(b) $\int_{-5/4}^{-1} \left[\left(-\frac{1}{2} + \frac{1}{2}\sqrt{4y+5} \right) - \left(-\frac{1}{2} - \frac{1}{2}\sqrt{4y+5} \right) \right] dy$

$+ \int_{-1}^{1} \left[\left(-\frac{1}{2} + \frac{1}{2}\sqrt{4y+5} \right) - y^3 \right] dy$

15. Figure A.6.1.1, area $= \frac{9}{8}$ **17.** Figure A.6.1.2, area $= 4$ **19.** Figure A.6.1.3, area $= \frac{5}{12}$

FIGURE A.6.1.1   FIGURE A.6.1.2   FIGURE A.6.1.3

SECTION 6.2

1. $\frac{1}{3}\pi$ **3.** $\frac{1944}{5}\pi$ **5.** $\frac{5}{14}\pi$ **7.** $\frac{3790}{21}\pi$

9. $\frac{72}{5}\pi$ **11.** $\frac{32}{3}\pi$ **13.** π **15.** $\frac{\pi^2}{24}(\pi^2 + 6\pi + 6)$

17. $\frac{16}{3}\pi$ **19.** $\frac{768}{7}\pi$ **21.** $\frac{2}{5}\pi$ **23.** $\frac{128}{3}\pi$

25. $\frac{16}{3}\pi$ **27.** (a) $\frac{16}{3}r^3$ (b) $\frac{4}{3}\sqrt{3}\,r^3$

29. (a) $\frac{512}{15}$ (b) $\frac{64}{15}\pi$ (c) $\frac{128}{15}\sqrt{3}$ **31.** (a) 32 (b) 4π (c) $8\sqrt{3}$

33. $\frac{4}{3}\pi ab^2$ **35.** $\frac{1}{3}\pi h(R^2 + rR + r^2)$

37. (a) $31\frac{1}{4}\%$ (b) $14\frac{22}{27}\%$

39. (a) 64π (b) $\frac{1024}{35}\pi$ (c) $\frac{704}{5}\pi$ (d) $\frac{512}{7}\pi$

SECTION 6.3

1. $\frac{2}{3}\pi$ **3.** $\frac{128}{5}\pi$ **5.** $\frac{2}{5}\pi$ **7.** 16π

9. $\frac{72}{5}\pi$ **11.** 36π **13.** 8π **15.** $\frac{1944}{5}\pi$

17. $\frac{5}{14}\pi$ **19.** $\frac{72}{5}\pi$ **21.** 64π **23.** $\frac{1}{3}\pi$

25. $\frac{4}{3}\pi ba^2$ **27.** $\frac{1}{4}\pi a^3\sqrt{3}$

29. (a) 64π (b) $\frac{1024}{35}\pi$ (c) $\frac{704}{5}\pi$ (d) $\frac{512}{7}\pi$

SECTION 6.4

1. (a) 8π (b) 8π (c) $\frac{128}{5}\pi$ (d) $\frac{128}{5}\pi$
3. (a) $\frac{2}{5}\pi$ (b) $\frac{2}{5}\pi$ (c) $\frac{5}{14}\pi$ (d) $\frac{5}{14}\pi$
5. (a) $\frac{80}{3}\pi$ (b) $\frac{80}{3}\pi$ (c) $\frac{56}{3}\pi$ (d) $\frac{56}{3}\pi$
7. (a) $\frac{704}{15}\pi$ (b) $\frac{704}{15}\pi$ (c) 8π (d) 8π
9. (a) $\frac{4}{15}\pi$ (b) $\frac{4}{15}\pi$ (c) $\frac{4}{15}\pi$ (d) $\frac{4}{15}\pi$
11. (a) $\frac{31}{5}\pi$ (b) $\frac{31}{5}\pi$ (c) $\frac{15}{2}\pi$ (d) $\frac{15}{2}\pi$
13. (a) $\frac{40}{3}\pi$ (b) $\frac{40}{3}\pi$ (c) 24π (d) 24π

15. (a) disc: $\displaystyle\int_0^2 \pi(x^3)^2\,dx$,   shell: $\displaystyle\int_0^8 2\pi y(2 - y^{1/3})\,dy$

   (b) shell: $\displaystyle\int_0^2 2\pi(2 - x)x^3\,dx$,   disc: $\displaystyle\int_0^8 \pi(2 - y^{1/3})^2\,dy$

   (c) shell: $\displaystyle\int_0^2 2\pi(2 + x)x^3\,dx$,   washer: $\displaystyle\int_0^8 \pi[4^2 - (2 + y^{1/3})^2]\,dy$

   (d) shell: $\displaystyle\int_0^2 2\pi x(x^3)\,dx$,   washer: $\displaystyle\int_0^8 \pi[2^2 - (y^{1/3})^2]\,dy$

   (e) washer: $\displaystyle\int_0^2 \pi[8^2 - (8 - x^3)^2]\,dx$,   shell: $\displaystyle\int_0^8 2\pi(8 - y)(2 - y^{1/3})\,dy$

   (f) washer: $\displaystyle\int_0^2 \pi[(x^3 + 1)^2 - 1^2]\,dx$,   shell: $\displaystyle\int_0^8 2\pi(y + 1)(2 - y^{1/3})\,dy$

17. (a) washer: $\displaystyle\int_2^3 \pi[(x^2)^2 - 4^2]\,dx$,   shell: $\displaystyle\int_4^9 2\pi y(3 - \sqrt{y})\,dy$

   (b) shell: $\displaystyle\int_2^3 2\pi(x + 1)(x^2 - 4)\,dx$,   washer: $\displaystyle\int_4^9 \pi[4^2 - (1 + \sqrt{y})^2]\,dy$

   (c) shell: $\displaystyle\int_2^3 2\pi(4 - x)(x^2 - 4)\,dx$,   washer: $\displaystyle\int_4^9 \pi[(4 - \sqrt{y})^2 - 1^2]\,dy$

   (d) shell: $\displaystyle\int_2^3 2\pi x(x^2 - 4)\,dx$,   washer: $\displaystyle\int_4^9 \pi[3^2 - (\sqrt{y})^2]\,dy$

   (e) disc: $\displaystyle\int_2^3 \pi(x^2 - 4)^2\,dx$,   shell: $\displaystyle\int_4^9 2\pi(y - 4)(3 - \sqrt{y})\,dy$

   (f) washer: $\displaystyle\int_2^3 \pi[5^2 - (9 - x^2)^2]\,dx$,   shell: $\displaystyle\int_4^9 2\pi(9 - y)(3 - \sqrt{y})\,dy$

SECTION 6.5

1. (a) 25 ft lbs   (b) $\frac{225}{4}$ ft lbs   3. $\frac{3}{2}$ feet
5. (a) $(6480\pi + 8640)$ ft lbs   (b) $(15120\pi + 8640)$ ft lbs
7. (a) $\frac{11}{192}\pi r^2 h^2 \sigma$ ft lbs   (b) $(\frac{11}{192}\pi r^2 h^2 \sigma + \frac{7}{24}\pi r^2 h k \sigma)$ ft lbs

9. $GmM\left(\dfrac{1}{r_2} - \dfrac{1}{r_1}\right)$ **11.** 788 ft lbs

13. (a) $\frac{1}{2}\sigma l^2$ ft lbs   (b) $\frac{3}{2}l^2\sigma$ ft lbs   **15.** 20,800 ft lbs

SECTION 6.6

1. 2160 lbs   **3.** $\frac{8000}{3}\sqrt{2}$ lbs   **5.** 2560 lbs

7. (a) 41,250 lbs   (b) 11 ft

SECTION 7.2

1. $\ln 2 + \ln 10 \cong 2.99$

3. $2\ln 4 - \ln 10 \cong 0.48$

5. $-\ln 10 \cong -2.30$

7. $\ln 8 + \ln 9 - \ln 10 \cong 1.98$

9. $\frac{1}{2}\ln 2 \cong 0.35$ **11.** $5\ln 2 \cong 3.45$

13. Figure A.7.2.1   **15.** 0.406

17. (a) 1.65   (b) 1.57   (c) 1.71

19. $x = e^2$ **21.** $x = 1,\, e^2$

23. $x = 1$

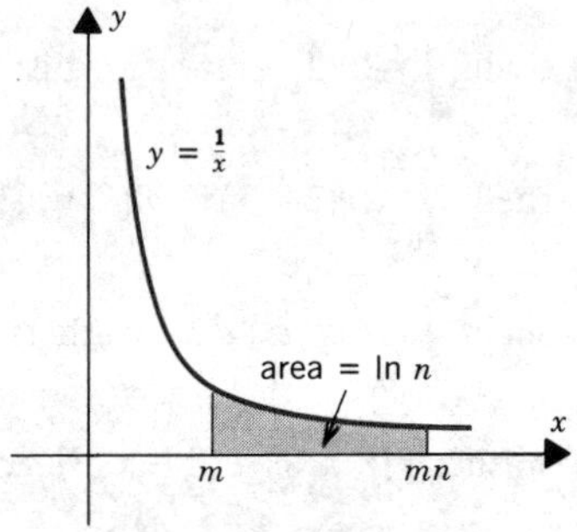

FIGURE A.7.2.1

SECTION 7.3

1. domain $(0, \infty)$, $f'(x) = \dfrac{1}{x}$

3. domain $(-1, \infty)$, $f'(x) = \dfrac{3x^2}{x^3 + 1}$

5. domain $(-\infty, \infty)$, $f'(x) = \dfrac{x}{1 + x^2}$

7. domain all $x \neq \pm 1$, $f'(x) = \dfrac{4x^3}{x^4 - 1}$

9. domain $(0, 1) \cup (1, \infty)$, $f'(x) = -\dfrac{1}{x(\ln x)^2}$

11. domain $(0, \infty)$, $f'(x) = 1 + \ln x$

13. domain $(-1, \infty)$, $f'(x) = \dfrac{1 - \ln(x + 1)}{(x + 1)^2}$

15. $\ln|x + 1| + C$

17. $-\frac{1}{2}\ln|3 - x^2| + C$

19. $\dfrac{1}{2(3 - x^2)} + C$

21. $\ln\left|\dfrac{x + 2}{x - 2}\right| + C$

23. $\dfrac{-1}{\ln x} + C$

25. $\frac{2}{3}\ln|1 + x\sqrt{x}| + C$

27. 1   **29.** 1   **31.** $\frac{1}{2}\ln\frac{8}{5}$ **33.** $\frac{1}{2}(\ln 2)^2$

35. $g'(x) = (x^2 + 1)^2(x - 1)^5 x^3\left(\dfrac{4x}{x^2 + 1} + \dfrac{5}{x - 1} + \dfrac{3}{x}\right)$

37. $g'(x) = \dfrac{x^4(x - 1)}{(x + 2)(x^2 + 1)}\left(\dfrac{4}{x} + \dfrac{1}{x - 1} - \dfrac{1}{x + 2} - \dfrac{2x}{x^2 + 1}\right)$

39. $g'(x) = \frac{1}{2}\sqrt{\frac{(x-1)(x-2)}{(x-3)(x-4)}}\left(\frac{1}{x-1} + \frac{1}{x-2} - \frac{1}{x-3} - \frac{1}{x-4}\right)$

41. $\frac{15}{8} - \ln 4$

43. $\ln 5$ ft

45. $(-1)^{n-1}\frac{(n-1)!}{x^n}$

47. $(-1)^{n-1}\frac{(n-1)!}{x^n}$

49. (a) for $t \in (1, x)$

$$\frac{1}{t} < \frac{1}{\sqrt{t}}$$

(b) for $x > 1$

$$\ln x = \int_1^x \frac{dt}{t} < \int_1^x \frac{dt}{\sqrt{t}} = \left[2\sqrt{t}\right]_1^x = 2(\sqrt{x} - 1)$$

(c) for $0 < x < 1$

$$0 < \ln\frac{1}{x} < 2\left(\sqrt{\frac{1}{x}} - 1\right) \quad \text{by (b)}$$

$$0 < -\ln x < 2\left(\frac{1}{\sqrt{x}} - 1\right)$$

$$2\left(1 - \frac{1}{\sqrt{x}}\right) < \ln x < 0$$

$$2x\left(1 - \frac{1}{\sqrt{x}}\right) < x\ln x < 0$$

(d) Use (c) and the pinching theorem for one-sided limits.

51. (i) domain $(0, \infty)$ (ii) increases on $(0, \infty)$ (iii) no extreme values (iv) concave down on $(0, \infty)$; no pts of inflection (v) Figure A.7.3.1

53. (i) domain $(-\infty, 4)$ (ii) decreases throughout (iii) no extreme values (iv) concave down throughout; no pts of inflection (v) Figure A.7.3.2

55. (i) domain $(0, \infty)$ (ii) decreases on $\left(0, \frac{1}{e}\right]$, increases on $\left[\frac{1}{e}, \infty\right)$ (iii) $f\left(\frac{1}{e}\right) = -\frac{1}{e}$ local and absolute min (iv) concave up throughout; no pts of inflection (v) Figure A.7.3.3

57. (i) domain $(0, \infty)$ (ii) increases on $(0, 1]$, decreases on $[1, \infty)$ (iii) $f(1) = -\ln 2$ local and absolute max (iv) concave down on $(0, \sqrt{2+\sqrt{5}})$, concave up on $(\sqrt{2+\sqrt{5}}, \infty)$; pt of inflection at $x = \sqrt{2+\sqrt{5}}$ (v) Figure A.7.3.4

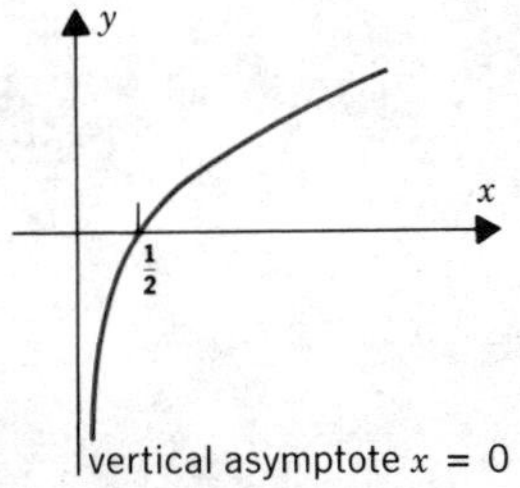
y
x
$\frac{1}{2}$
vertical asymptote $x = 0$
FIGURE A.7.3.1

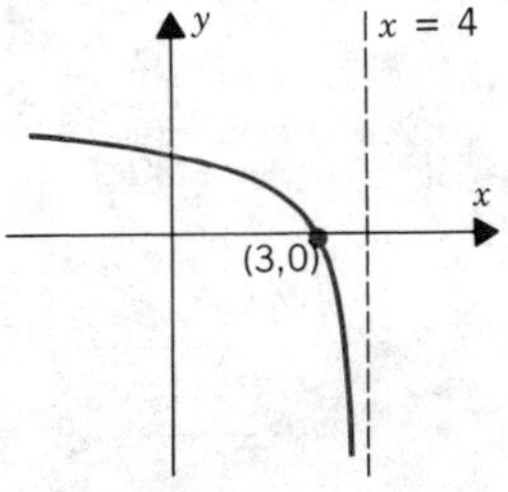
y
$x = 4$
x
(3,0)
FIGURE A.7.3.2

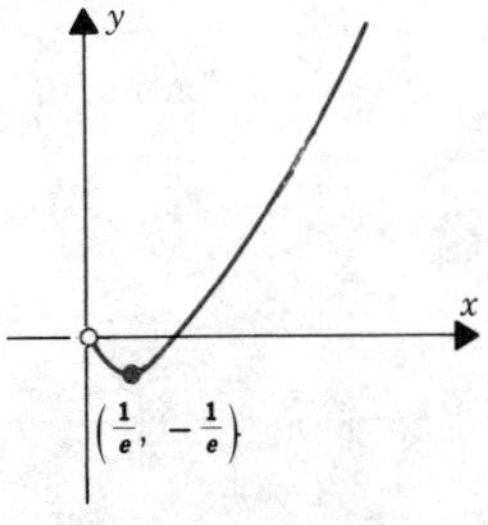
y
x
$\left(\frac{1}{e}, -\frac{1}{e}\right)$
FIGURE A.7.3.3

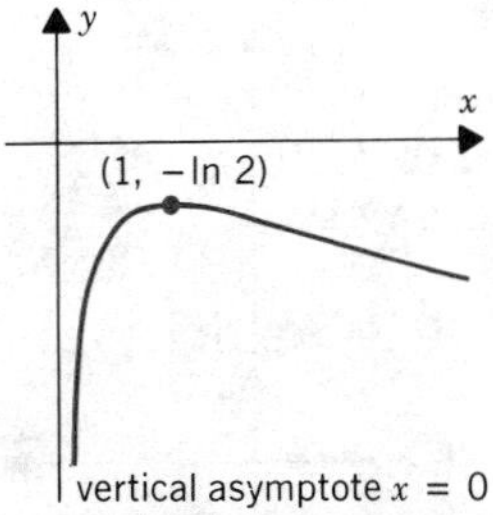
y
x
(1, −ln 2)
vertical asymptote $x = 0$
FIGURE A.7.3.4

SECTION 7.4

1. $\dfrac{dy}{dx} = -2e^{-2x}$ **3.** $\dfrac{dy}{dx} = 2xe^{x^2-1}$ **5.** $\dfrac{dy}{dx} = e^x\left(\dfrac{1}{x} + \ln x\right)$

7. $\dfrac{dy}{dx} = -(x^{-1} + x^{-2})e^{-x}$ **9.** $\dfrac{dy}{dx} = \dfrac{1}{2}(e^x - e^{-x})$ **11.** $\dfrac{dy}{dx} = \dfrac{1}{2} e^{\sqrt{x}}\left(\dfrac{1}{x} + \dfrac{\ln \sqrt{x}}{\sqrt{x}}\right)$

13. $\dfrac{dy}{dx} = 2(e^{2x} - e^{-2x})$ **15.** $\dfrac{dy}{dx} = 4xe^{x^2}(e^{x^2} + 1)$ **17.** $\dfrac{dy}{dx} = x^2 e^x$

19. $\dfrac{dy}{dx} = \dfrac{2e^x}{(e^x + 1)^2}$ **21.** $\dfrac{dy}{dx} = 2(a - b)\dfrac{e^{(a+b)x}}{(e^{ax} + e^{bx})^2}$

23. $\dfrac{dy}{dx} = 4x^3$ **25.** $\frac{1}{2}e^{2x} + C$ **27.** $\dfrac{1}{k} e^{kx} + C$

29. $\frac{1}{2}e^{x^2} + C$ **31.** $-e^{1/x} + C$ **33.** $\frac{1}{2}e^{2x} - \frac{1}{2}e^{-2x} + 2x + C$

35. $\frac{1}{2}x^2 + C$ **37.** $-8e^{-x/2} + C$ **39.** $2\sqrt{e^x + 1} + C$

41. $\frac{1}{4} \ln (2e^{2x} + 3) + C$ **43.** $e - 1$ **45.** $\frac{1}{6}(1 - \pi^{-6})$

47. $2 - \dfrac{1}{e}$ **49.** $\ln \frac{3}{2}$ **51.** $\frac{185}{72} + \ln \frac{4}{9}$

53. $\frac{1}{2}e + \frac{1}{2}$ **55.** $e^{-0.4} = \dfrac{1}{e^{0.4}} \cong \dfrac{1}{1.49} \cong 0.67$

57. $e^{2.8} = (e^2)(e^{0.8}) \cong (7.39)(2.23) \cong 16.48$

59. 7.61   **61.** 23.10

63. $x''(t) = Ac^2 e^{ct} + Bc^2 e^{-ct} = c^2(Ae^{ct} + Be^{-ct}) = c^2 x(t)$

65. $\frac{1}{2}(3e^4 + 1)$ **67.** $e^2 - e - 2$

69. (i) domain $(-\infty, \infty)$
  (ii) decreases on $(-\infty, 0]$, increases on $[0, \infty)$
  (iii) $f(0) = 1$ local and absolute min
  (iv) concave up everywhere
  (v) Figure A.7.4.1

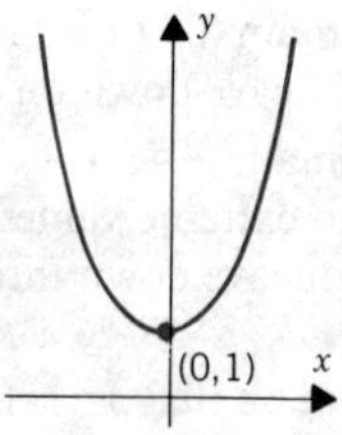

FIGURE A.7.4.1

71. (i) domain $(-\infty, \infty)$ (ii) decreases on $(-\infty, 0]$, increases on $[0, \infty)$
  (iii) $f(0) = 1$ local and absolute min   (iv) concave up everywhere
  (v) Figure A.7.4.2

73. (i) domain $(-\infty, \infty)$ (ii) decreases on $(-\infty, -1]$, increases on $[-1, \infty)$
  (iii) $f(-1) = -\dfrac{1}{e}$ local and absolute min
  (iv) concave down on $(-\infty, -2)$, concave up on $(-2, \infty)$; pt of inflection at $x = -2$
  (v) Figure A.7.4.3

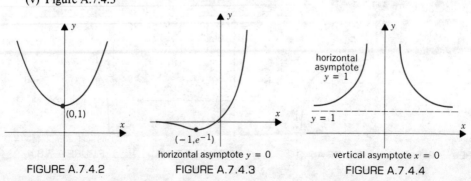

FIGURE A.7.4.2   FIGURE A.7.4.3   FIGURE A.7.4.4

75. (i) domain $(-\infty, 0) \cup (0, \infty)$

(ii) increases on $(-\infty, 0)$, decreases on $(0, \infty)$ (iii) no extreme values

(iv) concave up on $(-\infty, 0)$ and on $(0, \infty)$ (v) Figure A.7.4.4

77. Since for all $x > 0$

$$e^x > 1 + x, \qquad\qquad \text{(see the hint)}$$

the inequality is valid for $n = 1$. Suppose now that it is valid for $n = k$; that is, suppose that for all $x > 0$

(*) $$e^x > 1 + x + \frac{x^2}{2!} + \frac{x^3}{3!} + \cdots + \frac{x^k}{k!}.$$

Then, since

$$e^x = 1 + \int_0^x e^t \, dt,$$

we know from (*) that for all $x > 0$,

$$e^x > 1 + \int_0^x \left(1 + t + \frac{t^2}{2!} + \frac{t^3}{3!} + \cdots + \frac{t^k}{k!} \right) dt = 1 + x + \frac{x^2}{2!} + \frac{x^3}{3!} + \cdots + \frac{x^{k+1}}{(k+1)!},$$

and thus the inequality is valid for $n = k + 1$. This completes the induction and shows that the inequality is valid for all positive integers n.

SECTION 7.5

1. 6   **3.** $-\frac{1}{6}$ **5.** 0   **7.** 3   **9.** $\frac{3}{5}$ **11.** $-\frac{8}{5}$

13. $\log_p xy = \dfrac{\ln xy}{\ln p} = \dfrac{\ln x + \ln y}{\ln p} = \dfrac{\ln x}{\ln p} + \dfrac{\ln y}{\ln p} = \log_p x + \log_p y$

15. $\log_p x^y = \dfrac{\ln x^y}{\ln p} = y \dfrac{\ln x}{\ln p} = y \log_p x$

17. 0   **19.** 2   **21.** e^c, where $c = \dfrac{(\ln 2)^2}{\ln 2 - 1}$

23. $t_1 < \ln a < t_2$ **25.** $\dfrac{3^x}{\ln 3} + C$ **27.** $\frac{1}{4}x^4 - \dfrac{3^{-x}}{\ln 3} + C$

29. $\log_5 x + C$ **31.** $\dfrac{3}{\ln 4}(\ln x)^2 + C$ **33.** $\dfrac{10^{x^2}}{2 \ln 10} + C$

35. $\dfrac{1}{e \ln 3}$ **37.** $\dfrac{1}{e}$

39. $f(x) = p^x$

$\ln f(x) = x \ln p$

$\dfrac{f'(x)}{f(x)} = \ln p$

$f'(x) = p^x \ln p$

41. $(x + 1)^x \left[\dfrac{x}{x + 1} + \ln (x + 1) \right]$

43. $(\ln x)^{\ln x} \left[\dfrac{1 + \ln (\ln x)}{x} \right]$

45. $(x^2 + 2)^{\ln x} \left[\dfrac{2x \ln x}{x^2 + 2} + \dfrac{\ln (x^2 + 2)}{x} \right]$

47. Figure A.7.5.1   **49.** Figure A.7.5.2   **51.** Figure A.7.5.3   **53.** Figure A.7.5.4

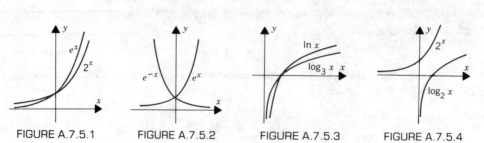

FIGURE A.7.5.1   FIGURE A.7.5.2   FIGURE A.7.5.3   FIGURE A.7.5.4

55. domain $(-\infty, \infty)$; increasing on $(-\infty, 0]$, decreasing on $[0, \infty)$; $f(0) = 10$ local and absolute max

57. domain $[-1, 1]$; increasing on $[-1, 0]$, decreasing on $[0, 1]$; $f(0) = 10$ local and absolute max, $f(-1) = f(1) = 1$ endpt and absolute min

59. $\dfrac{1}{4 \ln 2}$ **61.** 2   **63.** $\dfrac{45}{\ln 10}$ **65.** $(\ln 2)(\ln 10)$

67. $\dfrac{1}{3} + \dfrac{1}{\ln 2}$ **69.** $\log_{10} 7 = \dfrac{\ln 7}{\ln 10} \cong \dfrac{1.95}{2.30} \cong 0.85$

71. $\log_{10} 45 = \dfrac{\ln 45}{\ln 10} = \dfrac{\ln 9 + \ln 5}{\ln 10} \cong \dfrac{2.20 + 1.61}{2.30} \cong 1.66$

SECTION 7.6

1. $\frac{1}{3} \ln |\sec 3x| + C$ **3.** $\dfrac{1}{\pi} \ln |\csc \pi x - \cot \pi x| + C$

5. $\ln |\sin e^x| + C$ **7.** $\frac{1}{4} \ln |3 - 2 \cos 2x| + C$ **9.** $\frac{1}{3} e^{\tan 3x} + C$

11. $\frac{1}{2} \ln |\sec x^2 + \tan x^2| + C$ **13.** $\frac{1}{2}(\ln |\sin x|)^2 + C$

15. $x + 2 \ln |\sec x \tan x| + \tan x + C$ **17.** $\dfrac{1}{1 + \cot x} + C$

19. $\ln \frac{4}{3}$ **21.** $\frac{1}{2} \ln 2$ **23.** $\ln \left(\dfrac{1 + \sqrt{2}}{\sec 1 + \tan 1} \right)$

25. $\frac{1}{3}\pi - \frac{1}{2} \ln 3$ **27.** $\frac{1}{4}\pi - \frac{1}{2} \ln 3$

SECTION 7.7

1. 0   **3.** $\frac{1}{3}\pi$ **5.** $-\frac{1}{3}\pi$ **7.** 0

9. $-\frac{1}{6}\pi$ **11.** $\frac{1}{2}$ **13.** $-\frac{1}{4}\pi$ **15.** $\frac{1}{2}\sqrt{3}$

17. $\frac{1}{4}\pi$ **19.** $\frac{1}{2}\sqrt{3}$ **21.** 1.16   **23.** -0.46

25. 0.28   **27.** $\dfrac{1}{\sqrt{1 + x^2}}$ **29.** x **31.** $\sqrt{1 + x^2}$

33. $\sqrt{1 - x^2}$ **35.** $\dfrac{1}{x}\sqrt{1 + x^2}$ **37.** $\dfrac{x}{\sqrt{1 - x^2}}$ **39.** $\dfrac{1}{x^2 + 2x + 2}$

41. $\dfrac{2x}{\sqrt{1 - x^4}}$ **43.** $\dfrac{2x}{\sqrt{1 - 4x^2}} + \sin^{-1} 2x$ **45.** $\dfrac{2\sin^{-1} x}{\sqrt{1 - x^2}}$

47. $\dfrac{x - (1 + x^2)\tan^{-1} x}{x^2(1 + x^2)}$ **49.** $\dfrac{1}{(1 + 4x^2)\sqrt{\tan^{-1} 2x}}$ **51.** $\dfrac{1}{x[1 + (\ln x)^2]}$

53. $-\dfrac{r}{|r|\sqrt{1 - r^2}}$ **55.** $\dfrac{1}{1 + r^2}$ **57.** $\sqrt{\dfrac{c - x}{c + x}}$ **59.** $\dfrac{x^2}{(c^2 - x^2)^{3/2}}$

61. Set $\quad au = x + b, \quad a\,du = dx.$

$$\int \frac{dx}{\sqrt{a^2 - (x + b)^2}} = \int \frac{a\,du}{\sqrt{a^2 - a^2 u^2}} = \int \frac{du}{\sqrt{1 - u^2}} = \sin^{-1} u + C = \sin^{-1}\left(\frac{x + b}{a}\right) + C$$

63. $\frac{1}{4}\pi$ **65.** $\frac{1}{4}\pi$ **67.** $\frac{1}{20}\pi$ **69.** $\frac{1}{24}\pi$

71. $\frac{1}{6}\pi$ **73.** $\tan^{-1}(2) - \frac{1}{4}\pi$

75.

$$y = \sec^{-1} x$$
$$\sec y = x$$
$$\sec y \tan y \frac{dy}{dx} = 1$$
$$\frac{dy}{dx} = \cos y \cot y = \left(\frac{1}{x}\right)\left(\frac{1}{x\sqrt{1 - 1/x^2}}\right) = \frac{1}{|x|\sqrt{x^2 - 1}}$$

77. $\dfrac{d}{dx}(\cos^{-1} x) = -\dfrac{1}{\sqrt{1 - x^2}}$

SECTION 7.8

1. $2\sqrt{ab}$ **3.** $\left(\pm\dfrac{1}{\sqrt{2}}, \dfrac{1}{\sqrt{e}}\right)$ **5.** $x = \dfrac{1}{\sqrt{e}}$ **7.** 1

9. $\frac{1}{2}\ln 2$ **11.** $\frac{1}{6}\pi$ **13.** $\frac{1}{4}\pi$ **15.** $-\frac{1}{2}$

17. average slope $= \dfrac{1}{b - a}\displaystyle\int_a^b \dfrac{d}{dx}(\ln x)\,dx = \dfrac{1}{b - a}(\ln b - \ln a) = \dfrac{1}{b - a}\ln\dfrac{b}{a}$

19. $a^2 \ln 2$ **21.** (a) $45°$ (b) between $63°$ and $64°$ (c) about $31°$

23. $\pi \ln 4$ **25.** $\frac{1}{4}\pi^2$ **27.** $\frac{1}{2}\pi$

29. By the hint

$$\ln(m + 1) - \ln m < \frac{1}{m} < \ln m - \ln(m - 1)$$

$$\ln(m + 2) - \ln(m + 1) < \frac{1}{m + 1} < \ln(m + 1) - \ln m$$

$$\vdots \qquad \vdots$$

$$\ln(n + 1) - \ln n < \frac{1}{n} < \ln n - \ln(n - 1).$$

By addition

$$\underbrace{\ln{(n+1)} - \ln{m}}_{\displaystyle \ln \frac{n+1}{m}} < \frac{1}{m} + \frac{1}{m+1} + \cdots + \frac{1}{n} < \underbrace{\ln{n} - \ln{(m-1)}}_{\displaystyle \ln \frac{n}{m-1}}.$$

SECTION 7.9

1. $2x \cosh x^2$

3. $\dfrac{a \sinh ax}{2\sqrt{\cosh ax}}$

5. $\dfrac{1}{1 - \cosh x}$

7. $ab(\cosh bx - \sinh ax)$

9. $\dfrac{a \cosh ax}{\sinh ax}$

11. $\cosh^2 t - \sinh^2 t = \left(\dfrac{e^t + e^{-t}}{2}\right)^2 - \left(\dfrac{e^t - e^{-t}}{2}\right)^2$

$$= \frac{e^{2t} + 2 + e^{-2t}}{4} - \frac{e^{2t} - 2 + e^{-2t}}{4} = 1$$

13. $\cosh t \cosh s + \sinh t \sinh s = \left(\dfrac{e^t + e^{-t}}{2}\right)\left(\dfrac{e^s + e^{-s}}{2}\right) + \left(\dfrac{e^t - e^{-t}}{2}\right)\left(\dfrac{e^s - e^{-s}}{2}\right)$

$$= \tfrac{1}{4}(e^{t+s} + e^{s-t} + e^{t-s} + e^{-t-s} + e^{t+s} - e^{s-t} - e^{t-s} + e^{-t-s})$$
$$= \tfrac{1}{2}(e^{t+s} + e^{-(t+s)}) = \cosh{(t+s)}$$

15. $\cosh^2 t + \sinh^2 t = \left(\dfrac{e^t + e^{-t}}{2}\right)^2 + \left(\dfrac{e^t - e^{-t}}{2}\right)^2$

$$= \tfrac{1}{4}(e^{2t} + 2 + e^{-2t} + e^{2t} - 2 - e^{-2t}) = \frac{e^{2t} + e^{-2t}}{2} = \cosh 2t$$

17. absolute max -3

19. $[\cosh x + \sinh x]^n = \left[\dfrac{e^x + e^{-x}}{2} + \dfrac{e^x - e^{-x}}{2}\right]^n$

$$= [e^x]^n = e^{nx} = \frac{e^{nx} + e^{-nx}}{2} + \frac{e^{nx} - e^{-nx}}{2} = \cosh nx + \sinh nx$$

21. $A = 2$, $B = \tfrac{1}{3}$, $c = 3$

SECTION 7.10

1. $2 \tanh x \operatorname{sech}^2 x$

3. $\operatorname{sech} x \operatorname{csch} x$

5. $\dfrac{2e^{2x} \cosh{(\tan^{-1} e^{2x})}}{1 + e^{4x}}$

7. $\dfrac{-x \operatorname{csch}^2{(\sqrt{x^2 + 1})}}{\sqrt{x^2 + 1}}$

9. $\dfrac{-\operatorname{sech} x (\tanh x + 2 \sinh x)}{(1 + \cosh x)^2}$

11. $\dfrac{d}{dx}(\coth x) = \dfrac{d}{dx}\left(\dfrac{\cosh x}{\sinh x}\right) = \dfrac{\sinh^2 x - \cosh^2 x}{\sinh^2 x} = \dfrac{-1}{\sinh^2 x} = -\operatorname{csch}^2 x$

13. $\dfrac{d}{dx}(\operatorname{csch} x) = \dfrac{d}{dx}\left(\dfrac{1}{\sinh x}\right) = -\dfrac{\cosh x}{\sinh^2 x} = -\operatorname{csch} x \coth x$

15. (a) $\frac{3}{5}$ (b) $\frac{5}{3}$ (c) $\frac{4}{3}$ (d) $\frac{5}{4}$ (e) $\frac{3}{4}$

17. If $x \le 0$, the result is obvious. Suppose then that $x > 0$. Since $x^2 \ge 1$, we have $x \ge 1$.
Consequently,

$$x - 1 = \sqrt{x-1}\,\sqrt{x-1} \le \sqrt{x-1}\,\sqrt{x+1} = \sqrt{x^2-1} \quad \text{and therefore} \quad x - \sqrt{x^2-1} \le 1.$$

19. $\dfrac{d}{dx}(\sinh^{-1} x) = \dfrac{d}{dx}[\ln(x + \sqrt{x^2+1})] = \dfrac{1 + \dfrac{x}{\sqrt{x^2+1}}}{x + \sqrt{x^2+1}} = \dfrac{1}{\sqrt{x^2+1}}$

21. $\dfrac{d}{dx}(\tanh^{-1} x) = \dfrac{1}{2}\dfrac{d}{dx}\left[\ln\left(\dfrac{1+x}{1-x}\right)\right] = \dfrac{1}{2} \cdot \dfrac{1}{\left(\dfrac{1+x}{1-x}\right)} \cdot \dfrac{2}{(1-x)^2} = \dfrac{1}{1-x^2}$

23. (a) $\tan \phi = \sinh x$

$\phi = \tan^{-1}(\sinh x)$

$\dfrac{d\phi}{dx} = \dfrac{\cosh x}{1 + \sinh^2 x}$

$= \dfrac{\cosh x}{\cosh^2 x} = \dfrac{1}{\cosh x} = \operatorname{sech} x$

(b) $\sinh x = \tan \phi$

$x = \sinh^{-1}(\tan \phi)$

$= \ln(\tan \phi + \sqrt{\tan^2 \phi + 1})$

$= \ln(\tan \phi + \sec \phi)$

$= \ln(\sec \phi + \tan \phi)$

(c) $x = \ln(\sec \phi + \tan \phi)$

$\dfrac{dx}{d\phi} = \dfrac{\sec \phi \tan \phi + \sec^2 \phi}{\tan \phi + \sec \phi} = \sec \phi$

SECTION 8.2

1. $y = -\frac{1}{2} + Ce^{2x}$

3. $y = \frac{2}{5} + Ce^{-(5/2)x}$

5. $y = \frac{2}{3}nx + Cx^4$

7. $y = Ce^{e^x}$

9. $y = e^{-x^2}(\frac{1}{2}x^2 + C)$

11. $y = C(x+1)^{-2}$

13. $y = 3e^{-x} + 1$

15. $y = e^{-x}[\ln(1 + e^x) + e - \ln 2]$

17. $y = x^3 - x^2$

19. $y = e^{4-x^2}$

21. $y = 3x$

23. $y(Ce^x - \frac{1}{2}e^{3x}) = 1$

25. $y^2(1 + Ce^{x^2}) = 1$

27. $y^2 \sec^2 x = 2x + C$

29. $y^2_* = x^2(x^2 + C)$

31. Set $v = y^{1-k}$. Then

$$\frac{dv}{dx} = (1-k)y^{-k}\frac{dy}{dx}$$

and Bernoulli's equation

$$\frac{dy}{dx} + p(x)y = q(x)y^k$$

takes the form

$$\frac{y^k}{1-k}\frac{dv}{dx} + p(x)y = q(x)y^k \quad \text{or} \quad v' + (1-k)p(x)v = (1-k)q(x).$$

SECTION 8.3

1. (a) about \$411 $(e^{0.6} \cong 1.822)$
   (b) about \$613 $(e^{0.8} \cong 2.226)$
   (c) about \$859 $(e \cong 2.718)$

3. (a) about \$741 $(e^{-0.3} \cong 0.741)$
   (b) about \$670 $(e^{-0.4} \cong 0.670)$
   (c) about \$607 $(e^{-0.5} \cong 0.607)$

5. about $5\frac{1}{2}\%$

7. $20 + 5e^{-0.03t}$ lbs

9. $200(\frac{4}{5})^{t^2/25}$ liters

11. $\dfrac{4 \ln 2}{\ln 4 - \ln 3} \cong 9.5$ years

13. $5(\frac{4}{5})^{5/2} \cong 2.86$ gms

15. $100(1 - (\frac{1}{2})^{1/n})\%$

17. (a) $15e^{-(1/2)\ln 1.5} = 15\sqrt{\frac{2}{3}} \cong 12.2$ lbs   (b) $15e^{-(3/2)\ln 1.5} = 15(\frac{2}{3})^{3/2} \cong 8.2$ lbs

19. 640 lbs

21. $(\frac{227}{203})^2\, 203 \cong 254$ million in 1990, $(\frac{227}{203})^3\, 203 \cong 284$ million in 2000

23. about $16\frac{1}{2}$ years

25. (a) about \$3486 $(e^{0.15} \cong 1.162)$
    (b) about \$3813 $(e^{0.24} \cong 1.271)$
    (c) about \$4299 $(e^{0.36} \cong 1.433)$

27. The unique solution of $v'(t) + Kv(t) = 32$ that satisfies the side condition $v(0) = 0$ is the function

$$v(t) = \frac{32}{K}\,(1 - e^{-Kt}).$$

At each time t, $1 - e^{-Kt} < 1$.   With $K > 0$,

$$v(t) = \frac{32}{K}\,(1 - e^{-Kt}) < \frac{32}{K}.$$

29. $\dfrac{2 \ln 3}{\ln \frac{4}{3}} - 2 \cong 5.66$ min

31. $\dfrac{176}{\ln 2} \cong 254$ ft

33. $\dfrac{1}{k} \ln q$

SECTION 8.4

1. $2 \ln |y| + \cos (2x + 3) = C$

3. $\sin y - \cos x = C$

5. $y^2(x^4 + C) + 2 = 0$

7. $\frac{1}{3}x^3 + \frac{1}{2}e^{-y^2} = C$

9. $y^2 = C(1 + x)^2 - 1$

11. $y^2 = 2 \ln |Cx|$

13. $(2x - 3)(4 - y^2) = C$

15. $y + 2 = 2y\sqrt{1 - x^2}$

17. $y = \tan (e^x - 1)$

19. $1 + y^3 = 9e^{x^3}$

21. By the hint,

$$\left[\frac{1}{P(t)} + \frac{1}{M - P(t)}\right] P'(t) = k,$$

so that

$$\ln P(t) - \ln [M - P(t)] = kt + C'$$

$$\frac{P(t)}{M - P(t)} = C''e^{kt} \qquad\qquad (C'' = e^{C'})$$

$$P(t)(1 + C''e^{kt}) = C''Me^{kt}$$

$$P(t) = \frac{M}{1 + Ce^{-kt}}. \qquad\qquad \left(C = \frac{1}{C''}\right)$$

23. $y + x \ln y = Cx$

25. $\ln (x^2 + y^2) - 2 \tan^{-1} (y/x) = C.$

27. $(y^2 - x^2)^2 = Cx^3$

29. circles $x^2 + y^2 = K$

31. hyperbolas $x^2 - y^2 = K$

33. parabolas $x = -\frac{1}{2}y^2 + K$

SECTION 8.5

1. $x(t) = \sin (8t + \frac{1}{2}\pi); \; a = 1, f = 4/\pi$

3. $\pm \dfrac{2\pi a}{p}$

5. $x(t) = (15/\pi) \sin \frac{1}{3}\pi t$

7. $x = \pm\frac{1}{2}\sqrt{3} \, C_1$

9. $x(t) = x_0 \sin (\sqrt{k/m} \, t + \frac{1}{2}\pi)$

11. Set $y(t) = x(t) - 2$. Equation $x''(t) = 8 - 4x(t)$ can be written $y''(t) + 4y(t) = 0$. This is simple harmonic motion about the point $y = 0$; that is, about the point $x = 2$.

$$y(t) = C_1 \sin (2t + C_2).$$

The condition $x(0) = 0$ gives $y(0) = -2$ and thus

(∗)
$$C_1 \sin C_2 = -2.$$

Since $y'(t) = x'(t)$ and $y'(t) = 2C_1 \cos (2t + C_2)$, the condition $x'(0) = 0$ gives $y'(0) = 0$ and thus

(∗∗)
$$2C_1 \cos C_2 = 0.$$

It follows from (∗) and (∗∗) that $C_1 = -2$ and $C_2 = \frac{1}{2}\pi$. The equation of motion can be written

$$y(t) = -2 \sin (2t + \frac{1}{2}\pi).$$

The amplitude is 2 and the period is π.

13. (a) $x''(t) + \beta^2 x(t) = 0$ with $\beta = r\sqrt{\pi \rho/m}$

    (b) $x(t) = x_0 \sin (r\sqrt{\pi \rho/m} \, t + \frac{1}{2}\pi)$, taking downward as positive amplitude x_0, period $(2/r)\sqrt{m\pi/\rho}$

SECTION 8.6

1. $y = C_1 e^{-5x} + C_2 e^{3x}$

3. $y = C_1 e^{-4x} + C_2 x e^{-4x} = (C_1 + C_2 x)e^{-4x}$

5. $y = e^{-x}(C_1 \cos 2x + C_2 \sin 2x)$

7. $y = C_1 + C_2 e^{(4/3)x}$

9. $y = C_1 \cos 2\sqrt{3}x + C_2 \sin 2\sqrt{3}x$

11. $y = C_1 e^{-3x} + C_2 e^{(1/2)x}$

13. $y = 2e^{2x} - e^{3x}$

15. $y = 2 \cos \frac{1}{2}x + \sin \frac{1}{2}x$

17. (a) $y = Ce^{2x} + (1 - C)e^{-x}$ (b) $y = Ce^{2x} + (2C - 1)e^{-x}$ (c) $y = \frac{2}{3}e^{2x} + \frac{1}{3}e^{-x}$

19. $\frac{1}{2}x + \frac{1}{4}$

21. $\frac{1}{5}x^2 - \frac{4}{25}x - \frac{27}{125}$

23. $-\frac{13}{170} \cos x - \frac{1}{170} \sin x$

25. $\frac{3}{100} \cos 2x + \frac{21}{100} \sin 2x$

27. $\frac{1}{36}e^{3x}$

29. $C_1 \cos x + C_2 \sin x + \frac{1}{2}e^x$

31. $C_1 e^{-2x} + C_2 e^{5x} + \frac{1}{10}x + \frac{7}{100}$

33. $(y_1 + y_2)'' + a(y_1 + y_2)' + b(y_1 + y_2) = (y_1'' + ay_1' + by) + (y_2'' + ay_2' + by_2)$
$$= \phi_1(x) + \phi_2(x)$$

35. $-\frac{1}{6}x - \frac{1}{36} - \frac{7}{50} \sin x - \frac{1}{50} \cos x$

37. Set $s = r_1$ to simplify notation. Then $s^2 + as + b = 0$ with $a^2 - 4b = 0$, so $s = -\frac{1}{2}a$ is the only real root of the characteristic equation. First we show that $y_1 = e^{sx}$ and $y_2 = xe^{sx}$ are solutions:

$$y_1'' + ay_1' + by_1 = s^2 e^{sx} + ase^{sx} + be^{sx} = (s^2 + as + b)e^{sx} = 0,$$

$$y_2'' + ay_2' + by_2 = (s^2x + 2s)e^{sx} + a(sx + 1)e^{sx} + bxe^{sx}$$

$$= x(s^2 + as + b)e^{sx} + (2s + a)e^{sx} = 0 + 0 = 0.$$

Next we show that the Wronskian is never zero:

$$y_1(x)y_2'(x) - y_1'(x)y_2(x) = (e^{sx})(e^{sx}(sx + 1)) - (se^{sx})(xe^{sx}) = e^{sx} \neq 0.$$

39. (a) $y = C_1 e^{100(-5+\sqrt{5})x} + C_2 e^{100(-5-\sqrt{5})x}$
(b) $y = C_1 e^{-500x} + C_2 xe^{-500x} = (C_1 + C_2 x)e^{-500x}$
(c) $y = e^{-500x}(C_1 \cos 500x + C_2 \sin 500x)$

41. Follows directly from

$$(ve^{kx})'' + a(ve^{kx})' + b(ve^{kx}) = e^{kx}[v'' + (2k + a)v' + (k^2 + ak + b)v].$$

43. $D_1 e^{\beta x} + D_2 e^{-\beta x} = (D_1 + D_2)\left(\dfrac{e^{\beta x} + e^{-\beta x}}{2}\right) + (D_1 - D_2)\left(\dfrac{e^{\beta x} - e^{-\beta x}}{2}\right)$

$$= C_1 \cosh \beta x + C_2 \sinh \beta x \quad \text{with } C_1 = D_1 + D_2 \text{ and } C_2 = D_1 - D_2$$

SECTION 8.7

1. amplitude and frequency both decrease   **3.** at most once, at most once
5. if $\beta/\gamma = m/n$, then $m/\beta = n/\gamma$ is a period
7. $x = e^{-\alpha t}[c_1 \cos(\sqrt{\beta^2 - \alpha^2}\, t) + c_2 \sin(\sqrt{\beta^2 - \alpha^2}\, t)]$ or equivalently
$x = C_1 e^{-\alpha t}[\sin(\sqrt{\beta^2 - \alpha^2}\, t) + C_2]$
9. $x_P = \dfrac{F_0}{2\alpha\gamma m} \sin \gamma t$; as $c = 2\alpha m \to 0^+$, the amplitude $\dfrac{F_0}{2\alpha\gamma m} = \dfrac{F_0}{cm} \to \infty$
11. $(\beta^2 - \gamma^2)^2 + 4\alpha^2\gamma^2 = \beta^2 + \gamma^4 + 2\gamma^2(2\alpha^2 - \beta^2)$ increases as γ increases

SECTION 8.8

1. Figure A.8.8.1   **3.** Figure A.8.8.2

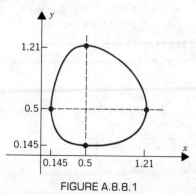

FIGURE A.8.8.1

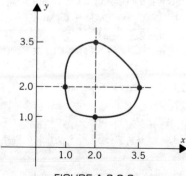

FIGURE A.8.8.2

5. $f(z) = e^{-mz} z^p$

$f'(z) = e^{-mz} z^{p-1} (p - mz)$

$f''(z) = e^{-mz} z^{p-2} [m^2 z^2 - 2mpz + p(p - 1)]$

The function has its maximum at $z = p/m$. Since p and m are positive, $f(z) \to 0$ as $z \to 0^+$ and as $z \to \infty$. The graph has an inflection point at $z = (p + \sqrt{p})/m$ and, if $p > 1$, at $z = (p - \sqrt{p})/m$. (We are assuming here that $z \geq 0$.)

7. Let $\bar{x}$ denote the average value of x on $[0, T]$. By the hint,

$$\int_0^T \frac{1}{y} \frac{dy}{dt}\, dt = \int_0^T (a - sx)\, dt$$

$$\underbrace{\ln y(T) - \ln y(0)}_{0} = aT - sT \underbrace{\left[\frac{1}{T} \int_0^T x\, dt\right]}_{\bar{x}}$$

Thus, $0 = T(a - s\bar{x})$ and $\bar{x} = a/s$.

9. We combine $\dfrac{dy}{dt} = \dfrac{b}{r}(a - sx)$ and $\dfrac{dx}{dt} = \dfrac{a}{s}(ry - b)$ to obtain

$$\frac{d^2 y}{dt^2} = -\frac{bs}{r} \frac{dx}{dt} = -\frac{bs}{r}\left[\frac{a}{s}(ry - b)\right] = -\frac{ab}{r}(ry - b)$$

and thus

(∗) $$\frac{d^2 y}{dt^2} + aby = \frac{ab^2}{r}.$$

Set $\beta = \sqrt{ab}$. The general solution of (∗) is given by

(1) $$y = C_1 \cos \beta t + C_2 \sin \beta t + \frac{b}{r}.$$

Then

$$\frac{dx}{dt} = \frac{a}{s}[C_1 r \cos \beta t + C_2 r \sin \beta t]$$

so that

(2) $$x = \frac{ar}{s\beta}[C_1 \sin \beta t - C_2 \cos \beta t] + K_1.$$

We can combine (1) and (2) as follows:

$$\left(y - \frac{b}{r}\right)^2 + \left(\frac{s\beta}{ar}\right)^2 (x - K_1)^2 = (C_1 \cos \beta t + C_2 \sin \beta t)^2 + (C_1 \sin \beta t - C_2 \cos \beta t)^2$$

$$= C_1^2 + C_2^2.$$

Taking $K_2 = C_1^2 + C_2^2$, we have

$$\left(y - \frac{b}{r}\right)^2 + \left(\frac{s\beta}{ar}\right)^2 (x - K_1)^2 = K_2. \qquad\qquad (\beta = \sqrt{ab})$$

11.
$$\frac{dy}{dx} = \frac{dy/dt}{dx/dt} = \frac{bs\,(a - sx)}{ar\,(b - ry)}$$

$$2ar(ry - b)\, dy - 2bs(sx - a)\, dx = 0$$

$$a(ry - b)^2 - b(sx - a)^2 = C.$$

With $C \neq 0$ the trajectory is the hyperbola

$$\frac{\left(y - \frac{b}{r}\right)^2}{C/ar^2} - \frac{\left(x - \frac{a}{s}\right)^2}{C/bs^2} = 1$$

with center at the equilibrium point $(a/s, b/r)$.

SECTION 8.9

1. (a) 2.48832, rel. error 8.46%   (b) 2.71825, rel. error 0.001%
3. (a) 2.59374, rel. error 4.58%   (b) 2.71828, rel. error 0%
5. (a) 1.9, rel. error 5.0%   (b) 2.0, rel. error 0%
7. (a) 1.42052, rel. error −0.45%   (b) 1.41421, rel. error 0%
9. (a) 2.65330, rel. error 2.39%   (b) 2.71828, rel. error 0%

SECTION 9.1

1. $-e^{2-x} + C$ 3. $\dfrac{2}{\pi}$ 5. $-\tan(1 - x) + C$

7. $\frac{1}{2}\ln 3$ 9. $-\sqrt{1 - x^2} + C$ 11. 0

13. $e - \sqrt{e}$ 15. $\frac{1}{2}\ln(x^2 + 1) + C$ 17. $\dfrac{\pi}{4c}$

19. $\dfrac{2}{3}\sqrt{3\tan\theta + 1} + C$ 21. $\dfrac{\ln|ae^x - b|}{a} + C$ 23. $-\frac{1}{2}(\cot 2x + \csc 2x) + C$

25. $\frac{1}{2}\ln[(x + 1)^2 + 4] - \frac{1}{2}\tan^{-1}\left(\dfrac{x + 1}{2}\right) + C$

27. $\frac{1}{2}\sin^{-1} x^2 + C$ 29. $\tan^{-1}(x + 3) + C$ 31. $-\frac{1}{2}\cos x^2 + C$
33. $\frac{1}{4}\sinh 2x - \frac{1}{2}x + C$ 35. $\frac{1}{3}\cosh^3 x - \cosh x + C$

SECTION 9.2

1. $-xe^{-x} - e^{-x} + C$ 3. $\frac{1}{3}x^3 \ln x - \frac{1}{9}x^3 + C$ 5. $-\frac{1}{3}e^{-x^3} + C$
7. $-e^{-x}(x^2 + 2x + 2) + C$ 9. $-2x^2(1 - x)^{1/2} - \frac{8}{3}x(1 - x)^{3/2} - \frac{16}{15}(1 - x)^{5/2} + C$
11. $\frac{1}{4}x^2 \ln x - \frac{1}{8}x^2 + C$ 13. $2\sqrt{x + 1}\ln(x + 1) - 4\sqrt{x + 1} + C$
15. $x(\ln x)^2 - 2x \ln x + 2x + C$

17. $3^x\left(\dfrac{x^3}{\ln 3} - \dfrac{3x^2}{(\ln 3)^2} + \dfrac{6x}{(\ln 3)^3} - \dfrac{6}{(\ln 3)^4}\right) + C$

19. $\frac{1}{15}x(x + 5)^{15} - \frac{1}{240}(x + 5)^{16} + C$ 21. $x \sin x + \cos x + C$
23. $\frac{1}{10}x^2(x + 1)^{10} - \frac{1}{55}x(x + 1)^{11} + \frac{1}{660}(x + 1)^{12} + C$
25. $\frac{1}{2}e^x(\sin x - \cos x) + C$ 27. $x \ln(1 + x^2) - 2x + 2\tan^{-1} x + C$

29. $\frac{1}{2}(x^2 + 1) \tan^{-1} x - \frac{1}{2}x + C$

31. $\dfrac{x^{n+1}}{n+1} \ln x - \dfrac{x^{n+1}}{(n+1)^2} + C$

33. $e^{2x}(-\frac{3}{13} \cos 3x + \frac{2}{13} \sin 3x) + C$

35. $x \sinh x - \cosh x + C$

37. $-\frac{1}{2}x^2 \cos x^2 + \frac{1}{2} \sin x^2 + C$

39. $e^x(x^4 - 4x^3 + 12x^2 - 24x + 24) + C$

41. Set $\quad u = \sin^{-1} x, \qquad dv = dx.$

$$du = \frac{dx}{\sqrt{1 - x^2}}, \qquad v = x.$$

$$\int \sin^{-1} x \, dx = uv - \int v \, du = x \sin^{-1} x - \int \frac{x \, dx}{\sqrt{1 - x^2}} = x \sin^{-1} x + \sqrt{1 - x^2} + C$$

43. (a) \$3700   (b) \$3425

45. (a) \$2008   (b) \$1913

47. (a) \$1009   (b) \$982

49. (a) \$2964   (b) \$2761

SECTION 9.3

1. $\ln \left| \dfrac{x-2}{x+5} \right| + C$

3. $5 \ln |x - 1| - 3 \ln |x| + \dfrac{3}{x} + C$

5. $\dfrac{1}{4}x^4 + \dfrac{4}{3}x^3 + 6x^2 + 32x - \dfrac{32}{x-2} + 80 \ln |x - 2| + C$

7. $5 \ln |x - 2| - 4 \ln |x - 1| + C$

9. $\dfrac{-1}{2(x-1)^2} + C$

11. $\dfrac{3}{4} \ln |x - 1| - \dfrac{1}{2(x-1)} + \dfrac{1}{4} \ln |x + 1| + C$

13. $\dfrac{1}{32} \ln \left| \dfrac{x-2}{x+2} \right| - \dfrac{1}{16} \tan^{-1} \dfrac{x}{2} + C$

15. $\dfrac{1}{2} \ln (x^2 + 1) + \dfrac{3}{2} \tan^{-1} x + \dfrac{5(1 - x)}{2(x^2 + 1)} + C$

17. $\dfrac{1}{16} \ln \left[\dfrac{x^2 + 2x + 2}{x^2 - 2x + 2} \right] + \dfrac{1}{8} \tan^{-1}(x + 1) + \dfrac{1}{8} \tan^{-1}(x - 1) + C$

19. Note that

$$y = \frac{1}{x^2 - 1} = \frac{1}{2} \left[\frac{1}{x - 1} - \frac{1}{x + 1} \right]$$

and thus

$$\frac{d^0 y}{dx^0} = \left(\frac{1}{2} \right) (-1)^0 \, 0! \left[\frac{1}{(x - 1)^{0+1}} - \frac{1}{(x + 1)^{0+1}} \right].$$

The rest is a routine induction.

21. (a) $C(t) = 2A_0 \left(\dfrac{t}{t+1} \right)$ (b) $C(t) = 4A_0 \dfrac{3^t - 2^t}{2(3^t) - 2^t}$

(c) $C(t) = A_0(m + n) \left(\dfrac{m^t - n^t}{m^{t+1} - n^{t+1}} \right)$

SECTION 9.4

1. $\frac{1}{3}\cos^3 x - \cos x + C$ 3. $\frac{1}{2}x - \frac{1}{12}\sin 6x + C$ 5. $\frac{2}{3}$

7. $-\frac{1}{5}\cos^5 x + \frac{1}{7}\cos^7 x + C$ 9. $\frac{1}{4}\sin^4 x - \frac{1}{6}\sin^6 x + C$

11. $\frac{1}{3}\sin^3 x - \frac{1}{5}\sin^5 x + C$ 13. $\frac{3}{8}\pi$

15. $\frac{1}{2}\cos x - \frac{1}{10}\cos 5x + C$ 17. $\frac{1}{2}\sin^4 x + C$

19. $\frac{3}{128}x - \frac{1}{128}\sin 4x + \frac{1}{1024}\sin 8x + C$ 21. $\frac{8}{15}$

23. $\frac{1}{10}\sin 5x + \frac{1}{2}\sin x + C$

25. $\frac{3}{8}\tan^{-1} x + \frac{x}{2(x^2 + 1)} + \frac{x(1 - x^2)}{8(x^2 + 1)^2} + C$

27. $\frac{1}{2}\left[\tan^{-1}(x + 1) + \frac{x + 1}{x^2 + 2x + 2}\right] + C$

29. 1   31. 0   33. 0

SECTION 9.5

1. $\frac{1}{3}\tan 3x - x + C$ 3. $\frac{1}{\pi}\tan \pi x + C$

5. $\frac{1}{2}\tan^2 x + \ln|\cos x| + C$ 7. $\frac{1}{3}\tan^3 x + C$

9. $-\frac{1}{2}\csc x \cot x + \frac{1}{2}\ln|\csc x - \cot x| + C$

11. $-\frac{1}{3}\cot^3 x + \cot x + x + C$ 13. $-\frac{1}{5}\csc^5 x + \frac{1}{3}\csc^3 x + C$

15. $-\frac{1}{6}\cot^3 2x - \frac{1}{2}\cot 2x + C$ 17. $-\frac{1}{2}\cot x \csc x - \frac{1}{2}\ln|\csc x - \cot x| + C$

19. $\frac{1}{12}\tan^4 3x - \frac{1}{6}\tan^2 3x + \frac{1}{3}\ln|\sec 3x| + C$

21. $\frac{1}{4}\sec^3 x \tan x + \frac{3}{8}\sec x \tan x + \frac{3}{8}\ln|\sec x + \tan x| + C$

23. $\frac{1}{7}\tan^7 x + \frac{1}{5}\tan^5 x + C$

SECTION 9.6

1. $\sin^{-1}\left(\frac{x}{a}\right) + C$ 3. $\frac{x}{5\sqrt{5 - x^2}} + C$

5. $\sqrt{3} - \frac{1}{2}\ln(2 + \sqrt{3})$ 7. $2\sin^{-1}\left(\frac{x}{2}\right) - \frac{1}{2}x\sqrt{4 - x^2} + C$

9. $\frac{1}{\sqrt{1 - x^2}} + C$ 11. $\frac{x}{\sqrt{1 - x^2}} - \sin^{-1} x + C$

13. $-\frac{1}{3}(4 - x^2)^{3/2} + C$ 15. $\ln(\sqrt{8 + x^2} + x) - \frac{x}{\sqrt{8 + x^2}} + C$

17. $\frac{1}{a}\ln\left|\frac{a - \sqrt{a^2 - x^2}}{x}\right| + C$ 19. $\ln|x + \sqrt{x^2 - a^2}| + C$

21. $\frac{1}{2}e^x\sqrt{e^{2x} - 1} - \frac{1}{2}\ln|e^x + \sqrt{e^{2x} - 1}| + C$ 23. $-\frac{1}{a^2 x}\sqrt{a^2 + x^2} + C$

25. $\dfrac{1}{a^2 x}\sqrt{x^2 - a^2} + C$

27. $\frac{1}{9}e^{-x}\sqrt{e^{2x} - 1} + C$

29. $-\dfrac{1}{2(x - 2)^2} + C$

31. $-\frac{1}{3}(6x - x^2 - 8)^{3/2} + \frac{3}{2}\sin^{-1}(x - 3) + \frac{3}{2}(x - 3)\sqrt{6x - x^2 - 8} + C$

33. $\dfrac{x^2 + x}{8(x^2 + 2x + 5)} - \dfrac{1}{16}\tan^{-1}\left(\dfrac{x + 1}{2}\right) + C$

35. $\sqrt{x^2 + 4x + 13} + \ln\left|\dfrac{x + 2 + \sqrt{x^2 + 4x + 13}}{3}\right| + C$

37. $\frac{1}{2}(x - 3)\sqrt{6x - x^2 - 8} + \frac{1}{2}\sin^{-1}(x - 3) + C$

39. $-\frac{1}{5}(8 - 2x - x^2)^{5/2} - \dfrac{243}{8}\sin^{-1}\left(\dfrac{x + 1}{3}\right) - \dfrac{1}{8}(x + 1)(43 - 4x - 2x^2)(8 - 2x - x^2)^{1/2}$

41. $\displaystyle\underbrace{\int \sqrt{x^2 - a^2}\,dx}_{(x\,=\,a\,\cosh\,u)} = a^2\int \sinh^2 u\,du = \tfrac{1}{2}a^2\int (\cosh 2u - 1)\,du$

$\qquad\qquad = \tfrac{1}{2}a^2(\tfrac{1}{2}\sinh 2u - u) + C$

$\qquad\qquad = \tfrac{1}{2}a^2(\sinh u \cosh u - u) + C = \dfrac{1}{2}x\sqrt{x^2 - a^2} - \dfrac{1}{2}a^2\cosh^{-1}\left(\dfrac{x}{a}\right) + C$

SECTION 9.7

1. $\tan\frac{1}{2}x + C$

3. $\dfrac{2}{1 - \tan\frac{1}{2}x} + C$

5. $\frac{1}{2}\sqrt{2}\,\tan^{-1}\frac{1}{2}\sqrt{2}$

7. $-\frac{1}{3}x + \frac{5}{6}\tan^{-1}(2\tan\frac{1}{2}x) + C$

9. $\frac{1}{2}(x + \ln|\cos x + \sin x|) + C$

11. $\tan\frac{1}{2}x + 2\ln|\sec\frac{1}{2}x| + C$

SECTION 9.8

1. $-2(\sqrt{x} + \ln|1 - \sqrt{x}|) + C$

3. $2\ln(\sqrt{1 + e^x} - 1) - x + 2\sqrt{1 + e^x} + C$

5. $\frac{2}{5}(1 + x)^{5/2} - \frac{2}{3}(1 + x)^{3/2} + C$

7. $\frac{2}{5}(x - 1)^{5/2} + 2(x - 1)^{3/2} + C$

9. $-\dfrac{1 + 2x^2}{4(1 + x^2)^2} + C$

11. $x + 2\sqrt{x} + 2\ln|\sqrt{x} - 1| + C$

13. $x + 4\sqrt{x - 1} + 4\ln|\sqrt{x - 1} - 1| + C$

15. $\ln\left(\dfrac{\sqrt{e^x + 1} - 1}{\sqrt{e^x + 1} + 1}\right) + C$

17. $\frac{2}{3}(x - 8)\sqrt{x + 4} + C$

19. $\frac{1}{16}(4x + 1)^{1/2} + \frac{1}{8}(4x + 1)^{-1/2} - \frac{1}{48}(4x + 1)^{-3/2} + C$

21. $\dfrac{4b + 2ax}{a^2\sqrt{ax + b}} + C$

SECTION 9.9

1. (a) 506   (b) 650   (c) 572   (d) 578   (e) 576
3. (a) 1.39   (b) 0.91   (c) 1.18   (d) 1.15   (e) 1.16
5. (a) $\frac{1}{4}\pi \cong 0.78$ (b) $\frac{1}{4}\pi \cong 0.79$
7. Such a curve passes through the three points $(a_1, b_1), (a_2, b_2),(a_3, b_3)$ iff

$$b_1 = a_1^2 A + a_1 B + C, \qquad b_2 = a_2^2 A + a_2 B + C, \qquad b_3 = a_3^2 A + a_3 B + C,$$

which happens iff

$$A = \frac{b_1(a_2 - a_3) - b_2(a_1 - a_3) + b_3(a_1 - a_2)}{(a_1 - a_3)(a_1 - a_2)(a_2 - a_3)},$$

$$B = -\frac{b_1(a_2^2 - a_3^2) - b_2(a_1^2 - a_3^2) + b_3(a_1^2 - a_2^2)}{(a_1 - a_3)(a_1 - a_2)(a_2 - a_3)},$$

$$C = \frac{a_1^2(a_2 b_3 - a_3 b_2) - a_2^2(a_1 b_3 - a_3 b_1) + a_3^2(a_1 b_2 - a_2 b_1)}{(a_1 - a_3)(a_1 - a_2)(a_2 - a_3)}.$$

9. (a) $n \geq 8$ (b) $n \geq 4$ 11. (a) $n \geq 238$ (b) $n \geq 19$
13. (a) $n \geq 51$ (b) $n \geq 7$ 15. (a) $n \geq 37$ (b) $n \geq 5$
17. Any polynomial function of degree 3 or less will do, for then $f^{(4)}(c)$ is necessarily zero.
19. First we justify the claim in the hint. Each of the given expressions is a weighted average and as such must lie between the largest and smallest of the quantities being averaged, here values of f. Thus, for each i, the expressions certainly lie between m_i and M_i.

Now we consider T_n. For each i, by the intermediate-value theorem, there exists x_i^* in $[x_{i-1}, x_i]$ such that $f(x_i^*) = \frac{1}{2}[f(x_{i-1}) + f(x_i)]$. Thus

$$T_n = \frac{b - a}{n}[f(x_1^*) + f(x_2^*) + \cdots + f(x_n^*)],$$

a Riemann sum. A similar argument shows that S_n can be written as a Riemann sum.

SECTION 9.10

1. $\dfrac{10^{nx}}{n \ln 10} + C$ 3. $\frac{1}{3}(2x + 1)^{3/2} + C$ 5. $\ln |\sec e^x| + C$

7. $\dfrac{1}{ab} \tan^{-1}\left(\dfrac{ax}{b}\right) + C$ 9. $x \ln (x\sqrt{x}) - \frac{2}{3}x + C$ 11. $\frac{1}{3}(x^2 - 2)\sqrt{1 + x^2} + C$

13. $\dfrac{1}{2} x - \dfrac{n}{4\pi} \sin\left(\dfrac{2\pi}{n} x\right) + C$ 15. $\dfrac{2\sqrt{x}}{a} - \dfrac{2b}{a^2} \ln |a\sqrt{x} + b| + C$

17. $-\frac{1}{3} \ln (2 + \cos 3x) + C$ 19. $\frac{1}{2} \tan^2 x + C$

21. $\dfrac{1}{2} \sqrt{2}\left[\ln \left|\tan\left(\dfrac{x}{2}\right) + 1 + \sqrt{2}\right| - \ln \left|\tan\left(\dfrac{x}{2}\right) + 1 - \sqrt{2}\right|\right] + C$

23. $a \sin^{-1}\left(\dfrac{x}{a}\right) - \sqrt{a^2 - x^2} + C$ 25. $-\left(\dfrac{1}{x}\right)\sqrt{a^2 - x^2} - \sin^{-1}\left(\dfrac{x}{a}\right) + C$

27. $\ln |x + 1| + \dfrac{1}{x + 1} + C$

29. $\frac{1}{3} \sec^3 2x - \sec 2x - x + C$

31. $\dfrac{x^2}{2} \ln (ax + b) - \dfrac{x^2}{4} + \dfrac{bx}{2a} - \dfrac{b^2}{2a^2} \ln (ax + b) + C$

33. $\frac{2}{3}(x + 1)^{3/2} + \frac{2}{3} x^{3/2} + C$

35. $x - \tan^{-1} x + C$

37. $\frac{1}{2} x\sqrt{1 - x^2} - \frac{1}{2} \sin^{-1} x + C$

39. $\dfrac{1}{4} \sinh 2x - \dfrac{x}{2} + C$

41. $\frac{1}{2} x - \frac{1}{4} e^{-2x} + C$

43. $\frac{1}{2}(x^2 - 8) \tan^{-1}(x - 3) - \frac{3}{2} \ln |x^2 - 6x + 10| - \frac{1}{2} x + C$

45. $\ln \left(\dfrac{x^2}{x^2 + 1} \right) + C$

47. $-\cot x - \frac{3}{2} x - \frac{1}{4} \sin 2x + C$

49. $\sqrt{x^2 + 4} + 2 \ln \left| \dfrac{\sqrt{x^2 + 4} - 2}{x} \right| + C$

51. $\dfrac{1}{3} \ln \left| \dfrac{3 - \sqrt{9 - x^2}}{x} \right| + C$

53. $\dfrac{\sqrt{2}}{4} \left[\ln \left| \tan \left(\dfrac{x}{2} \right) + 3 - 2\sqrt{2} \right| - \ln \left| \tan \left(\dfrac{x}{2} \right) + 3 + 2\sqrt{2} \right| \right] + C$

55. $\ln |1 + \sqrt{1 - e^{2x}}| - x + C$

57. $\sec x + \ln |\csc x - \cot x| + C$

59. $4 \sin x - \frac{8}{3} \sin^3 x + C$

61. $-2 \cos \dfrac{x}{2} + \dfrac{4}{3} \cos^3 \dfrac{x}{2} - \dfrac{2}{5} \cos^5 \dfrac{x}{2} + C$

63. $-\csc x + C$

65. $\ln |\sec x + \tan x| + C$

67. $\frac{1}{3} x^3 \sin^{-1} x + \frac{1}{3}(1 - x^2)^{1/2} - \frac{1}{9}(1 - x^2)^{3/2} + C$

69. $\frac{1}{3}(x^2 + 2x - 8)^{3/2} - \frac{1}{2}(x + 1)\sqrt{x^2 + 2x - 8} + \frac{9}{2} \ln |x + 1 + \sqrt{x^2 + 2x - 8}| + C$

71. $\tan^{-1} (2x - 1) + C$

73. $\frac{7}{8} x + \frac{1}{32} \sin 4x - \frac{2}{3} \sin^3 x + C$

75. $\frac{3}{2} \sin^{-1} \left(\dfrac{8x + 3}{\sqrt{41}} \right) + C$

77. $-x \sin^{-1} \left(\dfrac{x}{a} \right) - 2\sqrt{a^2 - x^2} + C$

SECTION 10.2

1. (a) $\frac{2}{13}$ (b) $\frac{29}{13}$

3. $(0, 1)$ is the closest pt; $(-1, 1)$ the farthest away

5. $\frac{17}{2}$

7. Adjust the sign of A and B so that the equation reads $Ax + By = |C|$. Then we have

$$x \frac{A}{\sqrt{A^2 + B^2}} + y \frac{B}{\sqrt{A^2 + B^2}} = \frac{|C|}{\sqrt{A^2 + B^2}}.$$

Now set

$$\frac{|C|}{\sqrt{A^2 + B^2}} = p, \qquad \frac{A}{\sqrt{A^2 + B^2}} = \cos \alpha, \qquad \frac{B}{\sqrt{A^2 + B^2}} = \sin \alpha.$$

p is the length of $\overline{OQ}$, the distance between the line and the origin; α is the angle from the positive x-axis to the line segment $\overline{OQ}$.

9. (a) $4x + 5y - 3 = 0$ (b) $4x + 5y - 11 = 0$
   (c) $4x + 5y + 17 = 0$ (d) $4x + 5y + 9 = 0$
11. (a) $(x - 3)^2 = (y - 4)^3$ (b) $(x + 3)^2 = (y - 4)^2$
   (c) $(x - 4)^2 = (y + 3)^3$ (d) $(x + 4)^2 = (y + 3)^2$

13. decreasing $\dfrac{8b^2\pi}{5}$ units/min

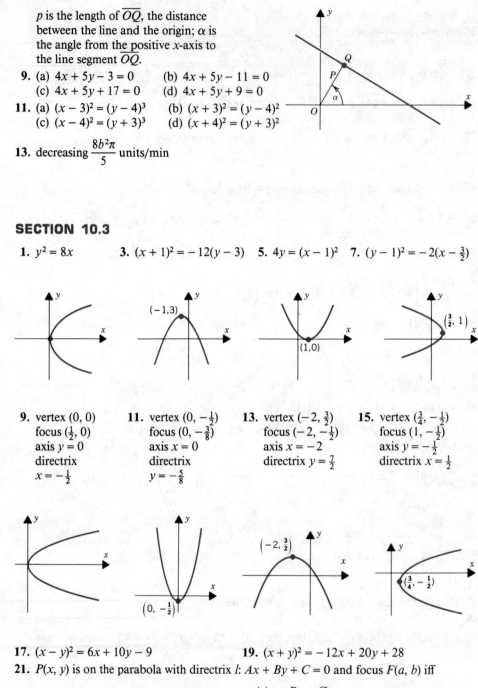

SECTION 10.3

1. $y^2 = 8x$ 3. $(x + 1)^2 = -12(y - 3)$ 5. $4y = (x - 1)^2$ 7. $(y - 1)^2 = -2(x - \frac{3}{2})$

9. vertex $(0, 0)$
   focus $(\frac{1}{2}, 0)$
   axis $y = 0$
   directrix $x = -\frac{1}{2}$

11. vertex $(0, -\frac{1}{2})$
   focus $(0, -\frac{3}{8})$
   axis $x = 0$
   directrix $y = -\frac{5}{8}$

13. vertex $(-2, \frac{3}{2})$
   focus $(-2, -\frac{1}{2})$
   axis $x = -2$
   directrix $y = \frac{7}{2}$

15. vertex $(\frac{3}{4}, -\frac{1}{2})$
   focus $(1, -\frac{1}{2})$
   axis $y = -\frac{1}{2}$
   directrix $x = \frac{1}{2}$

17. $(x - y)^2 = 6x + 10y - 9$ 19. $(x + y)^2 = -12x + 20y + 28$
21. $P(x, y)$ is on the parabola with directrix l: $Ax + By + C = 0$ and focus $F(a, b)$ iff

$$d(P, l) = d(P, F) \quad \text{which happens iff} \quad \frac{|Ax + By + C|}{\sqrt{A^2 + B^2}} = \sqrt{(x - a)^2 + (y - b)^2}.$$

Square this last equation and simplify.

23. We can choose the coordinate system so that the parabola has an equation of the form $y = \alpha x^2$, $\alpha > 0$. One of the points of intersection is then the origin and the other is of the form $(c, \alpha c^2)$. We will assume that $c > 0$.

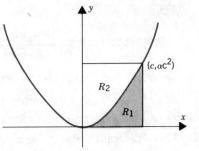

$$\text{area of } R_1 = \int_0^c \alpha x^2 \, dx = \tfrac{1}{3}\alpha c^3 = \tfrac{1}{3}A$$

$$\text{area of } R_2 = A - \tfrac{1}{3}A = \tfrac{2}{3}A.$$

25. vertex $\left(-\dfrac{B}{2A}, \dfrac{4AC - B^2}{4A}\right)$, focus $\left(-\dfrac{B}{2A}, \dfrac{4AC - B^2 + 1}{4A}\right)$, directrix $y = \dfrac{4AC - B^2 - 1}{4A}$

27. $2y = x^2 - 4x + 7$, $18y = x^2 - 4x + 103$

29. $y = -\dfrac{16}{v_0^2}(\sec^2\theta)\,x^2 + (\tan\theta)\,x$

31. $\tfrac{1}{16}v_0^2 \cos\theta \sin\theta$ ft

33. $\tfrac{1}{4}\pi$

SECTION 10.4

1. center $(0, 0)$
foci $(\pm\sqrt{5}, 0)$
length of major axis 6
length of minor axis 4

3. center $(0, 0)$
foci $(0, \pm\sqrt{2})$
length of major axis $2\sqrt{6}$
length of minor axis 4

5. center $(0, 1)$
foci $(\pm\sqrt{5}, 1)$
length of major axis 6
length of minor axis 4

7. center $(1, 0)$
foci $(1, \pm4\sqrt{3})$
length of major axis 16
length of minor axis 8

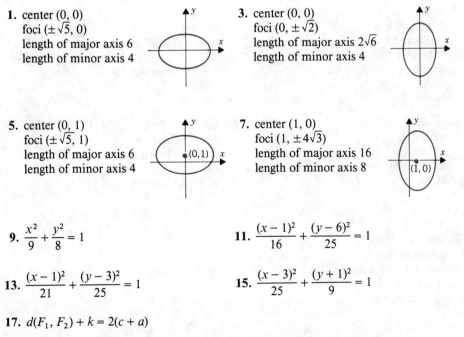

9. $\dfrac{x^2}{9} + \dfrac{y^2}{8} = 1$

11. $\dfrac{(x-1)^2}{16} + \dfrac{(y-6)^2}{25} = 1$

13. $\dfrac{(x-1)^2}{21} + \dfrac{(y-3)^2}{25} = 1$

15. $\dfrac{(x-3)^2}{25} + \dfrac{(y+1)^2}{9} = 1$

17. $d(F_1, F_2) + k = 2(c + a)$

19. We refer to Figure 10.4.7. The equation of the tangent can be written

$$(b^2 x_0)x + (a^2 y_0)y - a^2 b^2 = 0.$$

Thus

$$d(T_1, F_1)d(T_2, F_2) = \frac{|(b^2x_0)(-c) - a^2b^2|}{\sqrt{b^4x_0^2 + a^4y_0^2}} \frac{|(b^2x_0)c - a^2b^2|}{\sqrt{b^4x_0^2 + a^4y_0^2}} = b^2 \frac{|b^2x_0^2c^2 - a^4b^2|}{b^4x_0^2 + a^4y_0^2}.$$

The fraction on the right is identically 1:

$$|b^2x_0^2c^2 - a^4b^2| = |b^2x_0^2c^2 - a^2(b^2x_0^2 + a^2y_0^2)| = |(c^2 - a^2)b^2x_0^2 - a^4y_0^2| = |-b^4x_0^2 - a^4y_0^2|.$$

Thus $d(T_1, F_1)d(T_2, F_2) = b^2$.

21. The ellipse tends toward a line segment of length $2a$.

23. $\dfrac{x^2}{4} + \dfrac{y^2}{3} = 1$

SECTION 10.5

1. $\dfrac{x^2}{9} - \dfrac{y^2}{16} = 1$

3. $\dfrac{y^2}{25} - \dfrac{x^2}{144} = 1$

5. $\dfrac{x^2}{9} - \dfrac{(y-1)^2}{16} = 1$

7. $16y^2 - \frac{16}{15}(x+1)^2 = 1$

9. center $(0, 0)$
transverse axis 2
vertices $(\pm 1, 0)$
foci $(\pm\sqrt{2}, 0)$
asymptotes $y = \pm x$

11. center $(0, 0)$
transverse axis 6
vertices $(\pm 3, 0)$
foci $(\pm 5, 0)$
asymptotes $y = \pm\frac{4}{3}x$

13. center $(0, 0)$
transverse axis 8
vertices $(0, \pm 4)$
foci $(0, \pm 5)$
asymptotes $y = \pm\frac{4}{3}x$

15. center $(1, 3)$
transverse axis 6
vertices $(4, 3)$ and $(-2, 3)$
foci $(6, 3)$ and $(-4, 3)$
asymptotes $y = \pm\frac{4}{3}(x-1) + 3$

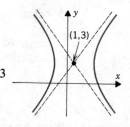

17. center $(1, 3)$
transverse axis 4
vertices $(1, 5)$ and $(1, 1)$
foci $(1, 3 \pm \sqrt{5})$
asymptotes $y = 2x + 1, \quad y = -2x + 5$

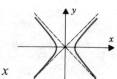

19. center $(0, 0)$, vertices $(1, 1)$ and $(-1, -1)$, foci $(\sqrt{2}, \sqrt{2})$ and $(-\sqrt{2}, -\sqrt{2})$, asymptotes $x = 0$ and $y = 0$, transverse axis $2\sqrt{2}$.

21. differentiate implicitly: $\dfrac{2x}{a^2} - \dfrac{2y}{b^2}\dfrac{dy}{dx} = 0.$ Thus, $m = \dfrac{b^2 x_0}{a^2 y_0}$.

23. Let $P(x_0, y_0)$ be the point of tangency and let l be the tangent line.

$$\text{slope of } l = \frac{b^2 x_0}{a^2 y_0}, \qquad \text{slope of } \overline{F_1 P} = \frac{y_0}{x_0 + c}, \qquad \text{slope of } \overline{F_2 P} = \frac{y_0}{x_0 - c}.$$

With θ_1 as the angle between l and $\overline{F_1 P}$ and with θ_2 as the angle between $\overline{F_2 P}$ and l, we have

$$\tan \theta_1 = \frac{\dfrac{b^2 x_0}{a^2 y_0} - \dfrac{y_0}{x_0 + c}}{1 + \dfrac{b^2 x_0}{a^2 y_0}\left(\dfrac{y_0}{x_0 + c}\right)} \qquad \text{and} \qquad \tan \theta_2 = \frac{\dfrac{y_0}{x_0 - c} - \dfrac{b^2 x_0}{a^2 y_0}}{1 + \left(\dfrac{y_0}{x_0 - c}\right)\left(\dfrac{b^2 x_0}{a^2 y_0}\right)}.$$

Using the fact that

$$b^2 x_0^2 - a^2 y_0^2 = a^2 b^2, \qquad (P \text{ is on the hyperbola})$$

it is routine to show that $\tan \theta_1 = \tan \theta_2$.

SECTION 10.6

1. parabola with vertex at $(0, -1)$ and focus at the origin

3. hyperbola with foci at $(5, \pm 2\sqrt{5})$ and transverse axis 4

5. ellipse with foci at $(-3 \pm \frac{1}{3}\sqrt{6}, 0)$ and major axis 2

7. parabola with vertex at $(\frac{3}{2}, -2)$ and focus at $(1, -2)$

9. ellipse with foci at $(\pm \frac{4}{15}, -2)$ and major axis $\frac{2}{3}$

11. hyperbola with foci at $(-1 \pm \frac{6}{7}\sqrt{21}, -4)$ and transverse axis $\frac{6}{7}\sqrt{35}$

13. the union of the parabola $x^2 = 4y$ and the ellipse $\frac{1}{9}x^2 + \frac{1}{4}y^2 = 1$

SECTION 10.7

1. $\alpha = \frac{1}{4}\pi,$
   $\frac{1}{2}(X^2 - Y^2) = 1$

3. $\alpha = \frac{1}{6}\pi,$
   $4X^2 - Y^2 = 1$

5. $\alpha = \frac{1}{4}\pi,$
   $2Y^2 + \sqrt{2}X = 0$

7. $\alpha = -\frac{1}{6}\pi,$
   $Y^2 + X = 0$

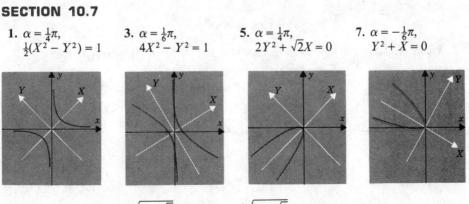

9. $\alpha = \frac{1}{8}\pi, \qquad \cos \alpha = \frac{1}{2}\sqrt{2 + \sqrt{2}}, \qquad \sin \alpha = \frac{1}{2}\sqrt{2 - \sqrt{2}}$

SECTION 11.1

1.–7. Figure A.11.1.1 **9.** (0, 3)

11. (1, 0) **13.** $(-\frac{3}{2}, \frac{3}{2}\sqrt{3})$

15. (0, − 3)

17. $[1, \frac{1}{2}\pi + 2n\pi], [-1, \frac{3}{2}\pi + 2n\pi]$

19. $[3, \pi + 2n\pi], [-3, 2n\pi]$

21. $[2\sqrt{2}, \frac{7}{4}\pi + 2n\pi], [-2\sqrt{2}, \frac{3}{4}\pi + 2n\pi]$

23. $[8, \frac{1}{6}\pi + 2n\pi], [-8, \frac{7}{6}\pi + 2n\pi]$

25. $[2, \frac{2}{3}\pi + 2n\pi], [-2, \frac{5}{3}\pi + 2n\pi]$

27. (a) $[\frac{1}{2}, \frac{11}{6}\pi]$ (b) $[\frac{1}{2}, \frac{5}{6}\pi]$ (c) $[\frac{1}{2}, \frac{7}{6}\pi]$

29. (a) $[2, \frac{2}{3}\pi]$ (b) $[2, \frac{5}{3}\pi]$ (c) $[2, \frac{1}{3}\pi]$

31. symmetry about the x-axis

33. no symmetry about the coordinate axes; no symmetry about the origin

35. symmetry about the origin

37. $r \cos \theta = 2$ **39.** $r^2 \sin 2\theta = 1$ **41.** $r = 4 \sin \theta$

43. $\theta = \pi/4$ **45.** $r = 1 + \cos \theta$ **47.** $r^2 = \sin 2\theta$

49. the horizontal line $y = 4$ **51.** the line $y = \sqrt{3}\, x$

53. the parabola $y^2 = 4(x + 1)$ **55.** the circle $x^2 + y^2 = 3x$

57. the line $y = 2x$ **59.** the vertical line $x = 0$

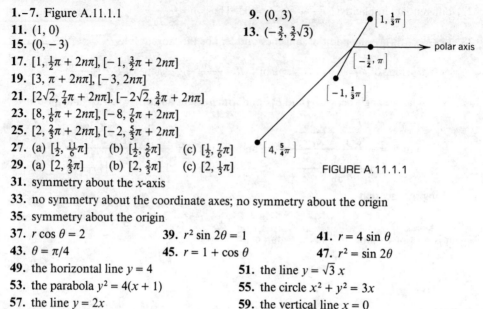

FIGURE A.11.1.1

SECTION 11.2

1. Figure A.11.2.1   **3.** Figure A.11.2.2   **5.** Figure A.11.2.3

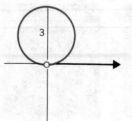

FIGURE A.11.2.1

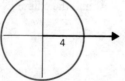

FIGURE A.11.2.2

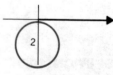

FIGURE A.11.2.3

7. Figure A.11.2.4   **9.** Figure A.11.2.5   **11.** Figure A.11.2.6

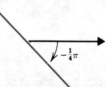

FIGURE A.11.2.4

FIGURE A.11.2.5

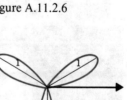

FIGURE A.11.2.6

13. Figure A.11.2.7

15. Figure A.11.2.8

17. Figure A.11.2.9

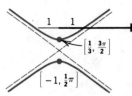

FIGURE A.11.2.7

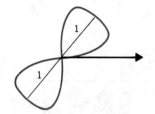

FIGURE A.11.2.8

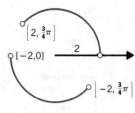

FIGURE A.11.2.9

19. Figure A.11.2.10

21. Figure A.11.2.11

23. Figure A.11.2.12

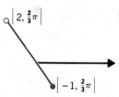

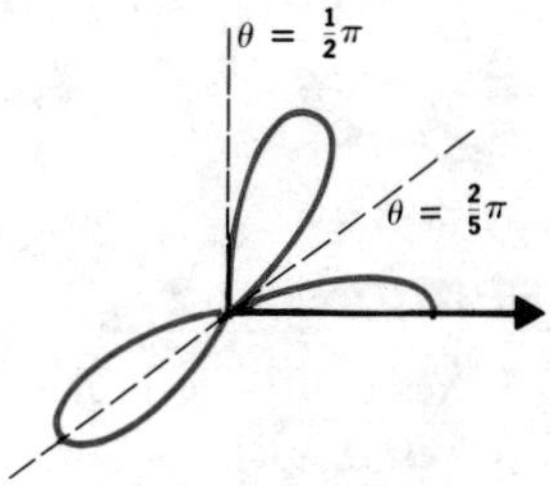

FIGURE A.11.2.10

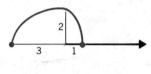

FIGURE A.11.2.11

FIGURE A.11.2.12

25. Figure A.11.2.13

27. Figure A.11.2.14

29. Figure A.11.2.15

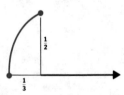

FIGURE A.11.2.13

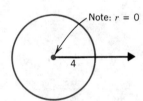

FIGURE A.11.2.14

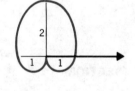

FIGURE A.11.2.15

31. Figure A.11.2.16

33. Figure A.11.2.17

35. Figure A.11.2.18

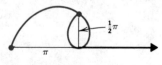

FIGURE A.11.2.16

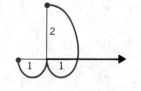

FIGURE A.11.2.17

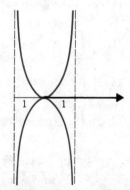

FIGURE A.11.2.18

37. Figure A.11.2.19   **39.** Figure A.11.2.20

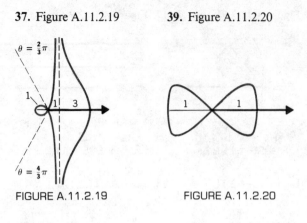

FIGURE A.11.2.19   FIGURE A.11.2.20

SECTION 11.3

1. yes; $[1, \pi] = [-1, 0]$ and the pair $r = -1$, $\theta = 0$ satisfies the equation

3. yes; the pair $r = \frac{1}{2}$, $\theta = \frac{1}{2}\pi$ satisfies the equation

5. $[2, \pi] = [-2, 0]$.   The coordinates of $[-2, 0]$ satisfy the equation $r^2 = 4 \cos \theta$, and the coordinates of $[2, \pi]$ satisfy the equation $r = 3 + \cos \theta$.

7. $(0, 0), (-\frac{1}{2}, -\frac{1}{2})$ **9.** $(-1, 0), (1, 0)$ **11.** $(0, 0), (\frac{1}{4}, \pm\frac{1}{4}\sqrt{3})$

13. $(\frac{3}{2}, 2)$ **15.** $(0, 0), (1, 0)$

SECTION 11.4

1. $\frac{1}{4}\pi a^2$ **3.** $\frac{1}{2}a^2$ **5.** $\frac{1}{2}\pi a^2$

7. $\frac{1}{4} - \frac{1}{16}\pi$ **9.** $\frac{3}{16}\pi + \frac{3}{8}$ **11.** $\frac{5}{2}a^2$

13. $\frac{1}{12}(3e^{2\pi} - 3 - 2\pi^3)$ **15.** $\frac{1}{4}(e^{2\pi} + 1 - 2e^{\pi})$

17. $\displaystyle\int_{\pi/6}^{5\pi/6} \frac{1}{2}([4 \sin \theta]^2 - [2]^2) \, d\theta$ **19.** $\displaystyle\int_{-\pi/3}^{\pi/3} \frac{1}{2}([4]^2 - [2 \sec \theta]^2) \, d\theta$

21. $2\left[\displaystyle\int_0^{\pi/3} \frac{1}{2}(2 \sec \theta)^2 \, d\theta + \int_{\pi/3}^{\pi/2} \frac{1}{2}(4)^2 \, d\theta\right]$ **23.** $\displaystyle\int_0^{\pi/3} \frac{1}{2}(2 \sin 3\theta)^2 \, d\theta$

25. $2\left[\displaystyle\int_0^{\pi/6} \frac{1}{2}(\sin \theta)^2 \, d\theta + \int_{\pi/6}^{\pi/2} \frac{1}{2}(1 - \sin \theta)^2 \, d\theta\right]$

27. $2\left[\displaystyle\int_0^{\pi/3} \frac{1}{2} (\sec \theta)^2 \, d\theta + \int_{\pi/3}^{\pi} \frac{1}{2}\left(\frac{1}{1 - \cos \theta}\right)^2 \, d\theta\right]$

29. $\displaystyle\int_0^{2\pi/3} \frac{1}{2}\left(\frac{-1 + \sqrt{3}}{\sin \theta + \cos \theta}\right)^2 \, d\theta + \int_{2\pi/3}^{11\pi/6} \frac{1}{2}(2)^2 \, d\theta + \int_{11\pi/6}^{2\pi} \frac{1}{2}\left(\frac{-1 + \sqrt{3}}{\sin \theta + \cos \theta}\right)^2 \, d\theta$

SECTION 11.5

1. $4x = (y - 1)^2$

3. $y = 4x^2 + 1, \quad x \geq 0$

5. $9x^2 + 4y^2 = 36$

7. $1 + x^2 = y^2$

9. $y = 2 - x^2, \quad -1 \leq x \leq 1$

11. $2y - 6 = x, \quad -4 \leq x \leq 4$

13. $y = x - 1$

15. $xy = 1$

17. $y + 2x = 11$

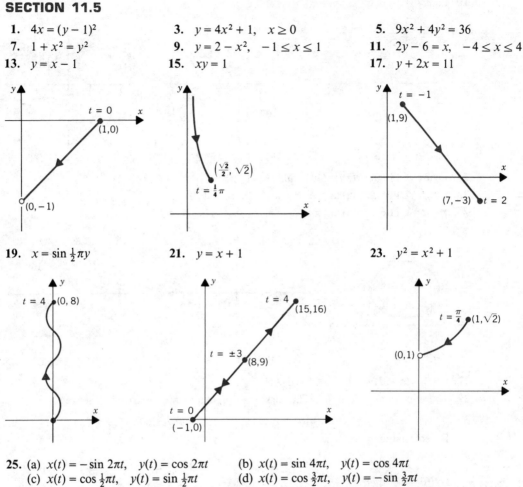

19. $x = \sin \frac{1}{2}\pi y$

21. $y = x + 1$

23. $y^2 = x^2 + 1$

25. (a) $x(t) = -\sin 2\pi t, \quad y(t) = \cos 2\pi t$ (b) $x(t) = \sin 4\pi t, \quad y(t) = \cos 4\pi t$

(c) $x(t) = \cos \frac{1}{2}\pi t, \quad y(t) = \sin \frac{1}{2}\pi t$ (d) $x(t) = \cos \frac{3}{2}\pi t, \quad y(t) = -\sin \frac{3}{2}\pi t$

27. $x(t) = \tan \frac{1}{2}\pi t, \quad y(t) = 2$

29. $x(t) = 3 + 5t, \quad y(t) = 7 - 2t$

31. $x(t) = \sin^2 \pi t, \quad y(t) = -\cos \pi t$

33. $x(t) = (2 - t)^2, \quad y(t) = (2 - t)^3$

35. $x(t) = t(b - a) + a, \quad y(t) = f(t(b - a) + a)$

37. (a) paths intersect at $(6, 5)$ and $(8, 1)$ (b) particles collide at $(8, 1)$

39. curve intersects itself at $(0, 0)$ **41.** curve intersects itself at $(0, 0)$ and $(0, \frac{3}{4})$

SECTION 11.6

1. $3x - y - 3 = 0$

3. $y = 1$

5. $3x + y - 3 = 0$

7. $2x + 2y - \sqrt{2} = 0$

9. $2x + y - 8 = 0$

11. $x - 5y + 4 = 0$

13. $x + 2y + 1 = 0$

15. Figure A.11.6.1; $x(t) = t, y(t) = t^3$; tangent line $y = 0$

17. Figure A.11.6.2; $x(t) = t^{5/3}, y(t) = t$; tangent line $x = 0$

19. Figure A.11.6.3;   (a) none;   (b) at (2, 2) and (−2, 0)

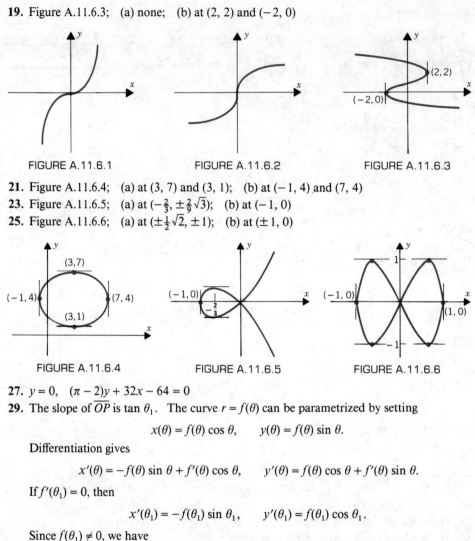

FIGURE A.11.6.1   FIGURE A.11.6.2   FIGURE A.11.6.3

21. Figure A.11.6.4;   (a) at (3, 7) and (3, 1);   (b) at (−1, 4) and (7, 4)
23. Figure A.11.6.5;   (a) at $(-\frac{2}{3}, \pm\frac{2}{9}\sqrt{3})$;   (b) at (−1, 0)
25. Figure A.11.6.6;   (a) at $(\pm\frac{1}{2}\sqrt{2}, \pm1)$;   (b) at (±1, 0)

FIGURE A.11.6.4   FIGURE A.11.6.5   FIGURE A.11.6.6

27. $y = 0$, $(\pi - 2)y + 32x - 64 = 0$
29. The slope of $\overline{OP}$ is $\tan \theta_1$.   The curve $r = f(\theta)$ can be parametrized by setting

$$x(\theta) = f(\theta) \cos \theta, \qquad y(\theta) = f(\theta) \sin \theta.$$

Differentiation gives

$$x'(\theta) = -f(\theta) \sin \theta + f'(\theta) \cos \theta, \qquad y'(\theta) = f(\theta) \cos \theta + f'(\theta) \sin \theta.$$

If $f'(\theta_1) = 0$, then

$$x'(\theta_1) = -f(\theta_1) \sin \theta_1, \qquad y'(\theta_1) = f(\theta_1) \cos \theta_1.$$

Since $f(\theta_1) \neq 0$, we have

$$m = \frac{y'(\theta_1)}{x'(\theta_1)} = -\cot \theta_1 = -\frac{1}{\text{slope of } \overline{OP}}.$$

31. Figure A.11.6.7   **33.** Figure A.11.6.8   **35.** Figure A.11.6.9
37. −8   **39.** 2

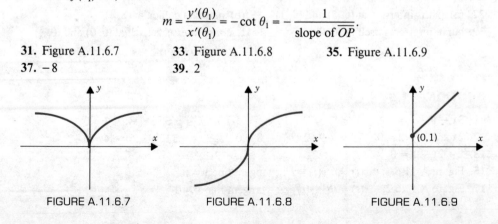

FIGURE A.11.6.7   FIGURE A.11.6.8   FIGURE A.11.6.9

SECTION 11.7

1. $x(t) = \overline{OB} - \overline{AB} = rt - r \sin t = r(t - \sin t)$

$y(t) = \overline{BQ} - \overline{QC} = r - r \cos t = r(1 - \cos t)$

3. (a) The slope at P is

$$m = \frac{y'(t)}{x'(t)} = \frac{\sin t}{1 - \cos t}.$$

The line tangent to the cycloid at P has equation

$$y - r(1 - \cos t) = \frac{\sin t}{1 - \cos t}[x - r(t - \sin t)].$$

The top of the circle is the point $(rt, 2r)$. Its coordinates satisfy the equation for the tangent:

$$2r - r(1 - \cos t) \overset{?}{=} \frac{\sin t}{1 - \cos t}[rt - r(t - \sin t)]$$

$$r(1 + \cos t) \overset{?}{=} \frac{r \sin^2 t}{1 - \cos t}$$

$$1 - \cos^2 t \overset{\checkmark}{=} \sin^2 t.$$

(b) In view of the symmetry and repetitiveness of the curve we can assume that $t \in (0, \pi)$. Then

$$\tan \alpha = \frac{\sin t}{1 - \cos t} = \frac{\sin t}{2 \sin^2 \frac{1}{2} t} = \frac{\sin \frac{1}{2} t \cos \frac{1}{2} t}{\sin^2 \frac{1}{2} t} = \cot \frac{1}{2} t$$

and

$$\alpha = \tfrac{1}{2}\pi - \tfrac{1}{2}t = \tfrac{1}{2}(\pi - t).$$

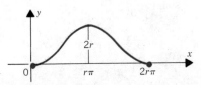

5. $x(t) = rt - b \sin t, \quad y(t) = r - b \cos t$

7. $x(t) = (a + r) \cos t - a \cos \left(\dfrac{a + r}{a} t \right), \quad y(t) = (a + r) \sin t - a \sin \left(\dfrac{a + r}{a} t \right)$

9. $x(t) = (r - a) \cos t + a \cos \left(\dfrac{r - a}{a} t \right), \quad y(t) = (r - a) \sin t - a \sin \left(\dfrac{r - a}{a} t \right)$

11. Since x and y parametrize the graph of f, we know that $f(x(t)) = y(t)$. Now set

$$u = x(t); \qquad du = x'(t)\, dt.$$

At $t = c$, $u = a$; at $t = d$, $u = b$. Thus

$$\int_c^d y(t)\, x'(t)\, dt = \int_c^d f(x(t))\, x'(t)\, dt = \int_a^b f(u)\, du = \text{area below } C.$$

13. area $= 2\pi r^2$

15. $\frac{3}{8}\pi a^2$

SECTION 11.8

1. lub = 2; glb = 0

3. no lub; glb = 0

5. lub = 2; glb = −2

7. no lub; glb = 2

9. lub = $2\frac{1}{2}$; glb = 2

11. lub = 1; glb = 0.9

13. lub = e; glb = 0

15. lub = $\frac{1}{2}(-1 + \sqrt{5})$; glb = $\frac{1}{2}(-1 - \sqrt{5})$

17. no lub; no glb

19. no lub; no glb

21. glb $S = 0$, $0 \le (\frac{1}{11})^3 < 0 + 0.001$

23. glb $S = 0$, $0 \le \dfrac{1}{10^{2n-1}} < 0 + \dfrac{1}{10^k}$ $\left(n > \dfrac{k+1}{2}\right)$

25. Let $\epsilon > 0$. The condition $m \le s$ is satisfied by all numbers s in S. All we have to show therefore is that there is some number s in S such that $s < m + \epsilon$. Suppose on the contrary that there is no such number in S. We then have $m + \epsilon \le x$ for all $x \in S$, so that $m + \epsilon$ becomes a lower bound for S. But this cannot happen, for it makes $m + \epsilon$ a lower bound that is *greater* than m, and by assumption, m is the *greatest* lower bound.

SECTION 11.9

1. $(d - c)\sqrt{m^2 + 1}$

3. $2\sqrt{3}$

5. $\frac{4}{3}$

7. $2 \ln (\sqrt{2} + 1)$

9. $\frac{1}{3}\pi + \frac{1}{2}\sqrt{3}$

11. $2 - \sqrt{2} - \ln (\sqrt{6} - \sqrt{3})$

13. $2 - \sqrt{2} - \ln (\sqrt{6} - \sqrt{3})$

15. $2\sqrt{3} + \ln (2 + \sqrt{3})$

17. $\frac{1}{27}(13\sqrt{13} - 8)$

19. $\sqrt{2}(e^\pi - 1)$

21. $\sqrt{2}(e^{4\pi} - 1)$

23. $\frac{1}{3}\sqrt{5}(e^{4\pi} - 1)$

25. $a[\pi\sqrt{4\pi^2 + 1} + \frac{1}{2} \ln (2\pi + \sqrt{4\pi^2 + 1})]$ $(a > 0)$

27. $\ln (1 + \sqrt{2})$

29. $f(x) = \cosh x = \frac{1}{2}(e^x + e^{-x})$

31. $p(0) = p(x) \cos [\theta(x)]$, $p(x) \sin [\theta(x)] = k \displaystyle\int_0^x \sqrt{1 + [f'(t)]^2}\, dt$

$$f'(x) = \tan [\theta(x)] = \frac{p(x) \sin [\theta(x)]}{p(x) \cos [\theta(x)]} = \frac{k}{p(0)} \int_0^x \sqrt{1 + [f'(t)]^2}\, dt.$$

Differentiation with respect to x gives

$$f''(x) = \frac{k}{p(0)} \sqrt{1 + [f'(x)]^2}.$$

Setting $z = f'(x)$, we have

$$\frac{dz}{dx} = \frac{k}{p(0)} \sqrt{1 + z^2}, \qquad \frac{dz}{\sqrt{1 + z^2}} = \frac{k}{p(0)}, \qquad \sinh^{-1} z = \frac{k}{p(0)} x + C.$$

Placing the y-axis so that the low point of the rope is at $x = 0$, we have $z = 0$ at $x = 0$, and therefore $C = 0$. Thus

$$\sinh^{-1} z = \frac{k}{p(0)} x \qquad \text{and} \qquad z = \sinh \left(\frac{k}{p(0)} x\right).$$

This gives

$$f'(x) = \sinh \left(\frac{k}{p(0)} x\right) \qquad \text{and} \qquad f(x) = \frac{p(0)}{k} \cosh \left(\frac{k}{p(0)} x\right) + K.$$

Setting $a = p(0)/k$, we have

$$f(x) = a \cosh\left(\frac{x}{a}\right) + K.$$

Placing the x-axis exactly a units below the low point of the curve, we have $f(0) = a$, $K = 0$, and $f(x) = a \cosh(x/a)$.

SECTION 11.10

1. $2\pi r$

3. $2\pi[\sqrt{2} + \ln(1 + \sqrt{2})]$

5. $\frac{1}{9}\pi(17^{3/2} - 1)$

7. $\frac{61}{432}\pi$

9. $3\pi\sqrt{13}$

11. $2\pi r^2$

13. $\frac{6}{5}\pi a^2$

15. $\frac{2}{5}\sqrt{2}\pi(2e^\pi + 1)$

17. See Figure A.11.10.1

$$S = \tfrac{1}{2}\theta L_2^2 - \tfrac{1}{2}\theta L_1^2$$
$$= \tfrac{1}{2}(\theta L_2 + \theta L_1)(L_2 - L_1)$$
$$= \tfrac{1}{2}(2\pi R + 2\pi r)l = \pi(R + r)l$$

19. $\pi a^2(20 + \ln 3)$

21. (a) $2\pi b^2 + \dfrac{2\pi ab}{e}\sin^{-1} e$ (b) $2\pi a^2 + \dfrac{\pi b^2}{e}\ln\left|\dfrac{1+e}{1-e}\right|$,

where e is the eccentricity $\dfrac{\sqrt{a^2 - b^2}}{a}$

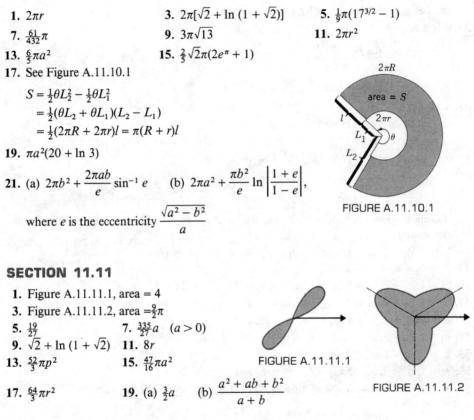

FIGURE A.11.10.1

FIGURE A.11.11.1

FIGURE A.11.11.2

SECTION 11.11

1. Figure A.11.11.1, area $= 4$

3. Figure A.11.11.2, area $= \frac{9}{2}\pi$

5. $\frac{19}{27}$

7. $\frac{335}{27}a$ $(a > 0)$

9. $\sqrt{2} + \ln(1 + \sqrt{2})$ **11.** $8r$

13. $\frac{52}{3}\pi p^2$

15. $\frac{47}{16}\pi a^2$

17. $\frac{64}{3}\pi r^2$

19. (a) $\frac{3}{2}a$ (b) $\dfrac{a^2 + ab + b^2}{a + b}$

SECTION 12.1

1. decreasing; bounded below by 0 and above by 2

3. increasing; bounded below by 1 but not bounded above

5. not monotonic; bounded below by 0 and above by $\frac{3}{2}$

7. decreasing; bounded below by 0 and above by 0.9

9. increasing; bounded below by $\frac{1}{2}$ but not bounded above

11. increasing; bounded below by $\frac{4}{3}\sqrt{5}$ and above by 2

13. increasing; bounded below by $\frac{2}{51}$ but not bounded above

15. decreasing; bounded below by 0 and above by $\frac{1}{2}(10^{10})$

17. increasing; bounded below by 0 and above by $\ln 2$

19. decreasing; bounded below by 1 and above by 4

21. increasing; bounded below by $\sqrt{3}$ and above by 2

23. decreasing; bounded above by -1 but not bounded below

25. increasing; bounded below by $\frac{1}{2}$ and above by 1

27. decreasing; bounded below by 0 and above by 1

29. decreasing; bounded below by 0 and above by $\frac{5}{6}$

31. decreasing; bounded below by 0 and above by $\frac{1}{2}$

33. decreasing; bounded below by 0 and above by $\frac{1}{3} \ln 3$

35. increasing; bounded below by $\frac{3}{4}$ but not bounded above

37. For $n \geq 5$

$$\frac{a_{n+1}}{a_n} = \frac{5^{n+1}}{(n+1)!} \cdot \frac{n!}{5^n} = \frac{5}{n+1} < 1 \quad \text{and thus} \quad a_{n+1} < a_n.$$

Sequence is not nonincreasing: $a_1 = 5 < \frac{25}{2} = a_2$.

39. boundedness: $\qquad 0 < (c^n + d^n)^{1/n} < (2d^n)^{1/n} = 2^{1/n} d \leq 2d.$

monotonicity: $\quad a_{n+1}^{n+1} = c^{n+1} + d^{n+1} = cc^n + dd^n$

$$< (c^n + d^n)^{1/n} c^n + (c^n + d^n)^{1/n} d^n$$
$$= (c^n + d^n)^{1+(1/n)}$$
$$= (c^n + d^n)^{(n+1)/n}$$
$$= a_n^{n+1}.$$

Taking the $n + 1$th root of each side we have $a_{n+1} < a_n$. The sequence is monotonic decreasing.

41. $a_1 = 1, a_2 = \frac{1}{2}, a_3 = \frac{1}{6}, a_4 = \frac{1}{24}, a_5 = \frac{1}{120}, a_6 = \frac{1}{720}; \quad a_n = 1/n!$

43. $a_1 = a_2 = a_3 = a_4 = a_5 = a_6 = 1; \quad a_n = 1$

45. $a_1 = 1, a_2 = 3, a_3 = 5, a_4 = 7, a_5 = 9, a_6 = 11; \quad a_n = 2n - 1$

47. $a_1 = 1, a_2 = 4, a_3 = 13, a_4 = 40, a_5 = 121, a_6 = 364; \quad a_n = \frac{1}{2}(3^n - 1)$

49. $a_1 = 1, a_2 = 4, a_3 = 9, a_4 = 16, a_5 = 25, a_6 = 36; \quad a_n = n^2$

51. $a_1 = 1, a_2 = 3, a_3 = 4, a_4 = 8, a_5 = 16, a_6 = 32; \quad a_n = 2^{n-1} \quad (n \geq 3)$

53. $a_1 = 2, a_2 = 1, a_3 = 2, a_4 = 1, a_5 = 2, a_6 = 1; \quad a_n = \frac{1}{2}[3 - (-1)^n]$

55. $a_1 = 1, a_2 = 3, a_3 = 5, a_4 = 7, a_5 = 9, a_6 = 11; \quad a_n = 2n - 1$

57. First $a_1 = 2^1 - 1 = 1$. Next suppose $a_k = 2^k - 1$ for some $k \geq 1$. Then

$$a_{k+1} = 2a_k + 1 = 2(2^k - 1) + 1 = 2^{k+1} - 1.$$

59. First $a_1 = \dfrac{1}{2^0} = 1$. Next suppose $a_k = \dfrac{k}{2^{k-1}}$ for some $k \geq 1$. Then

$$a_{k+1} = \frac{k+1}{2k} a_k = \frac{k+1}{2k} \frac{k}{2^{k-1}} = \frac{k+1}{2^k}.$$

SECTION 12.2

1. diverges

3. converges to 0

5. converges to 1

7. converges to 0

9. converges to 0

11. diverges

13. converges to 0

15. converges to 1

17. converges to $\frac{4}{9}$

19. converges to $\frac{1}{2}\sqrt{2}$

21. diverges

23. converges to 1

25. diverges

27. converges to 0

29. converges to $\frac{1}{2}$

31. converges to e^2 **33.** diverges   **35.** converges to 0

37. Use $|(a_n + b_n) - (l + m)| \le |a_n - l| + |b_n - m|$.

39.
$$\left(1 + \frac{1}{n}\right)^{n+1} = \left(1 + \frac{1}{n}\right)^n \left(1 + \frac{1}{n}\right).$$

Note that

$$\left(1 + \frac{1}{n}\right)^n \to e \qquad \text{and} \qquad \left(1 + \frac{1}{n}\right) \to 1.$$

41. Imitate the proof given for the nondecreasing case in Theorem 12.2.6.

43. Let $\epsilon > 0$. Choose k so that, for $n \ge k$,

$$l - \epsilon < a_n < l + \epsilon, \quad l - \epsilon < c_n < l + \epsilon \quad \text{and} \quad a_n \le b_n \le c_n.$$

For such n,

$$l - \epsilon < b_n < l + \epsilon.$$

45. Use Theorem 12.2.12 with $f(x) = x^{1/p}$.   **47.** converges to 0

49. converges to 0   **51.** diverges   **53.** converges to 2

SECTION 12.3

1. converges to 1   **3.** converges to 0   **5.** converges to 0

7. converges to 0   **9.** converges to 1   **11.** converges to 0

13. converges to 1   **15.** converges to 1   **17.** converges to π

19. converges to 1   **21.** converges to 0   **23.** diverges

25. converges to 0   **27.** converges to e^{-1} **29.** converges to 0

31. converges to 0   **33.** converges to e^x **35.** converges to 0

37. $\sqrt{n+1} - \sqrt{n} = \dfrac{\sqrt{n+1} - \sqrt{n}}{\sqrt{n+1} + \sqrt{n}} (\sqrt{n+1} + \sqrt{n}) = \dfrac{1}{\sqrt{n+1} + \sqrt{n}} \to 0.$

39. $\lim\limits_{n \to \infty} 2n \sin(\pi/n) = 2\pi$; the number $2n \sin(\pi/n)$ is the perimeter of a regular polygon of n sides inscribed in the unit circle; as n tends to ∞, the perimeter of the polygon tends to the circumference of the circle

41. $\frac{1}{2}$ **43.** $\frac{1}{8}$

45. (a) $m_{n+1} - m_n = \dfrac{1}{n+1} (a_1 + \cdots + a_n + a_{n+1}) - \dfrac{1}{n}(a_1 + \cdots + a_n)$

$$= \frac{1}{n(n+1)} \left[na_{n+1} - (a_1 + \cdots + a_n) \right]$$

> 0 since $\{a_n\}$ is increasing.

(b) We begin with the hint $m_n < \dfrac{|a_1 + \cdots + a_j|}{n} + \dfrac{\epsilon}{2}\left(\dfrac{n-j}{n}\right)$ Since j is fixed, $\dfrac{|a_1 + \cdots + a_j|}{n} \to 0$, and therefore for n sufficiently large $\dfrac{|a_1 + \cdots + a_j|}{n} < \dfrac{\epsilon}{2}$.

Since $\dfrac{\epsilon}{2}\left(\dfrac{n-j}{n}\right) < \dfrac{\epsilon}{2}$, we see that for n sufficiently large $|m_n| < \epsilon$. This shows that $m_n \to 0$.

SECTION 12.4

1. 0	**3.** 0	**5.** 0	**7.** a^2
9. 1	**11.** 0	**13.** 1	**15.** 0
17. 1	**19.** $-\frac{1}{2}$	**21.** 0	**23.** 0
25. $-\ln 3$	**27.** $\frac{1}{2}$		

29. Set $f(x) = 3x^{1/3} - \ln x$. That $f(x) > 0$ for $x \geq 1$ follows from observing that

$$f(1) = 3 > 0 \quad \text{and} \quad f'(x) = x^{-2/3} - \frac{1}{x} = \frac{x^{1/3} - 1}{x} > 0 \quad \text{for } x > 1.$$

Thus, for $x \geq 1$,

$$0 \leq \frac{\ln x}{\sqrt{x}} < \frac{3x^{1/3}}{\sqrt{x}} = 3x^{-1/6}.$$

Since $3x^{-1/6} \to 0$ as $x \to \infty$, $\lim_{x \to \infty} \dfrac{\ln x}{\sqrt{x}} = 0$.

31. If f has a limit as x tends to ∞, then f is bounded on an interval of the form $[K, \infty)$. Being continuous, f is bounded on $[a, K]$. It is therefore bounded on $[a, \infty)$.

SECTION 12.5

1. 0	**3.** 1	**5.** $\frac{1}{2}$	**7.** $\ln 2$
9. $\frac{1}{4}$	**11.** 2	**13.** $\dfrac{1 + \pi}{1 - \pi}$	**15.** e^2
17. π	**19.** $-\frac{1}{2}$	**21.** -2	**23.** $\frac{1}{3}\sqrt{6}$
25. $-\frac{1}{8}$	**27.** $-\frac{1}{2}$	**29.** $\frac{1}{2}$	**31.** 1
33. 1	**35.** $\lim\limits_{x \to 0} (2 + x + \sin x) \neq 0$, $\lim\limits_{x \to 0} (x^3 + x - \cos x) \neq 0$.		
37. $f(0)$			

SECTION 12.6

1. ∞	**3.** -1	**5.** ∞	**7.** $\frac{1}{5}$
9. 1	**11.** 0	**13.** ∞	**15.** $\frac{1}{3}$
17. e	**19.** 1	**21.** $\frac{1}{2}$	**23.** $\frac{1}{2}$
25. 1	**27.** e^3	**29.** e	**31.** 0
33. 1	**35.** 1	**37.** 0	

39. Figure A.12.6.1; y-axis vertical asymptote
41. Figure A.12.6.2; x-axis horizontal asymptote
43. Figure A.12.6.3; x-axis horizontal asymptote

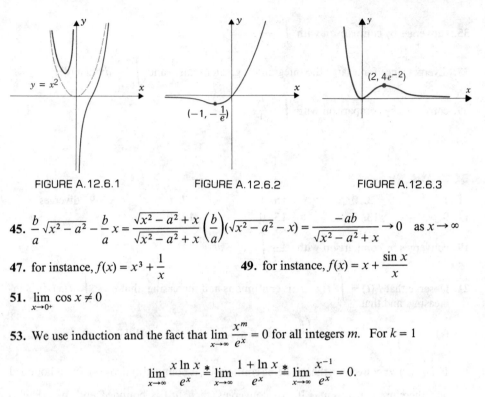

FIGURE A.12.6.1   FIGURE A.12.6.2   FIGURE A.12.6.3

45. $\dfrac{b}{a}\sqrt{x^2-a^2}-\dfrac{b}{a}x=\dfrac{\sqrt{x^2-a^2}+x}{\sqrt{x^2-a^2}+x}\left(\dfrac{b}{a}\right)(\sqrt{x^2-a^2}-x)=\dfrac{-ab}{\sqrt{x^2-a^2}+x}\to 0$ as $x\to\infty$

47. for instance, $f(x)=x^3+\dfrac{1}{x}$ **49.** for instance, $f(x)=x+\dfrac{\sin x}{x}$

51. $\lim\limits_{x\to 0^+}\cos x\neq 0$

53. We use induction and the fact that $\lim\limits_{x\to\infty}\dfrac{x^m}{e^x}=0$ for all integers m. For $k=1$

$$\lim_{x\to\infty}\frac{x\ln x}{e^x}\overset{*}{=}\lim_{x\to\infty}\frac{1+\ln x}{e^x}\overset{*}{=}\lim_{x\to\infty}\frac{x^{-1}}{e^x}=0.$$

Next suppose the result is true for some $k=p\geq 1$. Then

$$\lim_{x\to\infty}\frac{x^{p+1}\ln x}{e^x}\overset{*}{=}\lim_{x\to\infty}\left[(p+1)\frac{x^p\ln x}{e^x}+\frac{x^p}{e^x}\right]=(p+1)(0)+0=0.$$

Thus the result is true for $k=p+1$.

SECTION 12.7

1. 1   **3.** $\frac{1}{4}\pi$ **5.** diverges   **7.** 6

9. $\frac{1}{2}\pi$ **11.** 2   **13.** diverges   **15.** $-\frac{1}{4}$

17. π **19.** diverges   **21.** ln 2   **23.** 4

25. diverges   **27.** diverges

29. diverges

31. (a) Figure A.12.7.1   (b) 1

    (c) $\frac{1}{2}\pi$ (d) 2π

    (e) $\pi[\sqrt{2}+\ln(1+\sqrt{2})]$

33. (a) Figure A.12.7.2   (b) $\frac{4}{3}$

    (c) 2π (d) $\frac{8}{7}\pi$

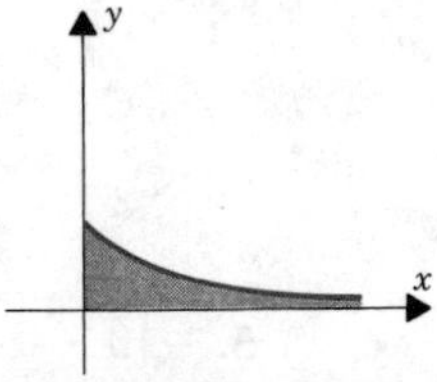

FIGURE A.12.7.1 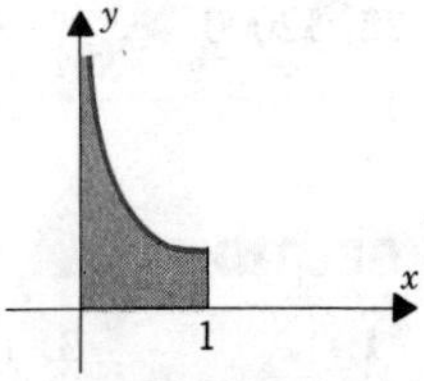   FIGURE A.12.7.2

35. converges by comparison with $\displaystyle\int_0^\infty \frac{dx}{x^{3/2}}$

37. diverges since for x large the integrand is greater than $\dfrac{1}{x}$ and $\displaystyle\int_1^\infty \frac{1}{x}\,dx$ diverges

39. converges by comparison with $\displaystyle\int_1^\infty \frac{dx}{x^{3/2}}$

SECTION 12.8

1. 1   **3.** 0   **5.** 1   **7.** 0   **9.** diverges
11. 0   **13.** 0   **15.** 0   **17.** 0

19. converges by comparison with $\dfrac{1}{\sqrt{2\pi}}\displaystyle\int_{-\infty}^x e^{t+1}\,dt$

21. Observe that $F(t) = \displaystyle\int_1^t f(x)\,dx$ is continuous and increasing, that $a_n = \displaystyle\int_1^n f(x)\,dx$ is increasing, and that

$$(*) \qquad\qquad a_n \le \int_1^t f(x)\,dx \le a_{n+1} \qquad \text{for } t \in [n,\, n+1].$$

If $\displaystyle\int_1^\infty f(x)\,dx$ converges, then F, being continuous, is bounded and, by $(*)$, $\{a_n\}$ is bounded and therefore convergent. If $\{a_n\}$ converges, then $\{a_n\}$ is bounded and, by $(*)$, F is bounded. Being increasing, F is also convergent; i.e., $\displaystyle\int_1^\infty f(x)\,dx$ converges.

23. (a) If $\displaystyle\int_{-\infty}^\infty f(x)\,dx = L$, then both

$$\int_0^\infty f(x)\,dx = \lim_{c\to\infty} \int_0^c f(x)\,dx \qquad \text{and} \qquad \int_{-\infty}^0 f(x)\,dx = \lim_{c\to\infty} \int_{-c}^0 f(x)\,dx$$

exist and their sum is L. Thus

$$\lim_{c\to\infty} \int_{-c}^c f(x)\,dx = \lim_{c\to\infty}\left(\int_{-c}^0 f(x)\,dx + \int_0^c f(x)\,dx\right) = \lim_{c\to\infty}\int_{-c}^0 f(x)\,dx + \lim_{c\to\infty}\int_0^c f(x)\,dx = L.$$

(b) $\displaystyle\lim_{c\to\infty}\int_{-c}^c x\,dx = \lim_{c\to\infty}\left[\frac{x^2}{2}\right]_{-c}^c = \lim_{c\to\infty} 0 = 0$, but $\displaystyle\int_{-\infty}^\infty x\,dx$ diverges since $\displaystyle\int_0^\infty x\,dx$ and $\displaystyle\int_{-\infty}^0 x\,dx$ both diverge.

25. \$2000

SECTION 13.1

1. 12   **3.** 15   **5.** -10 **7.** $\frac{15}{16}$ **9.** $-\frac{2}{15}$ **11.** $\frac{85}{64}$

13. $\displaystyle\sum_{k=1}^n m_k \Delta x_k$ **15.** $\displaystyle\sum_{k=1}^n f(x_k^*)\Delta x_k$ **17.** $\displaystyle\sum_{k=0}^5 (-1)^k\, a^{5-k}\, b^k$

19. $\sum_{k=0}^{4} a_k x^{4-k}$ **21.** $\sum_{k=0}^{4} (-1)^k (k+1) x^k$ **23.** $\sum_{k=3}^{10} \frac{1}{2^k}, \ \sum_{i=0}^{7} \frac{1}{2^{i+3}}$

25. $\sum_{k=3}^{10} (-1)^{k+1} \frac{k}{k+1}, \ \sum_{i=0}^{7} (-1)^i \frac{i+3}{i+4}$

27. (a) $(1-x) \sum_{k=0}^{n} x^k = \sum_{k=0}^{n} (x^k - x^{k+1})$

$$= (1-x) + (x-x^2) + (x^2-x^3) + \cdots + (x^n - x^{n+1})$$
$$= 1 - x^{n+1}$$

(b) converges to $\frac{3}{2}$

29. $|a_n - l| < \epsilon$ for $n \geq k$ iff $|a_{n-p} - l| < \epsilon$ for $n \geq k+p$.

31. True for $n = 1$: $\sum_{k=1}^{1} k = 1 = \frac{1}{2}(1)(2)$. Suppose true for $n = p$. Then

$$\sum_{k=1}^{p+1} k = \sum_{k=1}^{p} k + (p+1) = \frac{1}{2}(p)(p+1) + (p+1) = \frac{1}{2}(p+1)(p+2)$$
$$= \frac{1}{2}(p+1)[(p+1)+1]$$

and thus true for $n = p + 1$.

33. True for $n = 1$: $\sum_{k=1}^{1} k^2 = 1 = \frac{1}{6}(1)(2)(3)$. Suppose true for $n = p$. Then

$$\sum_{k=1}^{p+1} k^2 = \sum_{k=1}^{p} k^2 + (p+1)^2 = \frac{1}{6}(p)(p+1)(2p+1) + (p+1)^2$$
$$= \frac{1}{6}(p+1)(2p^2 + 7p + 6) = \frac{1}{6}(p+1)(p+2)(2p+3)$$
$$= \frac{1}{6}(p+1)[(p+1)+1][2(p+1)+1]$$

and thus true for $n = p + 1$.

SECTION 13.2

1. $\frac{1}{4}$ **3.** $\frac{1}{2}$ **5.** $\frac{11}{18}$ **7.** $\frac{10}{3}$

9. $\frac{67000}{999}$ **11.** 4 **13.** $-\frac{3}{2}$ **15.** $\frac{1}{2}$

17. 24 **19.** $\sum_{k=1}^{\infty} \frac{7}{10^k} = \frac{7}{9}$ **21.** $\sum_{k=1}^{\infty} \frac{24}{100^k} = \frac{8}{33}$

23. $\sum_{k=1}^{\infty} \frac{112}{1000^k} = \frac{112}{999}$ **25.** $\frac{62}{100} + \frac{1}{100} \sum_{k=1}^{\infty} \frac{45}{100^k} = \frac{687}{1100}$

27. Let $x = .\overline{a_1 a_2 \cdots a_n} a_1 a_2 \cdots a_n \cdots$. Then

$$x = \sum_{k=1}^{\infty} \frac{a_1 a_2 \cdots a_n}{(10^n)^k} = a_1 a_2 \cdots a_n \sum_{k=1}^{\infty} \left(\frac{1}{10^n}\right)^k$$

$$= a_1 a_2 \cdots a_n \left[\frac{1}{1-\dfrac{1}{10^n}} - 1\right] = \frac{a_1 a_2 \cdots a_n}{10^n - 1}.$$

29. $\dfrac{1}{1+x} = \dfrac{1}{1-(-x)} = \sum_{k=0}^{\infty} (-x)^k = \sum_{k=0}^{\infty} (-1)^k x^k.$

31. $\displaystyle\sum_{k=0}^{\infty} x^{k+1}$ **33.** $\displaystyle\sum_{k=0}^{\infty} (-1)^k\, x^{2k+1}$ **35.** $\displaystyle\sum_{k=0}^{\infty} (-1)^k\, (2x)^{2k}$

37. $4 + \frac{1}{3} \displaystyle\sum_{k=0}^{\infty} (\frac{1}{12})^k = 4 + \frac{4}{11}$ o'clock   **39.** 12 ft

41. $\displaystyle\sum_{k=1}^{\infty} n_k \left(1 + \frac{r}{100}\right)^{-k}$

43. $s_n = \displaystyle\sum_{k=1}^{n} \ln\left(\frac{k+1}{k}\right) = \sum_{k=1}^{n} [\ln (k+1) - \ln k] = \ln (n+1) \to \infty$

45. (a) $s_n = \displaystyle\sum_{k=1}^{n} (d_k - d_{k+1}) = d_1 - d_{n+1} \to d_1$

    (b) (i) $\displaystyle\sum_{k=1}^{\infty} \frac{\sqrt{k+1} - \sqrt{k}}{\sqrt{k(k+1)}} = \sum_{k=1}^{\infty} \left(\frac{1}{\sqrt{k}} - \frac{1}{\sqrt{k+1}}\right) = 1$

       (ii) $\displaystyle\sum_{k=1}^{\infty} \frac{2k+1}{2k^2(k+1)^2} = \sum_{k=1}^{\infty} \frac{1}{2}\left(\frac{1}{k^2} - \frac{1}{(k+1)^2}\right) = \frac{1}{2}$

SECTION 13.3

1. converges; comparison $\Sigma \dfrac{1}{k^2}$ **3.** converges; comparison $\Sigma \dfrac{1}{k^2}$

5. diverges; comparison $\Sigma \dfrac{1}{k+1}$ **7.** diverges; limit comparison $\Sigma \dfrac{1}{k}$

9. converges; integral test   **11.** diverges; p-series with $p = \frac{2}{3} \le 1$

13. diverges; $a_k \not\to 0$ **15.** diverges; comparison $\Sigma \dfrac{1}{k}$

17. diverges; $a_k \not\to 0$ **19.** converges; limit comparison $\Sigma \dfrac{1}{k^2}$

21. diverges; integral test   **23.** converges; limit comparison $\Sigma \dfrac{1}{k^2}$

25. diverges; limit comparison $\Sigma \dfrac{1}{k}$ **27.** converges; limit comparison $\Sigma \dfrac{1}{k^{3/2}}$

29. converges; integral test

31. (a) If $a_k/b_k \to 0$, then $a_k/b_k < 1$ for all $k \ge K$ for some K. But then $a_k < b_k$ for all $k \ge K$ and, since Σb_k converges, Σa_k converges. [The Basic Comparison Theorem 13.3.5.]

    (b) Similar to (a) except that this time we appeal to part (ii) of Theorem 13.3.5.

    (c) $\Sigma a_k = \Sigma \dfrac{1}{k^2}$ converges, $\Sigma b_k = \Sigma \dfrac{1}{k^{3/2}}$ converges, $\dfrac{1/k^2}{1/k^{3/2}} = \dfrac{1}{\sqrt{k}} \to 0.$

          $\Sigma a_k = \Sigma \dfrac{1}{k^2}$ converges, $\Sigma b_k = \Sigma \dfrac{1}{\sqrt{k}}$ diverges, $\dfrac{1/k^2}{1/\sqrt{k}} = \dfrac{1}{k^{3/2}} \to 0.$

(d) $\Sigma b_k = \Sigma \dfrac{1}{\sqrt{k}}$ diverges, $\qquad \Sigma a_k = \Sigma \dfrac{1}{k^2}$ converges, $\qquad \dfrac{1/k^2}{1/\sqrt{k}} = 1/k^{3/2} \to 0.$

$\Sigma b_k = \Sigma \dfrac{1}{\sqrt{k}}$ diverges, $\qquad \Sigma a_k = \Sigma \dfrac{1}{k}$ diverges, $\qquad \dfrac{1/k}{1/\sqrt{k}} = \dfrac{1}{\sqrt{k}} \to 0.$

33. (a) Set $\quad f(x) = x^{1/4} - \ln x.$ $\quad$ Then $\quad f'(x) = \dfrac{1}{4}x^{-3/4} - \dfrac{1}{x} = \dfrac{1}{4x}(x^{1/4} - 1).$ $\quad$ Since

$f(e^{12}) = e^3 - 12 > 0$ and $f'(x) > 0$ for $x > e^{12}$, we know that $n^{1/4} > \ln n$ or $\dfrac{1}{n^{5/4}} > \dfrac{\ln n}{n^{3/2}}$

for sufficiently large n. Since $\Sigma \dfrac{1}{n^{5/4}}$ is a convergent p-series, $\Sigma \dfrac{\ln n}{n^{3/2}}$ converges by the basic comparison test.

(b) By L'Hospital's rule $\lim\limits_{x \to \infty} \left[\left(\dfrac{\ln x}{x^{3/2}} \right) \Big/ \left(\dfrac{1}{x^{5/4}} \right) \right] = 0.$

SECTION 13.4

1. converges; ratio test

3. converges; root test

5. diverges; $a_k \not\to 0$

7. diverges; limit comparison $\Sigma \dfrac{1}{k}$

9. converges; root test

11. diverges; limit comparison $\Sigma \dfrac{1}{\sqrt{k}}$

13. diverges; ratio test

15. converges; comparison $\Sigma \dfrac{1}{k^{3/2}}$

17. converges; comparison $\Sigma \dfrac{1}{k^2}$

19. diverges; integral test

21. diverges; $a_k \to e^{-100} \neq 0$

23. diverges; limit comparison $\Sigma \dfrac{1}{k}$

25. converges; ratio test

27. converges; comparison $\Sigma \dfrac{1}{k^{3/2}}$

29. converges; ratio test

31. converges; ratio test: $\dfrac{a_{k+1}}{a_k} \to \dfrac{4}{27}$

33. $\frac{10}{81}$

35. Set $b_k = a_k r^k$. If $(a_k)^{1/k} \to \rho$ and $\rho < \dfrac{1}{r}$, then

$$(b_k)^{1/k} = (a_k r^k)^{1/k} = (a_k)^{1/k}\, r \to \rho r < 1$$

and thus, by the root test, $\Sigma b_k = \Sigma a_k r^k$ converges.

SECTION 13.5

1. diverges; $a_k \not\to 0$ 3. diverges; $a_k \not\to 0$
5. (a) does not converge absolutely; integral test
   (b) converges conditionally; Theorem 13.5.3

7. diverges; limit comparison $\Sigma \dfrac{1}{k}$

9. (a) does not converge absolutely; limit comparison $\Sigma \dfrac{1}{k}$

   (b) converges conditionally; Theorem 13.5.3
11. diverges; $a_k \not\to 0$

13. (a) does not converge absolutely; comparison $2 \Sigma \dfrac{1}{\sqrt{k+1}}$

   (b) converges conditionally; Theorem 13.5.3

15. converges absolutely (terms already positive); $\Sigma \sin\left(\dfrac{\pi}{4k^2}\right) \le \Sigma \dfrac{\pi}{4k^2} = \dfrac{\pi}{4} \Sigma \dfrac{1}{k^2}$
   ($|\sin x| \le |x|$)
17. converges absolutely; ratio test

19. (a) does not converge absolutely; limit comparison $\Sigma \dfrac{1}{k}$

   (b) converges conditionally; Theorem 13.5.3
21. diverges; $a_k \not\to 0$ 23. $\frac{10}{11}$ 25. (a) 4   (b) 6
27. No. For instance, set $a_{2k} = 2/k$ and $a_{2k+1} = 1/k$.
29. See the proof of Theorem 13.8.2

SECTION 13.6

1. $-1 + x + \frac{1}{2}x^2 - \frac{1}{24}x^4$ 3. $-\frac{1}{2}x^2 - \frac{1}{12}x^4$
5. $1 - x + x^2 - x^3 + x^4 - x^5$ 7. $x + \frac{1}{3}x^3 + \frac{2}{15}x^5$
9. $P_0(x) = 1$, $P_1(x) = 1 - x$, $P_2(x) = 1 - x + 3x^2$, $P_3(x) = 1 - x + 3x^2 + 5x^3$

11. $\displaystyle\sum_{k=0}^{n} (-1)^k \frac{x^k}{k!}$ 13. $\displaystyle\sum_{k=0}^{m} \frac{x^{2k}}{(2k)!}$ where $m = \dfrac{n}{2}$ and n is even

15. 1.65   17. 0.84
19. 0.54   21. (a) 4   (b) 2   (c) 999

23. For $0 \le k \le n$, $P^{(k)}(0) = k!a_k$; for $k > n$, $P^{(k)}(0) = 0$. Thus $P(x) = \displaystyle\sum_{k=0}^{\infty} P^{(k)}(0)\frac{x^k}{k!}$.

25. $\displaystyle\sum_{k=0}^{\infty} \frac{a^k}{k!} x^k$, $(-\infty, \infty)$ 27. $\displaystyle\sum_{k=0}^{\infty} \frac{(-1)^k a^{2k}}{(2k)!} x^{2k}$, $(-\infty, \infty)$

29. $\ln a + \displaystyle\sum_{k=1}^{\infty} \frac{(-1)^{k-1}}{ka^k} x^k$, $(-a, a]$

31. $\ln 2 = \ln\left(\dfrac{1 + \frac{1}{3}}{1 - \frac{1}{3}}\right) \cong 2\left[\dfrac{1}{3} + \dfrac{1}{3}\left(\dfrac{1}{3}\right)^3 + \dfrac{1}{5}\left(\dfrac{1}{3}\right)^5\right] \cong 0.693$

33. routine; use $u = (x - t)^k$ and $dv = f^{(k+1)}(t)\, dt$

35. $f(0) = 0$ by definition

$$f'(0) = \lim_{x \to 0} \frac{f(x) - f(0)}{x - 0} = \lim_{x \to 0} \frac{e^{-1/x^2}}{x} = 0$$

$$f''(0) = \lim_{x \to 0} \frac{f'(x) - f'(0)}{x - 0} = \lim_{x \to 0} \frac{e^{-1/x^2}(2x^{-3})}{x} = 0.$$

SECTION 13.7

1. $6 + 9(x - 1) + 7(x - 1)^2 + 3(x - 1)^3$, $(-\infty, \infty)$

3. $-3 + 5(x + 1) - 19(x + 1)^2 + 20(x + 1)^3 - 10(x + 1)^4 + 2(x + 1)^5$, $(-\infty, \infty)$

5. $\displaystyle\sum_{k=0}^{\infty} (-1)^k (\tfrac{1}{2})^{k+1} (x - 1)^k$, $(-1, 3)$

7. $\displaystyle\frac{1}{5} \sum_{k=0}^{\infty} (\tfrac{2}{5})^k (x + 2)^k$, $(-\tfrac{9}{2}, \tfrac{1}{2})$

9. $\displaystyle\sum_{k=0}^{\infty} \frac{(-1)^{k+1}}{(2k+1)!} (x - \pi)^{2k+1}$, $(-\infty, \infty)$

11. $\displaystyle\sum_{k=0}^{\infty} \frac{(-1)^{k+1}}{(2k)!} (x - \pi)^{2k}$, $(-\infty, \infty)$

13. $\displaystyle\sum_{k=0}^{\infty} \frac{(-1)^k}{(2k)!} \left(\frac{\pi}{2}\right)^{2k} (x - 1)^{2k}$, $(-\infty, \infty)$

15. $\ln 3 + \displaystyle\sum_{k=1}^{\infty} \frac{(-1)^{k+1}}{k} (\tfrac{2}{3})^k (x - 1)^k$, $(-\tfrac{1}{2}, \tfrac{5}{2}]$

17. $2 \ln 2 + (1 + \ln 2)(x - 2) + \displaystyle\sum_{k=2}^{\infty} \frac{(-1)^k}{k(k-1)2^{k-1}} (x - 2)^k$

19. $\displaystyle\sum_{k=0}^{\infty} \frac{(-1)^k}{(2k+1)!} x^{2k+2}$

21. $\displaystyle\sum_{k=0}^{\infty} (k + 2)(k + 1) \frac{2^{k-1}}{5^{k+3}} (x + 2)^k$

23. $1 + \displaystyle\sum_{k=1}^{\infty} \frac{(-1)^k 2^{2k-1}}{(2k)!} (x - \pi)^{2k}$

25. $\displaystyle\sum_{k=0}^{\infty} \frac{n!}{(n-k)!\, k!} (x - 1)^k$

27. (a) $\displaystyle\frac{e^x}{e^a} = e^{x-a} = \sum_{k=0}^{\infty} \frac{(x - a)^k}{k!}$, $e^x = e^a \sum_{k=0}^{\infty} \frac{(x - a)^k}{k!}$

(b) $e^{a+(x-a)} = e^x = e^a \displaystyle\sum_{k=0}^{\infty} \frac{(x - a)^k}{k!}$, $e^{x_1+x_2} = e^{x_1} \sum_{k=0}^{\infty} \frac{x_2^k}{k!} = e^{x_1} e^{x_2}$

(c) $e^{-a} \displaystyle\sum_{k=0}^{\infty} (-1)^k \frac{(x - a)^k}{k!}$

SECTION 13.8

1. $(-1, 1)$ **3.** $(-\infty, \infty)$ **5.** $\{0\}$ **7.** $[-2, 2)$

9. $\{0\}$ **11.** $[-\tfrac{1}{2}, \tfrac{1}{2})$ **13.** $(-1, 1)$ **15.** $(-10, 10)$

17. $(-\infty, \infty)$ **19.** $(-\infty, \infty)$ **21.** $(0, 4)$ **23.** $(-\tfrac{5}{2}, \tfrac{1}{2})$

25. Examine the convergence of $\Sigma |a_k x^k|$; for (a) use the root test and for (b) use the ratio test.

SECTION 13.9

1. $1 + 2x + 3x^2 + \cdots\, nx^{n-1} + \cdots$

3. $1 + kx + \dfrac{(k+1)k}{2!} x^2 + \cdots + \dfrac{(n+k-1)!}{n!(k-1)!} x^n + \cdots$

5. $\ln (1 - x^2) = -x^2 - \dfrac{1}{2} x^4 - \dfrac{1}{3} x^6 - \cdots - \dfrac{1}{n + 1} x^{2n+2} - \cdots$

7. $1 + x^2 + \frac{2}{3} x^4 + \frac{17}{45} x^6 + \cdots$ **9.** -72

11. $\displaystyle\sum_{k=0}^{\infty} \dfrac{(-1)^k}{(2k + 1)!} x^{4k+2}$ **13.** $\displaystyle\sum_{k=0}^{\infty} \dfrac{3^k}{k!} x^{3k}$ **15.** $2\displaystyle\sum_{k=0}^{\infty} x^{2k+1}$

17. $\displaystyle\sum_{k=0}^{\infty} \dfrac{(k! + 1)}{k!} x^k$ **19.** $\displaystyle\sum_{k=1}^{\infty} \dfrac{(-1)^{k+1}}{k} x^{3k+1}$ **21.** $\displaystyle\sum_{k=0}^{\infty} \dfrac{(-1)^k}{k!} x^{3k+3}$

23. 0.80 **25.** 0.60 **27.** 0.30 **29.** 0.07

31. Let $f(x)$ be the sum of these series; a_k and b_k are both $\dfrac{f^{(k)}(0)}{k!}$.

33. e^{x^3} **35.** $3x^2 e^{x^3}$

37. substitution of series for $y(x)$ gives $xy' - y = x^2 \displaystyle\sum_{k=0}^{\infty} \dfrac{x^{k2}}{k!} = x^2 e^{x^2}$

SECTION 13.10

1. $1 + \frac{1}{2}x - \frac{1}{8}x^2 + \frac{1}{16}x^3 - \frac{5}{128}x^4$ **3.** $1 + \frac{1}{2}x^2 - \frac{1}{8}x^4$

5. $1 - \frac{1}{2}x + \frac{3}{8}x^2 - \frac{5}{16}x^3 + \frac{35}{128}x^4$ **7.** $1 - \frac{1}{4}x - \frac{3}{32}x^2 - \frac{7}{128}x^3 - \frac{77}{2048}x^4$

9. 9.90 **11.** 2.08 **13.** 0.50

SECTION 13.11

1. $y = C \displaystyle\sum_{k=0}^{\infty} (-2)^k \dfrac{x^k}{k!} = Ce^{-2x}$ **3.** $y = \dfrac{3}{2} + C \displaystyle\sum_{k=0}^{\infty} (-2)^k \dfrac{x^k}{k!} = \dfrac{3}{2} + Ce^{-2x}$

5. $y = \dfrac{1}{2} x - \dfrac{1}{4} + C \displaystyle\sum_{k=0}^{\infty} (-2)^k \dfrac{x^k}{k!} = \dfrac{1}{2} x - \dfrac{1}{4} + Ce^{-2x}$ **7.** $y = Cx^3$

9. $y = \dfrac{1}{2} x + C_1 + C_2 \displaystyle\sum_{k=0}^{\infty} (-2)^k \dfrac{x^k}{k!} = \dfrac{1}{2} x + C_1 + C_2 e^{-2x}$

11. $y = a_0 \displaystyle\sum_{k=0}^{\infty} \dfrac{x^{2k}}{(2k)!} + a_1 \displaystyle\sum_{k=0}^{\infty} \dfrac{x^{2k+1}}{(2k + 1)!} = a_0 \cosh x + a_1 \sinh x = C_1 e^x + C_2 e^{-x}$

13. $y = \frac{1}{2}x - \frac{1}{4}$ **15.** $y = \dfrac{3}{2} + \displaystyle\sum_{k=0}^{\infty} (-1)^k 2^{k-1} \dfrac{x^k}{k!} = \dfrac{3}{2} + \dfrac{1}{2} e^{-2x}$

17. $y = \displaystyle\sum_{k=0}^{\infty} \dfrac{x^k}{k!} = e^x$ **19.** $y = - \displaystyle\sum_{k=1}^{\infty} \dfrac{x^k}{k!} = 1 - e^x$

SECTION 13.12

1. $\frac{4}{3}$ **3.** $\frac{2}{3}$ **5.** 1

7. $\dfrac{x}{1 - x^5}, \quad |x| < 1$ **9.** $\dfrac{3x}{2(1 - x^2)}, \quad |x| < 1$ **11.** $2e$

13. diverges   **15.** converges absolutely   **17.** converges conditionally

19. converges absolutely   **21.** converges conditionally

23. $[\frac{9}{5}, \frac{11}{5})$ **25.** $(0, 2)$ **27.** $(-1, 1)$

29. $\{-1\}$ **31.** $(-9, 9)$ **33.** $(-3, 7)$

35. $\displaystyle\sum_{k=0}^{\infty} \frac{5^k}{k!} x^{2k+1}$ **37.** $\displaystyle\sum_{k=0}^{\infty} \frac{(-1)^k}{2k+1} x^{k+1}$

39. $\displaystyle\sum_{k=0}^{\infty} \frac{(-1)^k}{(2k+1)!} (x^{4k+3} + x^{4k+4})$ **41.** $1 + x + \frac{1}{2}x^2 - \frac{1}{8}x^4$

43. $1 + \frac{1}{2}x^2 + \frac{3}{8}x^4$ **45.** 0.50 **47.** 3.92

49. $2/e$ **51.** (a) diverges   (b) diverges   (c) 1

53. Set $a_n = x_n - \dfrac{\epsilon}{4^n}$, $b_n = x_n + \dfrac{\epsilon}{4^n}$. Then $\displaystyle\sum_{n=1}^{\infty} (b_n - a_n) = 2\epsilon \sum_{n=1}^{\infty} (\tfrac{1}{4})^n = \tfrac{2}{3}\epsilon < \epsilon.$

$Area = \frac{1}{2}\,ab\cos a$

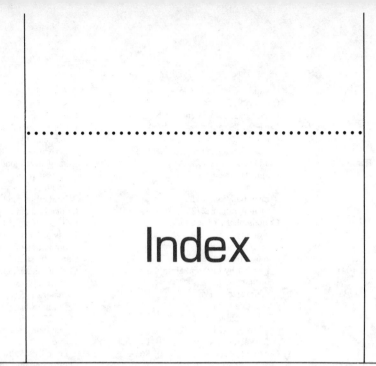

Index

Pages referred to in this index which do not appear in this volume can be found in Salas/Hille/Anderson: Calculus, Part Two, 5th edition.

inverse trigonometric functions

41. $\displaystyle\int \sin^{-1} x \, dx = x \sin^{-1} x + \sqrt{1-x^2} + C$

42. $\displaystyle\int \cos^{-1} x \, dx = x \cos^{-1} x - \sqrt{1-x^2} + C$

43. $\displaystyle\int \tan^{-1} x \, dx = x \tan^{-1} x - \frac{1}{2} \ln(1+x^2) + C$

44. $\displaystyle\int \cot^{-1} x \, dx = x \cot^{-1} x + \frac{1}{2} \ln(1+x^2) + C$

45. $\displaystyle\int \sec^{-1} x \, dx = x \sec^{-1} x - \ln|x + \sqrt{x^2 - 1}| + C$

46. $\displaystyle\int \csc^{-1} x \, dx = x \csc^{-1} x + \ln|x + \sqrt{x^2 - 1}| + C$

hyperbolic functions

47. $\displaystyle\int \sinh x \, dx = \cosh x + C$

48. $\displaystyle\int \cosh x \, dx = \sinh x + C$

49. $\displaystyle\int \tanh x \, dx = \ln(\cosh x) + C$

50. $\displaystyle\int \coth x \, dx = \ln|\sinh x| + C$

51. $\displaystyle\int \operatorname{sech} x \, dx = \tan^{-1}(\sinh x) + C$

52. $\displaystyle\int \operatorname{csch} x \, dx = \ln\left|\tanh \frac{x}{2}\right| + C$

53. $\displaystyle\int \operatorname{sech}^2 x \, dx = \tanh x + C$

54. $\displaystyle\int \operatorname{csch}^2 x \, dx = -\coth x + C$

55. $\displaystyle\int \operatorname{sech} x \tanh x \, dx = -\operatorname{sech} x + C$

56. $\displaystyle\int \operatorname{csch} x \coth x \, dx = -\operatorname{csch} x + C$

57. $\displaystyle\int \sinh^2 x \, dx = \frac{\sinh 2x}{4} - \frac{x}{2} + C$

58. $\displaystyle\int \cosh^2 x \, dx = \frac{\sinh 2x}{4} + \frac{x}{2} + C$

59. $\displaystyle\int \tanh^2 x \, dx = x - \tanh x + C$

60. $\displaystyle\int \coth^2 x \, dx = x - \coth x + C$

61. $\displaystyle\int x \sinh x \, dx = x \cosh x - \sinh x + C$

62. $\displaystyle\int x \cosh x \, dx = x \sinh x - \cosh x + C$